F

G

H

B

I

J

K

N

M

L

THE BIOTIC WORLD AND MAN

LORUS J. MILNE

University of New Hampshire

MARGERY J. MILNE

Second Edition

PRENTICE-HALL, INC.   Englewood Cliffs, N.J.

To those who have increased our enthusiasm:
our teachers—and our students

PRENTICE-HALL BIOLOGICAL SCIENCE SERIES
Henry Burr Steinbach, Editor

Preface To The Second Edition

WERE IT POSSIBLE to thank individually and publicly the many biologists who have generously written us, sending helpful suggestions based on the first edition of this book, we would gladly do so. These comments plus further personal experience have led to several new conclusions.

1. Although each teacher has his own preferred organization of biological subject matter, he should be so broadly based in his subject as to be able and willing to use whatever sequence of topics will best build interest, enthusiasm, and curiosity in his students.

2. Initially, no doubt because students are animals and not plants, discussion of topics related closely and obviously to man and mammals has a far stronger appeal to most beginners.

3. Transfer of comprehension from the more familiar vertebrate anatomy and physiology to the less familiar invertebrate and plant counterparts is easier than the converse approach.

4. Extensive use of the compound microscope is more successful when planned as a block, so that technical skills are built and maintained.

To match these conclusions we have rearranged chapter material. By entering the subject through its economic aspects, the student becomes quickly aware of the social ramifications of biology, and sees the need for a systematic arrangement of the plant and animal kingdoms. By following the discussion of values with a brief consideration of classification, the taxonomic framework comes more naturally. It then holds familiar knowledge and provides a basis for later expansion.

At an early stage, the familiar is met again in examination of the chordates, for which the chief tools are simple dissecting instruments. Non-chordate multicellular animals are presented as alternative designs which meet the same functional specifications. The single-cell organisms provide a logical bridge to the plant kingdom on the one hand, and through the viruses to the non-living chemical world on the other. We have amplified the consideration of plants to emphasize again the alternatives in design features and the limitations each design imposes. For ease of presentation, hormonal coordination is treated separately in connection with multicellular function of animals and of plants; from the teaching standpoint the common denominators in hormones seemed less important.

While up-dating on the basis of new discoveries has been incorporated in all chapters, we have continued to hold taxonomic and anatomical detail to a minimum. We believe that for the student of *general* biology, allocation of time and space to a discussion of the social implications of the subject—particularly conservation—is of far greater ultimate importance. The chapter on man's future has been reorganized to make its message clearer. We have inserted a selected series of references to informative supplementary material in books and magazines.

As in the previous edition, in lieu of a glossary, each technical term is indexed. We believe that a term or its definition has little importance on its own. It is but the hook on which to hang all future information on the topic. No one gains an understanding of baseball as an exciting game from nine, two-line definitions of the playing positions and a diagram of the field. No one gains an understanding of a community of plants and animals, or of the cooperating cells composing each one, or of the company of molecules in living substance, from brief definitions of the component parts. For this reason we encourage the student to develop instead a general understanding of each word.

L.J.M. & M.J.M.

Acknowledgments

THE LARGEST STOREHOUSES of ideas that we have tapped in preparing this volume are certainly the minds of those who taught us, the books we have read, and the conversations of colleagues. Our gratitude to these sources is nonspecific but strong. For definite and helpful criticism in the presentation of our material we are greatly indebted to Doctors H. G. Albaum and M. L. Gabriel of Brooklyn College, Harold C. Bold of Vanderbilt University, C. A. Lawson of Michigan State College, Louis B. Marks of Fordham University, H. Burr Roney of the University of Houston, R. L. Waterson of Northwestern University, and H. B. Steinbach of the University of Chicago. Dr. E. O. Dodson, then of the University of Notre Dame, suggested ways to improve our chapter on evolution. Editorial assistance of the friendliest and most judicious kind has been available to us in Mr. J. B. Plate, through numberless letters and conferences.

For illustrative material we are grateful to many: the American Museum of Natural History (Photo 403); *Arizona Highways* magazine (Photos 170, 341–342); the Army Medical Museum (Photos 23–24, 114, 203–205); the Australian News and Information Service (Photos 358–368); the Bausch & Lomb Optical Co. (Photos 50–52, 142–143); the Boyce Thompson Institute for Plant Research, Inc. (Photos 193–194); Dr. Ralph Buchsbaum (Photo 99, from *Animals Without Backbones,* University of Chicago Press, revised edition, 1948); the Canadian Department of Agriculture (Photos 16, 423–426); the Carolina Biological Supply Co. (Photos 91, 120, 136–137, 201–202, 347, 355); the Chanticleer Press (Photos 397–398, from L. Hogben's *From Cave Painting to Comic Strip,* 1949); Dr. G. W. Corner of the Dept. of Embryology, Carnegie Institution of Washington (Photos 222–225); the Cranbrook Institute of Science (Photos 98, 274, 378, 431); Dr. A. M. Elliott (Figs. 18-10, 20-7, 21-11, 21-18, 24-2, 24-3, from *Zoology,* Appleton-Century-Crofts, Inc., 2nd edition, 1957); the Elsevier Publishing Co. and Dr. Maurice Burton (Photos 138, 231, 302–304, 411, 458); the Federal Bureau of Investigation and Mr. J. E. Hoover (Fig. 19-14); Dr. Paul D. Foote and *Scientific Monthly* (Fig. 7-2); W. H. Freeman & Co. (Fig. 11-4, from G. Hardin's *Biology—Its Human Implications,* 2nd edition, 1954); the Fouke Fur Co. (Photo 446); Dr. J. L. Gamble of the Dept. of Pediatrics, Harvard Medical School (Photos 60–61); the General Biological Supply House, Inc. (Figs. 4-4, 20-2, 20-3, 21-5, 21-6, Photos 64, 79, 88, 103–104, 107, 127, 140–141, 153–155, 163, 197, 210–217, 250, 348–351, 457); Geological Survey of Canada (Photos 401, 407–408, 412–414); Dr. R. B. Greenblatt of the Medical College of Georgia (Photo 124); Dr. L. A. Kenoyer and the Armazy Sponge Co. of Detroit (Photo 87); Dr. L. O. Kunkel of the Rockefeller Institute for Medical Research (Photo 145); the McGraw-Hill Book Co. (Figs. 8-17, 23-4, from T. I. Storer and R. L. Usinger, *General Zoology,* 3rd edition, 1957); Marine Studios, Marineland, Florida (Photos 69–71, 101); Merck & Co., Inc. (Photo 151); the National Audubon Society (Photo 456); the New York Zoological Society (Photo 430); Dr. E. A. Park and the F. A. Davis Co. (Photos 62–63, from Park and Eliot, *Cyclopedia of Medicine,* 1951 edition); the Radio Corporation of America (Photos 54–56); R. C. A. and Dr. R. Wyckoff (Photos 144, 147, 149, from Wyckoff's *Electron Microscopy, Technique and Applications,* Interscience Publishers, Inc., 1949); Mr. C. G. Reather, Dept. of Embryology, Carnegie Institution of Washington (Photo 221); Miss Jane Roller of Washington, D. C., and Dr. L. A. Kenoyer of Western Michigan College of Education, and Harper & Bros. (Fig. 9-8, from Kenoyer & Goddard, *General Biology,* 1945); *Scientific American* and K. Chester (Photo 422); Dr. E. K. Shelton of the Shelton Clinic, Los Angeles (Photos 125–126); Mr. H. Spencer of Chester, Conn. (Photos 20, 22, 34, 157, 180–182, 219–220, 252, 256, 280, 387); E. R. Squibb & Sons (Photos 57–59); Dr. W. C. Stanley of the Virus Laboratory, University of California (Photos 146, 148); C. C. Thomas, Inc. and Dr. Z. P. Metcalf (Figs. 8-13, 8-16, 11-10, 23-10, from *An Introduction to Zoology,* 1932); Mr. H. F. Thornley of Utah State Agricultural College (Photo 26); the U. S. Department of the Interior, Fish & Wildlife Service (Fig. 21-12, Photos 36, 38–41, 49, 68, 288, 445, 447, 449–453, 459, 461–463, Endpaper Photo *O*); the U. S. Department of Agriculture, Forest Service (Photos 14–15, 19, 31–32, 373, 441–442), Soil Conservation Service (Figs. 24-6, 24-7, 24-8,

Photos 433–440), Bureau of Entomology and Plant Quarantine (Photos 27–30, 33, 35, 255, 320–322), Bureau of Plant Industry, Soils, and Agricultural Engineering (Photos 17–18, 21, 427); Ward's Natural Science Establishment, Inc. (Photos 77, 81, 92, 134–135, 162, 246, 261, 310, 316, 415, 419, 429); the Williams & Wilkins Co. (Photos 420–421, from P. Popenoe, *The Child's Heredity,* 1929); Mr. William Woodin III (Photo 2); and Dr. P. W. Zimmerman of the Boyce Thompson Institute for Plant Research, Inc. (Photos 188–190).

The remaining line drawings and photographs were freshly prepared for this book. For many of them we used Tessar and Microtessar lenses, Balcoted by the Bausch & Lomb Optical Co. to yield improved definition. Drs. Roy L. Donahue and Harry L. Shapiro kindly supplied data for Figs. 21-18 and 23-14, respectively. With many of the photomicrographs we had expert assistance from Mr. John W. Anderson. He has kindly permitted us to use his own photographs in the end papers (*I, K*).

For permission to include extracts from their books we are obliged to Harper & Bros. (Mark Twain's *A Tramp Abroad,* 1880 and G. Eckstein's *Everyday Miracle,* 1948); Houghton-Mifflin Co. (D. C. Peattie's *American Heartwood,* 1949, and D. C. Peattie and N. Peattie's *A Cup of Sky,* 1950); Oxford University Press, Inc. (A. Leopold's *A Sand County Almanac,* 1949); *Science* for the comments by W. M. Wheeler; William Sloane Associates, Inc. (L. J. Halle, Jr.'s, *Spring in Washington,* 1947, and J. W. Krutch's *The Twelve Seasons,* 1949); Mr. Roland Young (*Not for Children,* Doubleday, Doran & Co., 1930); and Dodd, Mead, Inc. for use of passages from our own *A Multitude of Living Things* (1947).

For much needed encouragement during the long gestation period of this book and for critical assistance in correcting errors or improving clarity we are particularly appreciative of the efforts of our friends and colleagues in the biology staff at the University of New Hampshire. Dr. Charlotte G. Nast and Dr. Emery F. Swan have been most helpful in these directions.

L.J.M. & M.J.M.

Foreword

IN THIS NEW BOOK on living things, the authors are expressing their own enthusiasm for the broad and integrated approach. They are convinced that a factual understanding of biological science improves chances for a successful, happy, and useful life.

The field of biology is so vast, and annual additions to it so impressive, that elimination of nonessential information seems of paramount importance. We have striven to include chiefly the background needed for intelligent evaluation of reports on scientific progress in modern magazines and newspapers. Yet appreciation of a science differs markedly from that of art, or literature, or history. Science is an edifice, built on interpretation of a growing mass of facts, whereas a picture or a play stands more on its own. Shakespeare, as studied in 1800, 1850, or 1900, remains basically unchanged. History can assume that driving forces go back only a small number of human generations, and any national or international situation can be analyzed in a definite period of years. But if any major body of scientific fact is omitted from consideration, the interpretations based on them no longer have validity. This is the essence of scientific method.

Biology differs vastly from decade to decade and, like other sciences, must be reviewed repeatedly. Only after 1800 was the significance of fossils appreciated widely; after 1850 the evolutionary point of view linked many previously unexplained correlations; that microbes cause disease became evident less than a century ago; in 1900 biology could offer no solid information on heredity; the use of antibiotic substances from living organisms in the treatment of human ills goes back little more than a decade. Vitamins and hormones are recent discoveries. In 1910 no one had done much to analyze the inter-relationships of animals and plants with their environment, or to survey possible needs for conservation practices. Whole new branches of biology arise at irregular intervals, each built on the old and seldom reducing the importance of earlier information.

To save space for emphasis on biological principles and the values of biological study to mankind, we have dispensed with much cherished terminology and detail. Facts are easy to memorize, to look up, and to forget. Principles require for their understanding both factual background and a higher category of mental activity. Understanding becomes a kind of adhesive web to which present and future facts can cling. Pulling information from any point in such an intellectual fabric stretches adjacent parts of the web and brings related data into use. The well-knit mind, supplied with a moderate load of facts, seems far more to be desired than a walking encyclopedia arranged only in alphabetical order. Details committed to memory may have a place in elementary schooling, and they must be a part of the working knowledge of specialists. But the information and approach of the present book are concerned with features needed for comprehension of scientific method, for presentation of biological principles, for understanding of human organization, and for a clear conception of the importance of other animals and plants. Through these avenues life takes on new possibilities and new freedoms.

A significant part of scientific method is analysis of a situation, and description of it in as precise terms as can be managed. We have tried to avoid terms for their own sake, introducing only those that would be needed and met again. Often they are familiar words employed with a more exact significance. To draw attention to them as they arise in the chapters, boldface type has been used. Beyond this vocabulary is the application of it, and this need not be technical. Often it is merely normal curiosity directed into profitable channels. Nor have we neglected the natural history approach that is the beginning and basic satisfaction in biology. A sympathetic interest in fellow living organisms brings greater pleasure in watching them, and provides a saner, better informed realization of the value of a sound conservation program. We hold that such is an essential foundation for every educated person.

An education is what remains as an individual's point of view and mode of thinking after most of the details learned in school have been forgotten. Many of the facts may seem useless in prospect and in immediate retrospect. So are the weary footsteps by which a person climbs a mountain. But without the steps there is no view.

Durham, New Hampshire   L.J.M. & M.J.M.

This book is written not for knowledge, but for action.

—ARISTOTLE

Contents

Endpaper Photos

A Eastern winter: paper birch trees overlooking a snow-covered, frozen lake at the base of Mount Chocorua, New Hampshire.

B Western summer: a young bull moose browsing on vegetation in a shallow beaver pond near Moose, Wyoming, in the broad valley of Jackson Hole.

C A bright-eyed robin watching for earthworms.

D Frontier vegetation along the milky stream issuing as meltwater from the Nisqually Glacier on the side of an extinct American volcano—Mount Ranier in Washington.

E A Pennsylvania katydid on a leaf listens to others of its kind, using "ears" located just below the knee joint of the forelegs.

F As a larva, this longicorn beetle bored galleries in a dying pine tree near Lake Ontario. The spread of the insect's sensitive antennae totaled 4½ inches.

G Sea purses are black leathery bags with a twisted projection at each corner. The projections become entangled in the seaweed among which these eggs are laid, until the young skate or ray hatches. Storms often toss the empty shells on the beach.

H The two large forward-facing eyes of this jumping spider allow it to leap accurately ten to fifteen inches, from branch to branch, or to capture prey. Such a leap amounts to from thirty to fifty times the length of the spider itself.

I Wind-catching parachutes provide transportation for the many seeds in a dandelion head. (Photo by courtesy of John W. Anderson.)

J Morning dew in the Florida Everglades places pearl-like spheres on every orb web strung by a busy spider during the quiet of the night. Some of these webs are six feet across, and stretch from tree to tree.

K A dogfish (shark) just prior to birth, still carrying a supply of food in the large yolk sac. (Photo by courtesy of John W. Anderson.)

L The sacred scarab of Egypt rolls a ball of dung to a suitable burying place, there to leave it together with an egg, as a food store for the hatching larva.

M A sand collar is the egg mass of a large carnivorous snail. It is formed of a mixture of mucus, eggs, and sand around the outspread foot; then the parent departs through the gap, leaving her six-inch product to wave in the sea water until the eggs hatch.

N The chrysalis of a swallowtail butterfly is supported both at the abdominal tip and also by means of a silken loop spun by the caterpillar just before metamorphosis. The transitions from caterpillar to chrysalis and from chrysalis to adult require only a few minutes, but the changes within the chrysalis require a number of days.

O Canada geese over an Arkansas wildlife refuge. (Photo by P. J. Van Huizen, U. S. Fish & Wildlife Service.)

P This large green turtle staring through a porthole of the giant marine aquarium ("ocean-arium") at Marineland, Florida, is a near relative of turtles at Key West, in pens awaiting conversion to turtle soup and turtle steak.

Q The many-branched arms of a basket star may confuse the apparent radial symmetry of its body. Nets reaching the bottom in sea-fishing operations often gather in one of these less familiar echinoderms.

R A young buck of the pronghorn antelope exercises by bouts with others of his kind, and by using his horns to uproot sagebrush or other tough bushes of the arid lands—playing with them as though with a ball.

S Carl Linnaeus reduced the long Latin descriptions of plants and animals to a pair of words which could serve as a scientific name.

T The adult stage of the antlion shows none of the ferocity of the larval stage. The antlion or "doodle bug" excavates conical pits in sandy soil and thrives on the juices of ants or other insects that blunder down the treacherous slopes.

1 · Introduction

EACH YEAR a new class of students begins college work, headed toward a bachelor's degree. Often the individual student lacks a clear idea as to the significance of the coveted letters.

The general public has a far firmer notion of what a college education means, although this notion is unrealistic. "They" expect the holder of a bachelor's degree to be widely read, familiar with the basic principles in every field of learning, and to have a mind ready to apply this knowledge to each problem or discussion that arises. The press may reflect disappointment that fresh graduates come short of these expectations. But the underlying conviction remains unshaken.

The student must exert himself in every one of his four years to merit even part of this esteem. He dares not specialize in language or science, in history or animal husbandry, to the point where his curiosity has no edge in other subject realms. Life is not so tightly compartmented. Prime interests of the moment often become secondary. Progress in a job may be barred because a graduate has deliberately narrowed his education and avoided the background for broader assignments.

1. FRONTIERS

In the liberal arts tradition, an education is a cohesive and cumulative experience. It is aimed toward helping a person toward intellectual maturity, toward informed, considered, nonemotional judgments. It seeks to develop a way of thinking that can be applied to any problem. The benefits of this education are expected to be more obvious ten or twenty years after graduation than during the educational process.

To be useful into an indefinite future and relate to unpredictable events in years to come, an introduction to biology must acquaint the student with the field as a whole, give some historical perspective to the subject, and encourage interest in its progress. Detailed attention cannot be given to any single aspect without sacrificing the breadth of overview.

Unlike some other fields of knowledge, however, biology requires for appreciation of even basic principles a consideration of underlying facts which are unfamiliar to many people. Moreover, the discovery of new facts may call for a change in understanding and a restatement of a scientific principle. But facts have an eternal quality about them, and give stability to the entire subject. This distinction must become clear before scientific progress can be understood.

A general biology course may provide the chief contact between a student and a research investigator. The student needs to learn what the biologist does to gain new information in the field or in his laboratory, and to see how fresh findings are integrated with earlier knowledge in planning future investigations. The frontiers of knowledge lie close enough in biological sciences for the student to see them. On these frontiers newsworthy discoveries are made every year. Gaining a perspective from which to appreciate new advances in biological and medical science is an essential part of a broad education.

2. EVIDENCE

A laboratory science is a way of thinking, of planning experiments, of analyzing results, of seeking implications from facts. The method, rather than the facts, may seem the most important feature.

Scientific method is a state of mind. It shows progress in a lack of finality in findings. It stresses open-mindedness, tolerance for judgments toward which factual support is ready, and caution over opinions lacking this background. It displays wide interest in every ramification of any piece of information. With practice, this way of thinking becomes a habit of thought. It encourages a person in any field of endeavor to inquire "What is the evidence?" And to expect an honest, verifiable answer.

3. GENERALIZATIONS

If biology were merely a cataloguing of information, a process of pigeonholing facts, of accumulating an encyclopedia, it would not be a science. But the facts are related to one another. A disease of plants has features in common with a different disease of animals. Human respiration is like the respiratory process in almost any living thing. Even the building blocks of which animals and plants are constructed are composed of corresponding materials throughout. Consequently, information learned about one type of life can often be applied (after testing) to others, including man.

In biology a search is made for generalizations that can be applied. The breadth of each is measured. Underlying causes are sought. And practical advantage is seen in this interchangeability of information. It becomes worth while to study every kind of living thing.

4. PERSONAL RESPONSIBILITIES

Each human being is a separate animal. Like every other living thing, he is a cooperating system of component parts. So long as the components operate normally and coordination is good, the individual is "healthy." If something goes wrong, symptoms of abnormality appear.

Usually the first observer of these symptoms is the person afflicted. This is true partly because a physician cannot live with his patient as intimately as the patient lives with himself. And to know when a physician's help should be asked, a person needs to know as much as possible about what each symptom can mean.

The value of personal understanding of body function and early recognition of significant symptoms can be seen in the statistics for death from cancer. A far smaller percentage of

medical men die from this malady than is characteristic of the population as a whole. Most medical men detect their own cancer symptoms early enough to be cured.

5. PUBLIC RESPONSIBILITIES

Whether he likes it or not, man is completely dependent upon green plants for all the food he eats, all the oxygen he breathes, for the continuous flow of many of the springs from which he obtains drinking water, for lumber, and for many other materials used in technology. His welfare is linked to the continued activity of green plants. Anything that is detrimental to green plants is harmful indirectly to mankind.

It is not enough for a few specialists to know how a plant operates, and to understand what affects plant welfare. The future course of civilization depends to only a limited extent upon scientists. It is the general public, their elected officials in government, and appointees of these people, who determine policies affecting the future of all.

The educated person must know enough of the structure, operation, and role of vegetation to be able to express an intelligent, informed opinion when his participation in public affairs demands it. The pros and cons of a new dam for electric power or irrigation may involve the submergence of vegetation. Is the overall picture worth while or likely to be detrimental? Installation of sewage disposal systems or smoke-abatement devices may raise the costs of local commodities. Is the expenditure advisable? What is at stake? The responsible citizen cannot depend entirely on the advice of experts. He must be able to evaluate their recommendations, to ask further facts, and to understand what he is supporting. These responsibilities require knowledge.

Man, with his civilization and domesticated animals, constitutes the chief hazard for plant life today. Unwittingly he can upset age-old balances between local plants and local animals. Neither the plants nor the animals concerned may be of any direct interest to him, but their balanced activities determine in large degree that the land he occupies has the characteristics he finds worth using.

This balance is not merely the problem of

the forester, the lumberman, the farmer, the rancher, the trader, or the businessman. The standard of living of the entire country is threatened. It becomes everybody's business to see that our lands are not wasted, that we build for the future by wise use of the present.

Many of these responsibilities are delegated to government agencies. Agencies, however, function properly only as long as they know the citizenry to be vitally interested in their operations, and aware of recommendations and practices. Agencies cannot succeed without the support, both financial and moral, of the people they represent.

To appreciate better these practical problems, it is important to have a reasonable awareness of the plants and other animals. A nodding acquaintance with the various kinds of creatures leads to a respect for them and their rights to life. This appreciation leads naturally toward enlightened cooperation with conservation programs. It develops at the same time a better understanding of the complexities of human existence.

Even the pursuit of happiness—guaranteed by our Constitution—is easier if hobbies are at hand. In the biology field, hobbies can have the double value of enjoyment by the individual and extension of scientific knowledge for the benefit of all.

Sometimes the information organized in biological science seems impressive. One central fact should be kept in mind: What is now known about living things is infinitesimal in comparison with what remains to be discovered.

EDUCATION

It has been said before that a fundamental aim of education is to enable men to live in time and space beyond the present and the immediate. The majority of uneducated men and women appear to lead entirely somnambulistic lives, never pausing between the cradle and the grave to look up from the immediate task in hand, never raising their heads to take stock of the long past or to survey the plains and mountain ranges that surround them. In their trade, in their daily occupations, even in the thoughts they express and the opinions they hold, they move without consciousness of worlds beyond their own. Ask the uneducated tailor for a description of the universe and see if it does not bear a striking resemblance to his own shop, even though the reality stretches away from his door. To the uneducated politician the goal of life is the advancement of his party, to the uneducated intellectual it is the advancement of his cause or the acceptance of his dogma. Each measures the world by his own shadow, overlooking the assistance he had from the sun in casting it. All these people are the victims of circumstances they cannot hope to understand, whether it is the American mechanic who shouts for democracy or the European barber who shouts for a dictator. In their somnambulism they are bound to the wheel of the immediate present, and will be freed only when education has awakened them to the breadth and scope of the universe they share in common.

—LOUIS J. HALLE, JR. in *Spring in Washington* (New York: William Sloane Associates, Inc., 1947), pp. 40-41.

2 · Methods in Biology

1. SCIENTIFIC METHOD—PROCEDURE, POINT OF VIEW. 2. LANGUAGE. 3. UNDERSTANDING.

A CATALOGUE of plants and animals according to the uses found for them is not biology, although the science of biology arose out of such practical information. Biology is the study of life, especially of the characteristics which plants and animals have in common.

Like so many scientific terms, the word **biology** stems from classic roots—in this case the Greek words *bios* (= life) and *logos* (= study). *Logos* also signifies reason, discussion, and consideration. These too are aspects of the study of living things.

Detailed examination of the plant kingdom alone is a specialty: **botany** (from the Greek *botane* = an herb). Corresponding study of animals is **zoology** (from the Greek *zoon* = an animal). These distinctions should be evident to anyone who has visited a botanical garden or a zoological park ("zoo").

People who study zoology professionally are **zoologists;** those who study plants are **botanists.** If they are interested in both primarily while the plants and animals are in their native haunts, the biologists usually consider themselves to be **naturalists.**

When all the animals of a region are considered together, they are referred to as the **fauna.** Correspondingly, the plants constitute the **flora.** All of these living things may be grouped as the **biota** or the biotic world, as contrasted with the inanimate world (the mineral kingdom). Often the general term **organism** is used for any plant or animal.

The number of different animals and plants is so vast that scientists must specialize for research work. Some are specialists on birds (**ornithologists,** from the Greek *ornis* = bird), on anatomical features (**morphologists,** from the Greek *morphos* = form or shape), on vital processes (**physiologists,** from the Greek *physis* = nature), and the like. Each specialty is a subdivision of the realm of biology. Botany, zoology, and the more general biology, by contrasts, are descendent parts of the older field of study called "natural history" or "natural science" (from the Latin *scientia* = knowledge).

1. SCIENTIFIC METHOD

In both the natural sciences and the physical sciences, a fundamental procedure has been found useful. It is called the "scientific method," and is a system leading to the discovery of facts and relationships between facts.

Facts do not constitute science any more than a pile of jigsaw puzzle pieces constitute a picture. The eternal quest of science is the relationship between facts. The goal is "understanding," as an overall picture which can be grasped when each fact is seen in its proper place. Without facts, however, a generalization may have no validity.

The essence of a scientific fact is its verifiability. If an observation can be repeated in almost identical form every time by any investigator who chooses to duplicate the conditions specified in the original scientific record, the observed phenomenon can be regarded as a fact. This repeatability is fundamental, and explains why so few claims are accepted until independent workers have done the work over again in the same or slightly different ways, and have obtained substantially identical results. Unless information is verifiable, it is not scientific and can not be considered reliable enough to form the basis for a prediction.

Thus a specimen of a plant or animal is itself a fact only so long as it can be re-examined. Museums are full of specimens ready for re-examination. The geographical locality at which a specimen was collected (latitude, longitude, altitude or depth) and the date (including the time of day) may be shown by a label. They are claims, not facts. They may be verified if another collector finds further specimens of the same kind of organism near the original locality on dates not far removed. After this verification, the earlier claim may be relied upon.

The respiratory exchange of carbon dioxide for oxygen from the atmosphere is a fact, since repeated observations show it to be a reliable occurrence. But this statement of a verifiable fact does not explain what happens to the oxygen or where the carbon dioxide comes from. Science accepts responsibility for discovering such relationships.

Scientific knowledge is. peculiarly democratic. The facts must be the same no matter who views them. Usually the method whereby a fact is demonstrated is part of that fact. It may be a statistical measure of the frequency with which an event can be expected.

Since scientific facts are in the nature of evidence, the aim in collecting them is to reach a conclusion. A valid conclusion linking scientific facts is regarded as a *law* (of nature). Scientific laws differ from civil laws, in that they are not "passed." Instead, each is guessed

at, and then offered for others to check. Each begins as a highly intelligent guess, based upon relevant facts.

Certain scientists seem to excel in making good guesses, just as some people are outstanding in devising ways to test each suggestion. Mention will be made of many of these men. Where space permits and interest warrants, a few details of their evidence will be related.

The growth of scientific knowledge to the point where a law can be stated is a slow process, usually requiring the efforts of many people. Yet when viewed in retrospect, the procedural steps seem comparable in any field of scientific endeavor:

Procedure

1. *Orientation*—A scientist's curiosity is aroused by an observation or an idea. He becomes aware that a problem exists.

2. *Exploration*—He tests the situation to see what he can observe about it, and if observations are repeatable. If he is thorough, he collects together all the information he can find on the subject. The accumulated observations or facts can be termed **data,** a plural word (the singular is *datum*).

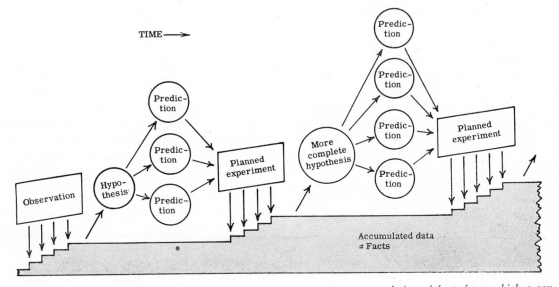

FIG. 2-1. *The steps in growth of scientific knowledge consist of an accumulation of facts from which a generalization (hypothesis) can be drawn, from which in turn predictions can be made leading to experiments and discovery of new facts that make a more complete generalization possible.*

3. *Explanation*—The scientist reasons out an explanation which will account for the inter-relations evident among the data. This is an **hypothesis,** often called a "working hypothesis" comparable to the "work sheet" full of preliminary calculations in solving a problem.

4. *Testing the hypothesis*—He designs experiments he can try, to provide him with new data which will extend knowledge and at the same time to try out the hypothesis by checking actual findings against predictions based upon the assumed explanation (Fig. 2-1).

He conducts the experiments under precisely known conditions, to learn the effect of varying a single factor at a time. He repeats the study again and again to make sure that the results do not vary significantly. He tries "control experiments" to satisfy himself that the factor varied is the only one causing any observed difference. In these control experiments he follows all the steps in the test experiment except those concerned with the studied factor. No significant variation is expected of a control experiment.

He repeats any experiments described by others if they do not fit into his hypothesis. If the results confirm the earlier reports, the explanation must be modified. If his new results contradict the old, he should attempt to learn why the earlier work gave different results.

5. *Communication*—After he has analyzed his experimental study, the scientist feels himself obligated professionally to present his findings and hypothesis at a scientific meeting or to publish them in a scientific journal read widely by those interested in the same line of research. Into this report should go not only details of his own work in a full enough form to allow any other scientist to repeat the experiments, but also a complete bibliography of previous investigations, a comprehensive review of the work of others, a concise summary of his own findings, and a clear presentation of his conclusions.

If the summary of relationships pertains to more than a very narrow field, and the explanation for the correlated data is detailed, it may constitute an outline so well supported as to be termed a **theory.** Presentation of an hypothesis or theory places it before others for criticism and appraisal, and at the same time claims modest credit for the work on which it is based.

If, as years pass, the explanation given is found adequate to include many new data, the acceptance accorded a theory may bring it into the category of a scientific **principle** or law. By then it has come a long way from the original highly intelligent guess, and by its stability becomes surer of continued importance.

Regardless of whether a generalization is at the level of hypothesis, theory, or principle, a single valid fact that completely contradicts it is sufficient to topple the entire edifice. A partial contradiction may require only a modification in the explanation, "bringing it up to date." Changes of a minor nature are common in scientific understanding.

The overthrow of a theory does not alter the facts upon which it was based. And the new fact that upsets previous ideas adds to the basis upon which a future theory will be built.

Point of View

As one "law of nature" after another has been discovered and analyzed, each has been found to depend upon the laws of chemistry and physics, and to be subject to restatement in precise mathematical terms. As a result, the mystical aspects of life have gradually decreased in number.

On this basis the scientist is willing to make another prediction: that all of the complex aspects of living things obey definite physical and chemical laws, in a purely mechanical manner. This approach to study is termed a "mechanistic" one, in contrast with a "vitalistic" point of view which would call upon unknown "vital forces" to explain living activities.

Observation, measurement, and recording go with the mechanistic approach. They lead to progress, to hypotheses, and to new investigations. Although there may be truth in vitalistic explanations, no experiment can be designed to elucidate the mystical. Vitalistic approaches cannot be verified experimentally and hence may be regarded as outside the field of science.

Keeping facts and interpretations separate is not always easy. A conclusion (= hypothesis) as to the relationship between observed phenomena may be so convincing that it is taken to be a fact itself. But when the scientist inquires "why" some phenomenon exists, he seeks a mechanistic explanation, a detailed account of the steps leading to the event.

The distinction between these two points of view can be clarified with an example: A person winds his watch with a definite end in view: to keep it running *so that* he can consult it and learn the correct time. It would be very foolish, however, to say that the watch runs in order to show the time. It runs because the main spring contains a supply of potential energy (supplied by winding it), and because the gears are arranged in such a way that the release of this energy moves the hands slowly at predetermined speeds.

Similarly a digestive gland does not elaborate its secretion in order to allow digestion of a meal. It elaborates that product because of its inherent structure (like the watch), because it is supplied with raw materials including energy, and because it is stimulated into activity.

A leaf manufactures foodstuffs used by the green plant, but the biologist carefully dodges reference to this as purpose. He states, instead, that the leaf is green because it contains a particular pigment, that the foodstuffs are manufactured because the organization of the leaf permits it, and that the leaf is there because certain parts of the plant became arranged into the components of a bud, and the bud underwent definite changes that made it into a leaf. Only by analyzing each detail in this objective, descriptive way can the facts be kept uppermost. Living activities are brought about by mechanisms, not by goals, though they may serve an end and do so astonishingly well. But interpretations based on goals are **teleological** (from *telos* = end) rather than scientific.

2. LANGUAGE

Part, at least, of the accomplishments of science are due to the care taken in describing each object or event in the most precise way possible. Where no satisfactory word exists for naming some aspect, a new term must be invented. Occasionally, loose usage is recognized and terms are discarded in favor of new ones that avoid ambiguity. Commonly, terms have a classical origin in Latin or Greek, and can be associated with other familiar words when one meets them for the first time. **Microscope, stethoscope,** and **telescope,** for example, make use of the same roots as *microbe, microphone, microtome, telephone,* and *television.* (Greek *micros* = small, *stethos* = breast, *tele* = far, *phone* = sound, *scopein* = see, *tome* = a cutting, and the Latin *visus* = a seeing.) Usually all parts of the word are taken from a single language; sometimes this procedure is not followed.

The multiplicity of terms used in a science like biology is sometimes discouraging to a beginner. Not infrequently the criticism is heard: "Scientific description consists of laboriously stating the obvious." But the obvious is usually an ill-understood whole, whereas the laborious and technical description draws attention to the component details on which further information should be found if the whole is to be understood—not merely accepted. Thus a beginner may have difficulty in such a seemingly simple task as describing where his navel is. First the scientist would avoid the English word navel (from the Anglo-Saxon *nafela*), in favor of the more universally understood Latin term **umbilicus.** He would describe the mark as a depression in the **mid line** of the body, and refer to it as being on the **ventral** surface. This would locate the navel with more precision. The ventral surface is contrasted with the **dorsal** surface (from the Latin *venter* = belly, and *dorsum* = back); between them on each side is a **lateral** surface. Similarly in biological terminology the head is the **anterior** end of the animal; at the opposite extremity is the **posterior** end (a tail, if any). Human arms are described as the anterior paired **appendages,** whereas the legs are the posterior pair of these. The upper arm or the thigh would be termed the **proximal** part of the appendage in each case, whereas the hand or foot would be the **distal** (from the same root as *distant*). Parts which are closer to the mid line than others are said to lie in a **medial** direction.

Unlike some living things, man is possessed of a right side and a left. His body is reasonably symmetrical, with the right half a mirror image of the left. The proper term for this type of symmetry is **bilateral** (from *bi* = two). A cylinder, on the other hand, has two ends but a **radial** symmetry; it can be cut lengthwise on any diameter to yield mirror images. A sphere has **universal** symmetry (Fig. 2-2).

The symmetry of the organism is usually considered carefully when studying animals of smaller size, where the body may be cut into

One pair of biological symbols should be acquired early. In both plants and animals, sex can usually be recognized. Often it constitutes an essential part of an observed fact. The scientist has adopted the symbol ♂ for male, following astronomical and astrological practice dating from before the dawn of written history. The ♂ sign represents the shield and spear of Mars, the paragon of maleness among the Greek gods. Correspondingly ♀ is the sign for female, and represents the hand mir-

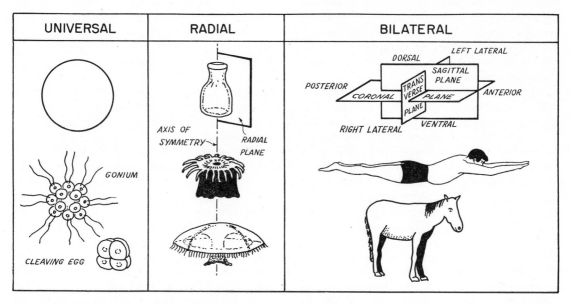

FIG. 2-2. *Universal symmetry involves essential similarity in structure along any radius from a central point. Radial symmetry is centered about a longitudinal axis, as in a cylinder. Bilateral symmetry shows mirror-imaging only between right and left. Conventional directions and sections for study are shown.*

slices and each of them examined in turn. These sections may be made *transversely*— in which case they are generally called **cross sections,** suggesting the units of sliced bread. Or they may be cut *longitudinally,* either horizontally (separating dorsal from ventral) as **coronal** sections, or vertically (separating right from left) as **sagittal** sections. Cross sections and longitudinal sections can be made through radially symmetrical animals or plants. The one longitudinal slice that includes the mid line in bilateral symmetry is unique; it is the mid-sagittal section, and it often shows enough more detail to be of particular interest. In radially symmetrical forms, the section including the axis of symmetry is the only one that gives an undistorted view of the radial arrangement of internal structures.

ror of Venus, most feminine of the Greek goddesses. The plural of ♂ is ♂ ♂, so that a foursome might be indicated biologically as 2 ♂ ♂ 2 ♀ ♀.

Care should be given to acquiring a basic vocabulary of scientific terms. Those used in this book have been held to a minimum consistent with accurate description and understanding. They constitute the essential language of biology and demonstrate the need for precise usage.

3. UNDERSTANDING

Animals and plants are not merely assemblages of named parts. They are working organisms with a wide variety of processes going on simultaneously as long as they are alive.

The architecture of each organism determines to a considerable degree the possible range within which it can operate. The mode of functioning is highly important to an appreciation of the structure, or of the conditions under which the plant or animal can live. Seldom is there only a single way in which organisms can meet living conditions. Usually different kinds exhibit a variety of answers to the same basic demands of life. An understanding of these solutions to common problems leads to a more complete visualization of the limiting factors which surround each organism. As such, a strong attempt should be made to become intimately acquainted with each major style of living thing, to evaluate the modes by which it operates, thrives, and reproduces, meeting competition for food and space in ways comparable to those employed by mankind.

TOO MANY "THINGS"

The following description of how they hitch up horses in Europe shows what a humorist can do with a lack of technical terms:

The man stands up the horses on each side of the thing that projects from the front end of the wagon, throws the gear on top of the horses, and passes the thing that goes forward through a ring, and hauls it aft, and passes the other thing through the other ring and hauls it aft on the other side of the other horse, opposite to the first one, after crossing them and bringing the loose end back, and then buckles the other thing underneath the horse, and takes another thing and wraps it around the thing I spoke of before, and puts another thing over each horse's head, and puts the iron thing in his mouth, and brings the ends of these things aft over his back, after buckling another one around under his neck, and hitching another thing on a thing that goes over his shoulder, and then takes the slack of the thing which I mentioned a while ago and fetches it aft and makes it fast to the thing that pulls the wagon, and hands the other things up to the driver.

—MARK TWAIN, in *A Tramp Abroad* (New York: Harper & Bros.), vol. 2, p. 19.

SUGGESTED READING (see p. 506)

Recent and Informative: Bahm, 1944.

3 · The Variety of Life

1. NAMES FOR ANIMALS AND PLANTS. 2. HIGHER CATEGORIES. 3. IDENTIFICATION. 4. THE PHYLA OF LIFE—THE VARIOUS PHYLA OF THALLOPHYTES, PHYLUM BRYOPHYTA, PHYLUM TRACHEOPHYTA, PHYLUM PROTOZOA, PHYLA OF THE "LOWER INVERTEBRATES," PHYLUM MOLLUSCA, PHYLUM ANNELIDA, PHYLUM ARTHROPODA, PHYLUM ECHINODERMATA, PHYLUM CHORDATA. 5. MAN AS A PART OF LIFE.

1. NAMES FOR ANIMALS AND PLANTS

And out of the ground the LORD God formed every beast of the field, and every fowl of the air; and brought them unto Adam to see what he would call them; and whatsoever Adam called every living creature, that was the name thereof. —Genesis 2:19.

ADAM may also have given names to the plants, but never since that day has there been universal agreement on what any living thing was called. Not only is a horse known as *cheval, Pferd, equus,* and *caballo*—according to the language involved—but in English the horse may be a stallion if a mature ♂, a gelding if desexed, a mare if a ♀, a foal if newborn, a coĩt if a young ♂, and a filly if a young ♀. Within a single tongue, too, the same kind of creature may be designated very differently according to the geographic locality, or several organisms may be confused under a single name. Thus in Texas there are "horn frogs" which are lizards, "toad frogs" (warty and phlegmatic) which would be simply toads in New England, and "green frogs" which may not be green but which are smooth-skinned and restricted to humid or wet localities. Even in the relatively small area of the northeastern states, the common earthworm is known variously as angleworm, fishworm, mudworm, easworm, eastworm, angledog, and night crawler. Such confusion has no place in science.

Far back in history the naming of plants and animals seems not to have provided so much difficulty. In the pre-Christian era there was little travel, and each educated person might come to know the common herbs, shrubs and trees, and the animals large enough to be of obvious importance to man. A heritage of plant names came down to the Greeks from the *Rhizotomoi,* the guild of root-cutters whose skill lay in collecting ingredients for early medicines. The Ebers papyrus (1500 B.C.) lists Egyptian drug plants and their uses. Animal names were from many sources—hunters, fishermen, and the priest cult who foretold the future from examination of the viscera of freshly killed birds and mammals.

From the time of Aristotle and his student Theophrastus (the "father of zoology" 384-322 B.C., and the "father of botany" 370-286 B.C., respectively), few names were added until the years of the Crusades (1096-1272 A.D.). Then men from northern Europe journeyed into Asia Minor and noted differences in the vegetation and animal life. Marco Polo brought back fantastic tales of far places. The Western Hemisphere was discovered and further unknown kinds of life came to Europe as trophies. The problem of naming animals and plants became acute, and the long Latin descriptions became painfully verbose. To keep the record straight, some men busied themselves with illustrated books telling about all the different animals known; these reference works were known as *bestiaries.* Corresponding volumes on plants were *herbals.* Classification rested on the economic uses of each kind.

Into this chaos came a young botanist who had traveled widely in and from his native Sweden (Photo 1). He was familiar with all the difficulties due to the unwieldy descriptions naming plants. A sentence-long diagnosis was the "name" of the buttercup, and still doubt remained as to whether a yellow daisy or a marsh marigold was indicated. Various suggestions had been made by previous and contemporary writers, but none of them had had courage enough to organize plant science on a systematic basis. Carl von Linné (1707-1778), known by his Latin pen-name as Carolus Linnaeus, carried through the arduous task, beginning with a little book called *Systema Naturae,* published at Leyden in 1735. After it came others, each a little better than its predecessor, until in 1753 he brought out *Species Plantarum,* and in 1758 the tenth edition of *Systema Naturae.* In both he had achieved consistency for the first time. The plants in *Species Plantarum* and the animals in *Systema Naturae* were arranged in groups according to **structural similarities,** and each received a two-word name. Neither notion was new, but the 1753 and 1758 books placed the method on such a clear footing that we begin our modern naming of living things at these dates.

The two words sufficing to name each kind were of classic extraction, and for many years the formal descriptions that accompanied the scientific names were invariably in Latin. Those for plants still are. But all individuals similar in form and life history were now classified together into the same **species,** and similar species were grouped into higher categories called **genera.** Each genus of plants was to have a name unique in the vegetable kingdom; each genus of animals must be unlike any other generic name in the animal kingdom. The same specific name could not be employed for more than one kind of organism within the same genus. Thus the various kinds of oak trees were grouped in the genus *Quercus,* but each kind had its proper species name: *Quercus alba,* white oak; *Quercus phellos,* willow oak; *Quercus virginiana,* live oak; *Quercus rubra,* red oak, and so on. Similarly, walnut trees were placed in the genus *Juglans,* and the black walnut became *Juglans nigra.* The American elm was named *Ulmus americana,* and one kind of goldenrod *Solidago sempervirens.* These names were adopted on a world-wide scale, so that *Q. alba* was the only name applied by scientific men anywhere to a white oak such as Linnaeus described.

Correspondingly, in the animal kingdom the mouse and rat took places in the genus *Mus;* one was *Mus musculus,* the house mouse, the other *Mus rattus,* the brown rat. Man became *Homo sapiens,* the house cat *Felis domestica,* and the lion *Felis leo.* The generic name was spelled with a capital letter, the specific name usually with a lower case initial, and both customarily are printed in italics.

By no means everyone followed Linnaeus' system at once. But as time went on, more and more persons adhered to his principles, and the work of nonconformists was given progressively less credit. His genus-and-species method came to be known as **binomial nomenclature,** and through international agreements reached at various times in the 1800's, standard rules of botanical and zoological nomenclature came into being. Beginning with Linnaeus' 1753 and 1758 books as the earliest acceptable, the name for an animal or plant is the first one applied to it under certain specified conditions—including the stipulation that the name must be a binomial. This is the **rule of priority.** Credit is often given to the author who first describes a species, by adding his name without punctuation between: *Ranunculus abortivus* L. (the small-flowered buttercup), *Fasciola hepatica* L. (the sheep liver fluke), or *Pinus rigida* Miller (the pitch pine). Only Linnaeus' name is abbreviated to a single letter.

2. HIGHER CATEGORIES

Linnaeus included 312 genera and close to 10,000 species of animals in his *Systema Naturae,* and grouped all of the insects into 72 genera. Knowledge of additional kinds has gone forward at a tremendous pace, until at present about 345,000 kinds of plants and 841,000 species of animals are recognized. New ones are found almost every day. To keep so many genera and species in an understandable array, it has been necessary to add further subdivisions to the plant and animal kingdoms, grouping genera into **families,** families into **orders,** orders into **classes,** and classes into **phyla.** Thus, a modern view of the classification of a white pine and a man would include the following categories, in sequence of increasingly limited significance:

Kingdom Plantae
  Phylum Tracheophyta (vascular plants)
    Class Gymnospermae (naked seeded)
      Order Coniferales (cone-bearing)
        Family Pinaceae (the pines)
          Genus and species:
            Pinus strobus L. (white pine)

Kingdom Animalia
  Phylum Chordata (mostly vertebrates)
    Class Mammalia (mammals)
      Order Primates (primates)
        Family Hominidae (men & sub-men)
          Genus and species:
            Homo sapiens L. (man)

An earthworm and a horse would differ from man and the degree of difference be evident from the classification:

Kingdom Animalia
  Phylum Annelida (segmented worms)
    Class Oligochaeta (bristle-bearing)
      Order Terricolae (earthworms and kin)
        Family Lumbricidae (earthworms)
          Genus and species:
            Lumbricus terrestris L. (the large earthworm of Europe and eastern North America)

Kingdom Animalia
  Phylum Chordata (mostly vertebrates)
    Class Mammalia (mammals)
      Order Perissodactyla (odd-toed hoof-bearers)
        Family Equidae (horses and kin)
          Genus and species:
            Equus caballus L. (the horse)

3. IDENTIFICATION

Since there are more than a million different kinds of living things to keep in order, the task of identifying specimens has become a distinct and highly technical branch of biology—the field of systematics or **taxonomy** (from the Greek *taxis* = arrangement). Taxonomists must be extremely critical of minute differences in structure, seeking those that are least variable, and watching for slight dissimilarities in life history and reproductive isolation which may involve the inability (or ability) to hybridize. These are criteria for distinguishing one species from another. Each year thousands of pages of scientific journals are given over to descriptions of newly recognized species and genera, and to clearer descriptions and new illustrations of kinds on which earlier writings were vague.

In accordance with the basic procedures of scientific verifiability, descriptions of new species are based on specimens preserved permanently in public and private collections, where they are available for restudy by anyone competent and interested. Each species is represented by as many specimens as possible (within reason) so that the full range of variation will be shown. Often the collection of a species is kept in some definite arrangement, as a series demonstrating, for example, the size of leaf or the blackness of pigmentation in feathers. Those specimens upon which the description of a new species is based are mentioned individually in the description (giving the "data"—geographical locality in which collected, date of collection, and the like) and are given special care as the **type specimens.** Whenever, at a future date, some ambiguity is seen in the original description, recourse to these type specimens allows further information to be gained and the confusion eliminated.

Collection and identification of plants or animals is an avocation for many who are not professional biologists. When such a collection is made, using proper techniques and careful study, the work takes on great scientific value. Collectors correspond with one another and exchange specimens by mail. Each person restricts attention to a sufficiently small portion of the plant or animal kingdom in order that a collection containing good representation of known species can be built up and the related literature thoroughly reviewed. To such self-trained specialists, specimens of new or rare species hold particular interest. Quite as much value, however, is derived when the specialist takes advantage of his knowledge and collections to bring published information up to date in a "revision," or as a more ambitious monograph.

Identification of specimens is often made simpler by preparation of **keys.** In a key, the person wishing to learn the name is offered alternatives which lead progressively to information about the particular species. The various phyla of thallophyte plants can be dis-

1. Carl von Linné, M.D. (1707-1778), Swedish naturalist, whose patient work toward a uniform method for naming plants and animals laid the foundation of modern procedures. He holds the American twin-flower (Linnaea), named in his honor.

THREE NATURALISTS WHO CONTRIBUTED TOWARD THE GROWTH OF BIOLOGY

2. Charles Darwin, B.D. (1809-1882), English naturalist, who presented a vast array of evidence showing that species change slowly. This monument to him is in the Galápagos Islands, on the Equator west of South America. Here, as naturalist aboard *H.M.S. Beagle* on a voyage around the world, Darwin found the island fauna so strikingly different from that of the mainland that he felt obliged to find a reason for the apparent change.

3. Louis Agassiz, Ph.D., M.D. (1807-1873), Swiss naturalist, the first full-time biology teacher in America, founder of the first marine biological laboratory in this hemisphere (on Cape Cod). Over its library door he wrote an admonition, "Study Nature, not Books."

4. Plants collected in the field are carried in the humidifier can (center), later spread flat and dried in the plant press (middle left). Each specimen is then mounted on a uniform sheet (front left) carrying a label with all essential data. These herbarium sheets are filed in folders and stored in insect-proof cabinets.

Scientific Specimens for Reference and Comparison

5. Animals collected in the field are preserved in various ways: Mammals and birds are made into "study skins"; insects are mounted on special pins. Each specimen bears a tag or label indicating where it was caught, when, and by whom. Here a group of biologists, back from a field trip, look on as three of their number begin preparing specimens for future study.

tinguished by selecting the correct alternative from study of a specimen in relation to the following key:

1. Chlorophyll absent 2
   Chlorophyll present 3

2. Organisms unicellular; no organized nucleus present .... bacteria
   Organisms usually multicellular; cells with a nucleus .... fungi

3. Plant multicellular but composed of two types of cells: spherical cells with chloroplastids, enmeshed in branched filaments lacking chlorophyll .... lichens
   Plants not of these two cell types 4

4. Chlorophyll dispersed in the protoplasm of each cell; no organized nucleus; a gelatinous matrix commonly secreted by the cells .... blue-green algae
   Chlorophyll in chloroplastids; nucleus distinct; a gelatinous matrix unusual 5

5. Flagellated single cells ...... euglenophytes
   Organisms without flagella or multicellular 6

6. Chloroplastids usually bizarre in shape; no masking pigment concealing the clear green of chlorophyll .... green algae
   Chloroplastids comparatively simple; masking pigments concealing the clear green of chlorophyll 7

7. Unicellular organisms with a silicious shell composed of two halves fitted together like a pill box; masking pigment golden yellow .... diatoms
   Multicellular; no silicious shell; masking pigment not golden yellow 8

8. Masking pigment brown ...... brown algae
   Masking pigment red .... red algae

Keys are meant to be referred to, not memorized. After a person is thoroughly familiar with a group of living things, he should be able to sift his knowledge to the point of writing a useful key. Similarly the specific, generic, familial, ordinal, and class names are not a necessary part of learned fact. They become as familiar as the names of friends often seen, whenever a person is specializing in a group of organisms. But the general scheme of the plant and animal kingdoms is well worth having in mind, in order that information may be kept in its proper categories. The accepted grouping is based on generalities of structure and becomes a sort of "dramatis personae" listing the kinds of organisms about which biology is concerned. These divisions are not

too numerous to grasp; those in the plant kingdom will seem less familiar at first:

Kingdom Plantae (plants)	
subkingdom Thallophyta	94,800 species
Phylum Cyanophyta	1,500 species
the blue-green algae	
Phylum Euglenophyta	300 species
most single-celled flagellates	
Phylum Chlorophyta	5,500 species
the green algae	
Phylum Chrysophyta	5,000 species
the diatoms	
Phylum Phaeophyta	1,100 species
the brown algae	
Phylum Rhodophyta	2,500 species
the red algae	
Phylum Schizomycophyta	1,400 species
the bacteria	
Phylum Eumycophyta	77,000 species
fungi and lichens	
Phylum Myxomycophyta	500 species
the slime molds	
subkingdom Embryophyta	284,000 species
Phylum Bryophyta	23,000 species
including liverworts	9,000 species
mosses	14,000 species
Phylum Tracheophyta	261,000 species
subphylum Psilopsida	4 species
subphylum Lycopsida	1,000 species
the clubmosses and kin	
subphylum Sphenopsida	25 species
the horsetails	
subphylum Pteropsida	260,000 species
Class Filicinae	9,280 species
the ferns	
Class Gymnospermae	630 species
Class Angiospermae	250,000 species
including dicots	200,000 species
monocots	50,000 species
Total plant species: about	379,000 species
Kingdom Animalia (animals)	
subkingdom Protozoa	30,000 species
Phylum Protozoa	
the single-celled animals	
subkingdom Metazoa	836,000 species
Phylum Porifera	3,000 species
the sponges	
Phylum Coelenterata	9,000 species
jellyfish and kin	
Phylum Platyhelminthes	6,000 species
the flatworms	
Phylum Aschelminthes	3,000 species
roundworms and kin	
Phylum Mollusca	40,000 species
clams and kin	

Phylum Annelida	6,000 species
segmented worms	
Phylum Arthropoda	723,000 species
including crustaceans	25,000 species
arachnoids	30,000 species
centi- and millipedes	8,000 species
insects	660,000 species
Other invertebrate phyla	1,000 species
Phylum Echinodermata	5,000 species
starfish and kin	
Phylum Chordata	45,000 species
including protochordates	
Class Agnatha	10 species
Classes Chondrostei and	
Teleostei (fish)	15,000 species
Class Amphibia	2,000 species
Class Reptilia	4,000 species
Class Aves (birds)	8,616 species[1]
Class Mammalia	15,000 species
Total animal species: about	841,000 species

4. THE PHYLA OF LIFE

Often so much thought is given to the differences by means of which unlike organisms can be distinguished, and the ways in which they can be grouped for "pigeonholing" that sight is lost of a more fundamental characteristic: that all of these many plant and animal types are successfully able to compete in the struggle for existence. Some are said to be "simple," meaning that their structure shows fewer visible complexities. Complexity of structure usually is evidence only of division of labor among the spatially separated parts of an organism. Division of labor is possible within even a single cell. Each organism is so complex merely in consisting of living substance that, in comparison, these differences among the categories of man's classification may seem trivial.

The Various Phyla of Thallophytes

(Photos 17-21, 136, 140-152, 156, 369.)
Structurally these are the simplest of plants; they vary in size from the smallest known living things to many-celled kinds reaching several hundred feet in length. The most conspicuous of them are seaweeds: including green algae (Chlorophyta), brown algae

---

[1] Probably less than 100 species of birds remain undiscovered—an approach to full listing not to be found elsewhere in any major group of animals.

(Phaeophyta), and red algae (Rhodophyta). These differ chemically in the types of pigments giving them their colors, and show an enormous range of life histories. The green algae are represented also by inconspicuous "pond scums" in fresh water and a few forms on land. Most blue-green algae (Cyanophyta) are aquatic but not marine; they are similar to the microscopic bacteria (Schizomycophyta) in a single-celled or colonial habit, and in the lack of a distinct nucleus and of sexual reproduction.

A relatively small number of fungi draw attention to themselves by achieving a size visible to the unaided eye. Like the algae, all fungi lack true roots, stems, and leaves. With a few exceptions, fungi are unable to manufacture their own food, but absorb nourishment from supplies produced by other living things. The fungi include the alga-like fungi, the sac fungi, and the club fungi. Some of the last-mentioned group produce reproductive structures familiar as mushrooms, shelf or bracket fungi, puffballs, and earth stars. The phylum Eumycophyta includes, in addition to fungi, the lichens, which grow commonly as incrustations on tree trunks, stones (including tombstones), and the ground. Each is a mutual benefit association of definite algae and fungi, where the fungus forms a covering that absorbs and holds water, protecting the alga from fatal desiccation, while the alga produces the food materials for both alga and covering fungus.

The other two phyla mentioned—the flagellates (Euglenophyta) and the diatoms (Chrysophyta) are composed entirely of microscopic, single-celled members. The importance of each to man and biology requires further discussion in later chapters.

Phylum Bryophyta

(Photos 153-157, 353.)
Liverworts and mosses are low-growing plants characteristic of moist, shaded land. None are marine. All manufacture their own food and are adapted to terrestrial life. The bryophytes need rain or other liquid water for reproduction, but ordinary growth processes can continue if the air about them is adequately humid. No special structures allowing rapid conduction of dissolved substances from place to place are found in bry-

ophytes, although they possess leaf- and stem-like parts. Their lack of true roots is in keeping with their delicate structure. Like the tracheophytes, however, they differ markedly from all of the thallophyte subkingdom in having an embryo stage in the life cycle— hence the classification of the two in the subkingdom Embryophyta.

Phylum Tracheophyta

The most spectacular characteristic of the many familiar plants in this phylum, from a biological point of view, is the possession of special parts in which dissolved substances are carried up and down. Together with the possession of true roots, stems, and leaves, this organization allows far more extensive spread into terrestrial situations.

Of the four subphyla, each includes members which grow to become far larger plants than any of the bryophytes. All but rare exceptions are essentially terrestrial, independent, and usually upright in growth.

The psilopsids are the simplest known of plants having conducting systems. Neither of the two living genera has a common name— *Psilotum* is tropical and subtropical, found in Florida, Bermuda and Hawaii; *Tmesipteris* is native to Australasia and the Philippines. Mention is made of psilopsids only because of the great antiquity of their fossil record and the fact that botanists regard extinct psilopsids as ancestral to all other tracheophytes.

Clubmosses (Lycopsida) and horsetails (Sphenopsida) are less complex both in structure and in their reproductive processes than the "higher plants" of the subphylum Pteropsida. (See Photos 174-176, 407.)

The three classes of the Pteropsida are all well known to everyone. Ferns (Filicinae) differ from the other two in that one part of each life cycle requires liquid water to be present for fertilization of the egg cells; at another stage, spores capable of starting new plants blow from place to place in the wind. (See Photos 177-182.)

Gymnosperms and angiosperms are often grouped as "seed plants," in contrast with the "spore plants" of the thallophyte phyla, the bryophytes and the ferns. "Seed plants" have come to dominate the earth's vegetation and to be most directly important to man eco-

nomically. Gymnosperms and angiosperms are also by far the most complex structurally; they vary in size from insignificant pondweeds that float on the water-film of ponds to giant trees with trunks up to forty feet in diameter and with known ages of 4,000 years. The gymnosperms, of which the cone-bearing trees such as pines are most familiar, differ from angiosperms in the development of the seeds. In gymnosperms the seeds are more or less exposed and not covered by accessory parts. In angiosperms a flower is usually more obvious and the seed is enclosed in a fruit. About 25 per cent of the different kinds of angiosperms agree in having flowers with parts in multiples of three, a characteristic type of seed and of stem structure, and leaves usually with parallel veins; these are the *monocots*. The remaining 75 per cent of the angiosperms are *dicots,* with netted veins in the leaves, flower parts in multiples of two or five (rarely in threes), and a different seed and stem structure. The monocots include the grasses, cattails, sedges, lilies, palms, and orchids; among the dicots are grouped the broad-leaved trees and most herbaceous plants.

(See Photos 6-22, 30-32, 145, 158-194, 234-248, 252-260, 323-329, 333-335, 340-343, 347-357, 368-379, 384-385, 406-410, 423-427, 433-442, 465-467.)

Phylum Protozoa

(Photos 24, 137-139, 246.)

Almost no member of this phylum is large enough to be recognized with the unaided eye; a few do barely reach these dimensions. Protozoans are the dashing denizens of pondwater, as seen under a compound microscope. With few exceptions their life processes are bound up in a single cell. Most of them depend on other organisms for food, but a few are sufficiently similar to the flagellate algae to have occasioned extensive arguments: are they animals or are they plants? At this level of organization the distinction is not always clear.

Most famous of the protozoans is the ameba. The "slipper animalcule" (Paramecium) is just a little larger than the lower limit of human unaided vision, and it can be watched easily with a hand lens. The variety of single-celled animals is great; many are free-living, but perhaps the greatest number are internal parasites, such as the ameba which causes one form of human dysentery.

Phyla of the "Lower Invertebrates"

Members of most classes in the phylum to which man belongs are distinguished by the possession of a backbone—a vertebral column —and are thereby different enough to describe colloquially as *vertebrates*. Any animal lacking a backbone is thus an *invertebrate*. The sponges, coelenterates, and worms are often grouped as "lower invertebrates," just as so many phyla of "lower plants" are conveniently discussed as thallophytes.

Sponges are familiar enough articles of commerce to require no introduction. The sponge as used by man, however, is merely the skeleton on which the living animal was spread out. Sponges are attached to the bottom of the ocean (one small group is found in fresh water), and they obtain microscopic food by straining it from water driven through their porous bodies. The phylum name, Porifera, refers to the food-catching pores. (See Photos 85-87.)

Coelenterates include a few fresh-water forms such as Hydra and the fresh-water jellyfish, but they are otherwise restricted to the ocean. Among the different kinds with common names are corals, sea fans, sea plumes, sea anemones, jellyfishes, and Portuguese man-of-war. Their structures have a common plan—an outer living layer, an inner living layer, and an intermediate zone of jelly-like material that is proportionately enormous in jellyfishes and much thinner elsewhere in the phylum. Most are radially symmetrical. Living animal food is captured and paralyzed through use of special nettling cells, and digestion takes place in a blind cavity occupying the center of the body. The phylum name, Coelenterata, refers to the digestive cavity. (See Photos 88-90.)

Flatworms are bilaterally symmetrical and may be equipped with fairly good sense organs such as eye spots. A small number are free-living scavengers in salt and fresh water, but most are internal parasites—for example, the flukes found in lungs, liver, and bladder, and the tapeworms found in digestive tracts. In many the life history is very complex, but there is never a true body cavity or a circulatory system. The phylum name, Platyhelminthes, is merely the Greek equivalent of flatworm. (See Photos 91-93, 207.)

Roundworms are bilaterally symmetrical and have a characteristic form. The body is circular in cross section, and consists of a digestive tube extending from end to end, and a body wall joined to the digestive tract at the two ends. Between the digestive tract and body wall is a sizable space filled with a blood-like fluid which circulates as the muscular body of the roundworm twists one way and another. Roundworms are regular inhabitants of soil, where they act as scavengers. Many are internal parasites in plants and animals, and are responsible for a variety of diseases (including elephantiasis in man). (See Photos 317-319.)

Phylum Mollusca

(Photos 44-47, 94-101, 229-230, 311, 402, 415, 431-432.)

Soft, unsegmented bodies, commonly surrounded in part by a sheltering limy shell, are characteristic of the snails, slugs, clams, oysters, scallops, chitons, octopuses, and squids which are grouped together as mollusks. The phylum name stems from the Latin *mollis* = soft. All but a few are aquatic, and the small number of terrestrial kinds are dependent upon humid air and water-filled vegetation for activity. The food includes plant material, and dead and living animal tissue; the degree of organization of the body is correlated nicely with the type of nourishment involved. Squid, which chase down their prey, are equipped in ways that allow rapid movement through the sea; they have the most advanced type of eyes among the invertebrate animals. Clams, on the other hand, may spend their lives buried in the mud, filtering their microscopic food from a water current they draw in and expel from a special siphon (the "neck" of a clam). They even obtain from the water current sperm cells from another clam, so that eggs are fertilized and then expelled through the siphon to drift and begin life at new sites.

Phylum Annelida

(Photos 210, 332.)

These are segmented worms. Usually the segmentation shows both in the external appearance and in the repeated duplication of internal organs. Bilateral symmetry is basic. Most annelids are marine, either swimming in the sea or burrowing in the bottom; a few are found in the mud of fresh-water lakes and ponds; still fewer are the terrestrial earthworms, the fresh-water and terrestrial (tropical) leeches. All are dependent upon adequate moisture, since their bodies have a delicate skin. The digestive tract is well developed, and each segment has a portion of the body cavity. A good circulatory system carries blood throughout, and a distinct nervous system may have definite sense organs. The phylum name refers to the small rings around the body which mark off the segments.

Phylum Arthropoda

(Photos 23, 25-35, 41-43, 102-119, 129, 131-133, 195-200, 208-209, 226-228, 255, 262-264, 269-273, 278-287, 290-293, 296, 303-309, 315-316, 320-329, 336-339, 370-371, 380, 386, 390-393, 400-401, 404-405, 428-429.)

In number of kinds and of individuals, the arthropods comprise over 80 per cent of the animal kingdom, and outnumber the plants two to one. As such they must be regarded as the most successful animals on earth. The characteristic from which the phylum name is derived is the possession of jointed legs (Greek *arthron* = joint, *podos* = foot) attached to a firm external skeleton. Extreme specialization is common, allowing members of the phylum to invade every known niche in which any life can exist. Most crustaceans are marine (like lobsters, crabs, shrimp, barnacles, and a great number of minute kinds); a few are found in fresh water (like the crayfish) or in moist sites on land (like pill-bugs, which are common in rotting wood). Spiders, scorpions, ticks, and horseshoe crabs (king crabs) are familiar members of the arachnoid part of the phylum; most of them are terrestrial and carnivorous. Centipedes, millipedes, and insects are also land forms, although some of the insects have invaded fresh water secondarily—especially in immature stages. Corre-

lated with the possession of an external skeleton is the habit of shedding the old skin periodically, allowing rapid enlargement of the whole body before a new skeleton hardens.

Phylum Echinodermata

(Photos 120-123, 211-217.)

All of these are marine. They show a false radial symmetry that is usually five-parted, a lack of segmentation, and generally have limy plates within the body wall. Starfish, sea urchins, brittle stars, sea cucumbers, and sea lilies are the most familiar members of the group. Most are scavengers, some extracting nourishment from the bottom ooze. Others attack clams and similar slow-moving sea animals. Echinoderms are unique in possessing a hydraulic mechanism for locomotion, with "tube feet" that enable them to move around and also to cling tenaciously. The phylum name signifies "spiny-skinned."

Phylum Chordata

(Photos 36-40, 57-84, 124-128, 130, 134-135, 203-206, 218-225, 231-233, 249-251, 261, 265-268, 274-277, 288-289, 294-295, 297-302, 310-314, 344-346, 358-367, 381-387, 394-398, 403, 409, 411-414, 419-422, 430, 433-464.)

The possession in embryonic stages of a special stiffening rod called a **notochord** (from the Greek *noton* = back and *chorde* = catgut), the occurrence of respiratory gill slits between the digestive tract and the outside of the body, and the dorsal position of a hollow tubular nervous system, separate the chordates from all other animals. Most of them, after the notochord is well formed, surround it with a vertebral column—providing the familiar backbone type of skeletal system for which the vertebrates are famous. The various chordate groups are commonly distinctive enough in body form and life history for every normal person to know them apart: fish, amphibians, reptiles, birds, and mammals. Exceptions are to be found in each class, and these sometimes give trouble to beginners in classification. Yet of all the animal kingdom, the vertebrates are those most widely recognized by man and most used by him in connection with his civilized activities. The human animal fits into the system, among one small group of the mammals.

5. MAN AS A PART OF LIFE

The relationship of man to the living world has interested thinkers since the dawn of folklore. In myths and fables handed down by word of mouth human beginnings were credited among the animals, from inanimate objects, and in various supernatural ways. Biologists are willing to weigh the evidence objectively, to analyze information on the structure and operation of the human body, its development through embryonic stages, and the scattered remnants of fossil history. None of these suggests that man occupies a place apart. His organization fits perfectly into the series of other animals. He agrees with the mammals in having hair and mammary glands.

His five nailed toes per foot and five nailed fingers per hand are borne on generalized limbs like those of other Primates. His lack of cheek pouches and of a tail; his proportionately larger brain; adaptations allowing erect, bipedal locomotion; and his ability to appose thumb and fingers but not big toe and lesser toes are all part of the differences that distinguish him as belonging to a separate family (Hominidae), but nothing more. The possession of speech and the development of language, the construction and use of tools, the desire and ability to modify his surroundings for his own comfort, and the capacity for thinking in abstract terms are prized characteristics that surpass corresponding features of all other living things. For man, they were fortunate extensions, since they made possible picture-drawing, writing, and records—and hence the ability to pass along information to succeeding generations.

SUGGESTED READING (see pp. 505-508)

Classics and Milestones: Aristotle, Theophrastus, Linnaeus.
Recent and Informative: Jones, 1951.

4 · The Value of Life

PARALLELING the progress of civilization is a rapid increase in the variety of plant and animal life for which mankind has found uses. Some kinds are valuable as food, others as the source of medicines, still others in technology. Man has come to rate nonhuman types of life according to whether they are beneficial to him, detrimental in some way, or neutral (meaning of no known economic significance at the moment).

Often someone inquires: "What good is a mosquito?" An equally proper question might be asked: "What good is man?" Nowhere in modern biology is man's egocentric point of view stressed so strongly as in the field of **economic biology.** The "value of life" is entirely in terms of its use to man.

Each year the list of useful and harmful plants and animals grows appreciably. One kind after another loses its negligibility among the "neutral" category and assumes an importance for mankind. If for no other reason, it would seem wise to protect the shrinking reservoir of noneconomic life—perhaps even more carefully than those kinds whose significance to man is already clear.

I. GREEN PLANTS

All of the food eaten by mankind or any other animal has its origin directly or indirectly in green plants. The energy it contains was captured originally from sunlight, in a process possessed by green plants alone. Without commotion or impressive change in temperature, they store this energy in the form of forces binding together chemical compounds. Green plants differ from all animals and from most of the non-green plants in the remarkable completeness of their chemical processes. From simple gases and dissolved minerals, they are able to construct all of the necessary ingredients of living substance. No animal and few non-green plants can do this.

Green plants, moreover, store food beyond their own requirements. Thereby they support as well the non-green plants, all the animals, and mankind. They also maintain in the atmosphere the oxygen supply without which the animals could not utilize the food.

The great majority of nutritional uses of

plants accrue to man either directly through his eating of raw or cooked plant tissue, or indirectly through inclusion in his diet of the meat of herbivores. Added to these are values in minerals and vitamins obtainable in especially rich sources where the accompanying energy content may be considerably lower—as measured in the customary units of carbohydrates, fats, and proteins.

1. ENERGY-YIELDING FOODS AND FLAVORINGS

A few seaweeds are used for food, often dried and powdered to make "sea moss farina," which can be turned into puddings and baked goods, or cooked as "dulse," or put in soups. Most dietary uses for seaweeds are local. Not only are they restricted to coastal areas where the seaweeds may be collected without cost, but they appeal chiefly on shores where funds are scarce and nutrition on little more than a subsistence level.

Indirectly, the more microscopic kinds of marine algae are enormously important in feeding fish, seals, whales, and shellfish that man finds valuable for food, as well as for furs and oil.

Neither mosses nor liverworts contribute to human fare, and among the less complex of higher plants, the main example of a food is the young "fiddleheads" of ferns which are gathered in many localities to be cooked as a springtime vegetable (Photo 178). Similarly, the gymnosperms contribute little to man's food supply, although "piñon nuts" from a particular pine of western states were collected and stored by scattered Indian tribes as an important source of proteins and needed calories.

Among the dicot angiosperms, however, food values are high. A large proportion of those esteemed for their leaves or buds belong to the Mustard family (kale, cabbage, cauliflower, broccoli, water cress, and others); to these should be added members of other plant families, such as parsley, celery, and lettuce. As roots, the turnip, carrot, and beet (including the sugar beet, the commercial source of much of our refined sugar—sucrose—and a molasses used for fattening cattle) have a prominent place, while the sweet potato and

the "Irish" potato (actually South American) divide the honors between foods from roots and from underground stems, respectively. In earlier days in America, during both Indian and pioneer times, maple syrup and maple sugar from the boiled sap of the sugar maple tree was the principal sweetening and the chief source of cash among the white settlers.

Rhubarb, for pies and "preserves," is an interesting example of the many instances in which man has learned to dodge poison in his foods. The part eaten is the tasty, nourishing, harmless, leaf petiole. The perennial plant body remains below ground, and the leaf tissue itself is poisonously full of oxalic acid crystals. Similarly, the starchy root of the South American cassava has become widely distributed through tropical countries of the world as the most important farinaceous food of warmer lands—though a dangerous glucoside must be removed in preparing the material for human consumption; tapioca is one of the products of the cassava root; another is the adhesive on postage stamps.

Forage for domestic animals includes alfalfa and various clovers which, as legumes, also enrich the soil because of the nitrogen-fixing bacteria in the root nodules. Indirectly these plants find their way to man's dietary.

Angiosperm fruits include an enormous list eaten in the wild form by man, or propagated by him as cultivated varieties, often with an increased yield of food values or palatability. Those of the Legume Family (pea, bean, and soy bean) and of the Rose Family (raspberry, strawberry, plum, apricot, peach, cherry, apple, pear, and others) are supplemented by fruits from other groups such as fig, avocado, orange, lemon, grape, blueberry, olive, tomato, pumpkin, and watermelon. In addition are fruits in which the outer parts are discarded in favor of the seeds themselves—nuts like walnut, pecan, peanut, and pistachio. To these may be appended a few where the value is taken as a spice needed only in small amounts—as in pepper, paprika, and clove, or in extracts such as almond. Some, like cocoa and chocolate (from cacao seeds) combine flavor and greater food value. Not all seasonings and flavorings have a fruit origin, however; cinnamon comes from a tree bark, and sage, peppermint, and bay are from leaves.

The monocot angiosperms contribute a variety of foodstuffs for man and his domesticated herbivores. In temperate climates and on the African plains, the Grass Family furnishes forage and hay for cattle and other plant-feeding animals that man values for meat. Cultivated members of this monocot group are called cereals, and include rice

ORIGINS OF CULTIVATED PLANTS*

Region†	Fruits		"Vegetables"	Cereals	Fibers	Flowers	Beverages & Narcotics
HOLARCTIC Nearctic [= Anglo- America]	blackberry[4] blueberry[4] cherry[4] cranberry[4]	pecan[5] persimmon[4] plum[4] strawberry[4]				bergamot lupine phlox rhododendron	
Palearctic [= Europe & northern Asia]	almond[5] apple[4] cherry[4] currant[4] date[4] fig[4] gooseberry[4]	grape[4] melon[4] mulberry[4] olive[4] pear[4] plum[4] quince[4] strawberry[4]	asparagus[2] beet[3] broccoli[6] cabbage[2] carrot[3] celery[1] lettuce[1] onion[1] parsley[1] parsnip[3] pea[5] radish[3] spinach[1] turnip[3]	barley[4] millet[4] oats[4] rye[4] sorghum[2] wheat[4]	cotton[5] flax[2] hemp[1,2] jute[2] ramie[2]	begonia carnation foxglove geranium larkspur lilac pansy rose spring crocus	hops[4]
NEOTROPICAL [= Latin America]	avocado[4] cashew[5] chayote[4] coconut?[5] grapefruit[4] guava[4]	papaya[4] peanut[5] persimmon[4] pineapple[6] tomato[4]	"Irish" potato[2] kidney bean[5] lima bean[5] manioc = cassava[3] peppers[4] pumpkin[4] squash[4] yam[3]	maize[4]	cotton[5] kapok[4] sisal[1]	canna cosmos dahlia frangipani fuchsia orchids morning glory nasturtium petunia poinsettia sunflower zinnia	cacao[4] maté[1] tobacco[1]
PALEOTROPICAL Ethiopian [= Africa]	gooseberry[4] grape[4]	pistachio[5] watermelon[4]	breadfruit[4] broad bean[5]	millet[4] sorghum[2] wheat[4]	flax[2]	calla lily castor oil crown-of- thorns poker plant poincianna	coffee[5] cola[4]
ORIENTAL [= southern Asia]	apricot[4] banana[4] cantaloupe[4] citron[4] cucumber[4] date[4] lemon[4]	lime[4] mango[4] orange[4] peach[4] plantain[4] plum[4]	egg plant[4] soy bean[4] taro = dasheen[3]	rice[4]		bleeding heart chrysanthe- mum Easter lily forsythia hibiscus hollyhock peony	hemp[1] poppy[5] tea[1]
AUSTRALASIATIC [including Pacific islands]					abacá[1]	bottle brush eucalyptus	

* Partly after Hylander and Stanley.
† For the exact extent of these regions, consult the map on p. 379.
NOTE: The economically important part of each plant is indicated by a superscript number: 1 = leaf, 2 = stem, 3 = root, 4 = fruit, 5 = seed, 6 = flower cluster. Thus the term "vegetable" is applied to products of every one of these plant parts.

(Photo 8), wheat, and maize (Indian corn). Other grasses in the broad sense are sugar cane (Photos 6, 7) and sorghum, from which molasses and a major part of the world's supply of sucrose are obtained. Onions are closely related. The Palm Family (Photos 257,

this great section of the angiosperm plants. Vanilla is extracted from an orchid.

2. MINERALS, VITAMINS, AND DRUGS

The fact that many green plants are rich in vitamins and minerals has been publicized extensively. Less obvious, however, is the extent to which man depends upon the green

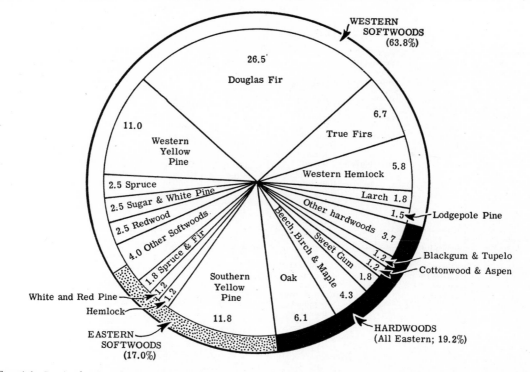

Fig. 4-1. *In Anglo-America, saw timber comes from a variety of softwoods and hardwoods. The proportions of each are shown as percentages (Data from U.S. Forest Service).*

258) furnishes dates and coconuts (used as a food in the tropics, as well as a source of dried coconut meat—called copra [Photos 9, 10]—from which oils are obtained for soapmaking), and sago from the sago palm. Sago is a farinaceous material when finally prepared, and vies for human attention in some areas with taro (= dasheen), from the roots of which comes the Hawaiian "poi." The pineapple is a monocot fruit (Photos 11, 12), as is the banana (Photo 13). Onions are essentially buds, whereas asparagus consists of young stems in which the conducting and strengthening tissues have not yet become mature and hard. Ginger is an example of a spice from

plants for drugs of various kinds—substances too complex or expensive to be produced by synthetic processes, but which can be extracted from plants with comparative economy.

Again, except for the antibiotics (see p. 28), only the seed plants are of particular importance. From the conifers comes ephedrine, a vasoconstricting extract of a Chinese shrub, used extensively in nose drops. Most other drugs are obtained from dicot seed plants.

Some drugs are decidedly helpful in medical practice. The leaves of foxglove (a close relative of the familiar snapdragon) furnish digitalis, one of the most valuable substances

6. Although sugar cane is a grass, its flowering tassels reach a height of 12 to 15 feet. At this stage the leaves are stripped or burned from the stalks, leaving the latter bare and ready for crushing to expel the sweet juice.

THE GRASS WHICH PRODUCES CANE SUGAR

7. Cane juice evaporating in a home syrup factory keeps this family busy for part of each year. The product is food and also a source of cash income, both hard to acquire in undeveloped parts of Florida.

8. Drying rice where the chickens cannot reach it—native style in the "interior" of Panamá. The large container of these bunches of rice is a dugout canoe, hollowed from a solid tree.

9. Drying the meat of the coconut as copra, for sale to coastal traders who send it on its way toward soap or other uses of coconut oils. Photographed in the San Blas country of Panamá.

SOURCES OF TROPICAL FOOD AND CASH INCOME ARE THE WIDESPREAD RICE AND COCONUT

10. Commercial drying of copra calls for roofs on wheels that can be pushed back to expose the coconut meat to the drying action of sunlight, yet shield it from rain when clouds gather.

11. A pineapple plantation consists of row after row of spreading plants, each with its dangerously saw-toothed leaves and central flower stalks.

12. A ripening pineapple.

TROPICAL FRUITS GROWING
IN SUBTROPICAL FLORIDA

13. Banana plants produce large flowers in a purplish red bud that peels off one broad petal for each "hand" of future bananas.

14. Western yellow ("ponderosa") pine.

15. Eastern white pine.

Neither of these symmetrical, lone trees would appeal to a lumberman. They are more horticultural specimens. For lumber trees are better when grown in dense stands that have branching (hence knots) only at the top of the tree. Under such circumstances each tree is self-pruning and grows straighter.

16. Sorting logs on their way to the saw mill.

THE MOST IMPORTANT WOOD
OF TEMPERATE AMERICA—PINE

available for treatment of some heart diseases. Quinine, from the bark of the South American cinchona tree, has long been an antimalarial drug used by man wherever the tropical malaria-carrying mosquitos are numerous. Castor oil, from the castor bean, is another example of a powerful substance of plant origin used extensively by man. In addition are aconite from roots; cascara from stems; belladonna and curare from leaves; chalmoogra oil (used in treating leprosy) from seeds.

A variety of poisons which may serve plants by discouraging animal attack have been used by human beings at almost every level of civilization. The oriental use of opium, obtained from poppies of one particular kind in which the alkaloid is most abundant, is to be balanced against the widespread chewing of "betel" with lime, to liberate cocaine from coca leaves, in South America and the East Indies. The use of marihuana (= hashish) from one species of hemp plant, the smoking of tobacco with its nicotine content, the drinking of strong coffee or tea rich in caffeine, or of various cola beverages with the same caffeine as the important constituent, are all habit-forming activities of man that take advantage of the stimulating effect of small doses of these poisons. The beverage use of alcohol is closely allied.

3. BUILDING MATERIALS

Most buildings (and the contents of almost all) have an origin in green plants. They are products of the forest. The kinds used (Fig. 4-1) are related closely to types available.

In temperate lands the list of building woods must start with pine (Photos 14, 15), whereas in the tropics bamboo thatched with palm is far more typical. Hardness or softness of woods determines some of their uses; grain shown in boards (Fig. 4-2), resistance to moisture (Photo 16), structural strength under strains of various kinds, and economy are all important factors.

4. FUELS, LIGHT, AND POWER

Although geologists are not agreed on the precise sequence of steps whereby coal, petroleum oils, and gas reached their present form, there is no dispute over their origin from green plants.

Peat

At the present time, in peat bogs, it is easy to see how the high acidity and abundance of organic toxins keep bacterial decay at a very low level, so that the plant parts covered by bog water or by peat moss do not disintegrate. Instead they consolidate into a mass of iden-

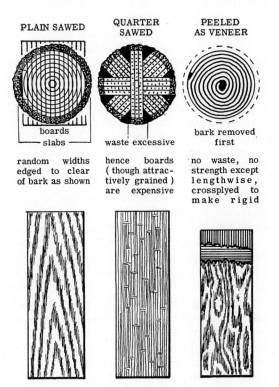

FIG. 4-2. *Grain in boards is dependent upon both the structure of the wood and the way in which the log is cut.*

tifiable plant remains—the peat that is dug and dried for fuel in many parts of the temperate zone where coal and petroleum oils are lacking or very expensive. In North America peat is used very little because other fuels are relatively abundant and inexpensive, but vast deposits are available. The fuel value of peat is very low, being comparable to that from an equal weight of wood (about 8,500 B.T.U. per pound).

Coal

Between peat and hard coal (anthracite) there is every gradation of coal, and many attempts have been made to trace a continuous series in terms of time. It is clear, however, that the coal seams used for fuel today were not the products of sphagnum bogs, since peat moss remains are absent or rare in them. Lignite and the so-called "brown coals" that are used extensively in Europe are somewhat lower than peat in fuel value (about 6,000 B.T.U. per pound), and the bulk of the plant remains in them have become so consolidated that identity has been lost. This seems to be partly the result of immense pressures of overlying strata and seas for great periods of time; partly, no doubt, the consolidation involved the leaching out of soluble mineral matter, leaving the percentage of insoluble carbon compounds increased. The fuel value is directly proportional to the carbon content. Higher temperatures, greater pressures, and perhaps longer periods at great depths have led to soft-coal formation from similar plant materials. Hard coal, with its semi-crystalline form, must have required still higher temperatures and pressures, resulting in the highest carbon content of all and in the most fuel value per unit of weight (about 14,000 B.T.U. per pound).

Since long periods of time were involved, one should not look for modern plants as the precursors of coal. More than half of the world's supply of good quality coal was deposited during the Carboniferous period, and consists of the remains of giant ferns, horsetails, clubmosses, and early seed ferns.

Part of the formation of coal seems to have been due to a sealing off of the plant debris from oxygen through sedimentary deposits in thin alternating layers. Bacterial decay was certainly far less effective than in modern swamps, except where acid conditions are prevalent today. The mud that covered the ancient vegetation appears in coal today in the consolidated form of slate, whereas the remains of mineral matter mixed with the plant debris form the rest of the ashes when coal is burned.

Gas and Oil

Coal beds contain gases as well as solid coal. When coal is heated without being burned, further substances evaporate and can be condensed by chilling the vapor. Kerosene ("coal oil" to many people) may have such an origin. Illuminating gas, once used extensively for homes, public buildings, and street lights, is now replaced by electricity, but as a fuel for kitchen stoves it is still sold under its former name in civilized economies. It may be obtained by distillation of soft coal, and leaves a porous residue of still lower vapor pressure—the coke used in blast furnaces and to some extent in heating of homes. The heat value of illuminating gas varies between 400 and 600 B.T.U. per cubic foot. Natural gas sometimes exceeds three times this figure, and especially prepared gases such as propane (sold in high-pressure tanks for home stoves beyond gas distribution and for automobile trailers) affords from 2,300 to 2,500 B.T.U. per cubic foot and requires special burners.

Natural gas, with a higher fuel value than gas made from coal, occurs naturally. Usually, however, it is in association with petroleum oil. Vast amounts of natural gas are burned to no one's advantage in many oil fields, because no economic value for the gas has been found. From other fields, the gas is piped to communities needing heat in winter, to keep homes and public buildings warm, to heat water, and to furnish fires for industry. The erratic distribution of oil fields in America restricts the number of regions where use of natural gas is easy. Extension of pipelines to the industrial northeastern states provides an important outlet for excess gas from Texas, and reduces the cost of manufacturing.

The oil itself gives less clue to its origin than do the coals, since the fluid contains no fossils. However, the fossil contents of overlying rocks in oil-rich areas indicate that most oil has a marine origin, probably from the stored oil droplets of countless microscopic diatoms, which have undergone some change and remain to represent incomplete decay in bygone times. One of the chief occupations for paleontologists in industry is the examination of fossils, particularly microfossils of invertebrates from presumed oil-bearing regions, to determine where drilling is most likely to bring in a new oil supply. A great part of the world's fuel for heat, light, and power now comes from oil wells, and through refining and synthetic processes with crude oil as the base are derived a vast number of lubricating oils, waxes, dyestuffs, and plastics.

5. STABILIZATION OF THE LAND

Water running down a slope tends to carry with it any soil particles that are not held firmly (Photos 434, 442). Vegetation not only breaks the force of down-pelting rain and hail, but its roots form a meshwork resisting erosion. Plants tend to increase the proportion of precipitation which sinks into the soil. This has two advantages: moisture is retained where roots can reach it, and the flow of rivers becomes more regular—less subject to sudden floods and periods of stagnation. Vegetation is important also in holding soil when winds blow over it (Photo 436).

Further consideration of these actions of plants in conserving soil and fresh-water resources appears in Chapter 24.

6. USES IN TECHNOLOGY

Closely related in form are the resins from coniferous trees, such as turpentine (used in paint), Canada balsam (used as a mounting medium in microscope slides and as a transparent cement in color-corrected lens systems), and kauri resins (used in varnish making). Copra (dried coconut) yields a great part of the fats needed for commercial soapmaking. The oil of the tung nut, grown originally in China but now on a large scale in this country as a semi-tropical tree, is important as a constituent of varnishes and in making special lubricating oils for aircraft. Some designers have even claimed that aircraft advance was delayed for years until a reliable source of tung oil was at hand. Certainly the use of rubber, from the latex of rubber trees, has altered the course of civilization in a host of ways.

Paper-making depends to a large extent on the availability of wood pulp from the conifers, particularly spruce and fir. Paper with a high "rag content" is more permanent and expensive, and is based on flax, cotton, and other fibers of non-coniferous plants which lack some of the resins and chemical substance that darken paper and induce brittleness. The extent to which flax is made into linen and cotton fibers into cloth is hard to realize. Related industries use hemp fibers for rope, and the cheaper jute fibers for cheap rope and burlap bags. Kapok as a filler for cushions and cheap upholstery has taken some of the place of cotton, although kapok loses its springy qualities far more quickly; it is the product of a tropical tree of the same name. Neatly cut pieces of bark from the cork oak of Spain and elsewhere provide stoppers for vast numbers of bottles; ground cork forms tight gaskets for all manner of sites in machinery.

Another substitute for cotton is sphagnum, the peat moss. It has been used for surgical dressings in place of cotton, since it is much cheaper, can be sterilized readily, takes up from 16 to 22 times as much liquid as the same weight of cotton, and in addition has an antiseptic quality that reduces contamination. This moss is almost the only one of economic value. It is used extensively also by nurserymen as a moist packing for roots of nursery stock, and by horticulturists as a humus material that can be mixed with soil to increase the organic content and water-holding capacities.

From the algae, the most important contribution is the jelly from certain seaweeds, known as agar-agar. Biologists use agar as the neutral, sterilizable medium on which bacteria can be grown and studied in terms of nutritional requirements. The geneticists now use agar to give body to the substrate on which they raise their fruitflies; the flies do not drown in agar jellies the way they did in banana mash, so that the yield of countable adults from each cross is improved greatly. Agar is employed medicinally as a harmless laxative that both gives bulk to the intestinal contents and competes with the body for water so that fecal material is eliminated more easily.

The growing of hops to give flavoring materials for beer; the use of wheat, corn, barley, rye, other grains, and grapes and potatoes as carbohydrate sources on which yeasts can act in alcohol formation toward beverage manufacture; and the cultivation of certain succulent members of the Lily Family to obtain saps for similar production of tropical beers and liquors are all uses of green plant products. Most early dyestuffs had a plant origin, but almost all of them have been replaced by the cheaper aniline dyes produced synthetically.

7. HARMFUL ASPECTS

Every year thousands of people in North America react painfully to poison ivy (Photo 22) or its close relatives, poison sumac and poison "oak." Thereafter the old warning "Leaves in three, let it be" has more meaning for them, and they may come to recognize the foliage on vine or herb or shrub—whatever the particular habit of growth. Even more people develop respiratory difficulties as allergic responses to various pollens, notably ragweed and cedar.

Economically more significant are the annual losses of livestock through poisoning by weeds among the forage. In most instances the basic cause is semi-starvation through overgrazing in areas where poisonous plants occur. Usually poisonous plants are less palatable and are avoided. Some of them, like Sudangrass, contain toxic concentrations (of cyanides in this case), only when young.

8. ESTHETIC VALUES

The distinction between use of coloring or flavoring agents derived from green plants as an aid to technology in the sale of manufactured products, and the appreciation of plants from esthetic angles, has no clear boundary. Except in terms of market price, it is difficult to place a money value on the psychological effects of ornamental shrubbery, flowers, lawns, or Christmas trees. The odor of a rose, a bunch of lilacs, or a balsam pillow; the regularity of a brilliant tulip or giant chrysanthemum; the irregularity of an orchid; the masses of color in a field of Texas bluebonnets or California poppies; or the cool shade of a summer forest path in the East, the cathedral stillness of a giant redwood stand in the West; these things have an appeal to the human mind that transcends price and reaches deep into the emotions, beyond the scope of modern science or economics (Photo 467). The extensive organization of garden clubs and the activities of these groups in highway beautification are indications of this wide appeal.

II. NON-GREEN PLANTS

Most of the chlorophyll-lacking plants are either fungi or bacteria. They obtain their energy and nutrients from the breakdown of molecules from dead or living organisms. In this way they prevent the accumulation of dead bodies, both plant and animal, and contribute importantly to the soluble substances which provide fertility in soil and lake or ocean. A few can be used directly as food, while others may be utilized in economic processes and sewage disposal. A comparatively small number of these non-green plants attack living organisms, causing diseases.

So important to man are the non-green plants that their study is divided into two major categories. **Bacteriology** deals with bacteria by methods which are specialized in relation to the microscopic size and methods of reproduction characteristic of these organisms. **Mycology** is the study of fungi. Scientists who identify the disease-causing fungi and consider means for preventing or curing the disease are **pathologists** (from the Greek *pathos* = suffering).

1. POLICING THE EARTH

Since the supply of molecules of each element available to living things is limited, and some elements are in comparatively short supply, it is hard to overrate the importance of decomposition by bacteria and fungi. They are the active agents of decay which keep the basic materials of life in circulation, available for building new living substance. Only when decay action is prevented in some way do energy-rich compounds accumulate in the form of peat, coal, and petroleum.

2. SOIL FERTILITY

Products of decomposition which are soluble in soil moisture or in the water of lakes and oceans are the nutrients upon which the larger green plants and aquatic animals depend, either directly or indirectly. "Fertility" thus depends upon decay organisms. In many of the higher plants, fungi also assist in absorption of water from the soil.

It is paradoxical that we—the animals and higher plants—live in an atmosphere rich in nitrogen and yet cannot use it. We need nitrogen constantly as an ingredient of proteins, but the inert gas itself—though 80 per cent of ordinary air—is unavailable to us. Death from nitrogen starvation is on every hand. Proteins are the most expensive foods.

Certain bacteria provide the only significant bridge between the gas and the nitrogen-containing compounds usable by more complex organisms. Much of the ocean is so poor in nitrogenous compounds that life cannot be rich or varied there. Coastal organisms are more numerous partly because nitrogen-fixing bacteria live there and release these valuable nutrients into the sea water. Vegetation is able to thrive on land because of the numbers of nitrogen-fixing bacteria in soil.

The kinds of bacteria involved in nitrogen-fixation chemistry are discussed on p. 402, the re-use of nitrogen in a cyclic pattern on p. 403, and the importance of soil organisms and soil fertility in man's future on p. 473.

3. SEWAGE DISPOSAL

If food materials or drinking water become contaminated, a round trip has been arranged for parasites, from man to man. Failure to deal scientifically with this problem has been an important cause of disease epidemics in the past. It continues as a threat at the present time.

Flushing raw sewage into streams and lakes appeals chiefly because of seeming economy. It has many disadvantages, some of which are discussed on p. 483. Sewage disposal can be handled in a way which takes advantage of water as a transport medium, yet salvages it for re-use. In sewage treatment plants, bacteria are put to work in huge settling tanks, where they digest the accumulated sludge and liquefy its components by breaking large molecules into small ones which are soluble. The supernatant liquid is drawn off, filtered by passing it through sand, aerated thoroughly, disinfected enough to destroy dangerous organisms remaining in it, and then drained into rivers or lakes or sprayed into the air to evaporate.

4. ECONOMIC PROCESSES

Bacteria may be used in the preservation of food. Shredded cabbage, suitably inoculated with microörganisms, becomes sauerkraut through fermentation; the acid content rises until further putrefactive processes are discouraged. Ensilage is produced in much the same way, as a winter food for dairy herds. Chopped green corn or damp hay is filled into a silo beside the barn; after oxygen in the soggy mass has been used up in respiration, fermentative organisms bring the material into an acid state in which it will keep, although still full of food values.

The curd of milk soured by bacterial activity and containing the valuable proteins, is subject to further action by bacteria and molds. If this process is controlled correctly, the product is cheese. The flavor and consistency depend upon continuation of the decay process under proper conditions. Limburger is a bacterial product. Camembert and other "soft" cheeses are formed by molds. The green or blue color in Roquefort, Gorgonzola, and blue cheeses is due to pigments in the molds. Swiss cheese derives its holes and some of its flavor from gas-forming bacteria. Cheddar cheese lacks holes because the bacteria which produce the decay are not gas-formers.

The stepwise nature of decay is evident in many commercial processes. Weak sugar solutions, such as fruit juices, can be transformed into hard cider or wine through the fermentative activity of yeasts. The weak alcohol solutions may be carried an extra step by acetic-acid bacteria, as "cider vinegar" or "white wine vinegar." A further bacterial fermentation can carry the weak solution of acetic acid to acetone—an important solvent. Other microörganisms produce acetone directly from the starches in cereal grains, after these have been cooked slightly.

The economic success or failure of alcohol production depends in large measure upon the particular species of yeast which carries on the fermentation. It is not clear whether alcohol production is checked finally by the toxic action of the alcohol on the yeast organisms or by accumulation of other by-products with similar effect. Some yeasts continue fermentation until the alcohol concentration has reached as much as 15 per cent, whereas others die when 3.5 per cent alcohol surrounds them. Man has selected from among the many wild yeasts the very few with high tolerance for alcohol. He has propagated these particular kinds, and endeavors by sanitary precautions to keep any others from the mash and fermentation vats in which alcohol is made.

Wood alcohol (= methyl alcohol) is produced by a bacterium which thrives on wood fibers through which an air current supplies oxygen while water drips from above. The alcohol is derived by breakdown of cellulose, and accumulates in the water, to be removed later by distillation.

"Cultured buttermilk" is a bacterial product. Commercial tea, coffee, and cocoa are prepared from plant products which have been worked on by fermentative bacteria and yeasts.

Putrefaction, a bacterial decomposition of proteins, is responsible for the tanning of leather; bacterial action dissolves away undesirable portions of the hides. Putrefactive bacteria also free the fibers of hemp, flax and other plants, toward textile manufacturing.

In the preparation of commercial sponges, the combined action of drying air, hot sun, and bacterial decomposition breaks down the dying cells of the sponge and converts their contents into soluble residues which can be washed away, and volatile components which go with the breeze; the spongin skeleton is left behind as a neutral, insoluble, porous, soft mass that can hold quantities of water or be wrung out fairly dry.

5. DRUGS AND ANTIBIOTICS

In recent years, man has discovered and taken advantage of a defense mechanism present in a wide variety of plants. The defense consists of chemical substances, known as **antibiotics,** which spread from the plant and inhibit bacterial growth. This action is selective, effective on only certain bacteria. But in the molds of the soil, man has found a great variety of different antibiotic substances. Penicillin (from the mold Penicillium), strep-

tomycin, aureomycin, terramycin, and a number of others are widely used in modern medicine (Photo 151).

Under soil conditions, each mold produces one or more of these antibiotic compounds and keeps down competition from bacteria while digesting organic compounds in ordinary decay processes. Man has found it possible to raise many of these molds on a mass-production basis, and extract the antibiotic compounds each produces. He has also been able to induce some of these molds to decompose an abnormal diet of foodstuffs, and produce unusual antibiotics as variants which have medicinal advantages. This use of a living organism on an artificial diet, to evolve modifications of the original antibiotic substance, is the technique of **biosynthesis.**

6. FOODS

Bacteria and fungi are essential foods for a wide variety of soil inhabitants and organisms living in water. A small number of fungi are large enough or cheap enough to be attractive as human food.

Puffballs and morels are all edible. In Europe, a relative of the morel is the truffle, which is hunted almost on a sport basis, using trained hogs to locate and root them from the ground.

Unfortunately there is no easy way to distinguish between a harmless mushroom with some food value and those with varying degrees of poison content. Delicate flavor (depending significantly on the method of cooking used) rather than nourishment is the lure in eating wild mushrooms. Much of the risk can be avoided by use of mushrooms grown commercially.

Yeast is a brewer's by-product with high protein content and a large number of vitamins in useful concentration. Actually, most of the vitamins in yeast are those least likely to be deficient in human diets. And some people develop disagreeable symptoms from eating raw yeasts. The food value, however, is potentially enormous, and much research has gone into seeking ways to transform yeast into a material with more attractive texture, taste, and form, so that it could compete with meats and other high-protein foods.

Lichens, which are chiefly of fungus cells,

form an important part of the regular diet of caribou, reindeer, and musk ox in the barren areas of the Far North. Lemmings depend largely on lichens. The manna that was eaten by the Israelites in the desert (Exodus 16) is a lichen native to that region, still used as food by local people; the description given is only slightly overdrawn.

7. PLANT PATHOLOGY

Bacterial and fungal diseases of plants are numerous. Some of them include in their life histories complex changes which parallel those found among parasitic animals. Plant lice (aphids) and leafhoppers often serve as **vectors,** transferring the disease organisms from one victim (**host**) to the next. In some instances, the plant disease organism undergoes transformations within the vector, so that there is an incubation period before the insect can infect new foliage.

Many plant diseases are wind-borne, and gain entrance to hosts via wounds, or even

through the breathing pores of leaves and stems. The damage done is dependent partly upon the host's resistance to the disease, partly on weather conditions, and partly on an unknown characteristic called the "virulence" of the parasite itself.

The chief types of action are these:

1. *Progressive destruction of the chlorophyll-bearing tissues* of leaves and stems, or a development of interlocking filaments over the surface of the leaves so dense as to reduce the amount of light reaching the host's cells. The latter is characteristic of the "powdery mildews" and is equally efficient in reducing photosynthesis and gradually starving the host of sun energy required for life (and for resistance to other disease organisms).

2. *Plugging of the conducting system* by fungus strands or by multiplying bacteria, reducing the efficiency of the transport system to the point where normal day-time water

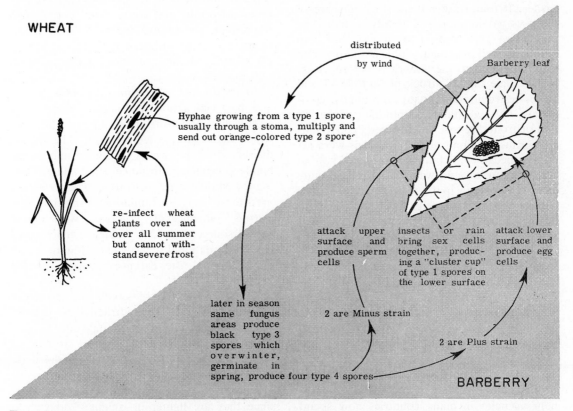

WHEAT

distributed
by wind

Barberry leaf

Hyphae growing from a type 1 spore, usually through a stoma, multiply and send out orange-colored type 2 spores

re-infect wheat plants over and over all summer but cannot withstand severe frost

attack upper surface and produce sperm cells

insects or rain bring sex cells together, producing a "cluster cup" of type 1 spores on the lower surface

attack lower surface and produce egg cells

2 are Minus strain

2 are Plus strain

later in season same fungus areas produce black type 3 spores which overwinter, germinate in spring, produce four type 4 spores

BARBERRY

FIG. 4-3. *By studying the entire life history of wheat rust, control measures can be found—such as eradication of barberry bushes near wheat fields—to break the chain of developmental stages.*

losses cannot be compensated for and the plant wilts—often irreversibly when the disease becomes advanced. The term "wilt disease" is applied to these types of attack.

3. *More extensive destruction of living tissues,* involving the death of large areas of woody plants, the invasion and rotting of fruits, the breakdown of stored wood in humid atmospheres, and many of the most serious plant diseases. The "rusts" and "smuts" that attack wheat and corn fall in this category (Fig. 4-3, Photos 17-19). Powdery scab of potatoes is another.

Few fungi have had more profound effects on human populations than the so-called "late blight" of potatoes which caused the great Irish famines of 1845 and 1846. Previously the disease had been unknown in Europe. Ireland demonstrated how effectively a human population can be ruined if it is dependent upon a single crop. The potato itself had been introduced into Ireland only about 250 years earlier. It found favor there since an acre of potatoes would support a family of five. The population grew rapidly from less than two million to well over eight—plus a million or so who emigrated to the Americas before 1845.

The "late blight" struck in both 1845 and 1846, destroying the potato crop almost completely. Over a million people died of starvation or from diseases which were effective killers because of famine. Soup kitchens were set up. But because any family who owned half an acre or more of land was denied relief, many died rather than part with their property. Others were evicted or gave up their land to be eligible for food. Emigration to the United States alone jumped from about 4,000 annually to 61,242 in 1845, 105,953 in 1846, about double that in 1847. This movement continued high throughout the rest of the century. Those who remained changed the land-tenure system, their marriage patterns, and the whole agricultural economy so radically that Ireland became stabilized with a population of just over four million.

To prevent financial losses in agriculture through attack of fungus organisms, government agencies in many countries now spend large sums annually on research. Both preventive measures and curative ones are sought, attempting in every way to avoid reduced yield of produce. Even disfigurements of surface or shape that reduce marketability are eliminated wherever possible.

4. *Destruction of growth tissue.* The chestnut blight, which virtually eliminated the formerly extensive areas of tall, vigorous chestnut trees in New England, takes this form (Photos 20, 21). Destruction may extend horizontally around a tree trunk from a minor wound, girdling the tree and ending its life in seeming suddenness. Deformations of growth produce visible abnormalities called "cankers." These often end the productive growth of one shoot after another, until a whole tree dies.

5. *Stimulation of abnormal cell proliferation,* forming galls on roots (often called "club roots"), stems (generally referred to as "witches' brooms"), or terminal buds (forming "crown galls"). Each of these is remarkably specific in form, indicating that the disease organism interferes with or supplements some of the steps in the normal chemistry of life, with results that are as definite as though the changes were controlled by heredity. Comments on animal-induced galls (p. 366) apply closely to those resulting from invasion of bacteria.

6. *Production of poisons* through fungus and bacterial action is a serious result of a pathogenic organism, if it affects plants in which man is interested for food. The fungus disease of rye known as "ergot" produces the highly poisonous substance ergotamine. During the Middle Ages in Europe, where rye was used extensively for human consumption, disastrous epidemics of "ergotism" were traced to this source. In 1951, a single French town made international news when a few died and many took sick after eating ergot-contaminated bread.

Ergot infects the blossoms and produces fruiting bodies that are attractive to insects. These—chiefly flies—disseminate the disease. The fungus replaces each ovary of an infected flower with a compact mass rich in the toxic chemical substance. With mechanical harvesting, however, it is easy to reject diseased seeds since they are lighter in weight. Today such rejection is so complete, and rye acreages have

17. Wheat with stinking smut is no longer valuable as food.

18. Corn destroyed by corn smut is unsalable and of no use to anyone.

FUNGUS DISEASES
OF PLANTS

19. The reproductive bodies of pine blister rust push out through breaks in the bark.

20. Almost every tree of the once common American chestnut died from an introduced fungus blight. Oriental chestnuts and hybrids with American chestnuts are immune. The disease has now spread to Europe and is attacking the native species with equal devastation.

21. Fresh damage by chestnut blight to a living branch.

shrunk so far because of human preference for other grains, that ergotamine has become one of the most expensive drugs on the market. It is an alkaloid useful in small doses for treat-

ing some forms of hemorrhage and of migraine headaches.

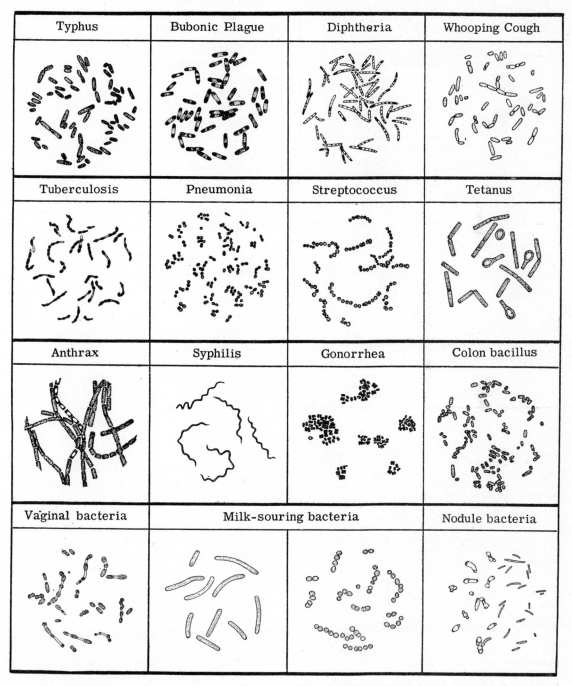

FIG. 4-4. *Harmful bacteria have become well known. Neutral and helpful kinds are often less appreciated.*

III. ANIMALS

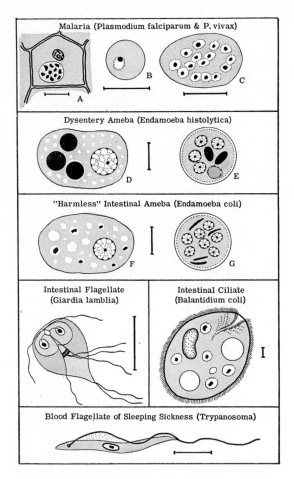

Malaria (Plasmodium falciparum & P. vivax)

Dysentery Ameba (Endamoeba histolytica)

"Harmless" Intestinal Ameba (Endamoeba coli)

Intestinal Flagellate (Giardia lamblia)

Intestinal Ciliate (Balantidium coli)

Blood Flagellate of Sleeping Sickness (Trypanosoma)

FIG. 4-5. *Protozoans which may cause human diseases are of many kinds. For centuries the most important has been the malaria organism, transferred from one victim to another by mosquitoes (see also Fig. 13-9). It has many forms, depending on the site of attack: at first it reproduces in tissue cells of the liver (A) and bone marrow; then it invades red blood corpuscles (B) and reproduces there, swelling the blood cell out of shape (C). The dysentery ameba destroys tissue lining the digestive tract, and engulfs red blood cells (shown in black at D); drought-resistant cysts (E) may be carried to new victims by contaminated drinking water or by flies; shown in black are pigmented bodies, in dark shading a food reserve of glycogen. The supposedly harmless ameba of man's intestine shares his food, engulfing particles (shown in black at F); it is distributed by cysts (G) containing several nuclei as well as pigmented bodies. Both the intestinal flagellate, Giardia, and the intestinal ciliate, Balantidium, cause diarrhea. Sleeping sickness (see also Fig. 13-5) is so disastrous to man that it determines what areas he can live in on the African continent. In each illustration the dimensions of the organism are shown by a line representing 10 μ at the same magnification.*

A major proportion of the economic values to be found in the plant kingdom have a counterpart among animals.

1. ANIMAL PATHOLOGY

Abnormalities among animals, the concern of animal pathologists, may be due to specific viruses; to bacterial or fungus infection; to protozoans; to many worms; and to a scattering of other organisms. The virus- and bacteria-caused diseases of man and domestic animals are discussed at some length on pp. 465-469.

Ringworm or athlete's foot is the most familiar of the several fungus infections of human beings; it is also the most common in the United States. In the tropics, however, other fungus infections and diseases are prevalent.

A somewhat arbitrary division of the field of animal pathology turns responsibility for recognition and treatment of bacterial and fungus diseases (and viruses) to a group of scientists versed particularly in bacteriological methods, whereas any symptoms arising from protozoan, worm, or arthropod invaders are referred to the parasitologists. This disposition of the field leaves pathologists themselves concerned chiefly with the problems of malignancies—cancers of various kinds. The parasitologists, moreover, are subdivided into those specializing on protozoa (Fig. 4-5, protozoologists), on worms (helminthologists), and on the arthropods (the medical entomologists). Ticks (Photo 23), although arachnids and not insects, are relegated to the entomologists; with the pathogenic members from three-quarters of the known kinds of life on the earth already constituting their field, the entomologists hardly notice the extra few problems the ticks and mites and spiders add to the load.

Amebic dysentery, sleeping sickness, kala-azar, and malaria are probably the best known human diseases caused by single-celled animals. Dysentery is prevalent in all tropical and Oriental areas where sanitation is at such a low level that water supplies become contaminated, or wherever human fecal material ("night soil") is used as fertilizer for the earth on which vegetables are raised. Sleeping sickness (African trypanosomiasis) is restricted to

22. Poison ivy foliage is characteristic, easily recognizable, and to be avoided. Some people are immune at some times, but few can escape its toxic action if consistently exposed to it for many years. Even smoke from burning roots, stems, or leaves affects many.

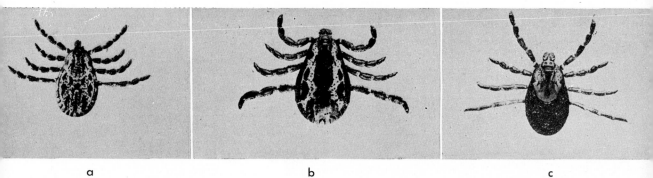

a   b   c

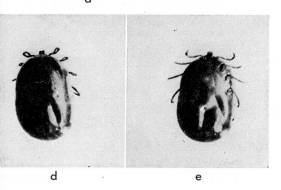

d   e

23. The tick vector of Rocky Mountain spotted fever and other diseases; ♂ ♂ *a, b;* ♀ *c.* An engorged ♀ in dorsal view (*d*) and ventral (*e*). The illustrations are not to one scale: unfed ticks reach a length of $\frac{3}{16}$ inch, whereas engorged specimens may exceed $\frac{1}{2}$ inch.

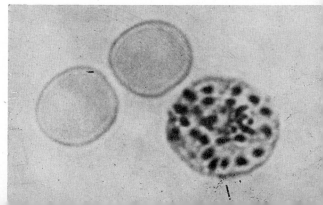

24. A malaria organism beside two red blood cells. On a world basis, malaria exceeds in importance any other single disease.

25. "Mormon crickets" are two-inch insects, heavy-bodied, and destructive to man's crops. Their attacks almost ruined the Mormon pioneers during their first summer (1848) in Utah. Sea gulls, one of their normal enemies in this area, finally controlled the outbreak of crickets.

26. Metal fences and poison baits are used extensively to reduce Utah's cricket populations where man attempts commercial raising of grains and other crops.

Africa. Malaria (Photo 24) occurs widely through warmer countries. Kala-azar is most widespread in India, but is a serious disease also in other parts of Asia, in the Mediterranean region and in some areas of South America. All four of these diseases may be fatal. Their economic significance, in terms of lives and working hours lost, is beyond estimation.

Tapeworms (Photos 92, 93), acquired by eating improperly cooked meat of infected animals; a variety of flukes which achieve entry in a number of different ways and produce difficulties for man and his vertebrate domestic animals by destroying tissue in lungs or liver; and a larger number of roundworms; all produce disease symptoms of degrees of severity ranging from slight fatigue (as from the toxic substances liberated by a heavy infestation of tapeworms) to fatal derangement of normal function. Three of the roundworms outrank all others in their effect on man: the hookworm of areas where disposal of human feces is handled carelessly and (usually) where walking barefoot is common; the trichina from improperly cooked pork (Photos 317, 318); and the filaria worms that cause elephantiasis (Photo 319). Pinworms and other roundworms of domestic animals may produce symptoms of disease, or merely weaken the victims to the point where other more serious agents are able to enter the system and cause fatal disorders.

2. DISEASE CARRIERS AND ALTERNATE HOSTS

Blood-sucking mites, ticks, and insects transfer disease organisms from one host to another. Frequently the parasite's life history is complex in that it requires developmental changes within the body of the vector before the parasite can successfully invade the next host.

Sleeping sickness is carried by the tsetse fly, malaria of birds by one kind of mosquito (Culex), malaria of man by a different mosquito (Anopheles), and so on. In many instances, man is only an incidental host to a disease normally affecting other animals. He enters the picture only by being bitten by an infected vector. Thus yellow fever is primarily a parasite of monkeys. But if man is bitten by

an infected mosquito (Aedes) he can develop the disease. Bubonic plague reaches man from rats by way of bites of rat fleas. He gets typhus fever from rats through lice. Tularemia and Rocky Mountain spotted fever come to him from rabbits and deer when he is bitten by infected ticks which are the normal vector in the wild animal populations.

When diseases that affect man or his domesticated animals have their major life cycle in wild organisms, the wild form serves as a reservoir of infection which no control measures within man's own sphere of operations will affect. Locating the wild reservoir and unraveling the parasite's life history often requires intensive sleuthing.

3. ANIMAL VENOMS AND POISONS

The Portuguese man-of-war and various of the larger jellyfishes, together with a few stinging corals of tropical reefs, provide enough toxic material through their stinging cells to affect man's skin, raising welts. If the affected area is extensive, enough poison may be absorbed to produce serious symptoms or even death.

The potency of the venom varies greatly and may be a more important factor in determining the degree of danger from a bite than the quantity involved. The larger centipedes, scorpions and spiders, and the many kinds of bees and wasps are less dangerous than some small ones (such as the "black widow," Latrodectes, of America).

Among vertebrate animals, the sting-ray, with its dagger-like spine on the tail, may inflict wounds through which microörganisms gain entry and produce infections. A few tropical fish have venomous spines. Some tropical frogs exude enough toxic material from their skins to have attracted human attention; extracts of the skin can be used as a highly dangerous arrow poison used in war or in hunting.

In the United States and Canada, no frog, toad, or salamander is harmful. Only four different snakes can do more harm than a kitten. These are (1) the **rattlers** of several kinds, all with a conspicuous and noisy tail tip that whirs a warning unless the snake is actually stepped on; (2) the **cottonmouth moc-**

casin (Photo 297) of wet situations from Virginia southward, through the lower parts of the Mississippi drainage area and south-westward where there are streams; (3) the rather widely distributed, cinnamon-brown mottled **copperhead** of woodlands; and (4) the brightly colored, yellow-red-black, banded **coral snake.**

Of these the rattlers, copperhead and water moccasin are of a single type, and an antivenin has been prepared for treatment of bites by these reptiles. The coral snake seldom bites human beings. Its venom, however, corre-sponds in type to various South American snakes. Antivenins for treating this type are made and maintained in South America, but not in the United States since call for them is so rare.

In the tropics and on other continents vari-ous other poisonous snakes are found. Of these, the cobras of the Orient are probably the most famous, most feared, and least perse-cuted (because of religious beliefs) among the people where the bite is frequently fatal.

Nonpoisonous snakes of America, such as the green snake, the black snake, the milk snake, the garter snake, and the water snake should be encouraged by every means possible. They are valuable to man in controlling insects and rodents. Many of these harmless snakes will strike and bite if cornered. So will a squir-rel or an angry cat, and the teeth in these lat-ter are so much larger than those of the harm-less snakes that the mammals are far more likely to do damage.

America has the only two poisonous lizards in the world: (1) the fat-tailed, black and pink Gila monster (Photo 298) of Arizona, and (2) the long-tailed, black and gray beaded lizard of Mexico (Photo 299). These animals have no fangs, but when the lizard clings to a bitten victim, a toxic saliva enters the wound. Both of these lizards can be provoked into bit-ing a person, but their poison is important pri-marily in subduing small animals slow enough to be caught.

4. OTHER DETRIMENTAL EFFECTS OF ANIMALS

In addition to animals which directly affect man are many which bear on activities closely enough to be listed as disadvantageous. Con-trol measures are planned and put into effect. Some of these receive further attention in Chapter 24.

Destruction of potential food

Because man strives to improve his effi-ciency as a food-raising species, he makes a vigorous attempt to grow crop plants or ani-mals in almost pure culture over wide areas. Such a concentration of a single species pro-vides an ideal situation for spread of disease organisms, and attracts predators or herbivores —giving all of these the best of living condi-tions and opportunity to multiply.

In lakes or the sea, where man sets his nets to catch fish, predators like shark and lamprey attack the captives and may do considerable damage to the nets as well, costing the fisher-men not only the fish they could no longer sell but also much time in repair of equipment. Where clams or oysters are "seeded" and allowed to grow to commercial sizes before harvesting, predators gather and make serious inroads. Starfish and the snails known as oys-ter drills attack the shellfish one at a time and remove the occupant, while some of the rays and skates munch the smaller shells in quantity and then separate the meat from the broken fragments of crushed shells.

Probably caterpillars (which are the larvae of butterflies and moths) and such sucking in-sects as plant lice and leafhoppers do more damage to foliage crops than any others of man's terrestrial competitors. Grasshoppers and crickets may reach alarming numbers and devastate large areas. Rabbits, mice, ground-hogs (marmots), ground squirrels, and pocket gophers reduce the yield of grain and garden crops. In the American Southwest, the so-called agricultural ant not only cuts and brings home sizable quantities of foliage but also diminishes the land area available to man's crops by keeping entirely free of vegetation rather large areas around the doorways of the anthill. The aridity of the land so limits the crop yield without interference that the activi-ties of these ants stand out as important dam-ages.

In many parts of the southern Mississippi drainage area, comparable difficulty is encoun-

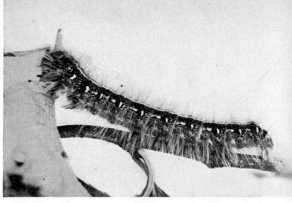

28. One tent caterpillar. (See also Photo 227.)

27. A tent caterpillar nest in a cherry tree.

29. Adults, ♂ *left,* ♀ *right,* of the tent caterpillar.

DEFOLIATION OF ORCHARD TREES AND FORESTS IS COMMONLY THE WORK OF CATERPILLARS

30. Leafless trees in midsummer after attack by gypsy moth caterpillars.

31. Following an epidemic of bark beetles in a stand of western yellow pine, lumbermen may remove all living trees to salvage the valuable timber. Dead and dying victims of the insects are left standing.

32. Destruction of cambium and phloem where the beetle larvae build their galleries provides easy entrance paths for disease organisms—adding to the girdling damage caused by the insects themselves. When the bark is peeled back, lines of frass show where bark beetle tunnels have destroyed tissue and left brown indigestible wastes.

33. The western pine bark beetle is actually less than a quarter-inch long. A pine tree, while healthy, may smother a few attacking pine bark beetles, but an old pine with declining vigor is usually overcome and girdled. Attack by a large number of beetles in an epidemic, however, kills off almost every tree of the susceptible species.

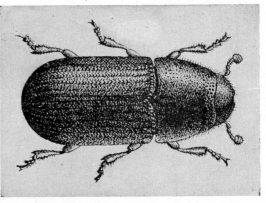

BARK BEETLE DAMAGE

tered among clay soils from the presence of large numbers of crayfishes. These crustaceans dig vertical burrows downward in the clay, each burrow ending in a larger chamber in which water stands because of the tight texture of the soil. From the burrow the crayfish emerges to forage each night, and the 8,000 to 12,000 crustaceans per acre in some areas effectively prevent the successful raising of the two chief crops—corn and cotton—by eating off the tops of the young plants as they appear.

Economic entomology manuals list a great array of insects which attack fruit—for example, the codling moth of apples and pears, the several corn borers of maize, and the leafhoppers of grapes. Still other insects, like the weevils of dried peas and grains, and the various mealworms and flour moths, damage food in storage. Ants and cockroaches raid the larder after foodstuffs have been bought and readied for human consumption. From the planting of seed to the appearance of vegetable food on the table, there is a continual competition with insects for man's use of his crops. A corresponding reduction in the yield of flesh on domestic animals in terms of food or time may be due to a variety of parasites which lower resistance to disease and retard growth. Maggot-laying or egg-laying flies which gain access to areas where food animals are being divided into "cuts" of meat, may ruin the material before man can get it to the table. In tropical regions, where refrigeration is lacking, the chief solution to this latter difficulty is to cook and eat the meat within minutes after the food animals have been killed.

Special mention is needed for the annual destruction of stored foods by rats and mice. Rats and mice make significant inroads on man's supplies both on shore and afloat, and they increase with remarkable rapidity whenever food opportunities become available through human carelessness. Actually, the rat is so resourceful and its teeth so strong (and quickly replaced) that building a rat-proof granary is both an engineering problem and a major expense. Rats can gnaw through cement walls and many other obstacles. Mice slide in and out through cracks that man often considers negligible or necessary for ventilation of the stored, living seeds.

Damage to property

Untreated wood exposed to sea water is almost sure to be destroyed by burrowing clams known as *shipworms*. These attack wharf pilings and ship bottoms, hollowing out living spaces for themselves but weakening the structure in the process. On ships, an encrusting layer of barnacles, mussels, and other clinging organisms provides great increase in friction; this reduces speed; collectively they are referred to as "bottom fouling" animals, and means must be found to remove them periodically or to discourage their colonization of ship bottoms.

Forest trees often are defoliated by such insects as tent caterpillars (Photos 27-29) or gypsy moths (Photo 30), or are doomed by activities of beetle larvae beneath the bark (Photos 31-33). Unless trees killed by persistent attacks are harvested promptly—often within a few weeks after they succumb—the wood is damaged further by insect invaders and by fungus, rendering it progressively less valuable for lumber.

Wooden structures on land in many areas are subject to damage by termites, which riddle the wood with galleries (Photo 34) and digest the cellulose (with the help of intestinal protozoans) as food. Carpenter ants may do similar damage in buildings by forming galleries in which to store food (seeds and fruits) and to rear young. Standing timber or freshly fallen trees often are penetrated by wood-boring young of various beetles, which reduce the value of the lumber and which make unsightly holes. Porcupines, rabbits, and starving deer or elk often girdle trees in winter by chewing the bark; they are detrimental to man's interests in lumber or tree fruit crops, and they upset the water-holding characteristics of forested hillsides.

Damage to textile raw materials, such as cotton through activities of the boll weevil, may be compared to damage to woolen fabrics after manufacture by clothes moths (Photo 35) and carpet beetles. Botflies attack cattle and horses and spend their final larval stages in ulcerous cavities in the skin; they leave holes in the hide and ruin it for leather. The starchy sizing used on many kinds of paper or to stiffen fabrics, and the glue employed in binding books, attract silverfish and book lice, in home or library. Continued rasping at the surfaces by these insects disfigures and defaces paper, destroys cloth, and causes bound volumes to fall apart.

Animals sometimes incur displeasure or endanger human life in other ways. Earthworms extruding their castings of earth on the putting greens of a golf course deflect the carefully aimed ball and bring down man's wrath. Alligators, cane rats, and muskrats tunnel through the levees with which man restrains flood waters of sluggish rivers, so that farm lands are inundated and homes swept away. Beavers may dam streams and flood roads or farmlands. Ordinarily, such efforts are very helpful in conserving the water supply and in preventing devastating floods, but in the wrong place (from man's point of view) beaver activities must be discouraged.

5. BUILDING MATERIALS

Coral rock—often known as "coquina"—is the product of coral animals (Photo 88) and a variety of tube-making worms. Limestone consolidated from these and similar materials of animal origin is used extensively for structural purpose, and is capable of being worked into fine decorative carvings. Marble is a limestone of extremely fine grain; it may be plain or variegated in color ("marbled" being a term widely used to describe the irregular patterns).

The function of coral animals in building reefs—and from reefs whole oceanic islands ("atolls")—in volcanic areas was elucidated first by Charles Darwin (Fig. 21-18).

6. FUELS, LIGHT, AND POWER

The contribution of animals in these directions is negligible by comparison with that of the plant kingdom. Yet the conventional measure for power is in horsepower, and the use of the various domesticated animals for traction and for turning mills extends from sled dogs in the arctic, through horse, ass (burro), mule, elephant, camels, to water buffalo, llama, and others. The use of dung for fuel is widespread in arid areas where trees are scarce and where

other wood must be hauled from great distances. The use of whale oil for candles (spermaceti) lit man's night activities for many years, and gives us the unit of illumination—the standard candlepower. The "oil sardine" was caught in earlier times to furnish fuel for European lamps. To a much lesser extent—and chiefly for esthetic purposes—fireflies have been used for illumination.

7. USES IN TECHNOLOGY

From the various kinds of sponges of warm waters come an assortment of products. The center for the industry (Photo 87) in the United States is at Tarpon Springs, Florida, with sponge fishing grounds extending from Apalachicola to Key West, in water to 150 feet deep.

From the cephalopod mollusks come cuttlebone (from the cuttlefish) such as is hung in cages with pet canaries as a source of lime, and India ink from the ink sacs of these relatives of the squid and octopus. Until recently, gastropod shells of cowries were used as a form of money in the South Pacific (Photo 432).

In the tropics—particularly in residences, churches, and other public buildings—the expense of importing glass panes for windows is often obviated through use of the translucent thin shells of the "window-glass shell" (Placuna) cut into three- or four-inch squares. Another clam—the giant of the group (Tridacna)—often contributes its pure white monstrous valves (Photo 98) to be used singly as baptismal fonts to hold holy water in churches not only of the tropics but of temperate areas as well. Fresh-water mussels are sought extensively for their shells, from which "pearl" buttons can be cut.

The value of the earthworm in soil movements and in aeration of the lower levels is merely a better-known example of similar benefits to crop-growing man from the activities of the greater number of still smaller soil animals.

During World War I, the difficulties in surgical treatment of gangrenous wounds led to the use of specially sterile cultures of blowfly maggots. These were introduced into a wound and there scavenged so thoroughly that they cleared out all the decaying tissue—eating

34. Wood and wood products such as paper are attacked by termites, although the insects themselves are unable to digest the cellulose they swallow. Instead, microorganisms in the termite digestive tract digest the cellulose, and release digestion products upon which the termites thrive. Termites are often called "white ants," although they are not ants of any kind. In the center of the photograph is a "soldier" member of the termite society, identified by the enlarged dark head. The other individuals are "workers"—both adult and immature.

DESTRUCTIVE, FIBER-EATING INSECTS

35. Adult clothes moths (right) do not eat, but they seek out a variety of fibers, often in the form of cloth, and show preference for wool or other substances with a fatty content. Their eggs hatch into caterpillars which attack these fibers, producing holes in fabrics; several sizes of these caterpillars are shown between the two buttons.

36. Seining for menhaden off the North Carolina coast. The ring of floats is attached to the upper edge of a net pursed in at the bottom to hold a catch of fish.

FOODS FROM THE WATER

37. At the Boston fish pier cargoes are unloaded from shiphold to carts for weighing and sale. Each kind of fish has its own price. Here a cartful of one particular species of flounder awaits its turn at the scales.

38. A pair of channel catfish being placed in brood pens at an Oklahoma fish culture station; ♂ *left*, ♀ *right*. Note the tactile appendages.

down to the healthy, living cells and no farther —and finally eliminated the infections, allowing normal healing processes to save the patient. The increased use of antibiotics in World War II largely eliminated the need for this interesting technique, but its availability should not be forgotten since many people develop adverse reactions to prolonged or repeated chemical treatments.

The increased use of nylon and other synthetic fibers has diminished the importance of the silk industry, wherein silkworms (caterpillars) were fed on mulberry leaves and were provided clean quarters in which to spin their cocoons. Later, cheap hand-labor unraveled the cocoons and prepared the fiber for use as thread. Spider silk still has an important place for the cross-hairs in the eyepieces of telescopes, theodolites, and the like; collecting it is a limited and highly specialized industry. Wool, from sheep or goat, retains its place as a fiber for warm clothing. Down feathers have not been supplemented satisfactorily for sleeping bags.

The use of leeches to withdraw blood from patients thought to have too much blood was introduced in very ancient times. Although no longer a part of modern medicine, "medicinal leeches" are still sold in large cities for use by the superstitious in self-medication, and by unscrupulous quacks who pose as miraculous healers. Yet they were reportedly used on Joseph V. Stalin, premier of the U.S.S.R., following his cerebral hemorrhage of March, 1953.

Tortoise shell and the skins of various lizards, snakes, and alligators, like the hides of some mammals, have a considerable commercial value as decorative and utilitarian leathers. The economic position of bird feathers and mammalian furs in decorative costumes as a luxury trade need only be mentioned to be appreciated. Down feathers are no longer used in bedding except for stuffing pillows, but in pioneer days they were highly important. Their use in modern times has extended into all manner of outdoor sleeping bags and insulating garments that allow activities away from fixed shelters in the coldest climates on earth.

Almost any animal material that can be dried and pulverized can be used as a fertilizer for soil. Excrement of domestic animals, bone meal, and fish meal, and its many variations, have economic importance in maintaining or building humus. Guano from sea birds on islands off the coasts of Chile and Peru has been highly important not only as a source of fertilizer but for phosphates and nitrates used in manufacture of explosives and other chemicals.

Highly malodorous secretions from the rectal "musk" glands of the skunk and other mammals have proven useful in the art of compounding perfumes. Toward this industry goes also the material ambergris, obtained from diseased whales. Ambergris is one of the most prized and peculiar substances known.

8. FOOD ANIMALS

Most of the animals man uses directly for food belong to vertebrate groups: fishes, birds, and mammals predominate, and their muscle tissue ("flesh") is the chief item of interest. Some food animals are caught from wild populations, but many of them are raised in captivity. The biological fields of fisheries and animal husbandry concern themselves with maintenance of a higher rate of yield in these industries.

MAMMALS. Of prime importance are the even-toed, hoofed ungulates—sheep, cattle, reindeer, buffalo, and goats which are domesticated, and the deer, elk, moose, antelope, and others (particularly on the African plains) hunted as game. Closely related, both taxonomically and in utility, are the pigs, hogs, and boars of the world, meat from which forms an important part of man's diet in almost every country. Rabbits and squirrels are the chief other food mammals of America, although opossum is considered a delicacy throughout much of the south, and the flesh of seals, walrus, and bear is sought farther north. Whale meat has had some economic value and is available in many places—either fresh, smoked, or canned. Horse meat has been used widely, but in America it is infrequently used except for pets.

BIRDS. Three groups of birds find important place on human dietaries: the hen-like kinds, including the domestic fowl, peafowl, turkeys, pheasants, partridge, quail, grouse, and prairie chicken; the ducks, geese, brants, and swans, collectively termed "waterfowl"; and the tinamous of southern Mexico and into southern South America. Both flesh and eggs form important parts of the diet of man in almost every country.

REPTILES. Only the large turtles have been used in civilized areas to any extent as food, but these are employed as steaks, in stews, and for giving both body and flavor to soups. The green turtle of tropical islands is the most valuable of these to man, but turtle eggs of all sorts are highly esteemed and actively hunted in many regions. In the Carolinas, land turtles (terrapins) are often maintained in penned enclosures, fed on garbage, and robbed of their eggs. In tropical areas many of the larger lizards are highly regarded as food by the natives.

AMPHIBIANS. Except for the hind leg muscles of frogs, approved as a delicacy and sought as a food in many places, man has few food uses for amphibians. Partly this is a matter of their small size, partly their unavailability in sufficient numbers to be economically valuable. Frog flesh is best in the fall and early months of hibernation, and frogs are caught for the market in fairly large numbers in New York, the states along the Mississippi, and in eastern Canada. Populations of French extraction are particularly fond of them.

BONY FISHES. A considerable assortment of true fishes find their way into man's diet. Those sought commercially (Photos 36-40) on the largest scale include the herrings, sardines (young herring and pilchard), and shad of the Herring Family; the tunas and mullets; the salmons; the eels; the mackerels; the various members of the Cod Family—cod, haddock, hake and burbot; and the flatfishes —flounder (Photo 422), halibut and sole. Vitamin concentrates are obtained from cod, halibut, and others.

ELASMOBRANCHS. The greatest food value from this group is in liver oils rich in Vitamins A and D, extracted from a number of different sharks now being caught deliberately for this product. To a small extent, shark meat appears on the market canned under trade names. Like so many other meats, it is completely acceptable as food as long as people are not told the name of the animal from which it is obtained.

ARTHROPODS. Honey from honeybees is a cash crop of considerable annual money value; considered in conjunction with the value of all fruits and vegetables resulting from the pollinating activities of honeybees, it will be seen that this insect is exceptionally valuable to man. Insects used directly as foods include grasshoppers and caterpillars (to be seen in the markets of Manila and of many Mexican and Central American towns). A major occupation of the children and women of the Australian aborigine tribes is the digging out of beetle grubs that feed on roots. Other tribes enjoy the honey-storing "replete" caste of ants, which they dig from the earth and eat raw.

Civilized man places more emphasis upon the crustaceans—lobsters, crayfish, crabs of the many larger kinds (Photos 41, 42), and shrimp or prawns. He overlooks, however, a great deal of food value in the hordes of horseshoe crabs that come ashore to spawn each spring, although these formed a regular part of the diet of Indians along the Atlantic and Gulf coasts and contain considerable nourishment. Man uses horseshoe crabs (usually dried) for fertilizer (Photo 43), though some are chopped and fed to hogs, some slit open and used to build strength in domestic fowl.

MOLLUSKS. Squid and octopus are human food in Portuguese, Spanish, Italian, and Greek communities, and in the Orient. Land snails are esteemed by the French and Japanese. The giant land snail Achatina, imported into the South Pacific, is now creating devastation—with no Japanese left in the area to eat them. Elsewhere among civilized groups, the chief mollusks of food value are believed to be the mussels, clams (Photos 44-47), oysters, scallops (adductor muscle only), and abalone (muscle only); all but the last are variants of the clam structural pattern.

ECHINODERMS. Often lumped with the mollusks as "shellfish," the chief echinoderms of interest to man as a food are the Oriental sea cucumbers sold as "trepangs" or "bêches de mer" in a dried condition, to be used to give body and flavor to soups. To the Occidental mind these are about as strange ingredients for a normal diet as the tough gelatinous saliva

39. Indians fishing for salmon in Oregon.

40. A large-mouthed black bass.

41. A box of shrimp from Alaskan waters.

42. Blue crabs, kept alive in pens, moult and are sent promptly to market as "soft shell crabs."

43. Horseshoe crabs, members of the arachnoid group and not crustaceans, are trapped in great numbers to be ground up for fertilizer. (See Photos 110, 129.)

in nests of the Chinese swifts, made into "birds' nest soup" on a sufficiently large scale for the abandoned nests to have a definite market value in the Far East.

9. HELPFUL ANIMALS

Much less credit is given than is deserved for the assistance man receives without asking from predators, large (mountain lion, wolf, coyote, fox, skunk, eagle, hawk, and owl) and small (bat, song bird, snake [Photo 78], frog, toad, spider [Photos 111, 112], dragonfly, praying mantis [Photos 131-133], ground beetle, and the like) in controlling the numbers of rats, mice, grasshoppers, mosquitoes, leafhoppers, caterpillars, and flies. Another honest vote of thanks is due the wild mice and seed-eating birds for their important part in destruction of weed seeds. The work of honeybees and other insects and hummingbirds in pollinating flowers has been mentioned but can scarcely be overemphasized in terms of man's unconscious benefits in food. Similarly, the scavengers—whether large (bear and vulture) or small (soil bacteria, protozoans, worms of many kinds, ants [Photo 281], dung beetles, carrion beetles, and many more) keep the cycles of carbon and nitrogen and other decay processes in active rotation, making raw materials available to plants and removing the remains of the dead before they can accumulate and clutter up the earth. Two groups of parasitic insects are worthy of special mention—the ichneumon flies (related to ants and bees) and the tachina flies (true two-winged flies with bristly bodies), which destroy countless insects (particularly those of caterpillar and beetle larva types) that would otherwise menace man's crops.

The forgotten smaller organisms, from plankton to crayfish or insect on which fish feed, or which supplement the diet of mosquito-catching birds, should not be overlooked. Their small size and inconspicuous habits tend to earn them no place in man's mind, but their activities do much to aid his projects.

10. ESTHETIC VALUES

The use of pink "precious coral" from the Mediterranean and of pearls from a variety of sources is a custom stemming from antiquity. A similar employment of fancy buttons, feathers, and furs extends the range of animal products for which esthetic values have been found. Collections of corals, mollusk shells, butterflies, and moths, and mounted bird or mammal skins have had considerable appeal apart from any scientific value. They are expressions of both man's hoarding instinct and the breadth of his curiosity; the curio cabinets in many living rooms contain souvenirs from human wanderings and all manner of animal or plant relics which hold continuing interest or about which further information is sought.

IV. AVOCATIONAL ASPECTS

Charles Kingsley wrote: "We act as though comfort and luxury were the chief requirements of life when all we need to make us really happy is something to be enthusiastic about." Often this enthusiasm is found primarily in a hobby. The avocation may entail more actual work than a person's gainful occupation, but its freedoms of choice compensate fully and bring pleasure out of all proportion. Few sciences afford such a wealth of avocational opportunities as does biology.

1. NONPROFESSIONAL SCIENTISTS

With a self-disciplined mind, a person may not only enjoy pursuing a restricted field in biology but actually make valuable contributions to scientific knowledge. In biology (as in astronomy, where a telescope of some kind is a requirement), the professional scientist encourages the cooperation of the amateur and respects his work. Perhaps the enterprises themselves are comparable: the vast numbers of stars to be studied on the one hand, and of kinds of life on the other.

Usually an avocational interest begins as a curiosity concerning the living things surrounding one's home. What are the correct names for the spring wildflowers, for the various birds, for trees and butterflies? Field guides to answer the early questions give a little information about each kind and open the door for further reading on topics of special interest.

With a minimal expenditure of money and with time taken only on weekends, holidays and evenings, it is possible to make important studies on the plants and animals of any given region—particularly on details of life history and ecological interrelationships. That significant research problems can be attacked with so little equipment sets biology off as a unique science. The well-directed curiosity plus patience and a sincere desire to learn the way living things operate, are requirements that cost nothing.

The collection of specimens from the home area can be supplemented by visiting other regions on vacation trips. Gradually the nonprofessional scientist can come to be better informed about the geographical distribution of some group of organisms than anyone else in the world. By correspondence and exchange of specimens with others interested in related subjects, progress can be made that otherwise would require costly expeditions.

The nonprofessional should preserve and care for his specimens according to methods that have been found effective. Specimens devoid of data concerning their origin are valueless scientifically. Similarly, information derived from their study is worthless unless it is made available freely to others. That so many nonprofessional reports of high caliber do appear annually indicates how possible it is for the amateur to master the restricted field in which he is working, to bring himself on a par with any professional in that area of knowledge, to know the vocabulary, the literature, the organisms, the points of view of other workers, and to be able to contribute facts of permanent value from his studies in spare time.

The insects, for example, are far too numerous for professional biologists in research laboratories to study adequately. In North America north of Mexico there are over 20,000 different species of beetles alone. All around the world are amateurs with sound knowledge of some genus, or family, or order of insects. These entomologists join together in clubs and societies, read technical journals, keep close track of literature in their specialties, correspond with others in the narrow field, and exchange specimens by mail so that each can build up a useful reference collection on which to base identification of unfamiliar species.

Aid in verifying identifications is available to most amateur zoologists, either from more advanced workers or from the staff of major museums. The prime requisite is that the specimens submitted be in good condition, carefully prepared, and supported by full data on details of origin (where and when captured being the fundamental facts for most places; elevation is important in mountain regions to identify the life zone). No charge is made for this cooperation.

As the amateur grows older he will be passing on the help to another generation of beginners. The accepted procedure for amateur collections that come to have scientific value is for the individual to donate them as soon as he is no longer active in his field—either to some other specialist-collector or to a responsible museum.

Much of our knowledge of habits and interrelations among mammals and among birds comes from the field studies of amateur biologists, who follow some particular group in spare time. Some of these band birds with numbered tags obtained from cooperating government agencies. A few such banded specimens are invariably picked up and returned to national headquarters, complying with a request on each band. The details of band recovery are then sent to the person who banded the bird, as payment for his care in attaching the band and sending in to headquarters the identification of the bird, date, and place of banding. These data make possible the plotting of migration routes and furnish data about the longevity of each species. Sometimes new knowledge is obtained about the enemies of the warm-blooded vertebrates from these studies of banded individuals.

Ornithologists, like garden club members, may be people who find in the avocational study of birds an esthetic outlet rather than a progressive scientific study. This should not be discouraged, but the consecutive observational approach to either field, if followed by presentation of the data obtained before a club or state academy of science with national con-

44. Where waves roll in over long Pacific beaches, the geoduck burrows in the muddy bottom.

THE LARGEST BURROWING CLAM HAS BE-
COME A SPORTS FISHERY ON THE WEST
COAST

45. An L-shaped board helps prevent water draining down the beach from filling the hole required to reach a geoduck—often four feet below the surface at points exposed only on exceptionally low tides.

46. The legal limit per day per digger is three geoducks (pronounced goo'-ee-ducks).

47. Preparing geoduck for dinner consists of severing and skinning the long neck (to be diced for chowder) and removing the thick edge of the mantle where it protrudes permanently between the edges of the valves.

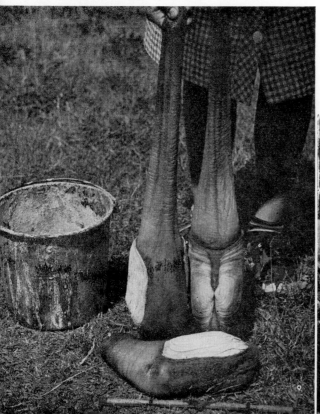

48. Fishermen who seek smelt through holes cut in the ice on Lake Champlain, Vermont–New York, tow wooden sheds to their chosen site on the frozen surface. The fisherman can then keep warm, protected from the wind while tending his lines into the water below him.

CROWDED PLEASURE

49. Near a big city, fishermen may stand almost elbow to elbow, each hoping for a bite at the end of the line. Whether fish are caught or not, the men can enjoy a day outdoors.

nections and officers who are active in the field, can have far-reaching and valuable effects, contributing to the total knowledge.

The nonprofessional's time and honest study of the problem chosen are his chief contributions—and they often lead to information of fundamental importance in the advancement of science. After all, Gregor Mendel was a rank amateur, but his work provided the foundations for all genetics.

2. WILDLIFE PHOTOGRAPHERS

Since the collection of specimens for scientific study usually implies willingness to maintain a museum, and also requires the killing and preservation of specimens for future reference, a number of people prefer to make and keep photographic records. These may be still pictures of orchids in their native habitats, high-speed flash photographs of animals in action, or even records of microscopic plants and animals studied at higher magnification. Motion pictures of animals or time-lapse records of plant growth and of flowers opening afford opportunities for later analysis. Often photographic records draw attention to unknown features of plant and animal activities.

3. HUNTING AND FISHING

These human activities seem properly to be considered as avocations (Photos 48, 49) since the total annual catch of fish and kill of birds and mammals provides only about one per cent of the meat eaten. Moreover, hunting and fishing have grown to be such big business —with cost of equipment, of trips, of guide service, and the like running over a billion dollars annually—that the cost of meat and fish caught as food runs between $8 and $16 per pound.

The chief scientific benefit arising from hunting and fishing has been an increase in accurate information concerning wildlife, stemming from subsidized research studies aimed at increasing the supply. It is clear now that game fish and game animals are like crop plants, crop animals, and people. All depend for success upon adequate nutrients in the soil or watery surroundings.

4. WATCHING

Outnumbering hunters and fishermen by about eight to one are people who enjoy watching birds or mammals or insects or growing plants. Many band themselves together into local "bird clubs" and nature organizations. No doubt attendance at meetings is motivated both by an interest in wildlife itself and by sociability. A major factor in the proven appeal of natural history lectures, motion pictures, illustrated books and nature writing is this same appreciation of living things and their activities.

The keeping of pets such as cats, dogs, rabbits, guinea pigs, parrots, parakeets, canaries, pigeons, peacocks, swans, goldfish and the many tropical fish now available to aquarium fanciers, demonstrates a similar appeal. Probably this habit arises partly from a feeling of kinship with the animals and an interest in their movements. Partly it may stem from an oversupply of parental instincts, and a wish to have something to fondle and fuss over. Another basis may be an unexpressed feeling of power, since the pets are dependent upon man for their food and quarters.

Beyond the purely economic value in conservation of wildlife and wild land is the increasing importance of these resources in relation to growing leisure time—the product of mechanization and specialization—to improved living standards, and to larger numbers of people surviving to beyond "retirement age." The right to enjoy the scenery of America has become a basic claim. To retain areas of outstanding beauty or interest for the traveling public is now a governmental responsibility—from town or city council that lays out a park, a parkway, or a "common" to a state, province, or federal authority authorized to set aside a tract for the people to enjoy. Thus have arisen our national parks, national forests, their state counterparts, and a series of national monuments to preserve into the future some more local feature.

Those of greatest biological interest, under the custodianship of the National Park Service include:

Acadia (Maine; 1919)	Crater Lake (Ore.;
Big Bend (Tex.; 1944)	1902)
Bryce Canyon (Utah;	Everglades (Fla.; 1947)
1928)	Glacier (Mont.; 1910)

Grand Canyon (Ariz. 1919)
Grand Teton (Wyo.; 1929)
Great Smoky Mts. (N.C.-Tenn.; 1930)
Hawaii (Hawaii; 1916)
Kings Canyon (Calif.; 1940)
Lassen Volcanic (Calif.; 1916)
Mesa Verde (Colo.; 1906)

Mt. McKinley (Alaska; 1917)
Mt. Rainier (Wash.; 1899)
Olympic (Wash.; 1938)
Sequoia (Calif.; 1890)
Shenandoah (Va.; 1935)
Rocky Mt. (Colo.; 1915)
Yellowstone (Wyo.; 1872)
Yosemite (Calif.; 1890)
Zion (Utah; 1919)

The establishment of a National Park requires an act of Congress. A National Monument may be set aside by Presidential proclamation. Among the most interesting of our National Monuments from a biological point of view are:

Chiricahua (Ariz.)
Dinosaur (Utah-Colo.)
Fossil Cycad (So. Dak.)
Great Sand Dunes (Colo.)
Jackson Hole (Wyo.)
Joshua Tree (Calif.)
Lava Beds (Calif.)

Muir Woods (Calif.)
Organ Pipe Cactus (Ariz.)
Petrified Forest (Ariz.)
Saguaro (Ariz.)
White Sands (New Mex.)

Constant guard must be maintained over these areas, to keep selfish local interests from making inroads on the lumber, mineral, or wildlife resources native to these public lands. Many of the national parks, national monuments, and national forests, as well as state reservations of smaller size but similar interest, furnish camping sites and some conveniences to encourage use of these areas by people with a liking for the out-of-doors.

V. VOCATIONAL ASPECTS

Aside from the relatively small number of artists, photographers, sculptors and technical assistants who have entered professions in biology in a roundabout way, most people engaged gainfully have combined a broad education and technical training at some college or university.

Those who retain the most general interest in the field of biology are ecologists (who study the interrelations of living animals and plants) and those applied ecologists, the wildlife managers and foresters. "Naturalists" as such have few paying positions open to them, for the field of natural history has been subdivided into areas more convenient to study. Mastery of a subject requires full familiarity with all published information on the topic. Scientific literature is now too vast for any one person to keep up with, let alone dig into

the past for proper perspective on more than a limited field.

For the most part, specialization in biology is based upon the classification of plants and animals. A person becomes an expert on algae or sponges or violets or mice. Alternatively, a comparative approach may be taken, as a study of vertebrate vision, or mollusk respiration, or blood pigments, or conducting tissues in plants, or the chemistry of some biological process. Each avenue provides research opportunities for scientific advances. Employers tend to be chiefly government agencies, educational institutions, and industrial corporations. Appointment is based usually upon some relationship between the field to be investigated and the research program on which the candidate was successful in graduate school.

TENANTS OF THE SOIL

Only an astounding fecundity saves the earth dwellers from their multitude of enemies and series of calamities. Every human step on soft earth kills hundreds by crushing their bodies between soil particles. Moles and mice tunnel through the ground to seek the living bits of food. Skunks, bears and 'possums hunt for earthworms, snails, and beetles by turning over stones and rocking logs aside. Man plows the fields to sow his crops and exposes the various small animals to light, dry air, and an appreciative following of birds. He clears away the fallen trees and piles the rocks in dry walls replacing moisture-holding hedgerows. Only the naturalist feels for the tenants of the soil, and his care has a selfish aspect too. Meticulously he replaces the roof over the many homes he studies, so that the creatures there will be less disturbed, and may continue to be present for an unannounced inspection on the next visit to the area. "Roll the log back" and "leave the stone exactly as you find it." As George Herbert wrote:

> *"More servants wait on man*
> *Than he'll take note of. In every path*
> *He treads down that which doth befriend him."*

—LORUS J. MILNE *and* MARGERY MILNE, *A Multitude of Living Things* (New York: Dodd, Mead & Co., 1947), pp. 106-7.

APPRECIATION

An appreciation of nature is the proper expression of our urban civilization. The savage does not glory in the wilderness as does the city dweller. Thoreau never acknowledged what Walden owed to Concord, though everything that Walden meant to him implied the imminence of Concord. If it were not for Washington and New York, I would take the wilderness for granted. I thank God that, having discovered the wilderness, I do not take New York and Washington for granted. New York and Washington are merely the walls without which you have no window. I would have them serve no better purpose than to direct the attention of men outward to the world of nature, to be the shadows that frame the sunlight.

—LOUIS J. HALLE, JR., in *Spring in Washington* (New York: William Sloane Associates, Inc., 1947), p. 129.

SUGGESTED READING (see pp. 507-511)

Recent and Informative: Chapman, 1950; Collins, 1948; Cooley, 1951; Fairchild, 1930, 1938; Howard, 1953; Kamen, 1953; Mangelsdorf, 1950; Milner, 1953, 1955; Quisenberry, 1954; Salaman, 1952; Schery, 1952; Weatherwax, 1950; Weiss, 1952; Yearbook of Agriculture, U.S.D.A., 1952, 1953.

5 · Protoplasm and Cells

1. SPONTANEOUS GENERATION. 2. THE MICROSCOPE AND THE CELL. 3. THE CELL THEORY. 4. PROTOPLASM. 5. BIOGENESIS. 6. LIFE.

PROGRESS in a science may come about in many different ways. Sometimes a man has a brilliant idea. He announces it in print, and then does little or nothing about it himself. Others, perhaps less original, pick it up and carry it through. The work of Linnaeus and of the taxonomists who followed him shows little that is original. And yet biology has progressed greatly as a result of their prodigious efforts. What had been a hopeless jumble of animals and plants became a manageable field for study. Moreover, grouping like with like has permitted some valid predictions and useful theorizing.

Taxonomy emphasizes the *differences* between organisms. Attention to the fundamental similarities among living things waited not so much upon a brilliant idea as on the invention of the microscope—a technological advance. The inability of the human eye to see objects smaller than a certain size led to conclusions that were full of error.

1. SPONTANEOUS GENERATION

Vertebrate animals laid obvious eggs, or brought forth their young alive. Many plants produced seeds from which new plants grew. But the lesser animals and plants had no apparent means of reproduction. It was thought that they must arise by **spontaneous generation.** Aristotle was a careful, conscientious observer but he could see no other way for smaller animals and plants to come about. The mystery of it clearly puzzled him. After Aristotle came other men who were less careful and scarcely conscientious. They repeated the spontaneous generation story and embellished it in many ways. Honeybees arose from rotting carcasses of horses; even Samson had observed this in a lion's disintegrating body. That

the insects involved were bee-like flies, with maggots in the carrion as their source, played no part in the explanation; the "bees" were spontaneously generated. Old books were full of recipes for accomplishing these and other wonders. Horsehairs dropped into rain barrels became worms and then snakes. Other worms arose from wet mud. Geese that had no known nesting ground were claimed to arise as barnacles on timbers of wrecked ships along the lonely coasts of northern Scotland. Frogs were generated in thunderstorms and fell to earth whenever it rained hard. These stories accumulated and achieved widespread approval.

Spontaneous generation received a sudden, incisive blow in 1668. An Italian with an ingenious and unfettered mind performed an experiment that seems adequate even by modern standards. Francesco Redi of Florence placed similar pieces of meat ("a snake, some fish, some eels of Arno, and a slice of milk-fed veal") into clean jars (Fig. 5-1). Four of these jars he left open to the air; four more he sealed shut; four more he closed only with cloth ("fine Naples veil"); four more he placed in frames covered with the same net. The July weather was warm, and soon the meat in the open jars was crawling with maggots; none could be seen through the veiling, though the flesh putrefied and the odor brought hundreds of flies to the outside of the containers. Redi was satisfied that the cloth did not exclude the air, and when he saw that only the jars into which the flies could go developed maggots and then a new crop of flies, he concluded that flies produced maggots and maggots produced flies. The sealed jars were opened after several weeks. In them the exclusion of air had made no difference; the meat was putrid, but no flies had developed, nor were any maggots to be seen. Hence flies came only from pre-existing flies. They were not generated spontaneously. Repetition of the experiment merely confirmed these findings. Redi described his work in a little publication that appeared in Florence under the title *Esperienze intorne alla generazione degl'insetti*.

Redi's work served to limit the broad application of spontaneous generation but not to destroy the idea. If insects came from previous

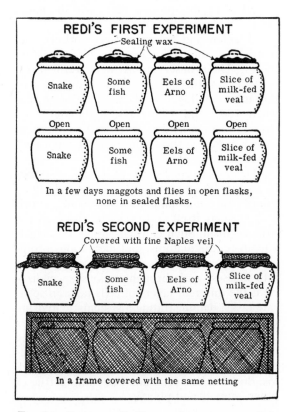

FIG. 5-1. *Francesco Redi's experiments were well designed and led to a definite conclusion (see text).*

insects, at least worms and other insignificant creatures arose from mud and slime in the mystical manner. The final end to widespread belief, even among scientists, did not come until within the past century. Then experimental proof was given that invisible particles carried by air currents are responsible for decomposition (Figs. 5-2 and 5-3). At last the standard method of boiling and sealing fruit to preserve it had a correct explanation. Diseases, too, might be caused by these "germs" in the air.

2. THE MICROSCOPE AND THE CELL

Contemporaries of Francesco Redi were another Italian, Marcello Malpighi, two Englishmen, Robert Hooke and Nehemiah Grew, and two Dutchmen, Jan Swammerdam and Antonius van Leeuwenhoek. These men made contributions of tremendous importance through the use of a new tool for biology—the first crude microscopes. Van Leeuwenhoek became very clever at grinding and mounting his own lenses, making high-powered simple microscopes (to 270X) and using them to explore the world invisible to the naked eye (Photos 51, 52). The others constructed true compound microscopes (Photo 50) and placed all manner of objects in the field of view.

One of Hooke's discoveries seemed of slight importance at the time. It occupies a single page and is accompanied by a little sketch in his 1665 book of curiosities, *Micrographia: or Some Physiological Descriptions of Minute Bodies Made by Magnifying Glasses. With Observations and Inquiries Thereupon.* Hooke examined the smoothly cut surface of a piece of cork, and noted to his astonishment that the microscope showed irregularities. Instead of the level expanse evident to his unaided eyes and fingers, he saw what suggested to him a downward view over a roofless building with walls standing to mark the position of a whole group of rooms. He described these units as cells (see p. 49). In his mind obviously was a concept similar to the dictionary definition of a cell as a "small room in convent, prison or monastery." This term, applied to dead plant material, persisted in biology and acquired a very different significance.

For a long time the cells Hooke described remained uninteresting. Both Hooke and Grew noted that cells, while alive, contained a liquid of some sort. The details, however, were beyond understanding.

In 1823 Robert Brown remarked that each cell appeared to include a small, spherical, transparent object whose form suggested to him a kernel or nut. His account of this cell inclusion seemed so trivial to him that he relegated most of the information to a footnote and gave the name **nucleus** to the unknown objects. Five years later, in a report published concerning *Microscopic Observations on the Pollen of Plants,* he added another footnote, mentioning that in the translucent contents of each pollen grain were minute particles that danced around. This was "Brownian movement," a characteristic behavior of bits of matter small enough to be pushed out of position by the erratic bombardment of still more diminutive molecules. The two observations which impressed Robert Brown so little— neither of them explicable on the basis of anything known to anyone at the time—proved to

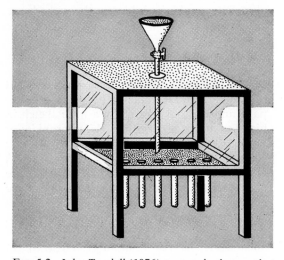

FIG. 5-2. *John Tyndall (1876) arranged a box so that he could pass a beam of light through it, over six empty culture tubes. When he could see no dust in the light beam, he filled the tubes with broth, boiled them, and noted no contamination. Stirring the air in the box, however, transferred dust to the open tubes and their contents spoiled promptly. Thus it is seen that bacteria remain alive in dust, and that ordinary air spreads their resistant stages into new places for growth.*

be the most original and valuable additions to science among all the pages of his publications. Both were at the lower limit of vision, made with a microscope, and concerned substances which were an absolute mystery.

3. THE CELL THEORY

Such was the background, slightly over a century ago, for two German biologists in correspondence with each other. One, M. J. Schleiden, was a botanist; the other, Theodor Schwann, a zoologist. Their conclusions, published in 1838 and 1839, established a

new theory in biology: that all plants and all animals were composed of cells, and that each cell contained a fluid material (**cytoplasm**) and a more solid structure, the nucleus.[1] Furthermore, they claimed, a cell could give rise to a new cell by a type of slow explosion, whereby cell contents emerged through a ruptured opening in the cell wall, expanded until the new and old were about equal in volume, and then a new cell wall formed around the extruded material. To this process they gave the name "free cell formation."

Schleiden and Schwann were entirely correct about the cellular nature of all living things. Their observations were verified repeatedly and became the **cell theory.** So important to biology is this point of view that when 1938 and 1939 arrived, biologists all over the world held a centennial celebration, commemorating the astute guess made a century before.

Our modern conception of the cell describes it as the basic structural unit of all living things. In some animals and plants, a cell may exist by itself and even constitute an entire organism. Such is usual among the flagellate algae, the diatoms, and the various protozoans. Elsewhere, cells are commonly grouped into masses, and through various specializations the different layers of cells take on separate tasks, demonstrating a systematic **division of labor** in each organism. But the activities of the whole organism, whether single-celled or multicellular, consist of the total of the activities of the cells of which it is constructed. We do what our cells do. The same is true of other animals and plants.

4. PROTOPLASM

The nucleus and cytoplasm together constitute the only known living material—the **protoplasm** of the cell (from the Greek *protos* = first, *plasma* = form).

Protoplasm is a highly complex and extremely variable substance, consisting of water (85-90 per cent of fresh weight), proteins (7-10 per cent), fatty substances (1-2 per cent), other organic compounds (1-1.5 per cent), and various inorganic compounds (1-1.5 per

---

[1] Their ideas were not unprecedented. In 1824 H. J. Dutrochet had offered the *same* view but his suggestions were not so fully expressed nor followed up.

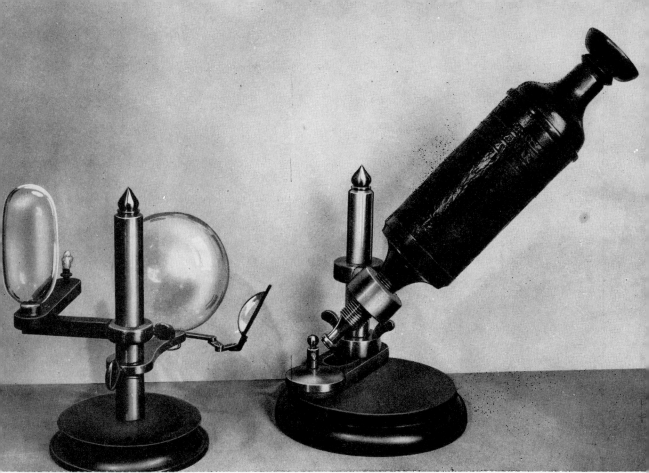

50. A replica of the early compound microscope and illuminator with which Robert Hooke discovered the cellular nature of cork, about 1665.

51. Antony van Leeuwenhoek made many simple microscopes of this design and used them with great care. His single lenses magnified as much as 270X, and permitted the discovery of animal life in pond water, starch granules, blood corpuscles, sperm cells, the true eggs of ants, the virgin birth of plant lice, the structure of heart muscle, and the existence of bacteria.

52. A replica of a Leeuwenhoek microscope.

THE INVENTION OF MICROSCOPES DURING THE 17TH CENTURY PERMITTED MANY GREAT DISCOVERIES

53. Leeuwenhoek's own drawings of bacteria (1676).

54. This table model electron microscope is focused by knobs on the control box to the right. The evacuating pump on the floor maintains an air-free path for electrons from the high-voltage source at the extreme right.

55. The senior-model electron microscope allows still higher magnification and flexibility; its pumps and high-voltage supply are in the rear cabinet. Since these devices cost many thousands of dollars and handle only specimens which can be exposed to high vacuum without evaporating, only well-endowed laboratories can afford to own one.

THROUGH ELECTRONICS, MICROSCOPY HAS BEEN EXTENDED TO THE SIZE RANGE OF THE LARGEST MOLECULES AND IN NEW DIRECTIONS WITH LIGHT

56. The television microscope consists of a special camera, sensitive to low light intensities and to the ultraviolet, over a conventional compound microscope. Any number of viewing screens may be used.

cent). Many of the characteristics of life seem to depend upon the ever-changing relationship between the water and the large molecules of carbohydrates, fats, and particularly proteins.

To obtain any final analysis of the constitution of these compounds is as difficult as trying to find a common denominator among the living inhabitants of a big apartment house. Nothing is so constant as the continual coming and going, plus the broad characteristics of the components. The chemical nature of these receives consideration at greater length in Chapter 6.

Additional structures have been discovered in living protoplasm. Small, ellipsoidal bodies called **mitochondria** are in the size range between 0.5 and 1.0 μ, and hence require for their study the highest magnification of the compound microscope. Since 1947, it has been possible to remove living mitochondria intact, and investigate their activity outside the cell. They appear to account for most (perhaps all) of the cell's respiratory exchange—using sugar, taking in oxygen, and releasing carbon dioxide.

Far smaller bodies, visible only through use of the electron microscope, are the **microsomes,** in which elaboration of proteins seems to be localized.

The outer boundary of the cytoplasm is a thin, jelly-like layer called the **plasma membrane.** It is living, tough, elastic, and important in the control of movement of chemical substances into and out of the cell. The selectivity of action found in the plasma membrane is one of the most characteristic features of living protoplasm.

Within the cytoplasm may be nonliving materials of various kinds. In animal cells, these usually are unabsorbed food or waste products not yet extruded. In plant cells, the most conspicuous nonliving portions are masses of liquid, which may be watery solution or an oil. Regardless of the type of nonliving inclusion, it is always surrounded by a membrane comparable to the plasma membrane around the whole cell. The presence of this membrane suggests that wherever protoplasm is in contact with nonliving substance, it reacts by membrane formation. Some of the behavior of unicellular organisms can be explained on this basis.

The term "cell sap" is often given to the large masses of watery solution in plant cells. A better term is **vacuole,** and around it there is said to be a **vacuole membrane.** The vacuole may contain dissolved coloring agents, such as the red, purple, or bluish anthocyanins which gives red cabbage leaves and many fruits their color. Anthocyanins are responsible for most of these hues in flowers and autumn leaves as well.

Plant cells commonly include in their cytoplasm living structures of larger size and great complexity. Each is a **plastid,** and a center of

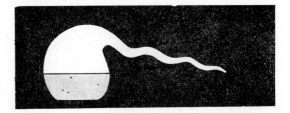

FIG. 5-3. *Louis Pasteur's flask of meat broth was open to the air through the long twisted side arm. But once boiled, it remained unchanged indefinitely, since "germs" did not have a means of moving in still air.*

special chemical activity—usually related to carbohydrates or carotenoid pigments. Most plastids have a characteristic shape, and they may be formed either directly from the cytoplasm or through division of previous plastids.

Some plastids are colorless (*leucoplastids,* from the Greek *leucos* = white) and serve in storage of starch. Others are colored (hence *chromoplastids,* from *chromos* = color). Those that include the important green pigment **chlorophyll** (from *chloros* = green, *phyllon* = a leaf) are called **chloroplastids.** They are the sites of carbohydrate formation when the plant has sun energy available.

Chromoplastids containing yellow and orange pigments not only make carrots yellowish orange but also are responsible for some of the bright colors of autumn leaves. They become evident only when the plant breaks down the valuable chlorophyll molecules and transports away the simpler parts into the trunk and roots before the foliage falls. When the masking green pigment is removed, the other colors and products of chlorophyll destruction are left—still in their chromoplastids.

Both plant and animal cytoplasm may include crystals and granules that seem to be either inert waste substances (such as calcium oxalate) or food in storage (such as particles of glycogen).

Young plant cells secrete around themselves a nonliving layer of a jelly-like substance—commonly calcium pectate—which serves to bind adjacent cells together. Between this adhesive layer and the protoplasm, an addi-

ments of Redi and the many scientists who followed prove basically that protoplasm arises only from pre-existing protoplasm. This is the fundamental concept that life begets life, and that life arises in no other way. The principle is called **biogenesis** (from *bios* = life, *genesis* = origin), and contrasts with the idea of spontaneous generation—**abiogenesis.**

A thorough search into every part of the plant and animal kingdoms has failed to find any evidence to show that abiogenesis occurs

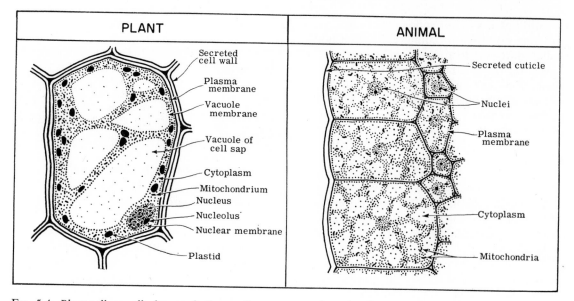

Fig. 5-4. *Plant cells usually have a distinct wall, many vacuoles of cell sap, and an assortment of plastids which are centers of chemical action. Animal cells lack a wall, seldom contain vacuoles or plastids, and commonly have smaller, less conspicuous nuclei.*

tional covering is secreted through the plasma membrane. This new layer is composed chiefly of the carbohydrate **cellulose,** and forms a reasonably rigid **cell wall** (Fig. 5-4). Even after a plant cell is dead, the cell walls may stand for years. It was these nonliving remains that Robert Hooke saw in his piece of cork (see p. 49).

Animal cells, by contrast, have no demonstrable cell wall. Sometimes they are covered by nonliving secreted substances that add to their rigidity (as in cartilage and bone).

5. BIOGENESIS

Study of the internal features of plants and animals serves to focus attention on protoplasm as the sole living material. The experi-

today. It would be unreasonable, however, to assume that life has existed forever in the past. Forever is too long. The one assumption with scientific acceptability is that if, in the past, life arose from nonliving materials, it did so under conditions which no longer exist. Such conditions are not beyond conjecture, and will be discussed in a later chapter (p. 444).

6. LIFE

Since protoplasm arises only through the action of pre-existing protoplasm, yet consists of nonliving chemical molecules, the essential feature of life must be in the arrangement of these molecules. The organization of molecular complexes has come to be a mutual problem for the chemist and physicist. These scientists usually call themselves biochemists and biophysicists when they deal with the organization of protoplasmic constituents.

One major difference between studying a living system and analyzing most problems in chemistry or physics is that the protoplasm continually changes in fine details, yet retains an overall constancy. Minor alterations in the concentration of each chemical component and the position of substances in a living cell occur continually. Simpler "raw materials" are taken in, energy is expended, and chemical processes continue at many speeds and with a multitude of end products—all in ways that produce more protoplasm.

In recent years it has become evident that carbohydrates furnish the main store of energy, that some of the fats can be converted into carbohydrates when energy supplies remain for a long time at a low level, but that other fats and the proteins provide the living organization itself.

In the chemical hierarchy of protoplasm the proteins appear to be dominant. Somehow, when organized in the living system, they have the ability to act on simpler raw materials (including inorganic salts), transferring energy from carbohydrate breakdown (which the proteins control), in making more carbohydrates, fats, and proteins (including more of themselves). The nature of these chemical processes becomes better understood each year.

Since so many chemical actions are in progress simultaneously within the confines of each single cell, they cannot occur in one general solution. Protoplasm is not a haphazard mixture. It is organized in fine detail and each chemical action has its own site. Each is associated with a surface—a membrane of some kind. Biophysicists and biochemists are investigating these surface actions, within the nucleus, the plastids, the mitochondria, the microsomes, and in the plasma membrane.

Man's study of the laws of chemistry and physics is very recent. During the billions of years through which living cells have existed, they have been exploring very thoroughly the limitations imposed by physical and chemical laws. The accumulated experience of protoplasm is hidden in its modern organization. Discoveries at the level of protoplasm and the cell can contribute not only to a better understanding of life but also of the molecular and atomic structure of the universe.

CELLS

Observ. XVIII. Of the *Schematisme* or *Texture* of *Cork,* and of the Cells and Pores of some other such frothy Bodies.

I took a good clear piece of Cork, and with a Pen-knife sharpen'd as keen as a Razor, I cut a piece of it off, and thereby left the surface of it exceeding smooth, then examining it very diligently with a Microscope, *me thought I could perceive it to appear a little porous; but I could not so plainly distinguish them, as to be sure that they were pores, much less what Figure they were of: But judging from the lightness and yielding quality of the Cork, that certainly the texture could not be so curious, but that possibly, if I could use some further diligence, I might find it to be discernable with a* Microscope, *I with the same sharp Pen-knife, cut off from the former smooth surface an exceeding thin piece of it, and placing it on a black object Plate, because it was it self a white body, and casting the light on it with a deep* plano-convex Glass, *I could exceeding plainly perceive it to be all perforated and porous, much like a honey-comb, but that the pores of it were not regular; yet it was not unlike a Honey-comb in these particulars.*

First, in that it had a very little solid substance, in comparison of the empty cavity that was contain'd between, as does more manifestly appear by the Figure A and B of the XI. Scheme, *for the* Interstitia, *or walls (as I may so call them) or partitions of those pores were near as thin in proportion to their pores, as those thin films of wax in a Honey-comb (which enclose and constitute the* sexangular cells) *are to theirs.*

Next, in that these pores, or cells, were not very deep, but consisted of a great many little Boxes, separated out of one continued long pore, by certain Diaphragms, *as is visible by the Figure B, which represents a sight of those pores split the long-ways.*

I no sooner discern'd these (which were indeed the first microscopical *pores I ever saw, and perhaps, that were ever seen, for I had not met with any Writer or Person, that had made any mention of them before this) but me thought I had with the discovery of them, presently hinted to me the true and intelligible reason for all the* Phænomena *of Cork. . . .*

—ROBERT HOOKE, *Micrographia*, pp. 112-113 (1665).

SUGGESTED READING (see pp. 505-507)

Classics and Milestones: Hooke, Redi, Schwann.
Recent and Informative: Baitsell, 1955; Gerard, 1940.

6 · Constituents of Life

1. CHEMICAL COMPOSITION OF PROTOPLASM. 2. WATER'S ROLE IN LIFE—IM-BIBITION, SOLUTION, DIFFUSION, DISSOCIATION, PERMEABILITY, ION EX-CHANGE, INTAKE AND OUTPUT, OSMOSIS, COLLOIDS. 3. DYNAMIC EQUILIB-RIUM—WATER BALANCE, EXCHANGE WITH THE ENVIRONMENT.

AS ANALYTICAL METHODS become increasingly sensitive, more and more of the 90-odd naturally occurring chemical elements are found as constituents of protoplasm. Twelve (shown in boldface type in the following list) are represented regularly by more than trace amounts. The others have been identified in protoplasm of some kind.

Element	Atomic Number	Symbol	Atomic Weight*	Periodic Position
hydrogen	1	H	1	Ib
lithium	3	Li	6.9	Ia
beryllium	4	Be	9	IIa
boron	5	B	10.8	IIIa
carbon	6	C	12	IVa
nitrogen	7	N	14	Vb
oxygen	8	O	16	VIb
fluorine	9	F	19	VIIb
sodium	11	Na	23	Ia
magnesium	12	Mg	24.3	IIa
aluminum	13	Al	27	IIIa
silicon	14	Si	28.1	IVa
phosphorus	15	P	31	Vb
sulfur	16	S	32	VIb
chlorine	17	Cl	35.5	VIIb
potassium	19	K	39.1	Ia
calcium	20	Ca	40.1	IIa
titanium	22	Ti	48.1	IVa
vanadium	23	V	51	Va
chromium	24	Cr	52	VIa
manganese	25	Mn	54.9	VIIa
iron	26	Fe	55.8	VIIIa
cobalt	27	Co	58.9	VIIIa
nickel	28	Ni	58.7	VIIIa
copper	29	Cu	63.6	Ib
zinc	30	Zn	65.4	IIb
germanium	32	Ge	72.4	IVb
arsenic	33	As	75	Vb
selenium	34	Se	79.2	VIb
bromine	35	Br	79.9	VIIb
rubidium	37	Rb	85.4	Ia
strontium	38	Sr	87.6	IIa
molybdenum	42	Mo	96	VIa
silver	47	Ag	107.9	Ib
cadmium	48	Cd	112.4	IIb
tin	50	Sn	118.7	IVb
iodine	53	I	126.9	VIIb
cesium	55	Cs	132.8	Ia
barium	56	Ba	137.4	IIa
lead	82	Pb	207.2	IVb

* Atomic weights are relative values useful in computing the mass of material taking part in chemical reactions. The reference point for these relative values is the weight of a definite volume of oxygen under standardized conditions of pressure and temperature. Under these conditions, a volume of 22.4 liters of this and every other gas contains 6.06×10^{23} molecules, and has the *molecular* weight in grams. For oxygen a molecular weight is 32.00000 grams. However, a molecule of oxygen consists of two atoms (and hence is represented by the symbol O_2). Hence an *atomic* weight of oxygen (symbol O) is 16.00000 grams.

A molecule of water consists of an atom of oxygen plus two atoms of hydrogen, as shown by the symbol H_2O. Its molecular weight is computed as $(1 \times 2) + 16 = 18$. Similarly 22.4 liters of carbon dioxide (symbol CO_2) under standardized conditions can be predicted to weigh exactly 44 grams $[= 12 + (16 \times 2)]$.

1. CHEMICAL COMPOSITION OF PROTOPLASM

It is easy enough to measure the total amount of each of the more abundant elements in protoplasm, and to represent them in graphic form (Fig. 6-1). Oxygen is clearly the most abundant element in a human body, with carbon, hydrogen, nitrogen, calcium, phosphorus, and sulfur following in rapidly decreasing proportions. Similarly, iron is the most abundant element in an automobile. This information, like a listing of the elements in protoplasm, does not lead directly to much understanding of the mechanism.

A far more informative approach is through

study of the molecules in which these elements are found. Some occur in small molecules, such as water. Others are part of large molecules, such as hemoglobin (probable formula: $C_{3032}H_{4816}O_{780}S_8Fe_4$—hence molecular weight 54,156.6 grams, or 3,000 times as large as a water molecule).

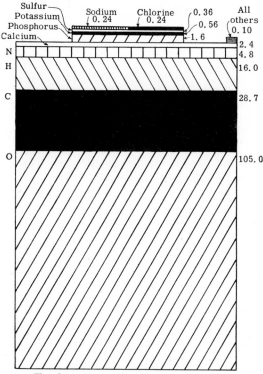

The elements in a 160-lb man—in pounds

FIG. 6-1. *A 160-pound man consists of 105 pounds of oxygen, 28.7 pounds of carbon, 16 pounds of hydrogen, and lesser quantities of other elements.*

If the total number of water molecules is measured in a given mass of freshly-killed plant or animal material, and this total is compared with a corresponding value for each of the other constituent molecules, it is seen that water molecules far outnumber all the rest. They constitute, in fact, about 99.5 per cent of the total *number* of molecules in protoplasm.

Depending upon the kind of organism and the stage in its life cycle when examined, the water content by *weight* may be anywhere between 25 and 99 per cent. Water accounts for a large fraction of the total amount of oxygen and hydrogen in protoplasm.

Almost all of the nonaqueous oxygen and hydrogen (as well as the bulk of carbon, nitrogen, phosphorus, and sulfur) is incorporated into **organic** chemical compounds—those containing carbon.

Carbon, hydrogen, and oxygen combine in the proportions of 1:2:1 to form the **carbohydrates,** such as the sugar glucose ($C_6H_{12}O_6$); or in approximately this ratio but with the hydrogen atoms still double the oxygen (as they are in water) in larger molecules, such as the sugar sucrose ($C_{12}H_{22}O_{11}$). These same three elements combine also in different proportions, with much less oxygen, to form **fats.** The same three, with nitrogen (and sometimes also with phosphorus or sulfur) are organized into **proteins.** Protein molecules are characteristically huge, with molecular weights ranging from around 35,000 (wheat gliadin) to above 17,000,000 (tobacco mosaic virus). Proteins account for most of the nonaqueous weight of protoplasm, and are responsible for many of the characteristics of life.

One of the most important types of proteins is the category known as **nucleoproteins,** since they were identified first in the nucleus of the cell. Each nucleoprotein consists of a protein part and a nucleic-acid part. Nucleic acids are organic derivatives of phosphoric acid. Great interest centers in the modern study of these compounds, because they are restricted to sites in the protoplasm which appear to control living chemistry of all kinds.

The nucleoproteins of the nucleus itself carry a nucleic acid whose chemical name is often abbreviated to DNA (desoxyribose nucleic acid). It is responsible for many of the staining characteristics of the nucleus, and is an integral part of the chemical basis of inheritance.

A different nucleic acid is characteristic of the nucleoproteins of mitochondria. It is designated RNA (ribonucleic acid) and consists of a single chain of molecular components, whereas DNA is a double chain. RNA appears to serve as a messenger substance between the DNA of the nucleus and the protein-producing chemical centers in the microsomes.

The chief fatty substances of protoplasm are the phospholipids, which are confined to the mitochondria, microsomes, and various surface membranes of the cytoplasm. They seem important in controlling income and outgo of other chemical substances.

Calcium is associated with surface membranes and this permeability control. Calcium pectate was mentioned (p. 48) as a substance binding plant cells together. A similar calcium compound has a corresponding role in multicellular animals.

In association with phosphorus-containing compounds, calcium is important also in bones and teeth. During bone- and tooth-formation periods, an adequate calcium intake is particularly important, and must reach rather high levels. Thus a child should get 1.0 gram of absorbable calcium daily, and a pregnant or nursing mother twice this amount regularly. Other adults can get along with 0.8 gram daily, but this supply should be maintained. We get our calcium most easily in milk, although beans, peas, and most cereals contain significant amounts. In old age, much of the brittleness of bones is due to calcium loss from the skeleton. The *relative* age can be read from an X-ray photograph, since the calcium in bones makes them opaque to X-rays.

Calcium is important also in the chemical reactions of blood clotting, and in the steps whereby iron is incorporated into the hemoglobin which gives red blood its oxygen-carrying capacity and red color.

Phosphorus is obtained from most meats in amounts beyond the small requirements of the organism. Iron is supplied adequately by many fruits and vegetables, by egg yolks, and by most meats (especially liver).

In crustaceans and some other arthropods, the blood pigment (hemocyanin) differs in containing copper in place of iron. Tunicate blood pigments contain vanadium. The important green pigment of plants, chlorophyll, contains magnesium.

Iodine is essential in the formation of the chemical substance elaborated by the thyroid gland. This element is obtained in sea foods. Unless these are a frequent item of diet, iodine must be sought deliberately to avoid the diseases caused by its lack. This point is discussed further in Chapter 10.

Animal protoplasm contains more sodium in comparison to potassium than does plant protoplasm. For this reason, herbivorous and omnivorous animals frequently develop "salt hunger," satisfied by such sodium salts as sodium chloride (NaCl). Valuable sodium may be lost in sweat, and is expended too in excreting the oversupply of potassium compounds obtained in a vegetarian diet. Wild herbivores such as deer and sheep may migrate for miles at irregular intervals to reach a "salt lick," where sodium salts are available to them. Human beings who sweat profusely may lose so much sodium that they develop "miner's cramp," with attendant pain and muscular spasms. Additions of sodium chloride to the drinking water clear up the difficulty, whereas excessive intake of unsalted water (in attempts to satisfy thirst from water loss) merely aggravates the trouble by increasing perspiration rate and sodium loss.

Where soils contain too little of elements required in trace amounts, plants may show deficiency diseases. Addition of the missing element to the soil corrects the condition. Animals eating plants deficient in the same elements may also show deficiency diseases. In some instances, as with iodine or cobalt, no pathological abnormality is evident in the plant, yet the animal disease is well known. Cobalt, for example, is part of vitamin B_{12}; its insufficiency causes "bush sickness," familiar in the United States and Canada, Australia and New Zealand, and Scotland.

2. WATER'S ROLE IN LIFE

A supply of water is almost as fundamental to living processes as is a supply of energy. Life's chemistry cannot use and transfer energy unless some water is present. Most organisms require a constant availability of water. Many characteristics of life processes are due to the peculiar properties of the water in protoplasm.

Imbibition

In reaching living protoplasm, water often must pass through nonliving layers of material, such as the cell walls of plants. These materials may hold a considerable quantity of water.

The addition of water to these substances in the dry condition causes them to swell. Primarily this is a demonstration of the readiness with which water wets the material. Wetting is a demonstration of mutual attraction (adhesive forces). When wetting has occurred, the water may be drawn into the structure, filling its submicroscopic pores by a process known as **imbibition.** Imbibition by even dead seeds in a closed container is often so forceful that the container bursts. Imbibition by a dry rowboat may cause swelling enough that seams close and the wooden bottom becomes watertight.

Soil water is held imbibed by the cell walls of plant roots. This action is a passive one, requiring no expenditure of energy. As the plant cell removes water at the inner surface of the cell wall, imbibed water moves through the intermolecular spaces and is replaced by more from the soil.

Solution

Water in and around living organisms is almost never pure. Usually some chemical compounds are dissolved in it. Since water is more nearly a universal solvent than any other substance known, it readily picks up from its environment a great variety of substances which are soluble in it. Other materials are said to be insoluble. Actually no sharp barrier exists between solubility and insolubility. The difference is in the amount of **solute** that will dissolve in the water (the **solvent**) before the solution becomes saturated with the particular solute. At this point an equilibrium is reached, with the rates of two processes equal: (1) dissolution of the substance, and (2) precipitation or evaporation of the same substance.

In a saturated solution of table salt, equilibrium is established when the rate at which some crystals are dissolving becomes equal to the rate at which others are being formed from the solution. Or water in equilibrium with air has the atmospheric gases dissolving in it at the same rate as the same gases are evaporating from the surface.

Since saturation is a matter of relative rates and not one of filling all the spaces between the water molecules, saturating a solution with one substance does not greatly affect the amount of another that will dissolve. An aqueous solution can hold very little silica, but

thereafter will be in equilibrium so far as dissolving the glass container is concerned. The same solution can be saturated with oxygen, with table salt, and still dissolve sugar readily, or take into solution unlimited quantities of alcohol.

Diffusion

The components of gas mixtures and of true solutions become uniformly distributed through the slow process of **diffusion.** If a crystal of copper sulfate is dropped into a tall jar of water, the crystal gradually dissolves. At the same time, the water near the crystal acquires a blue color that is evidence of the solute there. Little by little the blue color spreads through the jar. It continues to spread even after the crystal has dissolved completely (Fig. 6-4). Finally the solution is uniformly blue.

The principle is simple. Molecules of copper sulfate dissolved in the water are in constant motion—a form of energy responsible for the phenomenon of heat. When a molecule of copper sulfate approaches another of the same kind, both are deflected or bounce backward like struck billiard balls—each starting off in a new direction. The average time between repulsions is less where the solute molecules are more numerous—where the concentration of copper sulfate is higher. In directions away from the dissolving crystal, solute molecules travel farther on the average than in any other direction. Through the continual activity of the molecules, they gradually move away from the dissolving crystal.

This process continues until all parts of the jar contain the same number of solute molecules per unit of volume. The random movements continue, but there is no change in the overall picture. Diffusion accomplishes the eventual uniform distribution of each kind of molecule that is free to move. In general, the smaller the molecule, the faster diffusion occurs.

Dissociation

In water, many inorganic compounds that dissolve tend to lose their identities by becoming **ionized.** Thus sodium chloride (table salt) becomes **dissociated** into sodium-ion (symbol Na^+) and chloride-ion (symbol Cl^-), each with an electrical charge as indicated. The nature of the charge can be shown if an electrical current is passed through the solution between two conducting rods (called electrodes) dipping into the liquid. The Na^+ migrates toward the negative electrode (called the *cathode*) and is termed a **cation** (pronounced katt'-eye-on), whereas Cl^- accumulates and may emerge as gas bubbles at the positive electrode (the *anode*), showing Cl^- to be an **anion.**

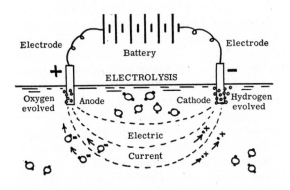

FIG. 6-2. *Electrolysis of water, liberating hydrogen and oxygen, may be the end result of passing an electric current through the ionized solution.*

Substances dissolved in the water of protoplasm or the ocean provide such ions as these:

anions	cations
bicarbonate	ammonium
carbonate	calcium
nitrate	iron
phosphate	magnesium
sulfate	potassium

Since any anion can combine with any cation, a rich variety of chemical substances is available in the watery medium. This feature makes possible a wide array of chemical reactions.

Water itself dissociates (Fig. 6-3) into hydrogen-ion (H^+) and hydroxyl-ion (OH^-). Only about one water molecule in every 10 million undergoes this change, but the results are striking because of the extreme activity of the two ions. Thus hydrogen-ion can combine with the chloride-ion to form hydrochloric acid (symbol HCl), which is a strong acid. Or the charge on the hydroxyl-ion can be neutralized by combination with the sodium-ion, to bear no electrical charge but to form sodium hydroxide (symbol $NaOH$), a strong

base. In a watery solution of sodium chloride, all four compounds may be present in addition to the four ions:

H_2O, $NaCl$, HCl, $NaOH$, H^+, OH^-, Na^+, Cl^-

Yet the proportions still leave the solution neither acidic nor basic (alkaline).

Addition of hydrochloric acid to pure water, by contrast, provides a solution rich in H^+ and relatively poor in OH^-. Its acid properties are due to the excess of hydrogen-ion. Or a solution of sodium hydroxide in water is basic because of the excess of hydroxyl-ion over the supply of hydrogen-ion. Hence solutions that have a greater proportion of H^+ to OH^- than the equality of water are acids. The greater the excess, the stronger is the acid. Solutions that have a lower proportion of H^+ to OH^- than the equality of water are bases. The smaller the proportion of H^+, the stronger is the base. The proportion of H^+ to OH^- is often discovered in terms of the colors of "indicator dyes" such as litmus (pink in acid solutions, blue in basic).

Permeability

Diffusion—an expression of the energy of movement in the solute molecules—accounts for the gradual spread of dissolved substances through the solvent. The mutual repulsion of particles bearing like electrical charges provides a mechanism whereby ions become distributed uniformly in an ionized solution.

Both solute molecules and ions meet a barrier, however, when they reach the plasma

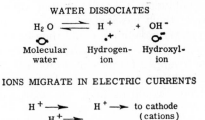

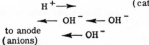

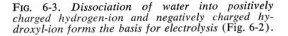

FIG. 6-3. *Dissociation of water into positively charged hydrogen-ion and negatively charged hydroxyl-ion forms the basis for electrolysis (Fig. 6-2).*

membrane of a living cell. The plasma membrane has little effect on the solvent water, and this material passes through the membrane in either direction with ease. To the solvent molecules the membrane is freely **permeable.** Other molecules and ions, on the other hand, are transferred through the membrane at rates which differ from one chemical compound or ion to another, and according to the direction of movement (into or out of the cell). To these materials the plasma membrane is *less* permeable.

To large molecules such as proteins, it is completely **impermeable.** Between the two extremes—water and proteins—is a whole range of relative rates. Accordingly, the plasma membrane is said to be **differentially permeable.** It is evident that the living system regulates the permeability of the plasma membrane, and that fatty materials associated with the surface play an important role in this control of permeability.

Ion Exchange

The plasma membrane has appreciable thickness—on the order of 5 to 10 millimicra ($m\mu$). It bears electrical charges, and these modify the transfer of ions through the membrane. The transfer is said to occur through **ion exchange.**

In the cells of a root, for example, respiration will release carbon dioxide (CO_2). Since this event occurs in aqueous solution, the actual compound formed is carbonic acid (H_2CO_3) or its ions, H^+ and HCO_3^- (bicarbonate-ion). At the plasma membrane the protoplasm may be in contact with soil moisture containing a small amount of sodium chloride which has ionized to Na^+ and Cl^-. The plasma membrane could then conduct an ion exchange. An ion of bicarbonate (HCO_3^-) can be swapped for an ion of chloride (Cl^-). Since both ions bear a single electrical charge, no change would occur in the charge on the plasma membrane. Yet the swap would put bicarbonate-ion into the soil, where it could combine with Na^+ to produce sodium bicarbonate ($NaHCO_3$). Simultaneously, the protoplasm would have disposed of a carbonate-ion (in excess due to respiration) and acquired a chloride-ion, which might be used.

Intake and Output

From studies in which artificially radioactive elements were used to label molecules and ions, biologists have learned that the living plasma membrane is highly active and expends energy in transferring substances from one side to the other. Upon this energy expenditure depends much of the selectivity so characteristic of the living system.

Nonaqueous molecules and ions do not "leak" into and out of living cells. They are transported. Often they are taken from solutions that are more dilute and moved to regions of higher concentration. This transfer is opposite in direction to that which could be predicted on the basis of diffusion. When the plasma membrane transports molecules or ions from the environment into the protoplasm and uses its own energy to effect the transfer, it is engaged in active **absorption.** The entrance of dissolved and dissociated materials from soil water into roots, and the movement of digested substances from the cavity of the digestive tract into the lining cells, are examples of absorption.

Similarly a cell may extrude material contrary to the gradient of concentrations, or at rates faster than diffusion could produce. If these substances are used outside the cell, the term **secretion** is ordinarily applied. If they are waste products, the word **excretion** is customary.

Often secretion and absorption are combined, as a cooperative process between adjacent cells. Sugar, for example, can be passed from one cell to another through expenditure of energy—one cell secreting the sugar toward another, and the second one actively absorbing the carbohydrate.

Osmosis

Diffusion appears to account for the transfer of water through plasma membranes. Substances retained within the cell by the differentially permeable membrane complicate the picture, though in an understandable way.

Sugar, for example, is a normal solute in the water of protoplasm. It does not escape through the plasma membrane to any detectable extent. The cell's sugar concentration may rise as high as 3 per cent, which means that the solution cannot be more than 97 per cent water. Actually the solvent concentration is usually much less, because of the presence of other solutes.

For illustrative purposes, a cell can be considered to contain in its protoplasm only 3 per cent sugar and 97 per cent water. If such a cell is surrounded by 100 per cent water, there will be a measurable passage of water molecules from outside into the cell (where their concentration is less). This movement of solvent molecules by diffusion through a differentially permeable membrane is called **os-**

out of the cell equal to that of solvent entry; the elastic force is obvious from the bulging of the cell, and the cell is described as turgid, or as exhibiting **turgor;** (2) the cytoplasm may utilize energy to excrete water toward the outside of the cell, at a rate equal to that at which osmosis brings in extra solvent; this activity is particularly obvious in some unicellular organisms in which the excretory mechanism is visible as a "contractile vacuole"; or (3) the cell may actually stretch until its plasma

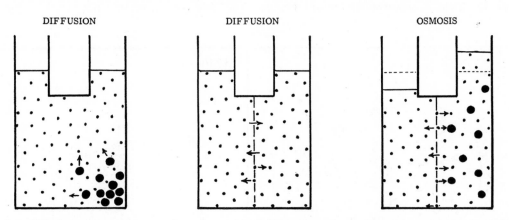

DIFFUSION   DIFFUSION   OSMOSIS

FIG. 6-4. *Diffusion of one substance through another* (left) *or of a solvent through a membrane* (center) *follows basic principles that explain osmotic movement* (right) *of solvent through a differentially permeable membrane.*

mosis (Fig. 6-4). It requires no energy from the cell, and is merely the result of random molecular movements.

As long as the concentration of water molecules inside the cell is less than that outside, the rate of entry of solvent should exceed the rate of exit of solvent. But since the sugar does not escape through the membrane, the concentration of water inside the cell can never reach 100 per cent. Equilibrium is permanently upset by the presence of solute inside the cell; hence water continues to enter by osmosis.

Ideally there would be no limit to osmotic entry of the solvent water. Actually, one of three different mechanisms provides an end point to the process: (1) in a plant cell, the protoplasm and vacuoles swell, pressing against the sturdy cellulose cell wall as though to burst it, until the mechanical pressure of the stretched cell wall ("wall pressure") is enough to make the rate of water movement

membrane is damaged and permeability changes allow the internal solutes to escape; this is what happens to a red blood cell when it is transferred to tap water; the cell then dies.

Osmosis can operate in either direction. If a cell containing 3 per cent sugar and 97 per cent water is placed in a solution of 10 per cent sugar and 90 per cent water, the solvent moves out of the cell faster than in. This is **exosmosis.** Carried to extremes in a plant cell, it causes the protoplasm to draw away from the cell walls, and the cell is said to be **plasmolysed.** Since animal cells lack firm walls, they merely shrink (Fig. 6-5). Hence **endosmosis** results in turgor, exosmosis in plasmolysis, if the cell is enclosed by a wall. In excess, either can bring about the death of the cell.

Aqueous solutions of the proper concentration induce neither endosmosis nor exosmosis. This would be true of a 3 per cent sugar solution surrounding a cell containing 97 per cent water. Such a solution is termed isos-motic or **isotonic** (from *iso* = equal). Solu-tions from which cells acquire water by os-mosis are correspondingly called **hypotonic** (from *hypo* = less, referring to the solute con-centration). The extreme in hypotonic solu-tions is distilled water; inability to tolerate pure water has been called "distilled water toxicity." Solutions to which cells lose water are **hypertonic** (*hyper* = greater). The ex-treme in hypertonic solutions is a saturated one. In high concentrations most soluble chemical substances are toxic to living things, and may be classed as poisons. Some have their fatal effect entirely through causing ex-osmotic water losses; the poison never really enters the cell. People often kill plants acci-dentally in this way, by adding too much fer-tilizer to plant roots and thus inducing fatal plasmolysis.

Colloids

The osmotic characteristics of an aqueous solution depend upon the concentration of water. This concentration is affected not only by dissolved molecules but also by suspended

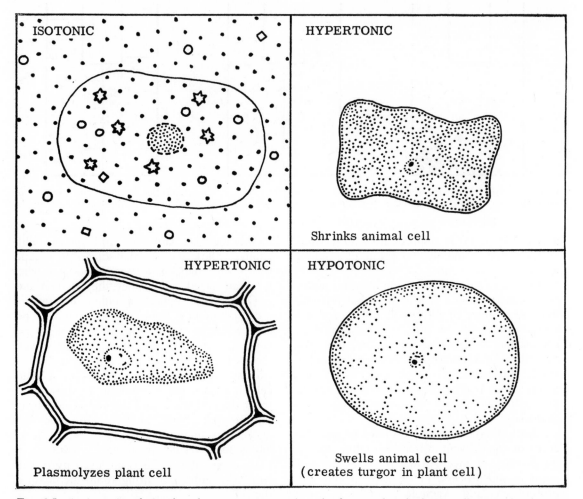

FIG. 6-5. *An isotonic solution has the same concentration of solvent as has the living cell exposed to it; out-ward movement of solvent is equal to inward movement. In a hypertonic solution, the solvent moves through the plasma membrane more rapidly in the outward direction. Animal cells, lacking a stiff wall, simply shrink, while plant cells come to contain a shrunken protoplast free from the cell wall. In hypotonic solu-tions, the solvent moves faster into the protoplasm. Plant cells swell and exhibit turgor. Animal cells swell and may burst.*

particles in the size range normal to large molecules such as proteins. Some of the characteristics of living protoplasm arise in this way.

A "suspension" differs from a solution. Suspensions tend to be cloudy, "milky," or turbid. Solutions, by contrast, are clear. Suspended particles can be separated from the water by mechanical means, such as filtration or centrifugation. Dissolved substances can be separated from the water only by electrical or chemical changes or by evaporation of the water.

The nature of the suspension is governed chiefly by the size of the suspended particles. If they are large and heavier than water, like sand grains, they will settle to the bottom upon standing, leaving the water as a clear liquid above them. The smaller the grains the more slowly they settle. If they are large and lighter than water, such as oil droplets coalescing from a mixture of olive oil and water, they rise to the top and fuse into a layer of water-free oil above the layer of oil-free water. Each of these liquids will be clear when free of the other, and an obvious boundary will mark their surface of contact. When shaken up together, however, the suspension is turbid and the oil droplets are so small that the boundaries between them and the water are invisible. A suspension of this type is described as an **emulsion.** Many medicines are emulsions, hence the common direction: "Shake well before using."

If the suspended particles are in the size range between 100 and 1.0 millimicra, they range downward from the limit of visibility with a light microscope to the dimensions of large protein molecules. Within this submicroscopic range are the various sizes of clay crystals in soils. Suspensions of this type do not separate so readily, and are called **colloidal suspensions,** from the Greek *kollodes* = glue-like.

Colloids may be liquid, or jellies of varying solidity. They constitute a special "state" of matter. Particles of colloidal size present to the water an enormous area of total surface. Thus a one-inch cube of material, if divided into cubes each 0.1 mμ on a side, would possess a total surface area of more than 1.6 million square feet. The smaller the suspended

particles, the larger is the surface area presented by a given weight of them.

All surfaces have a certain amount of electrical charge associated with them. On a surface as enormous as that in a colloidal suspension, the charge has great importance; it is termed the "surface energy" of the colloid. Many biological processes appear to be largely surface-energy reactions.

Apparently because of their electrical charges, colloids can hold on their surfaces

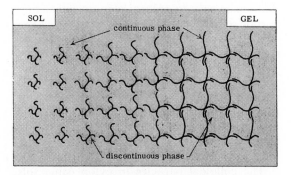

FIG. 6-6. *The transition from a liquid sol to a semi-solid gel may require no more than the extension of individual molecules until they overlap in three dimensions and resist displacement.*

surprising quantities of many ions. It may be that negative charges on colloidal particles attract positively charged cations, such as potassium. These ions are held firmly and taken out of solution—"adsorbed" on the colloidal surface.

The surface energy of colloidal suspensions is important also in maintaining the stability of the colloid. Repulsion between the negative charges so commonly found on colloidal particles seems to be responsible for holding the particles in suspension.

Liquid colloidal suspensions can be poured; they are called **sols.** Jelly-like colloids are **gels.** Often a sol can be transformed into a gel ("gelation") or a gel into a sol ("solation"). The "setting" of gelatine, seen in Jello and similar desserts, is an example of gelation.

Apparently a colloidal suspension may have the particles sufficiently separate from one another that the suspending water constitutes a **continuous phase,** and the particles themselves the discontinuous or **dispersed phase;**

the condition is then that of a sol (Fig. 6-6). But without losing water or changing its temperature, the suspended molecules may make contact with one another and become the continuous phase, isolating the water into discontinuous units; the suspension has then acquired the gel condition.

In an active cell, most of the cytoplasm is usually in the sol condition. The plasma membrane, other membranes within the cell, and much of the nucleus, ordinarily are in the gel condition. During movement of an ameba, gelation is easy to recognize in an advancing portion of the protoplasm, whereas solation appears to be an important function of the retreating end.

Soil water, "cell sap," and blood plasma are all dilute sols, whose osmotic activity is affected greatly by the proteins suspended in them. Cellulose cell walls, by contrast, are firm gels which can lose water by desiccation and regain it by imbibition, without losing their gross form.

The colloidal particles in cytoplasmic sols are not only free from one another, but they move around under the impact of smaller molecules such as those of water and dissolved materials. If a beam of light is passed horizontally through a colloidal suspension, its path is evident because the light is scattered —reflected by the many particles. When such a suspension is studied with a microscope, the light path is seen to sparkle or scintillate. This shows that each particle reflects light toward the lens briefly, then moves to a new position. The erratic movement of particles at and beyond the limit of vision as seen through a compound microscope was described first by Robert Brown (p. 46). Ever since, the term "Brownian movement" has been applied to displays of the effects of molecular activity.

3. DYNAMIC EQUILIBRIUM

The interaction of water, solutes, ions, and molecules in colloidal suspension in protoplasm is a characteristic of life itself. To survive, each organism must be able to maintain a balance—a dynamic equilibrium—between intake and loss of water, absorption of materials needed, and excretion of wastes. A living system can accumulate only the active in-

gredients of protoplasm and insoluble products such as starch grains, cellulose walls, and the limy skeletons of animals.

Water Balance

Since water is the commonest molecule in protoplasm, the solvent and suspending medium for most of the others, and one of the most active passing through the living membranes of each cell, the water supply is a critical factor in the welfare of protoplasm.

Fresh-water organisms live where they have an oversupply of water. Their external medium is so low in dissolved or osmotically active ingredients that the environment is chronically hypotonic. Their cells tend to take up more water than they need; some mechanism must be present to get rid of endosmotic excesses. The contractile vacuoles of protozoans, the rectal "gills" of many aquatic insects, and the kidneys (or equivalents) may all serve this important function.

The converse situation affects organisms living where water or soil contains large concentrations of dissolved substances, and exosmosis robs any unprotected cell of its water. Tidal pools and salt marshes provide these conditions whenever drought reduces their water content. These places, in fact, are subject to rapid and radical changes in water concentration during a single season. Heavy rains may carry off soluble salts, or tidal movements and storms bring the salinity to the full value of open ocean. Evaporation by the sun can raise the salt concentration to saturation. Organisms living under these conditions must be able to resist changes, to maintain their internal water concentration in spite of the external environment.

Fish such as eels, salmon, and lampreys shift from salt to fresh water or the converse in relation to their breeding cycle. Usually they spend several days in estuary areas before they continue their journeys. In this interval they become acclimatized to the altered environment, and are able to maintain their water balance in the new surroundings.

Exchange with the Environment

For years it has been clear that each organism took from its surroundings certain raw materials, maintained an almost steady supply for internal needs, and cast out fairly obvious wastes. Until recently, however, it was not possible to follow the movements of individual atoms or molecules, to learn how long each was retained in the body, whether it remained in one place or was shifted about, and how fast any changes occurred.

Georg Hevesy, Nobel laureate in 1943, appears to have been the earliest to use "tagged" atoms—radioactive tracers—to study exchanges between a living organism and its environment. In the early 1920's he experimented with bean seedlings grown in nutrient solutions containing a radioactive product of thorium's decay. The plants took up the substance and became demonstrably radioactive. They also gave out the substance, since when transferred after repeated washings into nonradioactive nutrient solution, the radioactive molecules began to appear in the solution.

At first these studies were limited to naturally radioactive substances—materials of small biological importance. A new tool was added (1931) with Harold Urey's discovery of "heavy hydrogen" (deuterium). Hevesy used it in the form of "heavy water" (deuterium oxide, symbol H^2_2O) to explore the intake and output of aqueous solutions by plants and animals, and to explore the "water space" inside these organisms. The chief difficulty in its use lay in the fact that, with a 3 per cent increase in weight above that of ordinary water, "heavy water" showed slightly abnormal permeability relations.

In 1929, E. O. Lawrence developed the cyclotron, making available artificially radioactive isotopes[1] of various chemical elements in millicurie quantities. Among these products the most important to the biologist was the atom "phosphorus 32" (symbol P^{32}), whose radioactivity decays to 50 per cent in 14 days as the substance disintegrates into sulfur—a harmless element useful to protoplasm. Hevesy adopted this too, to study the movement of phosphorus-containing phosphates into, through, and out of living tissues.

[1] An isotope is a variant form of a chemical element, identical in most properties, but unlike in having a different number of neutrons in the core of the atom. All isotopes occur in nature, but in quantities so minute that it is more expensive to extract them than to manufacture them. Some isotopes, like heavy hydrogen, are stable. Others are radioactive and "decay." Radioactivity is measured with a Geiger counter, and expressed in decimal parts of a "curie."

Artificially radioactive atoms became available in larger (kilocurie) quantities in the middle 1940's, after use of the atomic bomb (Aug. 6, 1945) and release of the secret that nuclear reactors had been built. Of the isotopes now priced within easy reach of experimental laboratories, the biologist has found greatest use for "carbon 14" (C^{14}), with which carbon dioxide could be labeled (as $C^{14}O_2$). The great advantage of these materials is in the smallness of the quantities that can be traced—a ten-millionth of a molecular weight, and hence a quantity unweighably small.

Hevesy's original technique—transferring an artificially radioactive organism into a nonradioactive environment and studying the rate at which the environment became radioactive—was retained. Two other methods were added: (1) after exposing the organism to a compound containing the isotope for a predetermined time at a known concentration, the organism is killed, cut into its component parts, and each of these is desiccated, powdered, and examined for radioactivity with a Geiger counter; or (2) slices of tissue or dissolved components from the tissue are spread out appropriately and dried, then brought into close proximity with sensitive photographic film. The film is affected by any radioactivity present, and shows this upon ordinary photographic processing.

Through use of these techniques and various modifications, an entirely new attitude has been found necessary. The organism is not only absorbing substances from its environment, but it is giving out some of the very same materials simultaneously.

The exchange can be amazingly rapid. For example, a mouse not only releases carbon dioxide into its environment as a result of respiration, but it also absorbs carbon dioxide at the same time. In the lungs the transfer must be in both directions—carbon dioxide from inspired air going into the blood stream, and *more* carbon dioxide coming from the blood stream into the gas to be exhaled. By using radioactive carbon dioxide ($C^{14}O_2$) instead of ordinary carbon dioxide with carbon 12, in an artificial atmosphere modified only in this one particular, it was learned that a mouse exposed for only a few breathing cycles (10 seconds) and then sacrificed for study, already had radioactive carbon (C^{14}) incorporated into glycogen molecules within its liver, and synthesized into many other compounds as well!

Calcium is highly mobile, moving between human blood and tissues at the rate of 20 per cent per minute. Water moves only a little more slowly. Half of the water molecules of the human body are replaced with fresh ones every week. Carbon, potassium, and sodium, move in and out on almost the same scale. Calcium and phosphorus in bones and teeth stay longer but are far from permanent. Altogether, it has been estimated that only about 2 per cent of the actual atoms present in a human body on one New Year's Day are there still a year later.

Of these 2 per cent, a majority are of an exceptional element: iron. This component of hemoglobin, of respiratory enzymes (cytochromes), and of a few other essential chemical mechanisms, is hard to obtain from the environment. Oxygen from the atmosphere and many other agents quickly change iron-con-taining compounds in nature to the ferric condition. Protoplasm can absorb iron only in the ferrous condition. One significance for the acidity of gastric juice is seen to be as an iron trap, transforming ingested iron compounds from the ferric to the ferrous condition, and permitting their absorption. And once the body absorbs the iron, it takes remarkable care of it. For example, when a red blood cell ends its useful life (after about 12 days of use in the duck, 125 days in man, still longer in the box turtle), the iron is recovered and used over again in the formation of new hemoglobin in fresh red cells.

Thus the constituents of life are in a constant state of flux, shifting about internally and being exchanged with the external environment. The vertebrate body does not "rob" materials from the skeleton when calcium or phosphorus is in short supply. It merely fails to replace atom for atom the normal withdrawal. A simple exchange has become one-sided, and the support mechanism may be seriously weakened as a result.

A dynamic equilibrium depends upon both suitable external conditions and healthy protoplasm.

WATER

The earth holds a silver treasure, cupped between ocean bed and tenting sky. Forever the heavens spend it, in the showers that refresh our temperate lands, the torrents that sluice the tropics. Every suckling root absorbs it, the very soil drains it down; the rivers run unceasing to the sea, the mountains yield it endlessly, in bubbling spring and far last slim cascade that flings away forever its bright similitude of life. Yet none is lost; in vast convection our water is returned, from soil to sky, and sky to soil, and back again, to fall as pure as blessing. There was never less; there could never be more. A mighty mercy on which life depends, for all its glittering shifts water is constant.

—DONALD CULROSS PEATTIE *and* NOEL PEATTIE in *A Cup of Sky*
(Boston: Houghton Mifflin Co., 1950), p. 41.

SUGGESTED READING (see pp. 507-510)

Recent and Informative: Fruton, 1950; Heilbrunn, 1951; Linderstrom-Lang, 1953; Pauling, Corey, and Hayward, 1954; Vallee, 1951.

7 · Energy Relations of Life

1. MEASUREMENT OF ENERGY. 2. FOOD SUBSTANCES—CALORIES, ORGANIC COMPOUNDS, ESSENTIAL FOODS, DEFICIENCIES. 3. STORAGE OF ENERGY—CHLOROPHYLL, THE LIGHT REACTIONS, THE DARK REACTIONS, ENERGY STORAGE, ENZYMES, DIGESTION. 4. NUTRITIONAL TYPES. 5. RELEASE OF ENERGY—AEROBIC RESPIRATION, ANAEROBIC RESPIRATION. 6. METABOLISM. 7. DEGRADATION OF ENERGY.

DISTINGUISHING between living and non-living substance is not always easy. Under most circumstances the decision is simple. Yet many of the characteristics of life may be dormant for a time; some of them are shown by nonliving materials.

1. Movement is usually a sign of life, but lack of movement does not necessarily signify absence of life. A leafless tree in February may show no movement even of the protoplasm within its cells. A hibernating snake or bat can go many minutes without a heartbeat. Still they are alive. Similarly, mixtures of chemical substances may move about—like a chip of camphor on a tub of water—without ceasing to be inanimate.

2. Growth by enlargement rather than accretion distinguishes living things from crystals. Such growth occurs in the absence of concentrated chemical substances. But an organism can achieve full size and cease to grow without dying. Hence absence of growth is no criterion by itself.

3. Reproduction is a capacity of all forms of life, but few of them can be counted on to reproduce within an hour of observation. Failure to reproduce does not indicate death or that nonliving substance is being studied.

4. Irritability is a characteristic of protoplasm. Changes in the intensity of illumination, sound, pressure, and the like evoke responses in living systems. Yet a stone is scarcely less irritable than a dry seed. The one lacks potential irritability; the other can become responsive.

5. Some definite form and range in size is a distinguishing feature of each kind of animal and plant. Nonliving things usually lack these limitations. The dead remains of an organism, however, may show its characteristic shape and dimensions. Hence this criterion also fails to distinguish between live and lifeless objects.

6. Chemical composition is a feature differing markedly in animate and inanimate objects. Protoplasm contains many very large molecules of carbohydrates, fats, and especially proteins. The molecular weight of these substances is high and remains high for a time even after death. But in substances that never have been part of living systems, molecular sizes are usually small.

7. Cellular organization is fundamental to living things exclusively. However, this organization is evident after death. It is not a reliable criterion of life.

8. Continuous demand for energy is a real measure of life, as contrasted with death, in objects that meet the previous seven requirements at some stage of their life histories. As long as any plant or animal is alive, it is employing energy in complex chemical and physical processes. Growth, response, reproduction, and movement all require expenditure of energy. The sources of this energy and its transformation in life determine to a large extent the form taken by plants and animals.

1. MEASUREMENT OF ENERGY

By definition, energy is the capacity to do work. Raising liquids in a plant, absorbing a meal in an animal, and growth of a cell are all processes involving work. The energy required for each type of work can be measured, but since the form of both the energy and the work varies widely, so too do the methods of measurement.

A physicist may evaluate energy as the momentum of a moving animal, or the position of a coconut that can fall from a tree, or as electrical energy, or as radiant energy such as light (Fig. 7-1). He may measure it in ergs—a

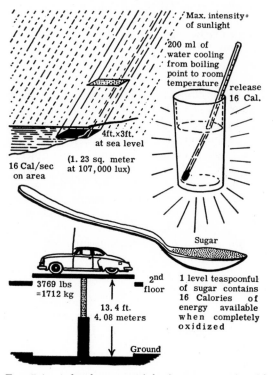

FIG. 7-1. *A level teaspoonful of sugar contains 16 Calories of energy, available if the sugar is completely oxidized. This much energy is received each second by a 4 ft. by 3 ft. area at sea level in brightest sunshine. The same amount of energy is released from 200 ml of water (about a teacupful) in cooling from the boiling point to room temperature. The same amount of energy is required to raise an ordinary automobile from one story to another.*

force of one dyne operating through a distance of one cm, where a dyne is the force required to give a gram an acceleration of a cm per sec. per sec. Or he may measure it in calories —the amount of energy required to increase the temperature of a gram of water from 3.5 to 4.5 degrees C. (a calorie equals about 4,860,000 ergs).

The chemist, by contrast, considers primarily the energy of chemical bonds—the

work required to bind molecules together or to break them apart.

All of these forms of energy concern the biologist, since each of them is found in living systems. The biologist (like the biological chemist), however, is likely to speak of Calories with a capital C—meaning a kilogram-calorie rather than the gram-calorie of the physicist. A Calorie is the energy required to change the temperature of a kilogram (1,000 grams) of water the one degree C. specified; hence 1 Calorie = 1,000 calories. The Calorie is the unit familiar in consideration of the energy content of foods. An apple, for example, affords about 100 Calories of energy.

2. FOOD SUBSTANCES

From his own experience, man usually thinks of foods in dietetic terms. He soon learns that milk contains water, dissolved mineral substances like calcium, carbohydrates like milk sugar (lactose), proteins like casein, and the many fats that rise to the top as cream and that can be made into butter. In addition, milk contains vitamins or their precursors—particularly Vitamins A and D. Other foods, though less "complete" than milk, may include larger percentages of some one or more of these important constituents.

A food may be considered either as any dietary substance utilized by an animal in its nutrition, or as only the energy-yielding constituents of that diet. The former view is preferable, because some essential materials are needed in such small amounts that their energy content must be negligible, yet their precise role in energy transfer is far from clear. Hence it is not possible at the moment to ascribe to them a definite place other than as vital requirements.

Calories

The energy content of any food or component of a food can be measured in terms of Calories per gram of dry weight. First, the foodstuff must be completely freed of water, which has no energy value but which is necessary for life. Then the dried foodstuff may be burned in a thoroughly insulated container in such a way that the number of Calories liberated in producing an incombustible mineral ash may be evaluated. The figures obtained are the "combustion values" of foodstuffs. They show that carbohydrates of any kind contain energy to the extent of 4.10 Calories per gram, proteins 5.65 Calories per gram, and fats 9.45 Calories per gram. The test apparatus, however, is somewhat more efficient than a living organism. The equipment leaves no fecal material with wasted foodstuffs. Hence a better approximation for the food value to an animal would be 4 Calories per gram of dry carbohydrate or dry protein, and 9 per gram of fat. As will be seen later, the energy in carbohydrates is available to the animal much more directly than is energy in the other two forms.

Measurements of the energy requirements of plants are much more difficult than an evaluation of the food requirements or energy economy of an animal. In each type of life, however, constructive processes hide energy and increase the total weight, whereas destructive processes liberate energy as heat and decrease the total weight. Over a reasonable period, if growth is not rapid, it becomes fair practice to keep account of the total heat output and to regard it as a measure of the processes by which life continues.

The chemical processes involved in life vary greatly with activity. Thus a 150-pound man transfers heat to the surrounding air at approximately the following rates:

	Calories per hour
1. while sleeping	65
2. awake but lying still; more muscular tension and mental activity	75
3. resting but sitting in a chair	100
4. light muscular exercise, such as writing or playing cards	170
5. moderate muscular exercise, such as walking on level ground	300
6. heavy work, such as climbing mountains, lifting rocks, digging ditches, pitching hay, running rapidly	600

It is possible to calculate the number of hours per day at each rate of activity and to compute the total number of Calories of heat liberated. If this is typical of ordinary routine behavior, the number of Calories of heat liberated should never be more than the number of Calories of food value taken in during the corresponding period. Representative approximations for the human animal indicate daily needs as shown below.

Warm-blooded animals (birds and mam-

Years of Age	Calories per day for		
	Children	Girls and Women	Boys and Men
0—2	1,000		
2—5	1,300		
5—9	1,700		
10—12	2,000		
12—14		2,200	2,600
15—16		2,600	
15—20			3,000
17—70		2,000—2,200*	
21—70			3,000* 3,200† to 5,000‡

* At light work; † at moderate work; ‡ at heavy work.

mals) maintain a higher rate of chemical activity when the surrounding temperature is low; their heat output and food needs rise as the temperature drops. Cold-blooded animals and plants have reduced rates of activity at lower temperatures, so that energy needs diminish in proportion to temperature. At any given temperature, however, the energy requirements are governed to a considerable extent by the weight of living protoplasm, by the degree of activity, and by the opportunity afforded for heat loss. In spite of the longer periods spent asleep, four 40-pound children use up far more energy each day than one 160-pound parent. Part of this is in growth, but a large portion of the energy is lost because the smaller individual has relatively more surface through which to radiate heat, in proportion to the volume (and weight) of body in which the chemical activities proceed.

Few people know how much surface they present to the world. It can be calculated using DuBois' formula for the area of the naked human body (S, in square meters), where W is the weight in kilograms and H the height in centimeters:

$$S = 0.00718 \times W^{0.425} \times H^{0.725}$$

On this basis the weights (84 and 58 kg) and heights (190 and 165 cm) of the authors indicate surface areas of 2.11 and 1.63 square meters respectively. Food requirements are approximately proportional to this surface area, the approximation being due: (1) to a slightly higher rate of energy expenditure in human females as compared with human males, and (2) to differences in heat loss rates because of unlike clothing.

In making studies of energy exchanges in smaller animals, the surface enters in the same way, without the clothing difference. Physiologists have even gone to the extreme of pinning out the skin of an experimental animal on squared paper, counting squares covered and getting individual measurements at the end of an investigation when the organism could be sacrificed. Sometimes unexpected features complicate the studies. For example, two mice in separate chambers show oxygen requirements, carbon dioxide output, and heat losses in proportion to their surface area. If they are in the same chamber and the temperature is comfortable or high, the same is true. But if the temperature is lowered, the mice huddle together. At once they cease to lose heat on the area of contact, and the total surface area of two mice is no longer the governing factor. The huddled mice are now one supermouse, the exposed area of which determines the radiation and convection losses of heat.

Organic Compounds

The Calorie content of foods is not the only consideration, however. Definite substances must be provided, out of which the organism can produce more protoplasm for growth and for replacement or repair. The chemical nature of the food is highly important. Through it the essential elements and groups of elements are obtained. The groups of elements are almost exclusively those in organic compounds—the carbohydrates, proteins, and fats discussed briefly in Chapter 6. Many animals must obtain these groups ready-formed—at least in basic linkages of the elements—because these animals lack the ability to produce the linkage if supplied only the raw materials (the carbon, hydrogen, oxygen, nitrogen, sulfur, and phosphorus).

The arrangement of the atoms within a molecule is subject to variation, and in different forms with the same overall constitution, the properties are different. Thus, carbohydrates contain only carbon, hydrogen, and oxygen, with the last two usually in the same proportions as in water. Glucose (grape sugar) and fructose (fruit sugar) are 6-carbon sugars,

$C_6H_{12}O_6$, whereas lactose (milk sugar) and sucrose (cane sugar) are both 12-carbon sugars, $C_{12}H_{22}O_{11}$. The 12-carbon sugars are **disaccharides,** the 6-carbon sugars **monosaccharides.** Starch and cellulose are carbohydrates with still larger molecules; they are **polysaccharides.**

Sugars and starches appear primarily in foods of plant origin. In the animal body the monosaccharides can be absorbed without digestion, but the more complex carbohydrates must be broken down to be taken into the body.[1] When excess carbohydrates appear in the diet, they may be converted to monosaccharides and then eliminated along with nitrogen-containing wastes, or converted to fats and stored at definite sites within the organism, or transformed to glycogen and stored.

Fats, with the same three types of atoms but with less oxygen in proportion to the hydrogen and carbon, have a characteristic structure based on the molecule of **glycerol.** Glycerol (= glycerine) is a triple alcohol, and can provide linkage for three extensive chains of carbon, hydrogen, and oxygen, in the form of **fatty acids.** The structure can be visualized readily as

$$CH_2—O—\text{fatty acid} \qquad\qquad CH_2—OH$$
$$CH—O—\text{fatty acid} \quad \text{since glycerol is} \quad CH—OH$$
$$CH_2—O—\text{fatty acid} \qquad\qquad CH_2—OH$$

Details of the fatty acid chains determine the characteristics of the fat, so that it may be a liquid oil, or a semi-solid grease, or a wax of some kind, each with its characteristic melting point. Among plants, fats are found chiefly in seeds, fruits, and growing regions. Those extracted from olives, cotton seed, corn, peanuts, castor beans, and flaxseed are particularly familiar oils. Fats are often referred to as **lipoids,** since this term includes as well a few fat-like compounds of slightly different construction. Lecithin, cholesterol, and ergos-

---

[1] Note that taking food such as carbohydrates into the digestive tract does not imply taking it into the body. Until an energy-containing substance passes through cell membranes into protoplasm it cannot be regarded as "inside." Instead, the body can be thought of as an elongated doughnut, with the hole represented by the digestive tube. The hole or the alimentary canal is merely a surrounded portion of the outside world.

terol are such nonfat lipoids; they may contain in their molecules both phosphorus and nitrogen. Many of the resins and "essential oils" in plants (for example, turpentine, vanillin, garlic, and camphor) are mixtures of closely related compounds, but commonly they contain other chemical elements. Thus, onion and garlic odors are definitely related to the sulfur content of these essential oils.

Butyric acid—one of the prominent components of milk fats—has the chemical form CH_3—CH_2—CH_2—$COOH$. Like most fatty acids found in nature, it has an even number of carbon atoms. Some of the fatty acids can be synthesized by the animal body; others must be obtained from foods and are thus among the essential nutrients. Fats beyond current requirements are usually stored by the body in special sites characteristic of each kind of organism.

Proteins complete the list of organic foods needed in quantity by animals. Each is composed of carbon, hydrogen, oxygen, and nitrogen, and many also contain either sulfur or phosphorus. Proteins are the most complicated and extensive molecules known. It is clear, however, that they are composed of definite building blocks called **amino acids.** There are about two dozen different kinds of amino acids occurring in nature, each with a name familiar to organic chemists. Proteins vary widely in the number of each of the amino acids that are linked together into the giant molecule, and also in the linkage itself. Probably no protein contains less than a hundred of them, however. Some proteins consist of relatively few of the total possible kinds; others seem to include some of each. Hence the variety of proteins is enormous, and has been compared to the number of different words that can be formed with the letters of an alphabet.

This remarkable variety of proteins is found in any well-balanced diet, and in animal digestive processes each protein is broken down into its component parts. The amino acids are absorbed, then reconstructed into the multitude of different proteins that are characteristic of the particular species. No chemical substances are more typical of protoplasm than are proteins. Yet in the normal diet, excess amounts of some amino acids are obtained and these are broken down to provide energy; their nitrogenous residues appear as dissolved wastes. In some situations, a high protein diet may provide the body with excess amounts of all the amino acids. Except in starvation, however, proteins are seldom employed as direct energy sources. Instead, they take part in much more complex chemistry, whereas the carbohydrates (and to a lesser extent the fats) yield the Calories that drive the reactions. The distinction between destruction of proteins as energy sources, and the destruction of excess amino acids to yield energy, is clear.

Essential Foods

It should be noted that organisms differ enormously in their food requirements. Green plants, for example, need only water, dissolved inorganic matter (containing no carbon compounds and actually only minute amounts of calcium, iron, phosphorus, sulfur, magnesium, and the like), carbon dioxide, and sunlight. Man and animals in general must have carbohydrates of no greater complexity than starches; proteins containing certain of the two dozen amino acids; definite vitamins; and water and inorganic substances. The reason for this great difference is that plants are much more able to **synthesize** (from the Greek *syn* = together, and *tithemi* = to place) the compounds they require, from carbon dioxide, water, inorganic nitrates, phosphates, and sulfates. They synthesize not only the complete variety of carbohydrates, lipoids, and proteins they need for protoplasm, but they also are far more thrifty in laying aside vast stores of these organic compounds. Animals (including man) and the non-green plants are able to synthesize fewer of the constituents essential to their own living substances, and must obtain the building blocks from green plants (or other animals that feed on green plants). Only in this way can they acquire these materials in a form that is neither too simple nor too complex to be usable. Since the molecules of proteins and fats are all too large to pass through a cell membrane, however, each cell of every living thing must contain a complete mechanism for synthesis of every protein and fat required for its activity, from simpler components (hence amino acids, glycerol, and fatty acids) that can be absorbed from the environment.

Deficiences

Animals need carbohydrates, proteins, and lipoids in considerable quantity. In the human instance, a ratio of 1 unit of protein to 1 unit of lipoid to 4 units of carbohydrates is often recommended. In addition, the animal must have traces (0.01 gram per day, or less) of definite chemical substances known as vitamins. Different animals require different vitamins. Apparently each vitamin essential to an organism represents a missing mechanism—a synthesis of an important substance—which, since lacking, must be provided in the diet; the particular animal cannot make its own. The vitamins are probably either compounds required for important chemical actions to continue (enzymes) or materials from which these substances can be made. Lack of an adequate supply of any vitamin brings about first a general decline in vigor, and then symptoms that have been linked together as describing a disease. Some diseases are due to parasites and infective agents; others are caused by improper function of body organs; those arising from dietary lacks of definite vitamins are classed as "deficiency diseases"—each an **avitaminosis.**

Some deficiency diseases have been known since antiquity. Descriptions of them appear in the writings of Hippocrates, the "father of medicine" (460-377 B.C.). And as early as 1720 it was evident that the malady called **scurvy** was not merely an affliction of the poor but was related to foods. Medicines could not cure it, but the symptoms vanished and the patient recovered if given "antiscorbutic" juices from oranges, lemons, citrons, and green vegetables. Captain Cook, whose famous voyage around the world took more than three years, kept his crew free of scurvy in spite of lack of fresh vegetables by feeding them lime juice, "sweet wort," and sauerkraut. For this accomplishment in health maintenance, Cook received in 1776 a special medal from the British Admiralty. Soon the whole of the British navy was insisting that its seagoing personnel eat lemons and limes daily to prevent scurvy. The order had the desired effect, and the British sailors came to be called "limeys" from their diet.

Experimental demonstration of vitamins began in 1881, when Dr. Lunin, a Swiss investigator at the University of Basle, looked into the nutritive value of the various substances known to be in milk. Lunin fed one group of mice on a diet of milk sugar, milk fat, milk protein, water, and the mineral substances of milk, while a control group of mice received milk alone. The latter remained healthy and vigorous, whereas the former (on a chemically pure diet) died within a month. Lunin concluded, correctly, that "additional substances," required for life, must be present in milk. He made no further attempt to learn what they were.

A few years later, a Japanese naval surgeon by the name of Takaki suspected that diet was the basis for the high incidence of the disease **beri-beri** among men in his charge. He could find no indications of the microbes that Pasteur and other Europeans indicated as disease agents. Neither sanitary conditions nor climate seemed to blame. Yet the disease was non-European, largely Asiatic. Accordingly, he selected for investigation two warships that were being sent simultaneously on long missions. Aboard one he ordered the usual rations, in which white "polished" rice was a main constituent. The other vessel was to be short of rice, but was to have large supplies of barley, vegetables, condensed milk, and meat. On the first ship several men died of beri-beri and about two thirds of the men suffered from its symptoms. Aboard the second vessel no one died of beri-beri, and the only men who showed any symptoms of the disease were the few who refused to change to the unfamiliar diet available and who tried to live on what little rice they were issued. Takaki arranged at once for the new diet to be used for all military personnel, and health improved immediately. The conclusion drawn from this experiment was that polished rice lacked enough protein in proportion to the carbohydrates.

A Dutch physician in Java, Dr. C. Eijkman, wondered whether the supposedly important protein-carbohydrate ratio was an adequate explanation of the beri-beri problem. He tested polished rice versus unpolished rice as diets for chickens and pigeons. In 1897 his findings were clear enough to publish: the birds fed on polished grain had developed a **polyneuritis** very similar to beri-beri in hu-

VITAMIN	Soluble in	Storage	Destroyed by	Physiological Action	AVITAMINOSIS SYMPTOMS or Deficiency Disease	CHIEF SOURCES
A converted carotene	fat	yes	cooking or exposure to air	(1) Component of visual pigments (see p. 231) (2) Essential for normal epithelia, especially glands	(1) "night blindness" (2) slackened growth, degeneration and death in young mammals (3) malfunction of body surface cells, especially glands; reduction of tear formation (xerophthalmia = dry eye) allows infection of eyes and nasal passages; similar infections develop in larynx, bronchi, salivary ducts, urogenital ducts—with sterility in ♂	yellow and leafy vegetables, egg yolk, fish liver oils, butter
B₁ thiamin	water	no	cooking if soda added	(1) Involved in carbohydrate and fat metabolism (2) Aids digestion and absorption (3) Required for normal nerve function	(1) reduced growth (2) loss of appetite (3) malfunction of digestive tract (4) improper carbohydrate and fat metabolism (5) **beri-beri**, with extreme weakness —in birds, a nervous "polyneuritis"	yeast, wheat germ, corn meal, enriched flour products
B₂ = G riboflavin	water	in liver		(1) Involved in cell respiration (2) Important to nerve function	(1) opacity of cornea (cataract) (2) cheilosis—an inflammation and cracking at corners of mouth, nose and eyes (3) faulty digestion (4) loss of hair —in dogs, "yellow liver disease" —in chicks, "curled-toe paralysis"	bran, enriched flour products, yeast, egg white, liver, kidney, muscle (especially pork, beef), cow's milk (twice as rich as human milk in B₂), green vegetables
niacin = nicotinic acid = P-P	water			(1) Involved in cell respiration (2) Important to normal skin and digestion (P-P = pellagra-preventative)	(1) **pellagra**, with inflammation of mouth, throat and tongue; skin blotched, first red, then bronzed, often scaly, subject to infections; mental irregularities may lead to insanity —in pigs, disease like pellagra —in dogs, "black tongue disease"	yeast, green vegetables, wheat germ, egg yolk, liver, lean meat
folic acid	water			Important to normal bone marrow function	(1) anemia (certain types) in man and monkeys —in rats and chicks, abnormal growth and blood formation	yeast, liver, green vegetables
biotin = H	water			Important in enzyme of respiration	—need for man entirely uncertain; specific disease in various birds and mammals	yeast, cane molasses, egg yolk, tomatoes
pyridoxine = B₆	water		light	Involved in metabolism of fatty acids	—need for man entirely uncertain; horny skin and granulated eyelids in experimental animals	yeast, cane molasses, egg yolk
pantothenic acid	water			Involved in growth and skin maintenance	—need for man entirely uncertain; skin ulcers and abscesses in experimental animals	yeast, cereal grains, milk, liver, wheat germ, egg yolk
B₁₂ cyanacobalamin	water			Proper formation of hemoglobin	**pernicious anemia** and some other anemias	liver; by-product of streptomycin manufacture
C ascorbic acid	water	no DAILY SUPPLY URGENT	cooking or exposure to air	Involved in maintenance of connective tissues, in defense against bacterial invasion and toxins. Part of enzyme complex in cellular respiration ("antiscorbutic vitamin")	(1) a few weeks' deficiency produces permanent damage to teeth (2) fragility of blood vessels with bleeding (hemorrhage) in mucous membranes, in joints, under skin (3) **scurvy**, with loss of weight, swollen gums (gingivitis) and loosened teeth (pyorrhea); ankles and lower leg areas swollen and painful to touch; anemia and shortness of breath; death	citrus fruits, green peppers, tomatoes, cranberries, bananas, apples, some leafy vegetables. Destroyed in raw milk by pasteurization — one of the few known disadvantages of this process.
D calciferol = activated ergosterol	fat	in skin, thymus, adrenals, kidneys, brain		Regulator of calcium and phosphorus metabolism ("antirachitic vitamin")	(1) **rickets**, with bones of children remaining soft, deformed; joints enlarging; ligaments and tendons elongating; muscles lax producing "pot belly"; "rachitic rosary" swellings in intercostal junctions; tooth formation and maintenance inadequate; spinal column may become deformed; extreme nervousness; anemia; loss of resistance to fatal infections	fish liver oils, enriched milk, enriched bread, egg yolk in summer ┆ man activates own ergosterol if in sun enough throughout year
E α-tocopherol	fat		ultraviolet light	May be needed for placenta formation and for sperm formation	—need for man entirely uncertain; in many mammals, lack brings paralysis; in others, e.g., rat, brings abortion of embryos; in ♂ rat and rooster must be present for proper sperm formation	wheat germ oil, egg yolk, some green leaves (lettuce, spinach)
K phylloquinone = menadione	fat			Essential for formation of prothrombin for clotting mechanism (Chapter 9) ("antihemorrhagic vitamin")	(1) slowness of blood clotting (2) liability to hemorrhage and appearance of small hemorrhages under skin*	leafy vegetables, alfalfa meal, tomatoes, liver, fish muscle and meal

* In many mammals, including man, Vitamin K apparently is produced in adequate amounts by intestinal bacteria, and is absorbed along with products of fat digestion. When fat digestion is abnormal, an avitaminosis-K is likely. Also common as a deficiency in newborn mammals (including man) since bacterial flora of intestine has not yet been acquired.

man beings, whereas those receiving unpolished grain remained normal. When the polyneuritic birds were fed rice "polishings" (really the bran which had been removed), they recovered quickly; the disease was due to a lack of some essential substance present in the bran. Eijkman called the required ingredient an "anti-beri-beri factor," but he did not learn its nature.

In 1912, Dr. Casimir Funk, a Polish physiologist, repeated Eijkman's experiment with variations, and concluded that the essential ingredient was an amine. He was wrong in his chemical diagnosis but his name for the material, *vitamine* (from *vita* = life and *amine,* the particular type of nitrogenous compound), has been shortened to **vitamin** and retained. The crystals Funk extracted from wheat bran, that cured polyneuritic pigeons, were neither an amine nor a simple substance. But a new field of study had been opened. In the following year, Doctors McCollum and Davis, of the University of Wisconsin, announced isolation of a growth factor which they called "fat soluble A"; this factor was essential for rats. Today, it has become known more fully as Vitamin A, while Funk's substance became Vitamin B—later recognized to be a whole complex of vitamins. Now a long series of these important materials is known (p. 69).

Fortunately, the initial excitement over vitamins has now disappeared, and with it have gone the bulk of extravagant claims and faddist aspects. It is still clear that small amounts (0.01 gram daily, or less) are essential but that addition of vitamins to an adequate diet achieves nothing (Photos 53-58). Excess vitamins are excreted in the urine. In fact, in some progressive countries like Sweden, tests for vitamins in the urine are used routinely to learn which ones are not in adequate supply.

Research has been directed toward learning the minimum daily requirement for man and his domestic animals of each vitamin. Other work has inquired into the chemical nature of the substances themselves as a step toward either extracting from food by-products greater quantities at lower prices, or toward synthesis of the vitamins themselves, for use as supplements to the diet. Together

with studies on the amino-acid content of various protein foods, and the amino-acid requirements in animal diets, these investigations have gone far toward providing an understanding of how energy is transferred from food to protoplasm or to activity in an animal body.

3. STORAGE OF ENERGY

Regardless of what chemical substances are required by an organism for living processes, the actual energy on which almost all life ultimately depends is sunlight. Each square centimeter of the earth's surface receives from the sun, on the average, about 2 calories of energy per minute. Of this a small fraction (not more than 3 per cent) is absorbed by green plants and utilized in a chemical process called **photosynthesis** (from the Greek *photos* = light, *synthesis* = putting together). In photosynthesis, water and carbon dioxide yield their component atoms to make up a more complex molecule—a carbohydrate. The proportions are very exact:

6 molecules of WATER
plus
6 molecules of CARBON DIOXIDE
plus
SOLAR ENERGY
(in the presence of
  LIVING PROTOPLASM
  and
  the pigment CHLOROPHYLL)
react to yield
6 molecules of OXYGEN
plus
1 molecule of SUGAR (monosaccharide)

The chemist writes this relationship in a single line with greater precision, using the symbols H_2O, CO_2, O_2, and $C_6H_{12}O_6$ for molecules of water, carbon dioxide, oxygen, and sugar, respectively:

$$6\,H_2O + 6\,CO_2 + \frac{sun}{energy} \xrightarrow{\text{(live protoplasm)}}_{\text{(chlorophyll)}} 6\,O_2 + C_6H_{12}O_6$$

The rate of this reaction depends upon a number of factors: the availability of water and carbon dioxide, the quantity and nature of the light available, the temperature, and the "physiological state" of the chlorophyll and the living protoplasm.

1. Water reaches the cell in which photo-

57. Avitaminosis A (100-gram rat on left) compared with the normal (140-gram litter mate on right).

AVITAMINOSIS SYMPTOMS IN TEST ANIMALS

58. For the first 2 weeks, both chicks were maintained on a diet deficient in vitamin B_{12}. The chick on the left was continued on this diet, whereas the chick on the right received a supplement of B_{12}.

59. Both baby rats are 14 days old. The rat at the left, like all its litter mates, shows a growth defect due to deficiency of vitamin B_{12} in its mother's diet.

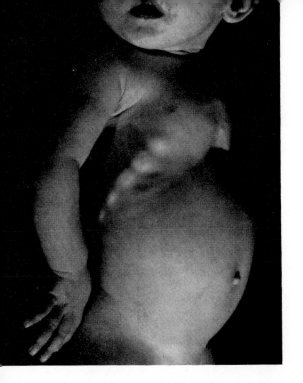

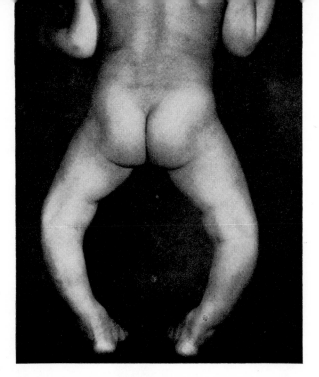

60. Protruding abdomen, marked off sharply from the chest by a groove, plus knob-like swellings at the ends of the ribs ("rachitic rosary"), and a bulging of the chest ("pigeon breast") are indications of an abnormal pull of the diaphragm—all signs of rickets.

61. Characteristic bowlegs, or knock knees of equal deformity, show the delay in calcification of the long bones which allows body weight and muscle tensions to produce permanent curvatures.

In the Middle Ages these symptoms were so common as to be considered normal for children.

Avitaminosis D (Rickets) in Man

62. X-ray of the arm of a child suffering from rickets, showing partial and complete "green stick" fractures through the poorly calcified bones at points marked with arrows.

63. X-ray of the same child as in Photo 62, after 216 days of treatment with vitamin D; the bone outlines are far more distinct, and some carpal bones in the wrist have become calcified (See also Photo 125).

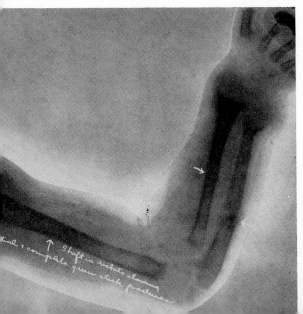

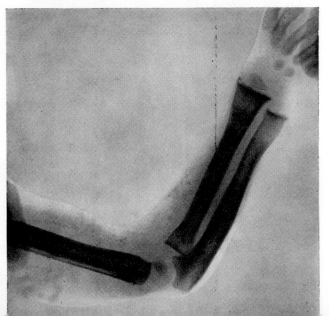

synthesis occurs either from its surroundings (in the case of aquatic plants) or adjacent cells. For land plants the supply is often limited enough that photosynthesis is restricted. By using "tagged" atoms in the water supplied, it has been shown definitely that the hydrogen in photosynthesized sugar comes from the water, and that the oxygen released has this same origin—hence does not come from the carbon dioxide required.

2. Carbon dioxide comes to the plant either dissolved in the water around it or from the atmosphere. Ordinary air contains about 0.31 per cent by volume (0.047 per cent by weight) of carbon dioxide. Under normal daylight conditions this supply is so low that it limits photosynthesis. A plant can utilize as much as 5 per cent. Above this, however, the gas proves toxic and inhibits photosynthesis. Both the carbon and the oxygen in carbon dioxide are incorporated into the sugar molecule.

3. Ordinarily light intensity by day is adequate for photosynthesis. The process is most active, in fact, at intensities about a tenth of full sunlight. Apparently intense light produces photo-oxidations that destroy some of the products of photosynthesis.

About half of the light energy reaching the earth is in the part of the spectrum visible to human eyes. Only in this region does chlorophyll absorb energy useful in photosynthesis. The pigment is most efficient in blue and red, less so in green—which is absorbed so much less completely that chlorophyll appears green. However, where plants grow layer above layer, the green light transmitted and reflected by the upper foliage is utilized by the lower, so that most of the visible energy may be absorbed. It is all about equally effective in photosynthesis.

As much as 20 per cent of solar energy absorbed may be used under ideal conditions. These conditions may be arranged in the laboratory: an artificial atmosphere with about 5 per cent carbon dioxide; limitless water and dissolved nutrients; and light intensities a tenth to a fiftieth as great as under field conditions.

Energy storage by photosynthesis normally comes nowhere near this figure. A good crop of corn (33 bushels to the acre) represents about 1.8 tons of dried organic matter, half of which is kernels, the other half roots, stalks, leaves and remainder of the plant. Since the crop grows in a third of a year, in light only half of whose energy is absorbable, in intensities that waste photosynthetic products, in carbon dioxide supplies as low as 0.04 per cent, and with the water often too scanty to allow full photosynthesis, it is remarkable that the plants do as well as this. A yield of 1.8 tons per acre represents storage of about 0.1 per cent of the annual supply of solar energy falling on the corn field. Sugar cane, which grows the year round in the tropics, does only about four times as well, even with abundant rain. Algae in relatively shallow sea water, with plenty of dissolved nutrients and water, store energy at comparable rates.

4. The actual utilization of light energy by photosynthesis is independent of temperature. Subsequent reactions, however, are speeded up if temperatures rise, and slowed if they fall. A conspicuous lowering of the rate of the entire process is noticed at temperatures below 20° C. Above 44° C., on the other hand, the protoplasm itself is so damaged by heat that photosynthesis falls off. Hence the range of optimum activity is small.

Chlorophyll

The green pigment required for photosynthetic use of sunlight usually consists of two closely related pigments mixed together. Chlorophyll a, $C_{55}H_{72}O_5N_4Mg$, and chlorophyll b, $C_{55}H_{70}O_6N_4Mg$, are normally associated with additional, non-green pigments, such as yellow carotenoids. Of these, xanthophylls (for example $C_{40}H_{56}O$) and carotenes (with the general formula $C_{40}H_{56}$) are most common.

Except in blue-green algae, chlorophyll is found only in chloroplastids. Within the chloroplastid still further organization locates the chlorophyll in small flattened discs. Here the pigment is associated with a protein exhibiting additional structural regularity.

Although photosynthesis will not occur in the absence of chlorophyll, the pigment does not enter into the overall chemical equation. Whenever a substance controls the rate of a chemical reaction without the substance itself undergoing change in quantity or chemical properties, it is spoken of as a **catalyst,** or as having catalyzed the reaction. The action of a catalyst can be shown by use of an analogy (Fig. 7-2).

Originally, photosynthesis was thought to be a single reaction. Now it is known to consist of a number of steps. The equation on p. 70 represents the overall changes but is comparable to a listing in parallel columns of (1) the carloads of steel, rubber, glass, and the like that might go into one end of a factory as the raw materials, and (2) the number of finished automobiles rolled from the assembly line at the other end. No intermediate steps in manufacture would be evident from the listing, no matter how accurate the totals were.

Chlorophyll serves as a trap for solar energy. It catalyzes one or more reactions in a mere 1/100,000th second. These chemical steps are described as the "light reactions."

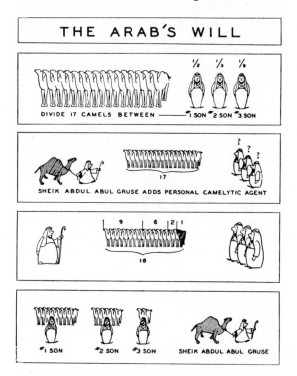

FIG. 7-2. *An old Arabian story tells of a father who willed to his three sons definite proportions of his wealth—consisting of 17 camels. The puzzled heirs called in a friendly sheik for advice. He tied his mount beside their camels, and suddenly the problem was solved. Yet the sheik's camel was left over at the time of the division—as is a catalyst at the end of the reaction it facilitated.*

Their products are processed in further steps for which light is not necessary. Collectively these subsequent events are termed the "dark reactions," although they proceed almost equally well in light or dark. In 1/100th second, the dark reactions use up the products of the light reactions. Hence if a plant is alternately illuminated for 1/100,000th second and shaded for 1/100th second, its rate of photosynthesis is the same as that found in continuous illumination. Yet it would actually be in the dark 99.9 per cent of the time.

Since photosynthesis is the process on which essentially all life depends, it is important to have a general outline of the steps.

The Light Reactions

Two different events requiring light energy appear to take place during the extremely brief time during which light is effective:

1. PHOTOLYSIS OF WATER (from *photos* = light, *lyo* = free). The water used in photosynthesis is split, and a hydrogen atom from its molecule is captured by an unidentified compound described as a "hydrogen acceptor." If the acceptor is represented by "A" the reaction could be written:

$$4\,H_2O + 2\,A \xrightarrow[\text{(chlorophyll)}]{\text{(light)}} 2\,AH_2 + 2\,H_2O_2$$

The products of this reaction include the compound indicated by AH_2—important in the synthesis of sugar—and the toxic material, hydrogen peroxide, which must be destroyed in a dark reaction.

2. CAPTURE OF ENERGY. Intimately tied to the photolysis of water is a series of at least three steps whereby inorganic phosphate is linked to the substance **adenosine monophosphate.** The linkages are remarkable in that they store unusually large amounts of energy in the molecule. Addition of one phosphate to adenosine monophosphate installs one "high-energy bond" and produces **adenosine diphosphate.** A second high-energy bond is incorporated along with a second phosphate, to produce **adenosine triphosphate.** The diphosphate and triphosphate are of such great importance in protoplasmic chemistry that they have come to be known by the abbreviations "ADP" and "ATP."

The mechanism within a chloroplastid

whereby energy can be captured and held in the form of ADP and ATP requires the presence of several chemical compounds, among them vitamin K.

The Dark Reactions

Dependent upon the light reactions are many chemical processes which use the energy stored temporarily in ATP and ADP. At least three of these reactions occur within the chloroplastid, since recent experiments have shown that the reactions continue even when the chloroplastid is removed from the cell. Hence a chloroplastid is a remarkably complete photosynthetic unit, and very much alive.

The multiplicity of dark reactions was studied by supplying isolated chloroplastids with an artificial atmosphere containing radioactive carbon dioxide ($C^{14}O_2$). The photosynthetic reactions were halted abruptly after a brief time by addition of boiling alcohol. The products of photosynthesis were then extracted, separated, and tested for radioactivity. Those which contained carbon-14 were then identified.

In this experiment the time element was critically important. A few minutes of photosynthesis was enough to put carbon-14 into a large variety of compounds, including sugars, fats, and proteins. By shortening the time for photosynthesis in the artificial atmosphere to seconds, the number of compounds with radioactive carbon decreased. From these data it was possible to reach conclusions as to the probable reactions following photolysis of water:

1. DESTRUCTION OF HYDROGEN PEROXIDE is a necessary step, as fast as it is formed by the photolysis of water:

$$2\,H_2O_2 \longrightarrow 2\,H_2O + O_2$$

This reaction accounts for the oxygen which is the by-product of photosynthesis. It is also an economical procedure which returns for photolysis one half of the water used in the light reactions.

2. CARBON-DIOXIDE FIXATION is probably restricted to the chloroplastid in the living cell. The reaction occurs only when light energy is used in photolysis of water, and hence must draw its raw materials or energy or both from the light reaction. Apparently an unidentified carbon-containing compound (a "carbon-

dioxide acceptor") is linked to the carbon dioxide in the synthesis of phosphoglyceric acid. Subsequent reactions convert the phosphoglyceric acid into a 3-carbon compound (triose phosphate), from two molecules of which a molecule of monosaccharide can be synthesized. Somewhere in these reactions the substance designated "AH_2," from the light reactions is used, and the high-energy phosphates of adenosine are degraded to release their energy again.

3. SYNTHESIS OF OTHER ORGANIC COMPOUNDS within the chloroplastid and perhaps adjacent cytoplasm of the cell utilizes further energy from the ATP system and some of the unknown material "AH_2." As many as a dozen reactions may be in progress simultaneously, explaining in part why radioactive carbon-14 quickly appears in so many different compounds.

The raw materials from which lipoids and proteins are synthesized appear to be among these intermediate materials. Amino acids may be formed along two different routes, and finally combined in the microsomes into proteins of almost unlimited variety.

Energy Storage

Monosaccharides are an obvious form of energy storage. The molecule is small enough that it can be transported from place to place. In every cell it can be broken down to make energy available for various processes. Its convenience is parallel to that of money in a human society. Money can be carried around, and it gets done a great variety of work in different situations.

Sugar can be present in only small amounts without introducing difficulties. Any large rise in its concentration is matched by increased endosmosis, and turgor in plant cells. Both plants and animals regularly use special chemical reactions to remove excess sugar from circulation. These steps produce larger molecules, such as insoluble starch or glycogen, which do not embarrass the protoplasm through osmotic activity.

The first step in the sequence involves expenditure of ATP, to attach phosphate groups to monosaccharide molecules. Thereafter the glucose-phosphate can be utilized to build a monosaccharide molecule into a disaccharide, a disaccharide into a trisaccharide, and so on. Eventually this sequence progresses to polysaccharides of large molecular size and insoluble nature, such as starch, glycogen, lignin, cellulose, and chitin.

Enzymes

To the chemist it is almost miraculous that so many different chemical reactions can occur in so small a space, at such low concentrations, and with so little change in temperature or electrical characteristics. Yet each reaction is found to depend upon its own cata-

cyanide, and most heavy metals). All enzymes are effective in minute amounts. Each is highly specific—related to a single reaction. Each increases the *rate* of the reaction without determining the direction taken, hence will catalyze action in either direction. The *direction* of the reaction is controlled by the concentration of substrates and products, and by the energy relations.

Enzymes are needed not only to permit synthesis of carbohydrates, lipoids, and proteins (and their precursors) from simpler substances, but also to split apart the large molecules and release the energy they contain. Enzymes must be present for synthesizing each enzyme required! If an organism lacks a

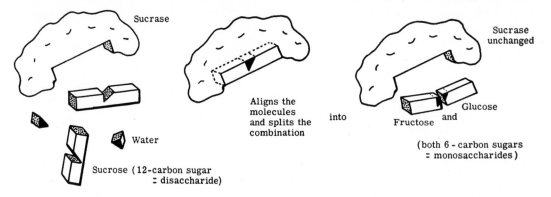

FIG. 7-3. *A model can suggest the lock-and-key relation between an enzyme and the compounds upon which it acts. Here the enzyme sucrase splits the double sugar sucrose into two simple sugar molecules. This enzymatic reaction is usually shown only by the equation:*

$$\begin{array}{ccc} \text{SUBSTRATES} & \text{ENZYME} & \text{PRODUCTS} \\ C_{12}H_{22}O_{11} + H_2O & \xrightarrow{\hspace{2cm}} & 2\,C_6H_{12}O_6 \\ \text{sucrose} \quad \text{water} & \text{(sucrase)} & \text{glucose} + \text{fructose} \end{array}$$

lyst. Moreover, the majority of these essential catalysts are of a protein nature—of huge molecular size. Collectively they are called **enzymes.** Usually each is named with a word ending in *ase,* and the word may be the substance **(substrate)** on which the enzyme works. Commonly the catalyst or enzyme name is shown in parentheses below the arrow of the chemical equation representing its reaction (Fig. 7-3).

Probably most proteins in protoplasm provide enzyme action. Many characteristics of enzymes, in fact, seem to arise from their protein nature. Enzymes are inactivated by heat (usually between 40 and 50 degrees C.), and by an assortment of poisons (such as

particular enzyme (or part of it), it must be assumed that some other enzyme system is lacking. The organism may then find it necessary to obtain the missing material by absorption, or to acquire the product of the missing reaction as an essential food. Vitamins in the diet of animals appear to supply essential parts of vital enzyme molecules—parts that the animal cannot synthesize. In the absence of the vitamin, some chemical process fails. The deficiency of its product shows as avitaminosis symptoms.

Digestion

Carbohydrates and fatty materials stored by plants would be wasted if it were not possible for the plant protoplasm to break down the big molecules again. The breakdown is intracellular (from *intra* = within) and constitutes a form of digestion. It releases the energy in the chemical bonds as this energy is needed for other processes, and furnishes atoms and groups of atoms as these are needed in synthesis. In addition, some plants (such as insectivorous ones, saprophytes, and parasites) may secrete digestive enzymes to the outside and carry on extracellular digestion (from *extra* = outside of), absorbing the products of digestion as food.

The chemical reactions in digestion are often quite different from those in synthesis. Carbohydrates, for example, may be simplified by **hydrolysis** rather than by steps involving phosphates (*cf.* p. 73). In hydrolysis, water molecules are added to the carbohydrate (Fig. 7-3) in a seemingly simple and direct reaction:

$$C_{12}H_{22}O_{11} + H_2O \xrightarrow[\text{(sucrase)}]{} 2\ C_6H_{12}O_6$$

Since the digestive processes of plants and animals appear to be comparable, and so much more direct study has been made of these reactions in vertebrate animals, a fuller discussion is reserved until the chordate digestive system has received consideration (pp. 102-105).

4. NUTRITIONAL TYPES

Since green plants can synthesize all of the chemical compounds required in their protoplasm from inorganic molecules and carbon dioxide, they are strictly "self-fed" **(autotrophic)** organisms. Non-green plants (with a few interesting exceptions) and animals require organic compounds as food; they are fed by others, hence **heterotrophic** in their nutrition. Green plants are the "producers," non-green plants and animals only "consumers" in the world of life. No biological concept is more fundamental than this difference in the source of energy (Fig. 7-4).

Since non-green plants and animals can synthesize fats from carbohydrates and carbohydrates from the building blocks of proteins, it is an inability to synthesize certain animo acids that distinguishes heterotrophic organisms from autotrophic ones.

Heterotrophic organisms can be subdivided

further. Those that thrive on decaying vegetation are **saprophytes,** gaining their energy by saprophytism (from the Greek *sapros* = rotten); most fungi are saprophytes. Many bacteria, by contrast, invade and destroy living plant and animal tissues, forcibly taking the raw materials they require. Such bacteria are **parasites,** feeding by parasitism. Most intestinal worms are parasites too.

Plant-eating animals ordinarily are called **herbivores,** in contrast to animal-eating animals, the **carnivores.** Carnivores that catch their prey alive are **predators;** those that find it dead and take nourishment from it are **scavengers.** These distinctions in the sources of energy among heterotrophic organisms should not conceal the basic fact that each of them depends, in the last analysis, on energy stored by green plants through photosynthesis. The carnivore that eats a herbivore is eating foliage by proxy, and obtains calories of energy bound by the green plant from sunlight.

A few algae and bacteria show an additional type of nutrition. Although their cells appear deceptively simple, these organisms obtain energy without sunlight and without involvement with other living things or their products. These are the strange **chemotrophic** organisms of wet places where iron or sulfur or other special chemicals abound. The chemotrophs catalyze changes in the constitution of these materials, and in doing so obtain energy with which to combine carbon dioxide and the hydrogen from water to form sugars and other complex chemical substances. The oxygen characteristic of photosynthesis rarely appears in chemotrophic activities. Instead it combines with the iron or sulfur to form oxides.

Bog iron ore—almost pure iron oxide—is apparently never produced except through the activities of "iron bacteria." A number of other substances left by chemotrophs seem equally distinctive.

Although chemotrophic activities are relatively rare, they have immense theoretical significance. They demonstrate the possibility of other systems on which life can depend. Under the present conditions of temperature, pressure, and available chemical substances, chemotrophic nutrition seems to offer few advantages. Yet other eras and other planets may have offered sites where chemotrophic organisms had a place of dominance, and where the familiar forms of living things could carry on, if at all, in a correspondingly minor role.

5. RELEASE OF ENERGY

Nearly 200 years ago, Priestley and Lavoisier discovered experimentally that a live mouse and a candle flame remove from the air in a closed container a chemical substance without which the mouse dies and the candle gutters out. In 1772 Lavoisier learned that green plants, by photosynthesis, can restore the "dephlogisticated air." Ever since, there has been a tendency to regard respiration and combustion as synonymous, and as the reverse of photosynthesis.

To burn sugar completely, oxygen must be supplied. The only products are water, carbon dioxide and energy. If the combustion is carried out in a special measuring device, the quantitative relationships can be shown to be:

$$C_6H_{12}O_6 + 6\ O_2 \rightarrow 6\ H_2O + 6\ CO_2 + energy$$

180	192	108	264	674
grams	grams	grams	grams	Calories

No further energy can be obtained from the products, water and carbon dioxide.

When protoplasm uses sugar as a source of energy, the maximum efficiency is only about 70 per cent. The remaining Calories escape as heat. The overall process is **respiration.** It appears to be the chief function of the mitochondria in each cell, and is essential to provide energy for all other reactions in living chemistry.

Respiration that uses oxygen is an **aerobic** means for releasing energy. Oxygen is required, carbon dioxide and water evolved, in the same proportions as are characteristic of

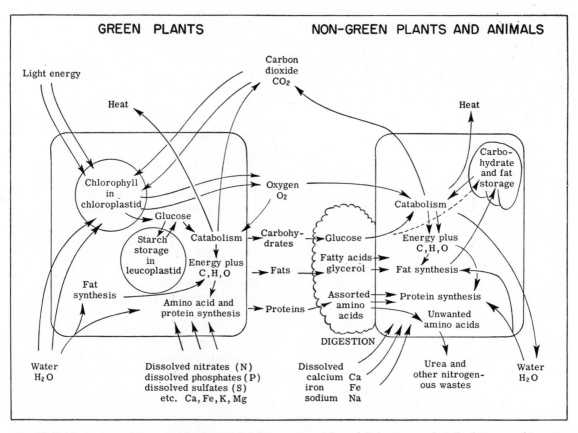

Fig. 7-4. *The autotrophic green plants use simple raw materials and light energy, but the heterotrophic non-green plants and animals must have as food various organic compounds of considerable complexity.*

combustion. Aerobic respiration consists of many chemical steps, and is not a reversal of "the" photosynthetic reaction. Protoplasm both stores and releases its energy a step at a time, but the steps are not the same.

Respiration without oxygen is also possible, as an **anaerobic** process. Both aerobic and anaerobic respiration begin, in fact, in the same way as does storage of carbohydrate: by addition of phosphate to monosaccharide at the expense of ATP molecules. The chemical steps proceed through triose phosphate and phosphoglyceric acid to pyruvic acid.

In these preliminary changes, the cell expends one molecule of ATP per monosaccharide molecule for the initial reaction. But it receives back *two* ATP molecules in the succeeding steps—a 100 per cent gain on the investment—merely in transforming each monosaccharide molecule into two of pyruvic acid (the substrate for further release of energy).

Aerobic Respiration

In aerobic respiration, pyruvic acid enters into a remarkable cycle of chemical activity (named for its discoverer, Krebs). This series of chemical reactions involves just under a dozen different organic acids, and represents a continuous process comparable to a conveyer-belt system. At various points in the cycle, raw materials (such as pyruvic acid) are added. Energy is added, products are removed, and energy is taken out again. For each molecule of pyruvic acid, the cycle requires 3 molecules of oxygen; it yields 3 molecules of carbon dioxide, 3 molecules of water, and as many as 15 high-energy phosphate bonds carried away in the form of ATP.

Hence, from each original molecule of monosaccharide, the protoplasm gains 2 high-energy bonds in reaching pyruvic acid, and 30 more by the time the Krebs cycle has turned out all the products of oxidation in the form of water and carbon dioxide. These high-energy bonds are the form of energy that can be used in synthesis and a host of other processes important to plants and animals.

Anaerobic Respiration

In many sites where living things thrive, free oxygen is not available. Parasitic worms and bacteria in the cavity of the digestive tract, and the various animals that live in the bottom mud of deep lakes, exist where oxygen is essentially absent. They respire anaerobically, wastefully, unable to get as high a percentage of the energy in their food to a usable form.

Brewer's yeast has been studied extensively while respiring without oxygen. This fungus organism is interesting, too, in that it can operate either as an aerobe or as an anaerobe. If enclosed in large closed vats of sugar solution, the yeast cells grow and reproduce, respiring aerobically until the oxygen is used up. So far the products are carbon dioxide, water, and energy (including more yeast protoplasm and heat lost into the solution). When the oxygen is gone, the yeast cells turn to anaerobic respiration, **fermentation:**

$$\text{monosaccharide (674 Calories per gram-molecular weight)}$$
$$\downarrow$$
$$\text{2 pyruvic acid} + \text{2 ATP}$$
$$\downarrow$$
$$\text{2 ethyl alcohol (655 Calories per gram-molecular weight)}$$
$$+ \text{2 CO}_2 + \text{ATP}$$

The high-energy bonds in the ATP gained are equivalent to from 22 to 28 Calories of energy per gram-molecular weight of monosaccharide. Without oxygen, however, the yeast cannot free the 655 Calories per 92 grams remaining as binding energy in the alcohol. Bubbles of carbon dioxide escape through the vat of yeast and sugar solution, but the alcohol concentration increases slowly until the yeast cells die. Yet if oxygen is bubbled through the vat of yeast and sugar solution, the yeast cells revert to aerobic means of obtaining energy, and the process continues until all of the sugar is used up and the yeast cells starve.

In anaerobic fermentation, each 1,000 Calories of energy requires 8,190 grams of sugar. In aerobic respiration, by contrast, 1,000 Calories of energy require only 267 grams of sugar. Thus the anaerobic process is nearly 30 times as wasteful of the sugar substrate as is ordinary aerobic respiration.

There are many other anaerobic reactions by which animals and plants get energy for life processes. One of these occurs at the same time as fermentation, if bacteria are not kept out of the yeast-sugar solution vats. These bacteria work on the alcohol produced by the yeast and degrade it into acetic acid, gaining thereby a few calories of energy. Vinegar is produced in this way.

Since yeast cells can operate either aerobically or anaerobically, they are often described as **facultative** anaerobes. Many bacteria, on the other hand, are **obligate** anaerobes, and free oxygen is fatal to them. Most plants and animals are equally much obligate aerobes, and, like ourselves, they die if their oxygen supply is diminished significantly.

The wasteful chemistry of anaerobic processes introduces a restriction in the living sites where such can be useful. Organisms that are opportunistic, taking advantage of each chance to multiply, often employ anaerobic reactions and gain through the greater speed characteristic of this method of obtaining energy. Parasites such as bacteria that cause disease are typical of this category. Cancer cells, parasitic on their neighbors, are thought to behave in this way also.

Anaerobic chemistry has a proper place in other situations in living organisms, where chemical reactions are called upon only intermittently. The first step in muscle contraction and the initial chemical response to light are two examples. In these a chemical reaction that is swift, though anaerobic and wasteful, can be followed by a recovery reaction taking a longer time but having the greater efficiency associated with use of oxygen.

6. METABOLISM

Respiration is a downtearing process, reducing the supply of stored foods, and is characteristic of all protoplasm at all times. No other criterion of life is so universal. Yet most of the energy it releases goes immediately into synthetic processes resulting in new compounds. The downtearing is accompanied by upbuilding. Both involve the same energy and the same atoms.

Building activities, such as photosynthesis, or synthesis of starch or glycogen, are collectively described as **anabolism** (from the Greek *ana* = up, *ballein* = to throw); they store energy in the form of chemical bonds. They conceal Calories, and are said to be **endothermic** processes (from *endo* = inward, *thermos* = heat).

By contrast, the breakdown of large molecules and liberation of energy are activities in the opposite direction. Collectively they are termed **catabolism** (from the Greek *kata* = down). They release heat and reduce weight, hence are **exothermic** processes (from *exo* = outside).

Anabolism and catabolism occur constantly in different chemical reactions in close proximity within each cell. Together they constitute the **metabolism** of the living system.

Often the respiratory exchange and heat output of an organism are measured as its **metabolic rate.** This is a number—liters of oxygen used, or carbon dioxide liberated, or Calories lost.

Measurement of the metabolic rate in an autotrophic organism (green plant) must be made in the dark. Photosynthesis hides respiration, since respiratory needs are met from the oxygen output, and respiratory carbon dioxide is absorbed quickly in synthesis of carbohydrate. In sunlight, liberation of oxygen may be 30 times as rapid as respiration. At low light intensities, it can be carefully balanced against metabolic needs so that atmospheric oxygen is neither used nor added to, and there is no net change in carbon dioxide around the plant. The light supplied then includes exactly the amount of energy required for the plant's anabolism.

In heterotrophic organisms and in green plants studied in darkness, measurements of metabolic rate may be made indirectly. Instead of placing the organism in an insulated chamber and recording both heat output and gas changes, the heat may be calculated. If the specimen studied is an animal, the total nitrogenous waste excreted will be recorded as well.

From the nitrogenous wastes it is possible to compute the amount of protein used in catabolic processes. The ratio of oxygen used to carbon dioxide released (called the R.Q. = **respiratory quotient**) differs according to whether metabolic energy is coming from breakdown of carbohydrate or fat or protein. For carbohydrates, the R.Q. = 1, since 6 molecules of oxygen are used and 6 molecules of carbon dioxide liberated for each molecule of monosaccharide utilized. For metabolism based entirely on fat digestion, the R.Q. is 0.7. Hence animals on a strictly plant diet have an R.Q. of 0.90 to 0.95—indicating that most of their energy comes from carbohydrates. Carnivorous animals have an R.Q. of about 0.75, whereas omnivores like man are usually between 0.80 and 0.84.

One clinical concept that has come from such studies is that of the **basal metabolic rate** (B.M.R.). This is taken to be the energy requirements or heat output while the organism —including its digestive tract—is in a state of complete rest; fasting prior to the measurement insures that the individual is not expending energy in rendering a meal ready for absorption. In man this might best be measured during sleep, and would represent the energy requirements for the beating heart, the respiratory muscles, the secreting glands, and the cellular processes of all kinds, including maintenance of body temperature and a general healthy state of slight contraction in all voluntary muscles, usually described as muscular "tone." The basal metabolic rate is often a clue to improper functioning of such glands as the thyroid. A low B.M.R. usually indicates either malnutrition or insufficient secretion from the thyroid, whereas a high value may indicate an oversupply of the thyroid's product. Sometimes the basal metabolic rate is calculated from a simple measurement of the oxygen used or the carbon dioxide output in a measured time, by assuming the respiratory quotient to be the average value for omnivorous man. Thus the normal B.M.R. for a 150-pound man of ordinary body proportions is about 1,600 Calories per day. A taller, leaner individual should have a slightly higher value; a shorter, stouter person should show a lower value. This is because more than half of the energy required goes to maintaining body temperature and making good any heat losses. These latter are proportional to body surface area, whereas heat production is proportional to volume (weight).

For clinical diagnostic purposes an approximation of this kind may have considerable value, though the information obtained is insufficient for complete analysis such as is possible on the basis of more elaborate direct calorimetry.

7. DEGRADATION OF ENERGY

Throughout considerations of chemical transformation in protoplasm, there is a conscientious attempt to balance each equation in terms of both the atoms and the energy involved. The first of these assumes the universal application among biological problems of the law of conservation of matter. The second takes for granted Newton's First Law of Thermodynamics, which states that energy can neither be created nor destroyed.[2]

The Second Law of Thermodynamics is quoted frequently in connection with biological processes. It states, in effect, that *in any closed system,* the available useful energy is continuously decreasing because every process degrades some of it to useless heat. This emphasizes the inefficiency of any mechanical or chemical action. Heat is a by-product that is lost in every energy transfer. In a closed system, heat accumulates but is not useful.

The physicist and chemist can demonstrate the accuracy of the Second Law because they choose to deal with isolated events and closed systems. But all organisms are open systems, constantly receiving energy from outside themselves—all of it, directly or indirectly, from the sun. Similarly, organisms are getting rid of heat, not accumulating it. They lose heat to the environment, and the environment radiates to outer space. Hence the accumulation feature of the Second Law is not pertinent to living systems.

Among the applied branches of chemistry and physics, there is discernible a distinct attempt to broaden considerations to include the open systems of continuous manufacturing processes. These are much more like those complexes of chemical reactions that concern the biologist. That the physical and mathematical scientists are just now beginning to think about them should be encouraging to the student of living things. The difficulty of analyzing energy relations where few limitations can be imposed without upsetting the continuity of a complex process, has so far deterred most other scientists from considering open systems. The biologist has admitted this difficulty, but he has nevertheless investigated

---

[2] In atomic disintegrations the substance of the atom is converted into energy—emphasizing that energy and matter are different forms of the same thing. Hence the First Law of Thermodynamics, as revised to include atomic understanding, now involves not only the principle of the conservation of energy but that of energy plus matter combined.

a multitude of aspects of his enormously variable subject.

The Second Law of Thermodynamics has been referred to as "Time's Arrow," because it points the direction of each chemical reaction —the direction in which some energy is released as heat. It has nothing to say about the rate. Yet the fact that each reaction has a direction can give a whole complex of reactions a direction too. This may well be the feature which has seemed to endow so many biological reactions with a purpose, giving them a consecutive rather than random quality. It has been used to account for the progressive evolution of the universe, the origin of life, and its subsequent evolution.

LIFE AND NOT-LIFE

On this earth, perhaps throughout the whole universe, the most fundamental of all antinomies, the most crucial of all struggles is that between life and death—or, as it might be more true to say, between life and not-life. And who, capable of realizing this fact, or of seeing himself as part of the Great Rebellion of the animate against the inanimate, can fail to find comfort in the fact that it is not alone in him that the one protagonist is embodied; perhaps even that the ultimate issues do not depend upon his success or his failure alone? Consider again the November trees which lift their arms to say that they have only temporarily yielded; that next spring they will again assert their determination to live. Those trees, like the frog now sleeping under the mud, are on our side.

—JOSEPH WOOD KRUTCH, in *The Twelve Seasons* (New York: William Sloan Associates, Inc., 1949), p. 126.

SUGGESTED READING (see pp. 505-510)

Classics and Milestones: Priestly, Eijkman

Recent and Informative: Arnon, 1955; Clayton & Delbrück, 1951; Green, 1949, 1954; Heilbrunn, 1954; Johnson, 1954; Kelner, 1951; Parker, 1953; Pearson, 1953, 1954; Pfeiffer, 1948; Rabinowitch, 1948, 1953; Stumpf, 1953.

8 · The Chordates

EACH KIND of animal has special means whereby it can obtain food, digest it, dispose of indigestible residues, absorb the products of digestion, distribute them throughout the body, carry on cellular respiration, bring oxygen to the cells, take carbon dioxide away from them, remove and dispose of wastes from metabolism, detect changes in the environment, respond to them, repair damage, grow, and reproduce.

In some animals these functions are handled within a single cell; in others the various cells of a multicellular body are specialized and each attends to a comparatively small number of functions. The unicellular types exhibit the apparent confusion of a one-room school, with everything going on at once in limited space. The multicellular types may be as segregated as a university—to the extent that the essential unit of effort is easy to overlook while examining the seemingly independent details.

1. GENERAL ORGANIZATION

In all of the multicellular animals more complex than sponges, the organism is not only a functioning mass of cells but a unit composed of definite layers, the **tissues.** Those animals with the greatest division of labor are organized further, in that their tissues are grouped into **organs,** and the organs into **organ systems.** Thus our digestive tract is an organ system, composed of mouth, esophagus, stomach, small and large intestines, rectum, and various glands such as the liver and pancreas. The stomach is an organ, composed of such tissues as a lining layer, muscular layers, blood vessels and nerves, and an outer covering layer. The layers are tissues, composed mainly of a single type of cell.

Before considering the general architecture and the functioning of various organ systems, the six chief types of tissues serving in the construction of such animals as mankind need review.

Epithelial Tissues

These form coverings over animal bodies and linings for all of the cavities and many ducts. One surface of each epithelial cell is characteristically faced against an external medium or toward some other organ. The cells in it are fitted together closely, with thin walls and little intercellular material

(Fig. 8-1). Often they rest on a "basement membrane." The cells may be flat and tile-like, or cubical, or packed together as parallel columns; the terms squamous, cuboidal, and columnar are applied to these variants.

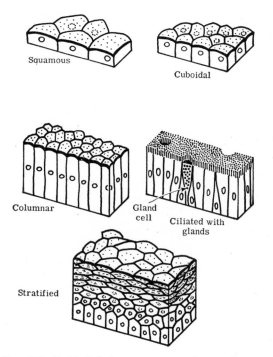

FIG. 8-1. *Epithelial tissues are named according to their form.*

The epithelium may be "simple" in consisting of a single layer, or it may be "stratified" as a considerable thickness of overlapping cells. The individual cells may be ciliated or flagellated on the exposed surface, or they may break open there to liberate secretions formed in the protoplasm; these last are **glandular** epithelia.

Simple squamous epithelium lines the body cavity of vertebrates, while stratified squamous epithelium forms the outer layers of human skin and the lining of both the mouth and nasal cavities. Cuboidal epithelium forms the interior of salivary glands and kidney tubules, while columnar epithelium lines most of the digestive tract. In the earthworm, the gut is lined with ciliated columnar epithelium; the same type of tissue is found in the air passages between mouth and lungs in land vertebrates.

Young larvae of many aquatic animals, such embryos as those of frog and toad, and others, are covered externally with ciliated epithelium that allows them considerable movement. Flagellated cells line the gastrovascular cavity of many coelenterates and assist in circulation of the digestible contents. Gland cells secrete a variety of substances in different sites on many animals: mucus, sweat, tears, saliva, milk, poisons, and digestive enzymes.

Supporting and Connective Tissues

These commonly give less evidence of the cells from which they develop, because of the large amount of intercellular material and the frequently slender extensions from one cell toward another (Fig. 8-2). They serve to hold the organism together. Among the most conspicuous are fibrous connective tissues,

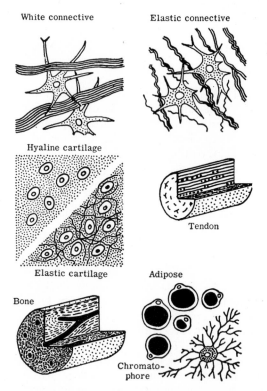

FIG. 8-2. *A disproportionately large amount of non-living, secreted material associated with the cell (either externally or internally) is the mark of connective and supporting tissues.*

with scattered small spherical cells among interlacing fibers; the fibers may be "white fibers" consisting of bundles of parallel, unbranched fibrils like those found in tendons and surrounding muscles and nerves, or "elastic fibers"—many of which branch—such as are located between the skin and underlying muscles, between one organ and another, and in the walls of the larger blood vessels and intestine. **Ligaments** and **tendons** are bundles of parallel white fibers enclosed in a sheath of the same material; the former serve to hold bone to bone, the latter bone to muscle. **Cartilage** (also called *gristle*) is composed chiefly of the firm, elastic intercellular material secreted by the small groups of spherical cells embedded inside; it may suggest a soft plastic, and is commonly a precursor of bone; it forms the final support and furnishes the basic shape for the human nose, outer ear, and voice box (larynx). **Bone,** such as is found in the skeletons of bony fishes, and in all amphibians, reptiles, birds, and mammals, is like cartilage except that it contains about 65 per cent by weight of a lime salt (particularly tricalcium phosphate). Both matrix and lime deposits are elaborated by bone cells which retain contact with one another and with blood vessels by means of long radiating protoplasmic processes.

Less obvious members of the connective tissue group are **adipose** tissue (with thinwalled cells, nucleus at one side, and globules of oily fat distending the cytoplasm), and the pigment cells **(chromatophores),** which contain coloring materials and from which many organisms derive a characteristic appearance.

Vascular Tissue (Sometimes Grouped with Connective Tissues)

This is the blood itself, with free cells (corpuscles—Fig. 8-3) in a fluid intercellular material, the plasma or lymph. The fluid in invertebrates such as crustaceans and arachnoids is colored blue with oxyhemocyanin;[1] in others, such as annelids and some insects, is definitely red with hemoglobin. Among vertebrates, however, it is free of pigment and some of the corpuscles, containing concentrated hemoglobin, are red. More detailed consideration of this important tissue is deferred to p. 122.

---

[1] In the absence of oxygen, oxyhemocyanin becomes colorless hemocyanin.

Nervous Tissue

This is a complex organization of specialized cells, each a **neuron,** which receive, transmit, and deliver electrochemical changes from place to place within the organism and which make possible prompt coordination of its activities (Fig. 8-3). Because of its significance, this aspect of biological action will be discussed separately in Chapter 11.

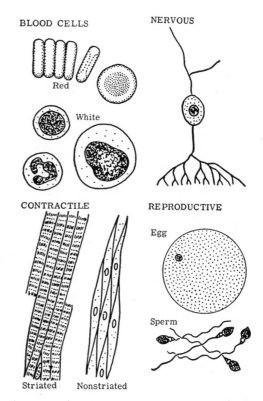

FIG. 8-3. *Other characteristic cell types of the chordate tissue systems.*

Contractile Tissue

Essentially, these are cells containing minute fibers called **myofibrils,** and they function through the change in shape resulting when stimulated to contract. The shortening in length and increase in diameter of the myofibrils acts to move some part of the animal or to place it under definite tension. Myofibrils are found in the T-shaped bases of the coelenterate epitheliomuscular cells, and in muscle cells of higher animals. Each muscle cell is usually referred to as a **muscle fiber** because of its cylindrical, elongate shape—not more than 50 μ in diameter but sometimes several centimeters in length. Commonly, muscle fibers are arranged in groups surrounded by connective tissue, as muscles; these may take the form of layers, sheets, or spindle-shaped links between parts of the skeletal system (Fig. 8-3). More extensive discussion of the entire muscular system begins on p. 91.

Reproductive Tissue

These cells are referred to frequently as **germ cells** in contrast with the body or **somatic** cells, and they differ markedly in that the reproductive cells are of no direct value to the individual organism containing them (Fig. 8-3). Somatic cells compose the body, but the reproductive cells merely make possible the development of future individuals. As such, they may be considered the most important of all cells, with potential immortality, while the same conclusion defines the somatic cells as a mechanism with limited life span, concerned primarily with insuring that the reproductive cells will find full use. These aspects of biology are dealt with in further detail in Chapter 18.

2. SPECIAL ORGANIZATION

With these same tissues, chordates are constructed by regular steps in their embryonic development. Throughout each maintains a regular bilateral symmetry, good indications of a segmented body, and a complete digestive tract. In having a single tubular (hollow) nerve cord in a dorsal position, a stiffening **notochord** of special connective tissue (which may later be replaced by a jointed vertebral column), and gill slits in the pharyngeal region of the digestive tract—at least in embryonic stages—they are different from all other animals. This combination of architectural features has made possible a remarkably efficient organization—one that has led to adaptations in vertebrates that make them masters of their environment to a degree far beyond anything found in any invertebrates.

Bilaterality in chordates (as elsewhere) usually indicates an emphasis on an anterior end, with accompanying specializations that make it a "head." In such a head come to be grouped major sense organs and a highly developed nervous mechanism—a brain. This is **cephalization** (from the Greek *kephalon* = head), and a process that may be followed on a comparative basis among the worms, crustaceans, insects, and some other groups. In chordates the head is associated with the mouth, with taste (and smell, if air-breathing), sight, and all the variations of touch, including orientation and sound perception.

The proximity of notochord and dorsal nerve cord makes easy the inclusion of both of these in a single skeleton, providing support for the viscera (because of the dorsal position), protection for the nervous system (hence emphasis on neuromotor development), and articulation for locomotory appendages. The design has, in fact, many of the characteristics of a cantilever bridge—with fore and rear appendages as abutments, the

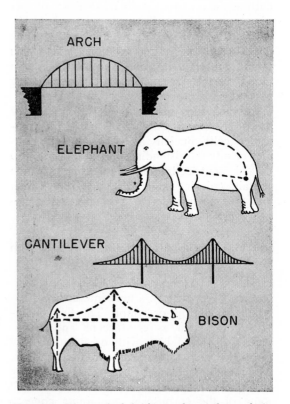

FIG. 8-4. *The arched bridge and cantilever design are duplicated in supporting structures of large chordates. The weight of the elephant's heavy viscera is hung from its arched back. The ponderous head of a bison at the end of a sizable neck is counterbalanced through ligaments along the neural spines of its vertebrae, just as an engineer would recommend in planning a cantilever bridge.*

main arch or span curved upward in proportion to the weight of viscera supported there, the head and tail extending in various amounts beyond the abutments in either direction and to some extent counterbalancing the visceral weight between them (Fig. 8-4). Such a pattern has potentialities extending downward in size to small animals where support is of less significance, and to large forms of elephant or

with a comparable development are seldom-met arrow worms (Chaetognatha) in the oceans—small, active swimming animals less than 2 inches long.

Chordate Groups

The most familiar chordate organization is

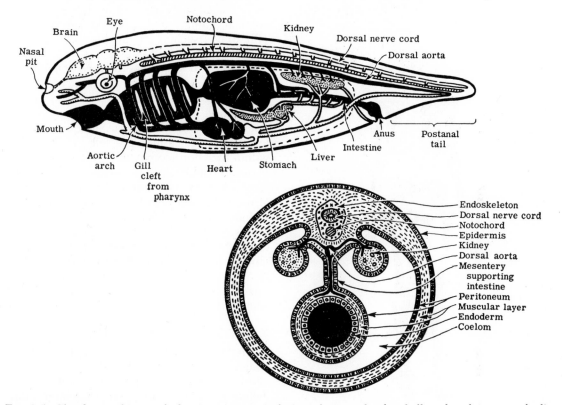

FIG. 8-5. *Chordate architectural plan is unique in inclusion of a notochord, a hollow dorsal nerve cord, slits between the pharynx and exterior, and the direction of circulation in the closed system. In the sectional diagram, the space in the body cavity is greatly enlarged; normally it is occupied by convolutions of the digestive tract.*

whale dimensions, approaching the physical limits of protoplasm for life in air and water, respectively.[2]

The post-anal tail is almost uniquely a chordate structure. The only nonchordates

that of the vertebrates: fish, amphibians, reptiles, birds, and mammals. Here (Fig. 8-5, Photos 69-84) a backbone provides support; jaws allow the catching, tearing, or grinding of food; and paired appendages aid in locomotion. The body cavity (coelom) is distinct, the vascular system closed, with a heart, arteries, capillaries, and veins; the blood contains cells with the respiratory pigment hemoglobin.

To this large vertebrate group must be added the less widely known lampreys (also called "round-mouthed eels"), in which there are no jaws (Photos 67, 68). Lampreys and

---

[2] The largest whale ever measured was 100 feet long and weighed 145 tons. This is the same length as the extinct monster reptile Brontosaurus, but the latter—mostly neck and tail—was far lighter. Even so the dinosaur depended upon the buoyant force of water to support its bulk while the long neck allowed the air-breathing head to browse on foliage at the water's edge.

other cyclostomes (from the Greek *cyclo* = round, *stoma* = mouth) are parasites of fish and such other aquatic vertebrates as they can reach. They cling by suction while horny teeth lining the mouth and studding the piston-like tongue abrade the host's skin and break blood vessels. Cyclostomes are the only vertebrate parasites, and their digestive tracts are simple

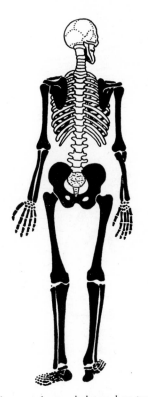

Fig. 8-6. *The vertebrate skeleton has two divisions: the axial skeleton (white—consisting of skull, vertebrae, ribs, and sternum) and the appendicular skeleton (black—consisting of the shoulder girdle and arms, the hip girdle, and leg bones).*

in correlation with their easily digested blood diet. One type of cyclostome, the hagfish, burrows into the body cavity of fish victims and curls up there while sucking away the host's blood supply. As such it is the only internal parasite among the chordates.

Nonvertebrate chordates include three minor groups of filter feeders, all in marine situations: (1) the lancelets such as Amphioxus (Photo 64), not over 2 inches long, which live partly buried in sand bars along many coasts; (2) sea squirts or tunicates,

which go through a free-swimming, tadpole-like larval stage that eventually affixes itself to some solid support and that degenerates into a highly specialized adult covered by a tunic of animal cellulose (Photo 66); a few tunicates after metamorphosis remain free-swimming in the open sea as **pelagic** organisms (these few include peculiar members that form chains and rings as indefinite colonies; the attached tunicates also include a few with colonial habit); and (3) the acorn worms (Photo 65) such as Balanoglossus, which burrow in sandbars and mudflats.

In all of these the chordate combination of notochord, hollow dorsal nerve cord, and pharyngeal slits are found at some stage in the life history, but the other features may or may not be present. Amphioxus has been of interest as indicating possible relationships within the chordate phylum; in its adult stages it is very similar in many ways to cyclostome larvae before metamorphosis. The lancelets also go through embryonic development in a fashion that can be considered a primitive representation of generalized chordate procedure; the outcome provides a notochord extending the full length of the animal—a situation without parallel among chordates. In none of the others does the notochord find such lengthy use in supporting the body.

3. THE VERTEBRATE SKELETON

The endoskeleton of the chordates at its simplest is the notochord alone. In all but the sub-vertebrates mentioned briefly in the preceding paragraph there are cartilaginous additions in the form of a segmented axial skeleton extending from the anterior to the posterior end of the body. In the head region, this **axial skeleton** takes the form of a supporting and protective structure related to the greater development of the nervous system there. In all vertebrates except the cyclostomes, the brain is roofed over completely. The sharks and their relatives among the cartilaginous fishes (Photos 69-71) never achieve a bony skeleton, but the anterior portion of the axial support mechanism is well formed. All higher forms develop a cartilaginous precursor of the skull and many other bones, but in later embryonic stages each advances these skeletal elements to true bone. In these the skull is recognized as being a **cranium.** Behind it

64. A young specimen of the lancelet, Amphioxus. Older ones are less transparent because of a row of flat rectangular reproductive organs along each side.

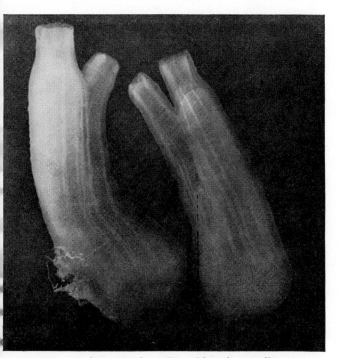

65. Acorn worms show in their structure so many chordate features that they have been placed in this phylum.

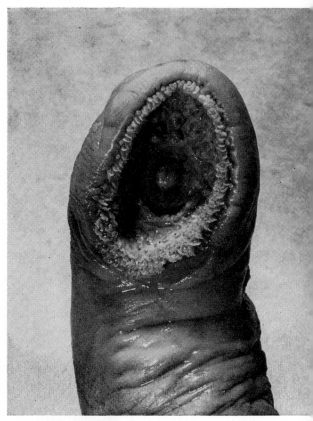

66. Sea squirts ("tunicates"), although usually attached as adults, come from a swimming, tadpole-like stages the structure of which includes most fundamental chordate features.

68. The jawless mouth of the lamprey is studded with rasping teeth.

JAWLESS CHORDATES

67. Seven gill openings can be seen behind the eye of the lamprey.

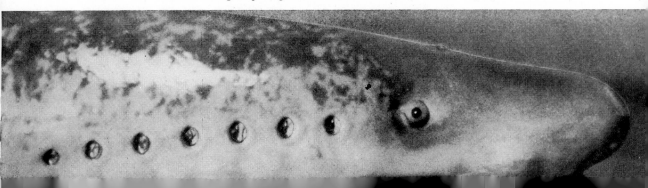

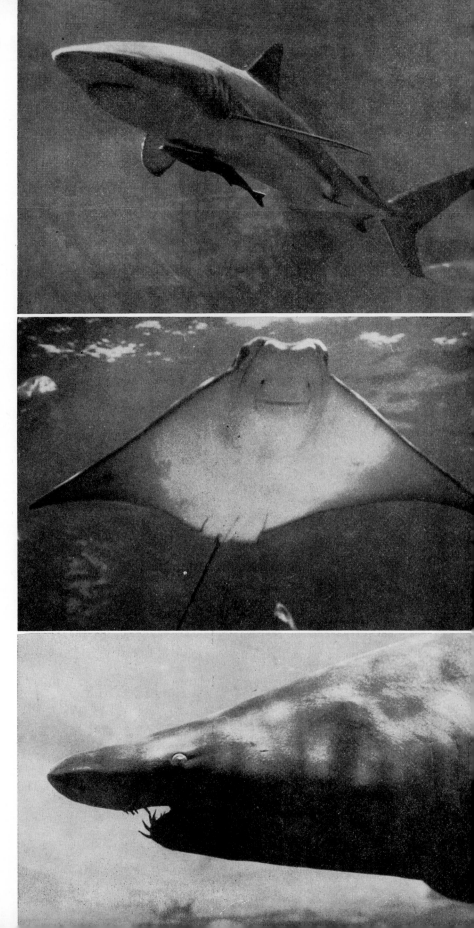

69. The characteristically unequal forking of the tail shows clearly on this large shark. The smaller fish below it is Remora, the "shark sucker," which does no harm but is carried along and is on hand when scraps from a meal are available.

70. A view from below a cow-nosed ray. The broad "wings" with which the fish propels itself are actually the greatly enlarged pectoral fins.

71. The mouthful of teeth seen in this sand tiger shark are the useful teeth, while still others are maturing in the roof and floor of the mouth, ready to move into active positions when the present teeth are worn down and shed. The separate gill slits may be seen.

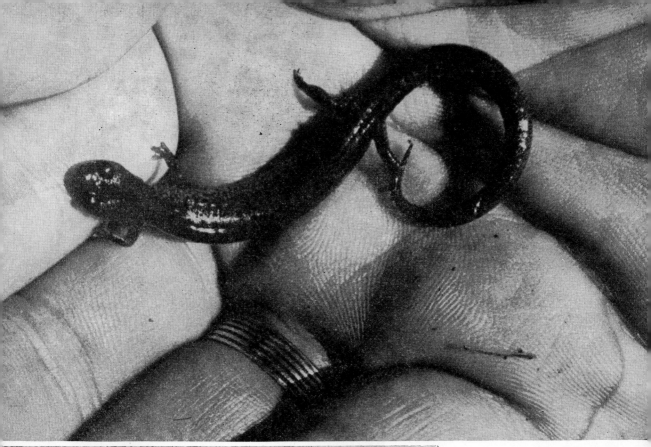

72. A common insect- and worm-eating inhabitant of rotting logs and humid places under fallen leaves is this salamander. Its aquatic larval stages possess gills, but the adult fails to develop lungs, and therefore must respire entirely through the skin surface.

73. The mud puppy reaches a length of a foot but never loses its feathery external gills although lungs develop as the animal metamorphoses from larva to adult.

TAILED AMPHIBIANS

74. Side view of the head and gills of the mud puppy (Necturus). The gills are bright red, the rest of the body mottled brownish gray. Note the marking through the eye.

75. A six-foot alligator sunning itself in a southern Georgia swamp. Hearing and vision are good, so that stalking these animals is not simple. The swish of the powerful tail can knock a man off his feet while the alligator escapes. (See Photo 128.)

REPTILES

76. The so-called American chameleon (Anolis) is a common insect-eating lizard of the southeastern United States. Its color changes from gray through browns to leaf green, but any matching of background appears to be fortuitous. Note the unusual placement of toes.

77. The skeleton of a harmless water snake shows the long series of ribs which, with the scaley scutes of the underbody surface, provide leverage for locomotion.

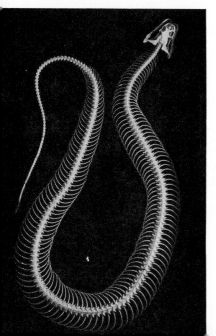

78. A harmless Red-sided Garter Snake in the sagebrush country of Wyoming.

stretch a series of segmentally arranged blocks—**vertebrae**—which surround, invade, or replace the notochord, and which surround the hollow dorsal nerve cord.

In all but the cyclostomes the cranial region has associated with it an upper and a lower jaw; these plus ribs that are distinct are parts of the axial skeleton. In all vertebrates except the cyclostomes (and some degenerate forms such as snakes), additional skeletal elements are present as support structures in a double pair of locomotory appendages. These constitute the **appendicular skeleton.** (Fig. 8-6).

Joints

Basically, all of these bones or blocks of cartilage (except the skull) form a series of levers moved by the force of muscular contractions. As such, they provide points about which the movement can occur—the fulcra of the physicist, or the **joints** of zoology. The physicist thinks of three classes of levers (Fig. 8-7), and in the framework of a vertebrate each has its examples: (1) The bell crank, with the fulcrum between the force and the load, is like the human head balanced on the end of the vertebral column, with the weight of the whole acting from its center of gravity toward the nose while the muscles that hold the head erect are in the back of the neck; when these muscles relax, as when a seated person dozes, the head falls forward, rotating at the hinge joint between the skull and the first vertebra of the neck. (2) The nutcracker, with the force applied at the end of the handle and the resistance provided between the force and the fulcrum at the other end, is like the vertebrate jaw, or the person who raises himself on tiptoe, lifting his own weight (pressing downward through his ankles) by contraction of muscles in the back of the calf of the lower leg; here the fulcrum is at the base of the toes, where the foot bends as the person rises on them. (3) The forceps, in which the power is applied between the fulcrum and the tips of the instrument where some object is to be held, is like the biceps muscle in the upper arm supporting the lower arm (particularly when the hand is holding some weight), with the elbow joint the hinge about which movement occurs if the biceps is allowed to relax. Each of the joints cited in these examples

is a **hinge.** In addition, the vertebrate skeleton includes **ball-and-socket** joints such as the knob on the end of the bone of the upper leg, which fits into a socket of the hip girdle and allows great freedom of movement in many planes, and **gliding** joints such as those between the vertebrae, in ankle and wrist. In

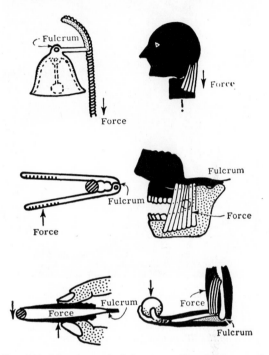

FIG. 8-7. *Muscles and skeleton act like the levers of the physicist: the bell crank, the nutcracker, and the forceps.*

all cases, connective tissue pads (usually of cartilage) keep the bones themselves from rubbing against one another (Fig. 8-8), while strong ligaments[3] plus a connective tissue capsule hold the bones in correct alignment. In many joints the cells of the joint capsule also secrete a special lubricating fluid (synovial fluid) that can withstand remarkable pressures without chemical breakdown. The capsule itself tends also to limit the movement of the joint, although with practice both it and the ligaments can be stretched enough to provide additional flexibility (and even to become valueless as stops). The vertebrae in many vertebrates, however, are equipped with bony

---

[3] Ligaments run from bone to bone; tendons connect muscle to bone.

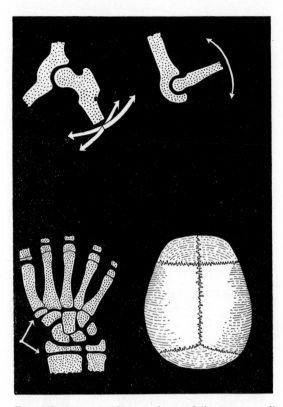

FIG. 8-8. *Joints in the vertebrate skeleton are well cushioned to prevent friction of bone on bone. The ball and socket* (upper left), *the hinge* (upper right), *and gliding joints* (lower left) *permit considerable freedom. Skull sutures* (lower right) *are immovable.*

projections that prevent twists and turns that might strain the enclosed nerve cord; at the same time these extensions furnish greater area for attachment of the controlling musculature.

Cranium

The cranium itself is a curious collection of skeletal parts (Fig. 8-9). As seen in the least complex vertebrates, it is merely a connective tissue trough under the brain in front of the anterior end of the notochord. To this, in the next higher forms, are added: (1) a cartilaginous capsule around each of the two nasal pits; (2) another pair around the eyes; (3) a pair enclosing the semicircular canals (or the ears of terrestrial forms); and (4) roofing plates that arise independently in the tissues over the brain. To these are added the

jaws and whatever hinging mechanism is present for their articulation.

Among the cartilaginous-skeletoned sharks and rays, the cranium is soon fused into a single complex piece. In higher vertebrates, where bone replaces the original cartilage, the component parts retain their individuality throughout the growing period, allowing increments to be added so that the cranium keeps pace with the rest of the body. In birds the thin cranium becomes so fused into a single bony shell when growth is complete that the individual bones cannot be identified separately. In most other vertebrates definite lines remain, marking the limits of each bone. Thus, in the human skull—although the bones are greatly fused at maturity—22 components can be recognized from the seam-like **sutures** that mark them off. The upper jaw has become fixed in relation to the cranium, while muscles from cranial surfaces control

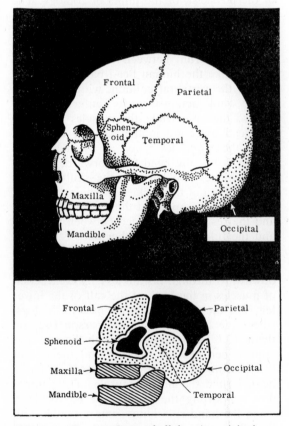

FIG. 8-9. *The vertebrate skull has its origin in an assortment of membrane bones and contributions from embryonic gill-arch support.*

the movements of the lower jaw in biting and chewing.

Vertebral Column

The cranium is articulated with the first vertebra of the axial skeleton and movement is possible between them. Knobs (condyles) on the skull fit into one or two cavities (the number depending on the group of animals involved) in the vertebra. In many vertebrates

axial skeleton into cranium, **cervical** region, **thoracic** region, **lumbar** region, **sacral** region, and tail or **caudal** region. The cervical portion includes the neck vertebrae, of which there are exactly seven in almost all mammals, whether mouse, man, giraffe, elephant, or whale. A thoracic section has ribs associated with it, whereas a lumbar region lacks them.

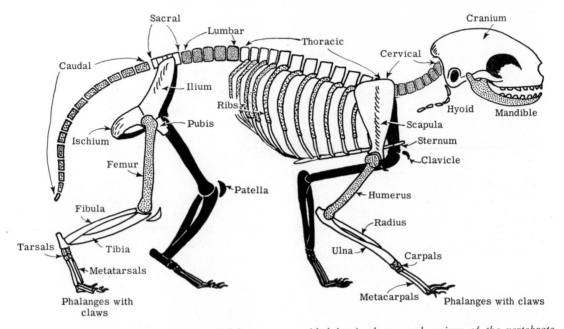

FIG. 8-10. *Unlike functions—a division of labor—are provided for in the several regions of the vertebrate skeleton.*

—including man—there are two such knobs, and the jointing allows nodding movements of the head. Rotation of the head takes place between the first and second vertebrae, so that skull plus first vertebra revolve on a single median projection fitting into a cavity in the second vertebra. These two vertebrae have names that make it easy to remember the divided function. **Atlas** supports the head, like the mythical giant of the same name who held the world on his shoulders. **Axis** provides for rotation. The cranium nods on atlas in the gesture of assent, while atlas and the skull rotate on axis when signaling "No."

The remainder of the vertebrae may be very much alike, or they may be specialized into a series of regions (Fig. 8-10). Man and many vertebrates show differentiation of the

Both are anterior to the sacral region which is modified in relation to the hip girdle and the hind limbs. The tail is usually unspecialized.

Fishes and amphibians usually have little or no neck, and correspondingly few or no cervical vertebrae. Reptiles—and to a far greater extent the birds and mammals—move the head independently of other body movements, and the neck becomes increasingly important. Long-legged birds and mammals which eat from the ground while standing have particularly long necks due to elongation of the individual cervical vertebrae; with this extension comes simultaneous elongation of the gullet connecting mouth with crop or stomach. But the elongation of a neck has further mechanical effects on the form of the organism and its mode of movement. If the head is large—

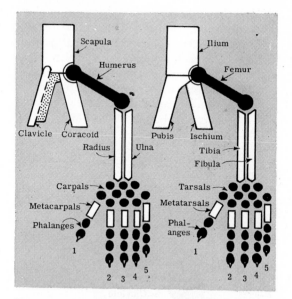

FIG. 8-11. *The basic design apparent in terrestrial vertebrate appendicular skeletons is the same for both fore and hind leg, wing or other modification.*

hence heavy—the supporting muscles must be brought from the thoracic region, and extra attachment surfaces must be present dorsally on the thoracic vertebrae; this alters the contour of the animal considerably (Fig. 8-4). Similarly, if the head is heavy in birds, it is brought back on the flexible neck and rested over the body in walking or in flight. Birds with smaller, lighter heads can stretch them in advance in flight, with improvement in streamlining and increase in speed. Pelicans, herons, and the like bend the neck; cranes, geese, flamingoes, and many others extend it as far as possible in the straight line of the flight's direction.

Related Support Structures

The remainder of the axial skeleton in the simplest vertebrates consist of a series of supporting bars between the gill slits that join pharynx to body exterior. There is good evidence that in the transition from the jawless Agnatha to the jaw-bearing fish, the first pair of gill slits spread ventrally far enough to join, and the cartilages that supported them before fusion became the jaw skeletal elements afterward. A further obliteration of a gill slit on each side—leaving it as a **spiracle**

such as is visible in the sharks and rays—furnished additional cartilages linking the lower jaw skeleton to the cranium. The embryos of higher forms demonstrate how still other gill support rods shifted their position in relation to the hinging of the lower jaw, converting the spiracle into a blind Eustachian tube to the middle ear and leaving remnants, which became the bones within this middle ear, as part of the hearing mechanism of land vertebrates. Thus it is that the jaws, both upper (maxilla) and lower (mandible) are regarded as more anterior representatives of the ribs and the breastbone **(sternum).**

Appendages

The appendicular skeleton consists of the supporting structures of fins, legs, wings, or other specialized limbs. These skeletal elements are in two main parts: (1) a series within the appendage itself, and (2) a group as an anchor in the body proper, providing areas for attachment of muscles moving the limb as a whole. In fish, the fins are supported on cartilaginous or bony rays of indefinite number and approximately radial arrangement. Amphibians, reptiles, birds, and mammals show a basic plan of bony parts that is uniform throughout; recognition of this fact is made in the application of bone names (Fig. 8-11). The appendage itself may be **pectoral** (the anterior pair, from *pectus* = breast) or **pelvic** (the posterior pair) in position, and the names of the bones differ though they correspond in every other way:

Pectoral Limb (one side)	Pelvic Limb (one side)
—shoulder joint	—hip joint
Bone: **humerus**	Bone: **femur**
—elbow joint	—knee joint (sometimes with a knee cap bone = **patella,** in the tendon)
Bones: **radius** (medial) **ulna** (lateral)	Bones: **tibia** (medial) **fibula** (lateral)
—wrist joint	—ankle joint
Bones in wrist: 10 **carpals**	Bones in ankle: 10 **tarsals**
Bones in hand: 5 **metacarpals**	Bones in foot: 5 **metatarsals**
Bones in fingers: 14 **phalanges** (5 fingers)	Bones in toes: 14 **phalanges** (5 toes)

WITHIN THE APPENDAGE. The humerus, radius, ulna, femur, tibia, and fibula are re-

79. The skeleton of a two-toed sloth adapts the animal for a life suspended from a tree limb by hooked claws. A large callused sole forms the opposing surface of each foot, enabling the sloth to cling without effort.

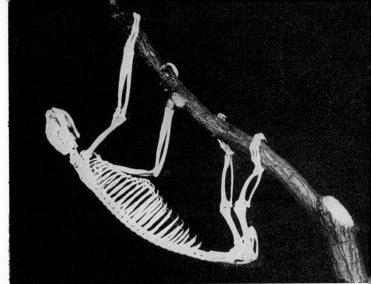

80. A mother two-toed sloth with her tightly clinging baby moves rapidly along a pipe railing at the Canal Zone Biological Area laboratory in Panamá.

THE SKELETAL SUPPORT
FOR LESS USUAL LIVING
HABITS AMONG MAMMALS

81. The skeletal framework on which a bat flies is actually the elongated finger bones which stretch the thin wing membrane.

83. A swimming beaver (see also Photos 394 to 396) with broad, paddle-like tail.

82. A pet mink, as much at home in the water as on land, yet little different in body form from a terrestrial weasel.

84. A porpoise is a small whale. This one leaps for fish at the giant oceanarium, Marine Studios, Marineland, Florida.

VARIOUS DEGREES OF MODIFICATION OF THE BASIC MAMMALIAN BODY PLAN ARE SEEN IN AQUATIC TYPES ferred to as the "long bones" of the appendages. In mammals, each develops as a three-part rudiment in the embryo: a **shaft** between caps. Growth ends when these parts fuse, either early (as in short-limbed dwarfs and dachshunds) or later (as in normal individuals). The shaft becomes longer, separating the caps further, and at the same time a sheath of richly vascular connective tissue over it lays down on it concentric layers of new bone. Also at the same time the center of the long bones in both birds and mammals (and the ribs of mammals) is removed by special multinucleate ameboid cells, and in its place "marrow" tissue develops. Throughout life, however, the cartilaginous precursor of bone remains as a reinforcing meshwork in which the hard, brittle salts of lime are deposited.

The distribution of lime is visible in an X-ray picture of a bone because the mineral matter is more opaque to the radiation than is the meshwork of cartilage. The more transparent portions are seen to follow a definite pattern, and this is not subject to variation in the same way as are fingerprints. Instead, the pattern follows closely the lines of force within the bone structure—in directions that resist deformation, whether crushing, stretching, twisting, or bending. In bone grafting, an implant may be cut to fit a gap in a damaged long bone. The stress patterns of the implant are those of its former site. But after the graft "knits," the living cells in the bone proceed to rearrange the lime deposits and reorganize the cartilaginous meshwork in the implant, until they too line up with the mechanical forces of the new situation. These alterations are not entirely due to position, however. Unless the appendage is used, and the actual stresses affect the implant, the rearrangement does not occur. Hence the skeleton is constantly adjusting its internal cellular patterns in relation to the forces it is called upon to bear.

GIRDLES. The anchoring mechanisms for the two pairs of appendages are spoken of as **girdles,** even though they do not go around the body. The pectoral or shoulder girdle of higher vertebrates consists of three bones on each side. They may fuse together in various ways, but at their junction point is always the socket fitting the knob on the end of the humerus. In man the coracoid bone degenerates into a mere process on the **scapula** (the shoulder blade), while the **clavicle** is well developed as the collar bone, bracing the girdle against the rib framework and preventing the shoulders from moving freely toward one another in front.

The pelvic or hip girdle also begins as three bones, again meeting in a socket—this one receiving the knob on the end of the femur. The **ilium** extends anteriorly and dorsally to meet the sacral vertebrae; the **ischium** projects posteriorly and dorsally, while the **pubis** is more ventral and anterior. The similarity to a girdle arises from the fact that the pubis from one side meets the pubis from the other, and the two share a cartilaginous connection on the midline. Together with the sacral vertebrae between the two ilia, the pelvic girdle makes a complete loop, with a space in the middle over which the tail (if any) projects, and through which the digestive tract and excretory and reproductive systems reach the outside of the body. In the human skeleton, the pelvic girdle is fused into a single hip bone, although the connection between ilia and sacral vertebrae remains as a ligamentous link—the sacro-iliac joint. The five sacral vertebrae are fused together, providing a broad attachment area for muscles, but the joint itself represents probably the weakest point in the axial skeleton. Man's bipedal gait puts his whole body weight on the junction, and frequently it proves inadequate for the strains provided.

4. THE MUSCULAR SYSTEM

Movements of the skeletal system depend upon muscular contractions. The muscles involved may be spindle-shaped or strap-like —or they may be formed into sheets—but in almost every instance two functionally different attachment points can be recognized: (1) fusion to a part which is *not* moved when the muscle contracts, called the **origin** of the muscle; and (2) attachment to a part which alters its position when contraction occurs— called the **insertion** of the muscle. In most skeletal muscles the origin is broader than the insertion, and the individual muscle fibers in their connective tissue sheaths may be linked directly to the connective tissue surrounding a bone. At the insertion end, however, there may be a tendon of connective tissue to transmit the force of contraction to some other region. Thus the gastrocnemius or calf muscle of the lower leg (Fig. 8-12) has its origin on the end of the femur nearest the

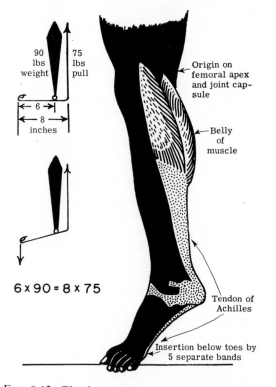

FIG. 8-12. *The lever action of the gastrocnemius muscle through the tendon of Achilles places considerable strain on the living tissues throughout its leverage system.*

knee joint, and sometimes partly on the joint capsule itself. The **belly** of the muscle extends down the back of the calf of the leg to a tendon known as the "tendon of Achilles" because it passes around the heel and spreads out below the toes by five separate bands that are inserted below the bones there.[4] When the gastrocnemius contracts, the origin cannot move; but the shortening of the muscle pulls the tendon and extends the foot. This helps a

[4] This tendon is also called the "hamstring"; when it is cut the animal is "hamstrung"—unable to extend its hind feet. African pygmy tribes render elephants helpless by stalking the big mammals until a single knife slash can sever the tendon of Achilles.

frog jump, a horse run, or a man raise himself on his toes. By contrast, many of the muscle sheets in the abdominal wall have their origins by multiple attachment points on a number of vertebrae, while their insertion is by connective tissue sheets on other muscles or as a line of fibrous material running lengthwise along the mid-ventral surface. The lack of blood vessels there may be visible through the skin as a landmark—the *linea alba* (white line)—or pigment may mark its position as a dark *linea nigra* (black line); these are familiar features of the human abdominal surface below the umbilicus.

Force

Often the force of the skeletal muscles is not appreciated. Since they actuate levers, the magnitude of the stress can be calculated in terms of the pull exerted, the weight lifted (or pressure provided), and the distances between the points of action of these two forces and the center of rotation—the fulcrum. Just as a 50-pound boy can counterbalance a 200-pound man on a seesaw if the boy is four times as far from the axle as the man is, so also the product of force times distance for clockwise rotation around a skeletal joint must equal the product of force times distance for counterclockwise rotation. And many of the lever systems operate to very poor advantage. Those that straighten the knee in man, for example, have to exert 10 times the force of any weight lifted. Yet most 180-pound men can take another of equal weight upon their backs—and straighten their knees in lifting. This is 3,600 pounds of force expressed in the two sets of muscles, or 1,800 in each leg. The muscles, tendons, and bony levers in the body of any large animal are constantly being subjected to forces of these dimensions. That living protoplasm and its secretions in connective tissue can resist is a true measure of the durability of their construction.

In this connection, it should be evident that there is a definite limit to the deforming (breaking and crushing) forces that can be withstood by the skeleton—particularly in its joints—and a limit to the pull that can be required of any muscle. In the architecture of an elephant this limit has been approached very closely. These tremendous animals are so heavy that they can walk rapidly, but they can neither run nor jump. Joints will not withstand the strain, and muscles are inadequate to provide enough force to overcome the great inertia. The only heavier animals are whales and a few other large sea-going forms. These are buoyed up by the water in which they float. If a whale is stranded on a sandbar by a receding tide, its own weight crushes internal organs, killing it. The seemingly sturdy bones may break; even the skin may burst and spill out the viscera. Often the lack of buoyancy prevents even fairly small whales from continuing respiratory movements. In such an event, the whales die of suffocation.

A considerable part of the energy expended by skeletal muscles is not apparent in movement. Instead it prevents movement. Each muscle can contract if stimulated to do so, but since it cannot expand again of its own efforts, muscles are arranged at least in opposing pairs (usually in much more complex coordinated groups). They function not only to cause skeletal movements but to prevent motions that are unwanted. The standing posture of a human being, for example, is tiresome to maintain in spite of the fact that it involves no movement. Muscles must be kept in a continued state of constantly-adjusted tension to keep the individual from falling forward, backward, or to the sides. Every position of unstable equilibrium requires for its maintenance a sizable amount of muscular work. Reference has been made already (p. 65) to the greater demand for energy (food and oxygen) when the individual is sitting or standing. The antagonistic action of muscles in maintaining balance is the chief reason for this increase above that of the resting (prone) position.

Muscle Types

Skeletal muscles are often described in terms of what they accomplish. Some cause hinge joints to fold up, and are called **flexors.** The flexing of the biceps in the upper arm is not only part of the work done in lifting but also a frequent human display feature to indicate degree of muscular development (Fig. 8-13). A muscle that becomes "hard" when contracted is clearly in better condition than one that is still so lacking in tension that sensitive fingers can deform it easily. Muscles

that open a hinge joint are **extensors;** the gastrocnemius is an example.

By no means all of the muscles of the body are connected to the skeletal system. Many are included in the wall of the digestive tract, where they knead and shift the food. Others surround arteries, invest the bladder and uterus. Still others compose the chief tissue of the heart. Somewhat over 50 per cent of the weight of a human being, for example, is muscle tissue.

Muscles may be considered as of three main types:

1. **Skeletal** muscles, which are under the control of the voluntary portion of the nervous system, are often referred to as **voluntary** muscles; they contract quickly (in less than a tenth of a second), tire easily, and are composed of unbranched muscle fibers having many nuclei and also prominent bands of alternating light and dark as seen under the microscope. For this reason they are often called **striated** muscles. The striae (stripes) are visible only under high magnification. Each of these muscle fibers has its own nerve connection.

2. **Visceral** muscles, such as surround the digestive tract, are not under much voluntary control, and are spoken of as **involuntary** muscles. They contract much more slowly (taking from one to 10 seconds for a full contraction), do not fatigue as skeletal muscles

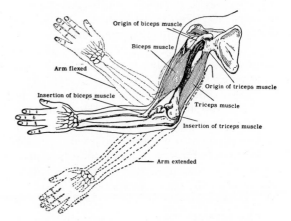

FIG. 8-13. *The action of the biceps and triceps muscle in the human arm is an example of the fact that muscles can only contract, and hence must be present at least in opposing pairs.*

do, and their fibers do not branch. They lack striations, and hence are termed **unstriated** muscles. Each muscle fiber has a single nucleus.

3. **Cardiac** muscle, in the heart, is highly specialized. Although involuntary, it has striated fibers. It contracts rather slowly, with remarkable regularity throughout life, and it recovers sufficiently during the interval between contractions (actually more than 50 per cent of the total time of each beat) to continue without showing fatigue. The fibers of cardiac muscle branch and fuse with one another so extensively that the whole heart consists, to all intents and purposes, of a single meshwork of continuous protoplasm. This meshwork, spoken of as a **syncytium** (from *syn* = together, *cytos* = cell) contracts as a single unit, in an "all-or-none" fashion.

Response

The response of a single muscle fiber is not easy to study. Usually a whole muscle is investigated—removed surgically from an animal and maintained in as suitable an environment as can be achieved. When such a surviving muscle is stimulated appropriately, it will contract. Its response, however, is a demonstration of the combined activities of hundreds or thousands of individual cells. A strong contraction represents the simultaneous effort of many cells; a mild pull is produced by relatively few of them. A sustained tension conceals the fact that the individual cells take turns in contracting, so that although the total population active at any moment remains about the same, no cell continues in a contracted state.

The individual muscle cell contributes its effect within the muscle through connective tissues which provide the real continuity from origin to insertion. Each muscle cell has only a single kind of response to an adequate stimulus: contraction. If it contracts at all, it does so all the way; this fact is expressed as the **all-or-none** law of muscle *cell* activity. It cannot extend itself again, and unless the connective tissue associated with a muscle cell stretches the cell after a contraction, further stimulation induces no response.

Contraction of a muscle cell is an outward display due to physical and chemical changes within its protoplasm. If the cell is not called upon to contract successively at too high a frequency, it has time to recover through further chemical action. When recovery is complete, the cell is ready to contract fully again. But if the cell is called upon to contract before recovery is complete, its contraction cannot be as great.

If the chemical products of contracting cells are not removed, the muscle reaches a state in which it will not contract at all. The muscle is said to be **fatigued.**

Because skeletal muscles are composed of so many individual cells and ordinary contractions involve only parts of the total population, a whole muscle can contract repeatedly and rapidly for a minute or more before signs of fatigue begin to show. The contraction phase of muscle cell activity requires no substance beyond the boundaries of the cell itself; it is an anaerobic process. Recovery, however, depends upon oxygen; it is an aerobic process. A sprinter can drive his muscles for an anaerobic dash to the finish line if he can count on opportunity then to breathe deeply and get oxygen to his muscle cells—permitting them to recover, ready for another race. During the run, the muscles incur an **oxygen debt** which they repay at the first opportunity.

Mild continuous stimulation of a muscle induces slight tension that may be maintained for days without fatigue. Skeletal muscles of warm-blooded animals normally maintain a tension of this kind, called **muscle tone.** It is part of the heat-control mechanism described on p. 199. Under conditions of extreme cold or nervous agitation, the muscle tone may become so forceful that involuntary movements ("shivering") occur.

Corresponding tension can be induced artificially or through disease, leading to continuous forceful contraction called **tetanus.**

All voluntary muscular action may be regarded as intermediate between tone and tetanus. The more forceful and prolonged a voluntary contraction of muscle, the sooner fatigue sets in. True fatigue prevents the muscle from contracting until it has had opportunity to recover through the aerobic changes referred to.

Since about three-quarters of the dry weight of any normal skeletal muscle is of the protein actomyosin, biochemists have given a great deal of attention to this material. In 1939, two Russians demonstrated that actomyosin not only contracts in the presence of ATP, but serves as an enzyme facilitating this reaction. Hence, the contracting structure and the enzyme are united in the same molecule. Actually, the molecules of actomyosin are organized within the cell into rope-like units called *fibrils*.

In 1952, actomyosin prepared in a new way gave the first clear demonstration of both the contracting mechanism and also the passive stretching seen in relaxed muscles. By changing the concentrations of ATP and of a mild solution of potassium chloride, the entire cycle could be repeated over and over.

A modern account of muscle contraction would require that fibrils of actomyosin in the living cell provide the change in length. A stimulus reaching the muscle cell must cause actomyosin to become an active enzyme, capable of splitting the cell's ATP and capturing the energy released. The energy appears in the contraction of the fibrils. Chemical changes occurring at the same time as this physical event must stabilize the shortened length of the fibrils, and then permit passive stretching. This would provide for the all-or-none characteristic of muscle contraction.

Another chemical step is known. As a muscle cell contracts, glycogen in its protoplasm breaks down anaerobically, producing lactic acid and releasing energy. The energy is utilized in a chemical cycle that rebuilds ATP. So rapid is this reaction that the lactic acid concentration plays a part in determining how much tension will be developed by the contraction. About 400 Calories of heat are generated per gram of lactic acid produced. So far as contraction is concerned, this represents lost energy.

Once the ATP concentration has increased and the muscle cell has been stretched (usually by contraction of some antagonistic muscle elsewhere in the body), the mechanism may be ready to contract again. No oxygen has been used. So long as the glycogen supply lasts and the lactic acid concentration does not rise enough to produce fatigue by

inhibiting the muscle cell from responding to nervous stimulation, contraction can follow contraction, as in the case of the sprinter.

The recovery phase is slower and its chemistry more obvious. The lactic acid formed from glycogen breakdown disappears in three different ways: (1) some is oxidized to carbon dioxide, water, and energy; (2) some is combined with this energy of oxidation and rebuilt into glycogen; about 500 Calories of heat are lost by the muscle for every gram of lactic acid oxidized; and (3) some escapes into the blood stream, where it stimulates respiratory movements. Simultaneously, oxygen and sugar enter the muscle cell from the blood; the oxygen is used in protoplasmic respiration and in the oxidation of lactic acid; the sugar is used in cellular metabolism and also converted into glycogen, rebuilding the supply. Carbon dioxide from oxidation of lactic acid diffuses into the blood stream and also stimulates respiratory movements.

A major part of the energy liberated in the stimulated muscle cell does not appear as contractile force. It escapes as heat and represents inefficiency of transfer (see p. 79). In birds and mammals, however, this inefficiency has been put to use toward maintenance of an even, near-optimum body temperature. The control is a function of the brain, discussed on p. 199.

5. THE INTEGUMENT

The superficial organ system described as the integument is more than just the wrapping of the package. Not only must it stand wear and tear, but through its specializations permit detection and capture of food, aid in battle or escape from competitors, and share in water and temperature regulation.

Temperature Control

Temperature control in warm-blooded animals is assisted greatly by features of their integuments: the fur or feathers that cover the skin; the fine blood vessels and delicate muscles within it; and the many glands that open through it. Both fur and feathers are highly efficient in trapping a "dead air" blanket around the animal. Muscles in the skin, inserted on the tissues surrounding the hair or feather base, are placed obliquely in such positions that on contraction they elevate the projecting structure and make the blanket of air deeper (Fig. 8-14). Simultane-

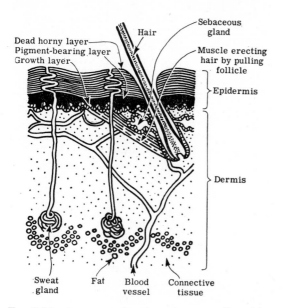

FIG. 8-14. *A cross section through mammalian skin.*

ously these muscles draw the skin at their origins between the hairs or feathers into small, tense furrows. The same reaction in a human being, despite the scanty hair, raises "goose pimples" familiar to everyone.

When temperature rises (if the organism is healthy), a bird or mammal relaxes these muscles in the skin, flattening the fur or feathers and allowing heat loss to proceed at maximum speed. Simultaneously the muscular coats around arteries leading to the skin relax, allowing blood to distend the fine capillaries near the surface, often making it a brighter pink, and affording more opportunity for loss of calories. If the blood temperature still remains high, sweat glands secrete a watery solution obtained from the blood over body surfaces where it may evaporate and take heat from the body for the change from liquid to vapor. Better than 135,000 calories are removed—chiefly from the body —for every eight-ounce glassful evaporated. Sweat itself is not much different in content from the liquid component of blood; it is

chiefly water, with dissolved sodium chloride and urea in enough quantities to provide a flavor. Some of the difficulties arising from salt loss were mentioned previously (p. 53).

Sweat glands are far from uniformly distributed. The cat, for example, has sweat glands only in the soles of the feet. Many mammals lack them entirely. Their existence in the cat, and the way in which their secretion is controlled by the nervous system, can be demonstrated in an entertaining experiment that does a pet no harm. The chief requirement, in addition to the cat, is a special plate constructed from alternating thin strips of metal and plastic, edge upward. The plastic acts as insulation between the metal strips. Every other metal strip is connected to one side of a three-volt battery circuit including a buzzer, while the remaining metal strips are connected to the opposite side of the same circuit. In a cool room, if a cat is placed on the plate with feet over the alternating strips, the buzzer does not ring; the cat's feet are dry. If a recording of a dog barking is played, the cat will not respond in any visible way; no dog is in sight. Mental agitation is evident quite quickly, however, since the buzzer commences to sound. The cat has perspired in the only place possible—the soles of the feet— and thereby completed the electrical circuit, proving the intimate relationship between nervous system and sweat glands. Raising the room temperature has the same effect on the cat.

At still higher temperatures, cats (like dogs and most birds) pant visibly. In this way the respiratory muscles propel air over the wet tongue and mouth interior, evaporating saliva in place of sweat. In man, direct disposal of heat from the skin, plus that used up in vaporizing sweat, accounts for about 80 per cent of the total. The rest goes chiefly into warming inspired air and evaporating into it enough moisture to saturate it, thus avoiding the danger of drying out the lung tissues. The percentages in other mammals and birds is not greatly different.

Corresponding to heat adjustments in the skin are cold adjustments, arising in the nervous system when excess of heat loss over heat production brings about a slight drop in blood temperature. Contraction of muscles in the various depths of the integument include not only movements that elevate hair or feathers, but also those that decrease the diameter of surface blood vessels, allowing the skin to grow pale and cool. Simultaneously the sweat glands cease activity altogether and the skin becomes dry.

Human Skin

The extent to which our skins diminish evaporative loss of water can be seen if the dead outer layers are removed. At a rate that is almost fast enough to watch, the plasma leaves the vessels and oozes through the cell membranes as a clear, slightly straw-colored liquid. If this dries, a thin film is left over the surface. Soon the superficial cells die of desiccation, then gradually become filled with waterproof substances. If infection sets in, white blood cells squeeze out, destroy the bacteria, and die themselves, accumulating as "pus."

The color of human skin depends partly on blood pigments visible through it, partly on the scattering of light from air pockets and clear granules within it, and partly on definite pigment cells. These last vary from one race to another, from one individual to the next, and from one region of the body to another. Two pigments are involved: black melanin and yellow carotene. Blonds among the white race have less melanin than have brunettes. Some seem almost completely unable to form melanin even when the skin is irritated by ultraviolet light; in others melanin formation is prompt and tanning results. Pigmentation that is not lost in ultraviolet-free light is characteristic of races which have been exposed for hundreds of generations to severe tropical sunlight. Freckles on the other hand, represent an unequal distribution in the skin of areas in which pigment formation can be elicited. Freckling, like skin pigmentation, is inherited.

Racial differences can be found also in the degree of development and activity of sweat glands. Commonly the amount of muscular work attempted and the frequency of well-soaped bathing (which is partly a matter of opportunity) determine how conspicuous this glandular mechanism will be. Diet also affects the volatile components which provide an odor to skin—freshly washed or otherwise. It is on these highly variable grounds that the statement rests: "Horses sweat, men perspire, and ladies glow."

Specializations

The superficial **epidermis** layer of the skin is responsible for the elaboration of the feathers and hairs of birds and mammals, the horn of the rhinoceros, the whalebone plates in the mouth of baleen whales, all nails, claws and most scales. The rhino's horn and whalebone, in fact, are scarcely more than tufts of long hairs fused together.

Nails, claws, hoofs. These are like the scales of some reptiles in extending beyond the secreting region of the epidermis (Fig. 8-15) as dead products which continue to grow from the base. Some replacement is possible in cases of accidental major damage.

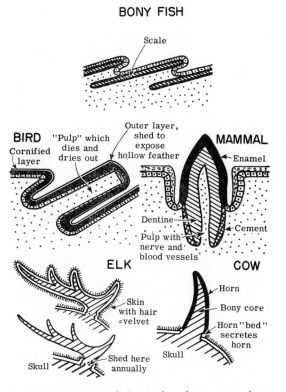

Fig. 8-15. *Feathers, hairs, and antlers are products of the epidermis, with no contribution from the dermis. A scale on a bony fish is entirely from dermis. True horns, such as those of the cow, arise from both epidermal and dermal components. A mammalian tooth is similar, with the enamel a contribution of the epidermis, and the dentine from the dermis; it fits a socket of the jaw bone.*

Scales of bony fish are produced below the epidermis, and are added to eccentrically at a rate sufficing to keep them overlapping. It is often possible to estimate the age of a fish by examining irregularities in the rate of scale growth.

kinds of feathers. Of these the contour feather is the most complex structurally (Fig. 8-17). The quill's extension—the shaft—bears side branches (the barbs) forming the "vane" of the feather. From each barb extend secondary branches, the barbules, some of which bear hooklets that aid in keeping the vane locked together into a single sheet.

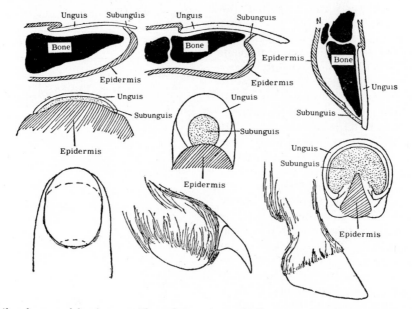

FIG. 8-16. *Nails, claws, and hoofs are epidermal secretions which arise in strictly comparable ways although the final products are so unlike in form.*

HAIRS AND FEATHERS. Hairs and feathers begin as an epidermal secretion over a minute, dome-shaped papilla of the deeper layer of the skin, the **dermis.** Normally this dermal papilla is sunken into the skin, and the hair or feather does not project until it is well formed. Each hair has a central core (the medulla) sheathed by a cortex, outside of which is a cuticular covering of scale-like flakes which show sufficiently characteristic patterns that an expert can often tell from which species of animal a single hair comes.

The entire hair (Fig. 8-14) is a non-living secretion. A feather (Figs. 8-15, 8-17), by contrast, has a living core for a brief time during formation. Later this core dries out, leaving hollow the quill of the feather. An outer covering, which shields the feather as it grows from its pocket within the skin, is shed to expose the final product.

Different sites on the bird produce various

ANTLERS AND HORNS. The antlers of deer, elk (Fig. 8-15), and moose differ in arising as dense masses of connective tissue within the dermis. They deform the epidermis upward, become impregnated with lime somewhat before the mating season, lose all living cells and the epidermal covering, and are finally shed each year by breaking away cleanly at the base. The epidermis with its hairs is the "velvet" that is rubbed from the surface when the antlers harden. Since a 5-point elk antler, when shed, may include 10 pounds of lime—all obtained from foliage eaten during a single year—the calcium requirements of the antlers alone in the diet of an elk may exceed the total lime content of 50,000 large heads of lettuce (a rich source) —150 heads per day!

True horns, such as those of cattle, sheep and the Old World antelopes, arise as epidermal secretions over a bony core arising from the skull; they are not shed. The pronghorn antelope of America (Photo 447) is unusual in shedding annually a thin, hollow, horny sheath from over a bony core.

TEETH. The teeth of vertebrate animals follow a common plan, with an inner mass of softer dentine material covered by a hard enamel. The former is a mesodermal product, the latter comes from epidermis. Mammalian teeth arise in sockets of the jaw bones. Ordinarily teeth cease growing after reaching a specific size. Among rodents such as rats, beavers, and squirrels, however, persistent roots allow replacement of the curved incisor teeth as fast as they are worn away. Occa-

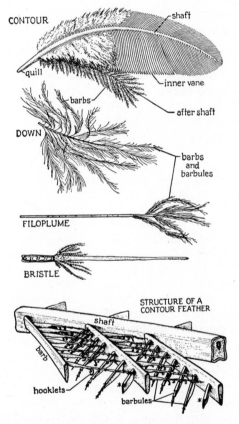

CONTOUR
shaft
quill
inner vane
barbs
after shaft
DOWN
barbs
and
barbules
FILOPLUME
BRISTLE
STRUCTURE OF A
CONTOUR FEATHER
shaft
barb
hooklets
barbules

FIG. 8-17. *Contour feathers, which provide the external covering of an adult bird's body, show full development of feather parts: a central shaft as an extension of the quill, a vane on each side consisting of parallel barbs locked to each other by microscopic barbules (as shown in the bottom diagram). Down feathers, in which young birds may be clad, have shorter quills and shafts; the barbs are longer and more flexible; older birds often bear down below the contour feathers. Filoplumes and bristles are specialized feathers found on some birds. (From T. I. Storer,* General Zoology, *McGraw-Hill Book Co.)*

sionally one of these teeth breaks off, or is twisted so that it no longer meets its mate in the other jaw. If this occurs in the lower incisors, the unopposed upper tooth may continue to grow in a circle, finally re-entering the mouth from below, and sometimes killing the animal by slowly penetrating the brain. Similarly deformed teeth, though without the continuous growth being counteracted by rapid wear, form the tusks of the boar and elephant and the spear of the narwhal; hence the age of the individual can be estimated from the dimensions in these teeth.

Teeth may be attacked by bacteria which secrete lime-dissolving acids. In fact, cavities ("caries") of this origin have been described as the most widespread human disease of this century. A correlation is seen with the amount of sugar in the diet. Sugar seems to be the only foodstuff the molecules of which are sufficiently small to diffuse into the fine structure of the tooth. And with this sugar, the bacteria can form the acid; without sugar, they fail to do so. The addition of fluorides to drinking water may affect the tooth structure during the formative years until even sugar molecules are too large to diffuse inward and nourish bacteria.

Some parallelism has been pointed out between the incidence of dental caries and that of poliomyelitis. Upon this is based the hypothesis that the virus invades the nervous system by way of dental nerves, and reaches these after bacteria and dietary sugar have opened the way.

GLANDS. The less cornified portions of the integument in terrestrial animals and the thinner skins of most aquatic forms are well supplied with glands. In fish and amphibians these supply mucus that makes the body more difficult for a predator to seize. The amphibian skin is studded, too, with poison glands that deter attackers. Frogs in air rely on secreted mucus to reduce skin damage from desiccation.

Most other terrestrial vertebrates have oil- or wax-secreting glands that furnish substances restricting water movements both from the environment into the skin and from the deeper skin into dry air. Our own **sebaceous** glands, secreting oily sebum, are mostly associated with the epidermal pits in which hairs arise—even when the skin in some area is devoid of vestiture, as it is, for example, on the sides of the human nose. These substances aid the body in shedding water during a rain.

It would be surprising indeed if the integument were less subject to variations and specializations. It is, after all, the outside of the package. It must protect the body against not only temperature difficulties and mechanical injury, but also from invasion by parasitic organisms and diseases, and from excessive action of ultraviolet light from the sun. It must make full provision for body movements by remaining flexible and elastic, yet must prevent excess water imbibition in aquatic animals and control water loss in terrestrial forms. In addition, the integument must contain sense organs capable of identifying a wide variety of external conditions, each sense organ responding to a specific stimulus. This aspect of the integument is treated more completely in Chapter 11. Further adaptations of the integument are considered in Chapter 20.

6. THE DIGESTIVE SYSTEM

In all vertebrates the alimentary canal (technically called the **gut**—a *singular* word) is a complete tube from mouth to anus. Usually it is modified into a mouth (= oral cavity), a pharynx, gullet (= esophagus), stomach, intestine, and rectum.

SUPPORT. All of the gut except the mouth and pharynx is enclosed within the body cavity. There it is supported by the **mesentery,** a median sheet of connective tissue originating just below the vertebral column and passing ventrally to surround the gut like a continuous pipe-hanger from gullet to rectum (Fig. 8-5). Through the mesentery, nerves and blood vessels pass to and from the gut. Covering the mesentery on each side and surrounding the connective tissue covering the gut is a continuation of the **peritoneum** —an epithelium that lines the body cavity.

As long as the gut is straight and hangs directly below the axial skeleton, this suspension is simple. But in almost every vertebrate, the gut elongates during embryonic development, and consequently falls into loops. A straight, simple gut is found in only a few blood-sucking kinds, for whom nourishment is quickly available from the food and little digestive action is required.

In meat-eating forms, somewhat greater chemical treatment must be given the food before its components are ready for absorption. The digestive tract accordingly is longer and more specialized (Fig. 20-3). Vegetarian organisms represent an extreme, since plant food contains so much more cellulose and other indigestible materials.

The suspension problem is altered enormously when the intestine falls into loops. In general, the structural solution to the difficulty has been to employ the muscles and connective tissues of the abdominal wall as an external hammock in which these internal organs can lie. The similarity to a bridge span, with fore and hind limbs representing the abutments, is retained. Extra weight hung from the backbone necessitates only a slightly greater curvature in it, plus additional connective tissues between the abutments to keep the pairs of legs from separating, the back from sagging, and the visceral hammock from dragging on the ground. A heavy herbivore cannot also be long in the torso if it is to stand on all fours (Fig. 8-4).

WATER CONTENT. The sequence of steps in digestion is remarkably similar throughout the vertebrates. Other than for those features related to the nature of the food the greatest differences are probably between those that take their nourishment from water and those that obtain it in air (usually on land). In the former, the mouth and pharyngeal portions of the digestive tract are concerned with separating the food from the water, wringing moisture from each piece before it is swallowed, and thus avoiding dilution of the digestive enzymes in the stomach; digestion then begins in the stomach. On land, this difficulty is not met, though the swallowing of completely dry food may involve enough friction to present a problem. In terrestrial forms, the mouth commonly is equipped with saliva-secreting glands, and this liquid (chiefly water plus some mucus) lubricates the food and enables it to pass readily through the pharynx. The saliva also maintains a slow current of liquid that sweeps food particles and bacteria from the mouth and that keeps the mouth sanitary. Without saliva, a terrestrial vertebrate mouth would become quite foul, and the organism would experience difficulty in preventing the tongue from adhering to the roof of the cavity.

Mouth to Gullet

The mouth is concerned primarily with the ingestion of food and the organization of the material into a form that can be swallowed. Most vertebrate mouths can be closed, and many of them have lips that effectively seal the cavity.

TEETH. Within the mouth a great majority have teeth, and these are of value in seizing prey, in tearing, and in grinding. Sometimes the teeth are attached rather loosely to the integument lining the mouth; in other vertebrates they are embedded firmly in special sockets in the jaw bones. Those of sharks and rays are examples of the former; the teeth arise toward the midline of the mouth, but as they mature in form and size, the tooth tissue dies and the integument carrying them gradually shifts toward the rim of the mouth; there the many teeth become erect (Photo 71) and for a short time are functional; later each wears away or breaks off. Some other animals achieve only a single set of teeth. Our own case (Fig. 8-18) is slightly less specialized in that we grow two sets: a "milk

dentition" of 20 teeth (each jaw with two incisors, one canine, and two molars on each side of the midline), and a "permanent" set with 32 teeth (the additions being two premolars and an extra molar—the wisdom tooth—on each side in each jaw). The teeth themselves usually show great modification in relation to food, and this aspect (as well as toothlessness) is dealt with among other adaptations in Chapter 21.

BOLUS FORMATION. When food reaches the back of the tongue, sensory structures there initiate the "swallowing reflex." This is a precisely timed collaborative effort by pharyngeal muscles that pack the food into a unit called a **bolus** and press it through the sphincter of muscles at the beginning of the gullet, just as these relax momentarily. When the bolus is once in the gullet, waves of contraction in the encircling muscles slide it down to the stomach. Gravity plays little part in the swallowing process. A man can swallow even liquids while standing on his head, and grazing mammals regularly swallow against gravity.

Where neck and gullet have no place in the animal's architecture (as in shark, frog, and others), the food passes directly from pharynx into stomach. In birds, where the lower end of the gullet is distended into a crop, the stomach is also separated into two parts—a sort of antechamber (the proventriculus) and a grinding gizzard. This and further modifications in the vertebrate digestive tract are adaptations to food. They will be discussed in Chapter 21.

Stomach

After food reaches the stomach, its movement ceases to be direct. Muscular contractions shift it back and forth, slowly dividing a bolus into parts, squeezing the parts into smaller portions, and all the while covering the newly exposed surface with digestive secretions.

SURFACE AREA. It is only on surfaces that enzymes can act. If, for example, a spherical mass of food four cms (1.6 inch) in diameter is divided by muscular action of the stomach into two equal spheres, the total volume remains the same (Fig. 8-19) but the

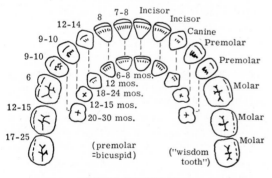

DENTAL FORMULAE

Milk Dentition	Adult Dentition
$\dfrac{\text{I}2 - \text{C}1 - \text{P}0 - \text{M}2}{\text{I}2 - \text{C}1 - \text{P}0 - \text{M}2} = 20;$	$\dfrac{2 - 1 - 2 - 3}{2 - 1 - 2 - 3} = 32$

FIG. 8-18. *The dentition of man, whether in early years ("milk dentition"—inner row) or as an adult ("permanent dentition"—outer row) is essentially the same for the upper and lower jaws. This is shown in the dental formulae given below the diagram:* I = *incisors,* C = *canines,* P = *premolars,* M = *molars.*

FIG. 8-19. *As food particles are divided by mechanical action of the digestive tract, the surface area per unit volume goes up rapidly. Spheres have the least surface for a given volume, yet three successive divisions double the surface area. The ratios are 1 : 1.26 : 1.59 : 2. Other shapes on division increase surface much more rapidly.*

ments, or **peristalsis,** from *peri* = around, and *stalsis* = constriction), all serve to separate large particles of food into smaller units with larger surface area exposed to digestive juices.

Because of an enzyme in the saliva, digestion in the human system, in ruminants such as the cow, and in some others begins in the mouth (Fig. 8-20). Often the action is very brief, since salivary amylase will split starch molecules into malt sugar (maltose) only if the solution is nearly neutral. Stomach acidity stops this completely as soon as the food bolus is broken up. The acid involved is hydrochloric, secreted at a concentration of 0.5 per cent by weight by glands emptying into the stomach. To some extent the acid sterilizes the food, preventing bacterial decay. It also activates part of the gastric secretion to form an active enzyme, gastric protease. This enzyme hydrolyzes proteins into peptones and proteoses. Part of this digestive action is recognized in the way the total secretion ("gastric juice") curdles milk by precipitation and coagulation of the main protein content. The curding action effectively delays what might otherwise be more rapid transport of fluid milk through the stomach, and thereby allows the protease to act on the milk protein in the same way that it does on other proteins.

Some water may be absorbed from the food through the stomach walls, but the primary functions of the organ in most vertebrates seem to be reception of the boli of food, and mechanical action on these until they are intimately mixed with gastric secretions to become a soup-like fluid called **chyme.** As consistency and acidity reach definite levels, the **pyloric** sphincter muscle at the posterior end of the stomach opens, discharging from time to time brief squirts into the intestine. In man, these contain about a teaspoonful each. *Pylorus* is Greek for "gatekeeper."

surface area exposed to digestive agents has jumped from 50.1 to 63.2 square cms. If each of these is divided equally again, so that four spheres result from the original food mass, the total volume is unchanged but the surface area of the four spheres now totals 79.5 square cms. Thus, as a food particle is divided progressively in half by volume, its surface area increases—in the case of a sphere, in the ratio of 1 : 1.26 : 1.59 : 2.00 : 2.52 : 3.17 : 4.00 : 5.05 : 6.35 : 8.00 : 10.05, and so on. A sphere offers the *least* surface area per unit of volume; in any other form, the increase of surface area is considerably more rapid as the bolus is divided.

LIQUIFICATION. The kneading action of the muscular stomach, and the characteristic waves of constriction (alternating with relaxation) in the intestine (called peristaltic move-

Intestine to Rectum

Usually two distinct regions can be recognized in the vertebrate intestine: a "small intestine" and a "large intestine" or **colon.** The former has a relatively small diameter but a heavier, more muscular and glandular wall, and it is customarily lined with ridges, tooth-like soft projections, or pile-like **villi.** The colon, by contrast, is thin-walled, much less muscular, and contains fewer glands.

THE SMALL INTESTINE. The folds, projections, and villi greatly increase the surface of the small intestine. This provides further space for glandular cells in the lining jejunum, thence to the ileum, then through a sphincter valve into the colon.

Two glands that arise in the wall of the duodenum during embryonic development be-

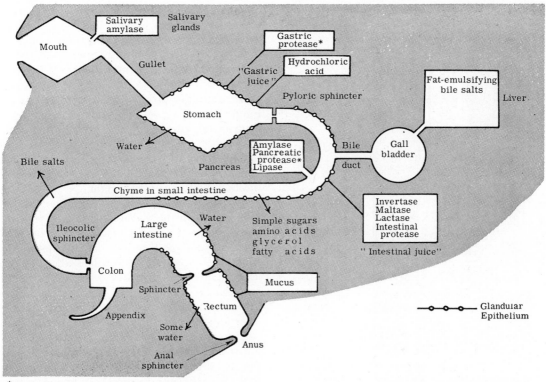

* Precursor only; activated after secretion.

FIG. 8-20. *The enzymes of the mammalian digestive tract and their sites of origin.*

epithelium, and greater opportunity for digestion products to be close to blood vessels into which they can diffuse. If the human intestine were smooth within, its surface area would total only about 6 square feet; the irregular surface, with its 5 million or so villi, presents an absorptive surface of over 100 square feet.

Each villus, if enlarged for study (Fig. 8-21) under the microscope, is seen to be composed of a thin epithelium around a finger-shaped mass of connective tissue largely occupied by fine blood vessels. Commonly the small intestine is modified further into three consecutive regions, the first of which is the **duodenum.** This portion is unique in receiving the ducts from liver and pancreas, and in occupying a fixed position with reference to the stomach. Food from the duodenum proceeds to the

come so large that there is no space for them within the wall itself. Instead, they extend out into the mesentery, one to become the liver, the other to form the pancreas. Each remains connected to the duodenum by a duct through which the digestive agents elaborated can reach the cavity (lumen) of the gut.

BILE. From the liver to the gut comes **bile.** In many vertebrates, the ducts from secretory cells in the liver enter a special **gall bladder,** in which the bile is stored between meals, before it passes down the **bile duct** to the duodenum. Bile is extremely important in the separation of fats into smaller units, making such fats an **emulsion** in the intestinal contents. The bile contains no enzymes, but its **bile salts** operate as "wetting agents" that reduce the tendency of fat particles to coalesce once they have been separated by mechanical action. This action of bile is similar to that of soaps, and it is fundamental in preparing fats for enzyme attack. The bile salts, incidentally, seem precious; after the fats have been hydrolyzed and

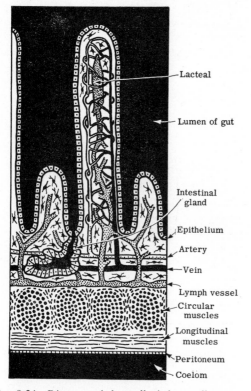

- Lacteal

- Lumen of gut

- Intestinal gland

- Epithelium

- Artery

- Vein

- Lymph vessel
- Circular muscles

- Longitudinal muscles

- Peritoneum

- Coelom

FIG. 8-21. *Diagram of the wall of the small intestine, to show vascular connections associated with food absorption and distribution.*

absorbed, the bile salts are reabsorbed by the posterior end of the small intestine, returned by the blood stream to the liver, and secreted there for use over and over again.

Human bile is normally a deep yellow-orange color, but that of other vertebrates ranges from red and yellow to a brilliant green (as in the frog), depending largely on the proportions of "bile pigments" in each. The chief bile pigments (red bilirubin and green biliverdin) are decomposition products from the blood pigment, hemoglobin. As such they are an excretion from the liver. When they reach the intestine, further chemical changes turn them brown or black. That

they are responsible for the characteristic color of fecal material is shown by the gray "clay-colored" stools that accompany blocking of the human bile duct. Commonly such a difficulty is indicated simultaneously by a marked increase of bile pigments in the blood, producing a yellow color to the skin and especially to the cornea of the eyes. The condition is described as **jaundice,** with a measured "icteric index" as a clinical estimation of how improperly the bile pigments are being discharged by their normal route.

Bile contains also the lipoid **cholesterol** as an excretory product from fat metabolism. Faulty emptying of the gall bladder or a drop in the reserve of bile salts (which help keep cholesterol in solution) may lead to precipitation of this material as **gallstones.** Gallstones may cause temporary stoppage of the bile duct and intense pain.

INTESTINAL JUICE. This is secreted by minute glands in the wall of the small intestine, and contains a number of enzymes, considerable calcium, and sodium bicarbonate. The sodium bicarbonate neutralizes the strongly acid chyme and provides a slightly alkaline reaction favorable to best activity of the intestinal enzymes. Chief among the enzymes of intestinal juice are **invertase** (hydrolyzing cane sugar—sucrose—to simple sugars such as glucose); **maltase** (breaking down maltose into simple sugars); **lactase** (similarly attacking milk sugar—lactose—and producing simple sugars); and an intestinal protease complex (continuing the breakdown of proteins, from the peptid and proteose stage left by the gastric juice action, into amino acids).

PANCREATIC JUICE. This reaches the small intestine through the pancreatic duct from the pancreas. Its digestive enzymes include an **amylase** (hydrolizing starches to maltose and either supplementing the work of saliva or taking its place in vertebrates in which the saliva is deficient or food swallowed too quickly); an enzyme precursor which is activated by a component of intestinal juice to become pancreatic protease (then breaking proteins, peptones, and proteoses into amino acids); and a **lipase** (converting fats emulsified by the bile into glycerol and fatty acids).

Collectively the enzymes attacking proteins (gastric protease, in the stomach; pancreatic protease, in the pancreatic juice; intestinal protease, from intestinal juice) are termed **proteolytic.** Those that hydrolyze fats (lipases, in pancreatic juice also) are called **lipolytic.** Carbohydrate-splitting enzymes (salivary amylase, in some saliva; pancreatic amylase, in pancreatic juice; invertase, maltase, and lactase, in intestinal juice) are **amylolytic.**

ABSORPTION OF DIGESTIVE PRODUCTS. Once broken down into their simplest forms, the carbohydrates and proteins can be actively absorbed as simple sugars (six carbon atoms per molecule) and amino acids. They pass through the wall of the small intestine into capillary blood vessels of the hepatic portal system, for transport to the liver and distribution throughout the body. Fats, on the other hand, either are absorbed directly or after hydrolysis into fatty acids and glycerol; they are then absorbed by intestinal wall cells and secreted into tissue spaces where they recombine as a fatty emulsion. These tissue spaces in the intestinal wall are so full of the whitish emulsion of fats that they appear engorged with milk, and for that reason the name **lacteal** has been applied to the small cavities. The lacteals intercommunicate and are drained by diffuse vessels of the lymphatic system (Fig. 8-21), to empty into the blood stream near the heart. The fats, carried by the blood throughout the body, are still not entirely available for use in catabolism or storage. Most of them, instead, are picked out of the blood by special cells in the liver, which chemically alter the fat before releasing it into the circulation again. Thereafter the fat is oxidized more readily by other tissues, which take it from the blood stream, either utilizing it for its energy content or storing it in characteristic sites where special cells become full of fatty materials as adipose tissue.

The chyme in the small intestine remains highly fluid, and flows back and forth under muscular compulsion while digestion continues. Gradually it shifts toward the large intestine, and at the same time about as much water is withdrawn as was added in digestive juices from glands beyond the pyloric sphincter. Hence the liquid passed from the small intestine to the colon is approximately of the same consistency as the chyme emerging from the stomach. Soluble materials—whether ions, sugars, or amino acids—and digested fats have been removed. But the slightly alkaline condition of the contents has allowed multiplication of bacteria in the residues. And depending on the nature of the food, various proportions of indigestible substances may still provide bulk.

Removal by absorption and hydrolysis due to enzyme action are both retarded when the content of indigestible material is high. Slow passage of food materials, however, favors greater development of bacteria. Where the intestinal contents include significant quantities of proteins, the bacteria engage in putrefactive operations that form many malodorous substances and much gas as by-products. But when the bulk filling the gut is chiefly cellulose, as in the diet of herbivores, these unpleasant aspects are less noticeable. In plant feeders, moreover, the colon frequently has an extensive blind branch, the **cecum,** at the junction of small and large intestines. Indigestible residues may be shifted into the cecum, along with the bacteria, and left there. The bacteria themselves ultimately reduce the large molecules to dimensions for which the herbivore has enzymes. Then the load in the cecum is returned to the small intestine for further hydrolysis and absorption before the rest is carried onward into the colon. Our own cecum is a fist-sized pocket with a projecting finger-like outgrowth, the **vermiform appendix.**

THE COLON. This portion of the gut functions primarily in absorbing water and in transferring indigestible residues from small intestine to rectum. In it, too, mucus is added as a lubricant, assisting in the defecation of solid or pasty wastes. In aquatic vertebrates, where water conservation is less important, the colon is commonly less extensive. In all, however, the bacteria multiply during the slow passage to the point where they may compose 50 per cent of the contents, with cellulose walls from plant food representing a still indigestible residue.

THE RECTUM. The final modification of the digestive tract, the rectum, has muscular walls that extrude the feces. Ordinarily the rectum remains empty except at the time of defecation, but it too may become distended with wastes.

Until a few years ago the retention of fecal material beyond a reasonable time was believed to result in excessive absorption from it of toxic products from bacterial action. The term "auto-intoxication" was given to the accompanying headache and other unpleasant symptoms. It is now known that such substances do not reach important concentrations in the blood, and that the discomfort of constipation is due to the unnatural and prolonged distention of the rectum with feces. The symptoms in man can be duplicated by packing the rectum with sterile cotton—proving that the discomfiture is entirely reflex in origin.

It should be noted as a practical point that almost all cases of constipation are due to irregular habits and a continued state of nervous excitement.[5] Routine use of cathartics is both habit-forming and contrary to the best interests of the gut. Least harmful, perhaps, is agar-agar, which is inert and indigestible but which increases the intestinal volume (providing more bulk for muscles to work on). Agar-agar competes with absorbing mechanisms so well that extra water is held in the feces and they are easier to egest. Mineral oil provides bulk and lubricates the passage of food through the intestine; unfortunately it also coats the villi of the small intestine so thoroughly that they cannot absorb digestion products normally, and the fat-soluble vitamins in particular remain in the oil and are lost in the feces. Salts such as magnesium sulfate (epsom salt) act osmotically to retain water in the gut and also irritate the gastrointestinal receptors, initiating powerful reflex contractions of the muscles around the intestine and expelling all contents. Castor oil is correspondingly irritating to the nerve endings in the intestinal lining and produces the same violent spasms. Still other drugs, such as cascara, act upon reflex centers in the brain, leading to nervous stimulation of the gut wall musculature and stronger than normal peristaltic movements.

The anus of mammals opens directly to the outside of the body. In many other vertebrates it discharges the rectal contents through an additional chamber, the **cloaca** (the Latin word for *sewer*). A cloaca differs from a rectum in that the reproductive system and the excretory system open into it also. Sometimes there is a strong sphincter muscle around the cloacal aperture, in addition to the one or two in the anus, between rectum and cloaca.

Ulcers

At intervals the question arises: "Why does not the digestive tract digest itself?" The answer is that it does whenever the cells that line it die and lose their control over the living permeable membranes. Self-digestion is quite evident in autopsy of dead animals when these have remained at temperatures conducive to digestive chemistry. And from time to time, the human organism loses control over the same living membranes in stomach or duodenum, leading to local self-digestion of the epithelium there, in the formation of ulcers. Unfortunately, the presence of an ulcer often stimulates the flow of digestive juice and aggravates the condition. From the distribution of ulcers among the population, it would seem that a continuous state of nervous tension and a reduction in physical activity are predisposing factors. Taxi drivers in big cities are very susceptible to ulcers, whereas postmen seldom experience this difficulty.

7. RESPIRATION

Respiration is a protoplasmic function, the mechanism whereby energy is obtained for all anabolic processes. Often, however, the term is used loosely for a secondary event that is properly called "ventilation." In vertebrate animals, the blood stream carries carbon dioxide from the respiring cells to skin, gills, or lungs, and at this site the waste material is exchanged for oxygen that the blood conveys to the tissues.

Chordate design includes provision for intake of oxygen and entrance of food to use common passages in the anterior end of the body. The simplest means for sorting out the two substances is through pharyngeal slits, and these are a conspicuous feature of all

---

[5] Constipation *may* be symptomatic of a functional bowel disturbance, of an organic gastro-intestinal disease, and of various maladies like hypothyroidism, lead poisoning, and spinal cord lesions.

chordates at some stage in their development.

Pharyngeal slit arrangement exhibits some versatility. Among the small and "less advanced" chordates such as the acorn worms, tunicates, and Amphioxus, and in larval cyclostomes, the food consists of microscopic organisms. These enter the mouth in a combined feeding and respiratory current induced by ciliary action. The water passes out through the pharyngeal slits (Fig. 8-22) and in doing so comes close to capillaries, permitting the exchange of carbon dioxide for oxygen. Meanwhile a moving film of mucus, secreted by the wall cells of the pharynx, traps a large percentage of the organic particles in the water, just as is done in the mantle cavity of a clam. This is filter feeding. And in the chordate pharynx, the mucus is shifted by cilia and formed into a rope which enters the gullet.

In "higher" chordates, by contrast, the larger food fails to escape through gill slits

and is swallowed by coordinated contractions of pharynx and gullet, without benefit of mucus ropes (as in fish); or the gill slits close in late embryonic life and the pharynx becomes merely part of the tube leading from mouth to stomach. Even here, however, it is the parting of the ways for food heading toward digestion and air passing toward the lungs. Yet pharyngeal slits are just another indication of the basic segmentation of chordate structure. The cartilaginous bars that support them, and the muscles that control their apertures, may function in breathing, or, where lungs replace gills, be adapted to other uses.

Gills

The mechanisms of respiration in forms too large to depend on ciliary drive for water currents are interesting and informative. Jawless

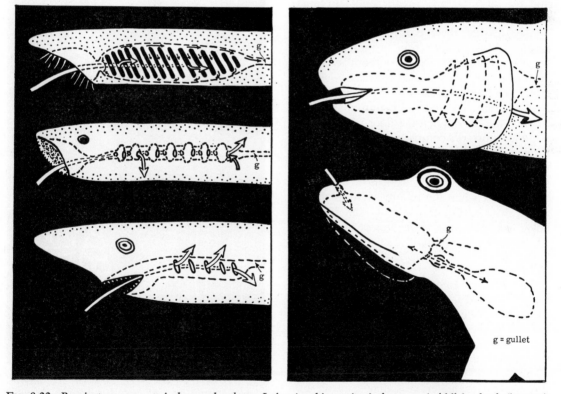

FIG. 8-22. *Respiratory currents in lower chordates. Left:* Amphioxus *(top),* lamprey *(middle),* shark *(bottom). Right: bony fish (top),* frog *(bottom). Valve action is provided between mouth and pharynx in Amphioxus. Respiration may involve the mouth or be independent of it in the lamprey. Each shark gill has its own valve. The bony fish has valves at its mouth opening and valve action in the gill cover. The frog has valves in nostrils and glottis.*

cyclostomes such as lampreys, which feed on fluid blood taken from living vertebrate victims, have "pouch gills" with a means for closing off the connection to the pharynx (Fig. 8-22, Photo 67). While sucking blood or holding by suction to a support, these animals breathe by drawing water into the gills directly, then expelling it by the same route. In fish, however, where true jaws are present and where external parasitism is not the mode of life, the water passes through the mouth cavity and leaves via the gill slits.

Among the cartilaginous-skeletoned sharks and rays—the "elasmobranchs" (from the Greek *elasmos* = a plate and Latin *branchia* = a gill)—with plate-like gills and separate gill slits visible on the outside of the body, the mouth itself is opened and closed in a regular sequence to keep the liquid moving in one direction. Among bony fish—the "teleosts" (from the Greek *teleos* = complete, and *osteon* = bone)—with a gill cover extending backward over the external openings of the gill slits, there is a membranous valve mechanism inside the front of the mouth that prevents reflux of water without complete closure of the jaws—hence with less muscular effort. In both kinds of fish, however, the mouth cavity is dilated by muscular action to draw in water. Then the floor of the mouth is pulled upward, compressing the liquid and forcing it out through the pharyngeal slits. In the elasmobranchs each gill slit has its own flexible valve to prevent return of water into the pharynx when the mouth cavity is dilated again, whereas in the teleosts the firm gill cover provides the valve action in a somewhat simpler way (Fig. 8-22).

Lungs

THE MOUTH FLOOR AS A PUMP. All of the aquatic, gilled stages of amphibians, such as newts (Photos 72-74) and tadpoles, breathe in the same way as do the bony fish. As adults they alter procedures to match development of lungs and of special nostrils communicating from external air to mouth through valves under muscular control. For breathing the mouth must be kept closed (Fig. 8-22). With nostril valves open, the floor of the mouth is dropped and air enters

the mouth cavity. The valves are now closed, the floor of the mouth raised, and the air driven between the firm cartilages of the **glottis** (a valve) through a **larynx** supported by cartilaginous skeletal elements, down the short **trachea** (windpipe), and into the simple lungs. By closure of the glottis, this air can be retained in the lungs for a time. If glottis and nasal valves are opened, the air emerges again rather suddenly, propelled by the **elastic recoil** of the lungs. Thus an amphibian demonstrates **pressure breathing** in that the lung air is under higher pressure than that of the atmosphere around the animal. Actually, both fish and most amphibians obtain a considerable part of their oxygen-carbon dioxide exchange through the moist skin, supplementing the gills or lungs in this function. Most terrestrial salamanders of fair size lack both gills and lungs as adults, depending entirely on respiration through the skin (Photo 72).

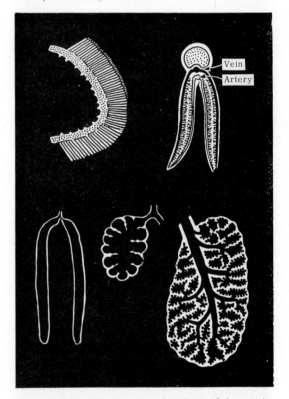

FIG. 8-23. *Respiratory structures. Upper left: a series of gill filaments on a gill arch. Upper right: the same in transverse section, indicating blood vessel connections. Lower left: a salamander's simple lungs. Center: a frog's lung. Lower right: a mammalian lung with its many alveoli.*

THE RIBS AS A PUMP. Although most fishes have ribs and rib-like bones, they do not use rib movements in ventilating the blood. Most reptiles and birds, on the other hand, have no means except rib movements for getting air in and out of the lungs.[6] In these latter, the ribs form a basket around the body cavity. Between each rib pair and the next are **intercostal** muscles, through contraction of which the whole rib mechanism is pulled obliquely forward, hinging on the vertebrae, to enclose a larger volume. When this muscular activity occurs, air rushes into the nostrils (or mouth) and into the lungs, filling them. Relaxation of the intercostal muscles allows the body cavity to collapse, and exhalation is accomplished passively—again with elastic recoil as an aid. (Fig. 8-23).

Birds have a unique device that increases the efficiency of this system (Fig. 8-24). It takes the form of tubes and cavities extending blindly from the compact, inelastic lungs into the spaces between the viscera and even out into some of the hollow long bones in legs and wings. Expiration leaves a sizable amount of **residual** air in the lungs, with almost no oxygen and with a fair concentration of carbon dioxide. Inspiration drives this residual air into the blind tubes and fills the lungs with fresh **tidal** air from which oxygen can be removed at maximum speed. Expiration empties the lungs of tidal air again, leaving them filled with residual air from the tubes. Thus the lungs, where blood capillaries are close to the surface for gas interchange, receive a complete change of air at each breath—a situation not found elsewhere among the vertebrates. The air sacs are important also in dissipation of heat, but the mechanism seems adaptive primarily for allowing efficient respiration in small lungs enclosed by a rib basket which must be more rigid for flight and which consequently can-

not produce large changes in the total volume of the body cavity. Bird lungs, in fact, are attached to the ribs, and if the connections are severed experimentally, the bird suffo-

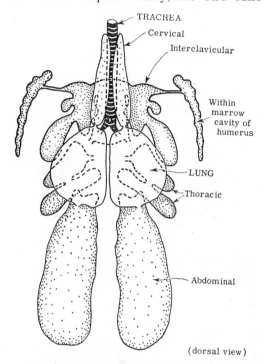

TRACHEA
Cervical
Interclavicular
Within marrow cavity of humerus
LUNG
Thoracic
Abdominal

(dorsal view)

FIG. 8-24. *The air sacs which allow a bird to replace completely its lung air at each inspiration.*

cates. Opening the air sacs, on the other hand, does not severely hamper respiration, although body temperatures rise promptly because of destruction of the normal means for heat removal.

THE DIAPHRAGM AS A SUPPLEMENT. Mammalian (and human) respiration involves not only action of intercostal muscles but also the movements of a muscular **diaphragm** (Fig. 8-25) which separates the body cavity into two parts—an anterior **pleural** cavity containing the lungs, and an **abdominal** cavity with the other viscera. The gullet runs through the pleural cavity, and the **pericardium** (with its enclosed heart) is surrounded by the lung space. The diaphragm is concave toward the abdomen, and contraction flattens it—expanding the volume of the pleural cavity at the expense of the abdominal. Simultaneously the intercostal muscles con-

---

[6] Turtles are an interesting exception among the reptiles, since the body is enclosed in a rigid shell formed by the dorsal carapace and ventral plastron. The ribs are fused with the bony plates of the carapace. Breathing movements involve muscles that flatten out the pockets into which the legs can be retracted, so that air is sucked into the lungs. Relaxation of the muscles allows the elasticity of the viscera to expel the air again. A startled turtle pulls its legs, head, and tail into the cavities under the shell with such vigor that the lung air is forced out in an audible hiss.

tract, drawing the ribs forward and increasing the pleural volume. Air enters the spongy, elastic lungs because of the excess of atmospheric pressure over the pressure in the lungs.

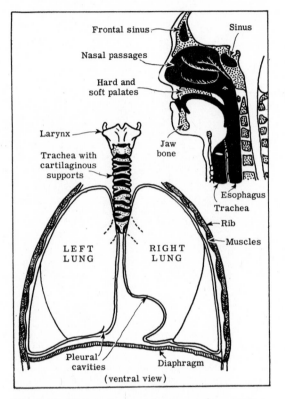

FIG. 8-25. *Human lungs and connected passages, as seen in ventral dissection* (lower), *and in median sagittal section through the head* (upper).

This is **vacuum breathing,** characteristic of most reptiles and birds and quite different from pressure breathing in amphibians. A mammal can force air from the lungs by relaxing the diaphragm and intercostal muscles and by simultaneously contracting the abdominal musculature.

A further difference in respiration is related to the size of the animal. Man breathes in and out about 18 times per minute (faster with exercise or emotion) from birth to death. A mouse or sparrow greatly exceeds this ventilation rate. In our case the tidal air amounts to about 500 milliliters, of which 150 have no effect in gas exchange since they remain in conducting tubes and never gain proximity to the capillary networks in the lungs. The deepest possible inhalation takes in another 2,500 ml, and with exhalation forced to the limit, an extra 1,000 ml can be expelled. Another 1,000 ml remains as residual air. Hence maximum exhalation followed by maximum inhalation may draw in 4,000 ml—the so-called **vital capacity** of the lung system (Fig. 8-26).

If a mammalian lung is removed from the body, it collapses of its own elasticity and lack of support, but it still contains enough air to float easily. The lung of a fetus or stillborn child, on the other hand, has never been inflated and will sink in water. This difference is often used by coroners at an inquest to determine whether a dead newborn infant died in birth or afterward (and hence possibly as a victim of infanticide).

High Altitude

In taking aircraft to high elevations for more economical flight, fliers reach atmospheric pressures too low to drive oxygen into their blood stream at an adequate rate (Fig. 8-27). They suffer from inadequate oxygen—**hypoxia** (usually misnamed "anoxia").

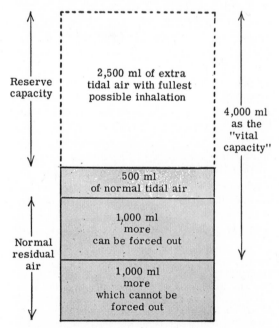

FIG. 8-26. *When at rest, we use only about an eighth of the total possible gas exchange in our lungs. Even with maximum inhalation and maximum exhalation, we can move only about 80 per cent of the total gas content.*

Three techniques have been helpful in counteracting this: pressurizing the cabin; or breathing an artificial atmosphere of pure oxygen (with a trace of CO_2 to stimulate the ventilation center in the brain); or deliberate pressure breathing.

If the cabin is not pressurized, pure oxygen becomes advisable above 5,000 feet in darkness (to support the high oxygen demands of the visual mechanism), and above 10,000 feet in daylight. Between 10,000 and 15,000 feet "most fliers remain conscious without oxygen, but their working efficiency is reduced." In the range from 18,000 to 30,000 feet "an unacclimatized man must have oxygen or lose consciousness in a maximum of 45 minutes, perhaps as little as 1½ minutes." Above this level, the oxygen must be supplied

under pressure—introducing further respiratory difficulties.

Combat airmen were trained to take into their lungs as much oxygen as they could, then to "hold their breath" and pull in the abdominal muscles as though trying to inflate a bag. This effectively raises the pressure in the lungs to a level more nearly comparable to the pressures at sea level, and forces more oxygen into the capillaries.

Flying an airplane requires attention to a host of instruments, but is sedentary work. Climbing a mountain is exercise demanding plenty of oxygen. Those who long to scale the world's loftiest peaks try to acclimatize themselves to high altitude for weeks prior to the

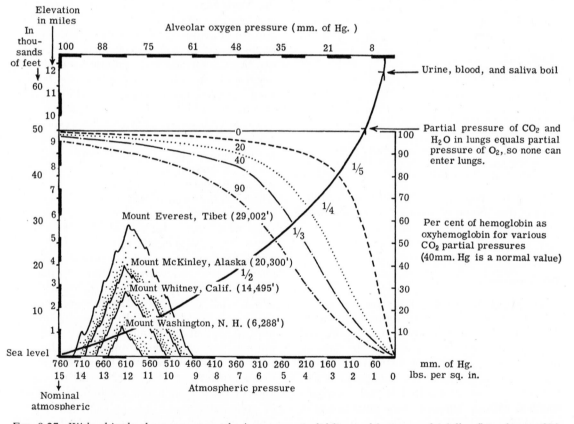

FIG. 8-27. *With altitude the gross atmospheric pressure (solid line and bottom scale) falls off to about a fifth at 40,000 feet (left scale). But oxygen accounts for only 20 per cent of this gross pressure, and by the time inspired air reaches the alveoli, dilution with residual air brings the initial partial pressure of oxygen still lower (scale at top). At high altitudes, this partial pressure of oxygen in the alveoli becomes too slight to drive the gas into the blood. Furthermore, at 40,000 feet, the oxygen-carrying capacity of hemoglobin begins to fall off sharply (broken curves), and the more carbon dioxide accumulates in the plasma, the worse the difficulty becomes (see scale at right). These factors determine what equipment is needed for high-altitude operations, whether on foot or by airplane.*

climb. Adaptation is through an increase in the numbers of red blood cells and in the hemoglobin content of each. For people from lower elevations this adaptation is reversible. Natives living at high elevations in the Andes and Tibet possess spectacularly high red-cell counts and hemoglobin levels, but for some unknown reason—perhaps related to this— they are unable to survive normally at lower altitudes.

With development of lighter equipment for supplying oxygen while climbing, and a better understanding of high-altitude physiology, many of the high peaks of the world became climbable in the 1950's:

Mt. Everest	29,002 ft.	1953
Mt. Godwin Austin (K2)	28,250	1954
Mt. Cho Oyu	26,867	1954
Mt. Nanga Parbat	26,660	1953
Mt. Anapurna	26,503	1950

More familiar peaks are far lower yet present problems in hypoxia:

Mt. McKinley, Alaska	20,269
Popocatapetl, Mexico	17,887
Mont Blanc, French Alps	15,781
Matterhorn, Switzerland	14,692
Mt. Whitney, California	14,495
Mt. Evans, Colorado	14,260
Pike's Peak, Colorado	14,110

The last two can be scaled in an automobile, but the trip should be avoided by people who suffer from "mountain sickness" in Mexico City (7,349 ft.) or Denver, Colorado ("A mile high").

Gas Transport

Transport of oxygen to the tissues by the circulating blood is made more efficient in vertebrates through the presence of the red pigment, hemoglobin, enclosed in special blood cells, the **erythrocytes** (from the Greek *erythros* = red, *cytos* = cell). These cells and the pigment are elaborated in an organ associated with the intestine but connected only to blood vessels—the **spleen.** In birds and mammals, after birth, the blood-cell-forming function of the spleen is taken over commonly by the marrow cells in the long bones. In all vertebrates, a steady replacement of cells is necessary to make up for the wearing out

that takes place. Hemoglobin inside the erythrocyte absorbs oxygen readily and takes the dissolved gas into a loose chemical combination to form **oxyhemoglobin.** This occurs wherever the concentration of oxygen in the surrounding blood plasma is slightly elevated. Disintegration of oxyhemoglobin to form hemoglobin and free dissolved oxygen takes place with equal facility whenever the oxygen concentration in the surrounding plasma falls —as it does in the capillaries near tissues needing oxygen. Almost all of the oxygen-carrying power of the blood is due to the one respiratory pigment.

Carbon dioxide, on the other hand, is carried principally by the plasma, either dissolved in it or in chemical combination as sodium bicarbonate. Aqueous solutions of carbon dioxide are acidic, but the acidity of the blood is scarcely changed by additions or evaporative losses of carbon dioxide. The control of acidity is in the sodium bicarbonate balance and in a chain of related chemical reactions described as a **buffering mechanism** because they adjust their concentrations in such ways as to resist changes in acidity. (See also pp. 55, 122.)

In terrestrial vertebrates, the respiratory system involves more than the lungs, trachea, glottis, and mouth. Between glottis and trachea is a **larynx,** usually supported by cartilages. In most the single trachea matches the length of the neck, either long or short, and is supported by a series of open cartilaginous rings which can deform to allow food to pass down the adjacent gullet. The trachea commonly forks into a pair of **bronchi** in the chest region, and each bronchus divides repeatedly into progressively finer **bronchioles,** which lead to the actual respiratory centers, the minute, sac-like **alveoli.** The term *lung,* as applied to that of an amphibian (Fig. 8-23), implies few of these complications. In bird or mammal, however, the lung includes the distal portions of the bronchi, all the bronchioles, the alveoli, and a considerable amount of connective tissue linking these structures. The lungs are then enclosed in a **pleural membrane** that is moist and allows movements within the chest cavity during the breathing cycle. Pleurisy, an inflammation of the pleural membrane, makes breathing difficult and painful.

ALVEOLAR EXCHANGE. The enormous number of alveoli in the lungs of warm-blooded animals provides a remarkable area of surface through which oxygen can enter the blood capillaries and through which carbon dioxide can escape. One human lung contains about 750 million alveoli, each about 0.004 inch in diameter—a total area of approximately 1,000 square feet. This entire surface in the alveoli is covered with a thin film of water, and the gas exchange corresponds closely to that in the wet surface of chlorenchyma cells in a photosynthesizing leaf.

In the lung, oxygen dissolves in the water film and diffuses through the membrane and protoplasm of the cells lining the alveolus, to reach the capillaries of the blood stream. Carbon dioxide, diffusing in the other direction, evaporates from the water into the air in the alveolus. That the moisture is essential in the process is demonstrated at intervals through the death of human beings who are untouched by fire and unhurt by smoke during a fire in a building. For example, a family trapped on an upper floor of a house by flames in the basement may thoughtlessly attempt to escape by the customary stairway. Someone opens the door to the upper hall and admits into the room a puff of superheated air that has accumulated at the top of the stair. In an instant, this air absorbs all the moisture from every alveolus—often hurried to these sites by an involuntary gasping inhalation by the victim. An open window may prevent the heat in the room from reaching fatal levels, and the fire department may extinguish the blaze before much economic loss is suffered, but all those on the top floor are dead of suffocation—dead before secretion of new moisture into the alveoli could make respiration possible again. Firemen constantly caution the public never to open a door which feels hot to the hand. It is better to wait for the arrival of the fire trucks or to leave through an open window than to risk desiccating the lungs and dying promptly from respiratory failure.

Accessory Structures

The majority of land vertebrates use the nasal route for admitting air into the mouth and thence toward the lungs. Basically, the nasal mechanism is sensory, and begins as a pair of pits on the outside of the head. These, in most higher forms, become connected to the mouth by a groove during embryonic development. The groove ordinarily closes, providing a tube through which air can be admitted. Occasionally, even in human beings, the groove fails to close and a child is born with a "harelip," which should be corrected surgically. In the mammalian mouth (Fig. 8-25), the nostrils do not communicate with the oral cavity directly, as is usually the case in other classes. Instead there is a **palate** as a partial partition separating off the tooth-equipped, chewing region of the mouth, from the nasal cavities, and directing air from the nostrils into the pharynx instead. In the congenital difficulty of harelip, the palate is often unclosed, too, and it interferes with speech as a "cleft palate." It should be closed surgically as early as possible.

The nasal passages are dorsal to the mouth but the lungs are ventral to the digestive tract. Both systems employ the same pharynx, and at this point the paths of air and food cross one another. Reflex operation of muscles and valves provide for the closure of the glottis when food is being swallowed, thus preventing entrance of foreign particles into the trachea. Occasionally the reflex is blocked at the critical moment and some object does enter the respiratory tract. Sensory endings identify its presence and call forth vigorous spasmodic exhalations as "coughing" at the same time that the ciliated epithelium is busy transporting the particle toward the open glottis. Sneezing, on the other hand, tends to expel irritating particles from the nasal cavities—even though much of the air volume may escape through the mouth.

Sniffing, however, is an intermittent vigorous inhalation that deflects air from its ordinary direct course from nasal openings to pharynx, and that spreads it out over the areas of sensory cells responding to odors, thus improving the chance that some odor will be recognized. The need to sniff demonstrates what a great transformation has occurred, from nasal pits that were completely sensory to through passages of the respiratory system wherein identification of chemical substances has become an accessory function.

Since, in birds, the whole sense of smell seems lost, the nasal pits are regarded as completely altered in use.

Related to the respiratory system in terrestrial vertebrates is the sound-producing mechanism. In amphibians, reptiles, and mammals, the larynx contains flat, ribbon-like

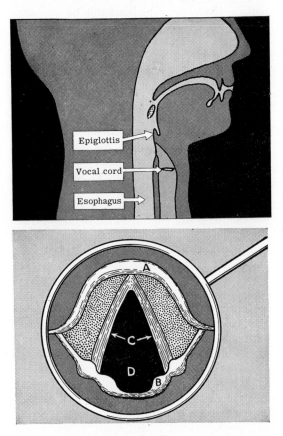

FIG. 8-28. *The vocal cords (C) are accessory structures in the respiratory mechanism. They may be examined* (lower figure) *by looking into the open glottis, down the larynx (D) bounded by the anterior (A) and posterior (B) walls.*

vocal cords stretched between the cartilages by muscular action (Fig. 8-28). Air from the lungs, exhaled rapidly over the taut cords, gives rise to various sounds. Pitch is controlled by adjustments of the tension. Other parts of the respiratory system provide resonant qualities that are frequently distinctive. In frogs, the throat contains a pair of air sacs communicating with the pharynx; toads have a single sac. In calling, air may be passed

from lungs to sacs and sacs to lungs, back and forth over the vocal cords, producing sound in both directions or in only one. In either situation, the sacs amplify the sound as efficient resonators. Birds, on the other hand, achieve their call notes by means of a syrinx at the end of the trachea, just at the point where the windpipe divides into the short bronchi. Air movements over muscle bands in the cavity of the syrinx produce the vibrations responsible for the familiar sounds. Some of the values to the organisms making these calls are discussed in Chapter 20.

Respiratory Problems

Man is susceptible to a number of diseases that produce respiratory difficulties. In pneumonia, the lung alveoli fill gradually with plasma and become useless for respiration; if the liquid is not reabsorbed quickly, the infected region solidifies and fills with connective tissue, making the loss of respiratory surface a permanent one; no significant regeneration takes place. In tuberculosis, there is destruction of lung tissue also, but no filling unless blood vessels break and hemorrhage occurs. Part of the difficulty in tuberculosis is the constant movement of the lung in ventilation. These movements can be avoided in man if the infection is unilateral (involving only one lung), since the pleural membrane separates the thoracic cavity into two. Injections of sterile air can be made between the lung and its sac, keeping the lung collapsed while respiration is handled entirely on the other side; this is the treatment called **pneumothorax.**

Pneumothorax treatments are impossible in dogs and many other mammals, because the two lungs are in a single sac. The significance of the double sac in man is not known, but full advantage is taken of it in treatment of unilateral tuberculosis.

Deep sea divers, or those who work under higher-than-atmospheric pressure in caissons while building tunnels under rivers, can stand the increased pressure for a limited time. Hours may be lost each day in transferring workers from the high pressure back to atmospheric levels. This down-pressure trip is particularly critical, since any hastening of it allows gas dissolved in the blood under pressure to emerge as bubbles in the circulatory system, damming capillaries and creating intense pain. These are the symptoms called "caisson disease" or "the bends," because of the cramping pains experienced by the sufferer. Now a helium-oxygen atmosphere can be used on the site of operations, in place of nitrogen-oxygen. If there is no nitrogen to dissolve, it cannot appear later as bubbles. Even under pressure, helium does not dissolve significantly in the blood. The diver or caisson worker can be returned to atmospheric pressure far more rapidly. If oxygen forms a bubble, internal respiratory processes use it up before any symptoms appear. The same technique could be applied to skin-diving, making it safer to go quickly from one depth to another.

In both the helium-oxygen mixture and the more common nitrogen-oxygen used for patients in oxygen tents, for fliers at high altitudes, and for victims of asphyxiation and drowning, a small quantity of carbon dioxide is essential. The carbon dioxide stimulates the respiratory center in the brain and keeps ventilation movements vigorous.

Carbon monoxide poisoning is recognized readily because of the unusual brightness of the blood color. Hemoglobin unites with the carbon monoxide, and this union is firmer than that with oxygen. Hemoglobin molecules linked to carbon monoxide will not break down and release the monoxide again rapidly at ordinary pressures of oxygen in atmospheric air. But in oxygen-reinforced gas mixtures, both gradual replacement of the carbon monoxide linkage with oxygen occurs, and also every unpoisoned red cell is called upon for its full oxygen-carrying capacity.

8. THE COELOM

When the ventral body wall of a chordate is cut through, the viscera lie exposed. They fit neatly against one another in the confines of the body cavity, free to shift slightly whenever the body position changes. The tissues which line the chordate body cavity are all derived during embryonic development from the third body layer—the mesoderm. For this reason the body cavity is called a "true" body cavity or **coelom.**

In all vertebrates an anterior part of the coelom is closed off around the heart as the "pericardial cavity," while in mammals a further subdivision by the diaphragm separates a thoracic cavity from an abdominal cavity. All three cavities are still recognized as representing the original coelom.

9. THE CIRCULATORY SYSTEM

That the heart and blood vessels are known so widely as the "circulatory system" pays tribute to the scientific deductions of an English physician, William Harvey. Prior to Harvey's time, anatomists had dissected the human body and named the parts, but no real agreement had been reached as to whether one side of the heart was filled with air, or the heart was the principal organ producing movement of the blood. The blood itself was believed to ebb and flow in the arteries and veins. Harvey published his analysis of heart operation in 1628, emphasizing three arguments:

1. When the heart contracts, it is firm to the touch; when it is distended with blood, it feels far softer. If some other organ were the pump, filling the heart with blood, the heart would be flabby when empty, and hard when full. Therefore the heart must be the pump, as a hollow muscle that becomes tense during contraction.

2. Within the heart are valves. They permit blood to flow from auricle to ventricle on each side, and from ventricle to arteries. They prevent flow in the reverse direction. Hence blood must pass through the heart in one way only. When the heart contracts, the arteries expand. Expansion must be due to blood forced into the arteries by the contractile force. Moreover, the veins contain valves and these are all arranged to limit flow to one direction—toward the heart. Therefore blood must come to the heart from the veins, be forced by the heart into the arteries. The valves make any other interpretation impossible.

3. At each beat the heart drives through itself a definite, measurable quantity of blood —about 3 fluid ounces. It beats 70 times a minute, 60 minutes an hour, 24 hours a day. Hence it moves between 9 and 10 tons of blood a day. But blood accounts for only about 8 per cent of the total weight of a living human body—perhaps 12 pounds in a

150-pound person. To have available so much blood to pump, the body cannot secrete it into the veins and destroy it as it comes from the arteries. Instead the blood must pass from the arteries to the veins by "motion, as it were, in a circle."

Harvey documented his studies by comparisons between man and various vertebrates, as well as crustaceans, insects, and worms. In man and four-footed animals with fur, a double circulation through the heart seemed a necessary explanation. Harvey proved his case, although he never saw the capillaries linking the arteries to the veins. He predicted them. Marcello Malpighi found them in 1661, using one of the earliest microscopes.

Now it is recognized universally that the vertebrate circulatory system is a closed sequence of arteries running toward organs and tissues, dividing there into a fine meshwork of capillaries that reassemble into veins leading back to the heart. The distinction between artery and vein is in direction of flow—from or toward the heart.

Arteries have heavy muscular walls (Fig. 8-29) and no valves. Veins have thin, less muscular walls, and frequent valves. The heart provides most of the propulsive force, although the activities of skeletal muscles through which veins run and the rhythmic movements of the mammalian diaphragm have an important effect in returning the blood from capillaries through the venous system to the heart.

Arteries to Veins

The direction of blood flow in chordates is the opposite of that in annelid worms, the only other major phylum with a closed circulatory system. In chordates the ventral (single) heart pumps the blood anteriorly (Fig. 8-5) to the pharyngeal region, where it passes laterally and dorsally to the midline into a **dorsal aorta.** The **carotid** arteries to the head and the **brachial** arteries to the fore fins or fore legs arise somewhat before this union into the dorsal aorta. From the aorta itself come **mesenteric** arteries to the digestive tract, **renal** arteries to the kidneys, and **iliac** arteries to the pelvic fins or hind legs; the aorta then

continues into the tail as the **caudal** artery. Smaller vessels pass to the heart muscles (the **coronary** arteries), to back and side muscles, and to reproductive organs.

In returning, the blood from the anterior end of the animal collects into the **jugular** veins. Blood from the digestive tract proceeds to the liver and there is distributed into capil-

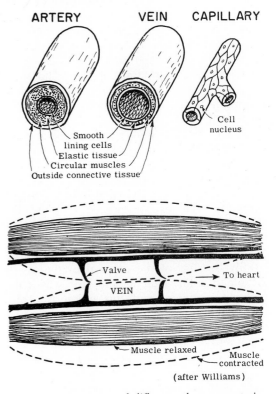

FIG. 8-29. *The structural difference between arteries, veins, and capillaries* (above) *lies in the thickness and musculature of the walls. At intervals, veins have valves* (below) *which limit the direction of flow when contraction of skeletal muscles expels the blood locally.*

laries; glucose and other products of digestion are removed for storage. Such a venous system—from capillaries in one organ (the gut wall) to capillaries in another (the liver)—is sufficiently different from the ordinary direct transfer from capillaries to heart to warrant a separate name, that of **portal system.** In this case, related to the glycogen storage function of the liver, the vein from the gut to the liver capillaries is the **hepatic portal** vein. It allows significant amounts of the products of digestion to be removed in the liver before the blood passes to the heart and thence to the rest of the body. From the liver, this blood continues toward the heart through the **hepatic vein.**

Fish and amphibians, which use the tail and hind legs to such a great extent in locomotion, have a further portal system involving the excretory system. In vertebrates, removal of organic wastes from the coelom is of much less significance than the extraction of nitrogenous substances from the blood. Accordingly, each shows an intimate interweaving of blood capillaries and excretory tubules in the form of complex kidneys, each with a duct carrying the excretion toward the outside. Renal arteries bring blood to the kidneys; **renal** veins remove it and return it to the circulation. But in fish and amphibians there is an added **renal portal** system, with a renal portal vein bringing blood from tail and hind legs, carrying products of muscle activity that are thus eliminated by the kidneys before the blood returns to the general circulation.

The jugular veins from the anterior regions, the hepatic vein from the liver and hepatic portal system, and the renal veins and others from the posterior regions of the body all empty into larger vessels leading into the heart. The details differ from one vertebrate class to another—and even among the orders within each class. In most, however, the final receiver for all of this venous blood is a thin-walled sac associated with the heart and known as the **sinus venosus.** In mammals this structure has been absorbed into the heart itself, and instead two major veins approach the heart, each a **vena cava**—one from the anterior end of the body (an anterior vena cava or precaval vein) and one from the posterior (the postcaval or posterior vena cava).

The Heart

Each vertebrate heart is composed of at least one **auricle** and at least one **ventricle.** Blood from the veins flows into the relaxed auricle. The auricle, with relatively thin walls, passes the blood to the relaxed ventricle. The ventricle, with thick muscular walls, provides the strong pumping action that sends the blood out into an artery.

In fish, the heart has a single auricle and one ventricle. The blood from the ventricle

proceeds along a **ventral aorta** to capillaries in the gills, then unites in the dorsal aorta to go to the many parts of the body (Fig. 8-5). The ventral aorta is peculiar to vertebrates using gills for respiration. Elsewhere there are no capillaries between heart and dorsal aorta. The amphibians begin life with gills and a ventral aorta, but as the gills are lost and lungs appear, the arteries become modified and the gill capillaries are no more. In frogs and other amphibians, however, the heart also changes. The auricle becomes divided into a right auricle receiving blood from the body veins via the sinus venosus, and a left receiving it from the lungs by way of the **pulmonary veins.** The two auricles empty their contents into the single ventricle in a sequence that insures minimum mixing of the unaerated blood from the right and the oxygen-rich blood from the left. Close timing on the valves allows the oxygenated blood to go chiefly through the carotid arteries to the head, and the **aortic arches** to the dorsal aorta and body, while the unaerated passes by way of **pulmonary arteries** to the lungs (and skin) for respiratory exchange.

Birds and mammals, including man, have a four-chambered heart through which the blood passes twice in a single cycle (Fig. 8-30). Venous blood returns to the right auricle, which empties into a right ventricle, forcing the blood through pulmonary arteries to the lungs. The aerated blood returns by pulmonary veins to the left auricle, thence to a left ventricle, to be pumped to the rest of the body by way of the dorsal aorta and its branches. The pulmonary circulation is thus distinct from the **systemic circulation,** and there is no opportunity for mixing of oxygen-rich with oxygen-poor blood. The four-chambered heart thus fully matches the presence of lungs for respiration. The two-chambered heart of a fish does equally well in a system using gills for respiration, since blood from the single ventricle reassembles after aeration into the dorsal aorta. In the fish heart, only oxygen-poor blood is present. By contrast, the single amphibian ventricle contains both aerated and unaerated blood simultaneously. Some mixture occurs, reducing the heart's efficiency. In bird and mammal hearts, the double circulation provides for complete separation of a lung circuit and a body circuit.

THE HEART CYCLE. The beating of the heart is remarkably regular. Its general tempo is under nervous and also chemical control, but the basic regularity is maintained by a

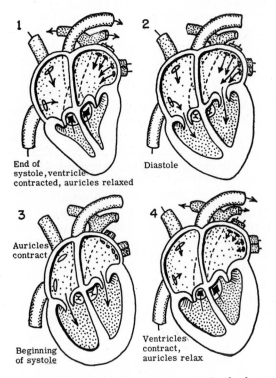

1
End of systole, ventricle contracted, auricles relaxed

2
Diastole

3
Auricles contract
Beginning of systole

4
Ventricles contract, auricles relax

FIG. 8-30. *The sequence of movements in the heart of a warm-blooded animal—bird or mammal—during a single cycle.*

local **pacemaker.** In lower vertebrates, with two- and three-chambered hearts, the sinus venosus, into which venous blood comes just before it enters the heart, has this timing function. In the four-chambered heart, where the sinus venosus is absorbed into the heart structure, it remains represented by a definite bundle of nervous tissue. This pacemaker, like the other in the complete sinus venosus, triggers the contraction of the heart muscle, and the movements of the valves where these have other than a passive role. In this way the regular alternation of contraction **(systole)** and elastic expansion **(diastole)** pumps out one lot of blood and admits another. The changes in pressure are felt all along the

arterial system, and there is even a measurable physical reaction in the body as a result of it squirting the blood out of the heart —throwing it, quite literally, around the aortic arch. As the blood leaves the heart in the direction of the head, the heart and the body shift with it slightly, though measurably, in the opposite direction. This action and reaction provide movements of the human body that can be observed on a good bathroom scale—slight but sudden variations in the weight that correspond to the rhythmic beating of the heart. This is the basis of operation in the clinical tool called a ballistocardiograph (from the Greek *ballein* = throw, *cardios* = heart, and *graphos* = write). The recorded ballistocardiogram is the basis for calculating a person's cardiac output.

Time studies of heartbeat rate allow understanding of several points. The rate at rest differs greatly in various animals. In general, the larger the vertebrate, the slower the beat:

Mammal	Pulse at Rest Beats per Min.	Blood Temp. °F.	Resp. Rate per Min.	Adult Weight Lbs.
Mouse	328-780	95-100	84-230	0.05
Rat	261-600	95-100	100-120	1
Rabbit	140-160	102	55	7-12
Cat	120-140	101.7	24	7-12
Dog	70-120	101-102	15-20	7-40
Pig	70-80	101-103.5	8-18	900
Sheep	70-80	104-105	12-20	100-140
Man	**60-80**	**98.8**	**15-20**	**100-200**
Lion	40-50	98.6	10	580
Dromedary	30	83-104	9-13	990
Horse	30-45	100.2	8-10	900-1100
Cow	40-70	101.5	10-30	1000-2000
Elephant	25-47	97.6°	5	12,000-13,000

° Heat production from the skin (two Calories per square inch per day) is the greatest known in any warm-blooded animal; the skin is about 10 degrees cooler than the blood temperature shown.

In man, the 72 beats per minute allow about 0.8 second per beat. Of this, 0.1 sec. is the duration of systole in the auricles, followed by 0.3 sec. systole of the ventricles, followed by relaxation in diastole. Hence the heart is in diastole—recovery—far more than half of each cycle.

BLOOD PRESSURE. The heart maintains a positive pressure in the arterial system—a pressure that changes from low at diastole to high at the peak of systole. The pressure depends upon two factors: (1) the vigor with which the heart pumps, and (2) the state of contraction of the muscular walls of the smaller arteries that lead to the capillaries.

Relaxation of these muscles, as in sleep or the lassitude induced by hot weather, allows the blood to pass through the capillaries under a lower pressure, and the heart has less to work against. Consequently the blood pressure falls.

If the blood vessels' muscular coats are somewhat contracted, and if an animal starts up from a state of rest, several changes are noted within a matter of seconds. The heart beats more rapidly—hence pumps more blood per minute. To allow the extra blood to pass through the capillaries without excessive increase in pressure, the muscles around the smaller arteries relax. Still the pressure rises. And as the pressure increases, so too does the volume of blood passing through the heart at each beat—still further augmenting the flow rate per minute. The heat liberated from muscular contraction causes a slight elevation of the blood temperature, and this, in a warm-blooded animal, leads to further dilation of the vessels near the body surface, allowing increased heat loss and keeping the body temperature from significant change.

In measuring human blood pressures, an inflatable rubber cuff is wrapped around the upper arm. The pressure in it is read from a mercury manometer, in mm of mercury. Two points are sought: the maximum pressure at the peak of systole, and the minimum pressure during diastole. If unimpeded, the blood flows through the arm arteries through both parts of the cycle. If the cuff blocks it completely, no sound of blood flow can be heard with a stethoscope beyond the cuff. But if the pressure is dropped gradually, the manometer can be read when the first sound is heard. This noise is due to the vibrations of blood squeezing through the space under the cuff, and the nearer the cuff pressure is to the maximum of systole, the briefer is the squeak. As the pressure in the cuff is permitted to fall further, the sound continues—once per heartbeat. But when the cuff pressure reaches the minimum diastolic value, blood is able to flow continuously and the squeak disappears.

The difference between systolic and diastolic pressure is known as the **pulse pressure.** In man these values vary not only with degree of activity, but with age and disease. For resting individuals they are considered normal when within the following ranges:

Age	Systolic pressure	Diastolic pressure	Average pulse
10	103	70	33
20	♂ 105-140	♂ 62-88	
	♀ 100-130	♀ 60-85	40
30	♂ 110-145	♂ 68-92	
	♀ 102-135	♀ 60-88	41
40	♂ 110-150	♂ 70-94	
	♀ 105-150	♀ 65-92	42
50	♂ 115-160	♂ 70-98	
	♀ 110-165	♀ 70-100	44
60	♂ 115-170	♂ 70-100	
	♀ 115-175	♀ 70-100	46

(Partly after Master, Dublin, and Marks, 1950.)

Thus, systolic pressures above 140 and below 100 are considered suspicious if the individual has not been exercising and is relaxed. Rise of pressure with exercise is prompt; its rate of return to normal after exercise is one measure of "youth."

The device for measuring blood pressure (sphygmomanometer) may be made to record variations in pressure as a graph on a continuously moving paper tape. To this device can be added another that measures rate and intensity of respiration, to form a Keeler polygraph or "lie detector." This apparatus operates on the principle that it requires more nervous energy to invent a lie, and more intense metabolism to suppress guilty interest in a subject, than it does to tell the truth and listen to questions about irrelevant matters. A slight rise in blood pressure and change in the breathing record are strong reasons to concentrate the questioning in the direction eliciting these responses. There are known instances where guilty people have failed to show anything on the polygraph, but none where guilt was indicated incorrectly; valid instances of men who have fallen from the top of a five-story building and who have walked away unhurt are about as infrequent and unexpected as those that "beat" the lie detector.

Capillaries and Lymph

In any closed circulatory system, the capillary network is the really significant part. In it alone the chemical exchanges are made: CO_2 goes from the cells and into the surrounding medium, whether air or water; O_2 goes in the opposite direction; products of digestion enter from the gut, and leave to all the tissues; wastes are received from each living cell, and are filtered out in the kidneys.

To accomplish these vital errands the blood must course through the capillaries at a pace neither too slow nor too rapid. Diffusion and absorption and secretion must occur in the smallest vessels, where the tube may be as small as 4 μ in diameter and the walls are a single cell thick—formed of characteristically flattened squamous "endothelium." Here alone the blood comes within a millimeter of every cell in the body—the limiting distance for effective distribution by diffusion.

The rate of flow through the capillaries is determined largely by the tonic contraction of the muscular walls in the arterioles leading to them. The total cross-sectional area of the arterioles is greater than that of the aorta, and the total cross-sectional area of the capillaries greatly exceeds that of the arterioles. Since the same blood courses through all of these vessels in turn, its rate of flow and its pressure drop far below those characteristic of the aorta (Fig. 8-31). At the same time, the frictional resistance of so many capillary wall surfaces effectively damps out the variations between diastolic and systolic pressure—transforming pulsating flow into steady flow.

The total volume of the capillary network is between 400 and 800 times that of the aorta, but this full "capacity" is never in operation at any one time. The system may be compared to the city water lines in a large house. So long as only a few faucets are open at any given moment, the pressure at each of them is acceptably high. But if too many demands are made upon the system simultaneously, the pressure drops rapidly. The blood circulates through every capillary pathway many times a day, but at any given time only a small proportion are carrying their fullest possible flow. The body is well supplied with alternate pathways, and if one becomes clogged, others take over.

LYMPH. The mechanical pressures produced by the heart at the arteriole end of a capillary network (about 40 mm Hg) and that at the venule end (about 20 mm Hg) are large enough to force fluid out of the vessels and into the tissue spaces. The delicate capillary walls leak. Some of this fluid is drawn back in through osmotic activity due to proteins and other molecules carried by the blood. The remainder of the exuded fluid is called **lymph.**

Lymph is formed in rather significant amounts. Each vertebrate carefully salvages the exudate by draining the tissue spaces through diffuse, connected, conducting channels (Fig. 8-32) called **lymph vessels** or **lymphatics.** In some animals, such as the frog, there are accessory pumps (lymph hearts) that help propel the lymph. Just as the lymph forms at the points where the pressure is high and the walls thinnest, it is returned to the general circulation at the point of lowest pressure. In mammals most of the lymph passes through the **thoracic duct** just before the blood enters the heart from the veins.

The slow return of lymph gives the body opportunity to use the fluid in two ways: (1) to carry fatty acids and glycerol from the villi to the general circulation without passing through the liver; and (2) to wash from the tissue spaces any bacteria or other foreign bodies, and carry them through special filters called **lymph glands** where these potentially harmful materials can be destroyed. The lymph and lymph glands are part of the body's defense system against disease.

Sometimes, as a result of infection or mechanical damage or faulty heart action, lymph is formed faster than it returns to the general circulation. It then produces local swelling known as **edema.** Bruised areas, infections,

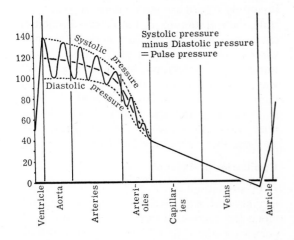

FIG. 8-31. *Variations in blood pressure along the cyclic pathway taken by the blood. The ordinate is pressure in mm Hg.*

bites, and stings may cause not only engorgement of lymph spaces locally but also lead to enlargement of the lymph glands if these become active in removing dangerous substances from the returning lymph.

Disorders of the Circulatory System

Wherever medical care is now widespread, only cancer competes with heart diseases and

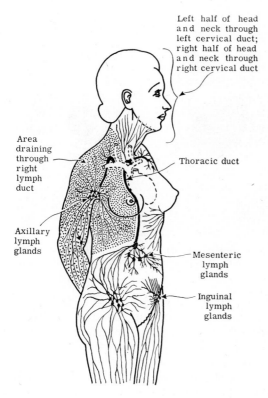

Left half of head and neck through left cervical duct; right half of head and neck through right cervical duct

Area draining through right lymph duct

Thoracic duct

Axillary lymph glands

Mesenteric lymph glands

Inguinal lymph glands

FIG. 8-32. *The lymphatic drainage of the human body.*

vascular damage (thrombosis and hemorrhage, particularly coronary and cerebral) for first place among the rising causes of death. At present heart disease leads by a wide margin (p. 469).

Heart defects are of many kinds: (1) the heart valves may fail to open fully, requiring the heart to work harder to move a given volume of blood; or (2) the valves may fail to close, permitting blood to flow back into the heart during diastole, reducing its efficiency. The former (stenosis) and the latter (leakage) can usually be distinguished with a steth-

oscope. In either situation the heart must use reserve power normally called upon only for times of muscular exertion. This places a strain on the organ, and also induces shortness of breath under conditions of mild exercise. Adjustment of activities to match what the heart can do seems to be the only therapy.

Or (3) the heart may fail to get its normal supply of food-bearing, oxygenating blood through the coronary artery. Pain symptoms appear promptly—the symptom known as **angina pectoris.** The condition may be due to (a) a nervous spasm of the smooth muscles in the walls of this artery, reducing the blood flow (nitroglycerin and other treatments can relieve this difficulty); or (b) a clot (thrombus) may block some of the branches of the coronary artery (coronary thrombosis) or a break in some part of the vessel system (coronary hemorrhage) sharply decrease the blood flow to an area of heart muscle. In these latter situations part of the heart actually dies, and can be replaced by noncontractile scar tissue only if the patient allows the heart to rest as much as possible.

Permanent increases in arterial blood pressure (in human adults to as much as 150 mm Hg) are not damaging in themselves. They predispose to other difficulties, however, in that this is a measure with the patient at rest. Exercise or emotional disturbance or hot weather or stimulants cause further rise. At elevated pressures, the capillary walls may burst and the ensuing hemorrhage deprive some vital organ of its blood supply. Accidents to vessels supplying the brain and the heart are particularly serious.

Chronic high blood pressure (**hypertension**) leads also to an acceleration of the ordinary slow increase in wall thickness and decrease in flexibility of arteries and arterioles (Fig. 8-33)—the condition of **arteriosclerosis.** Arteriosclerosis by itself also seems to bring on hypertension, so that a vicious circle is established. Hypertension plus arteriosclerosis makes thrombosis, hemorrhage and embolism particularly probable. Decrease in activities to keep the maximum pressure of the day within as safe limits as possible is the chief present therapy for these common disorders.

Blood

The distinction between the cellular material in blood and the fluid components is most obvious in the capillaries, where the thin walls can retain one and not the other. The fluid components, **plasma,** amount to between 50 and 60 per cent of whole blood in most vertebrates, and of this about 90 per cent is water, the other 10 per cent dissolved the red cells of man furnish a surface area in aggregate amounting to approximately three-fourths of an acre—32,500 square feet. This area is exposed to the plasma and accounts for the remarkable speed and seeming ease with which oxygen can pass by diffusion from plasma to hemoglobin in the gills or lungs, to unite loosely into oxyhemoglobin. Oxyhemoglobin is bright red, whereas hemoglobin is purplish. The difference in color between ar-

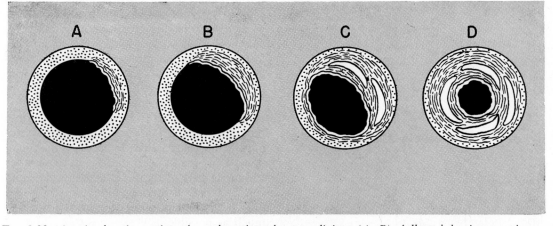

FIG. 8-33. *Arteriosclerosis consists of an ulceration of artery linings (A, B), followed by increase in connective tissue, deposition of the fatty substance cholesterol, and in severe cases, substitution with calcium and serious occlusion of the vessel (D).*

salts and suspended plasma proteins (Fig. 8-34). The cells, which comprise between 40 and 50 per cent of whole blood, are of two main types: (1) rather regular red cells, the erythrocytes, containing the important pigment, hemoglobin; and (2) irregular, almost ameboid white cells, the **leucocytes.** In addition, among the nonescaping components of whole blood are noncellular bodies called **platelets,** which are part of the clotting mechanism.

ERYTHROCYTES. Red cells are much more numerous than any others. They total about 4,500,000 per cubic millimeter in women, 5,000,000 in men. About 90 per cent of each by dry weight, or 50 per cent by wet weight, is hemoglobin ($C_{3032}H_{4816}O_{872}N_{780}S_8Fe_4$). The cell shape is characteristic for each kind of animal. Thus those of the frog are oval, while human red cells are small biconcave disks only about 7.7 μ in diameter. Because of their immense numbers, however, terial blood and venous blood is due entirely to the oxygen content bound in or lacking from the hemoglobin in the red cells. The difference in color between arteries and veins, however, is due only in part to the color of the red blood cells, since the arteries have heavier muscular walls that conceal the bright blood within.

Thanks to its red cells, vertebrate blood is able to absorb and carry about 50 times the load of oxygen that would be possible in an equal volume of plasma under corresponding conditions. Of this oxygen, about 98 per cent is in the cells, the rest being dissolved in the plasma and in the protoplasm of the erythrocytes. Carbon dioxide, on the other hand, is much more soluble in the plasma. Some of it remains in simple solution, but about 60 per cent is transported in combination as sodium bicarbonate. In the tissues, where CO_2 is in greater supply, the gas tension in solution is high, and the bicarbonates form from carbonates—thereby rendering the blood less alkaline. This change, in turn, assists the oxyhemoglobin in releasing its oxygen to become plain hemoglobin, allowing the oxygen to pass by diffusion to the cells. At the other end, in lungs or gills or skin, the dissolved carbon dioxide diffuses away, the bicarbonates decompose to carbonates (more alkaline) and carbon dioxide (which also leaves the blood stream). The greater alkalinity favors combination of oxygen with hemoglobin, and hence enhances the oxygen transport possibilities of the erythrocytes.

Red cells are formed in the embryo by the spleen, a small or medium-sized organ in the mesenteries near the stomach. After hatching of birds or birth of mammals the marrow tissue of the long bones and ribs supplements or even takes over the red cell production. The spleen then operates in large part like a lymph node, filtering out bacterial cells and other harmful materials. It also maintains in its sinuses a reserve of blood which becomes available under conditions of hemorrhage, and a

supply of red cells that are released into the general circulation during muscular exertion, at higher environmental temperatures, and at high altitudes. In this last situation, prolonged exposure to low atmospheric pressure and low oxygen availability also leads to increase in the pigment concentration in each of the red cells. Sometimes the spleen develops pathological anomalies and must be removed (splenectomy). Loss of the organ involves no harmful aftereffects, although there is a lowered resistance to bacterial disease.

The erythrocytes of almost all mammals are peculiar in that they lack a nucleus during their presence in the blood stream. Other vertebrates retain the nucleus. It has been suggested that the disappearance of the nucleus as mammalian red cells mature leaves more space for hemoglobin, and that the loss shortens the potential life of each erythrocyte. Certainly they do "wear out," and

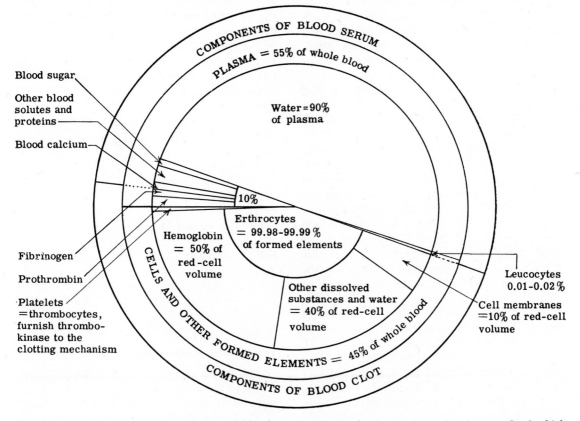

FIG. 8-34. *The components of whole human blood can be separated into numerous fractions, each of which appears to have an important function.*

failure to replace red cells at an adequate rate allows the erythrocyte count to drop—the diagnostic clue to the clinical symptom called **anemia.** Sometimes this is due simply to a lack of iron-containing foods in the diet, since hemoglobin involves this element in its complex structure. More often the cause is obscure, and a large number of different anemias are recognized. At least one is due to metal poisoning, which reduces the activity of human bone marrow, so that the supply of new red cells falls off. Another is due to excess red cell destruction in the liver, recognized by a rise in the pigments eliminated in urine and feces. Normally the removal of worn-out red cells (and possibly other functions) liberates into the human system some 25 grams of hemoglobin daily—roughly the amount present in 160 ml of blood, or about $\frac{1}{30}$ of the total blood supply of the body (slightly over five quarts). This fact would suggest that the average life span of a red cell cannot be much more than a month, but work with radioactive tracer elements indicates that 100 days or more is the actual life span. Hence the hemoglobin transfer measured is not all from this source.

Abnormal conditions in the blood may lead to escape of the hemoglobin into the plasma —the sudden, all-or-none process of **hemolysis.** It can be due to a decrease in concentration of plasma constituents until the solution is hypotonic and the red cells enlarge excessively, then lose control of their permeability. It may be caused by substances liberated into the blood stream by disease organisms or poisonous snakes. Malaria parasites invade the red cells and destroy the contents of large enough numbers to create a measurable decrease in the hemoglobin content of the blood. The hemoglobin, computed in terms of per cent of full content of all erythrocytes, then becomes a clinical cue to the state of health in the individual; it is measured in many routine physical examinations.

LEUCOCYTES. White cells in the blood are far less numerous than the red, even under conditions of severe illness due to infections, when the leucocytes seem particularly in evidence. For man, 5,000 to 9,000 white cells per cubic millimeter is an average number,

though in appendicitis and some other conditions the proportion may rise to 25,000 or above. Each cell is remarkably independent. Partly by ameboid movement, it can squeeze between the cells of capillary walls to leave the blood stream and enter the lymph as a **lymphocyte.** Indeed, the normal repository for a large proportion of the white cells of a healthy vertebrate is in the lymph nodes. Many white cells seem to remain there as permanent fixtures, called "stationary **phagocytes**" (from the Greek *phagos* = devour) because of the way they ingest bacteria and cellular debris. Other white cells in the lymph glands emerge into lymph vessels and join the general circulation in any emergency. The spleen again acts as a manufacturing and storage center for lymphocytes, and this function may explain the recently discovered protection that the spleen affords against damage from atomic radiations.

Leucocytes are of several kinds, but each can be recognized only in terms of the shape of the nucleus, the reaction to dyestuffs, and the presence or absence of granules in the cytoplasm. A majority are of a type which ingest bacteria or cellular debris and which react clearly to chemical stimulation; they have a rather granular cytoplasm and a definitely lobed nucleus. Possibly a third of the white cells in human blood are so similar to the nonwandering phagocytes in the lymph nodes that they are termed lymphocytes. They accumulate rapidly in regions of infection, and they seem to produce antibodies while alive, and enzymes that assist in digestion of dead tissue when they degenerate. Lymphocytes have a relatively large nucleus and a cytoplasm almost free of granules; they react but little to chemical stimuli. Other white cells include basophils, eosinophils (named according to their reaction to dyes), and the especially large monocytes which are particularly prompt in destruction of bacteria and cellular remains, and participate in repair of damaged tissues in cuts and bruises.

The Clotting Mechanism

The blood contains its own safety system, ready to close any small break in the enclosing vessels and prevent death by hemorrhage. If whole blood comes in contact with a foreign object which it can wet, or has added to it any extract ("tissue juice") from injured cells, its platelets break down into an enzyme. This substance, in the presence of calcium ions, catalyzes chemical interaction between plasma proteins, leading to the formation of insoluble strands of the protein **fibrin.** These strands form a meshwork across the wound and trap red cells to form a **clot.** Blood from which the clotting mechanism has been removed is **serum**—a clear straw-colored liquid familiar as the exudate which escapes through a fresh clot. Vitamin K, the antihemorrhagic vitamin, is needed for proper development of clot-forming proteins.

Sometimes clot formation fails in rather ordinary injuries. In man, there is an inherited deficiency in this direction, called **hemophilia,** in which the most apparent difference in the blood of the victim is that the platelets are especially resistant to tissue extract. Since they fail to disintegrate, the clotting mechanism does not even start. Beadle has found that certain of the blood proteins are lacking or abnormal, and he believes these to be an essential part of the clotting chemistry. The disease is usually fatal to girls before birth, and men afflicted with it seldom attain a reasonable life span. Probably hemophilia would never have attained very great notoriety had it not been a difficulty of the Spanish royal family. The disease is interesting to students of genetics, moreover, because of the peculiar sex-linked method of its inheritance. A strictly comparable disease, inherited in the same way, has recently been recognized in dogs.

Clot formation is prevented, too, if blood is drawn off into paraffined glassware whose walls it cannot wet, through paraffined tubes inserted far enough into blood vessels that no tissue extract reaches the blood to stimulate breakdown of platelets. In many blood transfusions, however, the whole blood is taken, clot formation is stimulated, the clot removed, and only the serum is used—as a replacement for water and the many dissolved and suspended noncellular components.

Occasionally clots form within intact blood vessels. With luck, they become lodged in some capillary area of relative insignificance, where the blood flow can largely bypass the mass, and the leucocytes perhaps isolate and destroy it. Such a clot is referred to as a **thrombus,** and the condition of embolism (shifting blood clots) is one filled with danger. For if an embolus lodges in a blood vessel supplying an important area of the brain, the cells there are cut off from their normal food and oxygen supply. Paralysis occurs if the brain area is concerned with body movements. Paralysis of important organs or vital functions, if prolonged, results in death, and the diagnosis is cerebral thrombosis. Coronary thrombosis, which deprives the heart of its blood supply through blocking off the coronary artery (or major parts of it) by an embolus, is another common cause of death.

Since clotting of blood in intact vessels is so serious, it would be surprising if the body did not contain compounds that inhibit clot formation. These are **anticoagulants.** One that can be extracted from liver or muscle, and concentrated, is **heparin.** It inactivates small quantities of clotting enzyme caused by occasional spontaneous breakdown of platelets. The concentrated extract is now used to prevent clotting in surgery, bridging the postoperative period while damaged cells are in contact with the blood stream. Use of heparin has greatly extended the range of operations, since grafting of blood vessels without it almost always causes prompt death from thrombosis. Another anticoagulant in present use is dicoumarol.

Anticoagulants such as citrates, oxalates, and fluorides are sometimes used to remove the calcium from a blood sample, interrupting the clotting mechanism at another point. Leeches add to their blood meal a powerful anticoagulant called hirudin; other bloodsucking forms have similar chemical secretions that keep the meal fluid. Hirudin and some others inactivate the clotting enzyme much as heparin does.

Other Plasma Components

In addition to components of the clotting mechanism and water, the plasma contains many other important materials. Simple sugars, fat globules, fatty acids, glycerol, amino acids, mineral ions of many types, and vitamins are among those removed from digested food in the gut. They are transferred to parts of the body where they are absorbed and used, or to depots where they can be stored.

Carbon dioxide, both in solution and combined with dissolved chemical substances, is transported by the plasma from the cells, where respiration is in constant progress, to the gills or lungs, where release of this waste can be accomplished. The products of muscular activity and of protein breakdown appear in the blood plasma as "nitrogenous wastes" —urea or other compounds eliminated through the kidneys into the urine. Proteins and simpler, inorganic compounds are present that maintain the slightly alkaline character of the blood in spite of addition or loss of carbon dioxide in the respiratory cycle; these substances also account for the osmotic relationships of the blood, for the low surface tension (the source of its foamy appearance as seen when mixed with water or whipped in a beaker), and other features.

Hormones are carried primarily in the plasma; the blood is the vehicle transferring these chemical messengers from the site of their formation to the organs they stimulate or inhibit.

ANTIBODIES. Still other substances in plasma provide the several separate mechanisms that combat disease and the basis for blood types:

1. OPSONINS, of a specific sort, developed in the blood as the result of the presence of bacteria in the blood stream. Either living or dead bacteria act as sufficient stimulus for opsonin formation. The result is an increase in the activity of leucocytes in engulfing the foreign organisms.

2. AGGLUTININS, of specific types (one agglutinin for each kind of bacteria) cause a clumping of the bacterial cells. In some way this renders the foreign materials more available to leucocytes, which then act as the removing agents.

3. LYSINS, of specific type, destroy the cell walls of invading organisms, releasing their protoplasm into the blood and bringing about their death. Again, even the presence of dead bacteria is a sufficient stimulus for development in the plasma of the appropriate lysin.

4. PRECIPITINS, of specific type, operate on molecules such as proteins, agglutinating them (causing them to go into the gel state and precipitate) as particles on which the leucocytes can work.

5. ANTITOXINS, of specific type, which neutralize the poisons called *toxins* that arise in the blood stream either as substances diffusing from the cells of living bacteria (especially from those of diphtheria, tetanus, and botulism) or as substances left in the blood stream when the bacterial cells disintegrate.

Collectively these agents are spoken of as **antibodies**—substances which the organism develops in its blood stream and body fluids in response to the presence of bacteria or foreign proteins or their breakdown products. The agents eliciting antibody formation are called **antigens.** Thus, antibodies are called forth by the presence of antigens, and they act in such a way as to hasten the destruction or neutralization of the antigens.

All antibodies function in protecting the organism against further invasion. Many of them remain in the system for years after the first entry of the agents that called them forth. Individuals protected in this way are said to be **immune**—meaning that the disease organisms are destroyed as rapidly as they gain entry into the immune individual, and that no symptoms of disease appear.

Active immunity may be acquired through having the disease itself, or injections of toxoids, or use of vaccines. It differs from passive immunity in that the person's own blood stream produces the effective antibodies. Ordinarily an active immunity lasts for a considerable time: influenza, paratyphoid, or typhoid for about a year; cholera, smallpox, tetanus, around seven years; diphtheria and lobar pneumonia, about 10 years; yellow fever, perhaps for life. Immunity to poliomyelitis through use of the Salk vaccine may last for years.

Toxoids are manufactured by treating the extracted toxins of diphtheria, tetanus, and the like with formaldehyde. The treated toxin no longer produces disease symptoms when introduced into the human blood stream, yet it continues to stimulate production of antibodies which are effective against virulent microbes of the disease.

Vaccination consists of introducing into the blood stream either a nonvirulent strain of the disease organism or organisms of a related, nondangerous disease, where presence of these organisms will call forth antibodies effective against the dangerous disease itself. Most famous of these is the deliberate application of cowpox vaccine to get a localized reaction which will confer immunity toward smallpox.

Passive immunity is obtained through injections of antitoxins or antibodies of other kinds, which have been produced by some other animal. Usually this is an emergency measure, and its effectiveness is strictly temporary.

Antitoxins are obtained in quantity by repeatedly injecting an experimental animal such as a horse with a specific toxin, such as that obtained as an extract of diphtheria bacteria grown in laboratory glassware. When the horse has built up a high concentration of diphtheria antitoxin in its blood, its serum (with the antitoxin) may be injected into a human diphtheria victim. The antitoxin is expected to neutralize the diphtheria toxin in the patient, eliminating the unpleasant effects of the live diphtheria organisms present, while other treatment gradually eliminates the infection itself. This prevents "side reactions" that may do permanent damage to the diphtheria sufferer.

Antivenin is another example. If a gradually increasing dosage of rattlesnake venom is injected regularly over a period of weeks into a goat, antibodies are built up which are effective in neutralizing venom from any of the rattlers or other pit vipers. Serum containing this high concentration of antibodies can be kept fresh for months in the refrigerator.

When a person is bitten by a pit viper, the venom ordinarily is injected subcutaneously into the connective tissue spaces—the ultimate portions of the lymphatic system. After all possible venom has been removed at the site of the bite, measures are taken to slow the rate at which lymph flow carries the residual venom into the general circulation. This may be by the modern, preferred method of applying ice to the bitten area, inducing vascular contraction and reduced blood flow to the area. Or it may through use of a tourniquet—tied tightly enough to block lymphatic flow but not obstruct circulation in arteries and veins (and removed for a minute every quarter hour to be sure that circulation in the vessels is not stopped, leading to death of tissue, i.e. "gangrene").

Antivenin (= goat serum rich in venom antibodies) is then injected judiciously by the attending physician over a 24- to 36-hour period. Only enough is injected to overcome distress symptoms arising as the residual venom reaches the general circulation. An overdose of antivenin can be just as serious as none at all.

The study of agglutinins and precipitins entails careful examination of the many reactions possible because of these special substances in the blood serum. It constitutes a highly restricted approach to the study of blood (hematology), and is called **serology.** A very practical use for serological examinations is in the diagnosis of low-grade chronic infections. The body develops antibodies and antitoxins because of the presence of the disease organisms and their waste products; the antibodies can be recognized (if agglutinin or precipitin) according to the action of serum of the tested animal when mixed drop for drop with blood of animals known to have the disease. If the tested animal has no antibodies for the disease, nothing happens, and the presumption is that the tested animal does not have the disease. But if antibodies are present in the tested serum, the blood cells of the known blood (diseased animal) may clump due to agglutinins, or colloidal material suspended in it may be precipitated due to precipitins. These reactions are studied under the microscope, and require anywhere from a few seconds to several hours.

Foreign Blood

Some of the possibilities of antibody action in the blood are not related to disease organisms and foreign proteins in the usual sense. They are inherited mechanisms that do not change, either by increase or decrease. Yet, like any ordinary antibody, they react in a definite way when in the presence of the appropriate antigen.

BLOOD GROUPS. Usually an antigen is thought of as a foreign protein, or as bacterial cells. This additional type of antigen was discovered early in the 20th century, in connection with blood transfusions. It was found that there are four blood groups in human beings and that transfusions between people of the same group cause little or no clot formation, but that where two different groups are involved, great care must be taken except when transfusing only plasma. The antigens are in the red blood cells of three of the four groups, and the blood groups are now named according to the antigens. Thus blood group AB has antigens A and B, in all red cells; group A has antigen A only; group B has antigen B only; and group O has no antigens at all. Correspondingly, the plasma of three of the four groups contain antibodies. Group AB has none; group A has antibody *b;* group B has antibody *a;* group O has antibody *a* and antibody *b*. These antibodies are peculiar in that they develop without the stimulus of the corresponding antigen.

If blood cells with antigen A are added to plasma containing antibody *a,* or blood cells with antigen B are added to plasma containing antibody *b,* clumping of red cells (agglutination) begins at once inside the blood system and the recipient is in desperate straits.

Even the antibodies contained in a donor's plasma may be significant, reacting with some of the recipient's cells. That more damage is not done apparently arises from partial absorption of antibodies by the tissues of an incompatible recipient, and from the dilution of the donor's plasma by that of the recipient.

In emergencies, the antibodies in the donor's plasma may be neglected and whole blood of type A, O, or B given to a type-AB recipient, or whole blood of type O given to type-A, type-B, or type-AB recipients. From this use, the term "universal donor" for type-O people, and "universal recipient" for type-AB people has arisen. That some agglutination of the recipient's cells is probable in any cross transfusion should not be overlooked.

The inheritance of blood groups is discussed on p. 320, and the percentages of various ethnic groups having each blood group is shown in a table on p. 459.

THE RH FACTOR. Whereas antibodies have a high degree of interchangeability among the vertebrates, antigens are usually unique for each kind of organism. Consequently surprise accompanied the 1940 discovery by Landsteiner and Wiener that an antigen in the red blood cells of the Rhesus monkey was present also in about 85 per cent of the white populations of Nordic and Mediterranean mankind. Since these 85 per cent carry the antigen, they do not form an antibody toward this normal component of their own blood.

The 15 per cent lacking the "Rh factor" (said to be Rh-negative) can and do develop antibodies to the Rh antigen if exposed to red cells containing it. The Rh antibodies are lysins which destroy Rh-positive red cells. If an Rh-negative person is given a transfusion of whole blood from an Rh-positive donor, antibodies usually develop. Such a person may react vigorously to a later transfusion of whole blood from an Rh-positive donor, even though in each instance the A, B, AB, or O relationships are completely compatible.

Shortly after discovery of the Rh factor, it was noted that over 90 per cent of newlyborn children and stillbirths suffering from *erythroblastosis fetalis* were Rh-positive babies with Rh-negative mothers. This disease is an anemia brought about by hemolysis of the fetal blood, and consequent jaundice.

The explanation seems to lie in a slow penetration of antigen-bearing red cells from the Rh-positive fetus into the maternal circulation, there stimulating development of Rh antibodies. Then these antibodies invade the fetus in sufficient concentration to damage its red cells and hence its ability to distribute oxygen efficiently to its developing parts. If the fetus obtains too little oxygen, death and expulsion may result.

In the United States alone, some 10,000 babies annually are born alive but ill from Rh incompatibilities. Some are saved by prompt transfusion—replacing all of the child's blood (containing antibodies derived from the mother) with blood free from Rh antibodies. Many pregnancies end in disaster from the same incompatibility.

Rh-positive babies in Rh-negative mothers result only when the father is Rh-positive. Determination of the Rh constitution of prospective parents allows some prediction of the occurrence of the disease. Testing of all human females for Rh should precede any transfusion of whole blood, to avoid sensitizing Rh-negative individuals.

Fortunately, only from 2 to 5 per cent of potential cases develop erythroblastosis, giving the disease an incidence of between 0.2 and 0.5 per cent in the whole population. By contrast, about 10 per cent of all pregnancies involve Rh-negative mothers and Rh-positive fathers. Apparently the integrity of the fetal circulation is good. And development of the antibodies to a toxic concentration is slow enough that one or more normal children may be born before an Rh-negative mother becomes a poor risk for further pregnancies.

The genetic basis for the Rh factor is discussed on p. 321, and its incidence among ethnic groups of mankind shown in the table on p. 459.

The interrelations of the proteins in blood plasma and the whole defense mechanism in the circulating medium are so intricate that it is difficult to see how it arose by orderly steps. Yet the various transport and protective mechanisms are no monopoly of man or the mammals, or even the vertebrates. They can be traced down the scale of organization into progressively simpler animals. In such a comparative study the plasma usually receives most attention. The goal is to make plasma artificially, since it is a nonliving, complex solution. Many of its normal components are now extracted as valuable therapeutic aids.

Artificial Blood

For emergency use, a simple solution of sodium chloride of the proper concentration can be employed in place of plasma to maintain blood volume and to stave off the effects of "shock." To be exact, a 0.9 per cent solution of table salt is effective; it neither causes cells and tissues to swell through endosmosis nor to collapse by plasmolysis. Still more suitable, however, is a balanced solution containing, in addition to sodium and chloride ions, rather definite amounts of such others as potassium, calcium, carbonate, and either sulfate or phosphate.

Foreign Proteins

Similar animals or similar plants have similar proteins in their blood streams or cell saps. This is demonstrated by making weekly injections of the serum of one animal (or the sap of one plant) into the blood stream of a quite different experimental organism, until the recipient builds up a good defense against the foreign injections, in terms of antibodies. Thus a rabbit might be "sensitized" to horse serum. Then a drop of serum from such a rabbit mixed with a drop of horse blood would cause prompt clumping of the cells and precipitation of proteins—visible changes that can be recognized and measured in terms of time required. But the serum of the sensitized rabbit will also precipitate proteins from and agglutinate cells in zebra blood—though the vigor of the reaction is less and the time required is longer. On cow blood the rabbit serum has no significant effect; nor on that from dog, cat, or rooster. The agglutinin and precipitin reactions, then, indicate that the chemistry of horse and zebra blood are more alike than that of horse and cow, or horse and cat, for example. These facts have helpful connotations that will be discussed further in Chapter 16.

The animal receiving regular injections of foreign proteins (such as the rabbit with horse serum) may show symptoms of discomfort with the first or second injection, but it soon develops an immunity that is closely similar to the immunity to a disease which so often follows recovery from the disease. Later injections or later infections are not harmful to the organism, since the blood is already equipped with the chemical substances that destroy the foreign material as fast as it is introduced. But if the rabbit were given, say, three injections at two-day intervals and then no more for six months, something different develops in the blood stream. The difference is seen at once if a further injection—even a much smaller one—is given at the end of the waiting period. The animal goes into convulsions, then into shock, and dies. The condition is called **anaphylaxis** (from the Greek *ana* = back, and *phylasso* = guard). Fortunately, such a disaster is rare in human beings, though two types of cases occur occasionally: (1) a man is stung by a bee, and suffers the usual aftereffects; six months or a year later—the time seems not to be at all critical—the same individual receives another bee sting and dies of it in a matter of minutes, often in convulsions; (2) one member of a party, all of whom ate the same meal, is taken suddenly and violently ill; an unfamiliar dietary article in the meal may be found to which the one individual had previously developed a sensitivity. The precise nature of such sensitization is not well understood.

In the human being, acute sensitivities are common enough but their symptoms are less violent—usually involving inflammation of the mucous membranes of the respiratory tract, with sneezing, itching, constriction of the air passages and consequent difficulty in breathing (asthma), or appearance of a rash on the skin (dermatitis); collectively these are described as **allergies** or allergic responses. Each is thought to be due to the introduction into the system of definite foreign proteins to which the organism is sensitive. The substance may enter through the nasal membranes, through the skin, the digestive tract, or by way of insect bites. Often the nature of the irritating substance can be learned by painting aqueous or alcoholic extracts of a wide variety of known foods, dusts, dandruffs, pollens, and the like on the skin of the forearm, over shallow sterile half-inch slits made through the outer skin layers. Local swelling with or without inflammatory dilatation of the capillaries is a clue to which of the variety of substances is a specific irritant. Those to which the individual is strongly responsive cause formation of great swelling and redness in the area around the particular cut. Those where the response is slight may involve only slight appearance of pink in that neighborhood.

Skin tests of this type are routine clinical procedures in dermatology. Sometimes it is easy for the allergy victim to avoid the source of irritation (cats or strawberries, for example) or to live remote from the source (perhaps cedar pollen or ragweed pollen). In some instances it is possible for a person to take injections of the irritant in repeated doses of increasing size until an immunity has been built up. Often immunities achieved in this way are short-lived, which may indicate some chemical deficiency inherent in the patient's system. That allergies apparently tend to run in families supports the idea that they represent variation with a genetic background

—perhaps an inability to form antibodies to some particular types of foreign proteins.

10. EXCRETION

Every living cell is constantly producing soluble wastes that cannot be allowed to accumulate if life is to continue. In multicellular animals, the substances absorbed from digested food often include toxic types and materials in amounts beyond the needs of the organism. One function of the vertebrate liver is in organizing waste substances from all sources into forms that can be transported by the blood stream and then excreted quantitatively by the kidneys.

Deamination and Detoxification

Since animals are characteristically unable to synthesize all of the amino acids required for formation of their own protoplasmic proteins, they depend upon absorption of certain amino acids from digested food materials. Unless the organism is acting as a cannibal, the proportions of the amino acids in its food will never be the same as the proportions that go into its own protoplasm. For this reason, some amino acids absorbed from the digested proteins of foods will be in excess supply. On a generous diet probably most amino acids are absorbed in amounts greater than can be utilized.

Amino acids absorbed into a vertebrate's blood stream circulate widely and are available as raw materials to all cells of the body. The liver serves as a monitor on the concentration of each amino acid in the blood. As the level rises beyond a critical point, liver cells commence to absorb the surplus and dispose of it by **deamination.** This is an oxidative process yielding hydrogen peroxide, ammonia, and organic compounds which may either be oxidized further to CO_2 and H_2O with release of useful energy, or disposed of in the bile. Hydrogen peroxide is itself a toxic substance, but with the enzyme peroxidase it can be converted into harmless water and oxygen useful in further deaminations.

Various other toxins entering the blood stream (such as those produced by bacteria in the gut) are acted upon by special enzymes in the liver. Thus benzoic acid is combined with the amino acid glycine to yield a soluble, neutral substance that can be eliminated by the kidneys. Others are linked and secreted into the bile. All of these reactions are grouped as **detoxification.**

Nitrogenous Wastes

Since a great proportion of excreted substances is nitrogenous—primarily the by-products of muscular activity and of protein metabolism—excretion consists chiefly in elimination of nitrogen. Yet gaseous nitrogen is never produced. Instead the nitrogen is incorporated into various molecules, each suitable for removal from the blood by the kidneys.

The various nitrogenous wastes can be arranged in a series of increasing complexity and this chemical form related to the life characteristics of the particular organism.

Substance	Formula	% Nitrogen	% Carbon
ammonia	as NH_4OH	40	0
urea	CN_2H_4O	47	20
allantoin	$C_4N_4H_6O_3$	35	30
uric acid	$C_5N_4H_4O_3$	30	36

Ammonia is characteristic of many aquatic organisms, and of mice. In most vertebrates, at least a small amount is eliminated, and may have importance in keeping the urine from becoming too acid. It is the most efficient of nitrogenous excretions, since it requires loss of no carbon from the food compounds. But its use introduces two difficulties. In concentrated solutions it is too alkaline to be tolerated by tissues, and hence must be discharged along with a great deal of water; only organisms which have access to copious water supplies can meet this demand. And the flavor or odor of ammonia is a strong cue, guiding a predator to an ammonia excreter.

Urea is highly soluble, colorless, almost neutral in terms of acid-base balance, odorless, but still easily recognized by flavor. Of all the nitrogenous wastes, it is the most widely met—from Hydra to man. By expending some carbon from the food supply, the organism buys an ability to concentrate the urine without serious consequence—saving water. Urea is formed in the liver of vertebrates using this excretory compound, as the principal product of a cycle of chemical changes taking its energy from ATP, regularly involving the useful amino acid orni-

thine, and utilizing the ammonia from deamination. The urea travels to the kidneys by way of the blood stream, and is lost also in sweat and saliva. Under the name carbamide, urea is a common ingredient of toothpastes.

Uric acid is used by far fewer vertebrates. It is the most expensive in terms of carbon loss, but has the advantage of almost complete insolubility. Many reptiles and birds employ uric acid for nitrogenous excretion, seemingly because they may then withdraw and conserve their water supply. The uric acid may accumulate as a paste or a powder. In flying animals, where weight is so important, freedom from watery urine may be a significant factor.

Allantoin is a somewhat similar insoluble waste characteristic of reptile and bird embryos. It accumulates in the allantois inside the shell, without altering the acidity or affecting the osmotic relationships of the water store, or betraying the presence of the egg to the sense organs of scent-guided animals.

Kidneys

Fundamentally, a kidney is a localized device removing fluid wastes and suspended particles from the coelom. Secondarily, however, kidney tubules may become closed off from the coelom and receive their wastes only from capillaries of the blood. In vertebrates this means blood as it passes from the renal arteries to the renal veins. Thus emphasis is placed on functions of the convoluted tubules with their blood supplies, rather than on open ciliated funnels and the discharge of coelomic wastes (Fig. 8-35).

In the process of excretion, any kidney acts as a combined filter and as a reabsorptive and secretory mechanism. The functional units in higher vertebrates consist of minute **renal corpuscles** and the various convoluted tubules. Each corpuscle is composed of a compact, three-dimensional mesh or knot of capillaries, almost completely surrounded by the cup-like end of a kidney tubule. As blood flows through the capillaries, cellular components and protein molecules are retained but small amounts of the remainder of the plasma are forced by mechanical pressures into the cavity of the corpuscle and start down the renal tubule. Included in this liquid are water, salts (both organic and inorganic), sugars, and amino acids—all in concentrations identical with those in the blood stream itself. But as the fluid progresses along the renal tubule, the tubule wall cells reabsorb water, inorganic salts, sugars, and amino acids, and return these to further meshes of capillaries. The

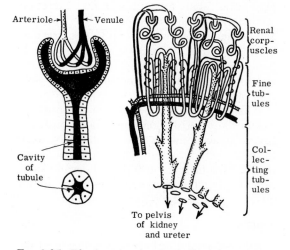

FIG. 8-35. *The functional unit of all adult vertebrate kidneys is the capillary knot* (left) *from which small molecules filter through into the cup-shaped end of a kidney tubule. Differential absorption and secretion bring the fluid in the tubule to the form of urine before it passes to the pelvis of the kidney* (right).

wall cells may also actively transfer from the blood stream to the fluid in the tubule additional organic wastes, but this is not diffusion; it is an energy-utilizing process of secretion. The product of this pressure filtration, reabsorption and active secretion, is urine. It may be from 50 to 70 times as rich in nitrogenous wastes as the blood plasma, reaching this concentration largely by the continued removal of water from a weak solution. Thus 125 ml of filtrate per minute may pass through a single human kidney, but only one ml turns up as urine.

From each kidney the urine passes toward the outside world through a single duct. The simplest kidneys, found in the adult stage of cyclostomes, fish and amphibians, empty through a pair of **Wolffian ducts.** Corresponding kidneys and Wolffian ducts arise during

the embryonic development of reptiles, birds, and mammals. But before becoming functional, these structures of higher vertebrates are replaced by a new, more posterior and more compact kidney on each side. New drainage ducts arise as a pair of **ureters.**

The Bladder

An odorous or flavorful urine may provide predators with telltale cues. Aquatic animals, in general, rid themselves of excretory wastes so continuously and inconspicuously that there is no difficulty. But terrestrial forms, if betrayed by a trail of urine, would be far easier to follow. Perhaps as an adaptation avoiding this possibility, most terrestrial forms have a collecting bag—a urinary bladder—in the cloacal region. In the frog, urine passes from kidney to cloaca via the Wolffian duct, then flows through the cloaca to its floor. There it collects passively in the bladder. At intervals, or when frightened, the animal contracts muscles in the abdominal body wall, compressing viscera and bladder and ejecting the urine through the cloacal aperture.

In higher forms, such as mammals, the termination of the ureters shifts during embryonic development from the general cloacal area to the mouth of the bladder, then along the bladder itself so that urine is delivered directly (though obliquely) into the storage container. The bladder walls also become more muscular, allowing separate control, and when distended tend to prevent transfer of any sudden increase in liquid pressure (such as might be due to a blow on the abdomen) to the thinner-walled, more delicate ureters. The connection between bladder and exterior becomes extended into a new duct, the **urethra.** The cloaca itself is obliterated in mammals, so that urethra and anus open separately to the outside of the body.

Throughout the vertebrates, the excretory system is related closely to the reproductive mechanism. The interrelations are considered in some detail in Chapter 24.

11. CONTINUITY

The vertebrate body plan must be regarded as a highly successful design. When properly coordinated, it operates with the smoothness required by an adaptable organism. Yet the degree to which functions interlock between the organ systems is less conspicuous when each of them is considered separately. This interlocking contributes to the continuity of the animal, and only occasionally introduces difficulties.

The gut, the respiratory and excretory systems are dependent upon the transport function of the circulatory system (Fig. 8-36).

also in passing through such filters as lymph glands and spleen where bacteria can be removed.

The plasma proteins serve as antibodies combating a wide assortment of antigens, and at the same time provide part of the chemical mechanism which maintains the slight alkalinity of the blood and its fairly constant osmotic

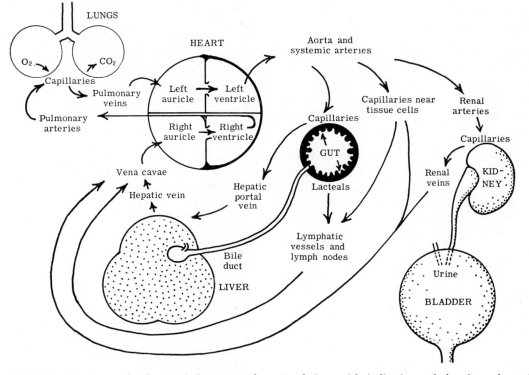

FIG. 8-36. *The fundamental scheme of the mammalian circulation, with indications of the sites where the blood stream gains or discharges its various types of load.*

From the gut the plasma receives water and the products of enzyme action—inorganic salts and sugars, amino acids, and the like. From the gills or lungs or skin (Photo 72) the plasma receives oxygen in exchange for carbon dioxide. The circulating medium carries these substances throughout the body, where they become available to the cells.

Plasma which escapes from the regions of high pressure and thin walls (the capillary beds) is gathered together into lymph spaces and vessels that return it eventually to the main "closed" circulation. This current is utilized too, both in bearing along with it the fats from the lacteals in the intestinal villi, and

character in spite of the extensive ingoing and outgoing of dissolved substances.

The water in plasma is effective as a solvent, as a means of maintaining uniformity of temperature among the various organs and, because of its great thermal inertia, moderating the effects of changes in temperature in the animal's environment. Even loss of water through the skin and mucous membranes of warm-blooded terrestrial animals has been utilized as an important part of their protection against high temperatures.

The gut exhibits functions in addition to the transport of food during digestion and absorption. It serves also as an avenue of elimination for certain wastes, and as part of the body's defense against invasion by parasites. The acid gastric juice and active proteolytic enzymes effectively destroy many potentially harmful organisms which enter along with food. The liver, which basically is an intestinal gland providing wetting agents used in fat digestion, has taken on a number of other tasks.

For one thing, it picks from the blood stream the small quantities of fructose and galactose (six-carbon sugars absorbed from digested foods) and converts them to more useful glucose. Secondly, it maintains in the blood a remarkably steady concentration of glucose, at about 0.1 per cent, by transforming any excess amounts into glycogen and by storing this, or by furnishing new supplies by breaking down its reserve of this complex carbohydrate.[7] Thirdly, it accounts for the principal destruction of excess amino acids, salvaging the carbon, hydrogen, and oxygen parts of the molecules for energy supply but transforming the nitrogenous portion into urea or other excretory waste. Finally, it detoxifies organic and inorganic substances appearing in the blood, stores raw materials needed in hemoglobin formation, and acts as a reserve center for Vitamins A, B complex components, and D.

The internal skeleton not only supports the viscera and forms a protective covering for the central nervous system, but it provides the basis for lever action in the appendages used for locomotion, and for the several types of muscular movements required in the different modes of respiration.

The flexibility of the integument, the presence of skeletal elements to which muscles are attached, and the contractile possibilities of

---

[7] A significant advance in understanding of this important two-way reaction was provided by the work of Carl F. and Gerty T. Cori, whose researches were recognized in 1947 through a Nobel Prize in medicine. In this glycogen-glucose balance, a product of the adrenal gland inhibits glycogen formation from glucose, whereas insulin restrains this inhibition.

a muscular system under good nervous control allow remarkable coordinated movements such as those in the various types of locomotion. Merely curving the compressed body from side to side, alternately to be convex to the right, then to the left, allows swimming. Where paired appendages are present, they also serve for movement in the most usual gait of all—the hind leg approaching the fore on one side (concave) while the fore leg reaches ahead on the opposite (convex).

PENALTIES OF CHANGE. So completely integrated are the various organ systems that a change in habit often introduces difficulties. Examples of this kind are numerous in the human body, clearly related to the fact that man is unique among vertebrates with four feet in that he habitually stands on one pair and uses the other two as hands. His vertebral column shows a compensatory change in having an S-shaped curvature in place of the usual inverted U. His pelvic girdle has almost a bucket form, and provides an unusual amount of support to the sagging viscera.

If man stands still for considerable lengths of time as part of his occupational habits, the blood accumulates in his legs. Partly this is because more pressure is needed to elevate the blood from the many capillaries to the level of his heart; in a four-footed position, with the spinal column horizontal, the heart is seldom higher than the hips. This is the basis for the gradually expanding leg veins of the store clerk, and the freedom from this **varicose** condition among postmen.

In this same upright position, man's sinuses fail to drain properly. In the four-footed position, sinuses merely extend upward and backward from the nasal passages. Like them, the sinuses are lined with mucous membrane. The frontal sinuses are located just below the eyebrows; the maxillary sinuses are slightly farther forward, while the single sphenoid sinus is behind the nose just below the brain. Each of the five has its own duct, but in man these lead upward from sinus to nasal passage. Thus, gravity can drain infective materials into the sinuses instead of out of them.

BLOOD

Thoughts of a medical man just prior to a bullfight in Madrid:

Blood—one could not get one's mind away from blood—blood so precious—so cheap—so frightening to the child when it drips from its cut finger—so curious to the student—blood that flows in the vessels but clots in the wounds—that may be dried and shipped round the world and revive the dying—the crimson that divides with green the honor of being chief color of life—fluid of life—a red Roman drink—laden with corpuscles—white corpuscles and red corpuscles—red because of the haemoglobin—haemoglobin a heavy-molecule pigment—many molecules assembled in such a corpuscle—a biconcave disk in shape—a shape to let the corpuscles squeeze through all the narrow places of the body—to let it swell reasonably without bursting and spilling—thirty-five million million such in a man and ten million made and destroyed every second—the blood of the bull different from the blood of the steed—the blood of the steed different from the blood of the toreador—the blood of one toreador as different from that of another perhaps as his nose—a hot ale that froths— that delivers and carries away—transporter of oxygen, carbon dioxide, food, waste, hormones, vitamins, the whole grand host of the body's chemicals—a shiny liquid that while it moves shifts from red to blue and from blue to red—that by passing from the hot vicinities of the liver to the cool vicinities of the fingertips equalizes the temperatures of the creature—that, as a great Canadian proved, represents the ancient salt water of the sea—the sea when our geological ancestors became terrestrial— stepped up out of it and in so doing carried some of it away with them— inside them—their own cells henceforth floating in their own sea—their own blood—this diluter in salts than the sea of today because that ancient sea was diluter—a fairy-tale fluid—good blood—bad blood—the coward with milk for blood—the writer with ink for blood—"who would have thought the old man to have had so much blood in him?"

—GUSTAV ECKSTEIN, *Everyday Miracle* (New York:
Harper & Bros., 1948), pp. 198-200.

SUGGESTED READING (see pp. 505-510)

Classics and Milestones: Harvey.

Recent and Informative: Burnet, 1954; Carlson & Johnson, 1953; Drinker, 1949; Fox, 1950; Gottlieb, 1948; Gumpert, 1948; Hayashi & Boehm, 1952; Katchalsky & Lifson, 1954; Kemeny, 1955; Kilgour, 1952; McLean, 1955; Page, 1948; Rodbard, 1953; Schick, 1948; Shapiro, 1951; Smith, 1953; Sognnaes, 1953; Surgenor, 1954; Szent-Gyorgyi, 1949.

9 · Other Multicellular Animals

1. COLONIES. 2. TWO CELL LAYERS. 3. BILATERAL SYMMETRY. 4. THE TUBE-WITHIN-A-TUBE. 5. SIMILAR SEGMENTS. 6. EXTERNAL SKELETONS—MOLLUSKS, ARTHROPODS. 7. INTERNAL SKELETONS—ECHINODERMS.

THE EXTREME to which division of labor has been carried among chordates seems reasonable to man—as one species of chordate. He has often concluded that other animals, especially the nonchordates, are simply less well designed and correspondingly limited in their possibilities.

This preoccupation with human and chordate characteristics can conceal our own limitations. It is easy to forget the vast living space in seas and lakes that is closed to us because we lack gills. Our size keeps us from leaping as many times our own length as a flea can, or flying with muscular wings as birds and bats do. Invertebrates of many kinds regularly surpass us by retiring into dormancy when water or food supplies run low.

Actually each plan of animal architecture has its good points and its bad. No one style can provide a combination of advantageous features only. No organism whose limitations outweigh its advantages can survive. Hence the tremendous variety of nonchordates—the real bulk of the animal kingdom, in total species or individuals—is worth investigation, if only to gain perspective for appreciating the chordate plan more fully. As Aristotle wrote: "We ought not childishly to neglect the study even of the most despised animals, for in all natural objects there lies something marvelous."

Since the vertebrate body plan includes certain features, we think of these as important, and rank higher those nonchordates that possess them:

1. Great division of labor
2. Bilateral symmetry
3. An internal skeleton
4. Evidence of segmentation
5. A closed circulatory system
6. Paired locomotory appendages
7. Ability to creep, swim, run, or fly

It has become customary to arrange the multicellular invertebrates in a series, starting with the simplest in structure, and ending with those that are most obviously complex. Some of these gradations can be seen easily from a table (p. 138).

1. COLONIES

The component cells of sponges possess a degree of independence unusual among multicellular animals. On occasion they go off on their own and begin new sponges elsewhere. If no interdependence were evident, each sponge (Photos 85-87) would be regarded simply as an aggregation of cells, each cell an individual. But some indications of a division of labor are present. To describe this balance between independence and interdependence, the term "colonial" is applied to sponge architecture. An individual sponge is a *colony*.

Sponge cells (Fig. 9-1) are of four main kinds: (1) thin, flat cells covering the outer surface of the colony; (2) tubular "pore cells"; (3) flagellated "collar cells"; and (4) free, ameboid cells wandering in a gelatinous matrix between the outer epidermal cells and the collar cells.

Through the beating of the flagella of the collar cells, water is drawn through the pore cells to a central cavity, and then returned to the outside. During this passage, oxygen is removed by all the cells, and the collars of the collar cells capture microscopic food particles. The food may be digested in vacuoles within the protoplasm of the collar cell, or passed to ameboid cells and distributed throughout the colony. All digestion is intracellular. Ameboid cells secrete the gelatinous matrix, and elaborate skeletal materials— lime, or glass, or a plastic-like material called "spongin." The familiar bath sponge is a spongin skeleton left after disintegration of the cells that originally covered it.

The skeleton keeps the sponge up from the bottom, where sediment might block the pores. It spreads the protoplasm in a form that permits maintenance of a feeding, respiring, waste-ridding current. Since the skeleton is diffuse, predators are deterred from attacking a sponge. Only by digestion of fragments can the food-rich cells be separated from the skeleton.

Sponges live attached to solid objects, hence are termed **sessile** organisms. Their feeding method limits them to aquatic situations where plenty of food is suspended. Almost all sponges are marine; they occur at all depths. A few kinds inhabit fresh water. To some extent, sponges rely on water to buoy

them up. They have no protection from desiccation. Since they lack means for locomotion, they must wait for food to come within range of the intake currents driven by the flagella.

In spite of their sessile habits, sponges should not be regarded as helpless. Damage to the colony is repaired quickly. Cells adjacent to a tear become ameboid, reproduce and fill the gap, then reorganize into a new part continuous and homogeneous with the old.

If a sponge is squeezed through a silk screen of fine mesh, its cells are either killed or separated one from another. The living residue can become ameboid, organize itself into a mass, and regenerate into a sponge like the original.

Many sponges will react even to a change in their orientation. If the rock to which they are attached rolls to a new position in which the sponge is inverted or even slightly disoriented, the animal may take one or the other of two courses: (1) it may slowly sepa-

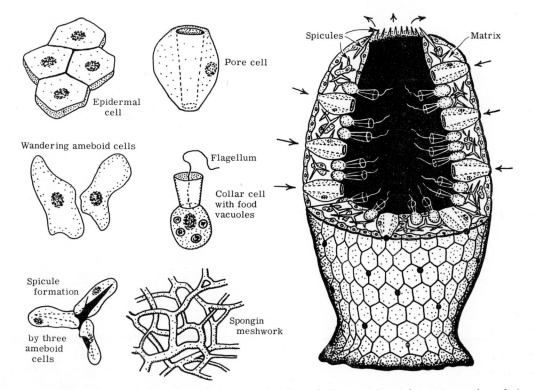

FIG. 9-1. *Sponge architecture depends on four types of cells and the secretions of one type—the gelatinous matrix, plus the spongin meshwork or the characteristic spicules.*

rate into fragments, each of which becomes an ameboid mass creeping to a new location and there reorganizing into a new individual; or (2) it may become disorganized as a single mass in the original site, reorganizing there

2. TWO CELL LAYERS

Division of labor and regularity of form are at a higher level of development among the coelenterates—a phylum which includes the familiar jellyfishes and coral animals. Here the organism is arranged in two definite cell

	SPONGES	COELENTERATES	FLATWORMS	ROUNDWORMS	MOLLUSKS	ANNELIDS	ARTHROPODS	ECHINODERMS	CHORDATES
Found in:									
oceans	x	x	x	x	x	x	x	x	x
fresh water	few	few	x	x	x	x	x		x
soil			few	x	x	few	x		x
air			few	x		few	x		x
Body symmetry:									
lacking	x								
true radial		x							
false radial								x	
bilateral			x	x	x	x	x	(x)	x
Organized tissues		x	x	x	x	x	x	x	x
Three germ layers			x	x	x	x	x	x	x
Digestive cavity		x	x	x	x	x	x	x	x
Organs & systems			x	x	x	x	x	x	x
Both anus & mouth present				x	x	x	x	x	x
Blood circulates				x	x	x	x	x	x
Heart & blood vessels					x	x	x		x
Closed circulation						x			x
Body segmented						x	x		x
Paired locomotory appendages						x	x		x
Diffuse skeleton	x								
Exoskeleton		few			x		x		
Endoskeleton								x	x
As adults, may:									
creep		some	x	x	x	x	x	x	x
swim		some	x	x	few	x	x	few	x
run							x		x
fly							x		x
Regeneration of whole animal from:									
a few cells	x								
fragments representing both layers		x							
large fragments			x					few	
Regeneration more limited				x	x	x	x	x	x

NOTE: *Usual* conditions are shown. Exceptions ordinarily are by degenerative loss, as in parasites.

(without moving away) and achieving a tolerable relationship with gravity. These behaviors indicate a more generalized cell, with greater potentialities, than is to be found in any of the "higher" animals.

layers around a sac-like digestive cavity (Fig. 9-2). The cavity is lined with a thick but single layer of tall cells concerned chiefly with secreting digestive enzymes and absorbing the products of digestion. On the outside of

85. A "finger sponge" from the Atlantic coast of Massachusetts is one of the larger forms found off shore. In tidal water most sponges are of encrusting types.

86. A "vase sponge" from Florida waters may reach height and diameter of a foot or more. This type has little commercial value except to the curio trade.

SPONGES

87. Tarpon Springs, Florida, is center of the American sponge industry. A great variety of sponges is available in the Gulf of Mexico, from depths to 150 feet, but only a few are commercially valuable.

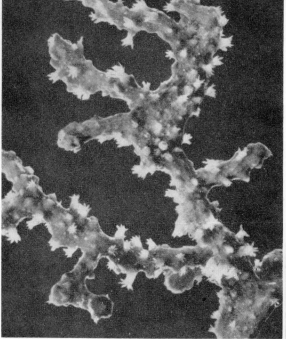

88. Each coral animal is a separate individual, secreting an external limy skeleton around and under its soft body.

90. One of the smaller jellyfishes of the Atlantic coast, seldom over two inches across.

89. A large sea anemone, cut transversely to show the folding of the body wall that increases absorptive surface area in the gastrovascular cavity; the mouth opens between the tentacles into the central chamber.

the animal, on the other hand, is a thinner layer, also one cell thick, of shorter cubical cells specialized primarily toward protective and sensory functions. Between the two is a noncellular gelatinous matrix of varying thickness.

Both cell layers of the coelenterates are composed of four main cell types: (1) **T-**

these are packed closely and secrete a common cuticle. Their bases lie parallel to one another, with the axes lengthwise of the animal along its parallels of radial symmetry. In the base of each of these cells is a contractile fiber which shortens under suitable

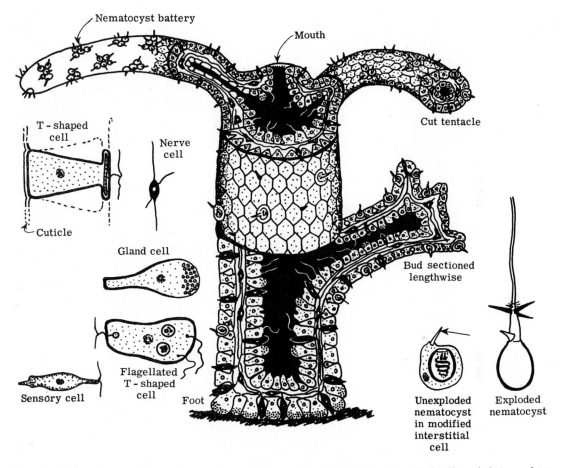

FIG. 9-2. *Coelenterate architecture is based on T-shaped cells, gland cells, interstitial cells and their products, and nerve-net cells.*

shaped cells with an elongate base following the contours of the jelly layer, while the bulbous body of the cell projects toward the outside of the organism or toward the central digestive cavity; (2) **gland cells;** (3) slender **sensory cells;** and (4) spheroidal **interstitial cells** as a reserve of undifferentiated protoplasm tucked into the spaces (interstices) between the bases of the T-shaped cells.

THE T-SHAPED CELLS. In the outer layer

stimulation. Simultaneous contraction of the basal fibers in many cells shortens the animal (and its tentacles) just as though muscle fibers were involved. In the inner layer, however, the T-shaped cell bases are attached to the matrix at right angles to those of the outer layer. On contraction, their fibers decrease the circumference of the digestive cavity and of the animal. Such action extends the body as a whole. Cooperation of contractions in the two layers allows the coelenterate a considerable range of movement and change of body form. Around the opening of the digestive cavity, and internally around the bases of hollow tentacles, additional T-shaped cells are arranged as **sphincters,** providing circular contraction that closes these openings.

T-shaped cells in the inner layer absorb digested food. Many of them bear one or two flagella, which aid in circulating the fluids in the digestive cavity. The enzymes which begin digestion, however, come from the many gland cells embedded in the inner layer; the initial steps of digestion are extracellular. This constitutes a slight advance over the type of organization in protozoans and sponges, where each cell attends to its own digestive processes on an intracellular basis. But as soon as the enzymes secreted into the central **gastrovascular cavity** have broken down the connective tissues of a coelenterate's prey far enough for it to fall into fragments, the T-shaped cells engulf the particles in food vacuoles and continue digestion on an intracellular level. Solid wastes are extruded into the gastrovascular cavity again, and eventually ejected at the mouth by a sudden violent contraction of the body.

GLAND CELLS. In the outer layer these secrete an adhesive in some coelenterates and both limy and horny substances in others. The adhesive aids free-living forms in adhering to surfaces—for example, allowing sea anemones to retain their hold on a rock while subduing a struggling fish. The other secretions mentioned contribute toward external skeletal structures which may support or protect according to the design. Among the corals, the animal perches on its limy product, and continued accumulation of the calcium carbonate from a large number of individuals builds up reefs hundreds of feet in thickness and acres in area (Photo 88).

SENSORY CELLS. The sensory cells are interconnected by a network of **nerve cells** embedded in the jelly layer. Along this network messages are passed that allow the animal to act as an individual rather than as an aggregation of cells. Yet the network is of the simplest kind, and represents a mere beginning toward the complex nervous system of higher animals. There are no main trunks, no nerves, and no brain. But the combination of sensory cells, nerve cells, and contractile T-shaped cells provides a fully cooperative **sensory-neuromotor mechanism** in which the sensory cells *receive* stimuli, the nerve cells *conduct* impulses, and the contractile fibers *react* to change the animal's position or shape.

INTERSTITIAL CELLS. These have wide potentialities. They may initiate growth and cell division, resulting in the development from an individual of side branches called **buds**. Buds may multiply until the organism is provided with many "heads," each with a mouth and a set of food-catching tentacles. Or a mature bud may constrict itself at the base and become a separate new individual.

Interstitial cells also migrate into surface positions in the outer layer and there elaborate within themselves one or more highly specialized structures called **nematocysts.** These are weapons or tools that are characteristic of coelenterates, yet unique in this phylum. Each nematocyst is a minute, nearly spherical body filled with fluid and containing a coiled tube. It lies below a cap-like door in the surface of the modified interstitial cell. The interstitial cell containing a nematocyst (or several as a "battery") develops a sharp, spine-like extension that projects into the surrounding water. This extension is not a trigger (as was formerly supposed) but a part of the cell with special chemical sensitivity akin to taste. Substances diffusing in the water from the small animals on which coelenterates feed appear to provoke discharge of the nematocyst. This event is explosively fast, knocking open the cap-like door, and everting the hair-like coiled tube into the water.

Some types of nematocysts penetrate the bodies of small animals on which coelenterates feed, then inject toxic fluids that paralyze the prey. Others coil like tendrils around projections such as hairs or bristles on the victim and prevent it from escaping. Still other types produce sticky substances that may be used to hold prey or to drag along the coelenterate itself. The poison-bearing nematocysts are responsible for the "stings" of large jellyfish, of some corals, and of the Portuguese man-of-war, which introduce hazards for swimmers in tropical and subtropical waters. The toxin, which appears to be an acid, can usually be neutralized with weak ammonia water.

COELENTERATE VARIATION. The two-cell-layer architecture provides opportunity for variation in form. The body wall may be thrown into longitudinal folds—as, for example, in sea anemones (Photo 89)—or, by vastly increasing the thickness of the jelly layer, the jellyfish type of organization is produced (Photo 90). Interstitial cells that secrete gas add the possibility of floats.

The coelenterate plan is relatively simple, but it is adaptable to two distinct modes of life: (1) as a sessile organism, with the mouth upward, as in the fresh-water Hydra, the marine corals (Photo 88) and sea anemones; and (2) as a free-swimming organism, with the mouth downward, as in jellyfishes. Many of the coelenterates alternate from one of these modes to the other (Fig. 9-3). An attached generation produces buds which float free and become jellyfish. Sexual activities of the latter produce fertilized eggs which settle to the bottom or arrive there in other ways

and begin the attached generation once more.

Where only two different body forms are involved in a complete life cycle, the animal is said to be **dimorphic** (from *di* = two, and *morphos* = form). Some coelenterates include additional stages, with still other specializations of the basic design. Such multiplicity of body forms in a single kind of organism is referred to as **polymorphism** (from *poly* = many). It represents an adaptation of the fundamental architecture allowing additional modifications and divisions of labor, separating feeding and food storage (in the attached generation) from dissemination and sexual reproduction (in the jellyfish generation).

All coelenterates are so deficient in skeletal support that for activity they must be buoyed up by water. Sea anemones reach as much as a foot or two in length; many are tough and rubbery on the outside when contracted. They can withstand body blows without damage,

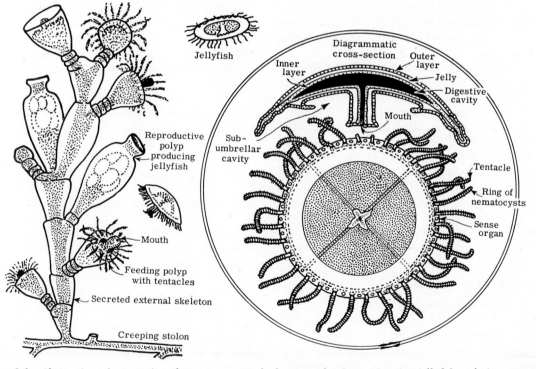

FIG. 9-3. *Alternation of generations between an attached type and a free-swimming jellyfish style is common among coelenterates. Colonies of attached individuals may be linked by a creeping stolon with upright branches; individuals may be specialized for reproduction (liberating jellyfish) or function solely in capturing and digesting food. The jellyfish generation* (inset) *reproduces sexually, producing new individuals which settle to the bottom and continue the cycle.*

but their tentacles are far more delicate. When danger threatens, both sets of T-shaped cells contract, drawing the animal into an almost spherical form—the smallest surface area for the existing volume of organism. Tentacles are pulled in to become mere knobs in a ring around the mouth.

Actual damage, however, can be repaired rapidly, and major pieces of the animal (with representatives of both the inner and outer body layer) are capable of reproducing a whole new individual. Jellyfish, by contrast, are much more delicate and seem less able to regenerate after substantial damage. Their tissues are still firm enough for rhythmic contractions of the bell to force water out of the cavity below, driving the body upward.

Radial symmetry, usually four- but sometimes three- or five-parted, is characteristic of coelenterates. The number of tentacles may far exceed this number. Radial symmetry and sessile habits usually mark a retiring animal. Most members of this phylum are sessile as well as radially symmetrical, and withdraw from any danger they detect. A radial plan permits withdrawal in any direction with equal ease.

Sea anemones and Hydra can accomplish a slow gliding movement, usually taking hours to move an inch. Hydra sometimes turns somersaults in slow motion (Fig. 17-9). Jellyfish, by comparison, seem to progress rapidly. But coelenterate design depends upon chance encounter with prey, whether crustacean or fish, that can be snared by nematocysts and pushed into the mouth. This feature limits coelenterates to aquatic (chiefly marine) situations, restricts activity to times when they are covered by fairly quiet water, and no doubt determines the largest size attainable.

3. BILATERAL SYMMETRY

A more efficient organization of a soft body is found in the flatworms, where in place of an inert noncellular jelly there is an active mass of cells forming a third body layer[1] (**mesoderm**). This third layer produces muscles and other organs between the outer and inner

---

[1] Since these layers arise during embryonic development they are called "germ layers."

body layers (**ectoderm** and **endoderm** respectively); it forms also internal sex organs with permanent reproductive ducts. Flatworms show an additional major advance in a bilateral symmetry, with a definite anterior end, and a dorso-ventral discrimination that defines a right and left side (Fig. 9-4). In the anterior end, the nervous system is more highly developed into masses of nerve cells called **ganglia** (singular, ganglion), and from these run **nerve cords** into the hinder part of the body, with branch **nerves** to various parts. The head end may also possess such special sense organs as eyes (Photo 91).

In the whole flatworm there is a definite gradient from anterior (high activity) to posterior (low activity). This gradient in metabolic rate can be demonstrated by comparison of the relative rates of disintegration in the presence of poisons, and also in terms of the regeneration of lost parts by individuals that are mutilated experimentally in various ways. Not only is the axial gradient of a flatworm found to descend from anterior to posterior, but from mid line to the sides of the body, and from ventral to dorsal. Thus, the obvious specializations of the body regions bear a relation to the whole organization. The potentialities of each cell are determined to a large extent by the position the cell occupies in the animal.

In spite of these advances, the body of flatworms remains depressed, and the lack of skeletal materials restricts them to aquatic situations or to keeping the full body area in contact with a supporting object such as a wet plant or rock. The body wall is covered by a single layer of cuboidal cells, through which deep-lying unicellular glands open to the surface and keep it lubricated with mucus. The ventral surface of free-living flatworms is densely ciliated, and much of their locomotion arises from ciliary action. Parasitic flatworms, however, secrete a tough cuticle over all surfaces, and as long as they are alive they are thus able to withstand the action of strong digestive enzymes and toxic substances. Both are able to contort the body through the contraction of muscle fibers which run lengthwise ("longitudinal" fibers), and around the body ("circular" fibers), just inside a basal membrane to which the outermost cell layer is attached and through the

91. These fresh-water flatworms, known as planarians, are effective scavengers. Each fully grown specimen is about one half inch in length.

FLATWORMS

92. Representative parts of tapeworms, mounted in transparent plastic.

93. The attaching scolex of a tapeworm may have hooks as well as suckers.

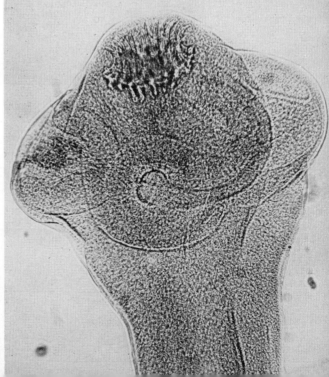

94. A tree snail (Liguus) of southern Florida and the West Indies.

MOLLUSKS OF THE SNAIL TYPE

95. A shell-less slug (Limax) from New Hampshire, is a land animal restricted to humid places.

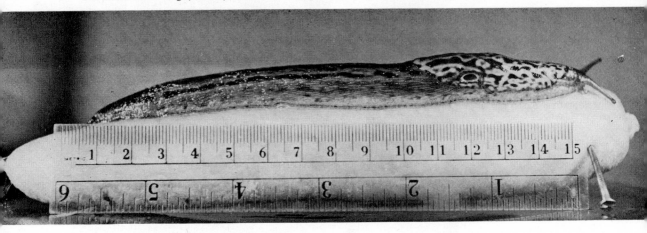

96. The queen conch of Florida, a marine snail, reaches a length of nearly two feet.

body ("dorso-ventral" fibers) from the basal membrane above to the corresponding membrane below. Free-living flatworms may crawl or swim by such muscular activities, and there is good evidence to believe that the internally parasitic flukes and tapeworms maintain their position in the digestive tract (or shift it) by corresponding sinuous body movements.

Where present at all, the digestive cavity of flatworms is blind like that of coelenterates, and undigested wastes must be eliminated through the mouth. But in flatworms the cavity usually branches, and a muscular sucking pharynx is commonly developed as an aid to drawing food into the digestive tract. Many free-living flatworms can evert the pharynx from the mouth as a hose-like elongated tube that is applied to large food and used to remove particles. Digestion is both extra- and intracellular.

This basic two-dimensional body plan is modified in the parasitic flukes to provide **suckers** which enable the worm to hold to its host. The tapeworms, which lack a diges-

tive tract entirely, are further specialized into an anterior anchoring unit and a series of reproductive segments (Photo 92) which may reach a collective length of 30 feet. The anchoring unit holds to the wall of the digestive tract with hooks (Photo 93) or suckers, or both, while the rest of the animal swims in the digestive fluids surrounding its host's meal in the intestine, and absorbs the products of its victim's digestive action; the worm lacks enzymes of this type.

4. THE TUBE-WITHIN-A-TUBE

The blind digestive cavity characteristic of coelenterates and flatworms carries the products of digestion to the immediate vicinity of the various cells of the body. Solid wastes are removed by a reversal of this movement. Such an inefficient distribution system places a handicap on the activities of an organism. Divorce of distribution from digestion through use of a circulating blood-like fluid eliminates

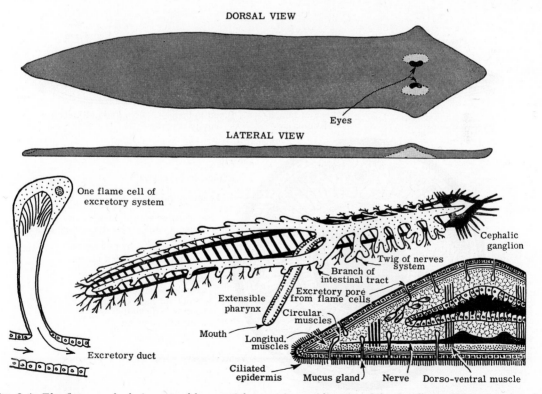

DORSAL VIEW

Eyes

LATERAL VIEW

One flame cell of excretory system

Cephalic ganglion

Twig of nerves system

Branch of intestinal tract

Excretory pore from flame cells

Extensible pharynx

Circular muscles

Mouth

Longitud. muscles

Excretory duct

Ciliated epidermis

Mucus gland

Nerve

Dorso-ventral muscle

FIG. 9-4. *The flatworm body is covered by a cuticle-secreting epidermis, while the digestive tract carries the food to all parts. Between epidermis and gut is additional cellular structure, with muscles, nervous system, and permanent reproductive ducts. Excretory cells, called flame cells, drive nitrogenous wastes to the exterior.*

one difficulty. Opening an anus at the end of the body opposite the mouth allows continuous passage of food materials and improves the other situation. These two steps have been taken by virtually all animals except sponges, coelenterates, and flatworms. They constitute the main advance in architecture shown by the roundworms. Here the body is bilaterally symmetrical and the mesoderm produces muscles and reproductive organs such as those in the flatworms. But the body is a cylindrical tube with a mouth at one end, opening into a cylindrical tube-within-the-body-tube that leads to an anus at the other end (Fig. 9-5). Food entering at the mouth is subjected to extracellular digestion, and unusable residues are eliminated at the anus. Between the two tubes is a space filled with a fluid which swirls back and forth as the roundworm wriggles. Products of digestion, absorbed by the endoderm cells lining the tubular digestive tract, pass to the fluid and are distributed to the rest of the body.

Roundworm design appears to have been less subject to variations than might be expected from comparison with other groups of successful organisms. Most roundworms are small or minute, although a few reach to as much as a meter in length. In active stages they require abundant moisture, but their eggs are microscopic and often highly resistant to chemical attack or desiccation. Yet in numbers of individuals, roundworms are probably outnumbered only by unicellular organisms and insects, and they compete strongly with both of these in number of niches regularly inhabited. Many roundworms are free-living in soil and water, but most are parasites in plants and animals.

Lack of a skeletal system restricts members of this phylum to creeping, unless buoyed enough by water to swim. Respiration depends entirely upon the moist body wall, and in conjunction with a comparatively small surface in proportion to volume, helps to limit the maximum size of roundworms. The gut is simple, matching the type of food taken (microscopic particles and juices from plant

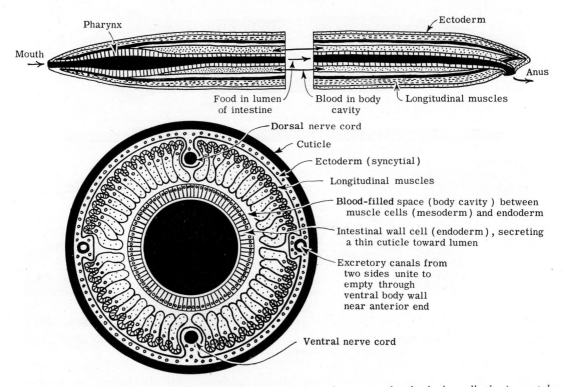

FIG. 9-5. *The roundworm plan is a simple tube-within-a-tube—the outer tube the body wall, the inner tube the digestive tract. Between them blood moves whenever the worm contorts its body.*

or animal hosts) and the requirements of a small animal, rather than a large one.

5. SIMILAR SEGMENTS

A higher degree of organization involving the tube-within-a-tube plan is characteristic of such worms as the earthworm, clamworm,

needing energy. But each segment of the worm has its own branches of the common blood vessels. Each segment also has its own branches of a common double nerve cord running along the ventral side of the series

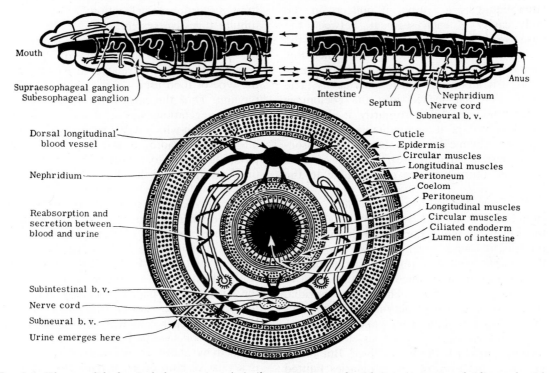

FIG. 9-6. *The annelid plan includes a series of similar segments, each with its excretory nephridia, each with its particular part of the nervous and circulatory system. Through all of them the digestive tract continues. Muscles are in sheets, with circular fibers toward the outside and the lumen of the gut, and longitudinal fibers nearer the body cavity.*

and leech. Here additional specialization has occurred through division of the body by transverse partitions into a linear series of similar compartments called *segments* (Fig. 9-6) or *metameres*. Through all of these units runs the central tubular digestive tract, and surrounding all of them is the tubular body wall, composed of epidermis and circular and longitudinal muscles. The organism has become a chain of similar parts, held together as an individual by several coordinating mechanisms. A closed system of tubes forming a blood-circulating system is found, and products of extracellular digestion absorbed from the endoderm-lined gut flow with the blood throughout the body to the various cells

of cavities, from an important ganglion in an anterior segment serving as a sort of brain. In this anterior region, the digestive tube is modified into a sucking pharynx, immediately back of which are segments in which the blood vessels are enlarged and muscular, forming a series of paired hearts that propel blood from the dorsal longitudinal blood vessel (above the gut) to a ventral longitudinal vessel (just below it). The blood thus circulates—forward in the dorsal vessel, backward in the ventral vessel—and a meshwork of fine capillaries among muscles and gut cells allow transfer of chemical substances to and from the liquid.

The cells composing capillary walls are

not only small and flattened, allowing transfer of materials through them to take place rapidly, but their contact with one another is sufficiently discontinuous to allow slight seepage of the blood fluid out of the blood vessels into the tissue spaces. The accumulated liquid is a lymph; it collects in the body cavity of each segment, between the digestive tract's muscular covering and the muscular lining of the body wall. Since this cavity is lined entirely by mesodermal material, it is a coelom or true body cavity. The lymph that has leaked into the coelom is called **coelomic fluid.** Primarily it is water, but dissolved in it are valuable substances, and also chemical wastes from living processes. Suspended in it are fragments of dead cells and other particles of no value to the animal.

A means for ridding the coelom of accumulated fluid and waste materials, and for salvaging the water and valuable components, is found in almost every segment of the compartmented worm as a pair of ciliated funnels leading into coiled tubes that open to the outside of the body. These are **nephridia,** suggestive in mode of action of the kidneys in vertebrate animals. They conduct coelomic fluid and suspended particles toward the medium in which the worm lives. But blood vessels in the form of fine capillaries knitted into the fabric of the fine tubules of the nephridium take away and return to the general circulation considerable water and most of the useful chemicals as these are absorbed by tubule cells from the liquid passing down the ducts. At the same time, other waste products are absorbed by tubule cells from the blood and excreted into the fluid passing toward the outside. This is an efficient system for ridding the body of wastes of metabolic processes, in a urine concentrated and eliminated by the nephridia.

It should be noted that the urine contains only waste materials that originate in the living cells of the animal or that have passed through protoplasm; much of this consists of nitrogenous by-products of protein breakdown. There is no connection between urine and the unabsorbed residues from food substances that are discharged through the anus

as feces. The latter have never really entered the animal, have never passed through a cell membrane. They are in the tube-within-a-tube, whose cavity is merely a partially surrounded portion of the outside world. Disposal of wastes in urine is excretion, and the nephridia collectively constitute an excretory system. Disposal of unassimilated matter from food is egestion or defecation, a function of a tubular digestive system.

The annelid worms of various kinds show digestive tracts that differ markedly from one another but that are related in each case to the type of food used—just as is usual in any phylum. Thus the earthworm, feeding on decaying vegetation, has a strongly muscular pharynx with which it can suck pieces of food into a gullet leading through the loops of the pumping hearts to a crop. The crop can be filled at night, and the next section of the gut —a gizzard—then breaks up the food mechanically before passing it on to the long intestine where glands add digestive enzymes and where products of digestion can be absorbed. The intestine of the earthworm has a single longitudinal fold mid-dorsally in the wall, which serves to compress the cavity of the gut into a C-shaped space. By this device the volume of the cavity (*lumen*) is reduced by about 50 per cent while the surface area available for secretion and absorption is increased by about 65 per cent; the net effect is a relative gain of more than 300 per cent! Yet the smooth, broad, longitudinal fold does not offer much resistance to passage of gritty meals. The leech, by contrast, has an enormous crop that distends readily with blood when the animal is able to gorge, and it has a short simple intestine through which food values can be absorbed; digestion of a blood meal is much simpler. An important adaptation in the leech's crop, in fact, is a series of glands secreting an anticoagulant substance that keeps the blood fluid; a clot would be more difficult to manipulate in the digestive tract and would offer much less opportunity for rapid action of digestive agents.

The origin of the segmented body plan is suggested among certain of the free-living flatworms where the body comes to consist of a series of individuals which separate by fragmentation of the elongate chain. A similar means of reproduction is found in some marine annelids, demonstrating how easily a segmented animal can be reorganized into a series of individuals, and suggesting that the single, metameric bands may have arisen originally from a series of individuals which failed to separate but which instead became more closely organized to act as a single cooperative unit.

As measured by chordate standards, the annelids show major advances: (1) metameric segmentation; (2) a closed circulatory system with capillary networks increasing the efficiency of movement for dissolved materials; (3) improved facilities for gas exchange with the environment by increased surfaces on paired paddles or special extensions of the body; (4) improved organization of the nervous system; and (5) greater division of labor along the length of the through-passage gut. Metameric organization is found again in the two most successful phyla of animals (the arthropods and chordates) and is believed to be responsible in part for their adaptability.

The annelid architectural plan is limited, however, in (1) lack of a skeletal support; (2) means for getting enough food to nourish a large animal; and (3) chronic danger of dessication. Except when buoyed by water, only the tropical leeches can get off the substratum for even half their length. These external parasites reach from foliage for a victim only when the air is so humid that water loss is no problem. Parasitic annelids are restricted by their ability to find a host and by the size of meal they can take without losing control of their stuffed bodies.

6. EXTERNAL SKELETONS

Addition of a skeleton frees an animal to some extent from dependence upon water's buoyant force, and reduces the need for passive flexibility as a means to survival under the tearing action of vigorous water movements. A skeleton alters the limits on size and also on the kinds of habitats that can be invaded.

Skeletal support may be achieved through secretion of a hard outer covering or shell— an **exoskeleton** (from *exo* = outside). Secondary advantages are evident: a reduction of water loss into air, and an armor useful in warding off enemy attacks. But a shell encases the living organism in a box with disadvantages: it adds weight, requiring additional energy to shift the inert skeleton from place to place; it restricts growth; it seems to predispose the animal to a passive way of life—retiring into the exoskeleton whenever danger threatens. Initiative is sacrificed in favor of blind security. This may lead toward degeneration and new limitations in life.

Two major phyla—the mollusks and the arthropods—have exoskeletons and balance the advantages against the disadvantages well enough for successful living in a competitive world.

Mollusks

These animals (Fig. 9-7) include (1) snails living in a spiral cone—a limy **shell** that can be extended around the ever-enlarging rim; (2) clams, with a pair of similar **valves** (a right and a left), also of lime but hinged together by a flexible ligament along one edge where growth is least (eccentric additions made internally enlarge the valves as the animal increases in size); (3) chitons, secreting dorsally a series of eight overlapping, transverse, limy plates to which additions can be made all around as the body grows; and (4) squid, cuttlefish, octopus and kin, in which the horny or limy shell is enclosed within the body or lost entirely. In all mollusks the shell (Fig. 9-8) is secreted by a **mantle.** The body is soft, unsegmented, and includes a circulatory system consisting in large part of open sinuses.

SNAILS. In snails, a muscular foot is extended and spread into a flat surface on which the animal creeps (Photos 94-96). A head is vaguely defined and usually carries such sense organs as tentacles and eyes. The mouth is provided with a rasp-like device which serves to scrape particles of food from the substratum. Snails also use a strongly digestive salivary secretion to initiate breakdown of complex food materials, which may then be sucked into the mouth through contractions of the muscular pharynx. Digestion is chiefly internal but entirely extracellular. Many snails use gills for respiration; others possess a lung and breathe atmospheric air. Similarly, most snails are aquatic, in both salt and fresh water; some are terrestrial but can be active only when the humidity is high. Those inhabiting desert regions may remain in suspended animation for years until a local rainstorm provides the proper conditions for activity. Snails range in size from minute forms less than $\frac{1}{25}$ inch in length, to the horse conch of the Florida coast (Photo 96), which

The mantle also limits the openings by which water enters and leaves, forming a double **siphon,** with incurrent and excurrent apertures. The water is drawn in at the former, passes through the gills, and emerges from the second opening. Food particles become embedded in mucus covering the gills. Cilia drive this mucus as a continuous sheet in a definite path that forms it into a food-laden

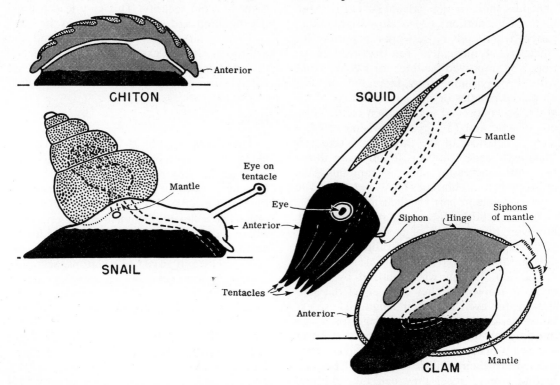

FIG. 9-7. *The fundamental mollusk architecture is firmly modified into several styles: the chiton, with eight overlapping limy plates as its flexible shell; the snail, with a single spiral cone housing most of the visceral mass; the clam, with its hinged pair of limy valves; and the squid, with its internal degenerate "pen."*

may grow to a length of two feet and a weight of several pounds.

CLAMS. Clams show a very different development of the mollusk architecture (Photo 97). When the strong muscles holding the two shells together are relaxed, the blade-like foot can be extended into the mud and the tip inflated with blood pumped from the heart. This knob-like distension anchors the foot, so that when the whole organ is shortened by muscular contraction, the shell is pulled along and into the mud. Clams have no head, and the food consists of microscopic organisms brought into the cavity of the shell by a water current propelled by cilia lining the mantle.

rope, entering the mouth between a pair of flap-like **palps.** Oxygen is removed by the gills, carbon dioxide disposed of at the same point, and the defecated matter from the anus, together with urine from a pair of kidneys, enters the breathing current just before it leaves through the excurrent aperture. The nervous system is usually more reduced than that in snails. Clams include kinds barely a quarter of an inch in length as well as Tridacna, the marine giant of the Australasian region reefs (Photo 98), which reaches more than three feet in length and a weight of at least 500 pounds.

CHITONS. Chitons are all marine, and in

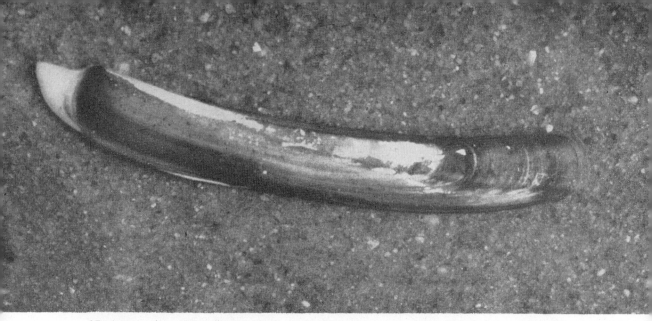

97. Among the more active of bivalve animals is the razor clam, which burrows vertically into sandy bottoms by vigorous action of its tongue-like foot. The whole animal may kick itself into the open or burrow downward very rapidly.

EXTREMES OF THE CLAM TYPE

98. A medium-sized example of the giant clam Tridacna, from a coral reef of the South Pacific. This particular pair of shell valves weighed 402 pounds. Small shells of this type are often used as baptismal fonts. In the reef, the clam lies with its hinge downward. If exposed at low tide or stimulated in any way, the animal may close its valves. Otherwise it extends a thick, fleshy mantle portion of the body and depends largely on the products of photosynthesis from microscopic green algae embedded in the mantle tissue.

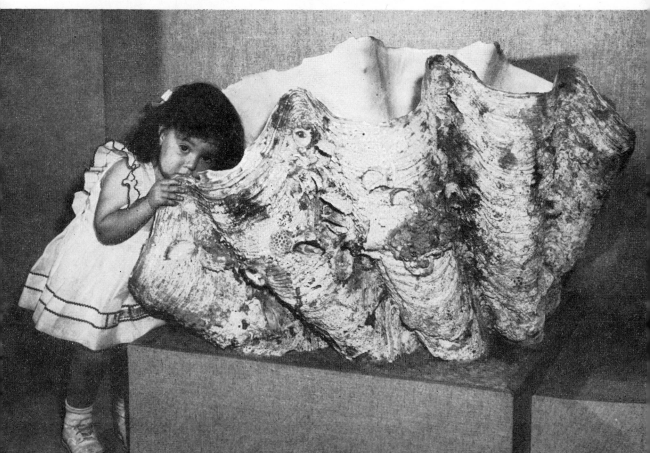

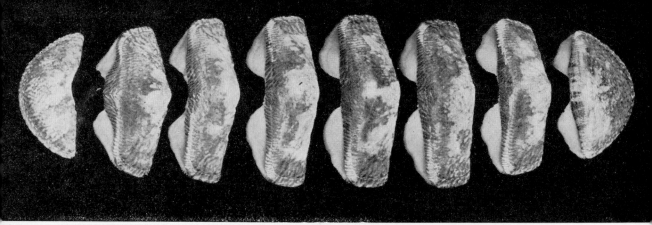

99. The shells of a chiton form a series of eight overlapping plates that allow the animal to curl up like an armadillo. (*Photo by Dr. Ralph Buchsbaum, from* Animals Without Backbones, *University of Chicago Press.*)

100. Squids are active animals, propelling themselves both by undulating movements of the tail fins and by jets of water expelled from the large mantle cavity.

101. An octopus with membranes between adjacent pairs of the eight arms. These organisms crawl rapidly, and also swim backwards by jet propulsion.

their broad foot and possession of a device with which they feed on seaweeds and microscopic organisms clinging to rocks, they resemble some kinds of snails. The plates on their backs form adequate protection from many enemies (Photo 99). If dislodged from the bottom, they usually roll up into a spherical, armored ball. Those on the California coast sometimes reach a length of thirteen inches.

SQUIDS AND KIN. In the squid (Photo 100), cuttlefish, octopus (Photo 101), and pearly nautilus, the external shell has been reduced and great freedom of movement achieved. The tissue is far firmer, and cartilages provide stiffening at important points and a case surrounding a highly developed nervous center. The sizable head bears two large eyes which are strikingly similar in anatomical details to the eyes of vertebrates. Each has a cornea, iris, lens, and central cavity, and forms a real image on a retina (except in the nautilus, which has a "pin-hole camera" type of eye with no lens). Fleshy arms or tentacles surround the mouth, eight (in *octo*pus) or ten (in squid and cuttlefish), with "suckers" on many (the pearly nautilus of Pacific and Indian Ocean bottoms lacks these). A mantle cavity contains the gills, and alternate expansion and contraction provides circulation of water; all are marine. Squids and cuttlefish have fin-like extensions of the mantle which enable them to swim or keep their balance in the water; all of this group, however, propel themselves more rapidly by clamping down the edge of the mantle around the head and forcing water out of the mantle cavity through a nozzle. This is jet propulsion, and the nozzle can be turned toward the tentacles for backward escape, or toward the tail fins for forward movement. Also opening into the mantle cavity is an ink sac from a special gland. With the secretion, an octopus, squid, or cuttlefish can becloud the water in its immediate vicinity. This may serve as an effective "smoke screen" in which to escape, or be most helpful as an anesthetic to the taste organs by which enemies seek it out.

All of this group of mollusks are predators. They range from an inch long to the giant squid off the Labrador coast, 20 feet long with 35-foot tentacles and a weight of several tons —the largest known invertebrate. The several kinds of octopus vary from two-inch to 28-foot spreads, but the body consists of only a minor part of these dimensions. The aggressive habits, well developed sense organs and nervous systems, and structural strength of these animals demonstrate the potentialities of the basic anatomical arrangement. Armored mollusks, and those like land slugs and sea slugs that differ only in lack of a shell, are

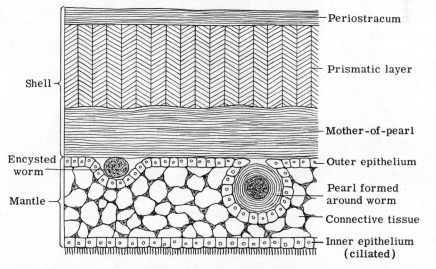

FIG. 9-8. *Between the shell of a clam and the mantle, pearls may form through a modification of the same process that lays down the layers of the valve itself. This diagram shows in section the several zones; the outer periostracum and intermediate prismatic layer are laid down by the outer epithelium at the edge of the shell.*

far more numerous as individuals and as species, but they show the restrictions in size and activity that go with emphasis on safety in a hard covering. No mollusk, moreover, can be active long in dry air.

Arthropods

Members of this phylum secrete a lighter exoskeleton of the inert polysaccharide **chitin,** with or without additional lime. The skeleton is jointed, giving flexibility and permitting active movement (Fig. 9-9). Growth is intermittent; the new exoskeleton develops under the old, which is then split open and shed. For a short time at each **molt,** the animal is helpless and unarmored. But the new exoskeleton soon hardens when exposed to air or water. While the body is soft, the animal expands it to new dimensions by swallowing air or water, and holds it distended until the freshly exposed chitinous plates become rigid, making the new size "permanent." That this

design is a successful one is attested to by the fact that more than 80 per cent of the animal kingdom employ it, and that arthropods thrive in the sea, in fresh water, in soil, on land, and occupy the greatest variety of niches. Insects are the only flying invertebrates.

Arthropod emphasis is ordinarily toward active lives. Their segmented bodies and jointed appendages permit great flexibility. The exoskeleton restricts water loss, and serves both as armor and for attachment of the well developed muscular system.

Typically, each segment of the body bears a pair of appendages, but various arthropods show different degrees of specialization whereby segments are fused together to form head, thorax (or cephalothorax), and abdomen, and whereby the appendages are modified into **antennae,** mouthparts, walking or swimming legs, **copulatory** organs, and parts of the tail fin. **Compound** eyes and a system of respiratory air tubes (**tracheae**) branching through the body are unique features of arthropods, but not all arthropods possess them.

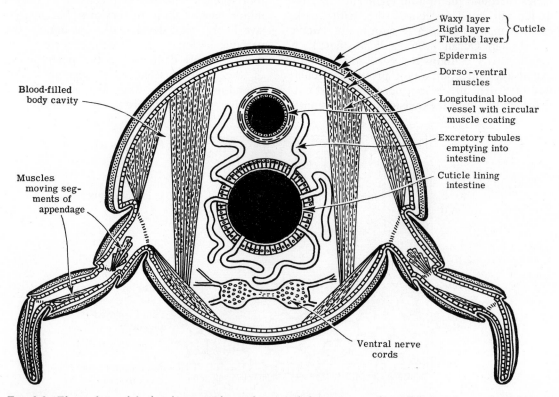

Blood-filled body cavity

Waxy layer
Rigid layer } Cuticle
Flexible layer

Epidermis

Dorso - ventral muscles

Longitudinal blood vessel with circular muscle coating

Excretory tubules emptying into intestine

Cuticle lining intestine

Muscles moving segments of appendage

Ventral nerve cords

FIG. 9-9. *The arthropod body plan provides a firm exoskeleton surrounding all living tissues, furnishing attachment areas for muscles that produce movements of appendages for locomotion, eating and the like, or movements of the body itself in respiration.*

102. A small spider crab. These animals grow to a leg spread of over two feet. The body is usually a creamy yellow.

103. A microscopic fresh-water form, Cyclops, carrying two egg sacs.

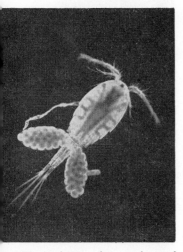

CRUSTACEAN ARCHITECTURE

IS SUBJECT TO MANY

MODIFICATIONS

104. The fresh-water "water flea," Daphnia, in side view. Like Cyclops, Daphnia swims by jerking its antennae.

105. A cluster of goose barnacles on a piece of wood left floating in the sea; each animal is attached separately, by means of a rubbery stalk. (Photo from preserved specimens, with feet extended.)

106. Acorn barnacles attached firmly to a rusting steel pile of a marine dock. The limy valves are opened when the tide covers the animals again, and each animal proceeds to strain water for food.

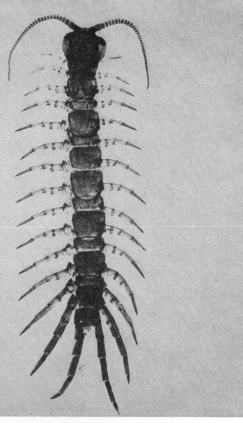

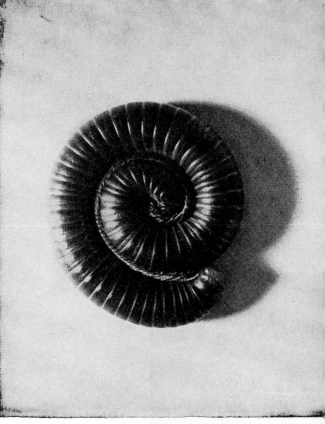

107. A centipede may have only 30 legs—never 100 —counting both sides.

108. Many millipedes curl up when disturbed, always with the head at the center.

MANY SEGMENTS, MANY LEGS

109. Waves of leg movements sweep forward along the length of a millipede, easily visible in silhouette as the animal walks along a string.

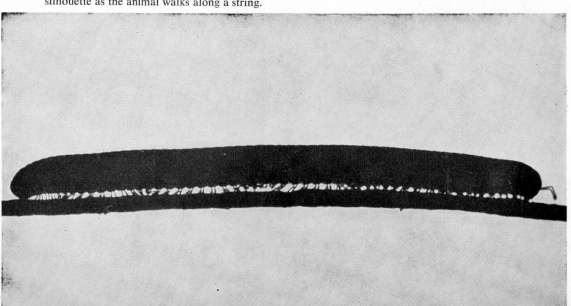

These details demonstrate a high degree of division of labor between metameric units.

CRUSTACEANS. Even the separate classes of arthropods show so great a range of body form and habit as to make generalizations difficult. Essentially, crustaceans like lobsters have a head with antennae (two pairs), **mandibles** for chewing (one pair), **maxillae** used to orient food toward the mouth (two pairs), and a **thorax** plus **abdomen** with a variety of paired appendages. Respiration is by means of gills or through the general body surface, and all but a few are aquatic, most of them marine. Lobsters and crayfish have five pairs of walking legs (of which the first pair are well developed as pincers) and an extended abdomen which can be curled under quickly to cup water in a tail fin and to propel the animal out of danger; the head and thorax are fused as a **cephalothorax.** Crabs are similarly equipped, but the small abdomen is held tight against the undersurface so that they appear tail-less (Photos 42, 102). These larger crustaceans depend to a considerable extent upon circulation of blood through the gills. The gills contain capillaries, and the vascular mechanism includes a pumping heart plus a few arteries. Most of the blood movement is through sinuses between the viscera. Other arthropods display few or no arteries or capillaries, and the blood movement serves chiefly for food and waste transport, with little function in respiration.

Most crustaceans are small or minute (Photos 103, 104), and are carried passively by surface currents in seas and lakes while they feed on the algae and other microscopic life there. Barnacles, on the other hand, become attached to the bottom after a free-swimming immature stage, and they degenerate within a limy shell, retaining the legs (Photos 105, 106) as a means for kicking a respiratory and feeding current toward the mouth. Still other crustaceans are parasitic, and in some instances degenerate into a mere mass of cells which branches and becomes root-like, absorbing nourishment from a host's body.

CENTIPEDES. Centipedes are rather uniformly armored and more conspicuously segmented than many crustaceans. The basic pattern of one pair of appendages per segment is followed through, the head bearing a pair of long antennae (and a pair of simple eyes), a pair of jaws, and two pairs of maxillae (Photo 107). The first body segment is equipped with a pair of special poison claws, on which ducts from glands open and furnish a toxic substance with which the prey is killed. These are the source of "bites" which may prove painful to man and serious to smaller animals. Centipedes have a straight digestive tract, as have so many carnivores. Into it posteriorly open a pair of **Malpighian tubules** —the excretory system of the animal. Respiration is by tracheae; all are terrestrial. Most centipedes are tropical in distribution and may reach lengths of as much as eight inches; one, the small "house centipede" with long banded legs, has become almost a domestic animal, and is both harmless and beneficial in cleaning the house of small insects.

MILLIPEDES. Millipedes are ordinarily much more cylindrical and the body wall is impregnated with lime like the exoskeleton of most crustaceans. Each body segment bears two pairs of legs (Photo 108), and the head carries two clumps of simple eyes as well as a pair of antennae, a pair of jaws, and a pair of maxillae. Millipedes are all harmless vegetarians and scavengers; many are protected by special malodorous "stink glands." When disturbed, some coil up into a tight spiral like a watch spring (Photo 109), with the head at the center of the whorl and the legs pressed against body surfaces that are sturdy enough to fend off mechanical damage. Tropical millipedes sometimes reach eight inches in length. All are slow-moving and restricted to humid situations among fallen logs and leaf litter.

ARACHNOIDS. The arachnoids represent a high degree of specialization of the basic arthropod plan. One ancient marine type, the king crab or horseshoe crab (Xiphosura, from the Greek *xiphos* = sword and *ura* = tail), persists from a subclass extinct otherwise for millions of years. Here the body is divided clearly into a large cephalothorax bearing six pairs of appendages underneath, and a narrower abdomen ending in a long spine-like tail that the animal uses for righting itself when it falls on its back (Photos 43, 110). The mouth opens among the leg bases, and the latter are used for chewing the mixed animal and plant food obtained in shoveling along the sandy bottom of shallow water from Maine to Yucatan. The cephalothorax bears dorsally two large lateral compound eyes and two simple median eyes. Under the abdomen are leaf-like plates that can be swung back and forth to drive water in and out of the **gill books** they conceal.

All other modern arachnoids are primarily terrestrial or parasitic, and none of them has compound eyes. Spiders (Photos 111, 112, Endpaper Photo H) are as widespread as the insects on which they feed, and must be regarded as highly beneficial to man. Rounded cephalothorax and abdomen give no indication of segmentation; the former usually bears eight simple eyes and six pairs of appendages: a pair of poison jaws, a pair of palp-like feet used to squeeze the food, and four pairs of walking legs. The poison jaws inject into the prey not only toxic substances which paralyze it, but also digestive agents which break down the living protoplasm into a liquid which the spider can then suck back, leaving the victim a hollow shell. Respiration is by means of **lung books,** opening ventrally at the anterior end of the abdomen. **Spinnerets** are commonly present around a silk-gland pore just ventral to the anus. Excretion is through Malpighian tubules and also by coxal glands such as are characteristic of the king crabs. The nervous system is highly developed. Most spiders are small, but the tarantulas and others may reach a body length of 3½ inches, with leg spreads considerably greater. Often the male is much smaller than his mate—an example of **sexual dimorphism.**

Scorpions are more elongate, with pincer-ended palp-feet and a segmented abdomen ending in a poison claw. Pseudoscorpions and whip scorpions lack a sting. Vinegarones and sun spiders appear more like spiders, but lack the constriction that gives true spiders a "waist"; they also lack poison. Harvestmen (Photo 113) have compact bodies with a turret of simple eyes above, and extremely long slender legs on which they run. They have stink glands for protection but no poison. Mites (Photo 114) and ticks (Photo 23) are usually minute, at most 1½ inches long when adult and engorged with blood; the whole body is fused into a single, unseg-

mented unit. The eight legs are on the sides. Mites include predaceous, scavenging, and parasitic forms, but ticks are all ectoparasites of reptiles, birds, and mammals, sucking their blood through needle-like mouthparts. Mites cause many plant and animal diseases, and, like the ticks, form vectors for other infective agents.

INSECTS. Insects, the most successful class of arthropods, are rather more uniform in body structure. The head, thorax and abdomen are distinct, and the thorax bears the locomotory appendages: three pairs of legs, and up to two pairs of wings in the adult stage (Photo 119). The head bears one pair of antennae (Endpaper Photo F) and mouthparts variously modified for biting, sucking, or lapping. Respiration is by tracheae branching throughout the body, or, in very small kinds, merely through the body surface. Excretion is by Malpighian tubules opening into the digestive tract. The nervous system is often highly developed, with good connections to such excellent sense organs as a pair of compound eyes, as many as three simple eyes, and a pair of antennae. Hearing and sound production are found in several orders. Most insects live alone, but many groups include gregarious or even truly social species. The latter, as in ant or bee colonies, may involve division of labor and polymorphism of body form. The insect design applies primarily to small animals, although some of the largest beetles are considerably bulkier than the smallest mammals. Other insects, such as some insect-egg parasites, are actually smaller as adults than the largest protozoans. Some fossil insects exceeded 27 inches in wingspread, but the modern maximum seems to be the 10-inch spread of the Atlas moth.

Insect architecture provides flexibility of operation that has enabled members of this class to invade literally every place—land, earth, fresh water, hot springs, and glaciers; they exist as scavengers, plant eaters, predators, and external and internal parasites. No other basic plan has allowed an invertebrate group the broad latitude in life histories found among the insects.

Even the molting of the exoskeleton has been turned to advantage. Many insects progress in regular and unspectacular steps from egg

110. King crabs come ashore to lay eggs. The ♂ clings tightly to the shell of the ♀ and is on hand to fertilize her eggs when she deposits them. (See also Photos 43, 129.)

111. A wolf spider running over a small fallen branch.

ARACHNOIDS
BEAR EYES
ON THEIR
BACKS

112. A jumping spider pauses atop a pencil eraser before leaping several inches after a fly.

Four Pairs of Legs

113. This harvestman has just molted. Its shed skin rests on the leaf above the newly emerged animal.

114. All mites are minute. Some are predators, other suck plant juices; many are parasites.

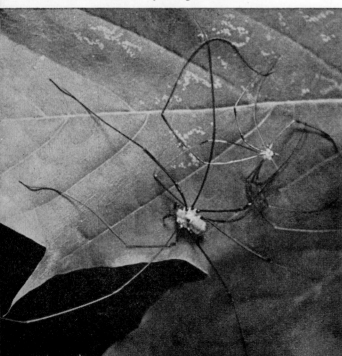

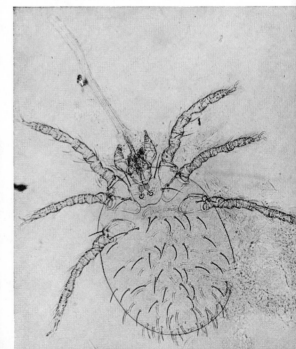

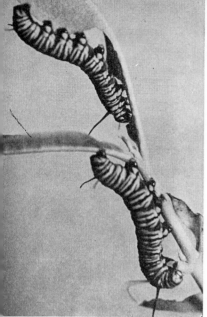

115. Caterpillars eat so much foliage every day that competition for food may develop. Often one insect will pursue another, biting at it, until the contest ends in routing the competitor.

116. Suspended from a button of silk (salivary secretion) ready to shed the larval skin and expose the chrysalis.

117. Colors of the adult show through the transparent skin of the chrysalis as time for emergence approaches.

METAMORPHOSIS FROM A CREEPING, LEAF-EATING ANIMAL TO A FLYING, NECTAR-SIPPING ONE;
THE TRANSFORMATION OF THE MILKWEED CATERPILLAR INTO THE MONARCH BUTTERFLY

118. Freshly emerged, clinging to the empty chrysalis while the wings dry and harden.

119. Exercising before the take-off. The flight may carry the insect from Maine to Florida and back.

120. Rows of tube feet mark the body of a sea cucumber. The anterior (oral) end is at the right, among the branched tentacles.

VARIATIONS

IN THE

ECHINODERM

PLAN

121. A far less flexible starfish on a southern Florida beach. The eight-to ten-inch spread and bright orange color attract beachcombers.

122. A sea urchin in aboral view is armed conspicuously with movable spines, between which are pincer-tipped structures policing the body.

123. The same sea urchin in oral view shows the five teeth in its mouth and a large number of flexible tube feet used in locomotion.

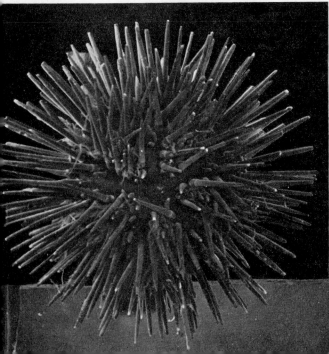

to adult. But in others the immature stages are highly modified for feeding and food storage, and entirely unlike the adult (Photos 115-119). After this **larval** life is completed, during the time out for the final molt, the individual becomes more than usually quiescent; a **pupal** stage is recognized, during which larval structures are transformed rapidly into those of the adult—equally highly specialized toward mating, dissemination into new localities, and other reproductive activities. This is a further division of labor, between successive stages in the normal life cycle of a single individual. For this reason it is referred to not as an example of polymorphism but one of **metamorphosis.**

7. INTERNAL SKELETONS

External skeletons are nonliving secretions of the ectoderm. Internal skeletons are intercellular secretions of mesodermal cells that continue to live and control the secretions; hence an endoskeleton is alive. Within this

difference, however, are two very divergent styles of endoskeleton: (1) relatively superficial skeletal units surrounding the body, either interlocking to form a rigid shell or jointed to produce a more flexible framework; and (2) a single linear flexible rod or series of skeletal units offering little or no advantage in resisting enemy attacks. The first of these, characteristic of the echinoderm phylum, seems primarily protection for delicate viscera—shielding them from mechanical damage of external origin. The fact that the skeleton is within the skin's limits does not alter this feature. The values in support, in muscle attachment, and in leverage become much less significant. And the phylum possessing these characteristics shows a far smaller range of adaptability than the phylum Chordata, in which the second of these architectural plans reaches full development. The echinoderms are almost radially symmetrical, with a unique water-vascular system, whereas

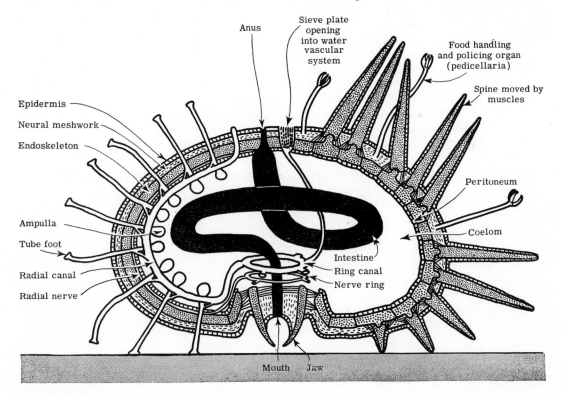

FIG. 9-10. *The echinoderm style of architecture assumes a false radial symmetry and a unique water vascular system. The diagram is an approximate representation of a sea urchin in longitudinal section through one radial canal. Note that the limy skeleton of fitted plates is internal in position.*

the chordates are bilaterally symmetrical and supplement their strengthening endoskeleton (the notochord) with gill slits, a hollow dorsal nerve cord, and a closed circulatory system. Actually, echinoderms begin as bilaterally symmetrical larvae, but before development has proceeded far, each goes through a curious metamorphosis that ends in approximately radial symmetry, and most are then associated with the sea bottom, either crawling on it, or, in a few instances, permanently attached.

Echinoderms

Echinoderms probably represent a degenerate type of organization (Fig. 9-10); the lack of a head, the rather simple nervous system, and the seeming radial symmetry, all evince a readiness to withdraw from danger threatening from any direction. When undisturbed, most of them show a definite preference in orientation for movement, so that in spite of the supposedly radial plan there is a functional bilaterality in behavior. Starfish (Photo 121), sea urchins (Photos 122, 123), and sea cucumbers (Photo 120) are equipped with tube feet and show remarkable control over this part of the water-vascular system in their slow locomotion. Brittle stars creep about more rapidly by muscular movements of their five arms. Sea lilies are flower-like in appearance and attached to the bottom; in a few instances they are free-swimming.

The echinoderm body plan shows great variation (Endpaper Photo Q), and the endoskeleton may be articulated as in starfish, almost fused as in the rigid sea urchins, or so discontinuous that it provides no appreciable support as in sea cucumbers. Radial symmetry, achieved by early metamorphosis of a bilaterally symmetrical larva, may be modified by elongation and habitual position to furnish dorso-ventrality as in sea cucumbers. The digestive tract in some is so specialized in relation to a restricted diet and mode of operation that the basic tubular form is lost and no anus at all is present. The coelom is well developed, but it carries on respiration and excretion as special functions; a part is modified into a highly unique water-vascular system, related in most forms to locomotion. Yet in all echinoderms, the nervous system is remarkably simple, with a nerve ring around the mouth and radial nerves having branchlets to the various organs. No important sense organs are elaborated, but special dermal appendages in many echinoderms help in feeding or in policing the body surface.

The internal skeleton of echinoderms does not compensate enough for inefficiencies elsewhere to permit life beyond the margins of the sea. In this single habitat representatives thrive at all depths, from tidewater to the great abysses. But those that move feed on particles in the bottom ooze or, as in the case of starfish, eat mollusks that are too slow to get away. Neither of these diets is conducive to large size or a need for specializations comparable to those of the chordates.

SUGGESTED READING (see pp. 510-511)

Recent and Informative: Ribbands, 1955; Scharrer, 1951; Steinbach, 1951; Williams, 1953.

10 · Chemical Coordination

1. CHORDATE COORDINATION—THE PITUITARY GLAND, THE THYROID GLAND, THE PARATHYROID GLANDS, THE ADRENAL GLANDS, THE PANCREATIC HORMONE, HORMONES OF THE MUCOSA, HORMONES FROM THE GONADS, THE SEXUAL CYCLE, MALENESS VERSUS FEMALENESS, AMPHIBIAN METAMORPHOSIS, FEEDBACK. 2. COORDINATION IN MULTICELLULAR NONCHORDATES.

AT THE CELLULAR LEVEL of organization, the nucleus appears to control activity in most parts of the cytoplasm. For a multicellular animal, with division of labor among the component cells, additional coordination is necessary if the whole is to act as an individual. A highly specialized animal is only as efficient as the central mechanism that coordinates its many activities.

This overall regulation of a complex organism may be achieved through extension of a basic principle among living things. Wherever two active cells are in proximity, each is constantly elaborating materials minute quantities of which spread out and influence the other cell. The closer the association between two or more cells, the more their activities are coordinated through this chemical means.

Unity in an organism is thus maintained through the mutual sensitivities of the participating units. The animal kingdom affords numerous examples in which chemical coordination is sufficiently important that centers of synthesis have become organized into definite glands. Ordinarily these glands pour their secretion into the blood stream, for distribution throughout the body. As such, they are glands without ducts—**ductless glands.** An alternative adjective is **endocrine.** In each case the product is a **hormone** (from the Greek *horman* = to excite), or "chemical messenger." Unlike enzymes, which are unaffected by the reaction they catalyze, hormones are used up and must be replaced by fresh secretion.

Hormones have been demonstrated in all classes of multicellular plants and animals. Those of vertebrates show remarkable interchangeability, permitting substitution of experimental animals while learning about man's own chemical coordination, and in planning treatment for disorders in the human mechanism.

Multicellular animals possess additional means of regulation—the system of nervous tissue, sensory cells, muscles, and glands, discussed in detail throughout Chapter 11.

1. CHORDATE COORDINATION

The discoveries of the past half-century have pointed to the importance of endocrine glands among vertebrates. The term "gland of internal secretion" has been applied to the **pituitary** (merged with a part of the lower surface of the brain); the **thyroid** and **parathyroids** in the neck region; and the **adrenal** bodies attached to the kidneys.

An endocrine function has been demonstrated also for the walls of the stomach and duodenum, for special cells in the pancreas, in the ovaries, and in the testes. The placenta, through which a mammalian embryo is nourished by the mother, is another source of specific hormones (Fig. 10-1).

The long delay in uncovering the role of these structures may be attributed to the small size of purely endocrine glands, and to the fact that several sources of hormones are compound organs, with another and more obvious function. Thus the earliest known civilizations practiced **castration** of men (producing eunuchs), of bulls (producing oxen), and of other male domestic animals. Removal of the scrotum with its testes in any of these mammals was recognized as a sure way to prevent reproduction. But the significance of the slower accompanying changes in body form and behavior was not interpreted in terms of hormones until within the past thirty years, when **endocrinology** became a separate field of study. Similarly, diabetes mellitus is described as a human disease in medical treatises from 500 B.C. Yet, until 1922 no one had demonstrated its relation to the pancreatic hormone.

Understanding of hormones in any situation is based largely upon two avenues of observation. In one, the effects of removing a suspected endocrine organ are studied (usually in an experimental animal), and then extracts from the gland material are introduced to see which, if any, are able to bring an end to symptoms arising from gland removal. This investigates the effect of an in-

adequate supply of the hormone. The other procedure consists of injecting extracts of a suspected endocrine organ into a normal individual, to learn the effects (if any) of an oversupply. Both under- and oversupply have their counterparts in the occasionally abnormal organism where the gland has shrunk **(atrophied)** or developed excessively **(hypertrophied)**.

The Pituitary Gland

From the tabular summary of presently well-established information on endocrine mechanisms (on p. 157), it is clear that the pituitary is a "master" gland—dominating the activity of many other centers. The pituitary itself, as seen in man, is a small body less than half an inch in diameter. Its location between and behind the eyes, above the base of the nose, suggested to early anatomists that it was the source of mucus in the nasal passages. Its name perpetuates this misconception (from the Latin *pituita* = phlegm, mucus). Actually, the gland has a dual origin. The anterior lobe arises from the roof of the embryonic mouth (though finally losing this connection), whereas the posterior lobe descends as an outgrowth from the brain (to which it remains firmly attached).

Of the numerous hormones from the anterior pituitary, some are elaborated throughout life: the thyrotrophic, parathyrotrophic, adrenocorticotrophic, and diabetogenic hormones. Others appear to be produced during embryonic life, and until the individual reaches maturity—for example, the somatotrophic hormone. Still others are formed in quantity only in relation to the primary reproductive organs, beginning at puberty and ceasing or decreasing markedly later in life: the gonadotrophic hormones, and the pituitary sex hormones. The names of many of these substances are derived in part from the Greek *trophein* = to grow, referring to their effect upon other endocrine centers.

Often the time at which undersecretion or oversecretion occurs determines whether abnormal production of a hormone will be evident. Thus inadequacy of somatotrophic hormone during the formative years results in a failure to achieve normal length of legs and arms. Commonly the torso has dimensions normal for a much taller individual, so that

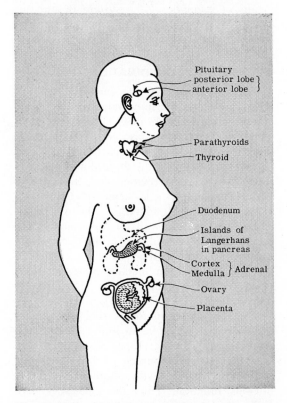

Fig. 10-1. *The chief sources of hormones and hormone complexes in the human body are the larger endocrine glands. Probably all cells, however, produce hormones important in maintaining proper coordination of the complex body. (After Parshley.)*

ENDOCRINE STRUCTURE	Controlled by	Hormone(s) produced	Affects the	Effect(s)	Undersecretion produces	Oversecretion produces
anterior pituitary	? blood thyroxin (I)	**thyrotrophic h.**	thyroid gland	secretion (S)	**hypothyroidism** (see thyroid)	**hyperthyroidism** (see thyroid)
	? blood parathormone (I)	parathyrotrophic h.	parathyroid gland	secretion (S)	hypoparathyroidism (see parathyroids)	hyperparathyroidism (see parathyroids)
	? cortisone in blood (I)	**adrenocorticotrophic h. ("ACTH")**	adrenal cortex	secretion (S)	(see adrenal cortex)	(see adrenal cortex)
	low blood sugar (S)	diabetogenic h.	glycogen stores	release of sugar (S)	low blood sugar (see pancreas)	high blood sugar
	unknown	somatotrophic h.	"long bones"	growth (S)	**dwarfism**	**gigantism** or **acromegaly**
	testosterone in ♂ (I); ? in ♀	gonadotrophic h.	gonads	maturation (S)	infantilism	sexual precocity
	blood estrogen & progesterone (I)	**follicle-stimulating** h. ("FSH")	ovarian follicles	maturation (S)	sterility	? sexual precocity
	? hormones from egg & embryo (S)	**luteinizing** h. ("LH")	corpus luteum	growth and maintenance (S)	abortion	
	? hormone(s) from embryo (I); nursing baby (S)	prolactin	mammary glands	enlargement & lactation (S)		
posterior pituitary	? blood concentration	oxytocin = pitocin	kidney tubules	reabsorption of water from filtrate (S)	water loss with thirst; diabetes insipidus	water storage; engorgement of tissues
	? blood pressure	vasopressin = pitressin	arterial muscles	contraction; blood pressure (S)	low blood pressure	high blood pressure
	? fetal hormone(s)	unnamed fraction	uterine muscles	contraction (S)		labor or oviposition
thyroid gland	ant. pituitary parathyrotrophic h. (S)	**thyroxin**	metabolic rate	fat storage (I) and sugar use (S)	low BMR; obesity; cretinism; **simple goiter**	high BMR; loss of weight; hyperactivity; exophthalmia
parathyroid gland	ant. pituitary parathyrotrophic h.	parathormone	blood calcium & phosphorus mobility	fixation of Ca & P (I)	muscle spasms; tetany from low blood calcium	softened bones and teeth; excretory loss
adrenal cortex	ant. pituitary ACTH (S)	**cortisone** & other components of "cortin"	joints; carbohydrate metabolism; blood sodium & potassium	maintenance (S)	Addison's disease	
		androgens	secondary sexual characters	maturation; male-female balance		sexual precocity; ♂ characters in ♀
adrenal medulla	sympathetic nervous system (S)	**adrenalin**	whole body	preparedness, pulse rate, muscle tone, nerve conduction rate (S)	passivity	irritability, hyperactivity
pancreatic isles of Langerhans	high blood sugar (S)	**insulin**	glycogen stores (antagonistic to diabetogenic h.; see ant. pituitary)	storage; fat metabolism	high blood sugar & loss through kidneys; **diabetes mellitus**	low blood sugar, starvation of cells especially neurons
gastric mucosa	products of protein digestion (S)	gastrin	gastric glands	secretion (S)		
duodenal mucosa	acidity (S)	[prosecretin]	pancreatic glandular epithelium	secretion of pancreatic juice (S)	NOTE: precursor is secreted into gut cavity, there activated by HCl, reabsorbed into blood as **secretin**)	
	acidity (S)	cholecystokinin	liver and gall bladder	secretion of bile (S)		
testis interstitial cells	unknown	**testosterone**	secondary sexual characters	growth and maintenance	infantilism	sexual precocity
ovarian follicles	ant. pituitary FSH (S)	**estrogen** = estrone = theelin	uterine mucosa (S) ant. pituitary (I)	proliferation production of FSH	sterility	sexual precocity
corpus luteum	ant. pituitary LH (S)	**progesterone**	uterine mucosa (S) ant. pituitary (I)	implantation of embryo; production of FSH	abortion	
placenta	growth of embryo	estrogen	uterine mucosa ant. pituitary (I)	retention of embryo (S); production of FSH	abortion	

NOTE: S = stimulates; I = inhibits; h = hormone.

the appendages in *dwarfism* seem quite out of proportion. In other instances, the torso is in keeping with the shorter limbs and the person is a true midget. The dachshund is apparently a clear example of the former in dogs, and follows an inherited course. By contrast, over-secretion of somatotrophic hormone during the growing period leads to excessive elonga-tion of the long bones, the diagnostic feature of *gigantism*. Sometimes, as a result of tumors or other causes, this growth-stimulating hor-mone is elaborated in quantity after normal growth is complete. This brings on a continua-tion of elongation in feet, hands, nose, ears, and sometimes chin, and to a state of distor-tion recognized clinically as *acromegaly*.

Prolactin is an interesting hormone in its effect upon behavior. In pigeons it appears responsible for the "mothering" instinct, and in other birds for a willingness to brood over "nest eggs" or even smooth stones. It is simi-larly effective if injected into virgin mice, and may induce them to secrete acceptable milk and adopt suckling offspring of almost any kind or age. Bereaved mother cats who nurse young rats or pups are reacting in the same fashion to their prolactin supply.

The term *pituitrin* was originally applied to the secretion of the posterior pituitary. Now this gland is known to produce at least three fractions. Damage to the posterior lobe leads to excessive water loss from the kidneys (8 to 10 gallons of urine daily, instead of the normal quart or two) and a consequent in-satiable thirst. Injections of hormone extract from the posterior pituitary are often used to aid in childbirth through the powerful con-tractions elicited in the smooth muscles of the oviduct and uterus. Thus the birth of mammals and the laying of eggs by birds and reptiles appear to be regulated and driven by this center.

The Thyroid Gland

Beside the larynx in air-breathing verte-brates are two small lumps of tissue; in man they fuse into a single mass. For many cen-turies it has been known that these thyroid tissues sometimes grow excessively large, pro-ducing a prominent bulge in the neck de-scribed as **simple goiter** (Photo 121). Even the distribution of the disease became apparent: the Alps, the Pyrenees, and the Carpathian mountain regions of Europe. Later additions to the list were the South American Andes, the Great Lakes country between the United States and Canada, and the St. Lawrence River valley draining these. The Chinese not only knew simple goiter; they found that eat-ing seaweeds was helpful. The Greeks recom-mended drinking small quantities of sea water as a curative measure. By 1180 A.D. a physi-cian and alchemist in Sicily prescribed ashes of seaweeds and sponges for the disease.

The correlation of these medications was not clear until iodine was discovered (1811), until the thyroid was found to contain the highest concentration of iodine in the body, and until the soils of the goiter-ridden areas were seen to have been leached of their iodine by the scouring action of glaciers in the last Ice Age. Sea water, seaweed, and sponges contain iodine.[1] And the hypertrophy of the thyroid gland was commonly a response to inadequate iodine in the diet. It was a compensatory overdevelopment of the gland, which ceased when iodine became available in food or medicine.

Science has established these facts beyond dispute, and simple goiter has become "one of the few diseases which might be conquered by Act of Congress," through mandatory ad-dition of a minute amount of iodine to all table salt sold in the country. "But thus far, Congress has rejected a law (such as Canada

---

[1] Iodine supplies available to man arise from the weathering of igneous rocks—hence in the craggy mountain areas of the world. Usually the streams in such places are very fast, seldom flooding mountain valleys, so that the iodine rarely is distributed lo-cally. Instead it may be added to the soil in regions where rivers empty slowly into the sea; most of the iodine reaches the oceans themselves. But when sea spray evaporates, sizable amounts of iodine are borne into the atmosphere as dust, and later the par-ticles may become nuclei of rain drops, fogs, or dews which fall on land. Loose soils retain a significant proportion of such iodine contributions, and acid humus acts as an efficient trap for it. Remote from bodies of iodine-rich salt water, however, the rains, fog, and dew contain little iodine. Hence there is a great variation in the iodine content of the soils of the world, a corresponding variation in the iodine content of plants growing on these soils, and hence in the availability of iodine to man in foods grown locally.

has) requiring all table salt in interstate commerce to be iodized." (*Time,* Sept. 19, 1949, p. 67.) Actually, only about a third of all American table salt is iodized, and in the iodine-poor areas large numbers of people distrust iodized salt as being "medicated" and harmful. In the 1949 *Public Health Reports* (U. S. Public Health Service) is the clear statement: "The thyroid gland takes up iodine from the blood stream and uses it to form a hormone, thyroxine. In turn, thyroxine regulates many body functions, including heat production, brain development, sexual maturity, and the growth of hair, skin and bones. A shortage of iodine may not be indicated dramatically by serious illness. Just as often, or oftener, the result may be lowered efficiency, nervousness or lack of energy. Too vague for any specific diagnosis, such a generalized malaise may weaken the individual's capacity throughout much or all of his lifetime." Moreover, iodine-deficient mothers often have feeble-minded children.

In addition to inadequacy of dietary iodine as a cause of abnormal thyroid activity, the gland may become inactive (**hypothyroidism**) or too active (**hyperthyroidism**). A deficient supply of the product **thyroxin** leads to different effects, depending on the stage of human life when the difficulty arises. In early childhood, hypothyroidism produces a peculiar type of dwarfing and idiocy called **cretinism;** the children remain cretins for life unless the condition is recognized and treated very promptly (Photo 125). Cretinism usually includes not only stunted growth but bow legs, defective teeth, enlargement of the tongue, sparseness of hair, a coarse leathery texture to the skin, and habitual exposure of the tongue. The disease may or may not bring on the hypertrophy of the gland itself as accompanying simple goiter. On the other hand, if hypothyroidism develops during adolescence or in later life, there is an obvious decrease in the metabolic rate, making the individual slow in reactions even to the point of feeble-mindedness. Such people gain weight in spite of honest attempts at dietary control. Injections of thyroxin are usually helpful and may allow return to normalcy. Where deficiency is due to a tumor of the thyroid gland, further destruction may be prevented by treatment with radioactive iodine—which becomes

concentrated in the gland and which often halts abnormal growth (Photo 126).

Overactivity of the thyroid gland is generally evident from a considerable increase in the basal metabolic rate, with inability to relax and rest. The individual becomes nervous and highly irritable, and in extreme cases other parts of the body become involved. Thus fat may be deposited behind the eyes in their sockets, leading to excessive prominence of the eyes—the condition termed *exophthalmia* (from *exo* = outward, *ops, ophthalmios* = eye). Such individuals are usually troubled also with loss of weight to the state of emaciation. The skin may become dry and the adrenal glands enter a state of inadequate activity further complicating the picture. Surgical removal of part of the overactive gland often brings relief, although the source of hyperthyroidism usually stems from the pituitary gland through excessive liberation of thyroid-stimulating hormone.

Thyroid glands are characteristic of all vertebrate animals, but among the cold-blooded forms the hormone may have quite different functions. Thus, in the amphibians, hypothyroidism postpones metamorphosis from the tadpole stage to the adult, and individuals given this handicap by experimental surgery grow to remarkable size without achieving mature anatomical details and behavior. Hyperthyroidism (or even feeding on thyroid gland tissue), on the other hand, hastens metamorphosis, so that a bullfrog tadpole which would normally reach a length of three to four inches before transforming will react to extra thyroxin at only ½ inch in length, absorb its tail, grow legs, develop lungs in place of gills, and achieve the adult skin type and markings—even many features of adult behavior—at a most precocious age.

The Parathyroid Glands

Embedded in the thyroid glands are two pairs of still smaller endocrine organs, the parathyroids, which elaborate the hormone *parathormone.* They are essential for life, since they control the concentration of calcium salts in the blood. So insignificant are the glands themselves, however, that their very existence was not demonstrated until

1891, and the results of their removal with superfluous thyroid tissue were not identified as separate from the sequelae of the more obvious surgery.

The chemical nature of parathormone is still unknown. Occasionally the parathyroids become excessively active, leading to a rise in blood calcium to the point where the kidneys lose this valuable ion into the urine. Maintenance of blood calcium at this high level then continues by removal of calcium from bones and teeth to the point where the former become pliable, deformed, and painfully twisted, and where the latter fall out or must be removed. Hyposecretion of parathormone, in contrast, allows a drop in blood calcium concentrations well below normal, to the point where the nervous system begins to suffer. Involuntary muscle twitchings, convulsions and even death may ensue if the condition is not recognized and treated correctly.

The Adrenal Glands

In close association with the kidneys are the paired adrenal glands, which in man reach the size of a golf ball, compressed against the upper curve of the larger organ. They have been known since 1663, but no better suggestion than that they were bumpers to keep the stomach from resting on the kidneys came until 1894, when the hormone **adrenalin** was recognized and described.

Adrenalin has been familiar in crystalline purity since 1901—the first hormone to be so completely purified. It has numerous effects and is released under nervous control. Fear and anger may provoke adrenal action, sometimes giving rise to the familiar "sinking sensation" in the abdominal area. The addition of adrenalin to the blood stream, whether naturally or through intravenous injection, causes contraction of the muscles around the visceral arteries, increasing blood pressure; simultaneously, the spleen releases more red blood cells into the circulation; the liver adjusts the blood-sugar level upwards by rapid hydrolysis of glycogen; the muscles attached to hair follicles may contract, elevating the hairs and often producing "goose pimples"; the pupils dilate; blood vessels in the skeletal muscles expand, bringing more blood into close proximity with muscle cells; and even coagulation rate for the blood is considerably increased in some peculiar way. All of these effects are reactions to an emergency—preparing the body for "fight or flight."

Because of its profound effect on the smaller peripheral blood vessels, adrenalin (usually as adrenalin hydrochloride) has been used successfully in stopping hemorrhage, shutting down the flow enough to allow a clot to form and seal the wound more effectively. Adrenalin solutions have been used, too, in contracting the nasal membranes in colds or allergic congestion, though this application is usually made under one of the alternative names of the hormone—epinephrine or suprarenin. Lack of adequate adrenalin may be due to disease of the gland; the symptoms are chiefly those due to lowered muscular tone.

Adrenalin is produced by only part of the adrenal gland—the central core or medulla. The outer portion of the adrenal body (the cortex) furnishes a hormone complex, known originally under the name "cortin." All of the components are steroids, and some of them (the **androgens,** from the Greek *aner, andros* = man) are involved in development and maintenance of the secondary sexual characters.

One component of cortin was identified and synthesized in 1949, under the name **cortisone.** It appears to be the active principle in therapy for Addison's disease—a malady marked by a bronzed skin (quite different from the effects of tanning), loss of appetite, muscular weakness associated with lowered metabolic rate, loss of sodium chloride and water from the body, and, in severe cases, prostration and death. Cortisone has proved valuable also in treatment of arthritis and related diseases, but the mechanism of its action is still unknown.

Androgens in the human body are produced in sufficient quantity that the fraction lost daily in the urine can be studied. A normal 20-year-old ♂ excretes nearly 17 milligrams, as compared to less than 12 in a ♀ of corresponding age. Moreover, if for some reason the androgen output in the ♀ rises to approach the level characteristic of the ♂, the normal femininity is replaced by assumption of ♂ characteristics such as facial hair and

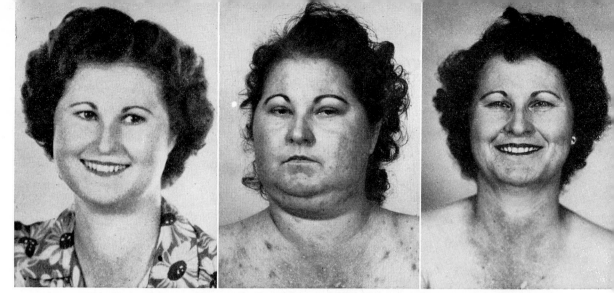

124. Hyperadrenocorticism ("Cushing's syndrome") is characterized by obesity confined to the face and trunk, hypertension, marked acne, purple striae in the inguinal area, and excessive development of body hair. *Left:* 10 years before onset. *Center:* at height. *Right:* 14 months after removal of whole right adrenal and ⅔ of left. Hypertension disappeared immediately. Cortisone and further hormone supplements are expected to maintain normalcy.

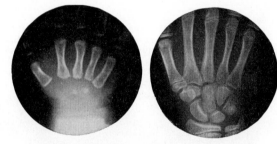

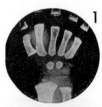

125. A cretin, age 10, height 3 ft. (*above, left circle:* bone age 6 months), was treated with thyroid for 8 years, reaching bone age 14 (*above, right circle*) and height 5 feet. The small numbered circles (*left and below*) show normal development of wrist bones and metacarpals at the ages indicated. X-ray diagnosis of physiological age thus is valuable in study of hypothyroidism and following its treatment in children.

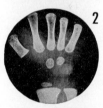

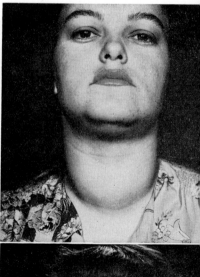

126. Abnormal growth and activity of the thyroid gland (*right, above*) raised the basal metabolic rate to 179 per cent of normal and produced other symptoms of toxicity. Treated for 3 months with a radioactive iodine compound from the Oak Ridge atomic plant (I^{131} with a half-life of 8 days), the patient recovered through selective internal destruction of the abnormal tissue (*right, below*).

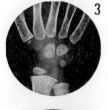

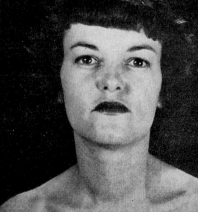

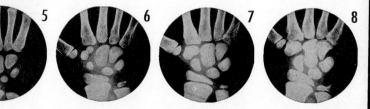

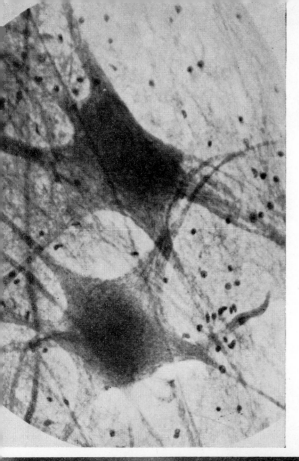

127. Giant motor cells with particularly large cell bodies may be seen in spinal cord smears. Axons extend the protoplasm often for several feet, to reach the muscles of the legs. Along this protoplasm pass the rapid electrochemical changes of repeated nerve impulses, which excite the effector mechanism into action. Activity of the effector, in turn, initiates sensory messages back to the coordinating centers of cord and brain.

Sense Organs and Nervous System Cooperate in the Coordination of the Animal Body

128. The eye of the basking alligator (see also Photo 75), like that of the basking cat, has a slit pupil that can be closed more completely than is possible with a circular pupil. In this way, additional protection is afforded the light-sensitive retina which is adapted for vision at low light intensities when the animal is stalking prey at night.

altered disposition of the fat stores—the clinical picture of masculinity in women (Photo 124). The parallel feminization of the ♂ with diminished androgen output is suspected but not yet proved. In children, excess androgens bring on precocious sexual maturity.

The Pancreatic Hormone

Special cells that the microscopic anatomist Langerhans termed "islets" are the secretory centers for the hormone **insulin** (from the Latin *insula* = island). But the "islands of Langerhans" did not become famous until 1922 when Frederick G. Banting (in collaboration with J. J. McLeod and Charles Best) prepared the first crude extract of insulin and demonstrated that it alleviated the symptoms of diabetes mellitus[2] in dogs from which the entire pancreas had been removed. The importance of this finding in medicine was recognized immediately, and a Nobel Prize was awarded jointly to Banting and McLeod in the following year.

Adequate insulin is a requirement for tissue cells, if they are to remove from the blood stream and oxidize the sugar they need. In hypoinsulinism, the cells release into the blood a still unidentified hormone that affects the liver and causes glycogen stores there to transform into blood sugar, thus raising the concentration to an abnormal height. The kidneys are unable to reabsorb so much sugar from the filtrate and it is lost in the urine. Even if sugar is withheld in the diet of a diabetic, the mobilization of glucose reserves and excretion of them in the urine continues at a high rate. With depletion of the liver stores of glycogen,[3] the blood sugar concentration drops suddenly and the patient must have more sugar promptly, or diabetic coma and death ensue.

2 Not to be confused with diabetes insipidus, which is the result of inadequate pituitary hormone (pp. 157, 158).

3 About six per cent of the weight of the liver in a well-fed human adult is glycogen (approximately 110 grams). An additional 250 grams of glycogen are stored in muscle cells as a reserve against exercise. This latter store amounts, by weight, to about 0.7 per cent of the muscles. The 350-gram total represents about 1,500 Calories—about half a day's energy requirements. Only an adequate insulin content in the blood keeps these glycogen reserves intact, as a stabilizing source of blood sugars from meal to meal, and as a means for keeping muscles normally resistant to fatigue.

Somewhere in this mechanism a secondary effect arises, interfering with normal metabolism of proteins and fats, and allowing these subsidiary sources of energy to be hydrolyzed and oxidized in such a way as to include serious poisons among their end-products. The unpleasant symptoms of diabetes seem due primarily to faulty fat metabolism, but recognition of the disease is generally by means of the simple test for sugar in the urine. It should be noted, however, that a positive sugar test does not necessarily imply diabetes mellitus. Not only do some other diseases induce this particular symptom, but the presence of sugar in the urine is not uncommon following ingestion of high carbohydrate meals. The person who absentmindedly eats through a pound box of candy in an evening is almost sure to show a high sugar concentration in the urine—an "alimentary glycosuria." This is quite different from the carbohydrate craving, excessive thirst, abnormal urine excretion, steady loss of weight, and general weakness found in diabetes mellitus.

Purified insulin is now obtained from the pancreas ("sweetbreads") of domestic animals (chiefly cattle, in slaughterhouses) and is available for injection into diabetics. With care, the possessor of deficient pancreatic hormone can live a fairly normal life, but the cells of the islets of Langerhans usually deteriorate progressively, so that the dosage must be raised gradually. Moreover, the diet must be watched with great care and related to the insulin injected—less carbohydrates, less insulin; more carbohydrates, more insulin. Hyperinsulinism can be caused easily by injecting too much insulin, and diabetics must be ready to drink sugary solutions or administer glucose intravenously if "post-injection shakiness" becomes evident. Hyperinsulinism causes an abnormal absorption of blood sugar by the tissues, a sharp drop to hypotonic levels,[4] and "hypoglycemic shock," with sudden coma and often death. In spite of precautions to the contrary, diabetics involved in accidents often suffer further harm because the insulin dose is withheld for more than a few hours. Recovery from an overdose is

4 The human blood sugar level must be kept just below 0.1 per cent to avoid collapse.

possible if more sugar is placed in the blood stream in time, but often the physician is unable to identify whether the coma is due to shock alone or to diabetic involvement.

Hormones of the Mucosa

A seemingly different category of hormones has been described from the mucosa of the stomach and duodenum. At least one of them, prosecretin, is not secreted into the blood stream directly. Instead it passes into the cavity of the gut. If acted upon by hydrochloric acid received by the duodenum in gastric juice accompanying food passed by the pyloric sphincter, it is changed to the active hormone, secretin. This, when absorbed into the circulatory system, reaches the pancreas and stimulates secretion of pancreatic juice.

Cholecystokinin, which stimulates bile discharge into the duodenum, may follow the same course. Gastrin, which induces secretion of gastric juice, is correspondingly affected by chemical substances within the stomach cavity, yet is conveyed by the blood stream and will affect even transplanted fragments of stomach mucosa sharing the circulation at remote points.

Secretin in the blood stream was the second hormone to be recognized. In 1902 the British physiologists, W. M. Bayliss and E. H. Starling, demonstrated that even an isolated loop of duodenum, when stimulated by weak hydrochloric acid in its cavity, elaborated a substance carried by the blood stream to the pancreas, stimulating it to secrete its digestive ferments. Even two dogs joined surgically by only their circulatory systems (Fig. 23-6) into a type of Siamese twin (properly termed *parabiosis*) reacted to the duodenal hormone. When food taken by one animal passed from its stomach to the duodenal loop following, that portion of the gut produced the hormone. The circulatory system then carried the substance to both dogs—the fed and the unfed—and both pancreases began to secrete. The term *hormone* was coined at this time.

Hormones from the Gonads

The reproductive centers, ovaries or testes, are the only true **primary sexual characters** in an animal. They elaborate the sex cells but are commonly at points in the body structure where they cannot easily be seen. Recognition of sex then depends on the **secondary sex characters,** and these, in turn, are controlled to a great extent by hormones elaborated in the testes and ovaries **(gonads),** respectively. In the human species, the distribution of fat; the development of hair on face, neck, shoulders, and chest; the lack of mammary development; and even the proportions of the skeletal system that make it easy to identify a manly man, are controlled by hormones from the gonads—in this case **testosterone** from the interstitial cells of the testes. The comb and wattles of a rooster, the mane and other hairy adornments of a lion, and the shining magenta-colored gluteal display areas of the ♂ mandrill are all developed under the "insistent compulsion" of this chemical.

The testosterone itself is elaborated by cells lying between the tubules of the testis where sperm arise and mature. As striking as the secondary sexual characters are in some animals, however, the psychic effects of testosterone are hardly less remarkable. Castration (removal of the testes and hence of both the source of sperm cells and of testosterone) allows the organism to change into a sort of intersex condition, in which the manly and womanly characters of the human species, the cow-like and bull-like features of cattle, and the rooster-like and hen-like aspects of domestic fowl become intermingled and unrecognizable.

The eunuch (if castrated before puberty) retains his high-pitched childlike (or feminine) voice; for this very feature, in former times, many children were castrated to provide older sopranos for all-"male" church choirs. The same operation, after adolescence, leads to considerable fat deposition on a semi-feminine pattern, a recession in muscular development, and a decrease in enterprise and mental force. The corresponding effects on a castrated bull (steer) show in increased fat production, decreased pugnacity, and a more vegetative life that leads to more weight per pound of feed (hence improved economic aspects in the sale for use as meat). Castrated roosters ("caponized" to become capons) are similarly lacking in competitive behavior, fatten up easily, and bring better prices.

The inability to reproduce and these hormonal irregularities are only coincidentally related to one another. Deficient sex cells have a significance only in terms of a future generation. In the undescended testes of a mammal (see Chapter 13, p. 281) the high temperature of the body cavity prevents maturation of the sperm and may even lead to degeneration of the seminiferous tubules. A suitable dose of X-radiation can accomplish the same sterilization while the testes are in the scrotum. But in neither instance is the inability to reproduce paralleled by any hormonal disturbance. Interstitial cells are unaffected and the individual still retains the secondary sex characters of the ♂.

Testosterone ordinarily acts to control the development of the sex organs and secondary sexual characters as the individual male reaches sexual maturity, and to lend strength to the sexual drive. In man it acts to increase the juvenile dimensions of testes and penis, to aid in the maturation of the sperm cells, to affect bone and muscle growth, and to co-operate with the androgens from the adrenal cortex in promoting hair development and other physical differences, including the enlargement of the larynx and the elongation of the vocal cords that causes the drop in pitch of voice.

In the ♀ vertebrate, **estrogen** (= estrin = estrone = theelin) from the ovary corresponds to testosterone. In mammals, estrogen arises in the **follicles** (Photo 235) as the enclosed egg cells come to maturity. It may serve comparably to an androgen, or stimulate the interstitial tissue into producing the hormones which maintain the secondary sexual characters and psychic behavior of the ♀. For the human ♀, these include deposition of adipose tissue providing rounded contours, a broadening of the pelvis, development of the breasts, additional growth of uterus and vagina, and other features.

Where eggs mature at one or more special seasons during the year, the added estrogen release may induce structural and psychic changes commonly seen in domestic animals when a ♀ comes "into heat." The importance of this change is clear, since only for a period measured in hours after discharge of an egg from its follicle can that egg be fertilized. If no sperms arrive in time, the egg disintegrates.

Hence the physiological and psychological changes in the ♀ correlated with the shedding of the egg from the ovary all cooperate to make fertilization more likely.

In many instances, the ♀ is completely uncooperative with the ♂ when not in heat. Under the stimulation of extra estrogen, however, she may not only display herself in a manner most attractive to him but may also seek his attentions. Her actions are often supplemented by vaginal discharges with a distinct odor detected at considerable distances by the opposite sex. Anyone who has kept an adult tabby cat knows when she reaches this condition by the congregation of tom cats from the whole neighborhood, calling, caterwauling, and fighting with one another outside the house in which the ♀ is confined.

The Sexual Cycle

The rhythmic nature of reproductive potentialities arises in the ♀ vertebrate through complex interaction. Part of this is the modification of sex-hormone output by the gonads, according to the endocrine stimulation received from the anterior pituitary. Part is the sensitivity of the pituitary to the concentration of sex hormones in the blood stream.

In many vertebrates the entire sexual mechanism is triggered by external events, such as change in the length of night—inducing synchronous ovulation in large populations. This is an **estrous cycle,** on an annual or semi-annual basis (from the Greek *oistros* = frenzy). In mankind and some of the other primates, by contrast, the rhythm appears to be entirely internal and follows a **menstrual cycle** (from the Latin *mensis* = month). In either instance, the central events concern the follicle with its developing egg cell, and the uterine lining (mucosa) which proliferates and prepares to house and nourish an embryo if the egg becomes fertilized.

Under hormonal stimulation from the pituitary, a follicle develops, liberates its egg into the body cavity by bursting, usually placing the minute cell where the funnel-like end of the oviduct rescues it and conveys it into the Fallopian tube toward the uterus.

A second hormone from the pituitary is effective in stimulating the formation of a

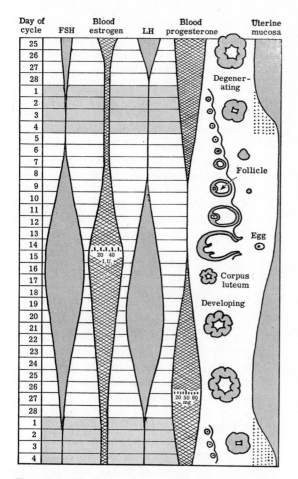

Day of cycle	FSH	Blood estrogen	LH	Blood progesterone	Uterine mucosa

FIG. 10-2. *The human menstrual cycle is controlled by four main hormones in the blood plasma. Following the end of a menstrual period, FSH from the anterior pituitary increases in concentration and stimulates development of ovarian follicles. From the growing follicles comes estrogen, which stimulates the uterine mucosa to grow in thickness. Estrogen also stimulates the anterior pituitary to produce LH. By the 14th day, estrogen has reached a maximum concentration, about 60 International Units (I.U.). Normally some one follicle has reached maturity and discharges an egg by the process of ovulation. Unless the egg is fertilized, the estrogen concentration gradually decreases. However, the pituitary continues to build up the LH concentration, and after ovulation the corpus luteum from the burst follicle grows rapidly, liberating progesterone into the blood stream. Progesterone inhibits the pituitary from production of FSH, and there is good correspondence between rise in progesterone and fall in FSH concentration. With decrease in estrogen by the 26th day, the pituitary is producing significantly less LH. The corpus luteum reaches a maximum of productivity. Unless the egg has been fertilized, the corpus luteum slowly degenerates and the blood concentration of progesterone falls off. With estrogen reaching minimum levels the uterine mucosa is no longer able to maintain its thickened condition. It is*

yellow gland in the empty follicle—a mass of tissue called the **corpus luteum,** from the Latin *corpus* = body and *luteus* = yellow. This small mass is an important endocrine organ in the menstrual cycle, since it inhibits the pituitary from production of the hormone stimulating further growth of follicles (Fig. 10-2). As a result, progress in the ovary is suspended until the fate of the recent egg is settled.

If the egg remains unfertilized for many hours, the egg disintegrates. Before long the corpus luteum regresses, its hormone disappearing from the blood stream. As a result the pituitary again is free to stimulate development of a new burst of growth in the ovarian follicles, leading to production of another egg ready for fertilization. Just before the new round begins, however, the uterine mucosa is shed—no longer supported by hormones from the ovary—as the menstrual discharge emerging over a period of several days from the vaginal opening.

If, however, the egg is fertilized as it descends the Fallopian tube, the first embryonic stages are passed through quickly and the resulting ball of cells burrows into the ready wall of the uterus. This **implantation** is actively assisted by the mucosa which, under normal stimulation, has become so receptive that it will envelop almost any small object—even inert foreign particles such as beads.

The reaction to implantation is formation of a sudden supply of estrogen from the uterine mucosa, affecting the pituitary and hence the corpus luteum. Thus the corpus luteum continues in its endocrine role, the pituitary produces no new supply of follicle-stimulating hormone, and menstrual cycles cease for the duration of pregnancy. No new follicles develop and the uterine tissue does not degenerate.

For the first three months of the human gestation period, the corpus luteum continues to enlarge. Its hormone seems to control the development of the placenta by means of which the embryo obtains its nourishment and disposes of its wastes, and prevents shedding

shed as the menstrual discharge, shown by shading on days 1 through 4. By the end of menstruation, the concentration of progesterone is sufficiently decreased (although the degenerating corpus luteum has not yet disappeared completely) that the pituitary is no longer inhibited from production of FSH, and a new cycle begins.

of the uterine wall containing the embryo— the event termed *miscarriage* or, medically, *spontaneous abortion.*

Later in the gestation period the placenta itself produces hormones. The amounts of these are large enough that excess is excreted in the maternal urine. After the 6th week of human pregnancy, this "pregnancy urine" injected into the blood stream of a mature but unmated ♀ rabbit is enough to induce ovulation. This can be recognized by sacrificing the animal and finding on the ovary surface the small clot of blood which regularly fills a freshly ruptured follicle. This is the Friedman test, one of several methods using biological reactions to detect pregnancy in early stages. Others use mice (the Ascheim-Zondek or A-Z test), or a South African aquatic toad (Xenopus). All are referred to as **bio-assays.**

Maleness versus Femaleness

Armed with a modern understanding of hormone interaction, many observations of long standing are seen to have a reasonable basis. Thus cattlemen have known for centuries that when twin calves of unlike sex are born, the ♀ frequently fails to develop normal sexual abilities; instead, she matures to a sterile cow called a **freemartin.** Her body build suggests that she is somewhat masculine; reproductive function is completely lacking.

This problem was clarified in the laboratories of the University of Chicago, when Dr. F. R. Lillie examined the uteri of pregnant cattle in the slaughterhouses of that city. He discovered that the extensive embryonic membranes of twin embryos overlap in the uterus, and that chemical substances can diffuse from one embryo's blood system into that of the other. Moreover, in the normal course of events, the maleness of the ♂ embryo becomes evident at an earlier stage than does the femaleness of the ♀; the hormones elaborated in connection with this genetically controlled sex difference diffuse from the more mature ♂ calf to the less mature ♀ embryo. The result is interference with normal development of the ♀ reproductive system; the genetically ♀ ovary precursors fail to develop into proper ovaries because of the presence of testosterone, and a sterile freemartin is produced.

Control of sex of offspring has long been a goal of mankind. So far he has learned to accomplish this chiefly in the domestic fowl. At the developmental age when chicks are hatched, their gonad precursors have not yet matured sufficiently for sex to be definite. Of course, the sex of the chick is included in its genetic makeup, and without interference each would become either ♂ or ♀, either rooster or hen. But if during the first ten hours after hatching an injection of testosterone is made into every chick, all become ♂ ♂; if estrogen is used, all become ♀ ♀. Actually, the rudiments of both ovaries and testes are present in each chick, and the hormone balance determines which of these organs will mature, and which type of behavior and other body features will accompany growth to reproductive adulthood.

Even at maturity, the rudiments of both sets of gonads remain—small bits of testis tissue in hens, in addition to their active ovaries, ovarian tissue in roosters supplementary to the active testes. If a tumor develops in the gonads of a hen, and so destroys them that little or no estrogen is produced, the suppression of testis growth ends; they develop, elaborate both testosterone and sperm cells, and change the hen to a rooster. Correspondingly, a rooster may become a hen and even lay eggs if something destroys the testis tissue that maintains his sexual characters by furnishing testosterone and sperm cells. Caponizing destroys all gonad material.

Such interchangeability of the sexes is possible within limits throughout the vertebrates. Even a human eunuch injected with testosterone grows facial hair and develops male musculature and fat distribution within the range of possibilities of his genetic constitution. No amount of testosterone, however, can make an Apollo or Hercules out of an individual lacking the hereditary basis. Nor can estrogen work more spectacular changes in the ♀. All that such injections can do is to make good a lack due to some abnormality of the endocrine glands themselves, and oversupply must be guarded against constantly. There is strong indication that the sex hormones, for example, are closely related to cancer-producing agents, so that excessive injections are most unwise.

Moreover, in an organism whose hormone control is so complicated, overdoses are most likely to produce unwanted changes—either compensatory or degenerative—in other endocrine systems that are essential to the health of the individual.

Amphibian Metamorphosis

Among amphibians, the transformation of the tadpole stage into the adult is dependent upon the thyroid's output of hormone. But if the supply of thyrotrophic hormone from the anterior pituitary is deficient, a normal thyroid will not produce enough thyroxin to induce metamorphosis—even if the supply of iodine in the diet is abundant. Injection of thyroxin, or feeding on thyroid gland from a mature animal, will bring on the change to adult body form. So will surgical union involving the blood stream to an individual with normal pituitary (Fig. 23-6). In fact, in this parabiotic existence, if one partner has a thyroid, the other an anterior pituitary, and each lacks the gland possessed by the other, the pair will achieve adulthood as though both were normally equipped.

A most instructive example of this dependence of thyroid on pituitary is found in the axolotl. This gilled salamander is native to the marshes near Mexico City, and is interesting to biologists because it reproduces without reaching adult form in many body features. It was learned that axolotls fed on thyroid will metamorphose, losing their gills and tail fin, gaining lungs, and acquiring a bright coloration of the skin in a pattern that never develops in a state of nature. Their own thyroid glands are normal, but produce no thyroxin. When pituitary injections were tried, however, axolotls used their own dormant thyroid glands to furnish the hormone needed for metamorphosis. Thus the reproductive habits of this amphibian are an adaptation to chronic deficiency in thyrotrophic hormone.

Feedback

Wherever the interaction of hormones in normal animals is well understood, the mechanism corresponds to a design feature of modern electronic controls. The system is planned to be self-correcting. Overproduction leads to reduction of output. Underproduction stimulates an increase. Thus a lowering of thyroxin concentration in the blood appears to induce the anterior pituitary to increase its secretion of thyrotrophic hormone—stimulating the thyroid to greater production. A rise in thyroxin concentration in the blood need not go far before the anterior pituitary is inhibited from further production of thyrotrophic hormone. And without stimulation, the thyroid gland reduces its output.

This is the principle of the "feedback" circuit in present-day radios, keeping the loudspeaker volume approximately constant in spite of variation in the strength of the signal picked up by the antenna. In radio and hormone network alike, the outcome is a "steady state." It is not an equilibrium. Thus nutrition, growth, excretion, maturation, reproduction, and the like are managed by hormonal feedback systems. They provide control without endangering the continuity of the multicellular organism.

2. COORDINATION IN MULTICELLULAR NONCHORDATES

The efficiency with which hormones can serve an organism in coordinating its activities depends not only upon the glands themselves, but also upon the speed with which the blood stream distributes the products. Animals in which blood flows sluggishly or passes through many open sinuses between the viscera cannot depend so much on hormones as those more like the vertebrate.

Well-organized ductless glands are known only among the arthropods and chordates. No doubt other invertebrates produce hormones too, but since the sources are less definite, the output minute, and the effects spread widely throughout the body, far less is known about them.

Among arachnids, crustaceans, and insects, however, the evidence now available points to a high order of complexity and of specificity in reaction and interaction. Growth, including molting and metamorphosis, is a primary field of hormone control in arthropods. So, apparently, is the cessation of activity known as "diapause." Among some of the higher crustaceans, at least, the coloration of the body surface varies according to the hormone output of glands stimulated by the nervous system.

A further hormonal mechanism is slowly becoming identified: the operation of "internal clocks" affecting metabolic rate, time of emergence from the pupal case, time of feeding, and the like. Some of these follow a 24-hour rhythm with remarkable accuracy (if

the average temperature remains constant). Others seem linked to a tidal rhythm, recycling every 24 hours and 50 minutes, and keeping in time with the moon's phases. Whether a counterpart of invertebrate lunar rhythms explains the regularity of the 28-day menstrual cycle in woman remains unknown.

SUGGESTED READING (see pp. 505-510)

Classics and Milestones: Bayliss & Starling, Banting & Best.

Recent and Informative: Brown, 1954; Constantinides & Carey, 1949; Funkenstern, 1955; Li, 1950; Thompson, 1955.

11 · Faster Coordination

1. ACTION AND REACTION. 2. SIMPLE SYSTEMS. 3. NEURONS AND NERVES. 4. SENSORY CELLS—SKIN RECEPTORS. 5. THE EYE—THE VERTEBRATE EYE, EFFICIENT USE OF EYES, THE COMPOUND EYE. 6. THE EARS—HEARING, EAR DEFECTS, EQUILIBRATION. 7. EFFECTOR MECHANISMS—GLANDS, LUMINESCENT ORGANS, ELECTRIC ORGANS, CHROMATOPHORES. 8. THE BRAIN—ACTION POTENTIALS IN THE CEREBRAL CORTEX. 9. THE CRANIAL NERVES. 10. THE SPINAL CORD AND SPINAL NERVES. 11. SELF-REGULATING CONTROLS—BREATHING, TEMPERATURE REGULATION.

UNITY OF ACTION in a multicellular animal depends upon coordinating mechanisms. Unified cooperation cannot surpass the means by which it is achieved. Hormones introduce an obvious delay—the time required for secretion, transportation, and response. If regulation depends entirely on hormones, the reaction is postponed in proportion to the slowness of the transfer method. The speed of blood circulation provides the principal limiting factor.

Insects and other arthropods, with relatively simple circulation and feeble heart action, employ hormone control chiefly for functions that can be handled satisfactorily on an hour-to-hour or day-to-day basis. In vertebrates, although the blood and hormones circulate far faster, regulation by chemicals alone is not sufficiently prompt to keep the animal from danger or help it find its food and mates. Active living in a highly competitive world, where energy for life cannot be obtained passively from the sun, usually requires an animal to have a faster method for coordination of its parts. The communication mechanism that answers this need is the nervous system. That nervous and endocrine regulation must themselves cooperate is obvious enough.

1. ACTION AND REACTION

Animals have need to detect and react to a considerable range of features in their environment. In general, the action that pro-duces a reaction in an animal is a *change* in some detail—an increase or decrease in illumination, a sudden noise that contrasts with the quiet before and afterward, or a new odor or taste. Such events, as they impinge on an organism, are referred to collectively as **stimuli.** If the stimulus comes rapidly enough so that the change is detected and the animal does something new, the action called forth is termed a **response.** But it should be noted that a stimulus, which means anything that excites action (and seldom provides the energy for it), must be strong enough to evoke response.

The weakest stimulus that is effective is referred to as a **threshold** stimulus. Each stimulus stronger than threshold can be expected to elicit a response, though the reaction to a very strong stimulus may be different from that to a very weak one. Thus we pour a dilute solution of acetic acid (vinegar) on some foods to enjoy the taste sensation produced. A strong solution of the same acid not only is unpleasant to the extent of producing pain, but may even be used to destroy unwanted living cells—such as the application of concentrated acetic acid to a wart to "burn" it and destroy the tissue of this benign (harmless) tumor.

A few of the higher plants show clear-cut responses to specific stimuli. These apparently are entirely on a hormonal basis, although there is an associated electrical change and alternations in permeability that are very closely similar to these characteristics of nervous action in animals. Growth movements and turgor movements, however, never achieve the speed characteristic of nervous mechanisms. Good sensory structures may be involved (as, for example, the tactile hairs in the Venus' fly-trap), and conduction may transfer the reaction to other parts of the plant as rapidly as 5 cms per second. No nervous system seems involved, and these cannot be correctly compared to the special mechanisms in animals.

2. SIMPLE SYSTEMS

The coelenterates possess the simplest type of specialization toward better coordination (p. 140). Commonly, their response to a stimulus is a change of shape or position. But the nature of the stimulus, its strength, the past history of the animal, and other features all enter into determining what reaction there will be. Spread of conduction of information has been measured and found to be of the order of 10 cms per second—a very leisurely performance when compared with nervous reactions of higher animals but enormously faster than hormone control would make possible in an animal lacking a good circulatory system.

The limitations of the network of sea anemones and other coelenterates have been studied. Ordinarily, these animals feed on microscopic living organisms that bump into the many tentacles, are stung and held by the nematocysts, and then brought by the tentacles to the mouth to enter the digestive cavity. But small bits of filter paper soaked in meat broth will be taken by a hungry anemone, passed by the tentacle touched to the mouth, and finally spat out when the broth has been removed. The reaction accepting the bits of brothy paper becomes faster as the experiment is repeated—but only for as long as the same tentacles (or immediately adjacent ones) receive the paper each time, and if the repeated offerings are made within a very few hours' time. Otherwise there is no increased rate of reaction and nothing resembling learning by experience. Yet even in this demonstration can be seen the suggestion of memory, and an ability to improve a response through repetition, however local.

3. NEURONS AND NERVES

Among the more advanced animals there is a true nervous system in place of cytoplasmic strands or nerve nets. Nervous systems imply the presence of **nerves,** and these in turn bear a definite relation to the cellular constituents of the system, the individual **neurons.** Each of the neurons differs markedly in that it conveys information normally in one direction only; in other words, each neuron shows polarity.

Typically, a neuron has a rather large mass of cytoplasm surrounding the nucleus to form a **cell body** (Fig. 8-3, Photo 127), and two sorts of long projections containing cytoplasm, called **nerve fibers.** Usually one type of projection is divided repeatedly, and each of the many forks ends in a little brush of secondary branching. These serve to pick up information to pass to the cell body, and the whole projection is called a **dendrite** (from the Greek *dendron* = tree). The other type of fiber from the cell body then carries the message away from the region of the nucleus. It is an **axon** and has few, if any, branches. Branches from axons are termed *collaterals,* and they have the responsibility of spreading the information more widely than is possible with an unbranched axon (Fig. 11-1).

The simplest arrangement of a neuron in an animal would be one in which the dendrites served sensitive areas such as the skin, and the axon carried messages to a muscle or gland. Stimulation of the skin area would arouse the dendrites to send information through the cell body, along the axon, to the region where a response could be forthcoming, as a contraction or secretion. To render easy discussion of these activities, the word **receptor** is applied to the part of the mechanism that receives the stimulus, and **effector** to the muscle or gland that actually does something by way of a response. Actually, the participation of a receptor, a single neuron, and an effector is rare in animals; usually several neurons are involved, and often more than one effector. Commonly, too, the receptor is itself part of a highly specialized cell or organ, termed a **sensory cell** or a **sense organ.** Examples are the sensory cells of the nasal region, which respond to minute amounts of chemical substances carried to them by inhaled air, or such sense organs as the eyes and ears. However, the arrangement of a receptor, neurons, and effector does form a mechanism for coordination that is basic in any nervous system; this shortest bridge from stimulus to response is termed a **simple reflex arc,** and the response to a stimulus in such a situation is often referred to as a **reflex** or a reflex act.

Neurons do not occur singly. They are organized into groups that comprise the nervous systems of all but the least specialized of animals. The axons and often parts of the dendrites near the cell bodies are commonly sheathed in a tough insulating layer of shiny white fatty materials—as electrically separated as are the individual wires of a telephone line. This **myelin sheath** seems to have a pronounced effect on the rate of message conduction. In myelinated fibers 100 meters per second is common, while in non-myelinated fibers the usual speed is one meter per second.

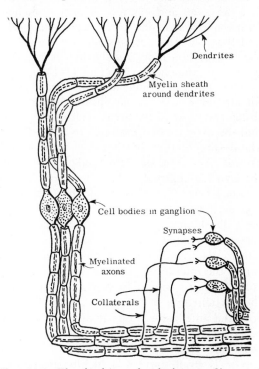

FIG. 11-1. *The dendrites, sheathed nerve fibers, aggregated cell bodies, and synaptic junctions of a vertebrate nervous system, in diagram form.*

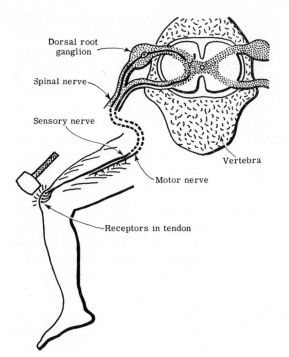

FIG. 11-2. *Nervous pathways of the knee-jerk reflex.*

As in the electrical analogy, groups of the sheathed extensions of nervous tissues are frequently grouped into parallel lines closely in association with one another, to form **nerves** (Fig. 11-1). The corresponding cell bodies may be clustered similarly into masses with less structural support, called **ganglia** (singular, *ganglion*). In vertebrates the nervous tissues at the anterior end of the central nerve are organized into a complex structure, the **brain,** whereas the dorsal nerve trunk itself contains further ganglionic matter that makes of it a complex **nerve cord.** Nerves which branch from the brain region and emerge through the protective portions of the enclosing cranium are called **cranial nerves,** whereas those that emerge between the vertebrae of the spinal column are termed **spinal nerves.** The brain, spinal cord, and spinal ganglia are referred to as the **central nervous system,** whereas the nerves and their branches represent the **peripheral** nervous system.

An example of a simpler reflex in a nervous system is the familiar **knee-jerk reflex** (Fig. 11-2). When the human lower leg is swung freely over a table or other support, and the kneecap is struck a smart blow, the leg kicks forward at the knee due to sudden involuntary contraction of muscles in the thigh. The receptors are in the tendon over the kneecap. When stimulated by the tap on the surface, the sensory cells affect the dendrites of the neurons associated with them. In the neuron a change passes rapidly from the dendrites to the cell bodies near the lumbar region of the nerve cord; thence each goes to a short axon. This, in turn, makes functional contact with the dendrites of a second neuron, the cell body located within the lumbar region of the cord, and through a short axon to pass the message to a third neuron with cell body in the cord. Thence an axon extends to branches among the muscle fibers in the upper leg.

The knee jerk is a seemingly valueless yet amusing reflex. Others with more importance to the individual include the quick withdrawal of the hand or foot from a hot or sharp object and the blinking of the eye on the approach of anything (even when known to be incapable of hitting because of intervening heavy glass plate). Each depends upon a sensory cell, but the sensory cell cannot in itself determine what the response will be at the other end of the reflex arc.

Most sensory cells, in fact, will respond to a number of different stimuli—each eliciting the same response. Retinal cells, for example, are most sensitive to light, but a blow on the eye can excite many of them to the point of sending messages down the optic nerve—producing the sensation of "seeing stars." Almost any sensory cell will respond to a direct current of electricity, and the evidence all points to an electrochemical change as the form of the message a sensory cell transfers to a neuron, or one neuron passes through its length and to another. But the same electrical current at appropriate points on the human tongue "tastes" salty, sweet, bitter, or sour, depending on which taste organs are stimulated. Yet under normal circumstances each sensory cell responds most readily to some one type of stimulus. This differential sensitivity, plus the interpretation placed on the information sent along the nerve fiber, determines most of the response obtained.

In the knee-jerk reflex used as an example, the electrochemical change (called an **impulse)** in the first neuron calls forth a new, similar, but separate impulse in the second neuron. The second impulse on arrival at the dendrites of the third neuron elicits a new, separate impulse within it. This third impulse eventually arrives at the terminations on muscle fibers, and stimulates these fibers to contract. The leg kicks forward.

Since the first of the neurons in this example is clearly associated with a sensory cell or group of them, and since it conveys impulses *toward* the spinal cord, it is described as a **sensory neuron.** Groups of the sheathed portions of the dendrites of such sensory neurons make up the major part of the nerve serving the kneecap area. The third neuron, on the other hand, is associated with an effector —in this case a muscle producing movement; hence it is a **motor neuron.** Actually, the sciatic nerve which connects the mid-dorsal nerve cord to the knee area of the leg contains both the sensory fibers of sensory neurons from the kneecap and the motor fibers of the motor neurons to the upper leg muscles. Because the nerve is neither purely sensory nor purely motor, it is referred to as a **mixed nerve.** Most of the spinal nerves have this nature.

The sensory and motor nerve fibers are separated in the region of the nerve cord of vertebrates. This is in relation to the internal structure of the cord itself. It has an H-shaped core of ganglionic tissue, and it is in association with the arms of the *H* that the connection is seen to the **dorsal root** and **ventral root** of each spinal nerve. The sensory fibers enter the dorsal root and have their cell bodies within an enlarged **dorsal root ganglion** from which only axons enter the upper limb of the *H* of ganglionic core. The cell bodies for the motor neurons are in the lower limb of the *H,* and only their axons pass out through the ventral root. Also in this ganglionic tissue are additional neurons serving as links between sensory and motor neurons, and between these and the brain; collectively they are described as **adjustor neurons,** and their existence makes possible the more complex types of reflex behavior. The second neuron in the knee-jerk reflex is an adjustor neuron.

Around the H-shaped gray-colored core of the nerve cord, filling it out to an approximately cylindrical form, are the elongated axons of neurons with cell bodies in the brain, as fibers extending backward in the animal to the many levels of the spinal nerves, plus the similarly far-reaching axons of neurons with cell bodies in the cord itself, conducting impulses forward to the brain. Since these lengthwise axons of two types are myelinated, the nerve cord is seen to be whitish, glistening, and tough.

Sensory, adjustor, and motor neurons are the basic elements of more complicated nervous systems. These units are not, however, in true physical contact or in actual electrical union. Instead, each neuron carries its own electrochemical impulse from dendrites to the end of the axon, and there initiates a chemical change that may stimulate the dendrites of the next neuron in the series. No spark leaps from one to another. The region where the axon of one and the dendrites of the next are in close proximity is a microscopic gap in the continuity—a space called a **synapse.** Nerve fibers can actually carry impulses in either direction, but a synapse is completely unidirectional. From it comes the polarity which is so characteristic of all higher nervous systems.

It would appear that the axon tip is able to secrete a chemical substance (a **neurohumor)** into the space of the synapse, and that this material may become sufficiently concentrated to cause the next neuron to respond. Since the distance from the site of elaboration of the chemical substance to the receiving component of the synapse is so short, any lack of continuity between one neuron and another produces delays measured in millionths of a second. The rate of conduction of the impulse in a neuron itself, on the other hand, ranges from 0.1 meter per second in such animals as worms, insects, and mollusks, to 100 meters per second in vertebrates with highly developed nervous systems.

Just as a sensory cell or sense organ has its threshold level below which a stimulus elicits no activity passed to the sensory neuron, so too does each synapse have a threshold. If the excitation reaching a synapse from the axon of the one neuron is too slight, the synapse acts as a block so that the second neuron is not caused to act. However, for excitation higher than threshold, the synapse carries across the chemical stimulus that initi-

ates a new electrochemical response in the second neuron.

Many drugs and some anesthetics seem to affect primarily the synaptic mechanism. Strychnine, for example, renders all of the synapses so indiscriminate in their conduction that almost any stimulus given the poisoned animal evokes violent convulsive contractions of all its skeletal muscles. Anesthetics, on the other hand, inhibit specific enzymes and prevent transmission of any impulses. Synaptic block also develops from prolonged excitation, as a form of fatigue. Thus the synapse is more subject to fatigue than the sites where nerve fibers reach muscle cells. And the nerve ending is more readily fatigued than is the muscle fiber itself. Nerve fibers, on the other hand, are practically immune to fatigue.

Often the synaptic mechanism conceals one fundamental feature of each neuron. A neuron, like a sensory cell, a muscle cell, or an individual gland cell, has its own threshold for activity—as a measure of its share in the general property of all living protoplasm, irritability. But if the stimulus reaching any of these cells is higher than threshold, the cell reacts in its characteristic way—fully, completely, and then relaxes again. The neuron conducts its electrochemical impulse and stops. Each impulse for any given cell is of one type and of one strength, without variation. The cell responds to its limit or not at all. Such is the basis for the **all-or-none law** of reaction.

Since all impulses conducted by each neuron are alike, it seems astonishing that different types of stimuli can be identified and the strength of each stimulus evaluated. The first of these depends entirely on which sensory cell—neuron train is excited. If it were possible to rearrange the nerve connections from nose and ear so that the auditory nerve served the nasal membranes and the olfactory nerve the sound receptor system, we would "hear odors" and "smell noises." The messages carried by these nerves do not differ in any respect, but the normal linkage of sense organ and remainder of the nervous system allows us to identify the stimulus with remarkable accuracy. This is the basis of ability to recognize distinct mechanical stimuli (such as contact, pressure, and sound), osmotic changes in the concentration of the environment, chemical changes in the kinds of substances in or around the organism, thermal stimuli (changes in temperature), photic stimuli (changes in intensity, direction, or color of light), and electrical

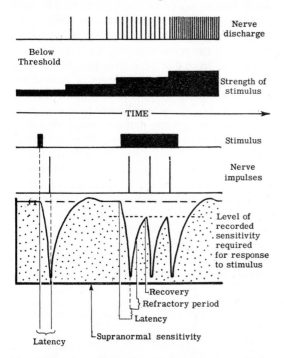

FIG. 11-3. *Upper half: The relation between stimulus (bottom), its intensity represented by steps, and nerve fiber discharge frequency (top). Lower half: A brief stimulus compared to a more extended stimulus, in terms of the changes in sensitivity and the related discharge of impulses on the associated nerve fiber.*

stimuli (alterations in strength or direction of electric currents).

There are only two variables in the impulses conducted by any neuron: (1) the number of them passing along its length per second (the **frequency**), and (2) the length of time during which a train of impulses continues (the **duration**). Actually, very few stimuli elicit single responses in nerve fibers; the usual event is at least a burst of several, repeated with the regularity of machine-gun fire (Fig. 11-3).

Only at threshold can a single impulse be expected. Above this critical point, each neuron carrying a response reacts repeatedly, and the frequency of impulses is related to the strength of the stimulus. Within limits, the more pronounced the stimulus is, the

FASTER COORDINATION · 173

more rapidly does one impulse follow another. Both oxygen consumption and carbon dioxide output rise in proportion to the number of impulses per second. In comparison with a contracting muscle, however, the energy involved, heat production, and fuel consumption are negligible. The heat has been measured: it represents one microgram of glycogen per gram of nerve per minute of prolonged stimulation. Hence the carbohydrate reserve of the nerve fiber is used up only very slowly, and the fact that nerve fibers are so immune to fatigue (as long as oxygen is present) should come as no surprise. Similarly, the energy for the impulse is obtained all along the length of its path. Thus, unlike electric currents, the impulse does not grow feebler with distance.

4. SENSORY CELLS

Rarely do the dendrites of a sensory neuron end simply in the skin and pick up stimuli directly. The more usual situation is for the dendrites to come into very close association with one or more specialized cells in which irritability is highly developed. These are sensory cells, which apparently elaborate and secrete toward the dendrite ends chemical substances that elicit responses from the neuron protoplasm. Some sensory cells are sufficiently different in form that they can be recognized by sight—appearance being linked to activity. Collectively they are referred to as *receptors*, and they are classified according to

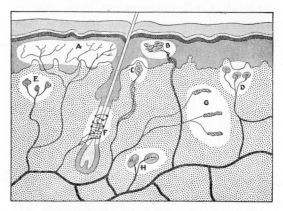

FIG. 11-4. *The various types of receptors in human skin. Probable functions are: A, pain; B, C, touch; D, cold; E, warmth; F, touch of hair; G, H, pressure.*

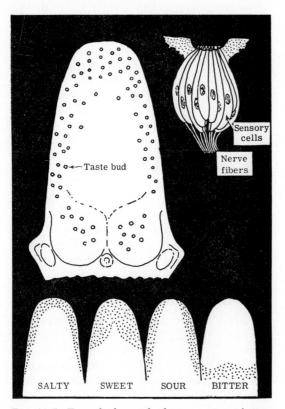

FIG. 11-5. *Taste buds on the human tongue* (upper left) *are of four physiological types with different distributions* (bottom row), *although in structure each taste bud has the same form* (upper right).

the nature of the stimulus to which they respond most readily and regularly. Those of man and many vertebrates include: (1) **tangoreceptors,** in the skin (Fig. 11-4), responding to touch; (2) **thermoreceptors,** in the skin, responding to either heat or cold; both types are present, with separate nerve supplies; (3) **chemoreceptors** for taste on the tongue (Fig. 11-5)—responding to dissolved substances[1] which are sweet or salty or bitter or sour; all four types are present, with separate innervation; (4) chemoreceptors for smell in the nasal

---

[1] Investigations reported for the first time in 1949 indicate that the substances may have to be dissolved in the individual's own saliva—that no water or salt solution or other person's saliva will allow operation of the sensory cells in the taste buds; this suggests an interaction of sensory cell and salivary chemical contents that had not been suspected before. Other substances apparently can be tasted with no saliva present.

membranes (Fig. 11-6), responding to infinitesimal[2] traces of chemicals suspended in air, and capable of identifying hundreds of different materials from these insignificant samples. Actually, the sampled molecules dissolve first in water or secreted fatty oils, and reach the living protoplasm in this form. Most "tasty" foods are recognized by odors that reach the nasal membranes from the rear —that is, from the pharynx; (5) **photoreceptors,** as retinal cells in the eyes of human beings, but merely as specialized nerve cells in such animals as the earthworm; they respond to light over a very definite range of wavelengths (approximately from 400 to 700 millimicra—violet to red—for the human eye), in an intensity range as much as a billion to one; (6) **tonoreceptors,** as special cells in the inner ears of human beings and of most other terrestrial vertebrates; they respond to sound waves in air over a definite range of frequencies—in us, from about 15 vibrations per second to 10,000 or 15,000, depending to a large extent on the age of the person. Greatest

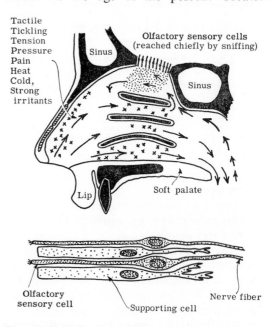

FIG. 11-6. *Cells of the olfactory tract of the human brain reach into the upper recesses of the nasal passages* (upper figure). *These cells are highly specialized and permit identification of a wide range of odors; supporting cells space out the receptor cells* (lower figure).

---

[2] The unpleasant odor of mercaptan can be identified from 0.000,000,000,002 gm inhaled; this is still a large number of molecules.

sensitivity is in the region of 1,000 vibrations per second (two octaves above middle C).

In addition, there are separate pain receptors in the skin (Fig. 11-7); sensory cells in the semicircular canals of the inner ear that

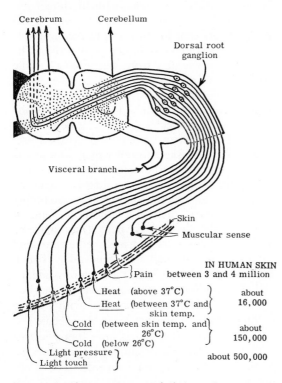

FIG. 11-7. *Skin receptors and their various connections through the dorsal root ganglion to nerve tracts in the spinal cord. Receptor functions underlined are highly discriminatory and are served by nerve fibers which regenerate slowly after injury. Others are less sensitive and regenerate more rapidly.*

help in maintaining body equilibrium; receptors in the muscles that inform the nervous system of the position of arms and legs; and a variety of sensory cells in the viscera that warn the animal if something goes wrong. Still other receptors are so remotely connected to the conscious portions of the nervous system that they create no sensations we feel, although they are essential to the successful control of involuntary actions such as movement of food through the gut, circulation of blood, sanitation of the respiratory system, and many more.

The general characteristics of sensory cells are important, since they influence the messages carried to the nervous centers, and hence the interpretation of an animal's sur-

roundings. One of these peculiarities is the relation between the immediately past experience of the receptor and the activity of the cell in stimulating the nervous system. Thus the first puff or two from a menthol cigarette is clearly mentholated, but the remainder of the tobacco "tastes" quite ordinary. Or the presence of a ten-cent piece resting on the bare forearm is soon beyond recognition by the sense of touch. When first it was placed there, the tangoreceptors responded, but soon they ceased to inform the sensory neurons associated with them. Or a foot that is uncomfortable when taking an initial step into a hot tub bath or a cold swimming pool soon becomes adjusted to the temperature and fails to report anything unusual. Other skin areas, not yet subjected to the change in thermal surroundings, still respond in the same way when stimulated, showing that the modification is in the sensory cells, not in the nervous system receiving the information. Such changes demonstrate **adaptation** of the receptors as they become accustomed to a stimulus that is continued, and elicit impulses in the sensory neurons only when a change is noted. Thus the nose can become adapted to one odor, but it does not change appreciably in its threshold for recognition of a different one. The significance of this type of **discrimination** is hard to appreciate in mechanical terms, for it seems unbelievable that the olfactory epithelium should have different receptors for each of the apparently limitless list of odors that can be distinguished.

The prize demonstration of adaptation is the experiment in which one hand is placed in a bowl of hot water, the other in another of cold water. After each has become accustomed to the surrounding temperature, the two hands are moved simultaneously to a bowl of water at intermediate temperature. The hand with the high temperature experience reports through its thermoreceptors and sensory neurons that the intermediate bowl is cold, while the hand with the low temperature experience reports that it is hot. The identity of the two responses is recognized separately by the nervous system, although the eyes can see the single bowl containing both hands, and although the individual knows that only a single temperature is present.

Adaptation, in terms of the electrochemical impulses in the neurons, is seen as a gradual decrease in the number of responses per second (Fig. 11-8). In all but eyes and ears, the frequency may drop to zero and the sensory cell show complete adaptation. Eyes and ears, however, continue to report light and sound, though the brightness of the light and the loudness of the sound may suffer changes in appreciation. As long as the light shines and the noise continues, the optic and

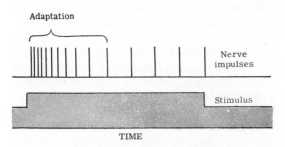

FIG. 11-8. *Adaptation in a sense organ subjected to continuous stimulation is evident from decreased frequency of nerve fiber discharge.*

auditory nerves pass a train of impulses that show partly the continuation and partly the degree of adaptation in the receptors involved.

The separate evaluation of temperatures by the two hands is a fair representation of the ability of the central nervous system to identify contrasts by awareness of two areas at once. The ability to see makes use of this same phenomenon, since the forms, brightnesses, and colors of objects all involve appreciation of contrasts simultaneously. But for pain, the nervous system has no such abilities. Pain can be slight, or worse, but it can't be double. If a hand aches because it is immersed in a pail of icewater, a bright spot of light focused on the forehead may actually burn the skin without being felt. If the light is felt, the hand is no longer painful—only the burn is appreciated; as soon as the light is turned off, however, the hand sensations are back again. The significance of this is not understood, but it is recognized to be a different mechanism from any involving other senses.

Skin Receptors

One of the more entertaining and informative of simple experiments with the intact human nervous system consists of mapping on the hand or back the position of receptors for pain, heat, cold, and touch (pressure). The subject is prevented from knowing what the exact details of the procedure are, while the experimenter touches the skin area investigated with, say, either a fine, blunt-tipped probe connected to an electric heating element, or an identical instrument containing crushed ice. The subject is asked to tell which stimulus is applied, the hot or the cold. Over a considerable part of each area no decision can be made, but at specific points in a seemingly random pattern, there is no question. Some of these points respond to heat (and may be marked with dots of red ink), others to cold (and may be marked with blue ink). Touch (identified with a bristle in a holder) is identified at still different points and may be marked in another color. Pain (identified with a sharp pointed instrument such as a fine needle) is separate again. Anesthetics are often selective with respect to these endings; thus cocaine prevents response of pain receptors, but does not affect heat, cold, or touch.

Not only can the whole body be mapped in this way, learning the distribution of these special sensory structures and seeing how nonuniform this aspect is, but double stimulation can be studied—two sensory points at a time—to plot the distribution of nervous connections. The subject is asked to tell whether one heat point is being stimulated or two, or whether one point of the pain stimulator is applied or two. Where sense endings are served by a single nerve fiber through the many branches of the dendrites, no difference is recognized as to whether one or more are stimulated. To some extent the fields of separate fibers overlap, and the distances across such fields vary greatly according to the body region involved. Hence sensory structures show **resolution**—the ability to identify the exact area stimulated as being separate from stimulation in an adjacent area, and this resolving power depends on the nervous connections to specialized mechanisms in the skin.

5. THE EYE

The eye and the ear have been mentioned as examples among vertebrates of a peak in organization for receptors with accessory structures. In each of these the sensory cells themselves represent little of the bulk of the organ, but the rest of the mechanism is essential for the receptors to express the full range of their possibilities.

compared to the sensitive film, and the eyelids to shutters, but the analogy has become too extended to have value.

The basic framework of the eye (Fig. 11-9) is a tough, fibrous envelope, almost spherical in form—the **sclera.** At its exposed center,

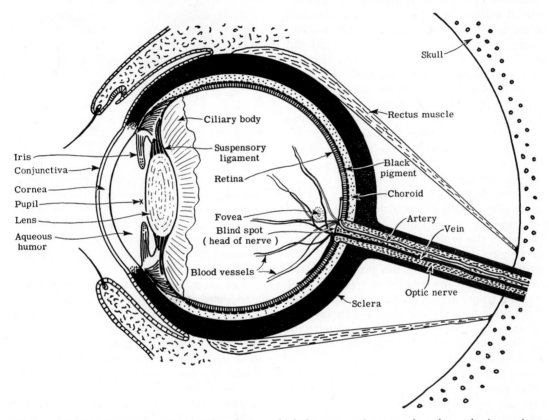

FIG. 11-9. *The vertebrate eye is a complex device which focuses an image and analyzes the image into a mosaic of recognizably different intensities in an identifiable pattern.*

The Vertebrate Eye

The vertebrate eye has often been compared to a camera. It has a lens system that produces a real image, inverted and diminutive, on the sensitive cells of the retina. There is an iris diaphragm that regulates the diameter of the pupil—the circular opening in the opaque portions of the eye through which the beam of light enters. The retina can be

this layer bulges outward a little and presents an area, the **cornea,** composed entirely of highly transparent living cells. Applied closely to the inner surface of the sclera except in the corneal region is a richly vascular layer, the **choroid.** The region of the choroid corresponding in position to the cornea is separated from the cornea by a space filled with a watery fluid. Oculists refer to this as the "anterior chamber," and the liquid content as the **aqueous humor.** In the center of the choroid curtain, on the optic axis of the cornea, is a hole—the **pupil**—around which is the actively muscular **iris,** with radially arrayed muscle fibers that expand the pupil, and with circularly arranged fibers that contract it. Behind the iris is a second, smaller, "posterior chamber" also filled with aqueous humor, limited away from the iris by the plastic **lens** and its surrounding suspensory ligament. The lens is actually a beautifully-formed mass of secretory material elaborated by the cells that were located in this position during embryonic development; the cells did their task, died, and degenerated to remarkable transparency. Lining the choroid beyond the suspensory ligament is the sensitive tissue of the eye, the **retina.** The large space between the lens and the retina is filled with a more viscous fluid, the **vitreous humor.**

Blood vessels enter the eye and spread out on its inner surface between the retina and the vitreous humor. Over this retinal surface, too, nerve fibers pass like roots from a tree, converging toward a central point where they join together as the trunk—the **optic nerve,** passing to the brain. Around the optic nerve are four rectus muscles which cooperate with two more in controlling the position of the eye; all six are inserted on the sclera. And over the front surface of the exposed portion of the sclera and the cornea is a thin layer of the animal's epidermis. It is continuous with the lining layer of the eyelids, and is called the **conjunctiva.** Over the cornea, the cells of the conjunctiva are also remarkably clear. No blood vessels enter this region, and the living cells are nourished entirely by sugars and other essential foods dissolved in the tears that wash the surface or diffuse from cell to cell from the periphery. Blinking the eyelids serves to distribute the tears, to sweep dust particles from the conjunctiva, and to prevent its delicate surface from becoming desiccated.

Optically, the exposed tear-wet conjunctiva, supported by the cornea below, is the most important part of the eye for any animal living in air. It accomplishes most of the bending of the light rays that produce an image on the retina. The lens of the eye is supplementary in action and serves to correct the optical system for near- or far-vision. Contraction of the **ciliary muscle** between the suspensory ligament and the sclera releases

tension on the lens and allows it to change shape, becoming more nearly spherical by bulging both forward and backward. The increased curvature of these two surfaces shifts the image, and, in a normal eye, is adjusted automatically to keep the image in acceptable focus on the retina when objects nearby are

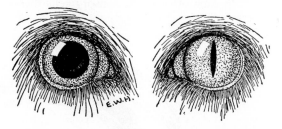

FIG. 11-10. *The slit pupil of a cat can open wide at night, and close by day much farther than a circular pupil can, thus protecting the sensitive retina from the strong sunlight in which the cat frequently basks.*

examined. When the ciliary muscle relaxes, the tension of the suspensory ligament is unopposed and it stretches the rim of the lens, flattening its anterior and posterior surfaces and focusing the eye for distant objects. These adjustments of the lens are described as **accommodation.**

The adjustments of the iris are also automatic, and serve to allow the eyes to examine objects in sun and shadow. In bright light, the radial muscles of the iris relax and the circular fibers contract; the pupil shrinks—in man to a minimum of two mm in diameter. In shade, the mechanism operates in the opposite direction, leading to expansion of the human pupil to a maximum diameter of about eight mm. These changes occur in a matter of seconds, and adjust the light reaching the sensitive retina. Through the dilated pupil 16 times as much light can pass as through the constricted one. Since the human eye can follow brightness changes exceeding a million to one, it is obvious that the iris attends to only a small part of these adjustments. Its prompt response, however, is an important factor in clear vision under daylight conditions.

Human pupils, like those of most vertebrates, are of circular outline. When they have closed as far as possible, there is still an opening through which a great deal of light can pass if the individual is on a sunlit white beach. The circular muscle fibers cannot contract farther, however; they are in their own way. A cat, on the other hand, with its slit pupils (Fig. 11-10), has in effect two curtains which muscular contractions can not only bring together but cause to overlap, shutting out the light. Slit pupils are characteristic of nocturnal feeders among the vertebrates (the cat and alligator—Photo 128—for example), where the animal habitually basks in the sun by day. In the brightest light a cat's pupils close to leave only a pinhole at each end of the slit. With its sensitive night eyes, this is fine for day vision.

The other eye adjustments that allow vision over such a spread of brightness take place in the retina itself. They involve changes in the concentration of light-sensitive pigments in the receptors. These latter are of two types, with characteristic shapes, pigments, and functions:

1. The **cone cells,** which are sensitive to light in the brightest range of day operations,

but blind at night. They contain the pale pinkish pigment, iodopsin. In man, and a scattering of other animals (some primates, many birds, some reptiles, and some fish), the cone cells also allow color vision.

2. The **rod cells,** which are largely dazzled by daytime brilliance but which operate well at night, containing another pale pinkish pigment, rhodopsin ("visual purple") or porphyropsin, depending on which animal is involved.

Rod cells are thus concerned with night vision, cone cells with day vision. The human eye includes about six million cones (of which 10,000 are in one special region, the fovea), and 160 million rods; they are served by 750,000 fibers of the optic nerve. Nocturnal animals have fewer cones; purely diurnal (day-active) animals have fewer rods.

Light reaching the pigments in the retinal sensory cells bleaches them. This is an example of a photochemical change (Fig. 11-11). The pigments are converted into a material called *retinene,* which is linked to a protein; at the same time a unit of energy is transferred to a nerve fiber. Independent of light, the sensory cells also convert the retinene-protein material back into light-sensitive pigment; this depends upon the availability of foodstuffs and oxygen from the blood stream. But at the same time the retinene-protein transforms into Vitamin A in combination with a protein, and this, too, can be synthesized back into photosensitive pigment in the light or dark. If the bright light shining on the retina continues, more and more pigment is bleached, and excess amounts of Vitamin A are carried away by the blood stream. In a dim light, Vitamin A is removed from the blood stream, combined with the protein in the receptors, and transformed into photosensitive molecules.

Since the pigments involved are all pale (and hence absorb only small amounts of light shining on them), any reduction in the concentration of pigment quickly reduces the number of pigment molecules receiving enough light energy to cause transformation into retinene-protein and the dispatch of a nervous impulse to the brain. For each brightness of light, there is an equilibrium estab-

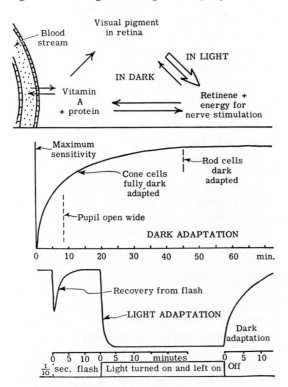

FIG. 11-11. Above: *The chemistry of light detection involves a delicate equilibrium between light-sensitive pigments, their decomposition products, and precursors.* Below: *The course of uninterrupted dark adaptation (partly dilation of the pupil, but mostly accumulation of light-sensitive pigment), and the effect of brief or prolonged exposure to light.*

lished in a matter of minutes, wherein the rate of synthesis of the pigments matches the rate of bleaching (Fig. 11-11). But the rate of bleaching is continuously reported to the brain and interpreted in terms of brightness. Any change of overall brightness upsets the equilibrium and a new balance is begun. To a bright light, a human eye may reach a steady state in two or three minutes and be completely "light adapted." To dim lights such as the still considerable illumination of the landscape under a starlit night sky, the equilibrium is not reached for as much as 45 minutes. And "dark adaptation" depends considerably on the amount of Vitamin A available in the blood stream. Lack of proper quantities of this vitamin leaves the individual unable to reach full dark adaptation. His in-

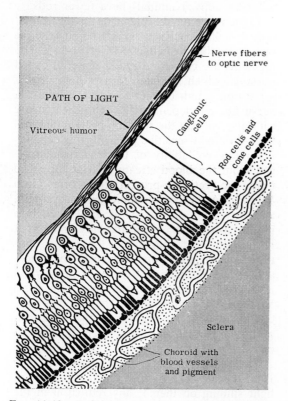

FIG. 11-12. *A diagram showing the path of light through the cellular layers of the vertebrate retina. Light unabsorbed by the pale pigment in the terminal segments of rod cells and cone cells is absorbed by the dense black pigment of the choroid. Blood vessels over the nerve-rich surface between vitreous humor and retina are not shown, although the light passes through these too.*

ability to see in the dark is called "night blindness."

A further characteristic of any light-sensitive structure in an animal is related to its photochemical nature. The response to a flash of light $\frac{1}{10}$ second long at one brightness is no different from the impression received from another flash $\frac{1}{100}$ second long at 10 times the brightness, or one $\frac{1}{1000}$ second long at 100 times the brightness. While this principle is used by all photographers in exposing their films, it is interesting to find it true of photoreceptors as well (Photo 129). As long as the duration is not beyond a critical length (say one-tenth of a second), the relation holds.

It is very doubtful whether any competent optical engineer would ever have designed the vertebrate eye in its actual form. After the light has come through the conjunctiva, the cornea, the aqueous humor, the pupil, the lens, and the vitreous humor, it still has to penetrate the full thickness of the retina in order to reach the sensitive ends of the rods and cones (Fig. 11-12). These important parts are faced away from the lens, toward the choroid. To reach them the light must pass through a network of blood vessels spread over the inner surface of the retina, through a maze of nerve fibers extending toward the head of the optic nerve, through layer after layer of ganglionic cells, and for almost the full length of the sensory cells themselves. And then only the light that is absorbed by a very pale pigment has any effect on the nervous system. Under the best possible conditions, for every 150 units of light reaching the conjunctiva, not more than 7 to 15 are absorbed, their energies used for stimulating the sensations of sight. In spite of this astonishing inefficiency, human eyes are able to excel any photographic or photoelectric cell device in responding with accuracy over such a broad range of brightnesses, in discriminating between such small differences in illumination, in evaluating so many shades of color, and in perceiving such a wealth of detail. Only larger eyes on the same plan, such as those of the horse (Photo 130) or the eyes of some birds (where more sensory cells are packed into the retina), do better than ours.

Two further features of the retina are worth attention. In the area of each eye at

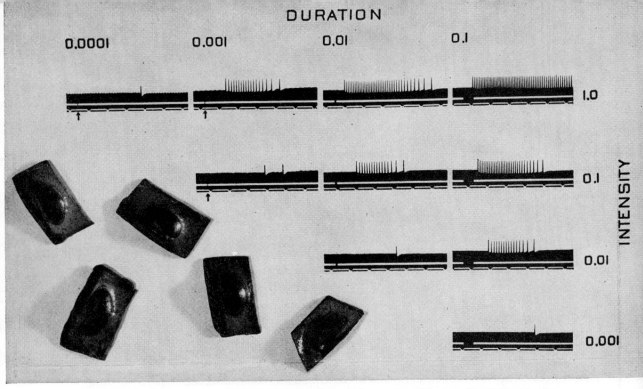

DURATION

0.0001   0.001   0.01   0.1

INTENSITY

1.0

0.1

0.01

0.001

129. Nerve impulses from excised eyes of living king crabs (Photos 43, 110) can be amplified and recorded as individual short vertical lines on a moving photographic tape. The response to a stimulating flash of light is the same for a 0.001-sec. flash of unit intensity as for a 0.1-sec. flash of 0.01 intensity. The arrows indicate the moment when the flash was given, and the notched white line on each sample record shows ⅕-second intervals.

LARGE EYES OFFER ADVANTAGES

130. The eye of the horse is the largest in any terrestrial vertebrate. Its lens is larger, admitting more light at night. Its sensitive retina receives a larger image on more receptor cells, permitting detection of finer detail.

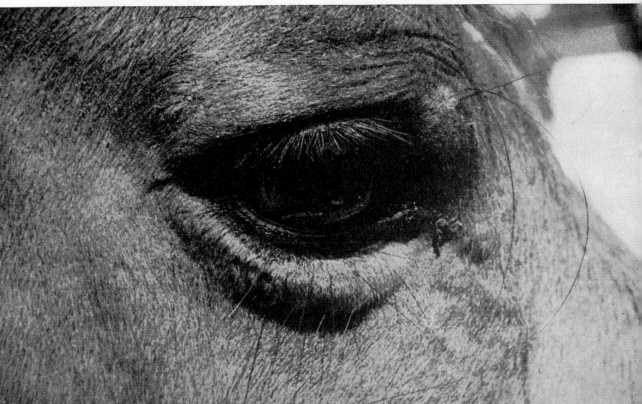

131. Most of the head of a dragonfly is occupied with the huge compound eyes which see forward, to the sides, upward, downward, and to some degree to the rear, all at the same time.

COMPOUND EYES MAY HAVE BINOCULAR FIELDS

132. A praying mantis by night has brown eyes.   133. The same mantis by day has pale green eyes.

    Pigments migrate within the eye, increasing sensitivity at the expense of acuity in dim light, and increasing visibility of fine detail at the expense of sensitivity in good light.

the end of the optic nerve, where all the axons from retinal ganglionic cells converge to leave for the brain, there are no sensory cells and the eye is blind. This is the **blind spot,** and although it produces a definite gap in our vision, we are not aware of it. Like the nerve fibers and blood vessels through which every image must pass to be seen, the blind spot causes us no concern. Actually, the human animal is very fortunate in having binocular vision, for the blind spot of one eye then coincides with a seeing area of the other. But in the many mammals and birds which see only monocularly, this blind spot is the source of danger—a blank area which must be investigated constantly by shifting the gaze either by eye movements or change of head position.

The other important retinal detail is the **fovea**—a slight depression or pit in the retinal surface, where the sensory cells are so tightly packed together that the cones are cylindrical in form and resemble fine rods. Yet in the human eye this fovea is provided only with cone cells, and they are unique to the extent that each has a separate nerve fiber connection to the brain. For these reasons the fovea is blind at night, but it is the area on which we carefully focus any daylit object in which we wish to see most detail. The retinal pit expands the image slightly, so that it covers more cells. And each sensory cell there can report to the brain the degree of illumination received—hence help analyze the image into its finest possible detail. Using the correct term, the eye reaches its highest resolution (or resolving power) in the fovea, since there it can distinguish between the smallest minutiae of any object in focus.

Elsewhere in the eye, the sensory cells are less densely packed and many of them share a nerve fiber to the brain. Resolution is much poorer, and in the human eye the percentage of cone cells decreases away from the fovea so that color vision fails in the periphery of the visual field. Correspondingly, however, the percentage of rod cells increases, and with them the sensitivity of the eye under night conditions. As a result, during the daytime we direct our eyes to fix the image of each object examined on the fovea in the "central field," for maximum recognition of detail and for full appreciation of color. The "peripheral field" (beyond the fovea in every direction) gives us only a supplementary picture with less detail, less distinct colors, but a very full appreciation of changes in brightness or of movement. At night, however, the fovea is blind (lacking rod cells), and to center a dimly lit object for study in the usual way is to lose it entirely. Instead, we must depend on the peripheral field, on our rod cells, and with practice can do remarkably well with the colorless, detail-less vision it provides.

The structural plan and the operation of the eye are remarkably uniform throughout the vertebrates. The mechanism of focusing in fish and some others involves no alteration in the form of the lens but shifts that part of the mechanism back and forward, much as is done in a camera. Fish and many of the lower vertebrates have no eyelids that can be closed over the eyes, and those forms that live in water receive little optic effect from the curved cornea and conjunctiva. They depend on the lens alone for image formation, since the water (unlike air) provides no sudden step in refractive index such as is required for bending light rays. Even the light-sensitive pigments in the retina differ slightly through the various vertebrate groups.

Often the question arises: If the lens system produces a small inverted image, why do we not see things upside down, and how can we see so much from so little? Resolution in the fovea is the answer to the second part, plus eye movements to get different parts of the image focused on this critical region. The inversion of the image is experience. A baby's eyes form an image, but time is required for appreciation that the toes seen with the eyes are the objects felt with the fingers. The orientation of this feature of the outside world is thus established by two senses. Later, objects farther off, such as the baby's mother, fit into the same pattern. The image translated to the brain in terms of illumination brightnesses in microscopic areas is related piece by piece to the position of the sensory cell in the retina, and to the nerve fibers that serve the many sensory cells. The interpretation by the brain is that the object seen must be a certain size and shape if it could be felt and measured. *To the brain the images have no orienta-*

tion. They merely allow appreciation at a distance of the visible world, and the mental image of that world is "as large as life."

Psychologists have demonstrated conclusively that the orientation of the image and its interpretation is purely a matter of learning. By wearing special prisms that inverted the images again in each eye, they saw images that were actually "right side up." For a few days the experimenters saw an upside down world and found moving around in it quite difficult. But, within a few weeks, the scene came to appear entirely normal, and the subjects performed all ordinary activities with accustomed precision. The world seemed cor-

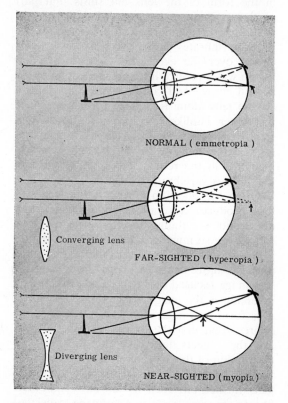

NORMAL (emmetropia)

Converging lens

FAR-SIGHTED (hyperopia)

Diverging lens

NEAR-SIGHTED (myopia)

FIG. 11-13. *The normal (emmetropic) eye is focused on distant objects when relaxed, and accommodates to focus nearer objects by bulging the lens. A far-sighted (hyperopic) eye must accommodate for even distant objects, and still more for close, since the relaxed lens focuses at a point behind the retina; the corneal curvature is too slight for the shortness of the eyeball. A near-sighted (myopic) eye, when relaxed, is focused for near objects and accommodation permits study of even closer objects; the curvature of the cornea is excessive in relation to the length of the eyeball.*

rectly oriented in vision and completely correlated with findings by touch or hearing. Then the prisms were removed and once more the world seemed upside down. A learning period of considerable length was necessary all over again, to become used to the old way of looking at things—to get the world back to normal by retraining the brain in its interpretations of impulses from the optic nerves. .

Efficient Use of Eyes

Two basic types of eye defects in human beings have a simple, understandable basis (Fig. 11-13). One type may involve a cornea that is too flattened to match the dimensions of the eye, and provides too little lens action; in this situation the person must strain his ciliary muscles and accommodate his lens to supplement the corneal action in order that the image may be brought forward and focused on the retina. The nearer the object examined is to the person, the greater this muscular strain must be. Hence the victim of this eye defect prefers to examine objects farther off, and is spoken of as **far-sighted;** *hyperopia* or *hypermetropia* are the proper terms.

The other variant of this type of refractive error in the eye construction involves a corneal surface that is too convex and, even when the lens of the eye is unaccommodated, focuses the image of distant objects at some point in advance of the retinal sensory cells. No matter how much such a person accommodates the lens by contracting the ciliary muscle, the image cannot be made to go back to the rods and cones; instead it moves away from them. When such a person comes close to an object, however, the image moves back automatically and finally reaches the retinal sensory cells and is seen clearly. This condition is described as **near-sightedness,** or more properly as *myopia.* The normal eye, by contrast with both of these defective varieties, is called an *emmetropic* eye.

With age, the lens hardens, and when the ciliary muscles release the tension of the suspensory ligament, it fails to bulge as much in the two directions. Hence it does not assist the corneal curvature as far as previously in accommodation to objects at different distances. For this reason, the far-sighted person becomes progressively more far-sighted, until use of eyeglasses becomes essential to any close work. The near-sighted person becomes less able to bring objects close to the eyes for scrutiny of detail, but his far limit for clear vision does not change. The alterations in the flexibility of the lens with age are called *presbyopia*.

Eyeglasses can be prepared to correct these difficulties. For the corneal surface that is too flat (or the eyeball that is too short—for it can be regarded in that way too), a supplementary lens is needed that provides additional convergence; this lens must be a positive lens, thicker in the center than at the edges. For the corneal surface that is too convex (or for the eyeball that is too elongate), the supplementary lens must reduce the convergence; it must therefore be a negative lens, thinner in the center than at the edges. And when the range of accommodation possible through contraction of the ciliary muscle becomes too small, either different eyeglasses for distance and for close work must be used, or the two corrections ground into a single bifocal lens. Trifocals, with three different corrections in a spectacle lens, are prepared where presbyopic losses become excessive.

The other major type of defect in human eyes is due either to the cornea or (less often) the lens having other than spherical refracting surfaces. Instead they have more curvature in one direction than in another at right angles to it. A cylinder represents the extreme condition of a lens with this characteristic; the parallel sides of the cylinder represent no curvature, while the circular form at right angles represents a definite curvature. In this defect of the human eye, the cornea or the lens tends away from a spherical form toward the cylindrical form, and shows a definite axis for this irregularity. The result of it is that horizontal lines in something examined are brought to a focus in one place, while vertical lines in the same object are focused at a different distance behind the lens. The two cannot be focused on the retina simultaneously, and vision is vague. This condition, described as **astigmatism,** can be corrected by placing in front of the eyes eyeglasses in which the compensating cylindrical form has been ground, with axes corresponding accurately.

In examining a pair of eyeglasses, the type or types of corrections can be recognized easily. If printed words seen through the lens appear larger than without it, the correction is for far-sightedness; if smaller, for near-sightedness. And if when the lens is rotated, the print appears to distort, a correction for astigmatism is present. These are refractive errors in the eyes. If an eye is both far-sighted and astigmatic, the one correction is ground into the front face of the spectacle lens, the other correction into the rear face.

The Compound Eye

An entirely different plan of eye is found among the arthropods, and no doubt it has

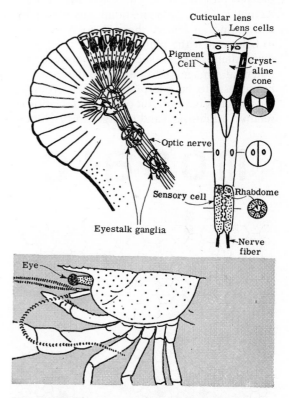

FIG. 11-14. *The compound eye of a crayfish is representative of the arthropod plan. The narrowly conical ommatidia (upper left) face in many directions, yet each unit has a limited field of view; the whole array detects changes in brightness in the surrounding scene, field by field. Each ommatidium (upper right) has its own lens system, pigment cell sheath and cluster of receptor cells; the receptor group may secrete a central rhabdome along which light reaches them. Sectional views at various levels show the relationship of the cells in a single ommatidium.*

contributed to the success of insects (Photos 131-133) and crustaceans Fig. 11-14), where the structure reaches highest complexity. Here the eye is composed of between 50 and 10,000 separate optical units, called **ommatidia,** each with its own lens, diaphragm, and 7 to 15 sensory cells. The ommatidia are elongate, slightly conical, and packed side by side into the surface of the body to form a convex outer contour. Each unit is responsible for only a very narrow angle of view—that part of the surrounding territory sufficiently close to the optic axis of the ommatidium for light from it to pass through the minute lens, miss being absorbed by a ring of blackish brown pigment forming an iris diaphragm, and reach the receptor region deep below the surface. Actually, while the ommatidial lens is capable of forming an image, there is good evidence to believe that the pinholing effect of the pigment diaphragm is such as to convert the potential image into mere differences in brightness, to be interpreted by the group of sensory cells beyond. But out of appreciation of relative brightness (and changes in brightness

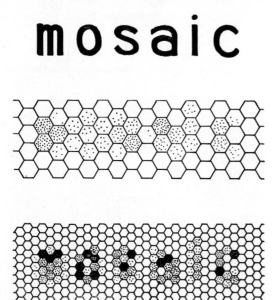

FIG. 11-15. *The relation between size of field of view of individual ommatidia and ability to identify patterns. Larger fields of view are characteristic of the compound eyes of night-active arthropods; smaller fields and more numerous ommatidia are found chiefly in day-active kinds.*

that denote movements of objects in the visual field), the compound eye sends to the brain a remarkably good picture of the surrounding scene. The brain sums up the information, just as it must in vertebrates, from similar nerve impulses sent from individual groups of receptors.

The surface of the compound eye is so clearly marked off into separate **facets,** each the lens at the end of an ommatidium, that the similarity to a tile mosaic is striking. Since each of these units contributes to the brain separate information, and since the nervous system then sums up the impressions, the term **mosaic vision** has been applied. There is little reason, however, to regard the nervous interpretation of the brain as being of a different sort from that in the vertebrate eye. The optics are different enough, but the relation between sensory cells and brain is approximately the same.

There is no attempt at focusing a compound eye, but objects near at hand are seen in more ommatidia than when more remote, so that depth and distance perception are possible. In many arthropods, binocular vision is achieved (Photos 131-133), with even greater precision of appreciation. But the limitations most obvious in the compound eye are those of resolution (determined by the fineness of the mosaic of facets—as shown in Fig. 11-15), of range of sensitivity (day or night vision or both), and of brightness discrimination (recognition of distinct differences among a series of neutral gray shades). Apparently some insects like bees and butterflies have abilities akin to color vision (if not precisely the same), and many are sensitive to ultraviolet radiations but scarcely so to red. These facts indicate that the limits of the spectrum may be quite different for the compound and camera types of eye.

6. THE EARS

For animal hearing, the energy identified as sound arrives in the form of rapid to-and-fro vibrations of the air. To pick up and present to the sensory cells such air vibrations, most hearing animals have a pair of tightly stretched, thin membranes, oval or circular in form. These vibrate in sympathy and synchrony with the air movements, and with a vigor proportional to the energy content of the sound. They are eardrums, properly called **tympanic membranes,** such as we have in our middle ears, or a frog has flush with the head surface, or a katydid has located on its front legs. The mechanism including the eardrums, and serving to interpret the vibrations to the animal, constitute the ears. As in the case of visual organs, the accessory structures vastly outbulk the actual sensory cells in the ear.

Our own ears consist of three main parts: an outer, a middle, and an inner ear (Fig. 11-16). The outer ear includes the funnel-like external member, the **pinna,** serving to collect the sound waves by reflecting them toward the small opening of the **auditory canal,** through which the sound passes to reach the more protected parts of the ear, deep in the head. The middle ear has a sizable cavity, too; it is separated from the auditory canal by the **tympanum,** and connected to the pharynx by a passage—the **Eustachian tube**—by means of which the air pressure on the two sides of the eardrum is kept reasonably equal and hence the tympanum as free as possible to vibrate. In the middle ear are small bones which act as levers that transfer the movements of the tympanum to the inner ear. Those in man and mammals are three in number, the smallest bones of the body with characteristic form, and in making the transfer of energy they amplify the mechanical forces by some 60 times. These bones in man have forms that are easy to recognize, and their names alone identify the shapes: the **hammer** (*malleus*) is embedded in the eardrum, but presses against the **anvil** (*incus*), which in turn transmits vibrations to the **stirrup** (*stapes,* with a central hole).

Hearing

The inner ear is a double mechanism, only one part of which (the **cochlea)** is concerned with hearing. Of the other part, the **semicircular canals,** more will be told presently. But the cochlea is coiled like a snail shell, allowing considerable length to be organized in a continuous compact spiral (Fig. 11-17). The larger, outer end of the cochlea approaches the middle ear, and at two small adjacent regions is separated from the cavity by only a thin membrane. One of these, the **oval window,** lies directly below the flat sole part of the stirrup bone. The other, the **round window,** has no such cover. Vibrations of the stirrup bone agitate the oval window, which in turn agitates the fluid filling the long V-shaped tube of the spiral cochlea by pressing

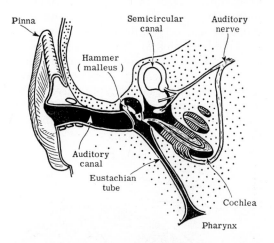

FIG. 11-16. *Sectional view of the human head exposing the cavities of the ear and several turns of the spiral cochlea.*

in and out on one end of the *V.* The other end of the *V* is the membrane of the round window; thus when the oval window is pressed in, the round window bulges out; and conversely. In this way the incompressible liquid in the cochlea is shaken at the same rate as, and with proportionately greater force than, the eardrum. The vibrations in the fluid agitate the sensory mechanism of the cochlea so that **hair cells** (20,000 of them in man) are touched against an overhanging membranous flap in the **organ of Corti** which occupies the space between the arms of the *V* (Photo 134).

Each hair cell bears a single "hair." Whenever this hair is touched against the overhanging flap, an impulse is sent along the auditory nerve. The series of hair cells respond at different points to different rates of vibratory excitation. The human ear is sensitive to sounds between 15 and from 10,000 to 15,000 vibrations per second, depending considerably upon age (less with advancing years). This greatest range corresponds in terms of the piano keyboard of from approximately four octaves below "middle C" to about six octaves above—10 octaves of range as compared to the seven on most pianos. The higher notes (high vibration rates) stimulate hair cells in the outer (upper) and wider end of the cochlea, whereas lower notes affect the lower, narrower end. Increasing intensity widens the band of responding hair cells, although the center of the excitation remains in the same place as long as the pitch of the note remains the same. And from these sensory cells, through some 4,000 nerve fibers, the auditory nerve conveys to the brain the impulses that can be translated into the sensation of hearing, the identification of musical pitch.

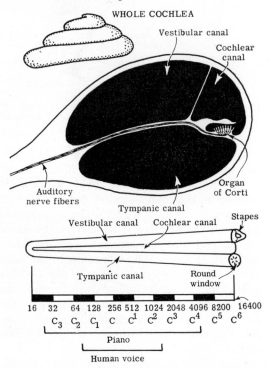

FIG. 11-17. *The cochlear spiral, when cut, is seen to be mostly fluid-filled canals. In a section through one turn* (upper right) *the position of the organ of Corti is evident. This contains the ribbon of receptors (hair cells) which are affected by vibrations of the fluid in the V-shaped canal system. Below is a diagrammatic representation of the continuity of the vestibular canal (beginning at the oval window and the stapes bone) and tympanic canal (ending in the round window), with the cochlear canal between. Parallel to this diagram is an indication of the frequency response of the various parts of this uncoiled spiral and the range of notes on the piano and in the human voice.*

No doubt related to the sympathetic way in which the hair cells respond in groups to vibration at any given rate within the audible range is the "pleasing" and displeasing combinations of pitches. Of these, the pair of notes we designate an octave is by all odds the least distressing; it corresponds to two vibration rates, one of which is exactly twice the other. All the common chords bear simple ratio relationships to one another in their frequencies of vibration—the feature that makes them easy for the ear to recognize and for the hair cells to respond to without interference, group with group.

Noise is defined as sound waves of assorted frequencies in which no single vibration rate can be recognized as a dominant pitch. A musical note, on the other hand, has such a dominant vibration rate, and musical scales are based on this fact. Thus, in the physics laboratory, "middle C" is 256 vibrations per second. But we distinguish between a violin, a flute, and a bugle all playing this pitch not by this "fundamental note" of 256 vibrations (or cycles) per second. They differ in the proportions of overtones and subharmonics that appear from them at the same time (Fig. 11-18). Each of these instruments playing middle C vibrates to some extent at all of these other octaves, below and above. Our ears distinguish the proportions of all as the "quality" of the note, and through this vague realization we can identify separate instruments from among the complexity of a symphony.

Ear Defects

There are three common ways in which the human ear begins to fail partially or completely in response to the ordinary range of audible sounds. Each corresponds to anatomical features of the ear, or to its related nervous system.

1. Central deafness—due to deterioration in the auditory nerve or in the brain centers to which the impulses pass. No treatment or hearing aid is known to help.

2. Perception deafness—due to deterioration of the organ of Corti in the inner ear, so that either the whole range of sounds or parts of it fail to produce a response. Ordinary aging reduces the sensitivity to high pitches. Disease or damage from other sources can

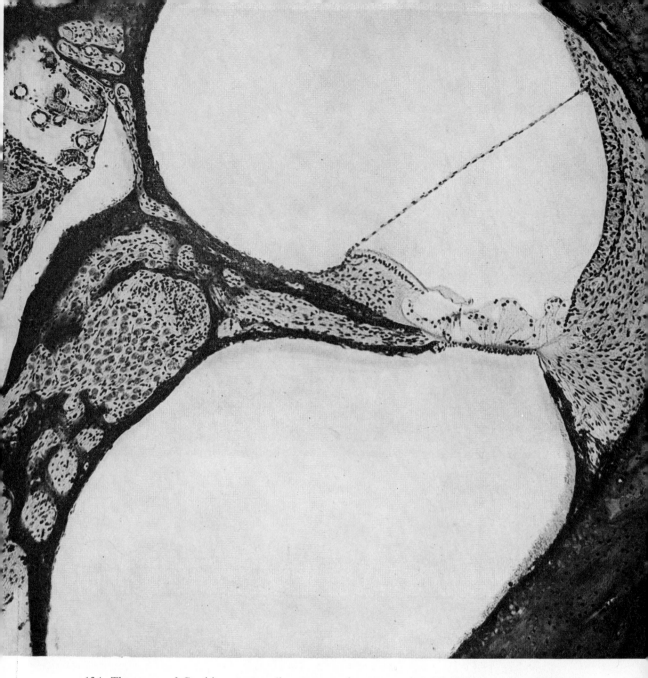

134. The organ of Corti in a mammalian ear, seen in cross section. The three parallel canals, the sensory cells, and overhanging flap of tissue are evident in this photograph. Evidence indicates that vibrations reaching the vestibular canal (*top*) through the oval window from the stirrup bone so agitate the fluid filling the continuous V-shaped vestibular and tympanic (*bottom*) canals that sympathetic vibrations are set up in the cochlear canal (*center*). At some region of the band-shaped organ of Corti, the membrane with its sensory cells moves sufficiently to touch its hair-like projections against the overhanging flap—thereby inducing those hair cells to start impulses along the auditory nerve. For each pitch of sound, a definite group of hair cells responds. Octaves and other chords are more pleasing than sounds of mixed pitch (dissonances or plain "noise"), apparently because only independent groups of sensory cells are stimulated and the brain can analyze the nervous messages into plainer information.

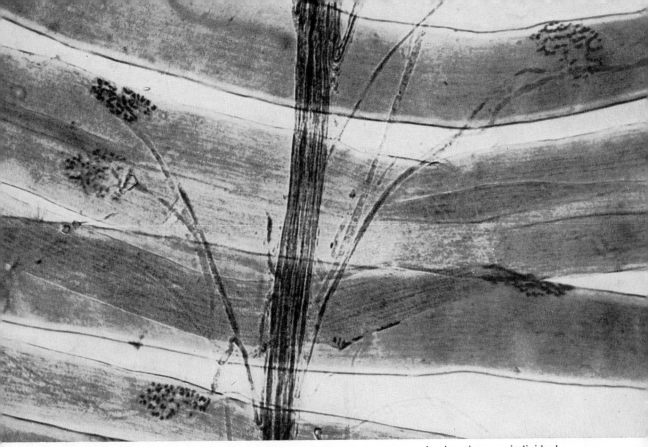

135. Nerve fibers separating to the motor end plates or neuromuscular junctions on individual muscle fibers.

136. In unicellular organisms a single mass of protoplasm is both the sensory and the effector mechanism. Here a culture of luminescent bacteria respond to their environment by producing enough light to illuminate a printed page upon which the enclosing tube is resting.

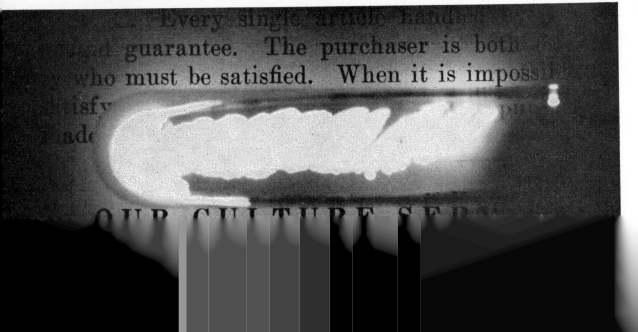

interfere in other definite patterns. Hearing aids are of no assistance.

3. Transmission deafness—involving the middle and outer ears. The difficulty may be as simple as an accumulation of wax in the auditory canal, or as complicated as a growth of bone over the round window membrane, blocking the vibrations of the fluid in the

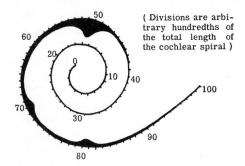

(Divisions are arbitrary hundredths of the total length of the cochlear spiral)

FIG. 11-18. *The distribution of stimulation from a musical instrument playing a single note as seen in terms of the cochlear spiral is a measure of the sensitivity of the ear to overtones and subharmonics— the "quality" of the note that helps identify the instrument producing it. Each overtone or subharmonic is one or more octaves away from the fundamental pitch sounded. (After H. Fletcher, Bell Telephone Laboratories.)*

cochlea. Often transmission deafness arises from middle ear infections that begin because disease organisms invade via the Eustachian tube from the pharynx. If attended to by a specialist, no permanent impairment may result. The surgery required in wax removal is very minor. That needed to re-open the round window or to provide an alternative (called *fenestration,* from the Latin *fenestra* = window) is highly technical and not always successful. Releasing the pressure of pus from an infection requires somewhat less skill, but usually involves draining the middle ear into the auditory canal through a small hole cut in the eardrum. This heals promptly and completely. Delay may allow the infectious agents to destroy the ear bone linkage between tympanum and cochlea, or seriously damage the eardrum itself. Hearing aids are helpful for transmission deafness, since they either increase the energy available or bring it to the cochlea by another route.

Equilibration

Except in cyclostomes, the semicircular canals of each inner ear are three in number,

arranged in such contrasting planes that movements of the head (or whole organism) cause a shift in the fluid filling them (Fig. 11-19). Each of the canals has an enlargement in which there are hair cells linked to the nervous system. Any motion of the fluid bends the hairs on the hair cells, and induces the discharge of a train of impulses along the auditory nerve. Hence the inertia of the fluid is used to trigger a response, advising the animal of turns taken or accelerations of any kind. It is curious that we are so accustomed to movements in the lateral (horizontal) canals that little or no discomfort is felt, whereas movements in a vertical plane (such as in an elevator) or in oblique planes (as in a rocking boat) produce gastric contractions

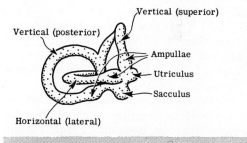

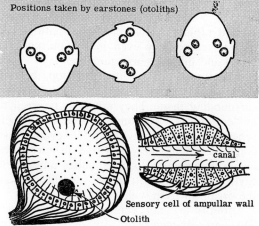

FIG. 11-19. *The semicircular canals and their ampullae* (top figure) *are supplemented by the otoliths in the utriculus and sacculus. The positions occupied by the otoliths* (middle figures) *advise the organism of its static orientation; movement of the fluid in the semicircular canals informs it of kinetic changes. The free-rolling otolith in its chamber* (lower left) *involves stimulation of hair-cells with nerve fiber connections in much the same way as the movement of fluid affects hair-cells within the three-paired ampullae* (lower right).

and even nausea. In addition to the semicircular canals are two other organs of static sense having a bulb-like form and enclosed stone-like spheroids (otoliths) of calcium carbonate secretion (Fig. 11-19). The otoliths swing or roll into fresh positions according to the static position of the head. In doing that, they stimulate different sensory cells lining the cavity enclosing them. The impulses from these keep the animal informed of its orientation in space.

A cat tossed in air is particularly adept at twisting its body to land on its feet, but without its semicircular canals, or with the nerve connections from these destroyed, the animal not only fails to make these righting responses but also shows difficulty in walking upright. Soon, however, it learns to depend on its other receptors, and once more can land upright again if allowed to see. Thus the otoliths supplement information derived from visual clues and from the many receptors in the muscles. These last report on the degree of contraction (position) and tension, and provide remarkably reliable cues for adjustments among cooperating skeletal muscles. The ear mechanism, however, is usually dominant, since if it is overstimulated (as may be done if a human being or a cat is whirled around rapidly), muscular coordination may be lost temporarily even in the presence of visual and muscle sense guidance.

Sometimes the otoliths develop beyond usual proportions and completely fill the space surrounding them. They are then referred to as "ear stones." Although this destroys their function for the individual, the event is so common among bony fish that fisheries men come to recognize specific shapes among the ear stones—enough to allow identification of the organism from which they came.

Otoliths are not confined to vertebrates. They are characteristic also of equilibrium-maintaining structures among invertebrates from coelenterates to arthropods. In all of these, because of their different origin, they are described as **statocysts.** The jellyfish design, for example, includes at least four statocysts at equal intervals around the rim of the bell; each has its lime particle in a cavity lined with sensory hair cells. The lobster bears a corresponding organ in the basal segment of the antennae, but this remains open for long enough during immature stages that a particle of sand becomes lodged in each and acts as a gravitational stimulator in place of a limy otolith.

7. EFFECTOR MECHANISMS

Motor impulses in an effector neuron may travel to a muscle (Photo 130) and provoke a contraction; to a gland and evoke a secretion; to a luminescent organ and initiate the chemical changes that release light energy; to a highly modified muscle mass capable of generating electricity; or to a number of specialized integumentary pigment cells and cause an alteration in the appearance of the animal. All of these are effector mechanisms. The muscles are widespread and complex in their activities. The other types of effectors are more localized, and information concerning them is somewhat less complete.

Glands

In the simplest situation, a gland may consist of a single cell whose protoplasm shows special ability to elaborate globules or granules of secretion. Upon stimulation, such a cell may change its permeability relations in such a way as to absorb water on one surface, sweep the secreted material toward the opposite side, and either so increase the differential permeability there for the secretion and water that they ooze together out of the cell, or entirely break down the plasma membrane on that opposite side, letting secretion plus protoplasm go gushing forth.

A few glands in the human being, such as tear glands and sweat glands, perform relatively little work, since their products are merely components of the blood from which the gland cells absorb a part. A small amount of concentrating activity goes on, since both tears and sweat are richer in salts than the blood but contain fewer organic compounds. Other glands, such as those that secrete enzymes and hormones, perform elaborate syntheses. Some of them indicate from their heat production that the energy required is greater than that for any other tissue in the body. In birds and mammals, the secretory activity of the liver and some other major glands seem to be an important part of the temperature control mechanism, and alters in rate according to nerve impulses received from the regulating centers in the brain.

Luminescent Organs

Light production is characteristic of a number of bacteria and some fungi. These luminesce when oxygen is available, and may give rise to surprise when dead fish glow in the dark (from bacteria over the surface) or the wet wood in a hollow tree gives off a pale light. Far more spectacular, however, is the illumination emitted by fireflies and a few other insects, and the light produced in the permanent night of the deep sea by all manner of squid, shrimp, and fish. Even in coastal water some of the comb-jellies (ctenophores) glow when stimulated, and a common protozoan (Noctiluca) turns the sea to glittering points of light around a person enjoying a night swim. In the mudflats, some of the tube-making annelid worms also produce significant amounts of light when aroused (Fig. 11-20).

In most multicellular forms the cells of a special luminescent organ secrete at least two materials. One, **luciferin,** is acted upon in the presence of oxygen by the other, an enzyme called **luciferase.** The light emission is due to the enzyme, and takes its color from the particular one of the many kinds of luciferase found in the animal kingdom. The luciferin is oxidized in the process, but only water has been identified among the several products of the reaction. Depending on the particular species of organism involved, the light may be a brief flash or a long glow. It may be made more conspicuous by the presence of highly-reflecting crystals of uric acid packed in cells immediately below the luminescent organ (as in many fireflies), or it may be obliterated under the control of the animal (deep sea fish) through covering by an opaque flap of skin acting as a muscular shutter. The phenomenon and its modifications are enormously interesting, particularly

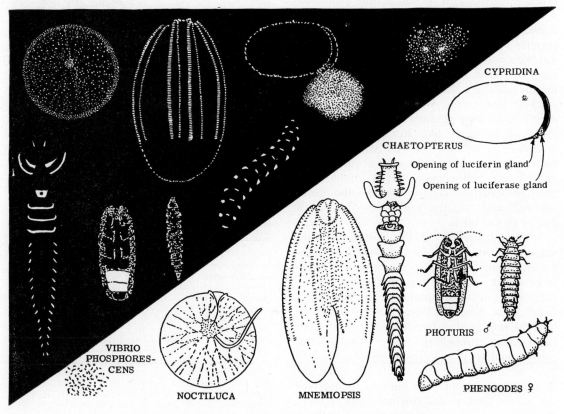

FIG. 11-20. *Luminescent organisms in the dark and the light.*

since the light is almost devoid of accompanying heat energy (it is composed almost exclusively of wavelengths within the spectral range visible to man). This "cold light," independent of the high temperatures customary in illumination sources constructed by man or to be found among the stars, affords a challenge. The efficiency is so much higher in terms of light output per unit of energy that it would be most advantageous were man able to duplicate the chemistry, or perhaps improve on it.

Electric Organs

Almost any cell is capable of some response to a stimulus, and in each instance there is a measurable change in the electrical characteristics of the cell immediately preceding the response. It usually indicates an accumulation of electrons on one side of the cell and a temporary depletion of them on the other, so that one becomes negative, the other positive. This is an action potential. The action potential of a contracting muscle is enough to stimulate a nerve and to induce another muscle to contract synchronously. In electric organs, highly specialized cells which seem to have an origin similar to that of muscle cells are usually found as flat disks, stacked like coins. When stimulated, each develops its own potential, and since all are arranged in series like storage batteries, a considerable voltage (to 400 volts) can be built up. The charge provides a current for only a few milliseconds, but it enables the chief possessors of electric organs—the "electric eel" and "electric ray"— to stun small fish or to kill them.

In many streams of the Amazon basin, where electric eels are fairly common, natives fording from one bank to the other are likely to be struck. To avoid this unpleasant experience, many tribes maintain on the two banks small herds of horses. When a party wishes to ford the stream, they free the horses and drive them ahead through the water. The electric eels expend their energies on the horses and have no appreciable charge left when the natives follow. One of their number then drives the horses back to the original bank, tethers them again, and rejoins his fellows without

danger of interference from the eels. A few hours later, the eels are ready to use their electric organs as before. Fatigue in these structures lasts only a short time, measured in minutes.

Chromatophores

The pigment-bearing cells of the effector system, called *chromatophores,* may consist of thin-walled spherical bodies full of granules, as in the squids and other cephalopod mollusks. In this case each is equipped with a set of radially arranged muscles under nervous control (Fig. 11-21). The muscles pull the sphere into a disk parallel to the body surface, and hence present all the pigment to view. The chromatophores in these animals have a curious twinkling quality which can

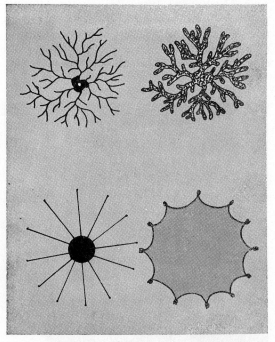

FIG. 11-21. *When the pigment in chromatophores is concentrated into dots, with wide intervening pigmentless areas, their existence is not evident. In most chromatophores the pigment is believed to migrate into previously existing channels with a constant pattern; one chromatophore's extensions overlap with those of neighbors, and the pigment becomes important in determining the over-all appearance of the animal. In cephalopod mollusks like squid and octopus, however, the chromatophores are controlled by contractile fibers that stretch the bags of pigment or let them shrink to insignificance. These changes may be rapid, in a fraction of a second, whereas pigment migration in the commoner type of chromataphore usually requires minutes or hours or even days.*

appear quite at random, or waves of activity can sweep over the surface, causing the skin to blanch or blush. Moreover, the pigments in different chromatophores are usually of more than a single color. Through red, black, brown, and white pigments a tremendous range of color can be achieved, since all of one color can be contracted (and vanish) simultaneously, leaving the rest; or one color can be expanded while the rest relax, producing sudden change to that deep shade; or an endless range of mixtures can be met. Most of these alterations seem related to temperature, level of metabolic rate, local stimulations, or general "emotions," and may be either restricted in area or affect the whole body surface.

The other chief type of chromatophore is a star-shaped cell with long branching processes that often interdigitate with those of neighboring chromatophores. This structure is frequent in vertebrates and arthropods, particularly among the fishes, amphibians and reptiles. The cytoplasm of each cell is densely packed with pigment granules but there is inadequate cytoplasm to fill all the processes and the central body simultaneously. As a result, the cytoplasm can move from one position to the other. When it is concentrated at the cell center, the minute flecks of pigment scattered in the skin have little effect on the overall appearance. But when the pigment is dispersed into the extensions of the cell through a shift in the cytoplasm, the skin acquires a definite color even though the cell centers may all be lacking in pigment.

The famed ability of the chameleons of the Mediterranean, Africa, and particularly Madagascar, to alter their colors is due to the presence of several colors of chromatophores in the skin, and to the control these lizards exercise over which ones are expanded, which contracted. Again the mechanism seems unrelated to background, but instead represents effects of temperature and nervous state. In the American Southeast there is a quite unrelated lizard (Anolis—Photo 76), often called a chameleon, with ability to change from ash gray to leaf green or chocolate brown. Most of the tree frogs have the same range. The shift from one color to another requires several minutes.

Among fish and some crustaceans, the al-

terations in color or distribution of black and white on the body are made more obvious in relation to the surroundings as interpreted through the eyes. Blinded individuals become very dark; those on which colored plastic "eyeglasses" are fitted adapt to match what they see. Among the flounders and others of the flatfishes, the correlation achieved between body pattern and surrounding bottom is quite remarkable. Sand, pebbles, and linoleum patterns are simulated both in terms of general hue and as continuations of the general mottling—that is, fine or coarse, contrasty or vague, according to the stimulation received by the eyes (Photo 288). In part, these modifications of chromatophores in fish and crustaceans are nervous, but the local control appears to be due entirely to substances liberated from the nerve-ending regions as hormones. They are called neurohumors, and they furnish additional means for correlating the parts of an organism. Experiments have indicated that the camouflage obtained in this way is of real value in allowing more frequent escape from predators.

8. THE BRAIN

The nervous system should not be thought of only as a compounding of reflex arcs from receptors in the skin, to muscles, glands, and other effectors. Nerve impulses arise also in the nerve centers themselves, often after a considerable delay, and hence without a clear causal relationship to any ascertainable stimulus.

A whole series can be traced through the animal kingdom, showing the relative development of the nervous system (Fig. 11-22) and its related sensory and effector mechanisms. Even within a restricted group, such as the orders of the class Insecta, the nervous tissue shows a great range of development, with increasing concentration of it into a few major centers as a mark of the most highly developed orders, whereas a more segmental chain of ganglia is to be found in the less specialized parts of the class. Properly speaking, the large mass of neurons present in the head of an insect is a **cephalic** ganglion; there is another, often even larger, in the thorax.

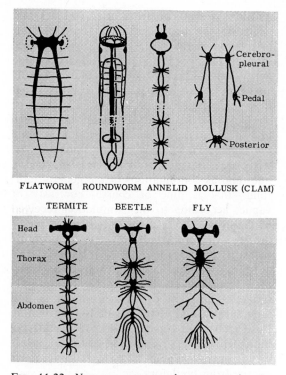

FLATWORM   ROUNDWORM   ANNELID   MOLLUSK (CLAM)

TERMITE   BEETLE   FLY

Head

Thorax

Abdomen

FIG. 11-22. *Nervous systems of representative invertebrates indicate the variation possible with linked neurons, receptors and effectors.*

The term **brain** is correctly reserved for the expanded anterior region of the hollow dorsal nerve cord of vertebrates (Fig. 11-23). During the embryonic stages of all, it becomes subdivided into three important regions: a fore brain, midbrain, and hind brain. Cyclostomes proceed no farther in subdivision, but all other classes of vertebrates specialize the fore brain into two components and the hind brain into another two—making a total of five regions to the brain, in a linear order. The most anterior of these extends toward the nasal pits of the embryo, and a pair of small masses of brain tissue become associated as an **olfactory tract**; the link between the neurons of the olfactory epithelium and the brain proper becomes extended, as the embryo grows, into a pair of **olfactory nerves**. Similarly, the lateral walls of the midbrain project and finally separate entirely as **optic cups** in the embryonic eye region. Later, the neuron components send from each eye a group of fibers which grow back to and make

intimate connections with the brain, as a pair of **optic nerves**. Associated with the hind brain are corresponding masses of nervous tissue which become incorporated into the developing auditory vesicles, and provide the basis for the **auditory nerves**.

The brains of cyclostomes, fish, and amphibians are arranged in a straight line; those of reptiles are scarcely less so. But in birds and mammals the excessive development of the roof and walls of the first and fourth of the five brain regions has been provided for in the compact brain case of the skull by a folding of the brain stem into a double S (as viewed from the side), dorsally in each of these regions, ventrally between them.

The roof of the first brain region, which is so complexly folded upon itself in the mammals—and particularly in man—is the **cere-**

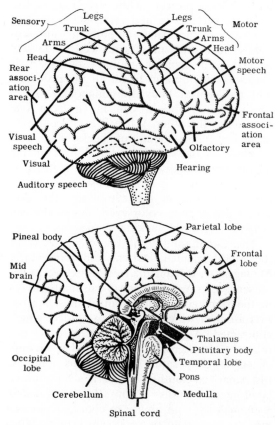

FIG. 11-23. *The mammalian brain shows a high degree of specialization, region by region, and also a remarkable ability to substitute functions of one area for an adjacent one when damage has incapacitated parts.*

brum. In the human example, it overgrows the rest of the brain to become its most conspicuous part. The roof and walls are covered by a layer of association neurons as a **cerebral cortex** in which are located all consciousness, all voluntary motor activity, many complex reflex actions, and all that is included in the general terms: thinking, psychic life, memory, and learning. The floor of this portion of the brain, in its anterior lateral corners, may be developed into definite **olfactory lobes** in which the senses of taste and smell are localized. The floor elsewhere acts as a conduit for nerve fibers from the cortical areas. In man the whole cerebrum includes about 10 billion neurons.

The second of the brain regions provides for respiratory exchange in the invaginated roof, and for connection to a structure of unknown function in most vertebrates, the mid-dorsal **pineal body.** The floor of this region extends ventrally into a special cup-shaped depression in the brain case, as the neural component of the pituitary gland—the upper, posterior lobe (hypophysis), which furnishes pituitrin. The walls of the second brain region furnish a place for the nervous connections between the ganglionic portions of the whole fore brain and the more posterior parts of the brain and nervous system, and in warm-blooded animals include the control centers responding to temperature changes.

The pineal body is an interesting puzzle. For years it was assumed to have an endocrine function, although no hormone could be demonstrated in it. Removal of the pineal body is invariably fatal, without distinctive symptoms. But in one reptile (Sphenodon—Photo 430), representing an otherwise extinct order (the Rhynchocephalia), the pineal body is as highly sensitive to light as if it were a degenerate eye. The fossil record lends weight to this hypothesis because many of the skulls of early reptiles had a gap in the skull where a pineal eye could perfectly well have looked upward at the Mesozoic world. And a number of modern fish have been shown to have unusual light sensitivity in this region, although the pineal body in their brains lacks any organization that would correspond to that of a vertebrate eye. Perhaps an answer will yet be found for these problems.

The midbrain of lower vertebrates is concerned primarily with vision, a function that in higher vertebrates has been shifted forward to the cerebral cortex. In fish and amphibians, the midbrain roof forms prominent bulging **optic lobes;** among reptiles some of the vision function has been transferred to the cerebrum; in birds and mammals the shift is complete. Reflex actions of eye and pupil remain controlled from the midbrain, and hearing has its seat there. Otherwise the midbrain structure is involved principally with nerve tracts passing anterior and posterior, linking other brain regions.

The fourth region of the brain, the **cerebellum** ("little cerebrum"), is greatly expanded dorsally in birds and mammals. It attends to reflex coordination of various types of movements of voluntary muscles—for example, equilibrium, a sense of position of the body parts, and the maintenance of muscular tone. It also provides the chief bridge between left and right sides of the brain; in higher vertebrates these transverse connections require so much tissue as to make recognizable a special region—the **pons** (Latin for *bridge*). The floor of the fourth region also functions for passage of impulses between more anterior and posterior parts of the nervous system. In man, the cerebellum contains about one billion neurons.

The final subdivision of the five-part brain, the **medulla** or **medulla oblongata,** continues this connecting function to the spinal cord, but it also involves the centers controlling most automatic activities of the body, such as respiratory movements, digestive movements, and some emergency involuntary spasms like coughing and sneezing. The roof of the medulla is extremely thin and allows a dense meshwork of blood capillaries to be separated only slightly from the fluid filling the cavities of the brain. Hence food and oxygen can diffuse into the cerebrospinal fluid and spread anteriorly and posteriorly in the hollow nervous system. Although the entire brain surface is covered by further capillary net, the respiratory needs are barely more than attended to, for any significant drop in the availability of oxygen to an animal produces profound loss of brain function.

The degree of development of any one of the brain regions depends in great extent upon the sensory mechanism associated with it, and upon the role of the brain in the activities of the animal (Fig. 11-24). Thus, where taste and smell are important, as they are in sharks that taste their prey long before

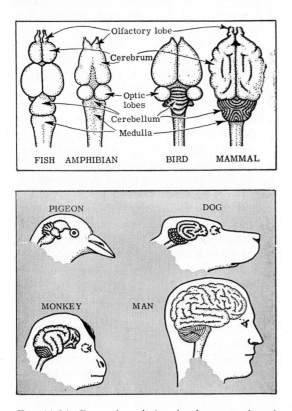

FIG. 11-24. *From the relative development of various brain areas, the habits and characteristics of the various vertebrate classes could be predicted.*

they can see it, the olfactory regions of the fore brain are most developed. In animals that rely more on the sense of sight, the optic areas of the nervous center are correspondingly enlarged. In birds, for example, where the sense of smell is lacking and taste appears to be much restricted, the olfactory lobes are much reduced, but the dorsal portion of the cerebellum is greatly expanded in correlation with the high degree of complexity in instinctive actions such as nest-building and migration.

Action Potentials in the Cerebral Cortex

The interactions of the billions of neurons in the human cerebral cortex give rise to electrical potentials extending through the skull and scalp, varying from moment to moment and corresponding crudely point for point from the brain surface to the overlying tissues. It is possible to record them on a moving paper tape as an **electroencephalogram.** The form of the irregular waves is recognizably different when the subject is asleep, awake, exercising, or mentally agitated. Moreover, where brain tumors are located in the cerebral cortex, their position (and, to some measure, their extent) can often be mapped in advance of surgical exploration, from study of the variations in the "brain waves" picked up by the sensitive instrument through wires in different locations. Even between the seizures characteristic of epileptics, the action currents are different enough from normal patterns for a specialist to identify. Thus the EEG (electroencephalogram) corresponds to the EKG (electrocardiogram) in using action currents from cellular metabolism to further medical diagnosis.

9. THE CRANIAL NERVES

No distinct demarcation sets off the medulla from the spinal cord. The one tapers backward indistinguishably into the other. Similarly, the terms "cranial nerves" and "spinal nerves" have little meaning other than that the former emerge through the skull, whereas the latter are related to vertebrae. Thus, the difference between those classes of vertebrates (reptiles, birds and mammals) in which there are 12 pairs of cranial nerves and the others in which these number 10 pairs is primarily a measure of the backward development of the skull, enclosing the bases of two more pairs of the continuous series.

10. THE SPINAL CORD AND SPINAL NERVES

The nerves of the spinal cord are far more uniform than are cranial nerves. Each has a double connection to the cord—a dorsal sensory root with enlarged dorsal root ganglion (containing the cell bodies of sensory neurons for that level of the body) and a ventral motor root that carries axons from the cell bodies in the cord. The cord itself is approximately cylindrical, slightly depressed, and marked by a deep groove on the mid line both above and below. These grooves provide additional possibility for blood capillaries to come close to cells within the cord. Between the grooves and in line with them is the small central spinal canal with some of the cerebrospinal fluid.

Enveloping the entire nerve cord are three successive layers of membranes, the meninges. The innermost—the *pia*—adheres closely to the cord and carries blood vessels into its dorsal and ventral grooves. The middle meninx—the *arachnoid*—is very delicate. Between it and the pia is most of the cerebrospinal fluid. The outermost membrane—the *dura*—lines the neural canal in the vertebrae and acts as a lining inside the skull. Inflammation of the meninges is known as *meningitis*. Study of cerebrospinal fluid is often used as a supplement to blood tests in seeking clinical information concerning suspected disease conditions. The fluid itself is similar in origin and chemical nature to lymph, and assists in diffusion of food substances and respiratory gases in the central nervous system.

The two roots of each spinal nerve are fused and enclosed in a common sheath before the nerve extends beyond the vertebrae, but at the point of juncture or just below, another branch can be noted in most spinal nerves. It is the *visceral branch,* carrying motor fibers to and sensory fibers from the organs monitored by the nervous pathways to be described presently as "self-regulating controls."

The gray and white appearance of the spinal cord represents structure in the same way that it can be recognized in the brain. But in the latter, instead of the "gray matter" being on the inside (in an H-shape as seen in section), it is external in the form of association neurons in the cortex of cerebrum and cerebellum. The "white matter" that covers the cord and composes its outer zones is less obvious in dorsal view of a mammalian or bird brain; it is the sheathed fibers that make up the longitudinal and transverse pathways, particularly along the ventral and lateral walls. Hence the familiar comment: "He's a genius; he must have plenty of gray matter!" The gray matter—the neuron cell bodies—is

on the outside of the brain chiefly because this is the one place where it is structurally possible to find space for so much of it and still have the cells adjacent to blood capillaries for respiration and food needs. The complex wrinkling and infolding upon itself found in mammals allows still more area without increasing the width or length of the brain beyond that which can be accommodated in a skull of convenient proportions.

In most of the vertebrates, the presence of paired appendages places particular emphasis on certain regions of the trunk and their associated nerves (Fig. 11-25). The result in all cases is a cooperative union of several spinal nerves on each side, forming a **brachial plexus** to the pectoral fin, fore leg, wing, or

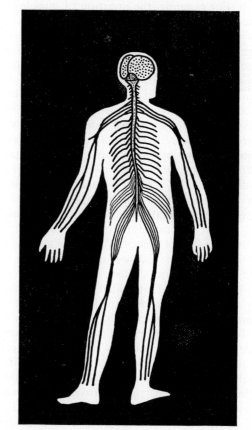

Fig. 11-25. *The mammalian spinal nerves and plexi form a network chiefly concerned with conscious sensation and muscular control. Below the cervical series are those of the brachial plexus to the arms, a thoracic series, a lumbar group, and the sciatic plexus to the legs.*

arm, and a **sciatic plexus** to the pelvic fin or hind leg. In addition, in those vertebrates possessed of a tail, the end of the spinal cord extends in a single, unpaired **caudal nerve** serving this appendage.

The proportion of reflexes mediated at various levels in the central nervous system is subject to differences according to the group of vertebrates. Thus, with a blunt stiff wire the brain of a frog or turtle can be destroyed in a few seconds. Thereafter the "spinal animal" (still having its spinal cord tissues intact) can hop, crawl, scratch, and swim if properly stimulated. Spinal birds and mammals have few reflexes left and no coordination whatever of any movements.

Even among mammals there is wide variation. For example, the insertion of muscles in the appendages can be transposed surgically so that a normal flexor extends the leg and the normal extensor flexes it. After such an operation, a rat can learn to use its fore legs as stiff crutches, but it never gains use of the hinder pair. In man, however, ordinary controls are soon established. Actually, the extensive transfer of motor controls from the cord to the cerebral cortex (called **corticalization**) shown in the human nervous system allows voluntary control over almost every individual muscle. Intense concentration may be required, but on this basis the abdominal muscles may be built surgically into a sphincter for an artificial anus near the umbilicus. Other "feats" of remedial surgery also have their basis in the extraordinary versatility of the human cerebral centers.

The degree of corticalization is shown also by sensory systems. Removal of the hindmost part of the cerebral cortex of the rat causes only slight impairment of vision. The same operation in the monkey destroys pattern sense but allows continued brightness discrimination. Man, however, becomes completely blind if this area is destroyed. Corticalization thus involves a progressive restriction of activities to definite parts of the brain, as well as the transfer to it of motor functions and reflexes from the spinal cord.

11. SELF-REGULATING CONTROLS

A phrase with seemingly mystical signifi-

cance has been applied to the portion of the nervous system that serves the viscera. Although it cannot be considered a separate, independent mechanism, the term "autonomic nervous system" has been widely used (Fig. 11-26). Just because we are not conscious

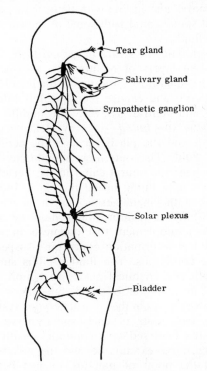

Fig. 11-26. *The autonomic nervous ganglia and trunks are concerned chiefly with control and coordination of organ systems about which consciousness is not ordinarily concerned.*

of the impulses that course up and down in loose nerve trunks paralleling the spinal cord, there has been a strong tendency to regard them as unique. Instead, they represent a further division of labor, and merely the nerve connections to the organs of the body cavity, for sensory cells and muscles and glands that do their part without disturbing the consciousness.

This portion of the nervous system consists of two rows of interconnected ganglia, one on each side of the spinal cord but not inside the vertebral sheath. Instead, these trunks are in the body cavity, and many of the spinal nerves make connections through visceral branches, while at the anterior end the vagus (an important cranial nerve) is intimately associated with them.

Functionally the autonomic components are in two opposing mechanisms: (1) the **sympathetic** fibers and ganglia (the largest of the latter being the "solar plexus" just below the diaphragm), which stimulate the heart and blood vessel musculature but which inhibit the activities of the intestinal tract; and (2) the **parasympathetic** fibers which act in the opposite way. Through the cooperative antagonism of these two groups, together with related sense organs among the viscera, unconscious control action originating in the brain, and hormonal interactions, normal activity and rhythmic function are maintained. Through their action, too, the animal is able to suspend digestive action quickly in an emergency, and to place emphasis on readiness for muscular feats that will enable it to escape from danger.

The sympathetic system liberates into the blood stream a definite hormone, **sympathin,** which is elaborated in the nerve endings and which serves to hasten synaptic transmission in at least the sympathetic ganglia. Its action is much like that of adrenalin, and sympathetic fibers call forth this hormone in addition. As a result, in any situation resulting from anger, fear or other excitement, the liver quickly transforms glycogen into sugar, raising the blood glucose level; the heart beats faster; and the capillaries of skin and intestinal tract contract (raising blood pressure, blanching the skin, and reducing digestive absorption). Capillaries of the voluntary muscles and brain dilate, however, bringing more energy-rich sugar and oxygen for use of these organs important in controlling vigorous activity.

A material corresponding to sympathin, and also acting as an excitatory agent, has been identified in parasympathetic synapses. Upon investigation[3] it proved to be a relatively simple organic compound, **acetylcholine,** available from chemical supply houses; hence it was available for experimental use. Its powerful action in parasympathetic synapses and at nervous junctions on muscle fibers, plus other evidence, has led to the belief that acetylcholine is the chief agent of synaptic transmission in the parasympathetic network. Many of the body tissues contain an enzyme, **cholinesterase,** which rapidly hydrolyzes acetylcholine and thus limits the time duration of any excitation. The nerve fibers themselves elaborate acetylcholine. Cholinesterase thus destroys the product after brief operation. The so-called "nerve gases," developed during World War II but never used, inactivate cholinesterase, hence lead to muscle spasms and obliteration of the soldier's "will to resist." Curare (a paralyzing poison used on arrows by South American Indians), nicotine (from tobacco), belladonna (used by some women to dilate the pupils as a beauty aid), and the deadly chemical ingredients of the mushroom Amanita, all act on the acetylcholine system.

These and other discoveries regarding the role of secretions from axon tips led to the general neurohumoral theory of synaptic action (see p. 172). Control of chromatophores (p. 191) then becomes a special case. This view provides an explanation for the polarity of the synapse, for the delay inherent in its operation, for summation of inadequate stimuli, and for the so-called after-discharge which is observed frequently as a continuation of impulses beyond a synapse after the series of impulses going to the synapse has ended. There are many difficulties, however, in applying this theory to action of the central nervous system, and some modification or extension of the hypothesis is needed before the operation of the brain will be clear.

The visceral branches connecting spinal nerves to autonomic trunks have been mentioned. Through this agency impulses from the viscera reach the same dorsal root ganglion as do impulses from superficial receptors in each area of the body. Transfer of impulses across some of these connections is not improbable. The same association neurons in the spinal cord as are related to sensory nerve cells in the outer body regions are connected at many levels to nerve cells of the autonomic system. For this reason, when chemical and mechanical difficulties arise that stimulate nerve channels of which we are entirely unconscious, the effect may be powerful enough to invoke pain sensations. These, how-

[3] For research work on this material, the 1936 Nobel Prize in medicine and physiology was divided between Sir Henry Dale of England and Professor Otto Loewi of Austria (now in the U. S.).

ever, are not interpreted by the brain as coming from the visceral sense organs. Instead they seem to come from body areas served by the sensory neurons of the same level. Hence stimulation of the diaphragm leads to pain sensations that appear to the consciousness as arising in the shoulders. Or the pain of ap-

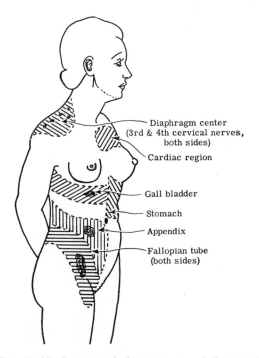

Diaphragm center
(3rd & 4th cervical nerves,
both sides)

Cardiac region

Gall bladder

Stomach

Appendix

Fallopian tube
(both sides)

FIG. 11-27. *Because of the joint use of the spinal nerve roots by superficial sensory pathways and by autonomic reflexes, stimulation and irritation of deep viscera result in "referred pain" seeming to arise from definite sensory areas on the surface or near it.*

pendicitis may begin in the lower left quadrant of the abdomen as a superficial ache or stabbing sensation, and then wander considerably. Somtimes it settles down promptly in the right quadrant, more or less over the position of the appendix. These pain sensations transferred from autonomic to sensory pathways are called **referred pains** (Fig. 11-27).

As examples of the reflexes controlled by the autonomic neurons, the ordinary automatic activities in human breathing may be outlined. Another, more extended, sequence is the series of well-timed events that attend to swallowing and to passage of food from the stomach, from the small intestine, and from the large intestine, together with secretion of digestive agents at appropriate phases.

Breathing

The control of respiratory movements in mammals originates in the medulla of the brain, where a specialized group of nerve cells is particularly responsive to increased acidity of the blood passing it in a capillary network. Ordinarily the respiratory center provides volleys of impulses along the nerves serving the diaphragm and intercostal muscles, causing the latter to contract—expanding the lung volume and bringing in tidal air as described in Chapter 8. Receptors in the pulmonary wall, however, respond to stretching with inhibitory impulses that suppress the respiratory center, allowing a cessation of inspiration and a passive expiration. Soon the respiratory center stimulates another contraction phase.

Repetition of inspiration is greatly hastened if the carbon dioxide content of the blood rises perceptibly, as takes place with any increase in muscular activity. The effectiveness of this mechanism is made particularly clear. For although, by cerebral action, a person can voluntarily "hold his breath" at any stage of the rhythmic cycle, these inhibitory impulses are destroyed in the respiratory center as soon as the blood carbon dioxide content rises enough to stimulate repetition of the volleys down the vagus nerve. Thus a person cannot asphyxiate himself with carbon dioxide by voluntary stoppage of respiratory movements.

Accessory mechanisms are present that supplement these activities of the respiratory center. The lung walls include sense organs that may send stimulating impulses to the brain if the exhaled position is held for long. And decrease of oxygen restricts the oxidation of lactic acid in working muscle cells; the lactic acid diffuses into the blood and may affect the acidity enough to stimulate the respiratory center. In addition, special receptors in the walls of a bulb-like swelling at the base of each internal carotid artery react to increased carbon dioxide and decreased oxygen in the blood by sending further impulses to activate the medullary mechanism. Receptors in the pharynx, on the other hand, inhibit the impulses from the respiratory center for the brief duration of the swallowing reflex, thus allowing the glottis to be closed and food to pass without danger of particles being sucked into the respiratory system.

The young mammal, prior to birth, depends entirely upon its parent for respiration. Immediately after birth is accomplished and the umbilical cord no longer provides for this function, the individual must begin respiratory movements and continue them for life. At first, however, the medullary center does not send the rhythmic volleys of impulses noted in later life. Instead the mechanism waits repeatedly until carbon dioxide accumulates before initiating a series of rapid inspirations and expirations. This irregularity, known as Cheyne-Stokes breathing, gradually disappears, as the respiratory center acquires its habitual rhythm. It is interesting, however, that the normal adult may return to Cheyne-Stokes breathing when in very deep sleep.

Temperature Regulation

As was pointed out earlier (p. 95) metabolic heat is put to use and controlled by birds and mammals. Heat from muscular contraction (plus about one-tenth as much, arising from other metabolic processes—particularly glandular activity) is distributed by the blood stream to all parts of the body. From the body surfaces it radiates away, or is lost by conduction and convection. If the heat loss becomes more rapid than the heat production, the blood temperature drops slightly. This affects a thermostat-like mechanism in the second region of the brain, and initiates an increase of nervous stimulation to the smooth muscles of the intestine and of the major blood vessels, and a slight increase in overall tension of the skeletal muscles. Together, these rises in contractile activity may liberate enough additional heat to match the heat loss, so that blood temperature returns to its "normal" level. If it does not, still greater muscular tone may give rise to irregular spasmodic contractions of many skeletal muscles, then the involuntary act of shivering. Still more heat is generated by this greater violence of contraction.

Similarly, if the environment is warmer, heat loss may be less than heat production. In that event, the blood temperature rises slightly. Again the nervous system responds by decreasing stimulation of the visceral muscles and by allowing a drop in tone among the skeletal musculature. Thus temperature regulation in a warm-blooded animal is responsible for a decrease in food (and oxygen) consumption with rise in environmental temperature. In cold-blooded animals, an increase in temperature of the surroundings is followed rapidly by a rise in body temperature and by a prompt acceleration of chemical reactions— an increase in both food and oxygen utilization. The converse applies to a drop in environmental temperature. Warm-bloodedness is thus an everyday term for uniform body temperature, whereas cold-bloodedness implies that the body is only a few degrees warmer than the surroundings and follows the temperature of the environment up and down quite passively.

SUGGESTED READING (see pp. 506-511)

Recent and Informative: Allen, 1951; Beidler, 1952; Evans, 1949; Gray, 1948; Haagen-Smit, 1952; Harvey, 1948, 1952; Kabat, 1949; Katz, 1952; Milne & Milne, 1948; Saunders, 1948; Wald, 1950, 1954; Walter, 1954.

12 · Behavior

INTERNAL STIMULI. EXTERNAL STIMULI. ORIENTATIONS. KINETIC RESPONSES. REFLEXES AND INSTINCTS. LEARNING. INSIGHT. FACILITATION AND INHIBITION. CONDITIONED RESPONSES. FRUSTRATION.

PERHAPS the most characteristic feature of animal life is its responsiveness to changes in its environment. In studying the organism as a whole, response to stimulation is rarely a simple reaction. The first step may be a reflex act, but subsequent events show that the animal has been generally affected by the change. If these delayed responses follow any regular sequence, they may be recognized as a **behavior pattern.** As such they become the concern of psychologists who, in the last analysis, are biologists restricting their attention to behavior of the whole organism— whether normal, intact, diseased, or experimentally modified.

Internal Stimuli

When examining a supposedly normal animal in terms of its behavior, a number of aspects must be kept in mind. For one thing, no matter how much the observer tries to keep the organism in a stimulus-free environment, it is receiving important impulses at all times from within its own body. The stimulation of the internal sense organs apprises the animal of a wide variety of needs: oxygen, water, food, bladder or rectal pressure, and sluggish circulation in an appendage on which the organism is resting. These are aspects of ordinary living, but they elicit definite responses without any external cue. Thus a rat in a squirrel cage becomes increasingly active as it grows hungry, and it expresses this inner stimulus by rotating the exercise wheel. Near noon, students in a lecture hall may unconsciously show a similar activity in general body movements, as a response to hunger pangs. These unavoidable behaviors must be allowed for in any study of an intact organism.

External Stimuli

Away from laboratory conditions, the animal is surrounded by a sea of stimuli, each of which expresses itself as a form of energy reaching the organism: light energy; air vibrations of sound frequencies; regions radiating heat energy toward the animal or absorbing heat; unequal pressures of all sorts. These affect the external sense organs. No response may be elicited, or the animal may do something. Part of the difference between a response and none is in the animal's internal state. Thus it is that the measurement of a stimulus as being sufficiently irritating to cause an organism to move from one place to another must always take into account the internal variables. Thereby the experiment becomes tremendously complex. Since no two individual animals are exactly alike, the difficulty of providing a valid control is enormous. Partly as a means for reducing this source of erroneous conclusions to a minimum, the psychologists commonly use as a test animal the laboratory strains of white rats and white mice—generally employing litter mates of the same sex (hence of practically identical age), fed on the same artificial foods, and representing an inbred line of spectacular purity. In this way the approach is very close to that expected from identical twins reared together, and correlations may be high.

Orientations

An attached animal, such as a hydroid or a worm inhabiting a secreted tube, may respond to a stimulus from a light source to one side, by turning the body either toward or away from the direction whence the stimulus comes. This is described as **orientation**. The older term for it was borrowed by one of the earliest investigators, Jacques Loeb, who believed he saw a definite correspondence between these movements of animals and the growth curvatures of plants. Present usage avoids the term *tropisms* in animal behavior, retaining only the directional signs and referring to such **postural relationships** as positive orientations or negative orientations. Some animals, of course, provide no response, and even an organism which gives a positive response under one set of conditions may orient in the opposite sense when those conditions are changed.

Kinetic Responses

Where the organism is free to move around, it may alter its position of rest to face toward or away from a source of stimulation; again this is orientation. Or it may move to an entirely new position—a more active response referred to as a *kinesis,* or a **kinetic response.** If to light, it would be a demonstration of a *photokinesis*. To a chemical substance, the term would be *chemokinesis*. To a current of air or water, it would be *rheokinesis* (Photo 131). Often an organism may show one threshold for orientation and a higher one for kinetic response. The sign of the two is ordinarily the same—either positive or negative. It should be noted that the stimulus calls forth an expenditure of energy on the part of the animal, and that the orientation or kinesis usually has a directional quality that implies detection by the animal of the direction from which the stimulus is coming.

Reflexes and Instincts

The structure of an organism determines the pattern of its responses. Reflexes come ready-made, as a special linkage of sensory cells, nervous pathways, and effectors. They are part of the animal's successful architecture.

In the human instance, a yawn, a cough, the blinking of the eyelids, salivation when some foreign object is in the mouth, and numerous other reactions are complex cooperative efforts, but the mechanism is on the structural level. Such responses need not be learned. Among animals with a central nervous system, examples seem endless. Even among coelenterates, however, corresponding activities are found.

In many unlearned responses there is some product of the reflex act that calls forth a second and different response. Touch a baby's cheek near the mouth and the head turns toward the object until the lips can investigate. If the object can be brought between the lips, the pharyngeal muscles provide suction. If something reaches the pharyngeal walls, swallowing ensues. Thus series and combinations of reactions are built into chains, and the stimulus that touches off the first, sets the whole mechanism to work. The machine-like activity resulting from such systems is usually referred to as an **instinct.** Many actions associated with reproduction (for example, nest-building in birds and the burying of mice by certain beetles) follow an instinctive pattern. Various courtship displays and autotomy in echinoderms or crustaceans may have the same basis. In man the instincts are so overlaid with learning that it is difficult to separate the two, though the instinctive patterns are visible in many behaviors.

Under laboratory conditions, animals often show great uniformity of response to artificial types of stimulation. Studies of this kind led Jacques Loeb to conclude that the organism had no choice. Its movements were "forced." A herring gull whose eggs have been treated with a poison will continue to brood over the dead eggs until the breeding season is past, whereas if the eggs are removed, a new mating and a new clutch will soon follow. Many of the inbuilt reflexes and instincts of animals are seemingly as automatic as these. Most of them are important in survival under "normal" conditions, although they introduce a definite loss of flexibility and block adaptation to new situations.

Loeb missed several points evident to the modern psychologist, and was misled as a result. Firstly, external stimuli introduce no new *types* of behavior. All an external stimulus can do is to modify the rate of a spontaneous behavior in response to internal stimuli. Thus a hungry animal will seek to satisfy its need for food; in doing so it will exhibit definite behavior patterns. If the hunger is satisfied, activity may cease. A circus lion performs before a meal, not afterward, and follows through routines that are meaningful to a cat in only one way: they lead to the desired reward—food.

Secondly, each organism contains the structural basis for several different responses to a given external situation. When the internal stimulus ("need") induces the animal to act, it may repeat over and over a single response to an external stimulus. But if this response fails to bring the organism to its goal, thereby reducing the internal stimulus to an intensity below threshold, the activity continues. Eventually a second response is tried. If this too is unsuccessful, a third may appear. The whole structural repertoire will be displayed if each attempt is blocked. This multiplicity of available responses in lower animals remained unknown until recent times.

Thirdly, some changes in behavior are due to structural maturation. A response at one age may be entirely different from that at another. For each species the sequence of new behaviors is remarkably uniform, and depends chiefly on modifications of the nervous system, not on completion of the effector mechanisms with which the response becomes obvious. Thus the human baby creeps, walks, and runs at ages that depend on nervous development; practice and assistance have little effect in hastening or retarding these activities. American Indian babies that are bound to a cradleboard allowing little or no exercise, develop usable muscles and walk as early as do other babies that have been given freedom and full opportunity. All walk when the nervous structure is ready.

Learning

Even the simplest organisms are capable of learning from experience. Jennings made this fact obvious from his studies of "trial-and-error" (or more properly, trial-and-success) among invertebrates. The heart of the matter lies in the multiplicity of responses available, all tested toward ending an internal need.

If an organism tries one response and is blocked, it may try a second response—after a time—a different reaction to the same environmental situation. This response also may

lead to failure. A third response may be no more successful, but a fourth may bring success. If the organism has learned from this experience and meets the environmental situation again soon, it will try the fourth response sooner when the internal stimulus leads to activity.

A hungry cat in a test box may seek to obtain food by (1) crying audibly; (2) scratching at the inside of the box; (3) pushing on the walls or door; (4) biting any exposed object; (5) pulling at things. If the box has a door whose latchstring hangs down inside the box, a continuation of response #5 may lead to freedom and food. The next time the cat is put in the box hungry, it may mew and scratch a little, then pull at things until the string releases the door. Each new test in which the #5 response brings satisfaction adds to the cat's learning, and reduces the time required for escape.

Insight

In the example of the cat in the box, an experienced cat will go promptly to the area of wall where the string hangs down, pull at it and escape. But if the string is arranged to hang at a new point along the wall, the cat may go to the old site, claw at the area where the string "should be" and fail to get out. The time required for the cat to find the new location of the string may be no less than was needed on the first trial in the box. And in its frustration the cat may resort to crying, scratching, pushing, and biting, before pulling at new sites. Clearly the cat has not associated the means (the string) and the end (escape).

If the test box is arranged originally so that the latchstring is close to the door, the cat may show a very different behavior. After it has learned that pulling at the cord releases the door, it may associate means and end enough to go quickly to the string in a new position. This is an example of **insight.**

The farther the means and the end are separated in space or time, the more difficult is the task of associating the two. Man often describes the means and the end as "cause" and "effect," but he too may fail to correlate them.

Facilitation and Inhibition

To some extent the learning phenomenon

is due to a characteristic of the synapse. There is less resistance to repetition of transfer of an impulse by a synapse than to conduction of the initial energy. The term *facilitation* is applied to this readiness to repeat. In habit formation, the neuronic pathways are kept in a continued state of facilitation, while forgetting or loss of habit consists in large part of the gradual loss of facilitation through prolonged disuse of the synaptic sequence.

Facilitation enters the picture also when the motor areas of the cerebral cortex of a mammal send to the skeletal muscles impulses that create a state of tone barely below that needed for movement. A stimulus to the nervous system may require far less time to elicit a contraction under these circumstances; the combination of stimulus and tone is highly effective. This type of reaction often makes people "jumpy." A man working with explosives may jump violently if there is any unexpected loud noise, even if it is only a door slamming. Another man handling high voltage electric circuits may leap back in terror if he pricks his finger on a sharp point. These, too, are examples of facilitation from general nervous tension and high muscular tone.

In higher vertebrates, the effector system involved in an unlearned and automatic reflex may also be under voluntary control. Human breathing is such a dual system; the automatic reflex pattern may be suppressed to varying extents by the exercise of voluntary nervous connections. In holding one's breath, there is an obvious limit that is reached as soon as carbon dioxide accumulates in the blood stream. But in such a complex series of contractions as constitutes a sneeze, the entire reaction may be prevented (and the stimulus hence ignored) by mental concentration on the initial muscular movements that are realized to be part of the performance. This is inhibition, and involves a chain of impulses on a voluntary basis occupying the nervous pathways needed for the reflex act. Even the knee jerk response may be suppressed or greatly reduced (or enhanced) by similar concentration and issuance of impulses to the muscles concerned.

Other responses of seemingly comparable type are actually very different. Thus, if a person is in deep sleep, tickling the sole of his bare foot with a feather has no effect whatever. In light sleep, however, the foot is usually withdrawn slightly, and even if the sleeper wakes, there is no recollection of the stimulus. When awake, on the other hand, conscious sensations are usually strong enough to cause muscular contractions. If continued, they may lead to hysteria. Clearly, a varying number of neurons are involved, and different numbers of muscles are called into action.

Conditioned Responses

More highly-developed nervous systems include means for associating with a reflex certain completely irrelevant stimuli. The classic demonstration of this was made by the Russian psychologist, Ivan P. Pavlov. He noted that when food was placed before hungry dogs, even the sight of it or the odor of it induced such copious secretion of saliva that the animals drooled. Pavlov tried ringing a bell at the same time that the food appeared. A bell alone drew the dogs' attention but did not affect their salivary glands. But after a week of this combination he rang the bell without providing the reward. The dogs drooled anyway. They had learned to associate the ringing of the bell with the appearance of food, and salivated for either. This was the first **conditioned reflex** investigated. It is to be contrasted with the unconditioned reflexes arising from structural features of the nervous system.

Further work showed that the dog could be conditioned just as readily to respond in this way to the flashing of a light instead of the ringing of a bell. Then a combination was tried, where food was furnished only when both the bell rang and the light flashed, but not when there was a ringing and no flashing, or flashing and no ringing. This too the dogs mastered, and they salivated only under the appropriate combination. More and more of these stimuli were added until the nervous system of the dog was no longer able to keep them in mind. There was a definite limit to the number of factors to which a dog could be conditioned simultaneously in terms of a single response. The chimpanzee can handle more factors than the dog. A six-year-old child can do still better. Thus the conditioned response is also a measure of nervous structure. The nearer two organisms are in structure, the more comparable is the behavior that can be expected.

Any stimulus that can be detected can serve as the basis for conditioned responses. A dog or a human being cannot be conditioned to ultraviolet light patterns because neither can see them, but a honeybee can learn to associate radiations of spectral purity well beyond the human range in this direction, and the conditioned response then becomes a tool for investigating the sensitivities in other animals.

Even unpleasant stimuli can be used to condition a response. They become tasks with a predictable reward. There is little difference between a dog becoming conditioned to salivate and to eat food when stimulated (and presumably hurt) by a strong electric shock, and the deliberate agreement on the part of a human being to do painful, dangerous or thoroughly unpleasant tasks in order to get money with which to buy meals that will induce salivation. In this respect, man is more willing than any other animal to work for distant goals instead of reacting in terms of the present alone.

Most of our own unaccountable likes and dislikes, our prejudices and hunches, and even many of our interests and hobbies, have conditioned reflexes at their base. In childhood the formation of unreasonable associations is particularly easy. A fondness for a color and type of cloth may be due entirely to the fact that when first the combination or components were met, they were the clothing of some well-liked person. Or an animal may be "friendly" because it was seen regularly through a window at mealtimes. Often our adult claims to have "learned by experience" that certain actions correspond to an accent of speech or a skin color have no more basis than a conditioned reflex—fear, anger, and anxiety—based on one or two vivid examples.

Sometimes claims to "mother love" and "intelligence" among nonhuman animals also prove to rest on unacceptable foundations. The domestic cow "mourns" the loss of her calf, but is quiet once more if a stuffed calfskin is provided in her stall. Often, however, in "solicitously" licking the dummy calf, her tongue accidentally rips open the sewed seams and exposes the hay used as stuffing. She then proceeds "calmly" to eat the hay, showing no return of the previous "mother love" until the calfskin collapses, emptied of its contents. Similarly, the brooding of birds seems based entirely on inability to find relief from reflex sensitivities of skin receptors, except by rubbing these against eggs in the nest. Crediting subhuman organisms with human motives is the practice of **anthropomorphism,** and a way of thinking that is to be discouraged at every opportunity, since a scientifically sound basis seems invariably to be lacking.

Conditioned responses are the basis of habit. They may also be the cornerstone of learning. Words, whether spoken or written, become substitute stimuli for the things and actions that normally elicit simple responses. And communication, from man to man and from generation to generation, becomes a means of building more tightly conditioned responses and of influencing the "thought" processes and actions of supposedly reasoning human beings, so that they behave in ways that are helpful or otherwise to the complex civilization in which they move. It is very difficult to follow the conditioned response to its end products in man. If one sits down quietly by himself and weighs a mass of evidence for and against some conclusion, usually the matter of judgment and estimated values enters; the problem is not a mathematical decision. Into the judgments and estimates enter the person's habits, personal beliefs, and prejudices—all the galaxy of condition responses that constitute his training and experience.

Frustration

Often a reward is achieved regularly from a response to one factor or group of them, but not to some very slightly different situation. The animal may then develop an extinction of response to the variant situations. Pavlov demonstrated this by feeding dogs when they approached a circular white sign, but not when they approached an elliptical one. Then he made the elliptical sign more and more nearly circular until at a ratio of 9 to 8 in the two diameters, the dogs could not distinguish between them. Two different reactions followed, depending on the individual dog: (1) the animal might go to sleep or into a trance, or (2) it might suddenly begin barking wildly and jumping around in an uncontrollable manner that might be called a "fit."

Pavlov pointed out the similarity between the sleep response and ordinary sleep. He contended that inhibitions involved in refraining from responding to the rewardless stimulus were comparable to the more broadly inhibited state of human sleep. This hypothesis would explain why fixing one's attention on a book or lecturer, by inhibiting response to other stimuli, could so rapidly lead to drowsiness. Even a droning sound or a lullaby could develop inhibitions that become similarly complete. No better explanation of sleep seems to be available at the moment, but this one is admittedly inadequate.

The responses of the dogs to the stimuli between which they could not discriminate correspond very closely to the two major types of "nervous breakdowns" known in human beings. As such, they are not in the same category with the normal inactivity of sleep. The trance-like state corresponds to *neurasthenia,* the wild barking and jumping to *hysteria.* Both are important **neuroses** of man, often brought on by similarly confusing situations. As in the dogs, recovery is possible only through long retraining with much encouragement, and repeated success with simpler problems, before any of comparable complexity or lack of reward can be endured.

SUGGESTED READING (see pp. 506-511)

Classics and Milestones: Pavlov, von Frisch.

Recent and Informative: Gerard, 1948; Milne & Milne, 1948, 1950, 1954; Montagu, 1950; Potter, 1950; Schneirla, 1948; Tinbergen, 1951, 1952, 1954; Warden, 1951; Witt, 1954; Yerkes, 1925.

13 · Single Cells and Smaller

I. ORGANISMS WITH AT LEAST ONE NUCLEUS: 1. ORGANISMS WITH PSEUDO-PODIA. 2. CILIATES. 3. FLAGELLATES—EUGLENA AND KIN, FLAGELLATES WITH MANY FLAGELLA, PARASITIC FLAGELLATES, CHLAMYDOMONAS AND KIN. 4. SPORE-FORMING PARASITES—MALARIA. 5. YEASTS. 6. DIATOMS. 7. NON-MOTILE GREEN ALGAE. II. ORGANISMS WITH NO DEFINITE NUCLEUS: 1. BACTERIA. 2. RICKETTSIA BODIES. 3. VIRUSES. 4. COMMUNITY HEALTH.

JUST AS Aristotle is regarded as the "Father of Zoology" and Theophrastus as the founder of botany, so also a cloth merchant of Delft, Holland, must be credited as the "Father of Microbiology." Antonj van Leeuwenhoek made and used his own high-powered simple microscopes (Photo 51), and discovered the existence of "animalcules" in hay infusions (1675), yeast (1680), and bacteria (1683). He communicated each discovery to the Royal Society of London. These descriptions with careful drawings appear in the early volumes of the *Philosophical Transactions*.

Most unicellular organisms ("microbes") live where water is in good supply, whether in the sea, fresh water, soil, or as parasites in other organisms. Ordinarily, dissolved minerals are available to them in adequate amounts. The surrounding water protects them from rapid changes of temperature (because of its high specific heat), from harmful ultraviolet in sunlight (by converting energy at these wavelengths into heat), and from gravity. Since the density of protoplasm and its inclusions is not much greater than that of the surrounding water, organisms tend to remain suspended. In those which elaborate a skeleton, the nonliving secretion is usually delicate and may provide additional frictional hold upon the supporting water, further reducing the effect of gravity.

Some unicellular types, such as the terrestrial green algae, retain a fixed position and become active if the humidity rises or rain falls. Others are carried passively in water (as "contamination") or by air currents (as "germs"). Those with their own means of locomotion move so slowly that distances covered during a single generation are microscopic. These movements serve chiefly to give each individual access to fresh territory in which food may be found.

All unicellular organisms are subject to the same general limitations. They must be able to remain dormant over months or years while living conditions are unfavorable, and to compensate through prodigious reproduction whenever circumstances permit.

The single-celled way of life places extreme emphasis upon large surface area in proportion to volume of protoplasm. In fact, the whole design is so unlike that of either multicellular animals or multicellular plants that many biologists have regarded unicellular organisms as constituting a third kingdom of life —the *Protista*. Those who object to this procedure are left with an insoluble problem. They must seek universally acceptable reasons for placing each unicellular organism in either the animal phylum Protozoa or one of the several phyla of thallophytes.

Since structural features are at a minimum among unicellular organisms, every scrap of information on life history and physiological activity must be considered in classifying them. On these bases, fair agreement has been found for recognizing certain categories:

I. ORGANISMS WITH AT LEAST ONE NUCLEUS

1. ORGANISMS WITH PSEUDOPODIA

Amebas are the best known of unicellular types moving about by means of protoplasmic extensions called **pseudopodia.** These organisms are referred to the protozoan class Sarcodina.

The fresh-water ameba (Fig. 13-1, Photo 137) has been popularized as an animal lacking all regularity of shape. Usually it is described as a naked mass of protoplasm, containing assorted food particles in various stages of digestion and, under proper conditions of nourishment, a peppering of glycogen granules.

The central part of an ameba's protoplasm is seen to flow (granules, nucleus, and all) toward and into the advancing pseudo-

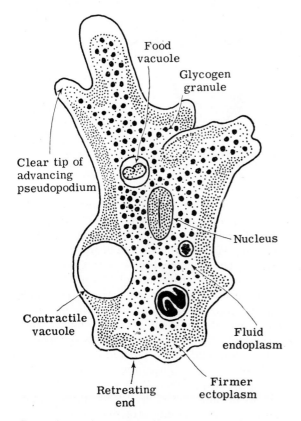

FIG. 13-1. *The supposedly simplest animal, the ameba, lacks even a definite shape, but its single cell carries on successfully all of the many physiological processes of a complex animal.*

podium. The fluid portion of the cytoplasm is thus distinct in behavior from an outer zone of the cell. The former is **endoplasm,** and clearly a liquid. Around it is **ectoplasm,** which seems to be a jelly. Endoplasm that flows into an advancing pseudopodium appears to jell and become ectoplasm. Similarly, at the trailing end of the cell, ectoplasm liquifies and becomes endoplasm. The sol and gel phases of cytoplasm are thus in a state of rapid interchange, and through these transformations and protoplasmic streaming, locomotion is achieved.

Until recently no real landmarks were known in an ameba. Now it is evident that the trailing end is a permanent feature of the cell. The organism thus possesses a retreating (posterior) end but no single advancing (anterior) region. Any part of the surface other than the trailing end seems able to form a pseudopodium.

The "nakedness" of an ameba's protoplasm may be more apparent than real. If a small piece of the outer surface of an ameba is cut away, the protoplasm begins to flow out of the opening as though pressure had been released. Only a little is lost, however, before a membrane forms across the cut place. Five minutes later the new membrane is still delicate and easily torn, but after half an hour the wound has "healed" and no longer can be found. Thus, the change from ecto- to endoplasm is not merely a reaction to water around the organism, as has been suggested. There is a thin, transparent surface layer over an ameba that can be torn and repaired. It may be nonliving, a secreted **pellicle,** rather than the true plasma membrane of the cell itself.

When an ameba encounters a suitable food particle, the cell flows around the object and encloses it. Invariably the food remains surrounded by a small sphere of water, and is a **food vacuole.** Into this water the protoplasm secretes digestive enzymes which break down the component molecules into small ones which can be absorbed into the protoplasm and used by it in growth or as a direct source of energy. Indigestible residues are disposed of by allowing the particle (still in its vacuole) to lag behind until the cell moves on and the vacuole is discharged.

In the sense that the food is surrounded by the protoplasm of a single cell, digestion can be described as intracellular. Yet, except in dissolved form, the food never enters the protoplasm itself. The vacuole represents the outside world, just as does the cavity of a digestive tract.

Ameba is like many other fresh-water organisms in possessing a mechanism used in ridding the cell of water entering by endosmosis. At intervals one or more **contractile vacuoles** appear, and fill with water secreted into them by the protoplasm. The transparent spheres of liquid reach the surface of the cell and burst. Usually the vacuole lies between the nucleus and the retreating end of the cell. When an ameba changes its direction, these relationships are quickly re-established, possibly by a lag in the shifting of the contractile vacuole.

In an ameba, a biologist has an ideal organism in which to study the role of the nucleus. It is not too difficult to cut an ameba in two—one half with the nucleus, one half without (Fig. 17-4). After surgery the halves recover and each continues to show its characteristic movements and irritability. The piece with the nucleus grows, feeds, increases its protoplasmic volume to a critical point and divides. The other portion—no matter how large a percentage of the original cytoplasm it contains—does not feed, but lives only until its food reserves are expended. Thus the nucleus is necessary for the capture and storage of energy as well as for reproduction.

Amebic dysentery in mankind is due to a very small parasitic ameba which gains access to the human gut in infected drinking water. This ameba attacks living cells of the gut wall, and anaerobically liberates by-products that induce symptoms of disease. The full name of this parasite, *Endamoeba histolytica,* refers to the tissue destruction characteristic of its activities (see Fig. 4-5). Like other amebas, it reproduces by simple division. Boiling the drinking water eliminates most sources of amebiasis, whereas treatment of diseased persons requires careful medication.

A sexual method of reproduction is known too in many kinds of amebas.

2. CILIATES

These organisms move about by means of multiple cilia. Paramecium, the "slipper animalcule," is widely known. Usually these organisms are grouped as the protozoan class Ciliata, the "ciliates."

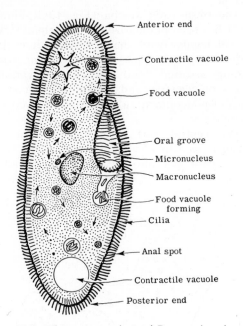

FIG. 13-2. *The entire surface of Paramecium is covered by rows of cilia which drive the active cell through the pond water.*

Cilia are short, hair-like processes which emerge at definite points in a thin, nonliving pellicle of horny material that surrounds the cell and gives the ciliate some degree of elastic rigidity. The cilia beat against the surrounding medium and drive the cell along.

Paramecium reaches a length of 0.01 mm —just large enough to see with the unaided eye if the light is good. Under the microscope the cell is found to be elongate, with a blunt end and a tapered end (Fig. 13-2, Photo 137). Since the animal usually moves with the blunt end foremost, this is said to be anterior (Fig. 13-3). Progression involves a spiral rotation of the body, so that no upper and lower surfaces can be recognized. There is, however, one point on the cell surface where the plasma membrane and pellicle are specialized as a pore through which particles enter the protoplasm. Since this mouth-like opening is part way back on one side of Paramecium, this surface is designated the **oral** surface; opposite it is the **aboral** surface. Such terms are useful in describing an object with no very conspicuous landmarks, since they allow reference of other structures to definite regions of the cell.

The cilia not only drive Paramecium through the water but they set up currents in the liquid that lead food particles to the oral opening in the pellicle. There a special group of cilia slap each particle and drive it into the protoplasm, enclosed in a microscopic drop of water as a food vacuole. Active movements of the living substance of the cell then conduct the food vacuole in a definite course through the cell—usually a somewhat incomplete figure of 8 (shown by arrows in Fig. 13-2). During this migration, the food vacuole is subjected to various digestive actions, and any indigestible residue at the end of the tour

reaches a second pore in the pellicle where it is thrust out. Again digestion is intracellular. Liquid wastes join excess water from endosmosis in one or more contractile vacuoles opening to the outside through still other pores in the pellicle. In Paramecium the number of contractile vacuoles and their position is a distinctive feature of the various species. Thus the large *P. caudatum* has two, one at each end of the cell.

The rapid beat of the cilia often conceals the fact that they follow a definite rhythm. Waves of each stage in the beat cycle pass rapidly over the surface of the cell. This is not synchronous beating but waves of activity. By suitable techniques the basis for the regularity may be demonstrated. It consists of a complex system of delicate fibers like a communication network extending from each cilium to its neighbors. Ingenious experimentalists have succeeded in thrusting fine-pointed glass needles into living Paramecium cells and destroying parts of this network. The cilia controlled by isolated parts of the network then failed to maintain any agreement in rhythm with those on the more intact remainder of the animal. Clearly, a wave of stimulation proceeds along the network and the cilia respond by beating. The rate of beating is usually between 10 and 17 per second, and in consequence the cell may be drawn forward as rapidly as 2 millimeters per second.

Another special mechanism of Paramecium consists of small sac-like modifications of the pellicle; these alternate in position with the rows of cilia. Each is called a **trichocyst,** and when they are seen in action it is hard to realize that they are merely secreted substances in a single cell. For when Paramecium gets into highly adverse situations— either chemical or physical—it discharges these trichocysts. Each explodes into the surrounding water as a fine thread-like extension as long as the greatest dimension of the cell. The great numbers of discharged trichocysts provide a felt-like covering over the animal, and have been presumed to provide protection to the organism. However, Paramecium can shed the discharged trichocysts, swim away, and reload with new secretion. Under normal conditions, it appears that the trichocysts are

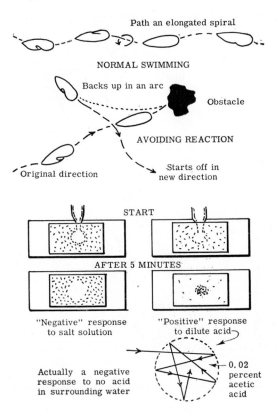

FIG. 13-3. *Even an organism consisting of a single cell is able to demonstrate unlearned responses to environmental stimuli.*

adhesive structures with sticky tips which Paramecium employs in holding to the substratum.

Paramecium, like other ciliates, reproduces asexually by elongating the cell, duplicating the nuclei, and separating the two equal halves transversely. This is **fission.** A sexual method of reproduction is used less frequently.

Paramecium is not unique in possession of these specializations of the single-cell design. Each of the features described has counterparts in other ciliated protozoans, and further complexities are common. They provide in a unicellular design the answers to problems presented regularly to each organism as it obtains energy and raw materials used in growth and reproduction. Some of the ciliated protozoans spend large portions of their life-spans in an attached condition, holding firmly to the bottom of pond or sea, or to some solid

object near the surface. The bell animalcule, Vorticella, provides a good example of such attachment (Fig. 13-4). The cell of Vorticella is approximately conical, with a row of particularly long cilia in a spiral on the flat end of the cone, creating a feeding current in the water that brings food particles to the oral opening. At the tip of the cone, the cell has a collapsible extension, and on the end of the extension an adhesive area. After swimming (also with the spiral of long cilia) to a new location, Vorticella turns into such a position that the tip of the cone is in contact with some solid object. There it adheres, and the adjacent region of the cell elongates into a very long spiral filament that raises the main body of the protoplasm well away from the supporting surface. In the filamentous portion of the cell is a contractile fiber under the control of the protoplasm. Through alternate contractions and passive elongations, the main body of Vorticella is thrust out in one direc-

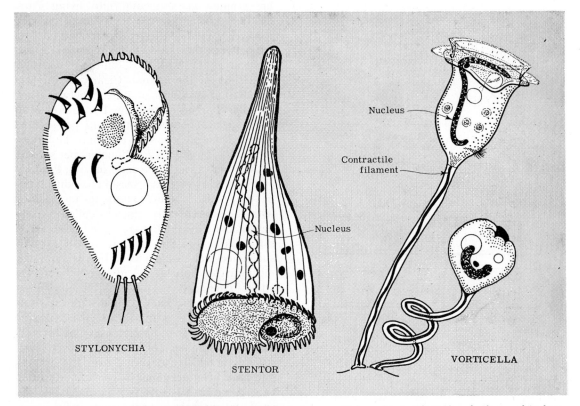

FIG. 13-4. *Examples of variation in ciliate protozoan design are Stylonychia (with its fused cilia used in leaping), Stentor (the "horn animal"), and Vorticella (the "bell animalcule") which can remain attached, feeding on bacteria brought in by the whorl of cilia beating the water, or can swim around actively in reaching other parts of the pond.*

tion after another, while the cilia beat and bring food from the surrounding water.

Experimental studies have shown that the contractile fiber in this single cell has many of the characteristics of muscle cells in higher animals. Vorticella demonstrates a high degree of specialization of one part of its protoplasm but in doing so actually expresses only the contractility that is a feature of all living substance. Through specialization this filamentous portion of the cell has become extraordinarily efficient in this one process. But in Vorticella the division of labor ends with the modification of part of a single cell; in higher animals, still further development of new adaptations is possible through the diversification of multicellular design.

Still other ciliated protozoans show further specilizations. Some, such as Stylonychia, have a row of cilia fused into a smaller number of long spine-like processes (Fig. 13-4). These are on the surface of the cell that rests regularly on the bottom of the pond or the surface of some submerged object. By pressing the tips of these spine-like processes into the substratum, and by flicking the whole row backward, Stylonychia leaps ahead. The mechanism also operates in the reverse direction. The development of these special structures not only provides the cell with an additional speed and mode of locomotion, but also involves it in a definite orientation within the water. The area of the cell against the substratum can now be called a lower, ventral surface; opposite it on the "back" of the animal is the dorsal surface. The organism now has also a right side and a left, the lateral surfaces. Thus the designations dorsal, ventral, lateral, anterior, and posterior are used regularly throughout the animal kingdom— even for single cells, when the organization allows the distinctions to be applied consistently.

3. FLAGELLATES

These organisms move about by means of one or more whiplash-like **flagella**, with which the cell reaches out into the water and draws itself along. Some kinds contain chloroplastids; others do not. Botanists tend to claim types with chlorophyll; they place these organisms in the algal phylum Chlorophyta if they store

starch, in the phylum Euglenophyta if they store oils or the polysaccharides glycogen and paramylum. Zoologists tend to claim all flagellates as protozoans of class Mastigophora.

Euglena and Kin

This flagellate in countless numbers gives the turbid green color to stagnant water such

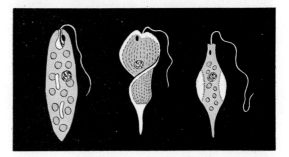

Fig. 13-5. *Euglena* (left) *and its relatives reach out into the water with the single flagellum and pull themselves along. The shaded granules are chloroplastids, the black spot the stigma.*

as duck ponds. In this way it is familiar to most people as a mass of green, although seldom as individual cells.

The active cell is spindle-shaped, with a highly flexible plasma membrane that bends and stretches as the organism moves (Fig. 13-5). The nucleus is relatively small, and several dozen minute chloroplastids shift around in the cytoplasm. At one end of the cell are four special structures: (1) a reddish *stigma* (often called an "eyespot") that seems to be part of the mechanism whereby Euglena can orient toward a light source; (2) a contractile vacuole; (3) a long, whip-like flagellum which lashes the water in complex rhythmic patterns and draws the cell after it through the pond; and (4) a small conical indentation, the "gullet," which appears to be a functionless vestige of a food-trapping device such as is used by many Euglena-like flagellates that lack chloroplastids.

Euglena's movements are primarily in one direction. Hence the cell shows polarity, with an advancing and a retreating end. No other symmetry is obvious, however, and in locomotion the cell rotates on its longitudinal axis.

FIG. 13-6. *Flagellates with many long, hair-like flagella inhabit the digestive tract of termites and woodroaches, there serving the larger organism by digesting cellulose in ingested wood fibers.*

As observed under the microscope, Euglena seems to show only random movements. But if a jar of pond water containing these organisms is illuminated from only one side, the green color that shows the organisms' abundance gradually becomes deepest at the illuminated side. On a cloudy day, Euglena migrates toward the surface of the ponds in which it thrives; at night the movements become more truly random and the organisms spread toward the bottom as though by diffusion. Too bright a light, such as direct sunshine, repels Euglena.

Many of the Euglena-like organisms lack chlorophyll and plastids too. These types are chiefly scavengers in fresh water, the sea, or in soil moisture.

Food storage in Euglena-like cells is in the form of paramylum (a polysaccharide quite different from starch) or glycogen or various fatty oils. Reproduction in the entire group is by duplication of the flagellum, stigma, gullet, contractile vacuole and nucleus, followed by longitudinal fission. No sexual activity is known in any of the Euglena-like organisms.

Flagellates with Many Flagella

Some chlorophyll-lacking flagellates have so many long flagella that they appear draped in hair (Fig. 13-6). Most of these organisms are found in the digestive tract of multicellular animals, and there serve an important function. Certain cockroaches and most termites, for example, depend upon these flagellates to digest the cellulose of the wood swallowed by the insect. The flagellates, on the other hand, benefit from the continual supply of wood fibers chewed by the insect. The products of cellulose digestion supply raw materials and energy to both the flagellates and the arthropods; neither organism can get along without the other. Some of the colonial habits of termites, in fact, seem due to the necessity for sharing the intestinal flagellates—implanting cultures in the gut of each newly-hatched or newly-molted insect.

Reproduction of these flagellates with many flagella is entirely asexual, by longitudinal fission.

Parasitic Flagellates

A fair number of parasitic flagellates are known and claimed by the zoologists. Few have received as much attention as Trypanosoma, a blood parasite of antelope and other mammals in the plains region of Africa (Fig. 13-7). Under ordinary circumstances, Trypanosoma lives in the plasma of these animals and absorbs energy-giving substances and oxygen from this restricted, aquatic site. Blood-sucking flies of the genus Glossina (called *tsetse flies*) bite the infected antelopes and obtain the parasitic Trypanosoma as well. The protozoan reacts to its new environment by a slight change in form, and by migration through the fly into its salivary glands. This change and migration requires about 20 days. If, after this time, the fly bites another antelope, it pours a little saliva (and the reorganized Trypanosoma organisms) into the wound, thus infecting a new animal. The fly is said to be the vector in this parasite cycle, and the antelopes are the host organisms.

Trypanosomes would be of no great importance to man but for the fact that tsetse flies bite human beings also, and man is unfortunately another suitable host for Trypanosoma. The multiplication of trypanosomes in human blood liberates toxic materials that result in trypanosome fever. Soon the protozoans invade the central nervous system, too. Depletion of food supplies there and accumulation of poisonous substances produce a lethargic condition of the victim, which increases as "sleeping sickness" and ends in death. Medically, the disease is known as *African Trypanosomiasis.*

The trypanosome itself is an elongated cell, somewhat longer than the diameter of a human blood corpuscle; on one end it usually bears a single flagellum which turns sharply to run parallel to the length of the cell, and is attached to the body of the trypanosome by a thin membrane. Undulations of the membrane, produced by movement of the flagellum, propel the trypanosome through the blood plasma or the salivary secretion of the tsetse fly. Thus the structure of Trypanosoma shows few visible complexities. Its life history, on the other hand, demonstrates how well the single-cell design can become adapted to highly specialized ways of life.

Chlamydomonas and Kin

Flagellates with chlorophyll in plastids and *two* flagella usually possess chloroplastids of forms as unusual as those of the non-motile green algae (Fig. 13-8); for this and other reasons, botanists place these flagellates in

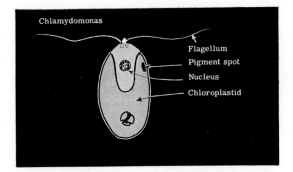

FIG. 13-8. *Chlamydomonas, with its two flagella, displays a single cup-shaped chloroplastid as well as a red pigment spot.*

the phylum Chlorophyta. They store starch, reproduce asexually by transverse rather than longitudinal fission, and have a sexual method

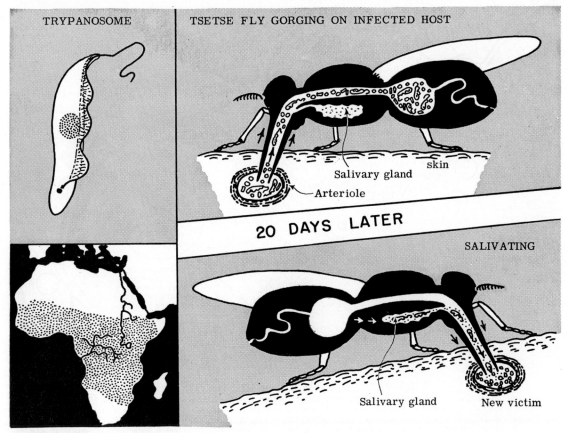

FIG. 13-7. *The trypanosome, a special unicellular organism, is responsible for trypanosomiasis ("sleeping sickness") in the area of Africa indicated by stippling. The tsetse fly serves as a transferring agent (vector) and is itself essential for development of the infective stages of the unicellular parasite.*

of reproduction as well. This is discussed on p. 311.

Many flagellates of this type build simple colonies (Photo 140), and the whole colony rolls along or swims through the combined activity of the many flagella. Gonium and Volvox (Photo 140) are common colonial forms in pond water. In each the colony has enough organization to show an axis of symmetry about which it revolves, and a direction of movement—usually in line with the axis.

4. SPORE-FORMING PARASITES

These unicellular organisms lack any direct means of locomotion, and thrive as parasites in the gut and blood stream of animals. The malaria organism is the most famous example. Usually these are classified as protozoans of class Sporozoa.

Malaria

Few parasites of mankind have done more to sap his energy, make him susceptible to other diseases, and limit the areas in which his civilizations might thrive than the malarial organism, Plasmodium.

In cellular detail, the mature parasite is apparently simple. Its life cycle is complex, and matches closely the habits of the vector mosquito, Anopheles (Fig. 13-9). By way of

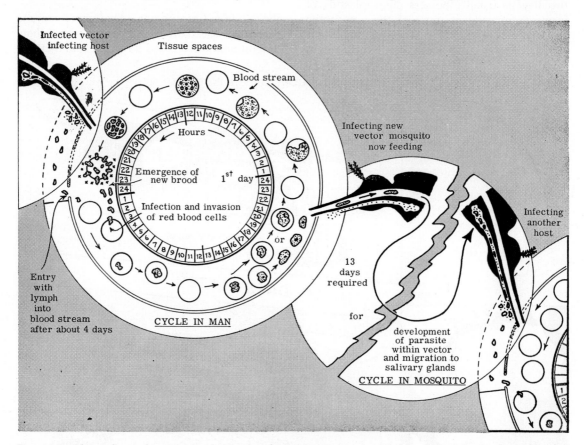

FIG. 13-9. *Plasmodium, the causative agent of malarias, has a complex life history both in the warm-blooded victim and in the mosquito which serves as vector. After entry into a bird or mammal from an infected mosquito's saliva, the malaria organism enters the bone marrow and there matures; soon its descendents invade the blood stream and attack red blood cells, multiplying within these (see also Fig. 4-5). This, the erythrocytic cycle, often follows a course of clock-like regularity; at emergence of each new brood, poisons are released into the plasma and the victim develops a new bout of chills and fever. Some of the new generations change into a form which can infect a new mosquito; others invade liver cells, and may remain dormant there for months, as a source of future relapses. Within the mosquito the Plasmodium organism undergoes sexual reproduction and changes to a form which can be introduced into a new bird or mammal when the mosquito bites.*

the victim's blood stream, the parasite reaches all tissues of the body. At first it appears to mature and reproduce in the bone marrow. Soon it returns to the general circulation, and in an ameba-like form invades red blood cells. Once inside it grows until almost all of the cell volume is occupied by parasite. Then Plasmodium reproduces, and the products break out of the cell into the plasma, ready to invade new red cells. At the time of emergence, quantities of toxic material are liberated, bringing on fever in the victim. Emergence frequently is so synchronized that cycles of chills and fever alternate with periods of seeming recovery.

When the disease is well established, certain of the parasite cells take up residence in the liver, and may remain there for months as a source of relapsing infection. Other Plasmodium cells become passive. If these latter are imbibed in a blood meal by the right kind of mosquito (Anopheles), they give rise to new generations of the parasite within the insect—including sexual phases. In a few days parasite cells enter the mosquito's salivary glands, ready for injection into a new host.

Some types of malaria affect birds exclusively; others attack mammals. A considerable number of comparable organisms are known.

Control of protozoan parasites requires not only a familiarity with their form, so that they can be recognized, but also an understanding of the chain of events in the life cycle so that the most vulnerable points may be attacked. Ridding the malaria-infested areas of the Anopheles mosquito removes the vector. Great strides have been made in this direction (Fig. 13-10). Quinine or atabrine or chloroquin, however, affect the Plasmodium organisms in human blood and prevent disease symptoms from appearing. So far trypanosomes have become immune to each drug with which control was sought.

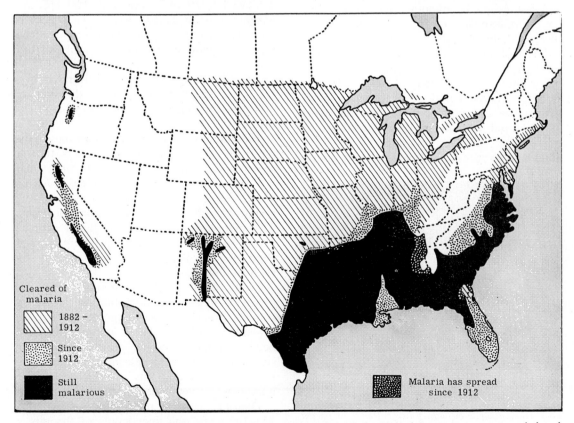

Cleared of malaria

1882–1912

Since 1912

Still malarious

Malaria has spread since 1912

FIG. 13-10. *Past and present distribution of malaria in Canada and the United States is a measure of the effectiveness of mosquito control and of the difficulty of such measures in some parts of the country.*

5. YEASTS

These are fermentative organisms without means of locomotion. Most of them are saprophytic; a few are parasites; all reproduce by budding. Usually they are placed in a subdivision of the fungi in the plant phylum Eumycophyta.

To most people, yeasts are known as the formative agents of carbon dioxide that "raise" bakery products, and of alcohols in breweries. Only a very few kinds are so used by man as "domestic plants." Other yeasts are "wild," and attend to the fermentative decay of fruits and many other sugary materials. All are unicellular fungi, and most of them can obtain energy for life either aerobically and efficiently in the presence of oxygen, or anaerobically and inefficiently in the absence of oxygen. In the former they liberate carbon dioxide and water, in the latter carbon dioxide and alcohol.

Yeast grows by budding. During budding the protoplasm spreads into a protrusion from the parental cell wall, until the new and the old are of about equal size; then cell wall formation proceeds to separate the protoplasm into two parts (Fig. 13-11). The two cells thus derived may separate or cling together. Under favorable conditions the process is rapid enough to watch through the microscope. In other situations (scant food, abundant oxygen), most yeasts form **spores**

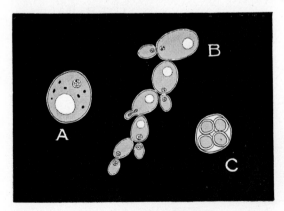

FIG. 13-11. *Each yeast cell is essentially a solitary organism, with a vacuole, glycogen granules, cytoplasm and nucleus enclosed by a chitinous cell wall (A). During rapid growth, loose colonies of parent cells and offspring are developed (B). Under some circumstances, drought-resistant cysts form (C).*

—usually four inside each cell; these spores withstand desiccation, allowing wind to distribute the yeast as dust particles which may fall into a new situation with abundant food.

6. DIATOMS

These are chlorophyll-containing organisms in which the green color is masked by a golden yellow accessory pigment. Locomotion is evident, but its mechanism is unknown. Each cell secretes a two-part shell of silica. Diatoms are regularly considered as a separate phylum of plants, the Chrysophyta.

In total number of individuals, diatoms probably outnumber all other unicellular green plants. They are extremely numerous in both fresh and salt water, with as many as eight million individuals to the cubic yard of water. In company with the flagellates, they serve as the food supply (directly or indirectly) for most aquatic animals and for many terrestrial forms that eat quantities of fish or crustaceans. The great blue whales, which achieve lengths of as much as 100 feet and weights as high as 145 tons, derive most of their food directly from microscopic algae, especially diatoms, which they strain from sea water.

Vitamins A and D, extracted from fish liver oils, arise initially by synthesis in diatoms and other marine unicellular plants on which these fish feed.

Individually, diatoms are strikingly symmetrical, with sculptured cell walls that fit together like the top and bottom of a small box. In addition to a single nucleus, each diatom cell possesses golden-brown plastids containing chlorophyll plus other pigments. The cytoplasm commonly encloses droplets of oil—apparently fatty materials in storage. Reproduction is complicated greatly by the skeletal covering.

Many diatoms glide smoothly along or progress in jerky motion, but no flagella or similar structures providing locomotion are evident anywhere. Their movements have been attributed to water currents caused by streaming of the protoplasm within the cell, but it is likely that this is a biological phenomenon not yet understood.

Diatoms are all of microscopic size (Photos 141-143) and the fine details of the pits in their cell walls have been used to test resolv-

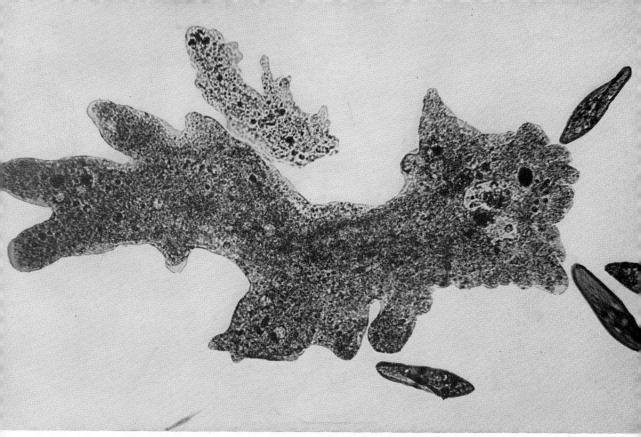

137. Two kinds of ameba (large and small) and several individuals of Paramecium.

. The silicious shells of radiolarians build up great thick-
ses of "radiolarian ooze" at the bottom of the seas. That any
anism can absorb silica from the minute amounts present in
an water, then fashion it into a transparent skeletal support
protoplasm, is a source of astonishment to many.

38. Limy shells of foraminiferans are also
roducts of single-celled animals. They too ac-
umulate to form great layers on the ocean bot-
om.

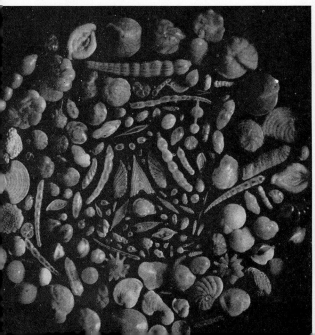

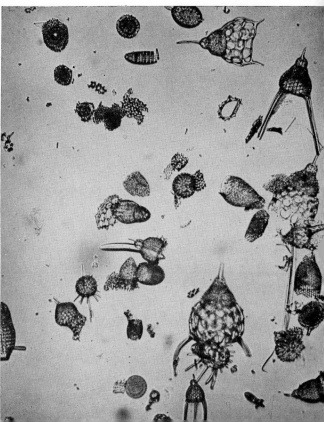

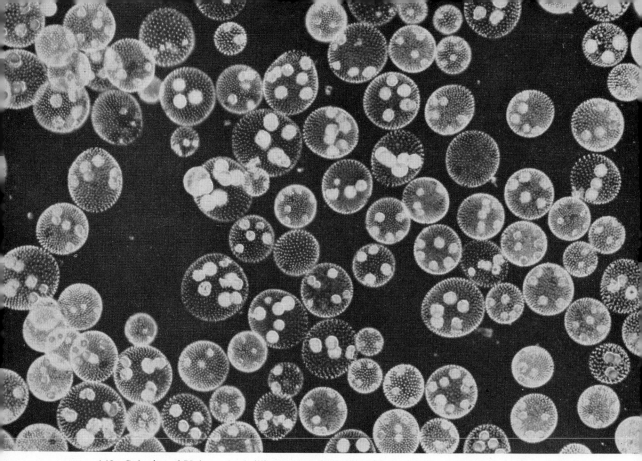

140. Colonies of Volvox are brilliant green from the chloroplastids of the many cells in each colony. They roll across the microscope field very rapidly as flagella on each cell whip the water surrounding them.

SPECIALIZATIONS

AMONG SIMPLER

ALGAE

142. One of the more slender diatoms, Amphipleura, when enlarged 900X, becomes a test object for good microscope lenses.

141. Circles of diatoms were favorite preparations of early microscopists, who delighted in the symmetry and fine detail of these silica-shelled plant cells.

143. A circular diatom, Arachnodiscus, enlarged 330X, shows an intricate pattern of pitted walls. Ten of this type can be seen in Photo 141.

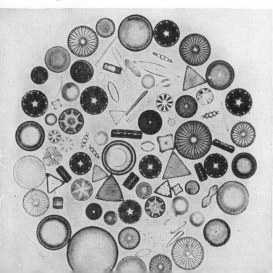

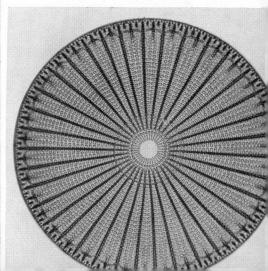

ing power in microscopes (a well-designed lens shows more detail). When diatoms die, their cell walls disintegrate but the silica skeleton within the walls remains. It sinks to the bottom, and through centuries may build up a bed of **diatomaceous earth** as much as 3,000 feet deep. Diatomaceous earth is used extensively in manufacturing neutral filters for removing bacteria from liquids, or impurities from oils and syrups, and also as the absorbent material mixed with nitrocellulose in dynamite. The oil droplets from dead diatoms of past ages have contributed extensively to the accumulation of petroleum. As such, these microscopic organisms are of great economic importance, and something of their nature should be appreciated by well-informed people.

7. NON-MOTILE GREEN ALGAE (phylum Chlorophyta)

On land the unicellular plant comparable in conspicuousness to Euglena in ponds is Protococcus. The greenish color of rough bark on the north side of tree trunks is due principally to this alga. It thrives where the sun does not reach it while at full daytime brilliance. Protococcus is undoubtedly the commonest terrestrial alga in the world.

Each of the approximately spherical cells is bounded by a nonliving, secreted, cellulose cell wall (Fig. 13-12). A single, large, cup-shaped chloroplastid contains its chlorophyll, and surrounds the nucleus almost completely. The two together occupy much of the cell's volume.

During dry or cold seasons, the protoplasm loses most of its water and suspends all possible activities. But when the air becomes humid or when rain wets the cells, water is absorbed. Soon growth and reproduction oc-

cur. Some cells break away and are carried by wind or other agents to new sites, where they lodge and begin new green areas.

In ponds are numerous other non-motile green algae. Some of them are handsomely symmetrical (Fig. 13-12), and known as desmids. Others, such as Chlorella, are interesting for other reasons. They have been adopted by a variety of animals which enclose them superficially and use them as a captive source of photosynthetic oxygen and perhaps also organic compounds. Man has used Chlorella in studying photosynthesis, and as a possible organism to domesticate as a food (see p. 484).

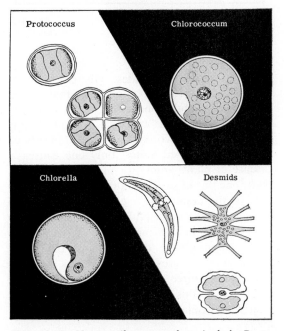

Fig. 13-12. *Non-motile green algae include Protococcus—inhabitant of tree bark surfaces—the commonest terrestrial alga, and Chlorella in ponds.*

II. ORGANISMS WITH NO DEFINITE NUCLEUS

1. BACTERIA

These are saprophytes and parasites[1] with a clearly cellular organization. All of them

[1] A few anomalous types are included with the bacteria: the "purple bacteria" which carry on photosynthesis, using a purple pigment, "bacteriochlorophyll"; the "iron bacteria" and the "sulfur bacteria" which are chemotrophic (see p. 75).

can be cultured on artificial media, and their size range falls usually between 1 and 5μ. They are assigned to a plant phylum by themselves, the Schizomycophyta.

Bacteria probably outnumber as separate individuals any other type of organism. In 1942 an eminent bacteriologist published a conservative estimate of the bacterial popula-

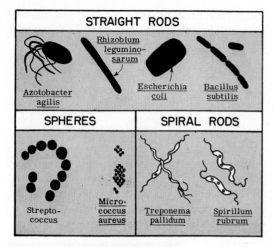

STRAIGHT RODS		
Azotobacter agilis	Rhizobium leguminosarum	Escherichia coli · Bacillus subtilis

SPHERES	SPIRAL RODS	
Streptococcus · Micrococcus aureus	Treponema pallidum	Spirillum rubrum

Fig. 13-13. *Bacteria can be distinguished by their shape, but more effectively by their nutritional requirements and staining reactions.*

tion of the United States. His calculations showed 10,031,000 quintillion that were "harmless, useful or necessary," as compared with 308 quintillion "bad ones." A quintillion is 10^{24}. In other words, of every 30,000 bacteria in the United States, only one causes a disease of plant, animal or mankind. By contrast, one out of every 17,000 human inhabitants of the country is a convicted murderer.

The "harmless, useful or necessary" bacteria engage in one main type of work: decomposition of the dead remains of plants and animals, wherever these remains may be. The same source of statistics (cited in the references to this chapter) gave an analysis of bacterial population according to habitat: For every

　　1.0 on a live plant, there are
　　5.6 in inland fresh waters,
　　62.5 in the human gut,
　　62.5 in the gut of other animals, and
　　62,500 in the soil.

Each bacterial cell (Fig. 13-13) is typically a single unit, which may have a spherical, rod-like, or spiral form. The names **coccus, bacillus,** and **spirillum** have been used widely for these three shapes of bacterial cells, but modern usage classifies bacteria into more than a hundred genera.

Ever since presentation of the "germ the-ory" of human ailments in the late 1870's and early 1880's, bacteria have been uppermost in the popular mind as causative agents of disease. Some of the genera have come to be known to many laymen, as well as the difficulties they cause:

Gonococcus	Gonorrhea
Meningococcus	Meningitis
Micrococcus (= Staphylococcus)	Boils
Pneumococcus	Lobar pneumonia
Streptococcus	Scarlet fever, septic sore throat
Various bacilli (each specific)	Botulism
	Diphtheria
	Gas gangrene
	Paratyphoid fever
	Tetanus (lockjaw)
	Tuberculosis
	Typhoid fever
Special spirilla a "vibrio"	Cholera
a "spirochete"	Syphilis
a different spirochete	Yaws

About 1,400 different species of bacteria have been identified, but of these only about 150 are clearly disease-producers (**pathogens,** from the Greek *pathos* = suffering, *genes* = to give birth), including all those affecting man and every plant and animal in which he is directly interested (see Fig. 4-4).

Beneficial bacteria are less familiar to most people. Those which are essential to economic processes were mentioned briefly on p. 27. Their significance in maintenance of soil fertility is almost incalculably great (see pp. 27, 402, 473).

The role of bacteria within the intestinal tract is becoming clearer every year. Those in the human gut appear to furnish our requirements of Vitamin K and possibly other substances. The abundant *Escherichia coli,* however, may be a bacillus which is along only "for the ride." It is still useful as an indicator of pollution (see p. 483).

The rumen of the cow and other ruminants has been found to be charged with active bacteria on which the animal's nutrition depends. The hay the cow eats is indigestible until these bacteria accomplish the initial enzymatic splitting of cellulose. Thereafter the animal not only continues the digestion and absorption of the carbohydrate but gains amino acids from the bacteria in two ways: (1) from excess amino acids liberated by the bacteria as they digest protein substances in the hay; and (2) by digestion of the protein content of the bacteria themselves, after the microbes have been killed by the cow's digestive agents farther along the gut. Hence any change in a cow's diet that favors the bacteria in the rumen is likely to be helpful to the cow's nourishment.

Recently it was learned that a hay diet supplies too little protein for maximum efficiency of these bacteria. Adding cheap ammonium salts to the hay was tried, to see if the bacteria could use this as a source of needed nitrogen. They could, but cows did not enjoy the hay as much. Low-cost urea was then substituted. The cows liked the flavor, and the cellulose-splitting bacteria in the rumen increased the food available to the ruminant. Thousands of tons of urea are used today by dairy farmers as an additive in cattle food.

All bacteria reproduce by fission. No doubt the rapidity of this asexual process is the main reason for their economic importance. Thus the typhoid bacillus reproduces every 20 minutes, and can soon build an enormous population.

Many saprophytic bacteria are "spore-formers," and can be carried as spores in dust. Fortunately, few pathogens have this habit, and consequently diseases are somewhat easier to control. An exception is *Clostridium botulinum,* a bacillus which develops on meat, alkaline vegetables such as string beans and lima beans, under anaerobic conditions (see p. 222).

The extremely small size of bacteria renders difficult any search for structural details. Even with the aid of the electron microscope, few details can be found. Most, perhaps all, bacteria lack a definite nucleus. Instead they have granules of nucleoprotein dispersed in the protoplasm. For this reason, bacteria are said to have "diffuse nuclei."

Many bacillus-type bacteria move slowly through the beating of one or more flagella (Photo 144). The spirillum type, by contrast, may swim rapidly by spiralling through the medium, driven by flagella.

2. RICKETTSIA BODIES

Whether these are cells or even alive is debatable. All are parasites in the size range between 0.2 and 0.8μ. They can be cultured in the laboratory only in the presence of living tissue. They cause many diseases, but are not especially specific as to host.

For study, the rickettsias are usually grown on chick embryos within the egg shell, either on the allantoic membrane or the yolk sac. Typhus fever, a rickettsial disease, is primarily a disease of rats, with the rat flea as the principal vector. Under crowded, unsanitary conditions, the disease is spread to mankind, as "plague"—a factor of great importance in the past history of civilizations.

Another pathogen among the rickettsias causes Rocky Mountain spotted fever. It is primarily a disease affecting various mammals native to the western United States, and is spread by ticks. Diseases of other animals which may infect man are known as **zoonoses.** They are difficult to eradicate because the wild population serves as a reservoir from which an epidemic may spread at any time.

3. VIRUSES

When watery suspensions of bacteria are filtered through special candle-shaped ceramic devices made of diatomaceous earth, the liquid passes through in a bacteria-free condition. Clearly the pores in the filter are too small to permit passage of bacteria. But the causative agents of certain diseases can go undiminished through such a bacteriological filter. They are termed "filter-passers," or **filterable viruses,** and their size range is now known to extend downward from 0.7μ in diameter.

All viruses are strict parasites. They can be cultured only on living cells, and are highly specific as to host. Antibiotics have no effect on viruses.

So many viruses are known today that a new subdivision of microbiology—virology—has come to the fore. Viruses cause serious economic loss annually to crop plants, through "curly top" of beets, the various leaf mosaic diseases of tobacco (Photo 145), beans, and melons, and stalk mosaic disease of sugar cane. Leafhoppers, mites (Photo 114), and aphids have been shown to serve as vectors. Still other viruses cause diseases of man and his domestic animals: chickenpox, cowpox, smallpox, measles, mumps, poliomyelitis (three types), rheumatic fever, virus influenza, virus pneumonia, yellow fever, the "common cold," rabies, distemper in dogs, and ornithosis (= psittacosis) in birds and man.

The specificity of a virus may extend even to the tissue level. Thus each of the three strains of poliomyelitis virus has a characteristic attack pattern, affecting special parts of the nervous system. It was only with great difficulty that Dr. John F. Enders of Harvard Medical School "adapted" these polio viruses to grow on monkey kidney instead of brain tissue. His work earned him a Nobel Prize, and made possible in 1954 the development by Dr. Jonas Salk of the first effective vaccine against the disease.

The virus causing mosaic in tobacco leaves (Photo 145) was purified in 1935 by Dr. W. M. Stanley. He used an ordinary low-speed centrifuge to separate a clear liquid from bacteria and cell debris in his extract of diseased tobacco leaves. The fluid retained its full ability to cause the mosaic disturbance. Next the liquid was subjected to centrifugal forces of about 500,000 times the force of gravity, in an ultracentrifuge. This force is capable of precipitating the largest of organic molecules, and in the laboratory of Dr. Stanley at the Rockefeller Institute for Medical Research, threw down a sediment of almost pure virus (Photo 146). It not only had remarkable potency but also a definite form. It was a nucleoprotein, and of almost chemical purity. Yet when this substance was injected into tobacco leaves it caused component chemical substances in the living cells to transform into further virus molecules. These, in turn, spread the disease, as a sort of self-catalyzing reaction. Stanley's work, and the many investigations that have checked, verified, and extended it, drew attention to a possible bridge in the gap between living and nonliving. No conclusion can be reached until further information is available on this important problem.

Other viruses, when purified, have obvious crystalline properties that can accompany only pure substances—though each seems to be a protein of high molecular weight (Photo 148). Many, however, show no such indications even when studied under the electron microscope at high useful magnifications (Photo 147). A great range in size is evident (Fig. 13-14).

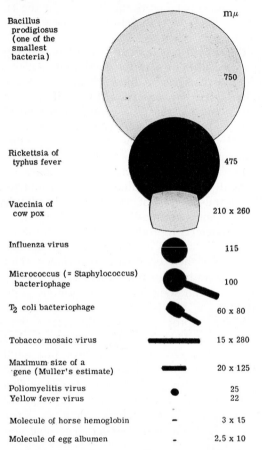

	mμ
Bacillus prodigiosus (one of the smallest bacteria)	750
Rickettsia of typhus fever	475
Vaccinia of cow pox	210 x 260
Influenza virus	115
Micrococcus (= Staphylococcus) bacteriophage	100
T_2 coli bacteriophage	60 x 80
Tobacco mosaic virus	15 x 280
Maximum size of a gene (Muller's estimate)	20 x 125
Poliomyelitis virus	25
Yellow fever virus	22
Molecule of horse hemoglobin	3 x 15
Molecule of egg albumen	2.5 x 10

FIG. 13-14. *Representative dimensions at the lower limits of size for self-reproducing organisms and substances. A human red blood cell is about 7,500 mμ in diameter, hence ten times the size of the large Bacillus prodigiosus shown.*

An additional category of submicroscopic particles was recognized in 1917 as a filter passer. It acted as a disease of bacteria, destroying them in conspicuous patches on culture plates. The name **bacteriophage** (literally "bacteria-eater") was applied, but until the development of the electron microscope little more was learned about them. Now it is evident that most of them have spherical bodies

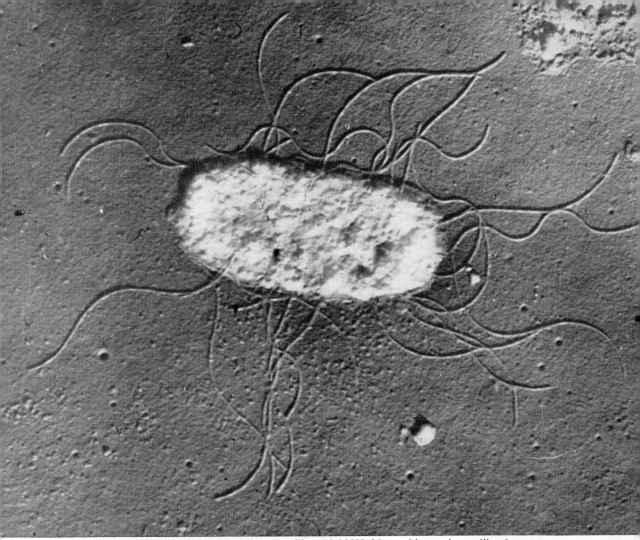

144. Electron micrograph of a flagellated bacillus; 19,000X. Note: this specimen, like those in Photos 146, 147 and 149, were shadowed obliquely with a metallic film prior to photographing them, to give an illusion of three-dimensionality.

AT THE SMALL END OF THINGS

145. A healthy leaf (*left*) of tobacco contrasted with a diseased leaf (*right*) with mosaic virus infections.

146. Electron micrograph of tobacco mosaic virus; 67,000X.

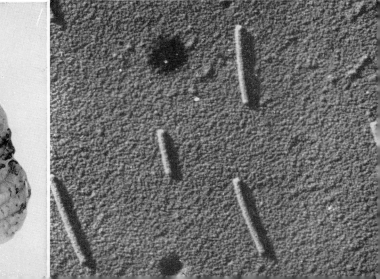

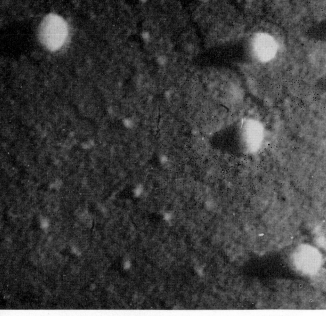 

147. Electron micrograph of influenza virus; 110,000X.   148. Bushy stunt virus crystals; low power microscope.

VIRUSES IN MANY GUISES

149. Bacteriophage particles forming in the surface protoplasm of infected colon bacilli; electron micrograph, at about 20,000X.

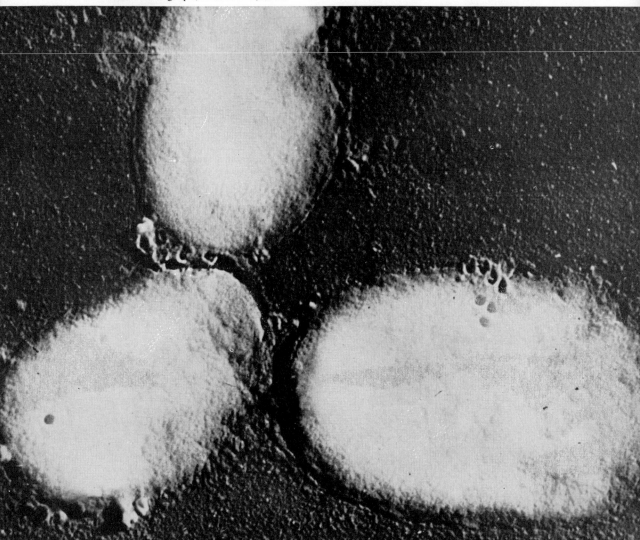

(Fig. 13-14), with short tails of various lengths. They are remarkably specific in action, attacking only definite strains of bacteria; they enter and multiply within the bacterial cell (Photo 149), destroying it completely. Breakdown of the cell is so sudden that the "phage" is said to "lyse" it and the action is called *bacteriolysis*. The extent to which bacteriophage act in a state of nature is still unknown.

Interest in viruses is twofold: (1) in learning how to reduce economic losses from the diseases they cause; and (2) in finding out how these particles operate. All of them lie at the border between the living and the non-living, consisting of protein molecules and hence violating the original form of the cell doctrine. They lack protoplasm, chromatin, and the like, hence technically are non-living. But they can and do undergo genetic changes (mutations) from forms to which some organisms are immune, to forms that can successfully invade and multiply. Or they may change in the opposite direction. These alterations may be due to rearrangement of parts of the big protein molecule, changing the enzyme form of the autocatalyst so that it operates on different substrates produced by living protoplasm.

4. COMMUNITY HEALTH

A fuller understanding of microbiology has been helpful to both medical men and the public. Popular magazines present new findings; newspapers headline each advance. Public opinion now supports changed living habits which bring about decrease in both the frequency and spread of epidemics. Usually this arises from knowledge of the mode of transmission of pathogens.

Spread occurs to only a limited extent through their own motility. Four other avenues of infection are the chief trouble-makers:

1. Through direct contact between an infected individual and a new host—by handling infected meat (as in brucellosis, tularemia, and others), or by kissing and sexual intercourse, where moist mucous membranes are brought together (gonorrhea, syphilis, yaws[2]).

2. Through air-borne droplets and spores (pneumonia, tuberculosis and other respiratory diseases, measles, mumps, and others). Commonly these are atomized into the air by sneezing and coughing or by waving and shaking infected handkerchiefs.

3. Through transmission by insect vectors such as the body louse (typhus fever), mosquito (malaria, yellow fever), and housefly (typhoid, paratyphoid, and possibly poliomyelitis), or by pets (cats, dogs, parrots, and the like).

4. Through food and water contaminated by sewage, by food handlers, by "fomites" such as dirty eating utensils or towels (cholera, amebic dysentery, paratyphoid, and typhoid).

To a considerable extent control measures correspond to these:

1. **Isolation** of individuals with the disease, so that they will not transmit it to others (chickenpox, diphtheria, gonorrhea, influenza, leprosy, measles, mumps, poliomyelitis, scarlet fever, smallpox, typhoid fever, and whooping cough), and sometimes **quarantine** of all persons known to have been exposed to a diseased individual until a full incubation period has elapsed without appearance of symptoms (diphtheria, measles, scarlet fever, smallpox, and whooping cough).

2. **Disinfection** of everything touched by the patient, and of the clothing and hands of anyone in contact with the patient or with anything that the patient has touched. Everything in the rooms occupied by the patient needs to be disinfected after the patient is no longer a source of infection. Thorough cleansing, using an antiseptic solution or spray, is usually sufficient. Complete renovation of walls, floors, ceilings, and furnishings is recommended after diphtheria and a few other diseases.

3. Ultraviolet light has proven highly beneficial in decreasing air-borne infections and is used routinely in many lavatories, school rooms, surgical operating rooms, and hospital areas.

---

[2] Yaws, like syphilis, is a spirochete infection transmitted by contact. It is widespread in many tropical areas. Often it is deliberately "transplanted" from one individual to another, to produce scars for purposes of adornment. Where natives have open lesions ("sores"—though they feel no pain), this is easily accomplished.

4. Recognition and control of carriers who can transmit a disease without showing obvious symptoms (typhoid fever, syphilis, and so on). Tests to locate these individuals are particularly important with domestic servants and food handlers in public eating places.

5. Immunization by vaccination (as for smallpox), or serum inoculation (as for diphtheria, rabies, tetanus, whooping cough).

6. Development of surer, faster curative measures.

7. Water inspection and purification programs—through chlorinating, filtration and storage. Mere storage in a protected reservoir usually results in the death of all pathogens within 30 days.

8. Milk inspection and pasteurization. Milk may carry bacteria of the Salmonella group (which cause acute irritation of the digestive tract), organisms of brucellosis (undulant fever), diphtheria, tuberculosis, typhoid and others. Consistently clean handling of milk from healthy cows (brucellosis-free, tuberculin-tested) should be followed regularly by pasteurization, since this process does no damage whatever to the milk, kills pathogens, and also reduces the activity of nonpathogens such as those that cause souring. Pasteurization consists of heating the milk to 140 degrees F. (60 degrees C.) for half an hour, or 176 degrees F. (80 degrees C.) for one minute, followed by rapid cooling to 50 degrees F. (10 degrees C.) or lower. At this point the milk should be sealed in sterile containers and delivered, then kept chilled until used.

9. Licensing and frequent inspection of all organizations handling food—whether manufacturing or distributing it. This involves canneries, butcher shops, bakeries, restaurants, and the like. One of the most potent toxins known must be guarded against constantly wherever foods contain significant amounts of protein—hence meats, cottage cheese, cream cheese, whipped cream, olives, and meat substitutes including beans, peas, and corn, where these are not kept frozen. The toxin is produced by a bacterium called *Clostridium botulinum,* is tasteless and odorless, and is not destroyed by ordinary cooking. The death rate from **botulism** or "food toxemia" is very high, and since antitoxins must be given before the symptoms develop (as also in tetanus and rabies), and no one knowingly eats food containing the toxins, treatment is of little use. Botulism from home-canned foods is a distinct probability if the foods and containers are not adequately sterilized. Botulism from commercially canned foods is now practically unknown because of the precautions taken under supervision of bacteriologists and chemists.

SUGGESTED READING (see pp. 505-511)

Classics and Milestones: Leeuwenhoek, Stanley.

Recent and Informative: Astbury, 1951; Bodian, 1950; Bovarnick, 1955; Burkholder, 1952; Burnet, 1951, 1953; Calkins, 1932; Dubos, 1949, 1955; Emerson, 1952; Gray, 1955; Kopac, 1950; Long, 1955; Luria, 1955; Lwoff, 1954; Maramorosch, 1953; Melnick, 1953; Moog, 1948; Morrison, 1949; Pollard, 1954; Pappenheimer, 1952; Pramer, 1955; Rahn, 1945; Raper, 1952; Russell, 1952; Salk, 1955; Stent, 1953; Went, 1955; Wood, 1951; Wyckoff, 1951.

14 · Multicellular Thallophytes

1. BLUE-GREEN ALGAE. 2. GREEN ALGAE. 3. BROWN ALGAE. 4. RED ALGAE. SUMMARY ON MULTICELLULAR ALGAE. 5. FUNGI—ALGA-LIKE FUNGI, SAC FUNGI, CLUB FUNGI. 6. LICHENS. 7. SLIME MOLDS. SUMMARY ON MULTICELLULAR FUNGI.

IN ADDITION to unicellular forms, the thallophyte subkingdom of plants includes a wide range of others. For convenience they can be lumped as algae, fungi, lichens, and slime molds. Most of the algae are aquatic; all of them possess chlorophyll; their architectural designs include thread-like chains of cells **(filaments)**, flat sheets **(thalli)**, or somewhat more three-dimensional bodies such as are familiar among the seaweeds and kelps. The fossil record shows clearly that algae are the most ancient type of multicellular vegetation on earth.

Fungi are primarily terrestrial saprophytes, aiding bacteria in decay processes; none of them have chlorophyll; the only part of a fungus ordinarily seen is the reproductive body in which spores are elaborated.

Lichens are cooperative organizations consisting of a meshwork of fungus strands and an enmeshed population of alga cells.

Slime molds behave like giant amebas during their feeding stages, and inhabit moist woodlands; in reproduction they erect complicated spore-cases, the products from which are distributed by the wind.

The architecture and life histories of these various thallophytes agree in certain features contrasting with the "higher" plants. All of them get along without roots, stems, leaves, flowers, fruits, or even embryonic stages in development. Most of them are attached to the substratum, but this anchorage is achieved through adhesion of individual cells or through a firm clasping of irregularities by parts of the plant. Division of labor is at a minimum. Food materials are synthesized or absorbed by the individual cells, or passed from the "haves" to the "have-nots" by a combination of secretion and absorption rather than through the assistance of special conducting cells.

Since the structural development of the thallophytes is comparatively simple, life-history details and physiological processes (such as pigment formation) are more helpful in grouping like with like. Seven main types have been recognized:

1. BLUE-GREEN ALGAE (Cyanophyta)

Although the most obvious feature of the blue-green algae is their blackish green color —caused by the presence of a dark blue masking pigment called phycocyanin—their true distinction is in an ability to manage with the least division of labor to be found in any multicellular plant. The individual cells contain no plastids, and the blue pigment as well as the chlorophyll are dispersed in the protoplasm. Granules and short filaments of nucleoprotein are found scattered through the cell substance rather than organized into a definite nucleus. These characteristics have convinced biologists that the blue-green algae are by far the simplest of multicellular green plants, and represent a style of architecture antedating the development of a distinct nucleus and plastids. As such they are the most ancient type of chlorophyll-bearing plant alive today.

In spite of this obvious simplicity in organization, the blue-green algae must be considered highly successful. They are widespread in fresh water. Some are amazingly tolerant of high temperatures (to 85° C. = 185° F.) and thrive in thermal springs such as those of Yellowstone National Park. These tolerant al-

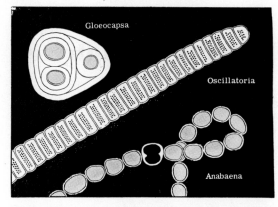

FIG. 14-1. *Representative blue-green algae* (see text).

gae precipitate calcium and magnesium salts as a porous rock (travertine), which may be colored in many pastel hues. One of the few marine types of blue-green algae has a red pigment as well, and gives the color for which the Red Sea is named. Additional members of the phylum thrive on the surface of damp soil and wet rocks. A few have invaded the digestive tracts of man and other animals, and live there as mild parasites. Otherwise the chief detrimental features found in the phylum arise from the unpleasantly fishy flavor and odor they may give to drinking water, or the occasional poisoning of cattle which swallow large numbers of certain blue-greens from stagnant pools. Some blue-greens add to soil fertility by utilizing nitrogen directly from the atmosphere, and can have importance in wetland agriculture, as in rice fields.

Blue-green algae store food as glycogen rather than starch. Their cell walls are double, and consist of an inner layer which may contain cellulose, plus an outer layer rich in pectic substances resembling gelatine. This latter holds water, making the wall thick, and gives the alga a slippery surface. The outer layer may be formed in successive coatings like an excretion and then degenerate into a slime covering the entire plant. Under adverse conditions, the individual cell may produce a drought-resistant wall, allowing it to be distributed in a desiccated state as a spore. Asexual reproduction is the only type known in Cyanophyta.

The multicellular habit is very loose in most blue-greens. Gloeocapsa, in fact, is often

described as unicellular, although the descendents from each original cell usually remain together. The "parent" cell divides within its slimy transparent coating, and each of the daughter cells elaborates a new gelatinous cover. A second division produces a total of four cells, but again the newly-separated units coat themselves. Thus a third layer is laid down between the inner cell walls and the pond water (Fig. 14-1).

In Nostoc, the cells adhere closely in filaments within a common gelatinous envelope. The mass may come to include dozens of separate filaments in a soft blue-green ball large enough to handle with forceps. Nostoc is often responsible for the slippery character of rocks near a waterfall, where spray permits growth in continuously humid air. At intervals in a filament, Nostoc develops large empty cells, which seem to be weak links favoring fragmentation—a major method of reproduction.

Oscillatoria is a common blue-green on flowerpots. It consists of long slender filaments with a comparatively thin outer layer to the walls. The individual cells are short and drum-shaped, packed closely into a smooth chain. The name Oscillatoria comes from the gentle swaying movements shown by each filament. Apparently this waving action is due to concerted changes in the shape of successive cells along the filament. At intervals, Oscillatoria may secrete mucilaginous material between cells, providing weak points at which fragmentation occurs.

Although the structure of blue-greens is never complex, some kinds have a branching habit. This may be either a false type of branching, each side member being another filament adhering by its terminal empty cell, or it may be true branching. A few genera build checkerboards of cells with fused walls.

2. GREEN ALGAE (Chlorophyta)

Division of labor is much more evident within the cells of green algae. The nucleus is distinct. All pigments are held in plastids. Starch is stored in special parts of each chloroplastid, and the chloroplastids themselves reach a complexity of form not equalled elsewhere in the plant kingdom. As a result, some of the green algae have been highly regarded as objects of beauty to be studied with the compound microscope. Their green color is usually clear, and the plants seem clean rather than slimy.

All multicellular green algae are delicate plants which must be buoyed up by water, either in the ocean, or in ponds and quiet parts of lakes. Some have a "holdfast" with which they cling to the bottom. Others drift freely with the water. A few, such as stonewort, accumulate lime in their cells and contribute to the formation of marl.

Many of the green algae consist of unbranched slender filaments, as in Ulothrix, Spirogyra (Fig. 14-2), and Oedogonium. Others are branched, and, as in stonewort, may show an approach toward stem-like specializations. Flat plates of cells are characteristic of some genera; this may be at the microscopic level and circular, as in Coleochaeta, or large and familiar enough to have a common name among beachcombers, as in "sea lettuce" (Ulva—Fig. 14-3).

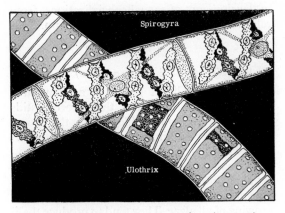

Fig. 14-2. *Representative green algae* (see text).

Filamentous, free-drifting, green algae fragment as a vegetative means of reproduction. But all genera also engage in sexual reproduction. And in this a whole series can be traced

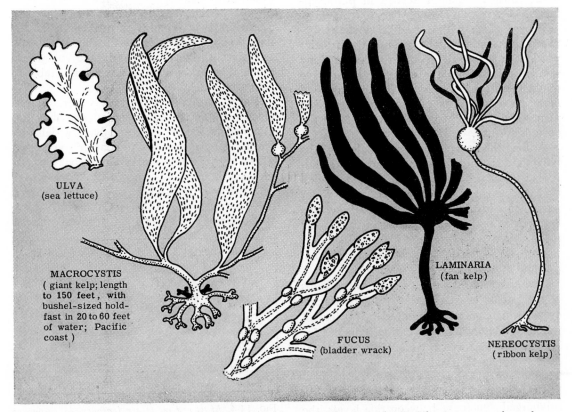

Fig. 14-3. *The larger seaweeds have characteristic forms. Of the types shown, Ulva is a green alga, whereas the others are all brown algae.*

in development of sexual specializations, from relatively simple to highly complex (pp. 312-313).

3. BROWN ALGAE (Phaeophyta)

Individual cells of brown algae contain a nucleus and plastids. But the chloroplastids contain, in addition to chlorophyll, the brown pigment fucoxanthin, which gives these plants their characteristic color.

A small number of brown algae are microscopic filaments. Most, however, are large and conspicuous along the seacoast, as the rankest growing of all algae. They tend to produce thalli many cells thick, with a tough, elastic, secreted covering that protects them from mechanical damage and from desiccation when exposed by the receding tide. All but a few species are marine, and many possess specialized floats in the thallus. Into these chambers they secrete gas, which keeps the plant extended in the water toward the light needed in photosynthesis.

Brown algae with rope-like portions between the point of anchorage and the broader portions of the thalli often develop long slender cells within the cylindrical part. No doubt these special cells aid in carrying food materials from parts of the plant receiving plenty of light to living cells farther from the ocean's surface.

Among the conspicuous brown algae of the Atlantic coast are the great ribbons of Laminaria, 10 or 15 feet in length and as much as 8 inches in width; they drift with water movements just beyond the rocks at low tide. Another is rockweed, Fucus, clinging to the rocks between tide marks (Photo 150). Sargassum, for which the Sargasso Sea was named, is found attached in deeper water.

The giants of the brown algae are the kelps of the Pacific coast. Biggest of all is Macrocystis, which may be anchored in 60 feet of water and extend its flat floating branches for 300 feet at the surface. Nereocystis, the "sea-otter's cabbage," has floats as big as a canteloupe which buoy up the ends of its long blades; most of the plant, however, is well submerged. On rocks between tide levels, the sea palm Postelsia manages to hold its place,

yielding to each wave but raising itself erect between one and the next.

Life histories of brown algae include two different "generations" of each species. These generations may have a similar appearance or be very unlike. One generation produces spores, and liberates vast numbers of them into the water; this is the **sporophyte generation.** The spores, however, cannot develop into another spore-producing plant. Instead each spore grows into a different plant, of the **gametophyte generation.** It produces **gametes** (sex cells). Union of the gametes in pairs is the sexual step in each life history. The product of the united gametes is a new sporophyte plant.

The conspicuous plant of Fucus, Laminaria, and the kelps is the sporophyte. The gametophyte generation of these familiar seaweeds is comparatively insignificant.

4. RED ALGAE (Rhodophyta)

The chloroplastids of red algae contain, in addition to chlorophyll, the masking pigment phycoerythrin. Whether its red color helps in photosynthesis remains a problem. That it may do so is suggested by the fact that many red algae thrive at depths in the sea where green algae and brown algae appear unable to get enough light.

Except for a few in fresh water, all red algae are marine. Characteristically they are attached to the bottom, and have a delicate, feathery appearance. A coarser type that grows between tide marks along rocky coasts in many countries is known as "Irish moss" (*Chondrus crispus*—Fig. 14-4); it is gathered for human food (p. 20). Other red algae, particularly in deeper and tropical waters,

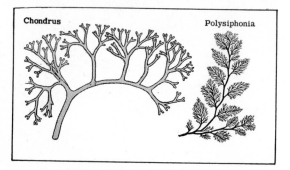

FIG. 14-4. *Most red algae are feathery, as shown at the right. The edible "Irish moss" (left), however, is much firmer in texture.*

150. Thallophytes reach their greatest structural development along rocky seacoasts. Fucus, the rockweed, is conspicuously exposed at low tide. In the foreground is a ribbon of Laminaria, torn loose by a storm; its holdfast is draped over the rock at the left.

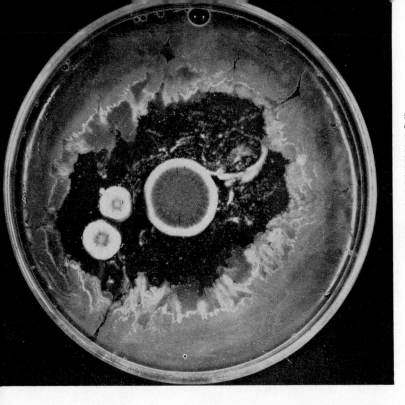

151. The dime-sized central area and two smaller disc-shaped patches to the left are colonies of the mold *Penicillium notatum*, from which penicillin is obtained. The dark region surrounding the colonies is almost free of bacteria, indicating the distance to which the antibiotic has diffused and inhibited bacterial growth; beyond the region of inhibition, bacteria have made a cloudy mass on the culture medium in this inverted Petri dish. The zone of inhibition is the phenomenon observed by Dr. Alexander Fleming in 1925, a discovery which led to recognition of antibiosis, medical use of penicillin, knighthood, and a Nobel prize.

FUNGI

152. These cinnamon-brown bracket fungi are at least eight years old. The rings show the extent of new growth each year.

secrete lime in such quantities that they are important in the formation of reefs. Several additional types of red algae, especially of the genus Gelidium, are the source of a gelatinous carbohydrate for which man has found many uses under the name "agar-agar" (p. 25).

Alternation of generations between a sporophyte and a gametophyte is a regular feature of reproduction in red algae. The gametophyte generation is either dominant in showing greater complexity of growth, or at least equivalent to the sporophyte generation. In many genera the life history is rendered more intricate in that the sporophyte generation is in two steps, the first step being a curious parasitic stage, the spores from which grow into a profusely branching second stage still attached to and being nourished at the expense of the gametophyte generation.

SUMMARY ON MULTICELLULAR ALGAE

All algae are dependent upon sunlight and autotrophic nutrition. They achieve large size only when buoyed up by water, and absorb their nutrients over all surfaces. In coastal, marine situations, however, the multicellular algae surpass all other plants in variety of structure and of life history.

Algal reproduction usually requires gametes or spores or both at some stage of each life cycle. Each is dependent for survival and distribution upon water. In consequence the algae large enough to attract public attention are the exceptional giants in a group of plants where small size is the general rule.

The multicellular habit among algae is clearly just an extension of tendencies evident among unicellular kinds. Both the blue-greens and greens include unicellular types as well. And to counterbalance the browns and reds, in which all modern species are multicellular, the algal group of phyla includes several which are restricted to single-celled ways of life.

5. FUNGI (Eumycophyta)

Saprophytic or parasitic habits are universal among fungi. The basic plant body is correspondingly simple: a branching mass of slender filaments. Each filament is called a **hypha,** and the mass is referred to as a **mycelium.** Ordinarily a fungus does not draw itself to man's attention until the hyphae begin to group together into a macroscopic "fruiting body" which produces spores. At this stage the mycelium has already grown extensively and accumulated reserves of stored food.

Most fungi are terrestrial (Fig. 14-5); a few are aquatic. A majority grow over the surfaces of organic matter on which decay bacteria are already active, and obtain nourishment by secreting enzymes and then absorbing the products of chemical action. Fungi can digest almost any organic compound.

Many fungi secrete also chemical substances classed as antibiotics. These stop or restrict bacterial activity near the fungus, and hence reduce competition for the available food.

Fungi that are parasitic in habit may develop special absorbing tips on branches of the mycelium, and press these tips into the protoplasm of the victim's cells. In this way the fungus gets as close as possible to its food supply.

High relative humidity is essential for fungus activity. Immense numbers of them die daily from desiccation. But those that meet suitable living conditions reproduce so prolifically that fungi are in no danger of becoming extinct. Their air-blown spores (produced either asexually or sexually) are highly resistant to drought, and form an important constituent of dust.

Members of three different classes of fungi draw attention to themselves:

Alga-like Fungi (Phycomycetes)

The vegetative portion of alga-like fungi consists of branching tubes filled with protoplasm containing many nuclei. For some reason, growth of the original cell is followed by division of the nucleus and expansion of the cytoplasm, but not by formation of cross walls. Usually the mycelium has a dense cotton-like texture.

Reproductive portions of the mycelium wall themselves off from the vegetative; the sexual and asexual reproductive cells are characteristically simple and microscopic (p. 312).

A colorless or grayish fungus growing on a fly drowned in an aquarium is usually Saprolegnia—the same organism that sometimes attacks the gills or wounds of pet fish or develops on the bodies of living aquatic insects. Adding a few crystals of copper sulfate to the aquarium water may kill the fungus without hurting the fish—or the insects.

Black mold of bread is usually Rhizopus, a harmless fungus. Spores from dust in the air settle on the bread as it cools in the bakery, and develop if the food is kept moist. Modern bakeries commonly add small quantities of calcium propionate to the dough. It has no effect on flavor or on human health, but it inhibits the growth of Rhizopus.

Among parasites of plants, the alga-like fungus attacking potatoes has greatly affected man's history (p. 30).

Sac Fungi (Ascomycetes)

The unique and distinguishing feature of sac fungi is the sac (an *ascus*) containing eight spores in a row, formed as a reproductive body after sexual union. Some sac fungi develop these spore sacs in a fruiting body large enough to see with the unaided eye; others are microscopic. Both saprophytic and parasitic styles of nutrition are common.

Ergot, a disease of wheat and barley, is due to one sac fungus (Claviceps). The powdery mildews which spread in and over leaves of lilac, phlox, willow, and the like in summer are destructive parasites. The saprophytic blue and green molds on oranges and other moist foods are more annoying than dangerous. One of them, Penicillium, is responsible for the blue color of certain cheeses, and has become highly regarded as the source of the antibiotic penicillin. Like so many other molds from which medicinally valuable substances are obtained, Penicillium is commonest as a normal inhabitant of soil (Photo 151).

A closely similar and common mold, Aspergillus, caused a fatal infection of the five Emperor penguins in the Washington zoo (July 10, 1955).

Because of their ability to form an ascus in reproduction, both brewer's yeast and the many wild yeasts that ferment cider are grouped with the sac fungi.

Saprophytic forms that may be found in woodlands include the edible "sponge mushroom" or morel, which pushes up through the soil from a mycelium growing below the surface on rotting wood. Another is the fruiting body known as a "cup fungus"—usually attached to the stick or piece of bark from which the mycelium obtained nourishment.

Club Fungi (Basidiomycetes)

The spores of club fungi are borne four (or in the cultivated mushroom, two) at a time on special club-shaped reproductive structures call *basidia*. Both saprophytic and parasitic types are common; the latter include the causative agents of corn smut, and of the red rusts of wheat.

Smuts destroy fruit or grain in which man is interested (Photos 17, 18); rusts attack the leaves and so weaken the plant that the yield of man's crop is reduced (Photo 423). In both smuts and rusts the life history is complicated in that, at various seasons, several different types of spores are produced. Rust fungi depend upon more than a single host plant; thus wheat rust requires barberry as well as the cereal (Fig. 4-3). Understanding these life history details is important in finding ways to reduce damage to man's crops.

Many club fungi form conspicuous fruiting bodies: mushrooms (toadstools), puffballs, bracket fungi. The basidia may be borne on the surfaces of radiating vertical plates open at the bottom (the "gills" of a mushroom) or stud the walls of vertical blind tubes open at the bottom (the "pores" below most bracket or shelf fungi). The spores are nipped off by the basidium, thrown with enough force to clear their neighbors, and dropped out into the breeze when the humidity is high. Each spore alighting in a place with enough moisture and suitable food can germinate into a hypha, develop a mycelium, and eventually erect a new fruiting body.

The slow subterranean growth of saprophytic mycelium is often evident in a field, woods, or even on a lawn, through the repeated crops of mushrooms rising from the periphery. After each rain the "fairy ring" of mushrooms is larger in diameter—a measure of the pace at which the mycelium is extending itself away from the central area where food has already been exhausted.

If spores of a mushroom are sowed at intervals on nutrient agar in a culture dish, cooperation between hyphae from separate spores may be demonstrated. In some mushrooms, at least, if the small mycelia developing from the various spores fail to obtain enough nourishment for each of them to form a fruiting body, they will pool their resources and produce a single large mushroom. From this one then come billions of spores, every one of them with another chance to find food and perpetuate the species.

6. LICHENS

Lichens cannot be said to be fungus or alga, since each is both (Fig. 14-5). In the cooperative association, most cells are the hyphae of the fungus partner. Usually it is a sac fungus, rarely a club fungus. The algal cells enmeshed by the hyphae may be in layers or separated. Green algae are more common components than blue-greens, but each lichen consists of one particular species of each partner. Both the fungus and the alga can be cultured separately. In reproduction they may be disseminated independently by

the wind. Factors still unknown govern the interaction of the two proper partners when they meet under field conditions, leading them to produce the characteristic lichen structure.

Lichens demonstrate particularly well the biological principle of **mutualism:** the alga benefits by protection and a prolonged water supply from the spongy fungus tissue; the fungus derives its food entirely from the excess energy stored through photosynthesis by the alga.

Although lichen architecture is relatively simple and individual plants rarely become more than a few inches across and a fraction of an inch thick, the cooperative arrangement is highly successful. Lichens grow abundantly on bare rocks in the arctic, where sunlight is available only part of the year. They manage under the harsh conditions on high mountains above the limit of trees. They encrust rocks in stone walls, and live on the bark of trees in the open. Dense mats of lichens coat

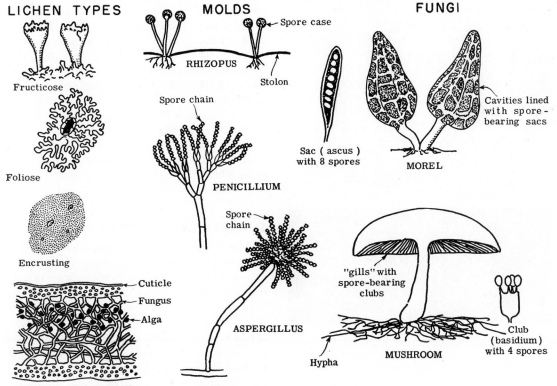

FIG. 14-5. *Representative fungi and lichens* (see text).

the branches of jungle trees in the humid tropics. Other lichens cover the ground wherever vegetation is restricted by adverse weather or certain soil conditions. Lichens, in fact, are among the first agents to hold water and dust on exposed rock faces, encouraging frost erosion and establishment of other plants in the new soil formed.

Three different styles of lichens can be separated easily: (1) an encrusting type, flat, and conforming closely to the substratum; (2) a low, lobed, leaf-like form somewhat more elevated from the support; and (3) an erect or pendant, branching style, clinging to trees, rock walls, or growing on rotting logs and the ground itself.

7. SLIME MOLDS (Myxomycophyta)

One of the strangest ways of life is that of the slime molds which inhabit moist woodlands. At one stage in each life cycle, a slime mold consists of a multinucleated mass of

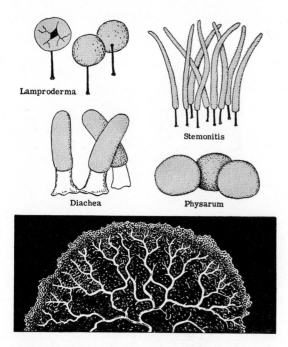

FIG. 14-6. *Slime molds seem clearly to be fungi when they send up elaborate spore cases* (upper figures), *but when the spores develop into a giant ameba-like plasmodium* (lower figure) *which extends pseudopodia over rotting logs and engulfs insects, an animal nature seems indicated.*

naked protoplasm, often an inch or more across. This mass (the "plasmodium") moves slowly like a giant ameba, avoiding sunlight, engulfing and digesting organic matter. Finally it moves into the light, is swept by concentric waves evident only in time-lapse motion picture records, and erects at one or more centers small spore-producing bodies. Often these are brightly colored and complexly organized (Fig. 14-6). The spores blow away. Those that fall on suitable ground may develop into single cells with two flagella, and swim for a time in the soil moisture. Later they transform into ameba-like cells that tolerate humid air. These cells swarm over the soil, feeding, undergoing nuclear division, and in some cases fusing in pairs before developing into a multinucleated mass large enough to see with the unaided eye.

For many years, before the full life-cycle was known, the ameba-like plasmodium was given a place both among the Protozoa and in a separate phylum of the animal kingdom, the "Mycetozoa" or "fungus animals" (from *mycetes* = fungus). Now biologists have agreed that the whole group is of thallophyte affiliation.

Most slime molds are saprophytic, or partly carnivorous if they happen to flow around some small animal. A few are parasites. One of the latter (Labyrinthula) is the causative agent of the "wasting disease" of eelgrass, a coastal flowering plant (see p. 371, Fig. 21-2). World-wide epidemics of this disease have been recorded at 25- to 50-year intervals. One in the 1930's so decimated the eelgrass population of America that many animals which depended for food upon eelgrass have almost disappeared.

SUMMARY ON MULTICELLULAR FUNGI

The hyphae of which multicellular fungi are composed consist of such slender filaments that they present a very large surface for absorption of food; hence they serve well both in saprophytic and parasitic nutrition. Fungi show high development of enzymatic chemistry, and in consequence can attack and be nourished by a wide variety of foods. Although fungus organization permits activity only under conditions of high humidity, periods of drought can be bridged through prodigious reproduction with desiccation-resistant spores. Only the fruiting bodies achieve conspicuous size. Those of large shelf fungi and puffballs probably demonstrate the practical limit. Size has importance chiefly in terms of a larger output of spores (as in the giant puffball, 15 inches across) or in perennial growth (as in big shelf fungi).

THE STUDY OF BOTANY

The standing objection to botany has always been, that it is a pursuit that amuses the fancy and exercises the memory, without improving the mind or advancing any real knowledge; and, where the science is carried no further than a mere systematic classification, the charge is but too true. But the botanist that is desirous of wiping off this aspersion should be by no means content with a list of names; he should study plants philosophically, should investigate the laws of vegetation, should examine the powers and virtues of efficacious herbs, should promote their cultivation; and graft the gardener, the planter, and the husbandman on the phytologist. Not that system is by any means to be thrown aside: without system the field of Nature would be a pathless wilderness; but system should be subservient to, not the main object of, pursuit.

Vegetation is highly worthy of our attention; and in itself is of the utmost consequence to mankind, and productive of many of the greatest comforts and elegances of life. To plants we owe timber, bread, beer, honey, wine, oil, linen, cotton, etc., what not only strengthens our hearts, and exhilarates our spirits, but what secures us from inclemencies of weather and adorns our persons. . . . The productions of vegetation have had a vast influence on the commerce of nations, and have been the great promoters of navigation, as may be seen in the articles of sugar, tea, tobacco, opium, ginseng, betel, paper, etc. As every climate has its peculiar produce, our natural wants bring on a mutual intercourse; so that by means of trade each distant part is supplied with the growth of every latitude. But, without the knowledge of plants and their culture, we must have been content with our hips and haws, without enjoying the delicate fruits of India and the salutiferous drugs of Peru.

—GILBERT WHITE, *The Natural History of Selborne,*
2 June, 1778.

SUGGESTED READING (see pp. 506-507)

Recent and Informative: Bonner, 1949, 1950; Crowder, 1926.

15 · Bryophytes

IN CONSIDERING each style of architecture among living things as a working design that meets requirements of food-getting, growth, and reproduction, it is to be expected that some examples encountered will be only moderately successful. The bryophytes fit this description. They show clearly the limitations which follow emphasis upon the gametophyte generation rather than on the sporophyte in the alternation met so regularly among the "higher" plants.

The main plant body of a bryophyte, whether moss or liverwort, is the gametophyte. The sporophyte generation never reaches independence, although in many kinds it may have enough chlorophyll to synthesize some of its own food. Otherwise it is parasitic upon the gametophyte plant.

To these generalizations a contrasting pair of statements can be added:

1. The gametophyte generation of any plant may consist of a filament or a thallus. In the latter case it may bear **rhizoids** as slender extensions one cell in diameter, reaching out from the surface layer and serving to anchor the plant to the substratum. Rhizoids of liverworts are unicellular; those of mosses are multicellular filaments. The maximum thickness of the thallus is found among liverworts —more than 50 cells one above the other, giving a vertical dimension less than an eighth of an inch.

2. The sporophyte generation of any plant is the only one in which division of labor reaches the degree of forming roots, stems, leaves, cones or flowers, and fruits. In the mosses and liverworts, the sporophyte remains at least partially parasitic upon the gametophyte. Hence no bryophyte has roots, stems, leaves, cones, flowers, or fruits.

1. LIVERWORTS (Hepaticae)

The familiar members of this class are flat green thalli, clinging closely to damp earth and stones (Photo 153). The lobed outline, from which the common name is taken, may suggest the lobes of a mammalian liver; *wort* is an old Anglo-Saxon word for any plant.

In some of the larger liverworts the thallus (Fig. 15-1) has distinct air chambers, communicating with the air above through a pore. Filaments, the cells of which are packed with chloroplastids, project into these chambers from below.

Since the customary manner of growth is by repeated forking of the plant, liverworts are said to have a **dichotomous** habit. After dichotomy, the old part of the plant often dies, leaving two separate individuals each expanding in the same manner. Another asexual means of reproduction in liverworts is through small cup-shaped structures that develop on the surface of the thallus. Each of these "gemma cups" bears internally small masses of cells ("gemmae") like so many eggs in a bird's nest. Each gemma separates from the parent plant, and may be distributed by the splash of rain drops or by wind; if it falls in a suitable location it may grow into a new individual (Photo 154).

Sexual reproduction is through liberation of microscopic sperm cells from the multicellular ♂ sex organs, the **antheridia.** The sperms swim through a film of liquid water from rain or dew to larger, non-motile egg cells enclosed singly in multicellular ♀ sex organs, the **archegonia.** Sex organs may be borne on the thallus itself, or on upright umbrella-like structures. In either case the fertilized egg grows by embryonic stages into a knob-shaped mass at the center of which is the spore case (**sporangium**) in which spores

153. From the branching thallus of Marchantia, slender stalks raise the reproductive structures into the wind. Most of those shown bear archegonia. The arrow indicates the top of an antheridium-bearing one. Approximately natural size.

154. Gemma cups with flattened, disc-shaped gemmae, on the surface of the thallus in the liverwort Lunularia, are about ³⁄₁₆ inch across. The thallus itself is marked off by grooves into areas surrounding air-pores.

155. In the spring, the liverwort Ricciocarpus floats on the surface of ponds like a coarse duckweed. Approximately natural size.

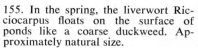

156. The term "moss" is often loosely applied. Above the pencil to the left is one true moss. At the pencil tip is a pedestal-shaped lichen. In the lower right is the "reindeer moss," another lichen. In the lower left is some peat moss (Sphagnum) mixed with the hairy-cap moss (Polytrichum), seen also in the upper right.

157. Moss sporophytes extend upward, raising the complex spore case where breezes can distribute the spores like dust.

are formed. This knob-shaped mass is the sporophyte plant. It may possess chlorophyll, but for water, salts, and probably sugars, it is parasitic upon the gametophyte and remains attached. Each spore is capable of growing into a new gametophyte thallus, thus completing the life cycle.

2. MOSSES (Musci)

Moss spores germinate into multicellular filaments known collectively as the **protonema.** By cooperative effort, these chlorophyll-rich cells produce an upright stalk-like structure consisting of filaments braided together (Fig. 15-2). At intervals this central portion of the gametophyte extends flat plates of cells, usually one or two cells thick. These plates appear to be leaves, but cannot be considered

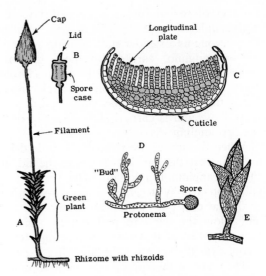

FIG. 15-2. *The moss gametophyte is the familiar green plant (A) which, at maturity, bears reproductive organs containing egg or sperms. A fertilized egg grows into the upright "fruiting structure" (the sporophyte), consisting of a filament and spore case. Leaf-like plates of cells on the gametophyte are far from leaf-like in section (C). Each spore is capable of developing into a protonema with conspicuous chloroplastids—the young gametophyte. This protonema sends up upright stalks (E) at intervals, and itself becomes the trailing rhizome—a horizontal stalk with rhizoids.*

LIVERWORT

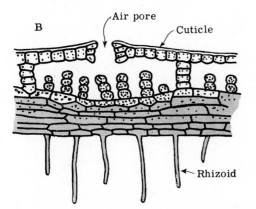

FIG. 15-1. *The bright green thallus of the larger liverworts clings to damp stones. In section the multicellular anchoring rhizoids are evident on the lower surface, whereas the upper surface has numerous openings into air chambers where chloroplastid-containing cells are exposed.*

such since they lack the division of labor typical of true leaves.

The core of the upright stalk-like portion of the gametophyte may include elongated cells comparable to those found in rope-like parts of some brown algae (p. 226); no doubt they assist in transportation of water and dissolved materials. But without better conducting tissue and cells specialized in ways that give mechanical support, a moss is limited to lowly growth—at most 6 or 7 inches from the ground. Even this height is a false indication of the potentialities in bryophyte architecture. A single moss plant cannot rise so high. Instead it must lean upon its neighbors. One rests on another, until at the periphery of the clump, members of the group lie prostrate on the ground or other firm foundation.

The mature moss develops antheridia and archegonia in a cup-shaped region at the top of the gametophyte. Again liquid water is required for the swimming sperm cells to go from the antheridia to the solitary eggs. The product of sexual fusion is an embryo—the multicellular sporophyte. This stage is familiar to everyone as a slender stalk bearing a terminal sporangium, carried by moss gametophytes at certain times of the year (Photo 157). Usually the archegonium neck grows for a time and covers the embryo. Later it tears loose and is carried aloft as a cap over the sporangium.

When the spores are ripe, the capsule dries and shrinks; the cap blows away; the lid of the sporangium topples off. The spores are still protected by a series of inward-pointing teeth that curl out of the way in dry weather and allow the wind to puff out the microscopic spores, or that curl together and form a roof over the spores if the humidity rises.

The stalk of the sporophyte often contains cells with chloroplastids, and helps nourish itself by photosynthesis. Otherwise it is dependent for food upon the green gametophyte that is the familiar moss plant.

3. SUMMARY

When viewed from the perspective of a review of the entire plant kingdom, two advances from thallophyte to bryophyte architecture seem particularly significant:

1. The gametes of bryophytes are formed in multicellular sex organs, not merely by separation of single cells; and

2. The sporophyte generation, although never independent, goes through embryonic stages while receiving nourishment from a preceding generation in the life cycle. Possession of embryonic stages is so unlike any of the thallophytes and becomes so important among seed plants, that the bryophytes and tracheophytes are lumped together in the same large subkingdom of plants—the embryophytes.

As compared with the tracheophytes, however, all bryophytes seem limited in several ways:

1. The delicate anchorage afforded by rhizoids and the complete lack of stiffening cells prevent bryophytes from achieving an erect habit of any height.

2. Since division of labor has not progressed far enough for bryophytes to have conducting tissue, transport is inefficient; it depends entirely on diffusion and cell-to-cell secretion and absorption; this inefficient distribution procedure will not suffice for a large plant; bryophytes must remain small.

3. At best a bryophyte secretes a thin waxy coating over the surface of cells exposed to air; it forms no waterproof cuticle and develops no mechanisms that restrict water loss into dry air; consequently bryophytes cannot grow in dry places, and must remain dormant during droughts.

These limitations keep bryophytes from offering much competition to tracheophytes in reaching light or access to wind useful in dissemination of spores.

16 · Tracheophytes

1. SPOROPHYTE TISSUES. 2. ROOTS—BRANCHING. 3. STEMS—BUDS. 4. LEAVES. 5. CONTINUITY—ROOT PRESSURE, ASCENT OF SAP, TRANSPIRATION PULL, BALANCE BETWEEN ABSORPTION AND TRANSPIRATION, DISSOLVED SUBSTANCES, AIR SPACES. 6. HABITS OF GROWTH—CONTINUED GROWTH, ANNUAL RINGS, LEAF FALL. 7. MODERN TRACHEOPHYTES—PSILOPSIDS, LYCOPSIDS, SPHENOPSIDS, PTEROPSIDS. 8. CHEMICAL COORDINATION—IRREVERSIBLE (GROWTH) CHANGES, REVERSIBLE (TURGOR) MOVEMENTS.

JUST AS the bryophytes emphasize the gametophyte generation and are limited thereby to the potentialities of thallus architecture, so the tracheophytes have developed the sporophyte generation. Of it they have made the highly successful land plants: the ferns, the evergreen conifers, the flowering plants and grasses. Increased division of labor in the sporophyte has been accompanied by gradual reduction of the gametophyte until, among the seed plants, this generation is hidden and nourished entirely by the sporophyte. The vascular plants—the tracheophytes—have thus explored the potentialities of the opposite alternative in the sequence of generations.

The sporophyte plan includes organs: (1) roots, (2) stems, (3) leaves, (4) cones or flowers. Each of these is composed of both simple and specialized tissues—sheets or cylinders or sheaths of cells showing essentially the same features in division of labor. By contrast with the structural details of the various thallophytes and bryophytes, the biggest improvement visible in tracheophyte anatomy is the conducting tissue, conveying water and dissolved substances upward in the plant, and elaborated foods downward. It is this feature which gives the group its phylum name—from the Greek *tracheia* = a rough tube. Tracheophytes are "vascular plants," from *vasculum,* the Latin diminutive of *vas* = a vessel.

1. SPOROPHYTE TISSUES

A number of biologists have tried to learn the shape characteristic of a cell in the middle of a multicellular mass, granting that the cells show no appreciable specializations. Tissue of this kind is common enough, particularly in the pith of stems. The "generalized cell" is roughly equal in diameter in every direction. It has flat faces where it is in contact with neighboring cells. If it is a small cell surrounded by large neighbors, it has fewer flat faces than if it is a large cell surrounded by small cells. But the average is remarkably close to 14 faces, of which 8 have 6 sides and 6 have 4 sides (Fig. 16-1, *pith*). This turns out to be the average, too, for the sides and faces of soap bubbles in a froth or of lead shot compressed in a container until no spaces are left between the pieces. Geometricians have named the figure a tetrakaidecahedron.

It would be wrong to assume that, because a "generalized cell" shows no special structural features, it has no function in a plant. Cells of this type are important as sites in which food is stored, in which a water reserve is maintained, as sites retaining potentialities of reproduction and growth, and as simple transfer systems through which water and foodstuffs are shifted for short distances. The term **parenchyma** is given to tissue the cells of which retain this generalized form, thin walls, and active protoplasm.

In leaves and a few other sites, parenchyma cells contain chloroplastids. The tissue is then called **chlorenchyma,** to show the slight degree of specialization.

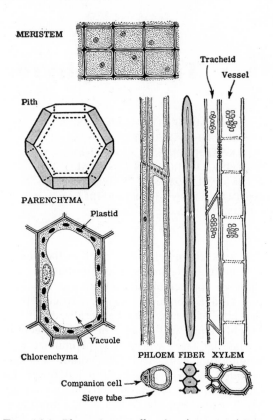

MERISTEM

Tracheid

Vessel

Pith

PARENCHYMA

Plastid

Vacuole

Chlorenchyma

PHLOEM FIBER XYLEM

Companion cell →

Sieve tube →

FIG. 16-1. *Plant tissues all arise from meristem. Meristem cells tend to be small, closely packed, often cubical, and so full of protoplasm that vacuoles of cell sap are absent. Meristem cells divide actively, producing new meristem cells and also cells which mature into other tissues. Those that mature into parenchyma are able to become meristematic again. Parenchyma cells are larger, with one or more vacuoles of cell sap; usually the cells are packed so loosely that intercellular air spaces are numerous. The "average" parenchyma cell of pith or cortex has 14 faces, of which 6 are rectangular and 8 are hexagonal. Photosynthetic parenchyma (chlorenchyma) contains chloroplastids.*

Greatly elongated cells produced by meristem may become specialized in the phloem into sieve tubes and companion cells, both retaining their cytoplasm but only the companion cell possessing a nucleus; the cytoplasm from one sieve tube continues through the perforated sieve plate at the end, maintaining intimate contact with the cytoplasm of the succeeding sieve tube. Or the elongated living cell may secrete a very thick wall and become a fiber; the protoplasm becomes restricted to a slender cavity and dies. Or the elongated living cell may become a tracheid of the xylem, with thickened wall except at areas where intercellular transfer is provided for; tracheids, when mature, are dead and lack protoplasm. Or a series of shorter cells may form a lengthwise pipe by loss of their end walls, to become a vessel; again the protoplasm is lost and the cell functions in the dead condition.

Cross sections of elongated mature cells are shown.

If parenchyma cells undergo repeated division, the resulting cells are smaller and more of their volume is filled with protoplasm, less with vacuoles of cell sap. The tissue has become **meristem,** or is said to be meristematic, and is characteristic of growth centers throughout the plant.

Perhaps the simplest specialization is that seen in cells at the surface of the plant, forming the **epidermis** layer. One face is exposed to water, or the soil, or air, and usually bulges from inner pressure. The epidermal cell may secrete a waterproof covering **(cuticle)** and reduce loss of moisture into dry air. This is usual on the surface of young stems, leaves, and reproductive structures exposed to air. Sometimes an epidermal cell bears a long extension, such as the **root hairs** of young roots or the **epidermal hairs** on stems, leaves, and fruits.

At various sites within a plant, cells may become very long and slim; several of these elongated cells usually lie side by side. Each may secrete additional material on all side walls, building up layer after layer until only a small central cavity remains. Any protoplasm in the cell is then walled off from a supply of nourishment, and dies. The dead, specialized cells give tensile strength to the plant, and are called **fibers.** Sometimes man values vegetation primarily for its fibers.

Additional stiffening is furnished by some of the specialized cells of vascular tissues. These tissues are "compound" in the sense that they include several types of cells. Nonvascular tissues are "simple" in having only a single type of cell. There are two vascular tissues: (1) **xylem,** concerned with upward transport of watery solutions; and (2) **phloem,** in which elaborated foods are carried throughout the plant.

Xylem commonly includes parenchyma and fibers as well as the cells in which longitudinal transport occurs. These latter are of two types: (1) long, slender cells, closed at the end, from which the protoplasm disappears after laying down extra thickening inside the walls; these are **tracheids;** and (2) long pipes of larger diameter, seemingly formed by removal of the end walls of large cells such as might otherwise form tracheids; again the wall is thickened over much of the inner surface before the protoplasm disappears; these are

vessels. At various points along the length of tracheids and vessels, thin places are left in the wall. These match thin places in adjoining cells and permit transfer of watery solutions in and out of the dead cells. In the living plant, both tracheids and vessels ordinarily are completely filled with watery solutions.

Phloem also may include parenchyma and fibers, but the characteristic cells are (1) **sieve tubes,** and (2) **companion cells.** In their functional condition, sieve tubes have fairly thin walls and terminate in perforated diaphragms called **sieve plates.** Sieve tubes develop large central vacuoles of cell sap, retain their cytoplasm throughout their useful life, but lose their nuclei. Control of conduction through sieve tubes appears to be the function of the companion cells, of which one or more extend the full length of the sieve tube, immediately adjacent to it. The sieve tube and companion cell (or cells) arise, in fact, from a single elongated meristem cell which pinches into two unequal portions from end to end. The larger portion becomes the sieve tube, the smaller the companion cell. Subsequent division of the companion cell may yield two or more of them along the length of the sieve tube.

All tracheophytes possess parenchyma, chlorenchyma, meristem, epidermis, fibers, tracheids in the xylem, sieve tubes and companion cells in the phloem. These may be considered the essential building blocks. In addition, special-purpose tissues may be found:

1. **Cork** consists of concentric sheaths of cells, lined up in radial patterns. Often the radial walls show accordion-pleating. All walls are heavily charged with a waterproof substance (suberin). Cork protects roots and stems that have grown so much that the original epidermis can no longer cover them.

2. **Resin canals** convey special secretions both vertically and radially in the vascular tissue of many coniferous plants.

2. ROOTS

The principal functions of any root are (1) to anchor the plant to the soil sufficiently well so that no ordinary storm will uproot it; (2) to absorb water and various dissolved materials from the soil, as useful chemicals in plant growth and reproduction; and (3) to conduct these materials to the stem above. The basic architecture of roots provides chiefly for anchoring, absorption, and conduction, but may be modified for accessory functions (for example, storage).

The strains on a root are vertical ones—tending to pull it from the soil. It is the type of strain for which man invents ropes and cables. These provide little resistance to bending but are highly effective in not stretching significantly when subjected to longitudinal forces. Roots are constructed in a comparable way. Their strengthening structures are located at the core and consist of reinforcements of the walls of cells in the region

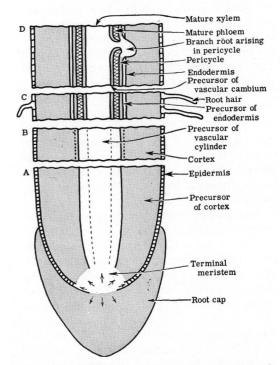

FIG. 16-2. *Diagram of longitudinal section through a dicot root. Back of the meristematic region (A) is a region of elongation (B), where little cell division is in progress but the cells are stretching lengthwise, thrusting the root tip into the soil. After this elongation is completed, the epidermal cells form root hairs, distinguishing a region of root hairs and active absorption from the soil (C). A still older region of the root (D) is marked by mature tissues, hence is a region of maturation; here branch roots frequently arise by development of meristematic centers in the pericycle. Arrows indicate the directions of spread of cells produced in the terminal meristem, to form more root cap tissue and the precursors of epidermis, cortex, and vascular cylinder in the root proper.*

where absorbed materials are conducted upward; more elaborate chemical nutrients are brought downward as food for root cells or for storage.

As long as a plant is healthy, its root system is constantly expanding. This activity is somewhat similar to the animation of a road crew constructing a new highway. At the advancing end of the root (Photo 158), where it is very small in diameter, is a region of rapid cell division. This corresponds to the area at the end of the highway where the paving materials are brought up and dumped.

Beyond this region of cell division, and pushed by it through spaces between the soil particles, is a thimble-like mass of loose cells, the **root cap** (Fig. 16-2). This serves as a three-dimensional bulldozer for the oncoming root. Cells of the root cap are crushed and broken by the pressure, but they are expendable, and more are formed constantly by the meristem they protect.

The meristem itself progresses through the soil, pressed forward by the force of recently-formed cells which are now dividing less frequently but which are rapidly increasing their volume by elongation. The root cap, meristematic region, and zone of elongation may move forward their own combined length every day.

Immediately behind and older than these parts are cells showing some specialization. Those in the surface layer (the epidermis) grow out into long filament-like extensions—the root hairs (Photo 159). Each square millimeter of root surface may bear 200 root hairs, and these extend 12 mm into the soil. They vastly increase the effective surface area of the root, and assist in the absorption of soil water and of various dissolved chemicals.

Immediately back of the root-hair zone, modifications are taking place in cells inward from the epidermis. Those comprising the central cylindrical mass of the root are changing into conducting cells (Fig. 16-2, *D*). Most of them elongate and develop thickenings in their walls internally (some spiral, some ring-like, and some uniform except for frequent gaps called *pits*); these cells are now tracheids. Near them, slightly farther from the axis of the root, other cells elongate, butt

against one another lengthwise, and develop openings in their ends as sieve plates. Beside each sieve tube lies a long, slim, and seemingly unspecialized companion cell.

Tracheids, sieve tubes, and companion cells, as they mature, are clearly unlike the parenchyma cells which are interspersed among them and which also surround them like a sheath. Tracheids and sieve tubes are the actual conducting cells, but for convenience the whole assemblage (tracheids, sieve tubes, companion cells, interspersed parenchyma, fibers, and sheathing parenchyma) is referred to as the **vascular cylinder.** The outer limit of the vascular cylinder is a parenchyma sheath which, since it has future importance, is given a name—the **pericycle.**

Outside the pericycle, most of the cells are loosely-packed parenchyma, and constitute the **cortex** of the root. This region serves in the storage of food and water, and is an avenue of transport toward the vascular cylinder for substances absorbed from the soil. Between the cortex cells are air spaces through which oxygen diffuses into and through the root, and is used there in respiration. Some carbon dioxide diffuses through the same spaces toward the soil, but most of the carbon dioxide from root respiration is carried in the form of carbonates to the leaves and there used in photosynthesis.

The innermost portion of the cortex is a special sheath, one cell thick, called the **endodermis.** Shortly after the vascular cylinder becomes well organized in the growing root, endodermis cells in regions radially outward from the phloem develop internal thickenings of a fatty nature that effectively prevent passage of nonfatty materials in a radial direction between xylem and cortex. The significance of this will appear shortly.

About four days after root hairs arise on a new root, they wither and disappear. For that section of the root, absorption has ended. Thus the root-hair zone maintains a spatial relationship with the root cap, the regions of meristem and of cell elongation. Yet at any point in the soil, the presence of root hairs on the root is a very temporary event. Only in this zone, however, are elaborated foods passed from the phloem into the cortex and to active surface cells. After root hairs die, any

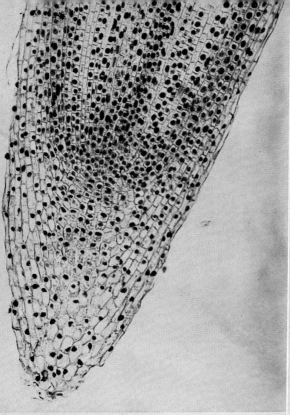 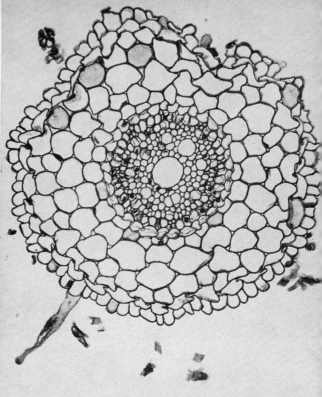

158. Longitudinal section through the root cap and growing point of an onion rootlet.

159. Transverse section through a young root in the root-hair zone; note the air spaces among the loose large cells of the cortex.

160. Longitudinal section through the terminal bud of a water plant stem (Elodea).

161. Longitudinal section through the terminal bud of a land plant (maple), showing the meristematic region and leaf primordia in characteristic pairs.

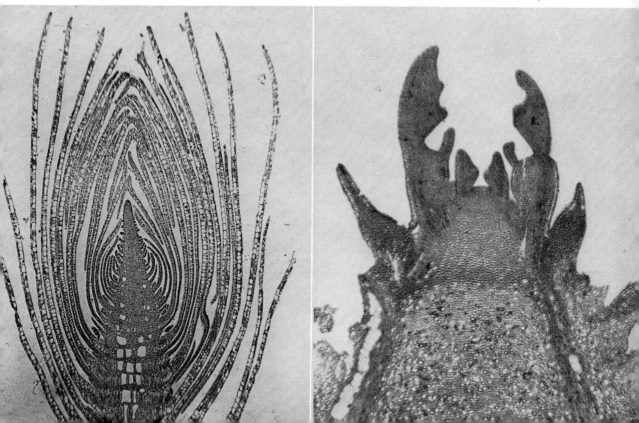

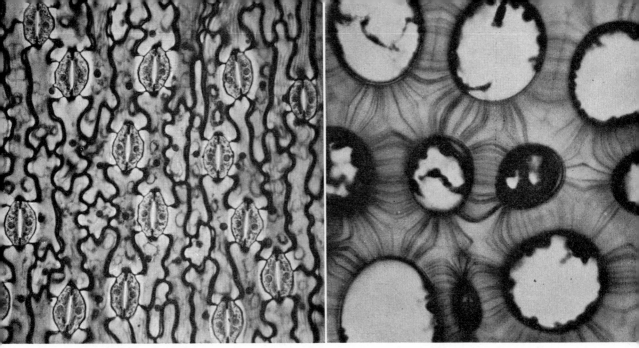

162. Stomata and epidermal cells of an onion leaf.

163. Plasmodesmata between persimmon endosperm cells.

164. Transverse section through a monocot leaf, with parallel veins and stomata on both surfaces. The large epidermal cells on the lower surface change size according to the water available. When they shrink, the leaf curls before wilting and shields the lower stomata from further loss of water.

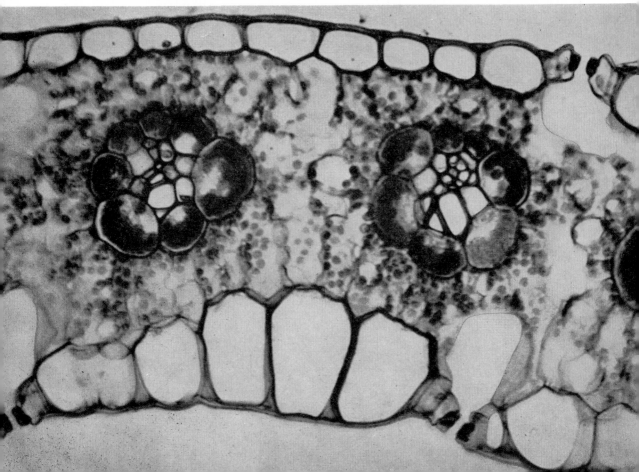

traffic in the root is in the direction of the xylem.

Slightly older than the region of root hairs is the maturation zone, in which the elongated cells of the vascular cylinder become tracheids, sieve tubes and companion cells, or fibers. In angiosperm xylem, larger elongated cells may dispense with end walls and become vessels.

At intervals, rows of parenchyma cells extend through the vascular cylinder to unspecialized endodermis cells, and communicate with parenchyma of the cortex. These rows are called **rays.** Pits in tracheids and vessels line up with them, facilitating transfer of solutions in radial directions. Otherwise the xylem pits match those in adjacent conducting cells, and solutions zigzag from cell to cell as they pass upward.

The thickened walls of fibers, tracheids, and vessels furnish the mechanical strength of roots, both toward lengthwise strains and against crushing forces within the soil.

Branching

Most roots develop secondary branches. Even when these branches are small—little larger than root hairs—they are constructed on the same pattern as the main root, although on a reduced scale. Each branch root originates in the pericycle of the vascular cylinder, at a point opposite a group of xylem cells. The branch root progresses toward the epidermis through the cortex partly by mechanical pressure due to growth and partly by digestive action. Once at the surface, a root cap forms and the sequence of events follows that described for the main root. Branch roots assist very greatly in resisting forces that tend to pull a plant from the ground, and also expand the potential volume of soil from which water and food materials may be absorbed.

3. STEMS

Stems are subjected to many more strains than are roots. They may be bent from any side or twisted in either direction. Ordinarily they bear leaves, which add surface on which wind can pull, and they have branches which extend the wind-leaf friction points away from the central axis of the plant and thereby increase the effect (moment) of each force. The architectural form that best resists such strains

with the minimum amount of skeletal material is the hollow cylinder, and most terrestrial stems at least begin with this design. Generally, a stem differs from a root in having a central **pith,** composed of relatively large, loosely packed parenchyma cells (Fig. 16-3).

Around the pith in a stem are vascular tis-

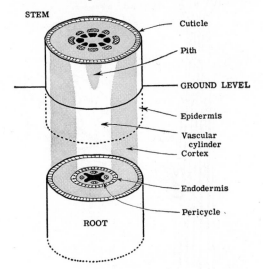

FIG. 16-3. *Diagrammatic representation of the modification in arrangement of parenchyma and vascular tissue at ground level as the structure changes from that of root to that of stem. The stem ordinarily is protected from desiccation by a cuticle secreted by the epidermis; normally the root possesses no cuticle.*

sues (xylem and phloem), cortex, and epidermis. Ordinarily the cortex is far thinner than in a young root. The epidermis normally is one cell thick—almost invariably waterproofed by a secreted cuticle. Roots, by contrast, usually lack a cuticle.

At intervals the stem epidermis normally is perforated by pores which communicate with air spaces between parenchyma cells. Older twigs may have visible gaps called **lenticels,** through which gas exchange occurs. These openings have characteristic shapes in each kind of plant, and are conspicuous on birch and cherry. Most of the dark markings in commercial corks are lenticels. Hence even the loose packing of plant parenchyma is useful: it permits gas exchange by diffusion, without any respiratory organs.

Buds

The growing point on a stem has no protective cap as does the corresponding region of a root (Fig. 16-4). Instead, the actively dividing cells (meristem) are covered by embryo leaves (Photos 160, 161) and by modi-

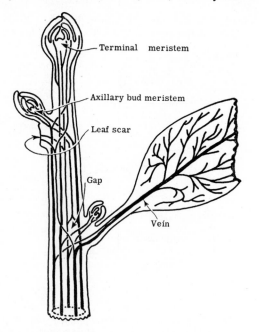

FIG. 16-4. *Meristems of the stem and its buds are at characteristic places along the lines of xylem.*

fied leaves, the **bud scales.** The growing region extends itself partly through cell division, partly through elongation of each cell. Slightly farther down the stem is a region of maturation. Over the outer surface is a single layer developing into epidermal cells with a waxy coating, while inwardly the vascular cylinder encloses parenchyma of the pith. Between these is the loosely organized cortex, usually green and carrying on photosynthesis, or like the pith, serving for temporary food storage.

Unlike a root, the stem's meristematic region elaborates also the **primordia** of leaves and cones or flowers, and **axillary buds** in the angle between the leaf and stem. Axillary buds may some day become side branches (Fig. 16-5). The vascular cylinder provides for xylem and phloem to each of these side structures, so that there are strands of the two conducting tissues extending to buds through the cortex; here they are called **leaf traces** (if to leaves) or **branch traces** (if to axillary buds or actual branches). In furnishing these strands

of conducting tissue, the vascular cylinder may show **gaps** called leaf gaps or branch gaps; each is filled with parenchyma like that of pith and cortex. Above a gap the cylinder closes again so that a sturdy mesh of supporting tissue is always present. Yet when a stem is seen in cross section at gap level, the discontinuity in the vascular tissue may seem a conspicuous feature that renders the actual continuity in a vertical sense less obvious and convincing.

Leaves occur at definite points on a stem, and the arrangement is characteristic of each kind of plant. In all, the place of origin of a leaf is a **node,** and the length of stem between one node and the next is an **internode.** At each node, however, there may be a single leaf, two leaves on opposite sides of the stem, or a group of leaves surrounding the stem. In the first instance the leaves are described as solitary or **alternate,** in the second as **opposite,** and in the third as clustered or **whorled.** If the stem is very short, a whorl of leaves at ground level is called a **rosette.**

Where leaves grow singly, their bases can be seen to follow a spiral arrangement up the stem. Where they are opposite, succeeding pairs are at right angles to one another. The

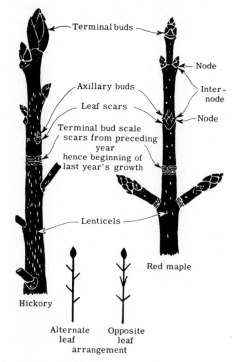

FIG. 16-5. *Buds, bud arrangement, bud scars, and respiratory lenticels.*

organization is clearly adaptive; it helps the plant place its leaves where one will shade another as little as possible, and it also distributes the leaf gaps in such a way that splitting of the stem structure is far less likely.

Between each leaf and the stem is the axillary bud, ready and capable of developing into a branch. This growth often is delayed until the leaf falls. Then the scar where it was attached can be seen below or surrounding the axillary bud or the new branch. Similarly, the terminal bud loses its bud scales when coming out of the dormancy that bridges a dry season or that is characteristic of winter. Scars remain, showing where the scales were attached. Often they can be identified on a branch until heavy bark develops. By counting backward to these terminal bud scale scars, it is easy to see how much of the branch grew in each of the recent years (Fig. 16-5).

4. LEAVES

Stem and leaf together compose an important combination. The stem's role in the partnership is holding the leaves to the light and air, and furnishing a two-way conducting system for materials going to and from the leaves, from and to the roots. The leaf itself is flat and characteristically green. Its form is the most thallus-like of any part of ordinary higher plants, and it provides the organism with a specialized site where oxygen and carbon dioxide can be obtained or lost easily, and where sun energy can be absorbed and used in life processes. Most leaves are so specialized, in fact, that they include no undifferentiated tissues which can repair damage or form new meristem. Those that constitute exceptions to this generalization are sufficiently unusual to be of great interest to horticulturalists (p. 307).

In the slender **petiole** by which the majority of leaves are linked to the stem, turgor movements are possible. This permits growth responses to light, as extensions or curvatures (differential or unequal growth) in ways that tend to keep the leaf at right angles to maximum light and as unshaded as possible by adjacent foliage. (The mechanism of this response is discussed on p. 259.) The result of these growth movements is a mosaic of leaves all facing the same way—outward on a wall, or toward the most exposed area of sky if in a free-standing plant.

The flatness of the leaf blade spreads chloroplastid-containing cells in the light, and affords opportunity for the gas exchanges inherent in their activity. Extensions of the stem's vascular tissue, the **veins,** pass close to these cells and keep them supplied constantly with water, the liquid substrate of photosynthesis. The chlorophyll-bearing portion of the leaf is composed of thin walled large cells, each well supplied with chloroplastids. Almost always the plastids are ovoidal in form, filled with ultramicroscopic granules which bear the pigment. Actually they enclose not only the bluish green chlorophyll *a* and green chlorophyll *b,* but also yellow carotene and orange xanthophyll. Sometimes a plastid contains only the yellow pigment—no greens. And many plants have in their leaves additional pigments (chiefly anthocyanins) dissolved in the cell sap, giving red, blue, and purplish colors in both reflected and transmitted light.

The large cells enclosing chloroplastids may either be a loose assemblage with many air spaces between, or they may be organized into two distinct layers—one (the lower) as described, the other (the upper) consisting

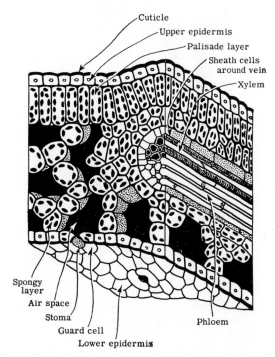

FIG. 16-6. *Stereogram of a portion of a leaf, showing air spaces* (black) *and a small vein (in section).*

of tightly-packed elongated cells with their long axes at right angles to the surface of the leaf. From their appearance in cross-sectional views of the leaf, the term **palisade** layer is given to the upper, **spongy** layer to the lower (Fig. 16-6). Where leaves are regularly exposed to particularly bright sun, several layers of palisade cells may be superimposed, with sufficient light passing through the plural upper levels to provide energy for the lower plus the spongy layer below. Movement of the cytoplasm **(cyclosis)** at rates of between 10 and 100 μ per second may present the chloroplastids in each cell to maximum light in a reasonably regular sequence.

The green color of vegetation indicates that the plants reflect or transmit (hence do not absorb and use) a greater amount of energy in this part of the spectrum. Chlorophyll absorbs chiefly in the blue violet and orange red, changing these parts of "white" sunlight and skylight into energy for photosynthesis plus heat.

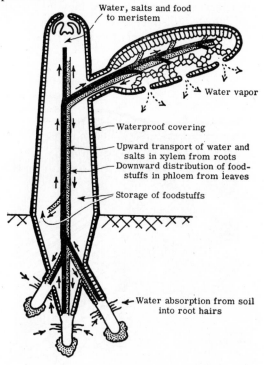

Water, salts and food to meristem

Water vapor

Waterproof covering

Upward transport of water and salts in xylem from roots
Downward distribution of food-stuffs in phloem from leaves

Storage of foodstuffs

Water absorption from soil into root hairs

FIG. 16-7. *The essential continuity of plant organs can be indicated in a diagram by arrows. Water, salts, and food are carried to meristems most conspicuously, but to all living cells as well. Downward movements are through phloem tissues; upward by way of xylem.*

Over both surfaces of the leaf is a water-proofed epidermis. Most of the epidermal cells lack chloroplastids, but at intervals (particularly in the lower epidermis) are specialized pairs of epidermal cells each with one or more chloroplastids. These are kidney-shaped **guard cells;** between them is a pore connecting the outer air with the intercellular spaces in the chlorenchyma (Photos 162, 164). The pore is a **stoma** (plural *stomata*), an opening which changes rapidly according to the activities of the plant. Each stoma may measure 6 x 8 μ, with from 50 to 500 of them per square millimeter of leaf surface. Hence, as much as five per cent of the leaf area may be given over to these pores.

When sunlight falls on a leaf, photosynthesis takes place both in the chlorenchyma and in the guard cells. Increased sugar concentration in the latter leads to endosmosis of water from surrounding epidermal cells and increased turgor. The greater turgor, because of the shape and skeletal stiffening in one wall of the guard cells, spreads the stomatal aperture and allows gas diffusion to proceed more rapidly—carbon dioxide entering, oxygen and water vapor emerging. With decrease in light comes decrease in guard-cell turgor, a closing of the stomata, and a rapid falling off of gas exchange possibilities and of water loss to the atmosphere.

5. CONTINUITY

The root system, the vascular tissue, and the chlorenchyma are the most active vegetative parts in a plant (Fig. 16-7). Each day the roots extend themselves into fresh regions of the soil, taking from it the film of moisture covering the mineral particles. The plasma membranes of root-hair cells swap by ion exchange for ions of many kinds and actively absorb still others. From this entry of materials into the root, there is a continuous passage across the young cortex, through the endodermis cells, through the pericycle parenchyma, into xylem tubes and upward.

That vast amounts of water and considerable quantities of dissolved minerals go along this route is a fact. But the mechanisms that handle these substances are less well understood. To a large extent the water and solutes travel together. This does not prove that the same forces move both in the same way. For this reason it is safer to consider the water as one problem, and the solutes as a separate one.

Root Pressure

One of the earliest experimental attempts to account for the rise of sap was described by Stephen Hales in his book *Vegetable Statics,* published in 1727. Hales had cut off the top of a growing plant and sealed a length of glass tubing to the stump. As the surviving root absorbed water from the soil, the fluid passed into the xylem and thence to the glass tube. Hales watched it rise. He tried filling the tube with water, to see if the plant's root could add more fluid against the weight of the column of liquid. They could and did, even when he extended the tube to produce considerable hydrostatic pressure. These experiments of **root pressure** became classic demonstrations. But no peak value for the root pressure had been found.

Part of the difficulty in understanding root pressure arises from the seeming simplicity of the anatomical basis for the phenomenon. Water enters the root hairs, passes to the cortex parenchyma, moves from cell to cell to and through the endodermis, continues through the pericycle and into the cells of the young xylem. Up to this point the solutions move only from one living cell to another. But in xylem they meet protoplasm-free, dead cells serving passively as vertical pipes.

The total number of young roots is adequate to account for the volume of flow observed. Thus a four-month-old rye plant has been shown to possess about 15 billion root hairs—a total absorptive area exceeding 3,000 square feet! The corresponding surface used by a tree is too large to comprehend easily.

It is obvious that the sequence of living cells within the root represents a graded series of sugar concentrations—highest in the pericycle, lowest in the root hair. The concentration of the solvent water decreases stepwise all the way from soil to xylem. Hence osmosis can explain transport of water.

The gradient, however, is nowhere nearly steep enough to account for much *force* in transfer of water. Nor does the entry of water into one rootlet do anything that can add to the pressure developed in a different rootlet. All rootlets operate in parallel. When Hales measured the total root pressure at the stem end of the entire root system, he could not be measuring more than the pressure developed by individual small rootlets.

In the 1930's the problem was attacked freshly by Dr. Philip White at the Rockefeller Institute for Medical Research. Using compressed air to resist water intake by small root tips held firmly by glass connectors of special design, White read the pressure applied on calibrated gauges. He found that a mere root tip from a tomato plant developed enough pressure to push water to the top of the highest tree—although pressures of this dimension have no known significance in a tomato vine.

White's work earned him the recognition of the American Association for the Advancement of Science, shown through its 1938 annual prize of $1,000 for the most outstanding piece of research reported at the general meetings of that year. But once again the limit of pressure found was not a measure of what the plant could do. How high a pressure a living root can produce is still unknown. White's measurement was merely an indication of the best joint he could make between root tip and measuring equipment!

Since osmotic pressures depend upon the gradient in concentration of the solvent water, and this is inadequate to account for such force, it is necessary to conclude that the living protoplasm of the cells through which the water passes must spend chemical energy in a combined secretory-absorptive transfer. Measurements of metabolism in rootlets do indicate disappearance of food at a rate that could support this transport activity.

One further problem is apparent in the nonliving nature of xylem tubes. Let us grant that the root protoplasm forces watery solutions into the tracheids and vessels at high pressures. But where is the mechanism preventing diffusion of the water and solutes back toward the soil? A protoplasm-free cell has no plasma membrane with which to resist this movement. Nor need the water encounter protoplasm of the living cells surrounding the vascular cylinder, since cellulose cell walls are freely permeable to all of the substances involved, and a continuous series of cell walls can be traced all the way to the cuticle-free epidermis.

The endodermis is seen as the answer to this difficulty. By the time a rootlet is specialized enough for absorption of soil water, endodermis cells have secreted fatty substances into all except their tangential walls. This fatty material seals in the vascular cylinder, preventing diffusion from it of any except fat-soluble substances. Water can still be transferred radially in the root at this level, but only through the protoplasm of the endodermis cells. No water can escape toward the cortex through the impregnated cell walls of this sheath.

Later on in a root's history, when absorption from the soil is no longer a feature of the mature portion of the root, the endodermis cells may fortify all of their walls against water transport, and end all movement of nonfatty substances in radial directions. Once water has been forced into the xylem tubes deeper in the soil, it has no other way to go but up.

Ascent of Sap

If the rise of sap in a tree were due to root pressure alone, any cut low on the trunk should release the pressure. The sap should gush out, draining the stem at a rate limited only by the zigzag transfer from tracheid to tracheid or to vessel.

Usually no such thing happens. Only when a deciduous tree is leafless or when a plant is in a saturated or near-saturated condition will any volume of sap exude from a bore hole. Even the stem of a leafless tree cut in winter will absorb water from the amputated root-end, and open its buds as though they were under pressure. Moreover, measurements show that the fluid in xylem tubes is normally under tension, rather than pressure. Water must be *pulled* up a stem, not pushed up.

Parenchyma cells with living protoplasm are frequent in the vascular cylinder, and must be the control centers which keep solutions moving vertically upward in xylem.

Transpiration Pull

The ascent of sap is far more vigorous when a tree has leaves, and is especially forceful when those leaves are engaged in photosynthesis. For this reason, another mechanism helping with ascent of sap should be sought in the leaves.

One logical step in this inquiry would be to follow the water reaching the leaves via the xylem in their petioles and veins, after this water has been received from the root and stem. Only about 10 per cent of the moisture entering the root system is used in photosynthesis. The rest is lost into the atmosphere, in a process called **transpiration.**

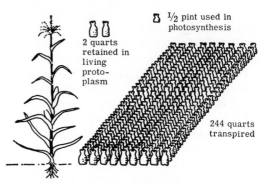

2 quarts retained in living protoplasm

½ pint used in photosynthesis

244 quarts transpired

FIG. 16-8. *A corn plant releases great quantities of water into the atmosphere by transpiration, employs only a little synthesis of new materials, and holds small amounts within the living protoplasm.*

This loss occurs primarily through the walls of the chlorophyll-bearing parenchyma in the leaf. The water evaporates into the intercellular spaces and diffuses out through the open stomata. Incredible amounts vanish in this way. For example, a single corn plant has been found to transpire at an average rate of 4 pounds of water per day throughout its life of three months or more (Fig. 16-8). An acre of corn, transpiring at this rate, loses 8,400 gallons of water in a day, producing about 200 pounds of sugar and other new solid weight.

A forest of giant trees is even more spectacular. A realization of this fact led Florence P. Jaques to refer in *As Far as the Yukon* to western cedars as "pulling a column of water from deep in the earth, lifting it to the far tree tips and spraying it out into the air—hidden fountains, far higher than the Yellowstone geysers, the most stupendous array of fountains in the world."

To a major degree, this water loss appears to be a price paid for getting carbon dioxide from the atmosphere. Ordinary air contains only about 0.03 per cent of this gas, and it must be one of the more difficult substrates for the plant to obtain in large amounts. Yet in the acre of corn described, the new weight (sugar and otherwise) represents organic compounds. The 200 pounds includes at least 80 pounds of carbon atoms absorbed as CO_2. This is 293 pounds of CO_2—which would be present in 12,100,000 cubic feet of air. This volume of air represents a segment of atmosphere extending vertically for 278 feet over the acre of ground.

But to get 293 pounds of CO_2 from the nearest 278 feet of air would require 100 per cent efficiency on the part of the corn plants. At 50 per cent efficiency—still incredibly high —the volume of air must be doubled: to 556 feet from the ground. The only conclusion possible is that through air movements a vastly greater volume of air was partly cleared of its CO_2 in achieving this "ordinary" growth of a familiar plant.

The water requirements of various plants have been measured carefully and calculated in terms of the number of pounds of water needed per pound of plant produced. Alfalfa heads the list, with 900; cucumber requires 713; potato, 636; wheat, 500; corn, 350; and cactus, 40. Each new pound of plant produced in photosynthesis requires of these totals only 0.6 pound. Transpired water accounts for most of the difference.

The immediate source of transpired water is easy to find. It is the moist surface of leaf parenchyma cells, exposed to the intercellular spaces opening to the atmosphere through the stomata. Each cellulose wall of a cell bordering an intercellular space has living protoplasm on one side of it, air on the other. Water fills the intermolecular latticework of the wall, and evaporates as though from an infinitely large number of small pores. Since these pores are too small to be seen with the best compound microscope, their diameters must be less than 0.1 μ.

Within each of these minute pores must be an equally minute water surface, concave toward the air. Extending behind this water surface is liquid in continuous contact with water molecules into the parenchyma cell, from cell to cell to the xylem of the leaf veins, down the petiole, the stem, the root, to the root hairs, and to the soil water. No break is visible for this entire length. The water can be considered to be enclosed in a tube, open at the top through submicroscopic pores.

For many years, physicists have studied water rise in tubes of considerably larger bore (Fig. 16-9). The rise is **capillary action,** which depends upon two characteristics of water: (1) its adhesive force, wetting and adhering to the tube walls; and (2) its cohesive force, whereby each water molecule clings to its neighbors and keeps the column from breaking. The height of rise is related to the radius of the tube at the point where the water is exposed to air.

A xylem vessel 0.1 mm in diameter would account for a capillary rise of only 30 cm (15 inches). But the submicroscopic pores through the walls of leaf parenchyma cells, even if as large as 0.1 μ in diameter, are 1/1,000th as big. Capillary action produced by concave water surfaces in pores of this diameter would support a liquid column at a height of 30,000 cm (1,233.3 feet)—several times the height of the tallest tree.

Physical chemists have shown that the cohesive force between molecules of pure water is 100 times as great as that required to prevent separation of the water columns from weight alone, if they were as high as those in the tallest tree. The factor of 100 surely is enough to allow for dissolved minerals and gases in the solutions raised by a plant, and for the friction inherent in moving liquid columns through xylem tubes.

Since the mechanism in leaves providing a

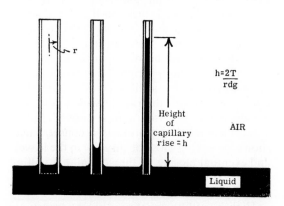

FIG. 16-9. *The height* (h) *to which capillary attraction between a liquid of density* (d) *and a tube is governed by the surface tension of the liquid* (T, *approximately a constant for dilute aqueous solutions*), *the force of gravity* (g, *approximately a constant*), *and the principal variable—the radius* (r) *of the tube.*

force supporting sap all the way up the stem is associated with the water-air surfaces through which the plant loses moisture in transpiration, the mechanism has been given the name **transpiration pull.**

Tensions as high as 1,500 pounds per square inch have been measured in vessels of tree xylem, at times when ascent of sap was particularly rapid. Velocities as high as 7½ inches per minute have been recorded. To withstand internal tensions of this magnitude and permit so rapid conduction of liquid, the xylem cells have real need for thick walls. This need is the modern interpretation placed upon the rings, spirals, and general reinforcement of walls found in tracheids and vessels.

Balance between Absorption and Transpiration

Either an inadequate or oversupply of water at the root end, and either an inadequate or excessive rate of transpiration at the leaf end, can cause trouble for a plant.

If a gardener moves a plant from one place to another, a considerable proportion of the root hairs may be sheared off through shifting movements in the soil. Water intake drops sharply. Transpiration losses continue. The gardener may shade the plant, decreasing the rate of photosynthesis in the guard cells and letting stomata close. Transpiration may be reduced enough to match the lowered absorption of water. Or the gardener may trim off a large number of leaves, until the reduction in transpiring surface matches the reduced absorption by the roots. In these ways the plant does not wilt beyond recovery.

When the sun is bright, the stomata are open widely. If the air is very dry, water loss into it may exceed the rate at which more can be absorbed from the soil or moved in the plant. General dehydration is a consequence, shown by wilting (loss of turgor) in the leaves, and eventual closing of the stomata. If wilting is too extreme, it becomes irreversible. The leaf or plant dies.

High humidity sometimes blocks transpiration. Occasionally, and particularly at night, a plant is seen in which the rise of water has continued—apparently by root pressure. Cells at the ends of leaf veins secrete the excess as globules of liquid on the outside. This is **guttation.** It suggests that the upward current of water has importance beyond supporting photosynthesis and preventing loss of turgor. An excess of water can be real, perhaps in relation to the transportation of solutes essential to the life of the plant body.

Dissolved Substances

Because water transpired from a plant is in the vapor form, it is pure water. The liquid absorbed by the roots contains measurable amounts of ions or salts. These diffuse or are transferred by secretion-absorption after entry into the root hairs, and are distributed widely throughout the plant.

Since the solvent water is removed in the leaves, the salt content within chlorophyll-bearing parenchyma may be expected to rise, increasing osmotic activity and bringing in more water.

Often crystals are found in plant cells. Many of them are insoluble calcium oxalate. They seem not to represent solutions saturated with any important substances, but rather a form of storage or the plant's way of handling waste materials.

A good many substances are at least as concentrated in soil moisture as they are in cell sap. Some clearly are concentrated by the plant. The silicious skeletal substances laid down by diatoms and horsetails are examples which must depend upon active absorption, since silicates (though abundant in soil) are nearly insoluble and very little diffusion could take place.

The iron salts absorbed by the root are essential for the formation of chlorophyll in the leaf, acting as a catalyst in this activity and not appearing in the pigment molecule itself. Magnesium is the mineral component of chlorophyll, and magnesium compounds in cell sap are involved also in fat and protein syntheses. The calcium in soil water tends to neutralize acidity within the protoplasm, and in particular to remove potentially toxic oxalates as crystals of calcium oxalate. Calcium is essential to maintenance of permeability relationships in the plasma membranes, and enters also as calcium pectates into the adhesive that holds cell walls together. The nitrogen-bearing compounds —chiefly nitrites and nitrates—supply the nitrogen for amino acids and hence proteins. Phosphorus and sulfur enter also into protein molecules, particularly those of nuclear materials. Sulfur occurs, too, in many plant oils, and appears to be essential for normal cell division. Potassium salts are required also in cell division, and in both photosynthesis and movements of carbohydrates from cell to cell. They may play a role, too, in resistance to disease.

While the roots are supplying water and dissolved substances essential for plant growth, and while the xylem is conducting these materials throughout the organism, the chlorenchyma, during sunlight, is active in photosynthesis. The products of this reaction—sugar and starches at first—are convenient ways of storing the light energy in quickly available form. During the day, the products of photosynthesis may accumulate to a considerable extent in the cells where they arise, but continually, both day and night, these carbohydrate energy stores are being translocated across cell boundaries and spread to all the living protoplasm of the plant. Apparently this translocation involves an expenditure of energy, but in some plants the cell walls are perforated by minute pores through which the plasma membranes of adjacent cells are in close and intimate contact (Photo 163). These protoplasmic connections, called **plasmodesmata** (singular *plasmodesma*), seemingly reduce the energy cost of carbohydrate movements.

A great part of the carbohydrate translocation takes place in phloem cells. These carry sugary solutions away from the leaves, and downward to living tissues as far as the ultimate root tip cells. Each cell in the plant, then, receives some of the watery solutions of calcium, iron, magnesium, nitrogen-containing compounds, phosphates, potassium, and sulfur, and some of the translocated carbohydrates. The last are sources of energy and supplies of carbon, hydrogen, and oxygen. Each cell elaborates its own complex carbohydrates, fats, and proteins from these substrates, and in growing tissues these syntheses proceed at remarkable rates. Many plants have special colorless leucoplastids in each large parenchyma cell, and in these plastids occur the synthesis of storable starches and the hydrolysis to provide sugars as needed.

Air Spaces

The stomata and intercellular spaces in the leaves communicate with air spaces between parenchyma cells in the leaf petioles, also with air spaces between parenchyma cells in stem cortex, leaf traces and pith, also with the lenticels that penetrate the bark there and provide fresh opportunity for gas exchange. They communicate with air spaces between the less tightly packed tissues of the trunk and with similar spaces in the root. Enough oxygen to supply respiratory needs in parts of the plant above ground is obtained and transported by diffusion. A considerable amount goes to the roots, too, but additional supplies of oxygen dissolved in soil moisture are usually necessary for active growth below ground.

6. HABITS OF GROWTH

With the standard building blocks available, a wide variety of designs are possible in the sporophyte architecture of vascular plants. In each, continuity must be provided for, and the combined advantages of rapid conduction and firm support exploited. Nearly three-quarters of the plant species known and over 90 per cent of those directly useful to man are tracheophytes. In this alone is a fair measure of the success of their fundamental plan.

A few of them are almost devoid of stiffening structures. Like aquarium plants and pond lilies, they must be buoyed up by fresh water and protected from desiccation. Others are trees, standing in spite of wind, drought, and wide changes in temperature. Among the smallest sporophytes are the "duckweeds," floating on ponds as minute leaves with short pendant roots. By contrast the California redwoods live thousands of years, rear to a height as great as 364 feet (*Sequoia sempervirens*) and diameter to 37 feet (*S. gigantea*). One specimen of the big Mexican cypress (*Taxodium mucronatum*) near Oaxaca is 112 feet in circumference at the base.

These plants show the ultimate known in division of labor toward efficiency in one direction: the autotrophic way of life for a land organism anchored to one site. They take full advantage of digging roots deeper, of spreading ever more leaves toward the light.

The fossil record shows that in the first long period when land plants became a well established design, trees were the principle form of terrestrial vegetation. This fact is significant, since it shows that permanency offered advantages not available in nontracheophyte styles of growth.

To build a tree takes time. The rate at which a plant can combine carbon dioxide, water, dissolved nutrients and sun energy into a woody edifice depends upon the plant's efficiency, upon the solidarity of architecture, and upon continuation of suitable weather conditions. The origin of land plants seems to have corresponded in time to a long period of unusually benign weather.

Growth year after year (the **perennial** habit) produces a reproductive body that can disseminate its products every year for decades or centuries. The plant may add annually to an erect stem, as a **woody perennial,** or die back to ground level each fall or dry season, as a **herbaceous perennial.** In some instances a compromise seems evident. A horizontal stem lies buried in the ground; together with a good root system, it is the perennial body of the plant; leaves or herbaceous branches bearing them are extended into air each spring or wet season. The underground stem is called a **rhizome.**

Unsettled weather and rapid changes (as viewed by comparison with perennial lives measured by decades or centuries) put a premium upon habits of growth that can reach reproductive maturity in shorter time. This may be as **biennials,** which store food in one year and part of another, but reproduce and die the second season. Or **annuals,** which pack both growth and reproduction into a single year, may have advantages. Both of these shorter life expectancies in the sporophyte require for their success some means for survival in the intervening dry season. Development of the seed habit appears to have been the step needed to permit biennial and annual growth to prosper where perennials, whether woody or herbaceous, met difficulties.

The seed habit, as a means for bridging periods of drought, is dependent in turn upon an earlier step in the life cycle: getting the eggs fertilized. Swimming sperms cannot maneuver in dry air. But wind and insects can transport dry pollen grains from which sperm-carrying pollen tubes might form. The cones of the gymnosperms and the flowers of the angiosperms take full advantage of this way to continue the reproductive cycle without need for liquid water.

Areas of the earth on which too little rain falls to permit tree growth have been colonized by seed plants whose architecture placed less emphasis on structures extending into air. These are the situations in which grasses grow, often with perennial roots, and all aerial parts at ground level. A few achieve greater height, as in maize and sugar cane.

Like the lilies, orchids, and palms, the grasses are **monocots** (monocotyledonous plants), with leaf veins running parallel from base to apex (Photo 164), with vascular tissue interweaving as bundles throughout the cortex and pith of stem and root (Photos 165-166), with flower parts in a three-rayed symmetry (Fig. 16-10). Some of them lose their pith at maturity and become hollow straws (Photo 167). None of them have a means for increasing the diameter of the trunk.

Monocots contrast strongly with the **dicots** (dicotyledonous plants), such as oaks, buttercups, roses, peas, and sunflowers. In these the leaves have conspicuous net-veining between the main veins, the vascular tissue is arranged in a single ring, and the flower parts show a four- or five-rayed symmetry. Monocot design represents emphasis on impermanence of the plant body. Only in tropical temperatures do monocots flourish in tree size (Photos 169-170). And then their growth is achieved in a fraction of the years required for corresponding height in most trees of dicot design. The terms *monocotyledon* and *dicotyledon* refer to the number of "seed leaves" in the embryo (one and two, respectively). These features are considered in detail in Chapter 18.

Continued Growth

In analyzing the structure and formation of roots and stems, some of the basis for the perennial habit was presented. The root has its meristem back of the root cap, furnishing

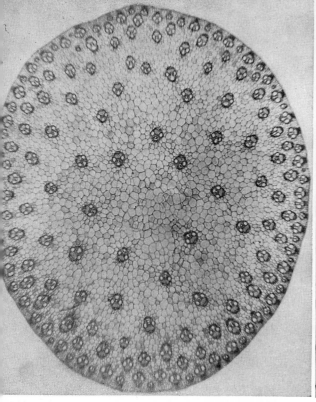

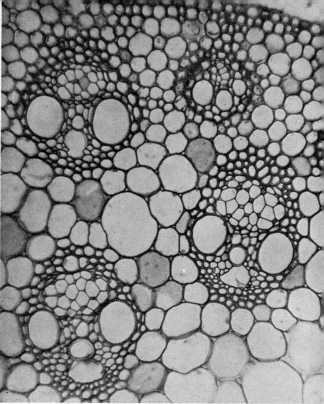

165. A corn stem has vascular bundles scattered throughout, but in each the phloem is to the outside.

166. Detail of corn vascular bundles; note large tracheae in xylem, also air space; note also air spaces between large cells of pith.

HERBACEOUS STEMS IN TRANSVERSE SECTION

167. A wheat stem develops a central air space, and becomes hollow.

168. In a dicot stem (Helianthus), the vascular tissue is arranged in a single circle of bundles.

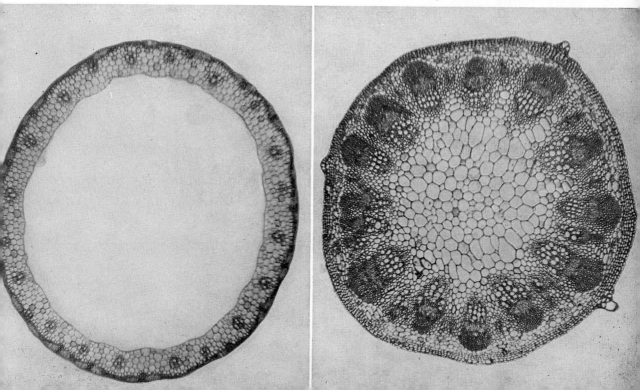

169. An avenue of royal palms in Matheson Hammock State Park, Florida.

WHERE THE WEATHER
IS WARM, MONOCOTS
MAY REACH TREE SIZE

170. A tree Yucca flowering in the Arizona desert.

new cells to the root cap as it wears away, and adding to the end of the root the new epidermis, cortex, and vascular cylinder. In the pericycle, parenchyma cells retain an ability to become meristematic and initiate the eruption of branch roots. The apical meristem of a stem provides all of the stem tissues, plus the primordia of leaves (and cones or

strictions may not be significant. Yet without additional meristems, tree growth would be impossible. Two unlike arrangements of supplementary meristems provide for continuous **secondary growth:**

1. A continuous sheath of meristem can

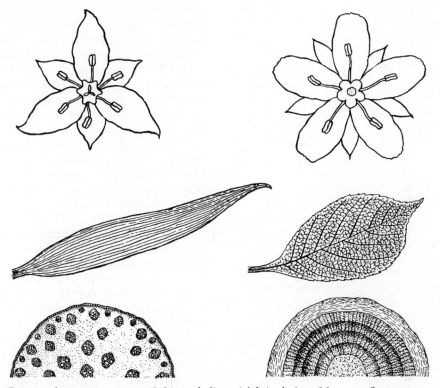

FIG. 16-10. *Contrast between monocot* (left) *and dicot* (right) *design. Monocot flower parts are in multiples of three* (top), *not fours or fives. Monocot leaves have parallel veins* (middle), *not net venation. Monocot vascular bundles are scattered* (bottom) *with no cambium, not arranged in a single circle. In addition, monocots have a single cotyledon in the seed, whereas dicots have two.*

flowers), and the dormant organization of axillary buds from which branches may develop later.

If a plant has no meristems beyond those listed, its **primary growth** is limited in two ways: (1) the diameter of root or stem can be increased only by cell expansion; and (2) since the number of xylem and phloem cells is fixed and there is a limit to the quantity of water with dissolved substances that they can transport, the addition of side roots and branches can provide for no greatly increased bulk of plant.

For low-growing vascular plants these re-

form in root and stem from parenchyma cells lying between the xylem and the phloem of the vascular cylinder. Its activity can furnish new xylem and phloem as additions to the original supply. New crops of leaves and new branches of the root system derive their vascular connections from the secondary xylem and phloem laid down by the sheath of meristem—the **vascular cambium.**

Since the woody heart of the tree is added to each year, the trunk's diameter enlarges. The original epidermis and cortex can no longer cover the growing plant body. Additional, overlapping patches of meristem form from parenchyma in the pericycle of the root and the cortex of the stem. These produce new parenchyma cells which may repeat the process as needed, and also layer after layer of the suberized cells of cork. The meristematic patches are the **cork cambium,** and serve to maintain a waterproof barrier around the

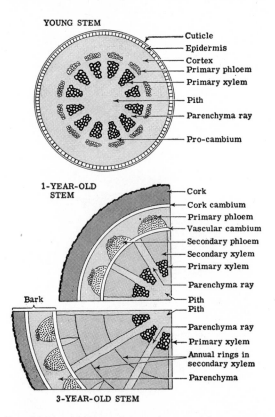

FIG. 16-11. *Addition of secondary growth to a stem serves principally to increase the number of vascular cells available for transport. But increase in girth requires replacement of the waterproof epidermis by a cork layer and the introduction of new spacing parenchyma cells between the points of primary phloem.*

plant body after growth has ruptured its original epidermis.

Tissues from the vascular cambium outward (new phloem, old phloem, cortex, cork cambium, cork, and tags of epidermis) are collectively described as **bark.**

This method of continuous growth is characteristic of gymnosperms and dicot angiosperms, even in plants with an annual habit. It is the basis for all firm tree growth, and for the wood which man finds so useful. It explains why a pine or an oak can hold more leaves to the light every year, and keep each one supplied with watery solutions.

2. The supplementary meristems may be restricted to the nodes. Growth and branching of roots then serves primarily to keep existing xylem charged with watery solutions by reaching fresh supplies of moisture in the soil. The stem, which commonly remains unbranched, may form new leaves year after year. But each leaf added corresponds roughly to an older leaf dropped. The vascular connections no longer needed by senile foliage are extended to the new. If branching occurs, each division may supplement its supply of conducted solutions by developing adventitious roots reaching directly to the ground.

This arrangement spends no energy on accumulating a comparatively idle woody center. It requires no expansion of the trunk beyond the diameter provided for by the terminal meristem. Hence no new waterproofing is needed. There is no bark, no stretching and cracking from internal growth. Slight elongation of internodes is possible, giving a cumulative increase in length or height of mature stems and trunks. This elongation and also production of new leaves or extension of old ones can be accomplished by the meristematic tissue at the separate nodes.

This style of growth is characteristic of monocots, whether grass or palm, and accounts for much of their success. Leaves with parallel veins are particularly well suited to continued growth from the meristem at the base (the node). Destruction of the leaf tips by fire, browsing animal, or lawn mower is not damaging to a plant of this type. By contrast, damage to the foliage of gymnosperms and dicots can be remedied only by unfolding of new leaves, either from primordia prepared by the terminal meristem or from adventitious buds arising in parenchyma and scar tissue.

Annual Rings

In a tree, the older xylem becomes filled with stored wastes and its cells no longer function in conducting materials. It has become **heartwood,** though still an important part of the structural strength of the plant. The active **sapwood** surrounds the heartwood, toward the cambium. The phloem never becomes correspondingly conspicuous, although it is no less important to the life of the organism. Girdling a trunk by removal of the bark leaves the wood intact; but without phloem to carry elaborated foodstuffs to the roots, the tree dies. Destruction of the outer bark down to the phloem has no appreciable effect unless it allows excessive loss of moisture or entrance of insects and disease organisms.

The combined activity of the vascular cambium, adding new xylem and phloem (and parenchyma cells in the radial transfer regions of the many rays), and of the cork cambium are not enough to keep the stem or root growing symmetrically. The cortex soon cracks because its growth does not keep pace with the increase in xylem and phloem tissues (Figs. 16-11, 16-12). Another cork cambium is then formed in the phloem. Thus the bark comes to contain much dead phloem in addition to the original epidermis, cortex, and products of early cork cambium activity. In an old root, the same has taken place but through the action of soil bacteria the outer dead cells rot away as the swelling root crushes them into the soil. The root then comes to have a large central core of xylem—from a few inches to two feet in diameter, depending on the size of the root—a vascular cambium, and a bark the inner part of which consists of living phloem and cork cambia and the outer part of dead phloem plus cork cells.

The activity of the cambium is correlated closely with the amount of water available to the plant. Rainy seasons correspond to periods of especially rapid plant growth. In dry seasons and winter, the plant may suspend many of its activities, including most of the cell multiplication and expansion in the cambium. Moreover, when the cambium is producing new vascular elements, the size of the new cells is related to the amount of watery solutions to be carried. The tracheids and vessels formed in a wet season are of much larger diameter than those originating when less moisture is available. Where seasons of wet and dry alternate with regularity, as in the temperate zones (dry in late summer, through autumn, and with water unavailable to the plant because of frost in the soil all winter; wet in spring and early summer), the successive sheaths of secondary wood formed by cambial activity show characteristic differences that can be detected with the unaided eye. Dry season wood is fine-textured and hard, the vessels having small cavities; hence in any given area of cross section the vessel walls make up a larger part. Wet season wood is coarse-textured and softer, the vessels having large cavities; hence in any given area of cross section, the vessels walls (which are the skeletal materials of the plant) make up a smaller part. The regular alternation of the two provides the grain in lumber, and the **annual rings** by means of which the age of a temperate zone tree can be determined. Photos 171-173, of transverse sections, show these details.

The "dating" of trees is a highly interesting procedure, made popular by A. E. Douglass, of the University of Arizona. The technique consists of removing a cylindrical plug in a

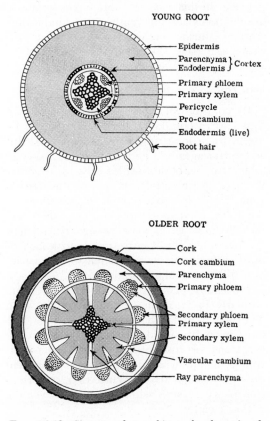

FIG. 16-12. *Since cork cambium develops in the pericycle—the outermost sheath of the vascular cylinder of the root—the endodermis, cortex and epidermis are all lost into the soil as the root ages.*

radial direction from the heartwood of a tree, and measuring the thickness of each annual ring in the xylem. In any area that has an annual cold (dormant) and spring-summer (active) season, or an annual wet season alternating with a dry one, the rings are true year indicators. The absolute thicknesses of the annual increments in growth are subject, of course, to enormous variation. But the ratio of thickness of succeeding rings is remarkably regular regardless of the location of the tree within a broad climatic area. Beginning with trees felled in known years, these ratios showing the irregular sequence of wet and dry years have been extended far into the past. Logs of unknown date, such as are found as beams in Indian ruins of the American Southwest, can be fitted into the series without the least uncertainty—often indicating definitely the period when these buildings were constructed. In this way, far more is known about the relation between weather and human migrations during prehistoric days (but still within the past 3,000 years) than could be ascertained from most other sources.

Leaf Fall

By contrast with the average life span of a root hair (a few days), leaves continue to be useful for a long time (several months). But as the leaf ages in a perennial plant, a special transverse disc of thin-walled cells grows across the base of the petiole. At first this **abscission zone** (from *ab* = off, *sciss* as in scissors, from the Latin *caedere* = to cut) may show externally only as a color change or a slight groove. Internally it corresponds to a lack of most stiffening tissue and often to a constriction of the vascular cylinder.

For many plants this development occurs regularly in late summer. In autumn, when chlorophyll and other materials in the leaf have been broken down and transported to the trunk or roots, the walls of abscission-zone cells liquefy, so that the leaf is supported only by vascular tissue. Wind, rain, or formation of ice crystals within the zone sever the petiole cleanly.

Corky scar tissue promptly seals the stem end, closing off the xylem and phloem tubes, keeping out disease organisms. The stem is marked by a **leaf scar** at the site; the closed ends of vascular strands are often visible. The shape of the leaf scar and the pattern of the vascular areas may be so characteristic in shape as to be useful in identifying trees in the leafless condition.

In north temperate regions, the autumnal fall of leaves is made spectacular because of pigments in the dying or dead leaves. Many of these colored materials are xanthophylls and carotene, evident as orange and yellow when the masking green is removed. More striking are the reds and purples due to anthocyanins. The particular shade depends partly on the amount of anthocyanin present or produced at the time—the more light or the more sugars, the more of them—and upon the acidity of the drying leaf. The more acid, the deeper the red; approach to neutrality or alkaline reactions yields purple and even blue. Strong light and low temperature favor pigment formation; low nitrogen in the soil has the same effect. Brown pigments, on the other hand, are largely tannins; these remain after the xanthophylls and anthocyanins disappear.

Wherever the fall of leaves shows no pronounced synchrony with the seasons, or the life span of each leaf is more than 12 months, the plant appears evergreen for the same reason that governments appear continuous— overlapping terms of office. So many gymnosperms have this characteristic that they are often described collectively as the "evergreens." Larch (*Larix* = tamarack) and bald cypress (*Taxodium distichum*), which drop their leaves in autumn, are obvious exceptions. Synchronous leaf fall is the mark of the **deciduous** tree.

7. MODERN TRACHEOPHYTES

In examining the life histories of all kinds of plants, it is easy to become impressed with the relative development of sporophyte and gametophyte on the one hand, and with the significance of the seed as a reproductive structure on the other. Neither of these features is now believed to be so fundamental as the possession of vascular tissue by those plants now grouped as tracheophytes. Formerly,[1] however, these same vascular plants

---

[1] Until 1942, most botanists followed the classification of plants proposed in a 23-volume mono-

were separated into (1) the "Pteridophytes," in which the gametophyte was an independent plant and no seeds were produced; and (2) the "Spermatophytes" or seed plants, in which the gametophyte was enclosed by and parasitic upon sporophyte tissue, and seeds carried the life history through a dormant stage.

Continued research work on plant life histories and anatomy has reached back into the fossil record and found extensive reasons for preferring the more modern arrangement—the one followed in this book and by botanists. Existing vascular plants fit the following scheme:

Subphylum Psilopsida—Psilotum and kin;
Subphylum Lycopsida—the clubmosses;
Subphylum Sphenopsida—the horsetails;
Subphylum Pteropsida—"leafy plants"
 Class Filicineae—the ferns
 Class Gymnospermae—conifers and kin
  including the Cycads,
   the Ginkgo, and
   the true conifers;
 Class Angiospermae—flowering plants
  including the Dicots and
   the Monocots.

Psilopsids (see p. 15)

The few living species of this group, like the several fossil representatives, seem to represent the earliest type of vascular plant—the first to rear up from the substratum with supporting tissue, xylem and phloem. As such they deserve attention.

In each case the sporophyte is a small plant (Fig. 16-13) that develops a reasonably good stem but no root and no real leaves. The stem shows dichotomous branching in two rather unlike parts: (1) a horizontal, underground rhizome, which lacks a pith; and (2) an upright, aerial portion with a central pith. On the latter, minute scales suggest the beginnings of leaves. Chlorenchyma forms the outer layer of the cortex in the upright stems, and in both parts the phloem surrounds the xylem completely. The modern "living fossils" Psilotum and Tmesipteris bear sporangia in the axils of the rudimentary leaves. Fossil psilopsids bore their sporangia at the tips of the branches (Fig. 16-13).

graph by H. G. A. Engler and K. A. E. Prantl, published between 1887 and 1915; it divided the plant kingdom into four phyla: thallophytes, bryophytes, pteridophytes, and spermatophytes.

Psilopsid gametophytes are minute; those of the fossil species have never been found. Each gametophyte is a thallus bearing multicellular sex organs, some of which produce swimming sperm cells, and some a single, nonmotile egg. Fertilization of the egg starts off the embryonic development of a new sporophyte generation.

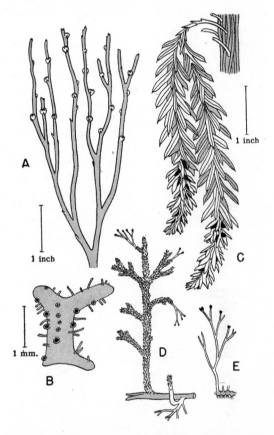

FIG. 16-13. *The modern psilopsids, Psilotum (A) and Tmesipteris (C) are regarded as the most primitive of living vascular plants. The gametophyte of Psilotum (B) is subterranean, devoid of chlorophyll, and saprophytic through the assistance of an enmeshed fungus. Rhizoids reach into the soil. Both larger antheridia and smaller archegonia are present. The swimming sperm cells reach the eggs through a liquid film of soil water, and the resulting sporophyte plant develops a horizontal rhizome with rhizoids (but no roots) and an upright, repeatedly branching series of stems (A) bearing the sporangia. Tmesipteris grows as an epiphyte on the bark of tree ferns. These two "living fossils" represent the subphylum which may be ancestral to the rest. The fossil members include the earliest of all land plants known: Asteroxylon (D), Hornea (E) and Rhynia, from the Ordovician period. Asteroxylon grew as much as 3 feet high; the others were shorter.*

Lycopsids (clubmosses)

Fossil "giant clubmosses" were all trees, some of them 135 feet high and 6 feet in diameter. Lepidodendron (the "scale tree"—Photo 407) and Sigillaria (the "seal tree") left abundant remains in the Carboniferous strata, showing that at that time this type of vegetation was among the dominant forms of land plants. Much of our coal is fossilized lycopsid wood.

Modern lycopsids seldom reach a height of one foot, and their greatest familiarity is from use as trailing greens at Christmas time (Lycopodium species) and as a novelty called a "resurrection plant" (Selaginella). Both genera are particularly common in the tropics, but various Lycopodium are found well into Canada in open woodlands.

The sporophyte has roots, stems, and small, evergreen, bract-like leaves (Photo 174). The stem includes a prostrate portion, forking repeatedly as it grows over the ground. At intervals, erect branches rise, bearing the leaves. Sporangia are borne on the upper surfaces of specialized leaves called **sporophylls.** In many instances the sporophylls are grouped at the ends of branches, forming small cones as the "clubs" of the clubmoss.

The many species of Selaginella are like

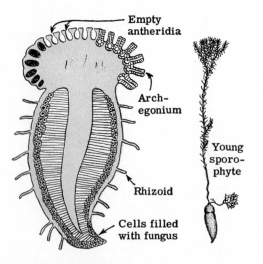

FIG. 16-14. *The gametophyte of the clubmoss Lycopodium is subterranean. From it arise the young sporophyte plants* (right) *which are more familiar denizens of woodlands* (see Photo 157).

most fossil lycopsids but unlike modern Lycopodium in that two types of sporangia are produced. One type provides small spores **(microspores)** from which ♂ gametophytes

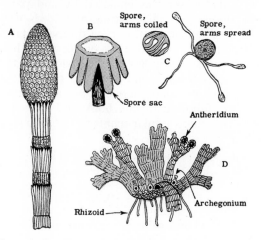

FIG. 16-15. *When the spores of a horsetail are ripe, the closely-packed side branches of the terminal reproductive structure* (A) *elongate, exposing a dozen spore sacs on each* (B). *Once free into drier air, the coiled arms of every spore* (C) *extend clubbed ends and push apart. Each spore can develop into a small gametophyte* (D). *From this the familiar sporophyte branches arise after fertilization* (see Photos 158, 159).

develop. The other produces fewer, larger spores **(megaspores)** from which ♀ gametophytes develop.

In each instance, the gametophyte is small (to ½ inch in length), carrot-shaped, and imbedded deeply in the ground or shallowly subterranean (Fig. 16-14). Its upper surface bears the sex organs in which swimming sperm cells and/or nonmotile eggs develop.

Sphenopsids (horsetails and scouring rushes)

Both the fossil and modern representatives agree in stem design. Rhizomes (with roots) and upright stems are both set off clearly at the well-spaced nodes by whorls of bract-like structures apparently derived from minor branches (Fig. 16-15, *A;* Photos 175-176).

Calamites, the giant horsetail, reached heights of 90 feet during Carboniferous times, and possessed a cambium. Modern sphenopsids all belong to the genus Equisetum. Most are less than 3 feet tall and herbaceous. The epidermis contains so much silicious material that the plants were used in pioneer days for scouring pots.

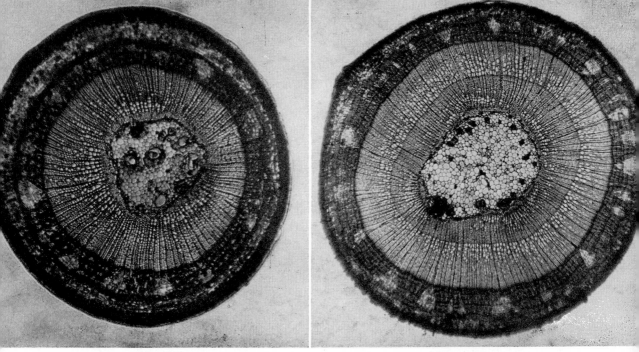

171. One year old.   172. Two years old.

A Basswood Stem Grows Through Activity of Its Cambium Tissues

173. Three years old.

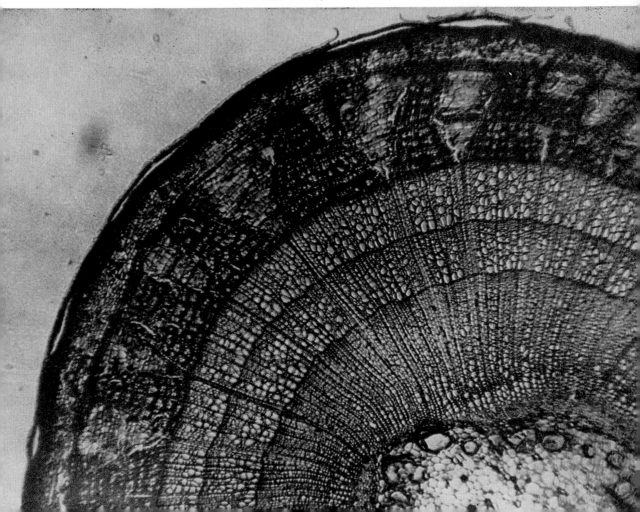

174. Clubmosses (Lycopodium), with their many spore-bearing clubs, may carpet a northern woods.

LYCOPSIDS AND SPHENOPSIDS

175. In spring the spore-bearing stalks of horsetails (Equisetum) are common along many railroad embankments and roadsides. The green sterile stalks (*right*) usually are present into summer.

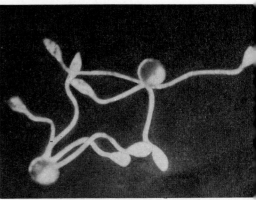

176. Each Equisetum spore bears four long knobbed arms which twist and untwist with changes in humidity, helping the spores to separate from one another as the wind sucks them from the spore cases.

177. In the tropics, tree ferns become tall; their long fronds unroll from "fiddleheads" just as do the leaves of smaller ferns.

178. Buried rootstocks of the interrupted fern (Osmunda) send up an annual crop of leaves that reach five feet in length. At this stage the fronds are called "fiddleheads."

179. A symmetrical frond of the maidenhair fern (Adiantum), easily cultivated and transplanted but wilts quickly when cut.

180. The spore-bearing areas (sori) of the leatherleaf woodfern (Dryopteris).

181. A fern gametophyte, seen from above.

182. The same from below, with its anchoring rhizoids.

Horsetails bear sporangia in whorls at the end of blunt side branches. The side branches themselves (Fig. 16-15, *B*) are grouped into a club at the top of the stem. When the spores are ripe, growth of the stem and of the side branches spreads the sporophylls, leaving gaps through which wind can reach the spores. The spores are unique in possessing four paddle-ended extensions apiece. These extensions writhe if the humidity changes, and appear important in separating one spore from another in wind dissemination.

Sphenopsid gametophytes are thalli with so many irregular lobes as to resemble a pincushion.

Pteropsids (leafy plants)

About 99 per cent of living vascular plants are pteropsids, with well developed leaves. Unless highly modified toward unusual features of environment, they have roots with good vascular tissue.

For every 16 kinds of ferns, there is one kind of gymnosperm and 397 kinds of flowering plants.

FERNS AND KIN (Class Filicineae). The geological period during which most of the world's coal supply had the form of living plants has been known as the "Age of Ferns." Within 50 million years after the first appearance of ferns of any kind in the fossil record, they and the early clubmosses and horsetails had spread as tall trees over the immense swamplands of Carboniferous times. Their dominance can be explained chiefly as an outcome of their vascular and supporting tissues. Early ferns had poorly-developed leaves, however, and in this respect resembled the psilopsids which led the way toward colonizing the land.

True ferns have prominent leaves with a strong midrib and pinnate lobing or subdivision (Fig. 16-16; Photos 177, 179); each leaf is popularly called a "frond." It seems to unroll from a bud called a "fiddlehead," and in this respect is almost unique among plants (Photo 178). Usually the vascular tissue is in separate bundles, the phloem radially beyond the xylem or surrounding it.

The prominent plant is the sporophyte. Special sporangia are developed on its regular leaves or on specialized ones. The sporangium wall includes a ring of reinforced

cells which serve as a spring hinge when the mature sporangium splits open. Its elastic recoil throws the spores into the air.

Usually the sporangia are borne in groups below the leaf. Each group is called a **sorus** or "fruit dot" (Photo 180). Often the sorus is covered by an extension of the leaf. The shape of the sorus and its cover is different in each genus, and can be used in identifying ferns.

On moist soil a fern spore can develop into a small, heart-shaped green thallus (the gametophyte), bearing rhizoids and multicellular sex organs (Photos 181-182). Swimming sperms travel through liquid water to reach and fertilize the solitary eggs. One fertilized egg from each thallus can develop into a new sporophyte plant.

Ferns and their kin include a few floating plants attractive in home aquaria, and tropical tree ferns (Photo 177) as much as 75 feet high, with trunks often clothed by adventitious roots. Their leaves reach lengths to 20 feet. Most ferns, however, are herbaceous denizens of shaded woodlands, growing with

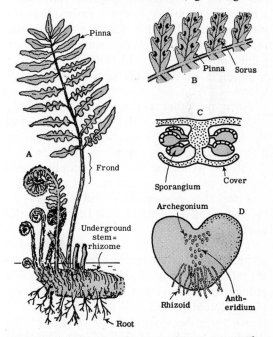

FIG. 16-16. *Ferns in temperate climates are evident mostly as the fronds which grow annually from a horizontal subterranean stem (rhizome). Commonly the under sides of the leaf divisions bear sporangia in groups* (B), *shown in section at* C. *Each spore may develop into a small gametophyte plant* (D).

rhizomes in the ground or clambering on larger vegetation.

GYMNOSPERMS (Class Gymnospermae). The most distinctive differences between gymnosperms and the fern class are found in the reproductive cycle: (1) The gametophyte generation is so reduced as to be microscopic, lacking in chlorophyll, and dependent for nourishment upon the sporophyte generation. (2) The sporophyte produces at one place spores which will develop into ♀ gametophytes and at another place spores which can develop into ♂ gametophytes. (3) A spore from which (or in which) a ♂ gametophyte develops is called a **pollen grain** (Photo 168); it is distributed by wind; it will not develop fully on the ground, however, but requires as stimulus a secretion from the ♀ gametophyte. (4) A spore in which a ♀ gametophyte can develop is called an **ovule; ovules** never leave the parent sporophyte. (5) Ovules in which a ♀ gametophyte develops contain one or more eggs that can be fertilized by a sperm cell from a pollen grain's ♂ gametophyte; the fertilized egg grows into an embryo sporophyte and then becomes dormant, with greatly reduced metabolic rate; the ovule wall and ♀ gametophyte tissue and enclosed embryo sporophyte constitute the **seed** of the gymnosperm.

Since no other parts of the sporophyte cover the seed, it is said to be "naked"—and the Greek *gymnos* = naked, with *sperma* = a seed, add up to the name for the class.

In most gymnosperms, the sporophyte produces its spores in special cones (Photo 183), and for this reason the word **conifer** (= "cone-bearer") is often applied loosely to the entire class.

Three different styles of gymnosperm are common: (1) the evergreen **cycads** which, except for their reproductive cones, resemble palms; their leaves are coarse, conspicuous, pinnately compound, and arise in a whorl or crown from the trunk (Photo 185); (2) the deciduous maidenhair tree (*Ginkgo biloba*), sole survivor of the ginkgoes—an ancient group—and hence a "living fossil"; the fan-shaped simple leaves have dichotomously branching veins (Photos 186-187); and (3)

the true conifers, mostly evergreens, in which the leaves are needles (as in larch or pine or spruce) or are scale- or bract-like (as in juniper or cedar).

Most gymnosperms are trees. Among them are the plant species holding the records for tallness (coastal redwood and Douglas fir), bulk (see p. 247) and age, and economic importance as wood (pine). They can be described as "conservative," building for permanency. The xylem develops no vessels, helpful in high-speed transport. Both wood and bark (and even the needles) contain resin canals, through which a protective gummy secretion can be shifted, plugging holes made by accidental damage or attack of animals, keeping out bacterial and mold infections (Photo 260).

ANGIOSPERMS (Class Angiospermae). The ultimate to date in reduction of the gametophyte is seen in angiosperms. The ♀ gametophyte consists of only 8 cells, and the ♂ gametophyte of only 2. As in the gymnosperms, the ♂ gametophyte develops from a spore known as a pollen grain, and the ♀ gametophyte grows as an inconspicuous tissue within the spore wall of the ovule. In angiosperms, however, the ovule itself is enclosed by additional parts of the parent sporophyte, and these contribute additional coverings for the seed. As a result, angiosperm seeds are enclosed in a **fruit**—the feature from which the class derives it name (the Greek *angeion* = a cover).

The spore-bearing parts of the sporophyte are usually organized into a **flower,** and angiosperms are often called the "flowering plants" for this reason. Flowers are devices which consolidate the reproductive function into one compact region, and serve also in many cases to attract animals (insects, birds, bats) that assist in transferring pollen from its place of origin to the site where it can develop and send sperm cells to fertilize eggs and start another sporophyte generation on its way.

Seed-production and the flowering habit appear to have freed the angiosperms from a need to become trees. Instead, they have exploited various ways that require less water, less time for a complete life cycle, and that achieve pollination or get seeds to places

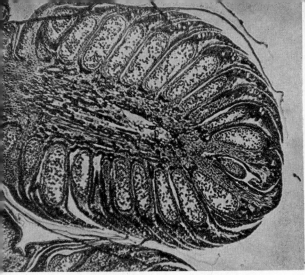

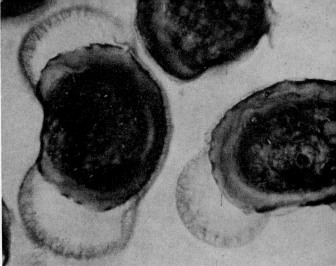

183. A young staminate pine cone in longitudinal section. Note the pollen grains in the spore cases attached to the leaf-like segments of the cone.

184. Pine pollen grains bear a pair of balloon-like wings which increase the drag of the wind that distributes them.

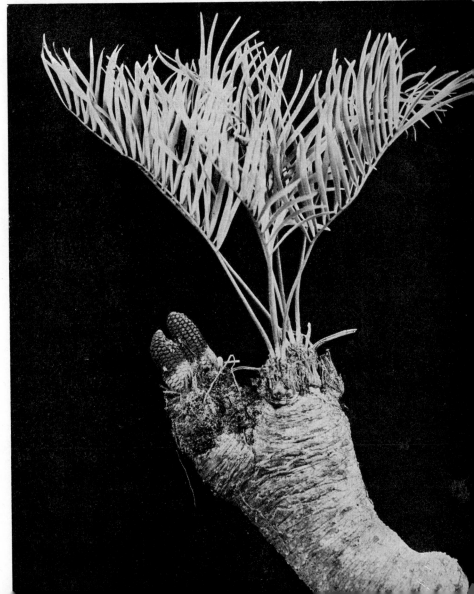

185. A cycad of Florida, the coontie or Seminole bread plant (Zamia), consists of a few green fronds, a large underground stem with roots, and upon occasion, staminate or carpellate cones with reproductive cells. Sandy soil covered this specimen to part way up the young staminate cones.

GYMNOSPERMS ARE
DISTINGUISHED BY
THEIR REPRODUCTIVE
STRUCTURES

THE GINKGO IS A LIVING FOSSIL—A BROAD-LEAVED GYMNOSPERM NOW USED FOR DECORATIVE PURPOSES ON PUBLIC GROUNDS AND STREETS

186. A well-formed specimen in New Hampshire.

187. The staminate catkins and the fan-shaped leaves with dichotomous venation are distinctive. Unlike so many gymnosperms, the ginkgo is like the larch in being deciduous.

where dormancy can end with successful growth.

Many of the angiosperms do retain the tree habit and produce wood of great economic importance. Others, such as bamboo and palms, achieve considerable height with less strength, making them more comparable to the cycads, tree ferns, and the unusual tropical giants among present-day horsetails.

The majority of angiosperms are herbaceous, either as annuals or retaining the perennial habit only in their roots. These lower styles of growth and briefer life histories permit a dormant root system or dormant seeds to bridge periods of drought or cold. They seem to exploit more fully the gain seen in both gymnosperm and angiosperm: freedom from liquid water for sperms to swim in while traveling from their site of origin to egg cells waiting to be fertilized.

Thus two unlike groups of plants have found ways to dispense with the liquid bridge between one generation and the next: the terrestrial fungi fuse hyphae from separate mycelia of unlike sexual strains, and use the wind to disseminate their dry spores; the seed plants employ pollen grains which develop only in the proximity of a ♀ gametophyte held by the parent sporophyte, and distribute dry seeds. Of these patterns, the angiosperm plan is clearly the more adaptable to life in the dry regions of the earth.

8. CHEMICAL COORDINATION

No doubt all multicellular plants develop hormones with which coordination is maintained. Unlike multicellular animals, however, plants lack distinct endocrine glands. Instead, hormones appear to be produced by parenchyma cells, and by meristems. Phloem appears to provide the avenue for distribution.

Hormones in plants are now known to be responsible for many complexly-coordinated processes. Even the existence of endocrine mechanisms in vegetation was not suspected until recently, however. And then it was detected through experiments designed to learn the basis for growth changes and gross movements of exceptional plants. Earlier studies had catalogued the effects of light, gravity, and other environmental stimuli without reaching any real understanding.

Irreversible (Growth) Changes

TROPISMS. For years it has been evident that potatoes, sprouting in a cellar bin, extend long pale shoots with poor leaves toward any light from a distant window. The petiole of a shaded leaf elongates itself and thrusts the leaf toward the light. Plants in a dimly lit room grow long and spindly. On a sunny window the same kind of house plant becomes bushy and sends out lateral branches all bearing leaves. Clearly, light discourages elongation.

Further evidence is obtained from seedlings. The developing shoot turns upward in the dark, the growing root bends downward. This is the reason that seeds need not be planted "right side up." But the mechanism was not clear for a long while after the basic behavior was described fully. Instead, the shoot was said to be negatively **geotropic—** it turned away from the earth (*geo* = earth); the root was positively geotropic (from *tropos* = a turning). The shining of a light on either plant organ alters the normal relationships. The shoot was described as positively **phototropic,** the root negatively phototropic, since the direction of growth of the one is toward, the other away from the source of illumination. This was mere terminology and provided no explanation. Hydrotropism (response to water), electrotropism (= galvanotropism, to electric currents), traumatotropism (to wounding), thigmotropism (= stereotropism, to contact), and the like, were added without reaching any useful hypothesis. All these tropisms were merely "reactions to stimuli."

The explanation should have been found in some 1888 experiments made by Charles and Francis Darwin. These ingenious experimenters placed a little black paper hat on a bean seedling, covering its shoot tip as soon as it became exposed (Fig. 16-17). Then the greenhouse flat containing several similar seedlings in addition to the tested one, was placed near a window where it got light from only one side. By the following day, all except the capped seedling had bent strongly toward the window. The capped one, instead, grew straight up. When its hat was removed, it too grew toward the window. On a fresh batch growing straight upward in the dark, the Darwins tried placing a sleeve of black paper around the developing shoot but pro-

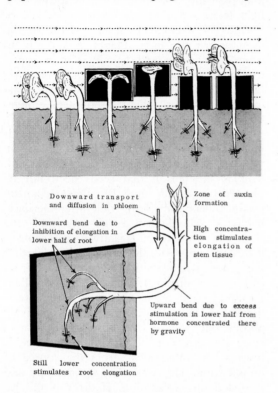

FIG. 16-17. Above: *The experiment on bending of seedling shoots tried by the Darwins shows the effect of paper caps and paper collars when light comes from the side.* Below: *The hormonal basis for a germinating seed's sending its shoot up and root down.*

viding no cover over the tip. All grew toward the light at the side. The scientists concluded that an "influence" from the stem tip moved down the stalk and caused the bending. They even placed marks on the stalk and found that the bending was due to greater growth on the dark side of the stalk than on the illuminated side. These experiments were repeated and quoted, time and again, with no understanding of what was happening.

Bending experiments in another plant added slightly to the picture. In 1910 it was discovered that the sheath (coleoptile) over the meristem of the growing shoot of the oat seedling was essential to elongation of the

shoot. By neat surgery, this tip could be removed, and at once growth in length ceased. But if a minute block of gelatine were balanced on the end of the seedling end of the cut coleoptile, and the tip of the coleoptile were replaced on top of the gelatine block, the "influence" diffused downward through the gelatine block and produced full growth, and all the usual curvatures to light. The "influence" had to be a chemical substance that could diffuse.

Between 1926 and 1928, in the laboratory of F. W. Went, the "influence" was described as a **growth substance.** Went placed coleoptile tips on a thin sheet of agar (Fig. 16-18), waited for a downward diffusion or sharing

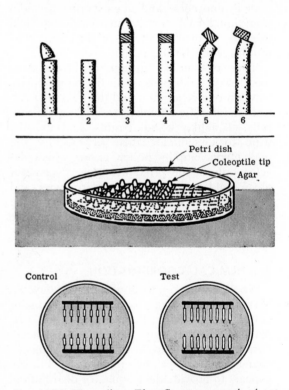

FIG. 16-18. Upper line: *The effects on growth of oat coleoptiles with the tip removed (growth stopped), with the tip separated by an agar block (no change from the normal growth), with only an agar block on which the tip has been standing (normal growth), and with the agar block placed asymmetrically (curvature) or with an asymmetric agar block on which the tip had rested for half the time (less curvature). Middle figure: A Petri dish with layer of agar jelly on which coleoptile tips have been placed to obtain test agar blocks. Lower figure: The "comb test," with oat sheaths mounted on a wire comb resting in a test solution of hormone. Elongation is measured readily in statistical numbers of cases, to evaluate suspected substances and methods of extraction or purification.*

to occur, then cut the agar into cubes and stood them on the decapitated coleoptiles. They elongated—and curved according to how the agar blocks were positioned. Also, the length of time allowed for the downward diffusion from the coleoptile tip to the agar determined how much curvature an eccentrically placed agar block could cause. Went proceeded to establish measurements in "curvature units." About this time the word **auxin** (from the Latin *augere* = increase) was applied to the growth substances, for there seemed to be several kinds. Although no special endocrine glands were involved, auxin seemed much like animal hormone material. It was definitely an organic substance produced naturally in these higher plants; it controlled growth or other physiological activities at sites remote from its place of production; and it was effective in minute amounts.

The search for auxins spread in all directions. They appeared in corn germ oil and in malt. They were found in human urine, particularly when the person was fed an oil-rich diet. The substance in human urine (on a diet rich in wheat germ) was recovered in enough quantity to learn its chemical nature; it was indole-3-acetic acid, related to the amino acid tryptophane. Soon it was available synthetically. Other auxins appear to be very similar. They are known now in every major group of multicellular plants.

Darwin and his son had found that the "influence" arose in the bean cotyledon and that shading the region including these seed leaves and the stem immediately below them prevented bending in relation to light. In the early 1940's the initial site of auxin formation in the oat seed was traced to the single cotyledon there. New methods for measuring auxin concentration were introduced. In the "comb test," coleoptile sheaths (minus their tips) were cut to known length and slid over the teeth of a fine comb (Fig. 16-18); the whole was then immersed in an auxin solution for a known length of time, and the increases in length were measured. The more auxin, the greater the extension. Or stem tips were split and immersed; inward curling was in proportion to the amount of auxin.

It became evident that the terminal bud of any plant contains the most auxin and must elaborate the substance in the embry-onic leaves. The material diffuses downward (but not upward) and gradually decreases in concentration. Neither temperature nor light seems to affect this downward movement, but, to be effective, auxin must have oxygen available; additions of sugar improve the growth reactions. Clearly, a metabolic process is affected by it. In the region just below the terminal bud, where the auxin is most concentrated, it stimulates elongation but inhibits lateral buds. Lower than this it is too dilute to affect stem growth but is still effective in inhibiting development of lateral buds on the same stem. Lower still, its concentration falls to a level where inhibition no longer occurs, and instead it stimulates bud development. Thus different processes have a variety of thresholds for auxin action.

These facts explain geotropism. Gravity forces auxin toward the lower surface of any horizontal shoot, causing elongation there that bends the shoot upward, away from the earth. The auxin diffuses on, and while growth is not stimulated, the substance inhibits elongation in root tissue, so that the lower surface of the horizontal root fails to extend. But the upper surface, being relatively free of auxin, grows normally; the resultant curvature swings the root tip toward the earth. Both forms of geotropism are now on a mechanical, chemical basis.

Light inhibits the action of auxin in stems, so that an unevenly illuminated stalk elongates on the more shadowed side, and turns its tip toward the illumination (Photos 188-189). In roots, light cancels the inhibitory action of auxin, and allows it to stimulate elongation—turning the root away from the light. Thus phototropism is part of the same mechanism. These conclusions have been checked in every possible way with agar blocks soaked in auxin solution. Even the following of the sun by sunflower heads and other blossoms **(heliotropism)** has this basis, but on a faster, day by day, time scale.

INHIBITORY ACTION. Removal of the terminal bud on a plant has long been known as a means of making it branch out. Housewives and horticulturalists cut or pinch off the leader, and their plants become shrubbier. The hormonal explanation is now available. Loss of the terminal bud stops the downward diffusion of auxin; lateral buds are no longer inhibited from development; their meristems become active and out they grow. As soon as one of them furnishes enough auxin, it takes over the inhibitory function, so that lower buds which have not passed a critical stage become dormant again. A block of auxin-soaked agar in place of the terminal bud will do just as well in inhibiting lateral bud development. Benefit to the plant can be seen in this mechanism. As long as foliage and buds toward the light are progressing, lower axillary buds and adventitious buds are inhibited —for a distance comparable to what the upper leaves may shade. If the upper foliage and buds are destroyed by frost, caterpillars or disease, the lower buds become active and provide replacements in which photosynthesis can continue.

ROOT FORMATION. At the end of a cut stem, scar tissue (callus) develops. This has been found to be very sensitive to auxins, and under their stimulation will initiate root formation. This discovery has been most helpful in getting plants to root from cuttings. Holly and others, ordinarily most resistant to attempts to induce root formation, yield very easily (Photo 190). Some kinds of plants still give no reaction in this direction to any plant hormone yet discovered, but rose bushes, apples, and others form excellent roots within a few days.

POLARITY. An astonishing reaction to auxins has been found when cuttings are inverted, the auxins applied to the upper (cut) ends. The substances diffuse downward and completely reverse the polarity of the whole stem—an event which has never been observed to occur naturally. Roots appear around the terminal buds, and new buds develop at the cut end. Polarity is such an interesting and elusive problem that this observation has opened up whole avenues for new investigation.

DISTORTED GROWTH. Leaves react to auxin by inhibition of blade development and elongation of the midrib. In weak solutions this affects merely the angle between the leaf petiole and the stem, but in stronger solutions the foliage becomes seriously distorted.

Leaves, however, are not so sensitive as coleoptiles; these require only one part of indole-3-acetic acid in 10 million of solution to produce a full one-degree curvature. Leaves respond only to higher concentrations.

Synthetic compounds which act as growth substances include 2,4-dichlorophenoxy-acetic acid, sold in every hardware store as "2, 4-D." It is selective in action, with little or no effect on monocot plants, although it induces dicots whose leaves are sprayed with it literally to respire themselves to death. In consequence it has been used widely as a weed killer in lawns.

OTHER ECONOMIC USES. Some of the hormones, like that in the oat coleoptile, induce cell elongation but no increase in the rate of new cell formation. Other plant hormones (phytohormones, from phyton = plant), common in wound areas, stimulate cell division. Thus, they either repair the damage or induce a covering layer of scar tissue. Still others are known. With some it is possible to inhibit potato eyes from sprouting, so that these stored vegetables need no individual care; other hormones will hurry this developmental process. One hormone used as a dust on apples and pears slows the formation of the abscission layer that ordinarily causes the fruits to drop. As a result, the crop remains on the trees, growing larger, and "waiting" to be hand picked—hence bruise-free. The drop of holly leaves from wreaths can be reduced in the same way.

Another valuable use for auxin has been found in that when it is touched to flower pistils, it initiates the changes that lead to fruit formation—without fertilization and hence without seeds. Seedless fruits (green pepper, watermelon, squash, cucumbers, strawberries, and tomatoes) are often larger than those with seeds and do not differ in taste. This technique effectively makes bees nonessential but requires the greatest care in hand application, since none of the hormone must be allowed to touch the leaves. The development of seedless fruits is called parthenocarpy, and corresponds to artificial parthenogenesis in animals (discussed in Chapters 18 and 19). The Greek root common to both—parthenos—signifies "virgin."

CIRCUMNUTATION. The growth movements of plants were commented upon and meas-

188. Potted tomato plants elongate with little bending when placed in various positions in a dark room.

189. A few hours' illumination from the right side modifies elongation into turning movements through inactivation of growth hormone on the lighted side.

Effects of Plant Hormones

190. Use of a growth hormone to induce root formation in holly cuttings. At the left are control specimens placed in water only, at the right are test specimens placed in dilute aqueous solution of the hormone.

Sleep Movements
in Sorrel (Oxalis)

191. Leaves with leaflets spread at midday.

192. Leaflets drooped, flowers partly closed, after dark.

5 HOUR DAY   7 HOUR DAY   12 HOUR DAY   17 HOUR DAY   19 HOUR DAY   24 HOUR DAY

193. Salvia grows luxuriant foliage if the night is short and day long, but as the Equinox approaches, it produces its scarlet flowers.

EFFECTS OF NIGHT-LENGTH ON FLOWERING

194. Lettuce flowers only when the night is short, and hence is a "long-day" plant.

5 HOUR DAY   7 HOUR DAY   12 HOUR DAY   APR. 7 1925   17 HOUR DAY   19 HOUR DAY   24 HOUR DAY

ured crudely before the days of time-lapse motion picture studies. Now the alterations in position of a growing tip of a twining plant are much more widely recognized. These circumnutations (or nutations) arise

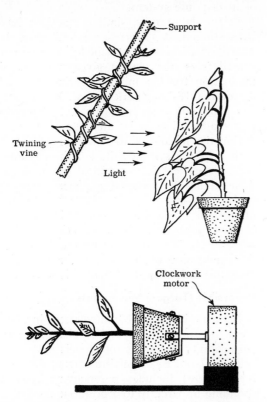

FIG. 16-19. *Twining vines show a response to touch stimuli that probably has a hormonal basis, though its nature is still unknown. Leaves turning toward one-sided illumination are shifted in this direction by unequal growth through hormone inactivation. A plant revolved slowly by a clockwork distributes its hormones so uniformly that it develops no curvatures.*

from differential growth in the tendril and may be due to unequal distribution of auxin. If a plant that is normally a twiner is placed horizontally on a clockwork device that rotates it several times per day, all twining movements cease (Fig. 16-19). This device was developed originally by the great plant physiologist, Julius Sachs, as a means of nullifying the effect of gravity in studying tropisms. Here it may be a means for equalizing the distribution of the hormones involved in growth.

This simple explanation is not a full enough mechanism to explain all of the facts, how-

ever, since some plants regularly twine clockwise and others counter-clockwise. In the wild morning-glory, two genetic strains are known —one of them a right twiner, the other a left —on a hereditary basis. The direction seems due to the spiral form of the growing meristem, though the circumnutations as shown by time-lapse studies are no more regular than in other forms where the inheritance is unproven and the embryonic basis undescribed. How the tendril or stem achieves its sensitivity to touch, whereby it responds by curling around an obstacle in the characteristic way, is even less understood.

NASTIC MOVEMENTS. Some movements involving growth differ in that they are not related to the position of the stimulus. Thus an embryonic leaf grows more rapidly along its edges than in the midrib region, and hence curves toward the axis of the stem in the bud. Later, under stimuli from elsewhere, the central area of the leaf begins to grow faster than the edges and it curves away from the axis of the stem, opening the bud. The opening of flowers has this basis, and in some cases responds clearly to the presence or absence of light. Chemical substances can cause this differential growth to appear. Some cause upper surfaces of leaves to grow, creating downward bending (epinasty), whereas others initiate greater growth of under surfaces and produce upward curling (hyponasty). One part of ethylene gas in 10 million parts of air cannot be identified by smell, but this concentration in a greenhouse can be demonstrated if tomato plants are brought in. Every one of them will respond by turning its leaves down, a curling due to epinasty. Many more nastics are known, but the causative agents are still undiscovered.

ETIOLATION. Another puzzle was mentioned briefly on p. 257—and is likely to have a hormonal explanation; it definitely involves plant hormones but as yet the mechanism is a mystery. Everyone knows how pale a plant becomes in the dark, or how colorless a potato sprout remains if no light reaches it. This lack of chlorophyll is termed *etiolation*. The aspect exciting curiosity is that in most cases ten minutes of light per day will prevent it, even though this amount is completely inadequate for food manufacture that will sustain the growth taking place.

PHOTOPERIODISM. The existence of another phytohormone, called *florigen,* has been demonstrated as arising in the leaves of some plants, and controlling their flowering. In some asters, for example, if the leaves on one branch are covered for a few hours each day during the early part of the summer, the whole plant will come into flower. Moreover, it will continue to flower through the autumn when control plants normally reach this stage. The number of hours during which the black covering is in place must be enough to reduce the length of the longer summer day to the same dimensions as the shorter autumn day when this plant ordinarily begins to develop buds.

On this basis, three different categories of plants have been segregated: (1) "short day plants," which will form flower buds only when the day is 12 hours or fewer in length (including aster, chrysanthemum, dahlia, ragweed, salvia—Photo 193, soy bean, tobacco, and, in terms of tuber formation on the roots, the artichoke); (2) "long day plants," which begin to show flower rudiments as soon as the day length exceeds 12 hours (including red clover, spinach and timothy); and (3) a large number of "indifferent" plants.

By covering "short day plants" or placing them in a dark room for part of each day, they can be induced to flower entirely out of season. Similarly, by providing these plants with artificial light for an extra period at the end of the day, they can be prevented from flowering even though mature. The "long day plants" respond in the opposite ways to artificially controlled periods of illumination.

Experiments reported on each year indicate how precise this mechanism may be. A florist wishing to have a good display of poinsettias for his show window at Christmas time, for example, placed his plants in a dark room until noon each day starting in late November, and then returned them to the light for all afternoon to allow photosynthesis to proceed. Half of a November or December day should certainly have been sufficiently less than the 12 hours the plant would tolerate if it were to form buds. But when no buds developed, he investigated.

The answer lay in the corner location of the greenhouse in which he left the poinsettias overnight. It was in line with automobile headlights as cars waited for the traffic signal, and this little light upset the poinsettia day-night response system.

In the laboratory, similar reactions have been studied. A "short day plant" on a six-hour day, 18-hour night schedule can be prevented from flowering if given moderate illumination for ten minutes during the middle of the 18-hour dark period. But a "long day plant" on a six-hour night, 18-hour day is not affected even by an hour of darkness during the middle of the 18-hour period. In both response systems, the length of uninterrupted darkness is the critical point. All of these studies are grouped as phases of *photoperiodism*—responses of plants to duration of periodic light and dark conditions. It is highly probable that the explanation for them will also elucidate the inactivation of auxin on the bright side of stems, and the release of inhibitory effect on the bright side of roots.

Reversible (Turgor) Movements

More rapid, reversible movements in plants seem invariably to be due to changes in the permeability relations of specialized parts called *pulvini*. Each pulvinus (from the Latin for *cushion*) includes parenchyma cells responding apparently to a hormone carried by the xylem, always by loss of water into intercellular spaces. Local wilting results, and unopposed mechanical forces—whether elastic or gravitational—provide motion.

RESPONSES TO TOUCH. The most spectacular of all plant movements are those shown by the Venus' fly-trap (Dionea) and by the "Sensitive Plant" (*Mimosa pudica*). Some members of the pea family (bean, clover, locust, and pea, for example) show the same reaction in much slower and milder degree than does the Mimosa.

The fly-trap leaf is highly specialized, with a long petiole that places the leaf in relation to others in the flat rosette on the ground (Photos 347-351). The blade of the leaf is in two symmetrical halves, and the margins are set with long stiff comb-like projections. On the upper surface of each half are two or three fine bristles acting as triggers for the reaction. If they are jostled—one of them several times within a minute, or more of them once in that time—the pulvinus extending the full length of the midrib loses its turgor, and elasticity folds the two symmetrical leaf halves together with their comb-like projections interdigitating. If the disturbance was an insect, it may be captured (Photo 349). In this event the upper epidermal surfaces of the leaf are brought firmly against it, and digestive enzymes are secreted which kill and disintegrate the body, rendering its nitrogenous compounds and carbohydrates into a form the plant can absorb. If no victim is captured, the leaf opens again after a number of minutes.

In the Mimosa, each leaf is twice pinnately divided. If a single leaflet is handled roughly, it transfers some chemical substance to the pulvinus at its base, and the change in turgor allows elastic forces to fold the leaflet against the midrib. Almost at once adjacent leaflets fold in the same way. And if the treatment was a particularly vigorous stimulus, the pulvinus where petiole joins stem also loses turgor, allowing the whole leaf to droop dejectedly; the reaction spreads to other leaves, both up and down the stem. Since the reaction spreads from a leaflet to the base of the petiole at a rate of from one to three cms per second, diffusion of a large molecule such as a phytohormone is not the most convincing explanation. Nothing resembling a nervous mechanism can be found. Electrical stimulation is effective in eliciting the reaction, but heat is also an efficient stimulus. Anesthetics like ether and chloroform (if increased in concentration slowly) affect the plant as they would an animal, blocking the response completely. The same and other anesthetics, if applied rapidly even in the surrounding air, stimulate the response in both Mimosa and the fly-trap. The description of these phenomena is now fairly complete, but understanding is not yet available.

RESPONSES TO LIGHT. Many people are aware of the daily "sleep movements" in the leaves of clover, wood sorrel (Oxalis), and other plants (Photos 191-192). At night they allow their leaflets to droop against the petiole of the compound leaf. By day the leaflets are erect. There is no true correspondence to sleep, and the term *photeolic movement* is preferable. Actually, the angle between the leaflet and the petiole changes very gradually and almost continuously, reaching a maximum near noon and a minimum near midnight. Flowers that open day after day and close at night have comparable mechanisms.

That this reaction is due to light, but not to light alone, is shown by transferring any plant showing photeolic movements to a dark room. Clover leaves, for example, continue on the same rhythm for from three to five days—raising and lowering the leaflets with remarkable regularity—but the reaction becomes less and less noticeable and finally disappears. The same is not true if continuous light is furnished, for the leaflets remain erect. The plant can be "trained" on artificial days, and a rhythm to 20 hours day and 20 hours night or six hours day and six hours night can be established. This, too, may continue for a few days in the dark. The reaction seems due partly to a chemical substance elaborated in the leaves during illumination, apparently due to the increase in temperature within the leaf when light energy is degraded into heat. The leaves can be "trained" to follow a changing temperature cycle in constant dim light. The timing mechanism remains a puzzle—one that has its counterpart among many animals, both simple and complex.

Journalists have made much of plants that can "tell time" in the dark, and also those that can "tell the date" as photoperiodism might indicate. Biologists have not yet been able to separate and identify the many mechanisms that allow these adjustments to light. The reversibility of photeolic movements suggests that here is an excellent place in which to study the phenomenon.

PINES

The pine's new year begins in May, when the terminal bud becomes "the candle." Whoever coined that name for the new growth has subtlety in his soul. "The candle" sounds like a platitudinous reference to obvious facts: the new shoot is waxy, upright, brittle. But he who lives with pines knows that candle has a deeper meaning, for at its tip burns the eternal flame that lights a path into the future. May after May my pines follow their candles skyward, each headed straight for the zenith, and each meaning to get there if only there be years enough before the last trumpet blows. It is a very old pine who at last forgets which of his many candles is the most important, and thus flattens his crown against the sky. You may forget, but no pine of your own planting will do so in your lifetime.

If you are thriftily inclined, you will find pines congenial company, for, unlike the hand-to-mouth hardwoods, they never pay current bills out of current earnings; they live solely on their savings of the year before. In fact every pine carries an open bankbook, in which his cash balance is recorded by 30 June of each year. If, on that date, his completed candle has developed a terminal cluster of ten or twelve buds, it means that he has salted away enough rain and sun for a two-foot or even a three-foot thrust skyward next spring. If there are only four or six buds, his thrust will be a lesser one, but he will nevertheless wear that peculiar air that goes with solvency.

—ALDO LEOPOLD, in *Sand County Almanac* (New York: Oxford University Press, 1949), pp. 82-3.

SUGGESTED READING (see pp. 505-511)

Classics and Milestones: Darwin & Darwin, Went.

Recent and Informative: Audus, 1955; Biale, 1954; Bosshard, 1955; Greulach, 1952, 1955; Jacobs, 1955; Kraus, 1954; Matske, 1942; Naylor, 1952; Platt, 1947; Schocken, 1949; Thimann, 1950, 1954; Yearbook of Agriculture, U.S.D.A., 1948, 1949.

17 · Growth

1. CELL DUPLICATION—MITOSIS, CELL DIVISION IN PLANTS, CELL DIVISION IN ANIMALS, CHROMOSOMES, THE ROLE OF THE NUCLEUS. 2. CELL NUMBER. 3. GROWTH AND FORM. 4. DIFFERENTIATION. 5. REGENERATION. 6. CANCER. 7. DEATH.

LASTING INCREASE in volume is the chief criterion of growth. It may be achieved through increase in cell number, or cell volume, or some combination of the two.

While presenting the cell theory in 1839, Schleiden and Schwann recognized that their idea had two parts: (1) all plants and all animals are composed of cells; and (2) since spontaneous generation has not been demonstrated, each cell must come from a previous cell by some method of reproduction. The two biologists presented evidence for both parts.

They had watched yeast cells becoming two, and described the microscopic event as completely as they could. The fully grown cell develops a bulge on one side; in a matter of minutes the bulge grows until it is about as large as the "parent" cell; sometimes it clings in place—a two-celled yeast plant—and sometimes it separates, becoming independent (Fig. 13-11). Even with modern microscopes, we have difficulty seeing much more in a living yeast culture. Yet in 1839, glass cover slips had been available for only two years. Microscopic technique was extremely primitive.

The first generalization offered by Schleiden and Schwann is correct. But their account of the yeast cell was incomplete and not representative enough to be useful. Most cells do not reproduce by the unequal division ("budding") shown by yeasts. Nor did this first explanation account for important events involving the nucleus of the cell. This oversight is easy to forgive, since Robert Brown had drawn attention to the nucleus and named it only in 1823. The material inside cells remained a mystery without even a name until 1846. It was in 1861 and 1863 that Max Schultze insisted on its importance, and referred to the cell as a "lump of nucleated protoplasm," and protoplasm as the "physical basis of life."

The biologist need not feel ashamed that his science was so slow in developing. The cell theory was announced a year before the chemists had distinguished between fats, carbohydrates, and proteins. And despite all the alcoholic beverages made and consumed in the years after invention of the microscope, yeast cells remained a curiosity with no known relationship to fermentation until 1857!

1. CELL DUPLICATION

Two separate and sometimes independent events are characteristic of the process that Schleiden and Schwann sought to describe: (1) duplication of the nucleus, so that from a single nucleus, two daughter nuclei arise; and (2) separation of the cytoplasm into two pieces. The first—nuclear division—is the process of **mitosis.** The second—cytoplasmic division—is called **cytokinesis.**

Under some circumstances the nucleus duplicates itself repeatedly, until a single cell is **multinucleate.** Chordate skeletal muscle cells and the alga-like fungi are good examples. Other cells, after becoming multinucleate, undergo cytokinesis later and regain uninucleate conditions in a multicellular mass. The angiosperm ♀ gametophyte is representative of this arrangement.

Mitosis

The chief hindrance to discovery of mitosis

was technological. The living nucleus is clearly visible in only a few tissues. Elsewhere its transparency is so much the same as that of the cytoplasm that the cell seems almost homogeneous.

A major advance in technique came in 1850 with the introduction of the first biological dye (carmine—a purplish red pigment extracted from cochineal bugs); it colored the cytoplasm and demonstrated that cells were full—not empty chambers. The second biological stain (hematoxylin—an extract from the logwod tree of Central America) was used in 1863; it blackened the nuclei and made them conspicuous (Photo 195). Unfortunately it also killed the nuclei, and to date no stain has been found which will color the nucleus without killing it.

To be able to locate the nucleus was one advance. To be able to see it clearly required others. The oil-immersion lens, permitting magnification of compound microscopes to rise to a useful 1,000X, came in 1872. The first device made especially for cutting uniformly thin slices for microscopic study was built in 1860; a better one, though still very crude, appeared in 1874. Embedding of specimens came later—1879 in celloidin, 1887 in paraffin. Without these tools and techniques a modern research worker in histology or cytology would feel helpless.

These improvements made it possible for Walther Flemming (1843-1915) to examine the nuclei of cells which had been actively dividing at the moment when he started the long chemical treatment needed to study the inner details. He noted that the nuclei differed greatly in their organization, and tried to arrange in his mind the various aspects, to reconstruct a living, continuous, transparent process from the dead nuclei his hematoxylin showed him.

In 1882, Flemming untangled the amazing cycle of changes, saw that they were correlated with division of the cytoplasm, and wrote a clear, well-illustrated description of a living process no one had seen in action. New techniques over more than half a century have not added greatly to understanding. Many of the details that have been filled in add to the puzzle rather than to the solution. And to

Flemming we owe much of our cellular terminology: cytoplasm, nucleoplasm, chromatin, aster, prophase, metaphase, anaphase, and telophase.

Briefly, the stages in mitosis and cytokinesis usually succeed one another in the following way:

1. When a cell is "ready," in physical and chemical features still largely a mystery, an unknown mechanism serves as a trigger that sets off changes in the cytoplasm. As much as 12 per cent of the cytoplasmic proteins become organized into a temporary apparatus that gives the whole cell a definite polarity.

2. Specific parts of the nucleus become shorter, denser, and easier to color with appropriate dyes. Soon it is apparent that the nuclear volume is occupied by several or many of these stainable structures (Photo 196), each elongated and twisted or bent, each called a **chromosome** (from *chroma* = color, *soma* = body). These consecutive stages during which the chromosomes become more condensed are referred to as the **prophase** of the nuclear cycle.

3. By the time that the chromosomes have become sufficiently stainable, shortened, and thickened to show the dye well, the rest of the nucleus has undergone chemical changes and there is no longer a clear boundary between the nucleus and cytoplasm of the cell; no nuclear membrane is visible, and it is said to have broken down in spite of the fact that no pieces of it remain. To all intents and purposes, the chromosomes are grouped centrally in the cytoplasm, and they move with relation to one another, demonstrating considerable freedom but great regularity of action. Soon they are seen to have arranged themselves in a definite pattern in almost a single plane (Photos 197, 198). Those chromosomes that have a V- or J-shape have the bend in the letter toward the middle of the group; I-shaped chromosomes in general occupy a radial position. This is the **metaphase** condition of the nucleus, and a chromosomal position in which a careful observer is likely to notice that there are two of almost every shape of chromosome, although the members of similar pairs may be nowhere near each other. Moreover, each cell of the same kind of organism has the same number of chromosomes and the same number of each shape.

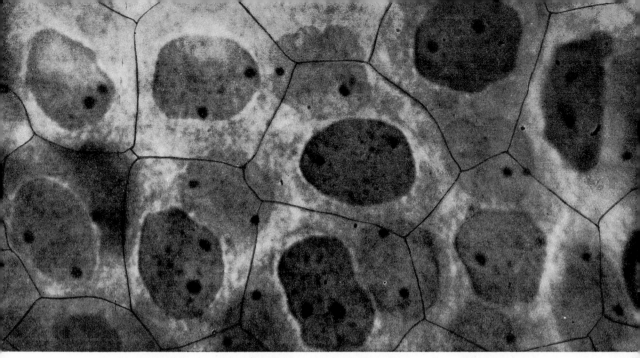

195. Nuclei with their nucleoli in the two levels of cells in the tail fin of a salamander larva stained with an appropriate dye. These nuclei are in interphase.

CELL DIVISION IN ANIMAL TISSUES

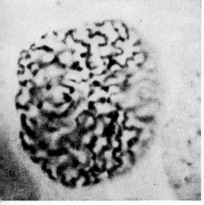

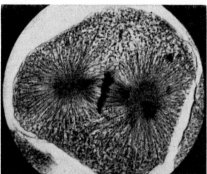

196. The same in late prophase with chromosomes becoming distinct.

197. Side view of metaphase in a dividing whitefish egg.

198. Polar view of metaphase chromosomes in salamander cells.

199. Anaphase in salamander.

200. Telophase in salamander.

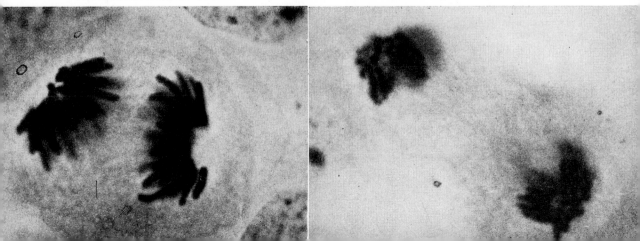

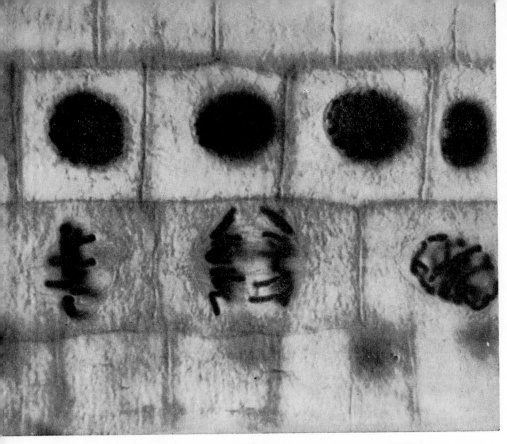

201. Interphase nuclei. Note also one in early anaphase, one in later anaphase, and one in late prophase.

MITOSIS AND CELL DIVISION IN PLANT TISSUES

202. Interphase nuclei. Note also one in early anaphase, one in late prophase, and one in early telophase.

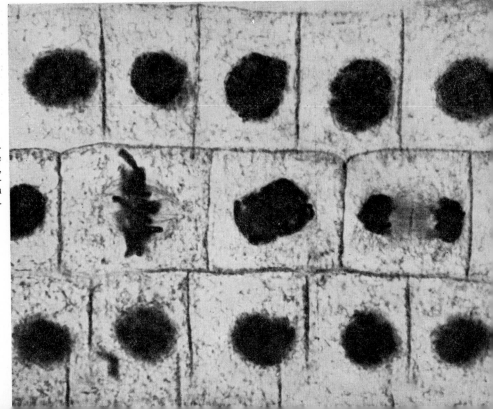

More of this aspect, and the significance of the facts, will be obvious shortly.

4. Another feature of each chromosome that is evident as soon as dyes will stain it and make the details visible, is a dual nature. Each consists of a parallel pair of thread-like parts, called **chromatids,** twined together something like loosely-twisted rope. But in the metaphase stage, the two chromatids in each and every chromosome begin to separate. In V- or J-shaped chromosomes, the disengagement occurs first at the bend of the letter; in I-shaped chromosomes, the parting usually begins at one end. Yet in every instance, the direction of this movement is at right angles to the plane in which the group of chromosomes lie. One chromatid of each pair is moving out of the plane on one side, while its mate is shifting in the opposite direction. The process continues until the two chromatids are completely free from one another, for every chromosome in the full set. The chromatids migrate in a converging group (Photo 199) away from the central transverse plane, and it will be noted that each of these groups contains a chromatid from every original chromosome—that is, two complete groups are now in the cell, separating from one another. The portion of nuclear activities in which the two chromatid groups become organized and shift apart is referred to as the **anaphase** stage in the cycle.

5. The separation of the two groups of chromatids continues until each group occupies a position approximately a quarter of the length of the cell from its boundary in the direction of movement. There each group stops (Photo 200), the chromatids (now properly chromosomes in their own right) commence to swell and lose their ability to absorb dyestuffs. Gradually the chromosomes come to occupy an approximately spherical region of the cytoplasm, and soon the more fluid portion of the protoplasm (between the waning chromosomes) becomes so different from the cytoplasm proper that it can be called *nucleoplasm;* the indication of this chemical change is the appearance of a nuclear membrane separating the nucleoplasm and chromosomes from the cytoplasm of the cell. The original cell now has two nuclei, but even as these changes occur in the chromosome contents at the two ends, separation of

the cytoplasm usually occurs and the original cell becomes two. Each of the daughter cells has its own nucleus, and in this nucleus is nucleoprotein material that arose as one twin of each chromosome in the parent cell. Reorganization of the nuclei after the anaphase migration is complete, is characteristic of the **telophase** period of the nuclear cycle. Thereafter, until the nucleus again begins its changes into prophase, it is said to be in an **interphase** condition, with full emphasis on its active functions as a coordinating region in the cell.

During the telophase, the cytoplasmic proteins previously forming the division apparatus usually vanish again.

The sequence just described, set forth in the main by Walther Flemming, encompasses the changes in the nucleus that provide two daughter nuclei each with a full set of chromosomes. Until the present century, however, the immense importance of the mitotic process was not realized; it was a curiosity, but scarcely more. Now it is clear that the chromosomes carry the inherited characteristics of each kind of plant or animal. Mitosis is the mechanism whereby every cell is furnished with a complete parcel of the genetic determiners.

Mitotic changes in the nucleus are remarkably uniform throughout multicellular life (whether animal or vegetable—except for the blue-green algae). Differences can be found, however, between plants and animals in the cytoplasmic division apparatus and in the mechanism of cytokinesis.

Cell Division in Plants (Fig. 17-1, Photos 201-202)

Rather late in prophase—but while the nuclear membrane is still visible—the cytoplasmic division apparatus appears in plant cells just outside the nucleus, and on opposite sides of it. At first there are just two curious little caps of thread-like lines, each set coming to an apex like the poles framing an Indian wigwam.

When the nuclear membrane vanishes and the chromosomes arrange themselves on the metaphase plane, the caps are seen to be at the ends of an axis of polarity passing through the center of the chromosome group. More-over, the fiber-like structure extends itself to reach the chromosomes, so that the cell seems to contain a symmetrical "spindle," <> in

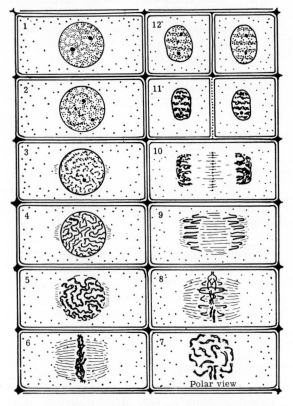

FIG. 17-1. *Mitosis and cytokinesis in plant cells, reading counterclockwise from the upper left. Interphase #1, 12; prophase #2-5; metaphase #6; metaphase polar view #7; anaphase #8-9; telophase #10-11.*

side view, with the chromosomes arranged on a transverse plane at its mid-point. At the same time fibers grow out from specific points, one per chromosome, into the pattern of "spindle fibers" toward each pole of the cell. For a time it was thought that, during anaphase, the chromosomes were pulled toward polar positions by the shortening of these fibers. Now it is apparent that the operation of the cytoplasmic apparatus is not that simple.

In a plant cell, as the chromatids separate during anaphase, they leave between them in the cytoplasm "interchromosomal fibers." At the end of anaphase, when the new chromo-

some sets have passed beyond the last part of the spindle, the cytoplasm secretes midway along the length of the interchromosomal fibers little droplets of a pectic substance. This fuses into a "cell plate" that reaches from wall to wall. Upon it as the "middle lamella" the daughter cells lay down cellulose cell wall, thus completing the separation in a way characteristic of plant cytokinesis.

In telophase the chromosomal fibers are absorbed back into the chromosomes and the cytoplasmic division apparatus vanishes without a trace.

Cell Division in Animals (Fig. 17-2, Photos 195-200)

In animal cells the cytoplasmic division apparatus is far more elaborate. Even during interphase, when the chromosomes show so little affinity for dyes, a small stainable body may be found closely applied to the nuclear membrane but definitely outside it—a **centriole.** Before any of the prophase changes can

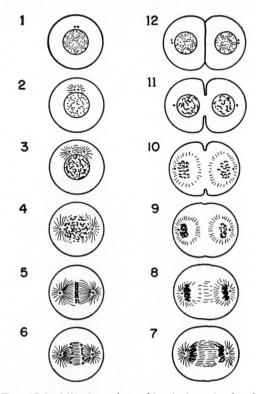

FIG. 17-2. *Mitosis and cytokinesis in animal cells, reading counterclockwise from the upper left. Interphase #1, 12; prophase #2-4; metaphase #5; anaphase #6-8; telophase #9-11.*

be recognized, the centriole divides into two, and the two new centrioles move along the nuclear membrane until they come to lie in the cytoplasm a little beyond the membrane and at opposite poles of the nucleus. In this position, each centriole soon is surrounded by a three-dimensional set of radiating lines of the same type of organization as spindle "fibers." In this case, however, because of the similarity in appearance to the lines of light drawn around diagrammatic stars, they are called **astral rays.**

As the nuclear membrane vanishes toward the end of prophase, some of the astral rays extend toward the chromosomes to provide a spindle much like that of typical plant cells. In anaphase, as the chromatid groups separate, there are interchromosomal fibers as in plants, but they vanish in telophase without furnishing any visible structure. Animal cells have no cell wall. Instead, during telophase, the cell membrane draws inward—a process called *constriction,* which effectively pinches the cytoplasm in two and provides a double layer of cell membrane between the cytoplasm of the two daughter cells. Cytokinesis is then complete. Meanwhile, the spindle fibers and astral rays vanish, and only the centriole is left, still just outside the nuclear membrane but associated now with the daughter nucleus rather than with the parent nucleus.

Chromosomes

When to call a chromatid a chromosome is one source of confusion in mitosis. The dual nature of the chromosomes can be demonstrated as early in mitosis as stains will differentiate between nucleoplasm and chromosomes. In some preparations, in fact, it is possible to see in late prophase that each chromatid is itself a dual structure, longitudinally twinned. Just when each chromatid reduplicates lengthwise is still a matter of conjecture, but for the basic importance of mitosis, the timing of this event is not significant. The essential feature is that regardless of the equality or inequality of cytoplasmic division between the two daughter cells, each of these new living units receives from the pre-existing parent a complete set of chromosomes—one from each chromosome of the parent nucleus.

Since all plants and animals fundamentally begin life with a single cell that has a nucleus with a definite number of chromosomes, and since in the embryonic development that nucleus becomes two, and then four and then eight, and so on to build up a multicellular organization or a number of separate cells, the process of mitosis insures that each cell produced has a nucleus with the exact same number of chromosomes in the precise assortment—one for each chromosome in the single cell from which the organism grew. Thus the modifications that make a cell a muscle fiber or a leucocyte, or a neuron or an epithelial gland, do not involve the chromosomes of the nucleus; in this respect all the cells of the body are alike.

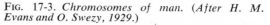

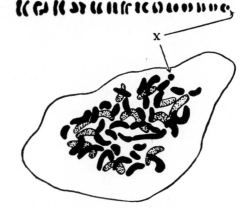

FIG. 17-3. *Chromosomes of man. (After H. M. Evans and O. Swezy, 1929.)*

Moreover, each organism is unique in its chromosomal content. The number of chromosomes is characteristic of each species, and details of the organization of each chromosome also differ from one kind to another. Thus man has 48[1] chromosomes per nucleus (Fig. 17-3), an ameba 6, a horse 60, a crayfish 200, a sweet pea 14, a bracken fern 144.

[1] Extensive study of human chromosomes reported in 1956 and 1957 indicated that 46 chromosomes may be a more representative number, perhaps with some variation in different genetic groups of mankind.

The Role of the Nucleus

Since every cell appears to contain the nucleoprotein material of which chromosomes are composed, and since all except the bacteria and blue-green algae have this nucleoprotein material organized into a nucleus, it is clear that the nucleus is important to life. Two lines of investigation have helped understand the significance: (1) experimental manipulation of living cells; and (2) research in cytogenetics—working out the detailed correspondence between events involving the chromosomes and events in the inheritance of body structure and function. The latter field of study is considered in Chapter 19.

By microsurgery (Fig. 17-4), it is possible to deprive a cell of its nucleus. The fragment lacking a nucleus may be able to continue

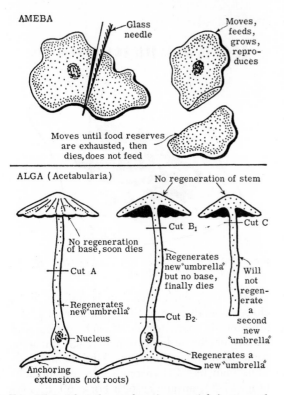

FIG. 17-4. *That the nucleus is essential for growth and other anabolic activites is indicated in experiments using microsurgery. Only the fragment of an ameba containing the nucleus can feed, grow, and reproduce. Parts severed from the alga Acetabularia vary in the amount of regeneration possible, but only the portion with the nucleus remains able to repeatedly replace severed parts.*

with many life processes, but not with extensive repair and never with reproduction. The red blood cells of mammals are famous as naturally enucleate cells.

Apparently, substances from the cytoplasm pass into the nucleus, are arranged or rearranged through the action of substances in the chromosomes, and emerge from the nucleus again and migrate to the microsomes, there determining the constitution of proteins undergoing synthesis. Since these proteins then serve as enzymes controlling all metabolic chemistry, the nucleus can be regarded as carrying the blueprints according to which the chemical processes of the species are established and maintained.

No doubt these chemical activities differ from species to species in ways that produce the structural dissimilarities by means of which we identify each kind of organism. Yet within a single individual, the various cooperating cells are not alike—even though they appear to have the same chromosomal complement.

Experimental investigation of these aspects of nuclear control was extended in 1952 through the new technique of transplanting a living nucleus from one cell to another. Early work with the method was restricted to the growing embryos of animals (amphibians). Some interchangeability within the same species seemed possible even between cells at different developmental ages.

On the other hand, mitosis and development of the cytoplasmic apparatus seen during the process seem to depend upon the cytoplasm. Experiments by M. Hartmann, published in 1928, demonstrated that if an ameba is prevented by repeated surgery from building a critical volume of cytoplasm, it will not divide; instead the cell appeared to be potentially immortal. Cells in which mitosis is not followed by cytokinesis must follow some other triggering mechanism.

2. CELL NUMBER

Following the discovery of mitosis, it was assumed that growth meant an increase in cell number. Then it was recognized that some of the rotifers in pond water go through an embryonic development resulting in as few as 128 cells, and that from then on they increase in size only by enlargement of that fixed number of units. Although the rotifer is small in comparison with most other metazoans, this principle has wider ramifications than was first appreciated.

Thus, H. H. Donaldson, working at the Wistar Institute of Anatomy in Philadelphia, found that in rats the number of cells in the cerebral cortex reaches its maximum 20 days after birth—long before the rat is full grown. The brain continues to enlarge, but the mitoses of the cortex are ended and increases in dimensions do not involve new cell formation. Similarly, William Trager, investigating flesh-fly larvae at the Rockefeller Institute for Medical Research, learned that when these maggots hatch from the egg, their embryonic development has already provided the full quota of larval cells. Each cell is small, and during the several stages of growth (interrupted briefly by molting), the cell number remains constant although the volume of the individual increases many fold. In later maggothood, new cells do form, but they are precursors of adult tissues and preparatory to the amazing changes during pupation. This latter occurs within the fixed dimensions of the hardened skin of the last larval stage, and includes disintegration of all the maggot tissues into what seems to be a "soup"—almost as though digestion had taken place. Within this liquid medium, the new adult structures develop, fuse, and become organized into the complex functional anatomy of the adult fly. The controlling factors are a complete and challenging mystery.

3. GROWTH AND FORM

Repeated duplication of cells and elongation along a single axis produces a filament. Along two axes growth produces a flat plate of tissue, such as a thallus. Growth in three dimensions might form a sphere—as it does in the early stages of a vertebrate embryo.

Enlargement at a uniform rate is rarely met in multicellular plants or animals. Instead, some parts grow faster than others and produce local enlargements. Thus the final form of a multicellular organism is a result of **differential growth**—enlargement at unlike rates in different parts.

Sometimes differential growth rates are responsible for seemingly strange disproportionate development. Each new set of antlers grown by deer, elk, or moose are larger than the preceding set to a degree far greater than the increase in body size. By contrast, the human head at birth is a far larger proportion of the total volume of the individual than at maturity; the head does not continue to enlarge as rapidly as do the body parts.

4. DIFFERENTIATION

Among some plants and most animals, the growth process is most rapid early in life, and slows perceptibly with age. The individual cells become more specialized or "differentiated."

To learn more about the normal growth process and the basis for differentiation, an experimental program was begun in 1912 at the Rockefeller Institute for Medical Research. On January 17, Alexis Carrel opened a hatching hen's egg and by neat surgery removed a small piece of tissue from the beating heart. This sample he placed in a warmed, humidified chamber with a few drops of chick blood plasma. For a time the fragment of heart continued its regular beating, then it slowed down and showed every sign of stopping. Carrel and his assistant, A. H. Ebeling, gently washed the fragment with warm isotonic salt solution, to learn if products of contraction or other metabolic activity might be accumulating and poisoning the tissue. Almost at once it resumed its beat. The two men then arranged for a regular replacement of nutrient plasma. Beating continued, and soon the dimensions of the cell mass began to change; the fragment of tissue was growing. Mitoses occurred and each cell enlarged to reach normal size. Eventually the tissue became so bulky that it was in difficulty again, since nutrient materials did not diffuse rapidly enough to the central regions. The experimenters divided the cell mass and discarded half. Soon a routine was established: replace nutrient plasma and divide the tissue every 48 hours.

Nearly 50 years have passed since that January day. The tissue was still alive and beating regularly until the late 1940's, when the experiment was terminated deliberately. From two to ten years is the life span of a chicken. Carrel received a Nobel prize in medicine (1912), retired, and died. Still the heart tissue grew and pulsated. Ebeling continued as custodian of the "tissue culture," but since he found no reason to expect new developments, prolongation of the time-consuming care seemed futile. The tissue seemed potentially immortal under the conditions of the experiment. Had all the cells been left, and had means for sustaining their growth been possible, the total volume would now be several times that of the earth. That they do not differentiate into mature heart tissue, go through senile deterioration, and die is the most fascinating part of this study.

A corresponding experiment involving tomato root tips has been carried on for many years by P. R. White, also of the Rockefeller Institute. A fragment of embryonic tobacco stem tissue is similarly thriving in nutrient solution, growing in volume about 50 per cent each day. Other men, in various laboratories, have demonstrated the same ability to grow cells in tissue culture, without differentiation —whether the cells come from assorted plants, miscellaneous animals, or man.

The ability to grow at such a rate is recognized as a characteristic of "youthful" tissues. With increase in bulk, changes set in that reduce the rate of mitosis, limit the volume attainable per cell, and modify the protoplasm in some way that restricts its future possibilities.

So long as a tissue is able to grow, it can be described as "competent." But progressively under ordinary circumstances the tissues of an organism become mature, differentiated, and incompetent. Eventually the point is reached where even repair of minor accidental damage is no longer possible. With no reserves for emergencies, the organism has become senile and will succumb to the first serious difficulty encountered. Author and playwright G. B. Shaw stated the case simply on the occasion of his 90th birthday, when he was questioned about how long a man can live. He replied: "I do not admit any limit to human life except the statistically certain fatal accident, which must occur to everyone sooner or later."

5. REGENERATION

The healing of a wound is a highly interesting process, because the steps follow one another with such regularity. The vertebrate reaction begins with a blood clot, together with exuded serum that seeps through and then dries, forming a scab and furnishing some mechanical protection to the delicate exposed tissues below, allowing better control of water relationships in those tissues, and localizing the region of probable infection. In a terrestrial animal the scab keeps underlying tissues from drying out. Instead, their cells can both maintain ordinary activity (for the most part) and also undergo some extraordinary growth, so that new connective tissues bridge the gap—from intact cells on the one side of the wound to those on the other. These preliminary tissues are lacking in normal waterproofing and are deficient in mechanical strength. If the scab is removed, the area below it soon wrinkles through desiccation; it may crack open as dying cells give way, and it tears very easily. But as time goes on while the scab forms a covering, the bridging tissue gains in thickness, in strength, and in waterproof qualities, until through its own action the scab comes loose and falls away. The exposed area is covered by a temporary coating of scar tissue—largely connective, with interlocking fibers. But with further time, the adjacent cells of the body surface duplicate themselves and extend into the scar zone, gradually obliterating it.

The repair process is due both to undifferentiated cells that remain scattered over the body (hence happen to be in the vicinity of the wound) and to the "dedifferentiation" of cells in the damaged area. These multiply themselves and bridge the gap. But more than this, healing is a measure of the growth energies in an individual. In the early portion of a lifetime, these growth energies vastly outweigh the fairly regular deterioration of the body through normal activity. As age accumulates, the growth energies diminish and eventually reach a level approximately equal to the regular disintegration; such is characteristic of maturity. When the deteriorative processes outweigh the remaining growth energies (Fig. 17-5), the organism has reached senility. Death then becomes more likely from even minor damage.

The relative position of the growth energy level and the disintegrative level can be evaluated in terms of the rate of repair of a wound. It is true that within reasonable limits the

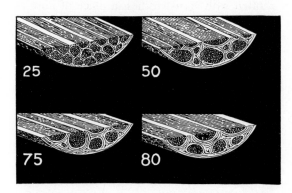

FIG. 17-5. *Decrease in contractile tissue and increase in inactive connective tissue is a mark of aging in human muscle. (After Hardin.)*

rate is roughly proportional to the size of the damaged area, but the late Lecomte du Nöuy showed how regularly the rate of repair falls off with age (Fig. 17-6). He measured rates of healing as change in wound areas with time, and concluded that from such information a different interpretation could be placed on the biological processes. He proposed, in fact, that in place of the ordinary chronological age of an individual (measured in hours, days, months, or years from birth, or from fertilization), a truer "biological age" could be determined, measured in rate of tissue repair. In these terms, the hour or day of a

child contains a number of biological events comparable with a week or year of an old man. Learning or growth or tissue repair are completed in the short chronological period of youth or the long chronological period of old age. On a biological basis the events are comparable, but the time scale is less familiar. In other words, an organism does slow down measurably as it gets older, and resistance to damage is one indication of how far the slowing has proceeded. The rate of slowing is not uniform from individual to individual, nor from year to year, nor from tissue to tissue.

Repair of damage is possible on considerably more elaborate scales among the lower vertebrates and among the invertebrates. A young salamander in the gilled stage will replace a complete limb if it is severed—experimentally or in escape from an enemy. Lizards grow new tail tips. Spiders and crabs

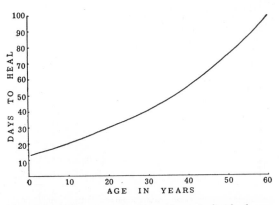

FIG. 17-6. *The rate of aging of an individual can be plotted in terms of the number of days required to heal over a wound two inches across. Or different individuals can be compared in terms of their "biological age" according to this rate rather than their chronological age. (Data from Lecompte du Noüy.)*

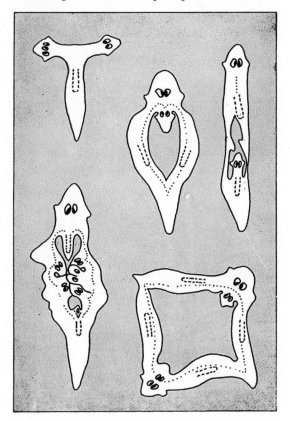

FIG. 17-7. *The nature of controlling forces in repair and regeneration may be studied in Planaria, a free-living flatworm. Some of the resulting monsters are striking. (After Hull.)*

regenerate legs, yet the lobster can replace an antenna or leg but not an eye (it forms an antenna-like organ in place of an eye if the entire eyestalk is removed). Earthworms will regenerate the first few segments and replace the posterior half of the body, but

dividing them through the heart and reproductive segments is invariably fatal to both halves. The flatworm Planaria, on the other hand, recovers from all manner of mutilation —often with monstrosities in place of normal individuals (Fig. 17-7). Hydra received its name in the 16th century when the Abbé Trembley discovered that he could cut the

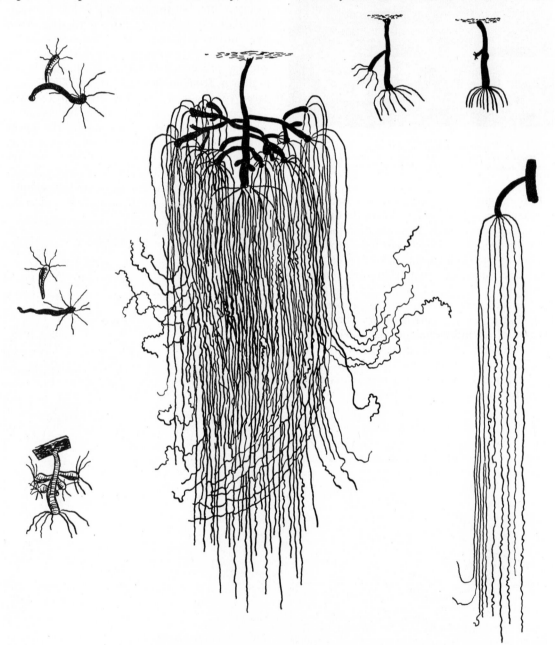

FIG. 17-8. *The first scientific studies of regeneration were those of Trembley, who examined and experimentally cut the fresh water coelenterate, Hydra, and gave it its name. (Redrawn from Trembley, 1744.)*

animal with a scalpel and induce formation of new tentacle-bearing "heads" seemingly without limit (Fig. 17-8); *Hydra* in Greek folklore had this characteristic. Regeneration of sponges pressed through a silk screen has been commented on earlier (p. 137, 138). Thus, with increasing complexity as well as with increasing age, the ability to repair and to replace is progressively less.

6. CANCER

Reappearance of active cell division and growth after an organism has achieved full size is often a sign that something has gone wrong with the central control mechanisms. Uncontrolled growth is cancer's chief characteristic.

The general name **neoplasm** is preferred to the loosely used terms *tumor* and *cancer*. Often a distinction is made between the relatively harmless "benign" neoplasms (such as warts) and the dangerous "malignant" types. But a benign neoplasm can become malignant, or the malignancy may be arrested spontaneously. No real understanding has been reached for the mechanisms involved.

The two most important types of human malignancies are *carcinomas* of epithelial tissues and *sarcomas* of connective tissues. The danger from a malignant neoplasm is partly from the inroads made by the developing tissue upon adjacent and often vital organs, and partly from the unpredictable ability of neoplasms to release parts of themselves into the blood stream—which carries them throughout the body and starts new cancerous growths in dozens or hundreds of sites. The medical term for such duplication is **metastasis** (from the Greek *metastasis,* from *methistanai* = to place in another way); the cancer is said to *metastasize,* and it is then referred to as metastatic. On this basis even very small cancers, such as minute *melanomas* of the skin (containing the black pigment melanin, hence the name) can multiply until they prove fatal.

One strange feature of secondary neoplasms is that the areas contain cells with the same type of tissue as the original neoplasm. The site of the metastasized cancer does not affect the tumor cells.

Neoplasms may continue, spreading farther and farther (Photos 203-205), with no restriction based on the welfare of surrounding tissues. They may lay aside ordinary aerobic nutrition, become wastefully anaerobic, or attack and digest surrounding tissues parasitically.

The causative agents in cancer are being sought diligently. It is known that excessive and continued exposure to certain wavelengths in sunlight can cause cancer of the skin. A number of chemical compounds called "carcinogenic agents" may induce cancer. A few of these agents are related in their molecular structure to the sex hormones. A limited amount of success has been found experimentally in arresting hopeless cancers by surgical removal of sources of androgens, such as the adrenal glands.

Public support for research in this field is of the utmost importance. At present only heart disease kills more people annually in civilized areas than does cancer; one in five die of cancer, usually well before "old age." Moreover, the incidence of cancer in civilized society seems to be increasing (see p. 470). For these practical reasons, every intelligent person should be informed that (1) there is *no* conclusive evidence that human neoplasms are hereditary; *anyone* can develop cancer; (2) a majority of neoplasms can be cured completely *if treatment is prompt*—with the promptness measured in weeks, not months or years; (3) only three ways have been found to cure cancer: X-ray, radium, and surgery.

Each individual should be thoroughly familiar with the 7 danger signs that *may* mean cancer; they give the best possible warning to seek a prompt medical checkup:

1. Any sore that does not heal.
2. A lump or thickening in the breast or elsewhere.
3. Unusual bleeding or discharge.
4. Any change in a wart or mole.
5. Persistent indigestion or difficulty in swallowing.
6. Persistent hoarseness or cough.
7. Any change in normal bowel habits.

Free diagnostic clinics are maintained in every state by the American Cancer Society, Inc. (47 Beaver St., New York 4, N. Y.); at many of these, therapy is available.

7. DEATH

Death is an individual affair. It happens cell by cell, as the cessation of metabolic processes. Once a cell loses the ability to reproduce itself, its death is predictable.

Multicellular organisms do not die at a single time. Xylem cells and fibers die in reaching mature usefulness; a cork cell provides no waterproofing until it is dead. Our own bodies have begun to die even before birth: the outer layers of the skin must be dead, loaded with waterproofing materials, ready to resist desiccation in the event of birth anywhere during the last few months of pregnancy. And after birth, not only are these dead skin cells constantly sloughing off and being replaced by fresh ones from below, but the lining of our digestive tracts from mouth to anus is continually losing dead cells worn from the surface by contact with food and waste.

There is no such biological event as a "moment" of death. When cessation of activities occurs in cells essential to the coordination of an organism, the *individual* can be regarded as dead. Irreversibility is the essential feature of this cessation. But the separate cells die one at a time, and some may remain functional for hours or days after the life of the individual organism is irretrievably ended.

SUGGESTED READING (see pp. 505-511)

Classics and Milestones: Flemming, Thompson.

Recent and Informative: Ashby, 1949; Braun, 1952; Conklin, 1949; Danielli, 1952; Gray, 1953; Greene, 1948; Lansing, 1953; Lüscher, 1953; Mazia, 1953, 1956; Moog, 1948; Rose, 1949; Schrader, 1952; Smith, 1954; Waddington, 1953; White, 1950.

203. The basal cells of the skin may proliferate at the expense of their neighbors, as a basal cell carcinoma.

ALMOST ANY TISSUE CAN BECOME CANCEROUS, BUT IDENTIFICATION USUALLY DEPENDS UPON CAREFUL STUDY OF STAINED SECTIONS

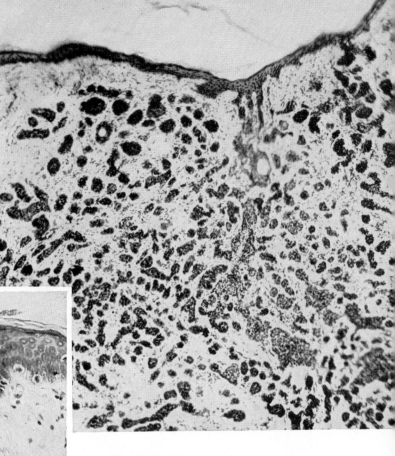

204. Normal skin for comparison.

205. The squamous cells may lose their normal control, as a squamous cell carcinoma.

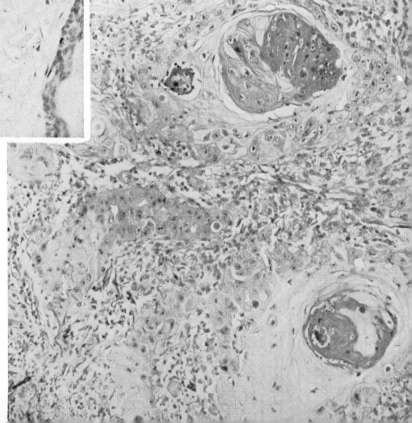

206. Frogs in amplexus are almost impossible to separate. The stimulus of the fore legs of the ♂ clasped around the body of the ♀ is the final factor required to induce egg laying. Emergence of eggs somehow stimulates the ♂ to discharge sperm suspension over them before the jelly layer has swollen with pond water.

207. Mating flukes (Schistosoma), in which the more slender ♂ uses a specialized penis in introducing sperm into the larger ♀ worm's body.

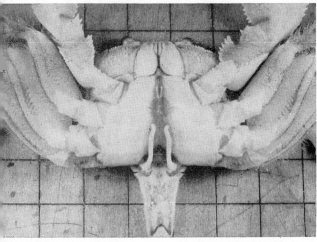

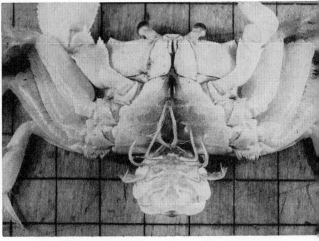

208. Ventral view of a crab (Ocypoda), showing the specialized swimmerets of the ♂ (normally concealed by the abdominal apron) with which sperm are transferred to paired openings of the ♀.

209. The corresponding view of the ♀ crab, showing the broader abdomen (turned back) and relatively unspecialized swimmerets to which the fertilized eggs remain cemented until hatching.

210. Copulating earthworms, in which each worm receives sperm from the other and each has its own eggs to be fertilized. Somehow, large earthworms find and mate with large earthworms, small with small, and medium-sized with their equals. Only in this way can sperm-carrying ducts be formed through apposition of longitudinal grooves on each worm.

18 · Development of the Individual

1. THE GERMPLASM. 2. ANIMAL EMBRYOS—FERTILIZATION, ACCESSORY STRUCTURES, THE SPERM, EMBRYONIC BEGINNINGS, ORGANOGENY, DIFFERENTIATION, TOTIPOTENCY, THE EGG, EXTRAEMBRYONIC MEMBRANES, STORED FOOD, THE FETUS, DEGREE OF DEVELOPMENT, METAMORPHOSIS. 3. PLANT EMBRYOS—GYMNOSPERMS, ANGIOSPERMS, DORMANCY, DISPERSAL.

THE STEPS taken by a single cell in becoming a whole new individual are so numerous, interesting, and varied that a special subdivision of biology is needed to encompass their study. The investigation of these successive changes is the domain of embryology.

In each instance, a seemingly simple cell divides into two, the two into four, and so on, establishing a cell lineage that ends in great diversity. Differential growth and differentiation may occur simultaneously or in sequence.

At the beginning of its development the single cell contains within it both the inheritance of its species and also the full potentialities of a new individual. It is **totipotent.** But as mitosis and cytokinesis succeed one another, there may be a gradual loss of potentialities in individual cells. In proportion as they become differentiated they lose their interchangeability, and can be said to be only partipotent.

1. THE GERMPLASM

The development of animal embryos differs from that of plant embryos in that the animal soon sets aside certain cells which retain totipotency whereas the rest lose this feature progressively. The cells set aside become reproductive tissue. They constitute the **germplasm,** as a contrast to the body or *soma*. This distinction was emphasized first by the embryologist August Weismann in the 1880's. He was impressed by the continuity of the germplasm, forming new germplasm plus soma at each generation (Fig. 18-1). The germplasm thus has potential immortality, whereas the death of somatic cells (and of the body as a whole) is predictable as soon as the two lineages of cells have separated.

Viewed in these terms, it is easy to see why attention centers on reproduction when considering a multicellular organism. Adaptations in structure and function of the organism's body serve primarily the task of reproducing the species. To the classic question, "Which came first, the hen or the egg?" there is a clear biological answer. The egg *always* comes first. The hen is merely a device that makes more probable that the egg will attain this dominant position. Man and woman too, are only the tools of the sex cells—expendable masses of tissue in each instance that further the immortality of the germplasm.

Among plants the reproductive tissue is less confined. Totipotent cells are retained at many sites, and form the basis for both vegetative reproduction and the development of sex organs in embryophytes.

In either kingdom, however, specializations of the parent organism are intimately associated with embryonic development. These may serve to improve the chance that each egg will be fertilized by a sperm (Fig. 18-2). Or they may furnish the food supply and whatever protection is essential until the fertilized egg has developed through embryonic steps into an independent, self-feeding individual. Often it is impossible to understand the embryonic steps without simultaneously considering the mechanisms and conditions under which the sperm reaches the egg and the embryo subsequently develops.

2. ANIMAL EMBRYOS

Even though the great majority of animals move around, a central problem remains in getting a sperm cell to each egg. A wide variety of modifications improve this chance meeting.

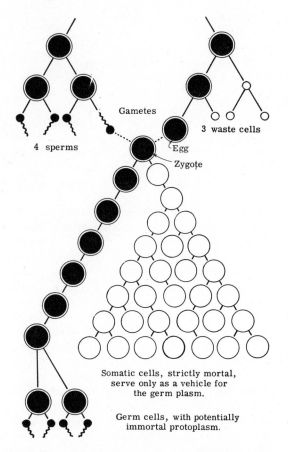

Gametes

3 waste cells

4 sperms

Egg

Zygote

Somatic cells, strictly mortal, serve only as a vehicle for the germ plasm.

Germ cells, with potentially immortal protoplasm.

FIG. 18-1. *The continuity of the germplasm is a fundamental principle among animals that limits the soma to being a mere carrier of the reproductive cells.*

Fertilization

The many specializations related to achieving fertilization may be considered from the standpoint of the relative role of chance, or in terms of devices which provide a fluid medium for sperm travel. Each represents a successful solution to the basic problem.

1. AQUATIC ORGANISMS IN WHICH EGG CELLS AND SPERM CELLS ARE BOTH LIBERATED BY THE PARENT(S) AND IN WHICH FERTILIZATION IS COMPLETELY EXTERNAL: The echinoderms, such as starfish and sea urchin, are excellent examples, although there are many more among the worms, mollusks, and smaller phyla—so many, in fact, that in spring the upper levels of the ocean, where these gametes collect, become a sort of thin soup. The number of sex cells liberated by *each* parent usually runs into the millions or higher. Each gamete is provided with a small amount of stored food, which in the ♂ must give sufficient energy for locomotion toward chance meeting with an egg, and in the ♀ must be both adequate to allow time for a sperm to arrive, and also to feed the embryo until it reaches a stage of development where it can feed itself. Usually the embryonic period until the time of self-feeding is very short, and the complexity reached is not impressive. That it is adequate for survival in a highly competitive existence is partly indicative of the vast numbers that begin. Death to countless hordes still leaves many to carry on the species in each case.

2. AQUATIC ORGANISMS IN WHICH THE SPERM CELLS ARE LIBERATED FREELY BUT IN WHICH THE EGGS ARE RETAINED BY THE PARENT UNTIL THEY HAVE BEEN FERTILIZED: This is characteristic of Hydra, most jellyfish, many tapeworms, some clams, and others. The number of sperm cells far exceeds that of eggs, and the latter are provided in most instances with more food stores. The younger proglottids of some tapeworms (nearer the attaching scolex) become sexually mature as males and emit sperm into the intestinal contents of the host; the gametes reach other coils of the same or other tapeworms, to older proglottids in which the testes have atrophied and the ♀ sex organs are fully developed, ready with ripe eggs; later the proglottids with fertilized eggs separate from the chain and pass out with the feces (Fig. 20-6).

3. AQUATIC ORGANISMS IN WHICH THE EGGS AND SPERM ARE LIBERATED INTO THE WATER, BUT ONLY WHEN EACH PARENT IS STIMULATED BY THE PRESENCE OF THE OTHER: This method is characteristic of many fish which cooperate in pairs, the ♀ laying a few dozen or thousand eggs, then the ♂ spraying them with milt (sperm suspension), then more eggs, and so on. A variant of this system is to be noted among certain toads and frogs, in which

the ♂ clasps the ♀, and liberates sperm when the ♀ extrudes eggs (Photo 206). The pressure of the ♂ just behind the forelegs of the ♀ stimulates her to egg laying; the response can be elicited by placing a wire clip or clothespin suitably padded with cloth in the same position.

4. AQUATIC ORGANISMS IN WHICH THE EGGS ARE RETAINED BY THE FEMALE UNTIL AFTER FERTILIZATION, AND IN WHICH THE MALE INTRODUCES SPERM INTO THE BODY OF THE FEMALE: This is the process of **copulation.** In **hermaphrodite** animals (♂ and ♀ combined, from Hermes and Aphrodite, the ♂ and ♀ deities of ancient Greece), such as free-living flatworms, leeches, and many snails, this is more properly considered an exchange of sperm cells, since each individual receives sperm from the other and since the eggs of each are fertilized. In most there is a specialized **penis** that may be extended, carrying the duct from the testis, and a receptive **genital atrium** or **vagina,** leading either into a bladder-like, blind, **seminal receptacle** in which the sperm may be stored and nourished until the time of egg laying, or to an enlarged, modified portion of the oviduct where fertilization takes place as the eggs arrive from the ovary.

Where the sexes are separate (as, for example, in some worms, many mollusks, crustaceans, a few fish, and the whales and porpoises), copulation may involve an intromittent organ, or the openings of the reproductive ducts may be simply apposed while sperm are transferred from ♂ to mate. All of these devices save greatly on the volume of sperm suspension needed, since wastage is much reduced,

5. TERRESTRIAL ORGANISMS WHICH ARE HERMAPHRODITES: These chiefly include mollusks and that unusual group of annelids, the earthworms. The mechanism in many of the latter is particularly complex and interesting: the worms copulate above ground by overlapping the first few dozen segments and apposing the ventral surfaces, while the two worms face in opposite directions (Photo 210). On the under side of each worm are four longitudinal grooves; these, when matched properly, form four canals external to the worms' bodies, made fluid-tight by slime secreted cooperatively by the two individuals. Sperm emitted from the testes through short ducts

lead into these external longitudinal canals, pass lengthwise between the worms to enter seminal receptacles in each, and are stored

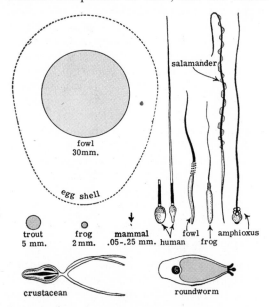

FIG. 18-2. *Great variation is evident in the form and size of reproductive cells among animals. The egg may be smaller than that of a mammal or as large as that of a bird (not counting the "white" of the egg or the shell). Sperm cells are all microscopic. (After Storer.)*

internally for a time. After the worms separate, each secretes a cylindrical sheath in the region of the glandular enlargement of the body known as the **clitellum;** the completed sheath slips over the body toward the anterior end of the worm, but it is so elastic that it conforms closely to the surface. As the sheath passes over the openings of the ducts from the ovaries, the eggs are discharged into the space between sheath and worm—causing the sheath to bulge out from the body. As the sheath passes the ducts from the seminal receptacles, the sperm are added and fertilization occurs outside the body but within the sheath. The sheath continues to slip forward until it slides off the anterior end of the worm. As it does so, it purses in still more and allows no significant loss of eggs or fluid. It is now called a **cocoon,** which remains in the earth until the eggs hatch and the young crawl out and away.

6. TERRESTRIAL ORGANISMS IN WHICH THE

SEXES ARE SEPARATE: These are chiefly the insects, arachnids, millipedes and centipedes, reptiles, birds, and mammals. All of them are highly adapted for transfer of sperm without returning to a pond or ocean in which the ♂ gametes can swim. Most exhibit some degree of display by the ♂ before the ♀, a behavior commonly referred to as "courtship." In most birds and some reptiles, copulation is entirely through apposition of the cloacal openings, with muscular movements of the genital ducts responsible for transfer of sperm to the ♀, and subsequent conduction of the sperm to the oviducts where the eggs are ready. In other reptiles and some birds, and in mammals, there is a penis and vagina; insects have an analogous intromittent organ plus a genital atrium and seminal receptacle.

Accessory Structures

In the vertebrates, the accessory parts of the reproductive system are extensive and so much involved with the excretory system that the two are referred to jointly as the **urogenital** mechanism. Each individual during its embryonic stages begins with precursors of both ♂ and ♀ reproductive systems,

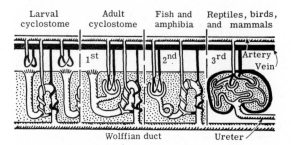

| Larval cyclostome | Adult cyclostome | Fish and amphibia | Reptiles, birds, and mammals |

1st   2nd   3rd   Artery Vein

Wolffian duct   Ureter

FIG. 18-3. *Primitively, the vertebrate kidney is a series of tubules emptying coelomic fluid with wastes into a longitudinal Wolffian duct, which opens to the outside world. This arrangement is functional in larval lampreys, but in adult cyclostomes a more intimate connection with the blood stream is established as a "first-type" kidney. Openings to the coelom are present in higher vertebrates only during early embryonic development. The kidney of fish and amphibians is "second-type" because the tubules are closed off, and only the posterior portion of the primitive kidney mass grows into the final organ. In reptiles, birds, and mammals an entirely new rudiment posterior to first- and second-type kidney rudiments becomes the functional kidney; it has its own duct, the ureter, to the bladder. The Wolffian duct then has importance only in the male, as a tube conveying sperm—the vas deferens.*

and these develop a considerable distance before the genetic control of sex exerts itself through the hormones.

Among the various vertebrates, three different types of kidneys are found (Fig. 18-3), and they arise consecutively in the embryonic development of those having as adults the second or third type. Each kidney occupies the dorsal part of the coelom on each side of the aorta. The simplest and most anterior kidney is that of cyclostomes, where there are ciliated nephrostomes opening to the body cavity, strongly reminiscent of the nephridia in the earthworm. This type reaches functional form but is replaced by a second kidney in fish and amphibians. The second kidney type is somewhat more complicated and also more compact; it involves further development of capillary meshwork around the kidney tubules. Like the first type, it empties into the cloaca by way of a longitudinal tube called the *Wolffian duct.*

In reptiles, birds and mammals, the Wolffian duct is retained only in males—as a functional part of the reproductive system. Otherwise the second-type kidney is gradually replaced during embryonic life by a third and final type, a functional unit that arises posterior to the embryonic precursors of previous kidneys and that has its own duct, the ureter. This last type has no connection with the coelom, but in the male its ducts become involved with the ducts of the reproductive system.

The vertebrate gonads arise adjacent to the kidneys. If the embryo is to become a ♂, fine tubules called *vasa efferentia* connect the rudimentary testis through the kidney into the cavity leading to the Wolffian duct (Fig. 18-4). In mature amphibians, the sperm follow this route to the cloaca and the outside. Even in the ♂ frog adult, however, there is usually a rudimentary oviduct on each side, leading from the anterior end of the body cavity to the cloaca. It is non-functional—a vestigial organ left from the embryonic stages prior to the assumption of dominant ♂ sexuality.

In the ♀ amphibian, this oviduct becomes enlarged and considerably convoluted, with heavy glandular walls. Eggs bursting from the ovary into the coelom are carried by beating cilia of the peritoneal lining to the anterior end of the coelom, there to enter the open end of an oviduct and proceed posteriorly, gaining on the way the jelly coating that corresponds to the white of a bird's egg and that after fertilization swells up in pond water as a protective buffer around the developing embryo.

In ♂ mammals, the reproductive mechanism develops the same connections through the kidney, but later a new third-type kidney develops with its own duct, the ureter. The second-type kidney degenerates (except for the fine tubules from the testis). These tubules become glandular and convoluted as an **epididymis;** they still empty into the old Wolffian duct, but now this has only a sperm-carrying function and is called a **vas deferens.** It maintains its connection with the excretory system at the base of the penis, where it joins the urethra from the bladder to form a common **urogenital** canal through which both urine and sperm can pass to the outside.

In most mammals, the picture is complicated further late in fetal life by the migration of the testes through an **inguinal canal** into a special external protrusion of the coelom, the **scrotum.** In some mammals this descent of the testes occurs only during the mating season. In others, as in man, it takes place normally somewhat before birth. The need for the migration is evident from study of those occasional individuals in which the testes fail to descend. In this condition of cryptorchy (*cryptos* = hidden, *orchis* = testis), the gametes fail to mature properly and the individual is sterile. The cause of the difficulty seems entirely due to temperature. In the scrotum, the testes are sufficiently cooler than they would be within the body cavity for maturation to proceed.[1]

In man, the inguinal canals ordinarily close more or less completely after the testes are in the scrotum. Connective tissue may fill them, but they remain a weak place in the coelomic wall. In lifting heavy weights a person may hold his breath and compress the abdominal musculature over the intestines so

forcibly that the inguinal canal on one or both sides opens and allows a loop of the gut to project as an **inguinal hernia.** The strain is definitely beyond that allowed by human structure. If the inguinal canals hold, corresponding hernias can be formed by parting of the muscle coats, allowing a loop of intestine to protrude through the abdominal wall. In woman, corresponding inguinal hernias form into the outer labia, which are homologous to the ♂ scrotum.

The sperm cells of mammals mature at a fairly steady rate during the period of reproductive life (Photo 251), and, gradually, move passively into the epididymis. Here the sperm accumulate, still not activated, but with nourishment supplied and with excretory and

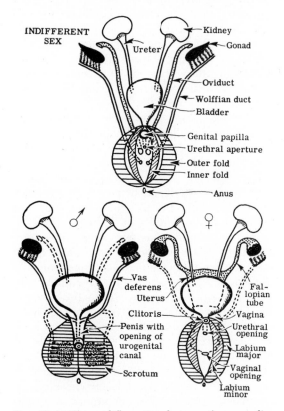

FIG. 18-4. *The undifferentiated stage of mammalian development shows the precursors of parts needed for both adult ♂ and ♀. In the ♂, the outer folds of the genitalia close to become a scrotum into which the testes descend, carrying with them a vas deferens each (broken lines); the oviducts remain rudimentary or disappear. In the ♀ the oviducts fuse into a vagina and uterus, and the Wolffian duct is lost.*

---

[1] In birds, where body temperatures are sometimes even higher by a few degrees, and where no descent of the testes occurs, it has been found that special air sacs of the respiratory system surround the testes, and ordinary breathing keeps them considerably cooler than the rest of the viscera.

respiratory needs taken care of by the tubule walls. From this point, two steps are involved in transfer of sperm to the ♀ during copulation:

1. The reflex control of blood from the penis partially blocks the veins returning from the organ, leading to distension of spongy vascular tissue within it, and enlarging and stiffening it as a hydraulic mechanism that derives its force from the ventricular contractions of the heart. By this **erection,** the terminal segment of the sperm-carrying urogenital canal is provided with sufficient support so that it can be inserted for some distance into the vagina.

2. Ciliary currents and muscular contractions similar to peristaltic waves bring the sperm cells from the epididymis down the vas deferens, past the glandular **seminal vesicles** and the prostate gland which add accessory fluids, and along the urogenital canal into which Cowper's glands also throw a supplementary secretion. The sperm is then ejaculated with some force from the end of the erect penis into the region of the vagina nearest the uterus. The accessory fluids add bulk to the ejaculate so that the sperm suspension becomes a **semen,** and also serve to activate the sex cells themselves until they lash their flagella and are ready to move under their own power through the ♀ genital tract. Muscular contractions of the ♀ reproductive system aid considerably in this migration.

The ♀ mammal has few comparable complications in the anatomy of reproduction; her complexities are hormonal. In connection with the habit of nourishing the developing embryo through a placenta within the oviduct, one portion of this tube is enlarged into a **uterus.** The oviducts from the two sides, in fact, are fused in varying degrees, but always have a single opening to the outside from a common vagina. In some mammals, such as the cow, the vagina is single but the uterus is strongly divided into two. In woman and some others, the uteri too are fused completely into a single central structure, into the antero-dorso-lateral corners of which the eggs are conducted by the two **Fallopian tubes**—the sole representatives of the embryonic oviducts. Fertilization in mammals usually occurs in the Fallopian tubes. Occasionally an embryo implants itself in this location instead of in the uterus—as a tubal (ectopic) pregnancy. More rarely the sperm reach the abdominal cavity and fertilize an egg which somehow has escaped the funnel end of the Fallopian tube (wrapped around the ovary though not attached to it)—and an abdominal pregnancy results. A few such instances in human beings have proceeded to full term before being identified. More frequently the blood supply available is too restricted, the embryo dies, and white cells from the blood remove the remains.

The Sperm

Of the three parts of the vertebrate sperm cell—head, middle piece, and flagellum—only the first two ordinarily enter the egg (Fig. 18-5). The head contains chiefly the nucleus, whereas the middle piece holds the centrioles. Commonly sperm entry precedes completion of egg maturation, but in all the sperm nuclear components eventually travel through the egg cytoplasm while an aster like that of mitosis develops around the approaching nuclei. The chromosomes become distinct and the two nuclei lose their identity, unite as a double group of chromosomes, and generally proceed from this point directly into the first mitosis of the developing embryo. Meanwhile, the delicate membrane that invested the egg separates slightly from the protoplasm as a "fertilization membrane" that seems to reduce the attractiveness of the egg for inducing the approach of further sperm.

Embryonic Beginnings

The activated egg—no matter how started

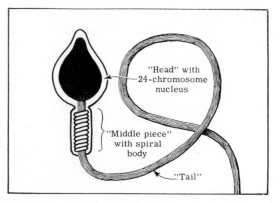

FIG. 18-5. *The structure of a human sperm cell.*

on its way—is a single cell. Usually it divides into two cells which cohere (Photos 211-215), the two into four, and so on, until a group of 16 to 64 have been formed. This is the

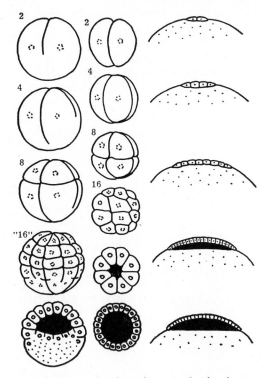

Fig. 18-6. *The essential similarity in the development of an animal embryo through cleavage to the blastula stage is seen as a development of a roof, one cell thick, over the cavity of the blastocoel. In a medium-yolky egg, such as that of an amphibian* (left column), *the process seems somewhat more comparable to that in a relatively yolk-free egg, as in Amphioxus and many invertebrates* (center column). *A very-yolky egg, as in birds* (right column) *achieves the same result though in a more restricted way.*

segmentation or **cleavage** stage of development. Then, as these cells continue in division, they rearrange themselves slightly as a hollow sphere in which each cell is at the surface; this stage in development is called a **blastula,** and the enclosed space is the **blastocoel** or segmentation cavity (Fig. 18-6).

Almost at once, in the least complicated cases, one side of the hollow sphere begins to indent, producing first a dimple toward the outside world, then a deep pocket which becomes more and more extensive as the cells of one hemisphere move into position close inside those of the other (Fig. 18-7). The product is a double walled cup—a two-lay-

ered animal—with an **ectoderm** toward the outside and an **endoderm** toward the center (Photos 216-217). The blastocoel is almost obliterated in this process, but a new cavity occupies a central position. It is the precursor of the digestive cavity, and is called the **archenteron** (from *arch* = primeval, *enteron* = gut). The archenteron may continue to communicate with the outside world through the open **blastopore,** or the lips around the blastopore may close to isolate the archenteron in the center. The embryo is now a **gastrula,** a stage produced by the infolding changes of **gastrulation.** The similarity of a gastrula to an adult coelenterate such as Hydra is striking and considered to be significant; only the secreted jelly layer, the tentacles, and differentiation of the cells in outer and inner layers are lacking.

The succeeding steps depend more upon the type of animal into which the fertilized

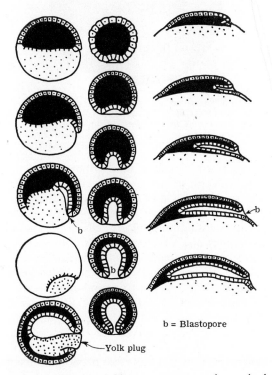

b = Blastopore

Yolk plug

Fig. 18-7. *The infolding or overgrowth or both whereby a blastula becomes a gastrula in medium-yolky eggs* (left column), *in relatively yolk-free eggs* (center column), *and in very-yolky eggs* (right column).

egg will develop (Fig. 18-8, Photos 218-220). Among the vertebrates, three events follow gastrulation but occur simultaneously: (1) Folds of ectoderm rise up beside the mid-dorsal line of the embryo, meet above, and

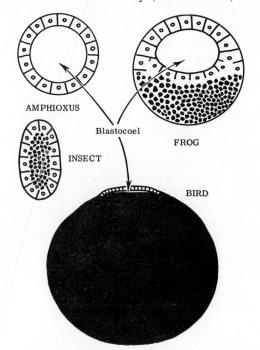

FIG. 18-8. *Sectional views through the blastula stage show the degree of yolkiness* (black granules or solid black area) *and the position of this food store. In insect and bird embryos the yolk never becomes cellular before it is absorbed as nourishment.*

separate off a longitudinal tube that is the hollow dorsal nerve cord—precursor of brain and spinal cord; this is the **neural tube,** produced by **neurulation** (Fig. 18-9). (2) At the same time, undifferentiated cells in the region of the blastopore (where ectoderm joins endoderm) migrate or proliferate between the two primary tissues as **mesoderm,** the **third germ layer** of the body. (3) Corresponding in time to these events, a solid rod of tissue arises over the roof of the archenteron, in some forms as a contribution from the endoderm, in others from the mesoderm, and in still others from the lip of the blastopore itself between the mesodermal rudiments; this is the **notochord,** an embryonic stiffening structure characteristic of vertebrates and extending from the region just behind the brain-to-

be to the tip of the developing tail. The mesoderm soon extends throughout the body of the embryo, and in the region of the notochord soon shows signs of organization into paired blocks in a series from anterior to posterior—a demonstration that the vertebrate body is derived from a segmental plan.

As the embryo of a vertebrate progresses, it becomes clear that the ectoderm and endoderm contribute relatively little to the final body structure. Most of the mature organs are mesoderm, and very few are devoid of a large mesodermal component (Fig. 18-10). Thus the ectoderm contributes the neural tube material and the epidermis of the body surface (but the dermis is from the mesoderm). Other ectodermal derivatives include the lining of the mouth and the outer part of the rectum; the olfactory epithelium and other lin-

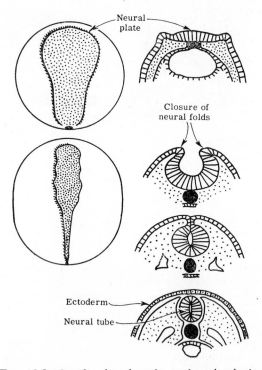

FIG. 18-9. *On the dorsal surface of a developing amphibian embryo, shortly after gastrulation, a thickened neural plate shows the organization of nervous tissue* (upper left); *it is evident in transverse section* (upper right). *Later the sides of the neural plate grow upward and toward the mid-line, finally closing and separating off the neural tube. At the same time, the roof of the archenteron rises and frees a rod of tissue as the notochord. Meanwhile the mesoderm becomes better organized between the ectoderm and endoderm, along each side of the neural tube and notochord* (lower right).

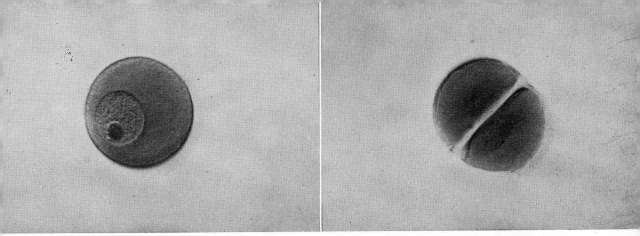

211. One cell.

212. Two-celled stage.

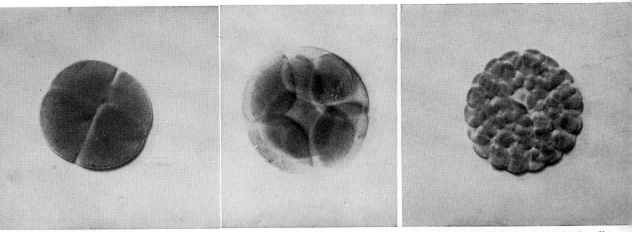

213. Four-celled.

214. Eight-celled.

215. Approximately a hundred cells, rearranged as a hollow blastula one cell thick.

EMBRYONIC DEVELOPMENT OF AN ANIMAL EGG CONTAINING LITTLE YOLK (Starfish)

216. Early gastrulation.

217. Late gastrulation.

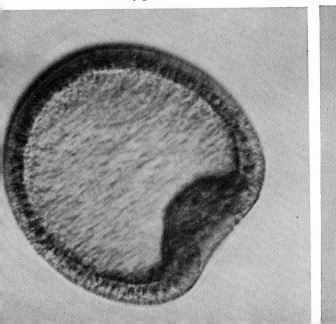

218. Frog eggs among water-logged leaves on the bottom of a pond in spring.

EMBRYONIC DEVELOPMENT IN AMPHIBIANS

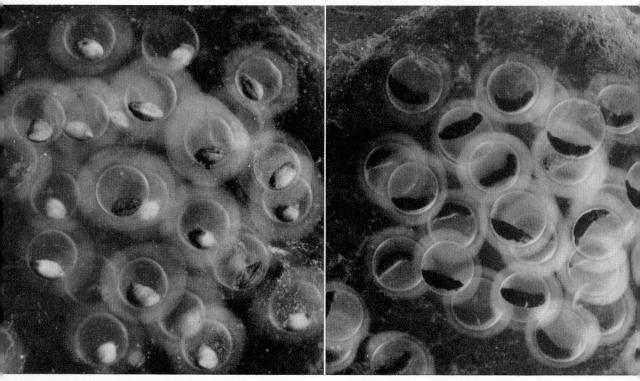

219. Salamander embryos which have recently closed the neural groove.

220. Salamander embryos a few days older, showing developing gills.

ings of the nasal region; the lens and conjunctiva of the eye; much of the ear; and part of those specializations familiar as scales, nails, claws, hooves, teeth, antlers and horns, and hairs and feathers.

The neural tube provides the cells of brain and spinal cord, of cranial and spinal nerves, and of the retina of the eyes.

The endoderm, in contrast, furnishes only the lining of the digestive tract from pharynx to rectum, including the lining of the lungs

and urinary bladder, the glandular parts and duct linings of the liver and pancreas.

The rest of the body is mesoderm: all muscles, all skeleton, all blood vessels, all centers of carbohydrate or fat storage, the excretory system, and the reproductive system. The endocrine organs are mesoderm, except for the pituitary (the posterior lobe of which comes from brain tissue whereas the anterior

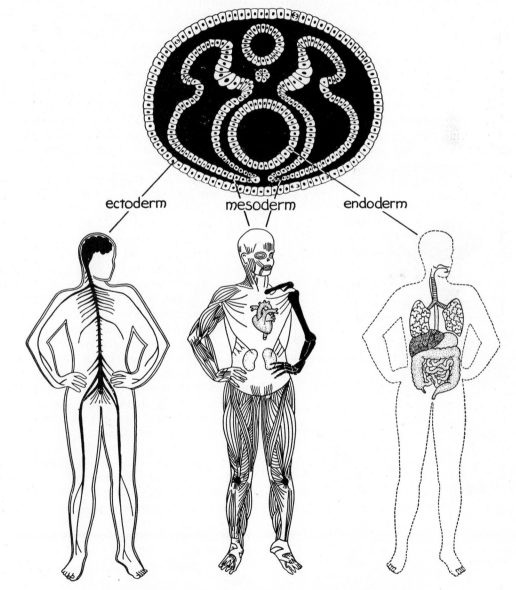

FIG. 18-10. *Products of the germ layers in a mammalian embryo.*

lobe is ectoderm from the mouth region), the thyroids, parathyroids, and pancreatic islets (all of which are endoderm).

Thus, refraction in the eye (by conjunctiva and lens) is an ectodermal contribution, supported and given both form and control by mesoderm (as the cornea and ciliary muscle—suspensory ligament mechanism). Light sensitivity is an extension of brain function (the retina and optic nerve). The rest of the eye, like so much of the body, is of mesodermal origin.

Organogeny

After the spread of mesoderm, development is on a cooperative basis, with the three germ layers interacting to lay down the beginnings of organs and organ systems. Disproportionate growth results in the characteristic final form of the various parts, and it is not difficult to trace the steps through which each organ appears. The general term **organog-**

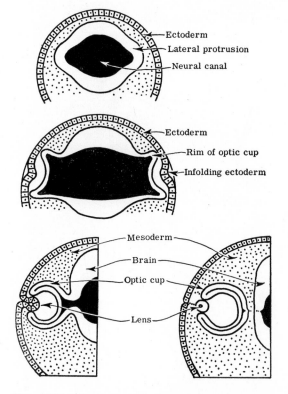

FIG. 18-11. *Formation of the ectodermal components of the vertebrate eye.*

eny is given to the process of formation. Thus, in a vertebrate embryo the fertilized egg undergoes segmentation to become a blastula with a single cell layer. Gastrulation distinguishes ectoderm from endoderm. Mesoderm develops, neurulation occurs, the notochord forms, and organogeny brings the embryo into a functional condition. Four examples will suffice to show how continuous is the series of changes that achieves the final result:

1. The brain arises from enlargement, folding, and specialization of the anterior end of the neural tube. Even as the ridges of ectoderm arise in the late gastrula, to meet on the mid-dorsal line and separate off the neural tube within, the anterior end of the tube is of larger diameter than the posterior end. Further growth in the anterior region takes place in three distinct rings, to give rise to a fore, mid, and hind brain. Among all those that develop a skull, a further division separates the fore brain into two and the hind brain into two, so that the complete structure consists of five regions one behind another, leading to a nerve cord that extends through the line of vertebrae. Further differential growth provides the further features described in Chapter 11.

2. The eyes commence as a pair of lateral outgrowths (Fig. 18-11) from the sides of the embryo's brain. Rapid enlargement transforms these extensions into cup-shaped bodies with a double wall, the hollow of the cup facing the ectoderm of the head region. Further disproportionate growth provides a fold extending brainward from the cavity of the cup, while the rim of the projection achieves a circular form. At this point in time, the whole **optic vesicle** may separate completely from the brain tissue. The rim of the cup comes into contact with the overlying ectoderm and stimulates the latter in some vertebrates to buckle inward ("invaginate" is the proper term), separating a ball of cells that later become organized into a lens for the eye. In other vertebrates the ectoderm when stimulated thickens and separates as a mass (by delamination), forming a lens of strictly comparable type. Meanwhile, the layers of the optic vesicle consolidate to become the retina, while mesodermal materials organize around them, providing the tough sclera and cornea, the iris and supporting structures around the

lens, and a film of vascular choroid plus connective tissues elsewhere and a net of capillaries over the inner surface of the retina. Meanwhile axons of nerve cells in the retina itself grow toward the notch in the rim as the optic nerve; they emerge from the eye and make their way to the brain. Soon the notch closes, so that the optic nerve appears to leave the eye from near the center of its optic axis. Then the lens becomes transparent, the cornea and ectoderm (the conjunctiva) over it clear up, and light can enter the eye to form an image on the retina. The nervous connections are complete, and the mesodermal contributions of eyeball and muscles to move it bring the organ into a functional condition.

3. The heart, blood vessels, and circulating fluid arise early in embryonic development. Among the mesodermal cells, "blood islands" appear as open tissue which fills with fluid and scattered cells. Gradually the walls become organized into veins leading toward a central straight tube which forks into arteries among the tissues of the forming embryo. Muscles appear around the central straight tube and soon it commences to contract in irregular rhythm. The tempo becomes more regular, the rate faster, and contractions propel the blood with its plasma and cells from veins to arteries. Valves and capillary connections come soon, and the embryonic circulation has begun a continuous operation that will cease only on death.

The heart elongates while a mesodermal sac (the pericardium) forms about it. The elongation throws the heart into folds (Fig. 18-12), so that the blood comes anteriorly from the veins, rounds a corner at the auricle, and passes posteriorly to the ventricle; there it turns again and is forced anteriorly into the arterial system. If the embryo becomes a fish, little more complexity is added. Among amphibians, however, at the stage when provisions are being made for terrestrial and aerial life, and when lungs develop, the auricle becomes divided into two and the new circulation from the lungs empties into the left auricle while venous blood from the body continues into the right. These modifications require neither cessation of the heart beat nor diminution in its function. Among bird and mammal embryos, the final division of the beating heart into a right and left auricle, a

right and left ventricle, is accomplished while the heart circulates blood through the embryo; the septa form and new pulmonary circulation is added to the functions already present.

4. Limbs arise as outgrowths of meso-

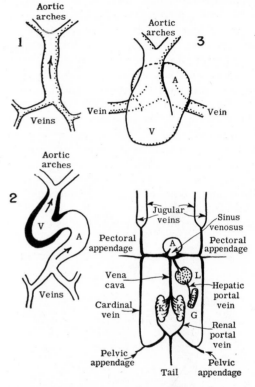

FIG. 18-12. *Formation of the vertebrate heart, and the fundamental plan of veins in a chordate embryo* (lower right).

dermal material covered by ectoderm. Just prior to the appearance of limbs in a fish, reptile, bird, or mammal embryo, the mesoderm becomes organized along the two sides of the notochord into definite paired blocks, each called a **somite**—a "body division." A pair of spinal nerves grows out in relation to the somite blocks in such a way as to lie in the space between the developing vertebrae. Cooperative growth of somites and nerve cord leads to mesodermal enclosure of the notochord and nerve cord as intersegmental precursors of the vertebrae themselves. To these the mesodermal cells that will produce skeletal muscles become attached, and progress in providing a skeletal support continues.

But at two regions along each flank of the

body, several somites together with their nerve supply become organized into limb buds (Photos 222-225). The anterior one produces a fin or a front leg or wing or arm, together with its nerve supply (as a plexus from several spinal nerves), while the posterior limb rudiment becomes a fin or a hind leg or a leg in the human sense, again with its plexus of nerves uniting to form a special supply for the appendage. Within the appendage, mesoderm becomes organized into muscles and skeletal support, and into blood vessels and connective tissues, while nerves gradually invade by extension away from the plexus and from the spinal cord. The nerves follow the muscles as these are differentiated from the more generalized mesoderm. Soon a functional, recognizable limb has evolved from an indefinite mass of embryonic limb bud. By special techniques it is possible to identify the source from which cells come into

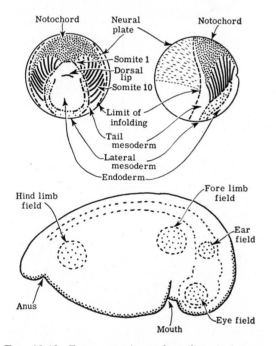

FIG. 18-13. *From experimental studies, it is possible to indicate on an amphibian egg in earliest gastrulation the areas that will become definite tissues and organs of the tadpole* (upper figures: left, *facing dorsal lip fold;* right, *at right angles to the lip); in later embryos the presumptive areas of limbs, ear, and eye can be identified and used for investigations of potentialities—totipotency or partipotency.*

all of these developing parts. The information may be charted (Fig. 18-13) but so far has not led to a satisfactory understanding of forces involved.

Differentiation

The interactions between one embryonic tissue and another are undoubtedly chemical, but the actual substances involved are still unknown. Certainly something (called an "organizer") passes from the optic cup tissue to the overlying ectoderm and stimulates the production of a lens, since a lens will form from almost any ectoderm experimentally placed over the optic cup, or an optic cup moved elsewhere on the body under undifferentiated ectoderm will call forth a lens at the abnormal site. Possibly the ultimate example of such experimental embryology was the test in which a transplanted optic cup was grown successfully under the skin of the tail on a frog tadpole. A lens formed, and a complete eye—even to representatives of the muscles for rotating the eyeball—formed in the strange situation. No connection to the nervous system was achieved by the optic nerve, so that the organ was functionless though perfect. And when the tadpole metamorphosed to a frog, its tail shrank until the eye came to be located on the midline at the most posterior point on the animal—glaring blindly backwards.

In this example, the eye tissue must have possessed some chemical difference from the surrounding tail tissue that prevented the eye from degenerating and being absorbed as were all adjacent cells. The nature of this difference is completely unknown.

Other studies have investigated the degree of differentiation in a limb bud area, and the terms totipotent and partipotent are applied on the basis of part of a limb bud's ability to produce a whole limb or only part of a limb. Where a limb bud is divided and still totipotent, it is usual for two complete limbs (each almost perfect) to form at the same general position on the animal's side. Spontaneous divisions of a limb bud or even of a presumptive head region are rare, but occur at intervals—producing animals with extra legs or double-headed monsters.

Separation of the first two cells formed by division of a fertilized egg (Fig. 18-14) may result in two individuals with exactly the same inherited characteristics—hence identical twins.[2] Or one of these two cells may ten identical triplets are the three survivors of identical quadruplets, where the first four cells from division of the egg separate. Among human beings, twins (counting both identical

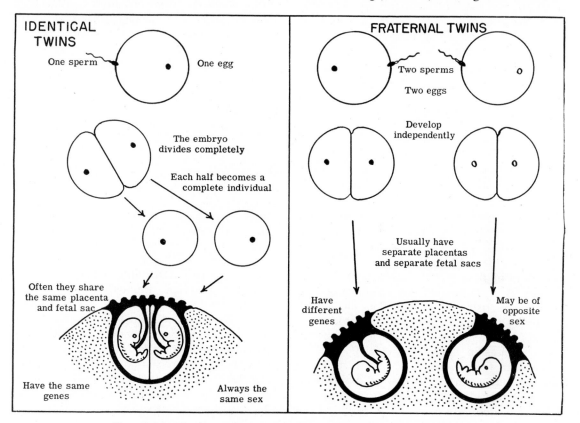

IDENTICAL TWINS

One sperm   One egg

The embryo divides completely

Each half becomes a complete individual

Often they share the same placenta and fetal sac

Have the same genes   Always the same sex

FRATERNAL TWINS

Two sperms
Two eggs

Develop independently

Usually have separate placentas and separate fetal sacs

Have different genes

May be of opposite sex

FIG. 18-14. *The physical basis of identical twins and of fraternal twins.*

again divide and separate, so that three individuals—identical triplets—are formed. Of-

[2] The closeness of the similarity in identical twins has been subject to statistical study. A mathematical expression, the **percent of correlation,** has been used, where 100 per cent represents complete correlation—hence identity—and zero a complete lack of correlation. In identical twins the correspondence in I.Q. is 91 per cent; correspondence in number of friction ridges in the finger-print patterns is 95 per cent. For fraternal twins (same birth but not identical, hence may be brother and sister), these values are 59 per cent and 46 per cent, respectively, whereas for siblings (brothers and sisters not born at the same time) the values are 50 per cent and 50 per cent. The correspondence for I.Q. of first cousins, however, is only 25 per cent. Such data suggest strongly that intelligence as well as physical makeup is largely hereditary.

and fraternal) are born about once in each 88 births, triplets once in each 7,600 births, and quadruplets once in each 670,000 births. A few instances of identical quintuplets that survived are on record. The Dionne family of Calendar, Ontario, has been observed with interest. Careful examinations of fingerprint patterns and other characteristics of the five girls have led to a reconstruction of the divisions producing them (p. 290).

Thus multiple births—whether identical (from the same fertilized egg) or fraternal (from separate fertilized eggs)—are not very common among human beings. In a few animals, however, this *polyembryony* is the customary event. The nine-banded armadillo is an example where each birth regularly involves identical quadruplets.

The Egg

Basically, each egg contains a single cell with the potential ability to grow into a reasonable facsimile of the parent. Accompany-

the least important of proteins in terms of food value.

The single cell in a snail's egg is not very different in size or appearance from that with the potentialities of becoming a man, a mouse, or a mackerel. The frog, the fowl, and the fishworm start from a single cell that is scarcely bigger or smaller than that giving rise to a hummingbird or a whale. Yet the

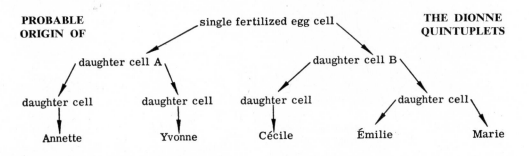

ing this single cell is a greater or lesser quantity of food in the form of clear oil globules or of yellow yolk granules. The amount is determined largely by the number of hours or days that the embryo must grow before it is large and vigorous enough to obtain nourishment outside of the egg—either by tapping a new food supply from its parent (as a mammal does) or by actively foraging (as in tadpole or chick). Another important feature in most eggs is a water supply, but again the degree of difficulty to be experienced by the embryo in obtaining further water determines how much of an aquarium will be provided by the parent. The white of a hen's egg is the water store (Fig. 18-15). The albumin it contains is a protein that preserves the neutral nature of the aquarium in spite of toxic substances added by the hemmed-in embryo. Quite incidentally, the albumin is nourishing, but it is one of

eggs of these animals are obviously unlike—in overall dimensions, amount of stored food and water, and in the protective covering or shell. But the shell is governed by the way in which the parent handles her eggs (Photos 226-233; Endpaper Photos G, M). Its presence generally means that the egg is designed to be deposited on land and exposed to air, without the buoyant support of water. The parchment-like covering of a turtle egg and the limy shell of a bird's are mechanical structures that keep the contents from spreading out like a pancake on a griddle. They serve, too, in deflecting chance blows, and in reducing water loss by evaporation.

An egg shell is not all gain. Its presence slows down the important exchange of carbon dioxide from the growing embryo for oxygen from the surrounding air. Yet this process must go on or the egg will never hatch. The thinner and more porous the shell, the better the exchange can take place, but also the poorer is the protection and support it affords. Each kind of creature seems to produce a shell that is as light as can be, considering the size of the egg. Thus the larger the egg, the heavier it is, and the stronger must be the shell that keeps it in shape. There is a definite limit to the size of an egg, because of the mutually incompatible requirements of strength and respiration. Without internal struts or partitions to aid in the support (and to offer additional complications for the em-

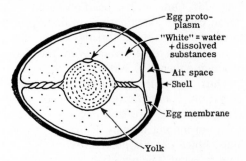

FIG. 18-15. *The structure of a bird egg.*

bryo), an egg cannot be successful if it is much larger than that of an ostrich.

For years there were claims that the non-existence of much larger eggs was due to the inability of any living organism to put into one shell a larger proportion of its own body materials. Then someone found the goose-sized Kiwi—a flightless bird of New Zealand —that is so profligate in egg-laying that its products weigh almost a third as much as the bird itself. Two such eggs in rapid succession (the normal clutch) is the physical limit of possibility. Yet the Kiwi hen survives. A corresponding effort on the part of an ostrich would yield 100-pound eggs that would either fall apart because of their own weight, or suffocate because of the increased thickness needed in the shell. The actual limit in size was approached most closely by the ostrich-like Aepyornis of Madagascar—now extinct for several centuries—which laid the largest known eggs: nine and one-half inches in diameter and thirteen long, with very thick shells (Photo 231).

The protoplasm of the single living cell of a bird's egg comes to lie centrally on the upper surface of the massive yellow yolk, as a small grayish-white spot (Fig. 18-15). Around this are wrapped successive layers of the white of the egg, then a tough membrane and the limy shell. Down the tube connecting the ovary to the outside world, the whole is driven by contraction of ring after ring of strong muscles. This rough treatment leaves its mark on the egg. The walls of the tube drag on the shell while it is still flexible, polishing its surface except over the two ends. The muscles impress a taper on the egg, giving it a streamlining like a tear-drop. The "round end" and the air cushion inside are at the front, to be laid first. The "pointed end" trails in conformity with the best principles of dynamic design. The eggs laid by young birds are not only smaller (due to a less generous food and water supply for the embryo), but also are more pointed or elongate because the passageways have not yet been stretched. An old hen, with distended oviduct, lays more nearly spherical eggs.

The great amount of stored food in a reptile or bird egg provides so much resistance to division of the cytoplasm with cell membranes that cleavage involves only a surface

layer; the yolk remains in a continuous mass (Fig. 18-8). Gastrulation is accomplished by an inward growth at the edge of the layer of cells produced by cleavage, and the embryo comes to develop on top of the yolk like a kitten on a big cushion. But as the new individual enlarges, the yolk is used up, the yolk sac shrinks, and, somewhat before hatching, is reduced to a small, wrinkled, yellow bag attached to the abdomen of the embryo.

Extraembryonic Membranes

Three structures in these very yolky eggs improve living conditions for the embryo (Fig. 18-16). One is a separate sac, the **allantois,** attached to the abdomen, into which nitrogenous wastes are transferred for storage. The other two are the **amnion** and the **chorion,** which arise from a rim-like fold of ectoderm plus mesoderm originally surround-

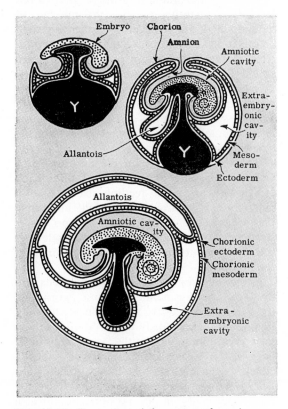

FIG. 18-16. *Formation of the extra-embryonic membranes, the amnion, the chorion, and the allantois. Yolk is shown in black; when enclosed by extension of membranes it is referred to as a yolk sac.*

ing the embryo on the yolky mass. As this converges to enclose the embryo, it closes off a fluid-filled amniotic cavity lined with amnion, and at the same time provides a richly vascular chorion which comes to line the shell and provide for more efficient respiratory exchange. Gradually, the amniotic cavity spreads beneath the embryo, until only a slender connection remains leading from the mid line of its abdomen and carrying blood vessels plus the slender neck of the allantois. As these structures develop inside the egg, the embryo appears more and more as a small animal surrounded by its private aquarium, and free to engage in considerable movement within the limits provided by its vital abdominal tether.

Stored Food

On a comparative basis, a hen's egg is close to the maximum in terms of total stored food. The quantity matches the number of days a chick must develop inside the shell before it is ready to brave the outside world. At the other extreme are organisms that are able to fend for themselves in as many hours. In their case the parent takes the other alternative: producing a vast number of eggs in a single season (Photos 226-233), providing little parental care, and leaving survival of the offspring largely to chance.

Toward this latter plan the eggs are provisioned for only a brief period until each individual can begin feeding itself. A thin membrane is sufficient protection, and since the ocean itself is the aquarium, no water store need be included with the single egg cell. The parents, moreover, need never meet each other.

Somewhat similar egg-laying methods are used by the degenerate parasitic worms in the vertebrate digestive tracts. These, too, are in a liquid that is chiefly water. Many of them broadcast minute eggs, either separately or in bags. These eggs, however, require shells—chiefly because of the likelihood of being digested by the parasite's host. To resist the potent ferments in an intestine requires a particularly impervious coating. Tapeworms and roundworms provide their young with such protection.

The mammalian egg (Photo 251) represents modification in another direction. Dissolved foodstuffs in the cytoplasm are sufficient for the early cleavage stages, and these are undergone while the beginning embryo descends the oviduct toward the uterus. Once in the uterus, the young individual moves into the maternal uterine tissues—seemingly a joint action, with the parental cells engulfing and the embryo "eating its way in." Soon it is embedded, and diffusion of foodstuffs from parent to embryo accelerates. But as the embryo enlarges through the gastrula stage its requirements apparently become too great for diffusion through the simple surface, and new structures, similar to the amnion and chorion of the bird or reptile embryo, appear. Again the amnion comes to surround an amniotic cavity and the embryo, while the chorion interlocks with the maternal tissues. It provides additional area for food transfer, for respiratory exchange, and for disposal of soluble wastes.

In some mammals, the chorionic tissue destroys the maternal uterine epithelium (Fig. 18-17), digesting it away until the embryonic covering is in direct contact with the walls of the mother's capillaries. It may stop at this point, and the nourishment, respiration, and excretion of the embryo go on through its own capillary walls, through the covering layer of cells composing the chorion, and through the capillary walls of the mother. But still other mammals go a step farther—in that the embryonic tissue invades the capillaries of the parent, ridding itself of even this slight barrier to diffusion. Why the mother's blood is not stimulated to clot by the invasion of the foreign embryonic matter, no one knows. Yet the embryo's chorion comes to be surrounded by little lakes of blood, in the most intimate possible contact consistent with completely separate vascular systems.

Collectively, the combination of maternal and embryonic tissues involved with the metabolism of the new individual is called the **placenta,** and no mixing of blood supplies should take place. As a result, offspring are commonly of a blood type different from that of the mother—the particular type following the chromosomal genes just as does any other character of the developing entity.

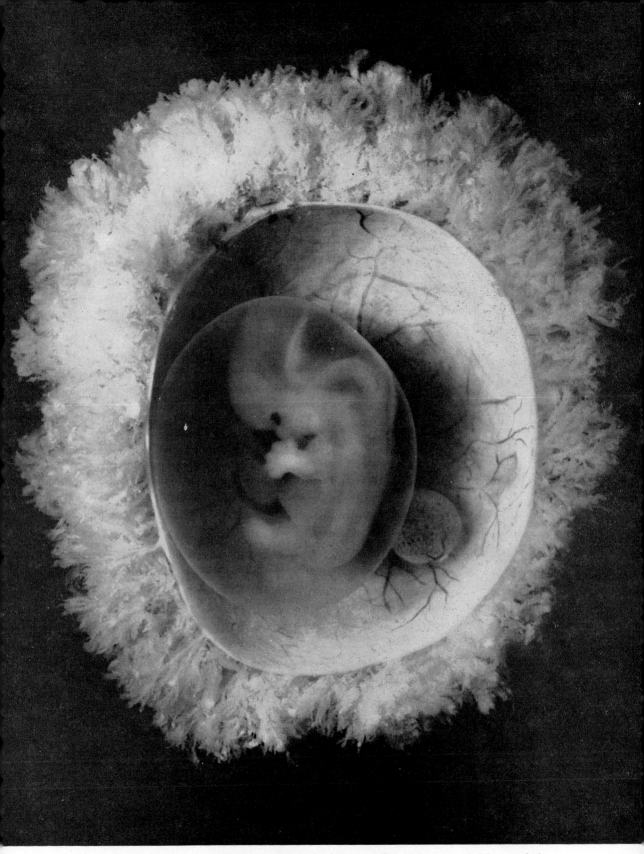

221. A 40-day human embryo still enclosed in its intact amnion and surrounded by amniotic fluid. One side of the chorion has been cut away to expose the amnion. The embryo's heart pumps its blood through the umbilical cord to the vessels in the chorion, and into the feathery extensions of its wall which fit intimately into the uterine lining of the mother. At this stage the amnion is about ¾-inch across.

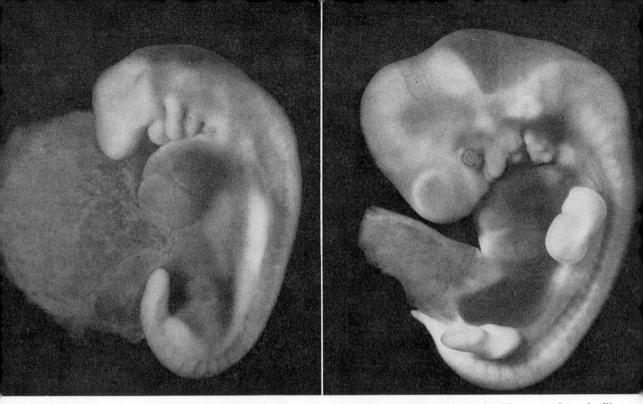

222. Twenty-six and a half days old. Note gill clefts, blocks of muscle tissue (somites), hind limb bud, distinct tail, and protruding, disproportionately large heart.

223. Thirty-four days old. Note remains of gill clefts, increased number of somites, development of fore and hind limb buds, and appearance of rudiments of eye and ear.

DEVELOPMENT OF A HUMAN FETUS (REMOVED FROM ITS MEMBRANES)

224. Forty-three days old. Tail is disappearing as adjacent body parts grow more rapidly. Hands and feet are "paws." The eyelids have not yet covered the eyes and the nose lacks any semblance of human form.

225. Fifty-six days old. Although recognizably human, with distinctive fingers and toes, nose proportions, indications of ribs, and the like, this fetus still lacks the anatomical and physiological development needed to survive if born.

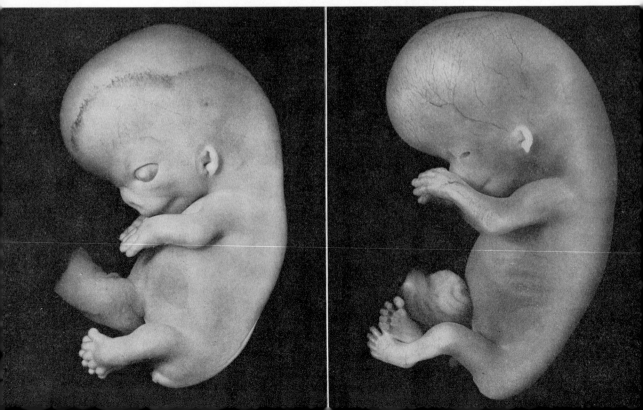

After a mammal embryo has a recognizable placenta, it is usually referred to as a *fetus*. Both continue to enlarge, but at birth the fate of the placenta is subject to some variation. In some mammals, the placenta is retained and its tissues are absorbed by the parent. More usually, however, it is discharged like so much debris shortly after the emergence of the fetus, and is known as the "after-birth." This is the situation in mankind, but occasionally the placenta tears away from the uterine wall at the time of birth, so that the fully-developed fetus emerges still in its embryonic membranes. The condition is known as being "born in a caul," and is a rarity on which many superstitions are based —predicting strange futures for babies so delivered. The distinction between placentae that are discharged and those that are not is one that makes use of approximately the same terms as are met in trees that shed their leaves in the fall and those that are evergreen. Deciduous leaves or deciduate placentae are those that free themselves from their attachment to the parent organism.

Most mammals, but not all, begin life as eggs lacking shell, yolk mass, or albumin covering. They develop a little, then have a placental connection with the parent, and continue as an internal parasite until the moment of birth. Between the moment of fertilization ("conception") and the sudden change of environment involved in birth (parturition) extends the **gestation period,** a characteristic number of days for each kind of mammal. Forty weeks is a good value for a "full term" human fetus, but like almost every other biological measurement, this one is subject to considerable variation. Premature births may occur at any time during this period. Those prior to 28 weeks after fertilization are ordinarily called abortions or "miscarriages," and yield a baby that is usually too immature to live. From 28 weeks onward, however, the human embryo may be sufficiently well developed to survive in an incubator.[3] In physiological features and behavior

[3] According to Dr. Curtis J. Lund (1949), birth weight—especially the fourth pound—is probably the most important factor in infant survival. Survival increases from 25 per cent for three pound babies to 75 per cent for four pound babies.

aspects, however, the premature baby is at a distinct disadvantage. It is a fetal-infant, in proper terminology, arising from a pre-term birth, and although it may become adjusted to a schedule of feeding and care imposed on it, no significant advantage is found when the premature individual is compared at a later age with those that remain in the uterus for the full 40 weeks. Nor, among those less frequent cases where birth is delayed for as much as 44 weeks after fertilization, is the extra (10th) month in the uterus to be considered as lost time. The post-term infant simply is farther along functionally and psychologically, and is neither behind nor ahead of other offspring born at the end of the normal 40 weeks. Hence chronological age,

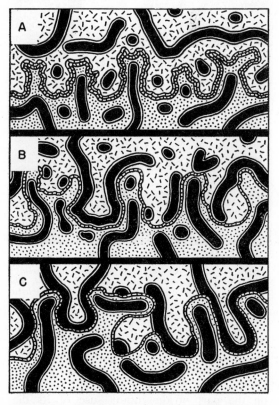

Fig. 18-17. *Degrees of placental invasion of maternal tissue* (shown by short lines) *at boundary of contact with embryo* (stippled): *A, Simple interdigitation with maternal epithelium intact; B, fetal epithelium in contact with blood vessel walls of parent; C, fetal epithelium invading maternal blood stream for most intimate contact. Note that fetal circulation remains intact and parental blood does not clot from invasion.*

based on date of birth, gives a false representation of the physiological age, and leads to faulty comparisons of the achievements and behavior of children.

The change from uterine existence to life in air is sudden and profound. Nourishment

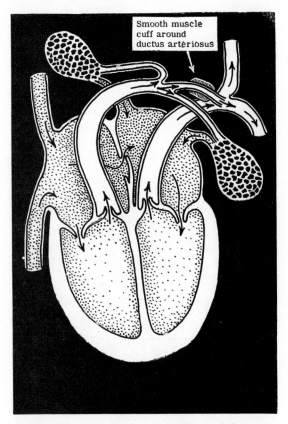

Smooth muscle cuff around ductus arteriosus

FIG. 18-18. *The circulation of the fetal heart includes provision for redirecting the blood through the pulmonary circuit as soon as birth occurs. The interauricular valve closes and the ductus arteriosus is constricted; both by-passes become obliterated as connective tissue forms.*

is no longer received continuously through the placenta, but comes spasmodically to a digestive tract which hitherto had had no function. Respiration requires physical effort on the part of the infant—use of its diaphragm and intercostal muscles, and of air passages that were in a state of relative collapse before birth. Excretion involves the kidneys, and again the mechanism is an untried one. Temperature control, water balance, and defecation of intestinal residues are all

new functions that must operate well enough to allow survival. The blood stream must change radically at birth. The umbilical artery and vein are severed and tied off, and they soon degenerate into solid fibrous structures within the body. For gas exchange the blood must course through the pulmonary system, whereas in the fetus most of the fluid bypassed the lungs, through short circuits provided between the right and left auricles, and between the pulmonary artery and the aorta (the *ductus arteriosus*). At the moment of birth, the interauricular opening must close and a cuff of muscle constrict around the ductus arteriosus (Fig. 18-18). Failure of these two mechanisms would allow too much blood to miss aeration in the lungs. The arteries would carry a high percentage of hemoglobin rather than oxyhemoglobin; the difference in body appearance is obvious enough for such a baby to be termed a "blue baby."[4] It is remarkable that so many of the body systems are in operable condition, and that these safety mechanisms in the blood vessels are ready for the moment of birth, when this event can take place over such a wide range of time. Yet viable (= able to survive) human babies may make the change from uterine to aerial life at any time from the 6th to the 10th month of pregnancy—40 weeks, minus 12 or plus 4. No wonder a leading expert on development of human nervous responses refers to the howling infant as "durable and docile!"

The ductus arteriosus is itself remarkable for its origin. Each vertebrate vascular system begins as a generalized series of six paired aortic arches between a ventral aorta and the dorsal aorta (Fig. 18-19). In each class of vertebrates the final circulation uses a part of this basic set of pathways. In an amphibian, the change from the fish pattern to the style illustrated occurs at metamorphosis. Correspondingly, in bird and mammal, the 6th aortic arch on one side serves as a bypass for the pulmonary circulation until the lungs can function. Thereafter this arch (the ductus arteriosus) shrivels to become a piece of connective tissue, the *ligamentum arteriosum*.

---

[4] Additional causes of this appearance are known.

26. Katydid eggs overlapped like shingles on a wooden stake.

227. The egg mass of the tent caterpillar appears varnished against winter weather. (See also Photos 27 to 29.)

228. Moth eggs in a cluster under a goldenrod leaf.

229. A pair of whelks (the smaller is the ♂) on the muddy bottom of a shallow bay. The tip of the string of egg capsules was pulled from the mud. New capsules are still being added to the series as the ♀ produces more egg string.

230. One of the egg capsules opened a few weeks later. Ordinarily the small whelks emerge through a pore in their capsule.

231. From smallest (hummingbird) to largest (extinct Æpyornis of Madagascar) among bird eggs. The other two eggs are a hen's egg and an ostrich egg.

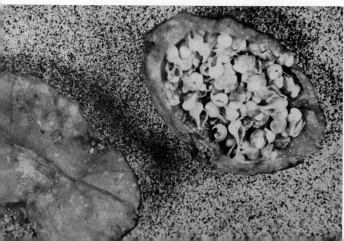

Eggs Come in Many Kinds of Containers

232. Most horned toads (Phrynosoma) bring forth active young—as many as 22 in a single litter.

DIFFERENT SPECIES OF THE SAME GENUS SOMETIMES HAVE DIFFERENT REPRODUCTIVE HABITS

233. A few kinds of horned toads, like the Texan species, bury two dozen or fewer eggs in a burrow under dry sand. (See also Photos 345 to 346.)

The activities of the newly-born or newly-hatched animal are subject to a wide range of limitations. In some, such as the colt and the chicks of pheasant or domestic fowl, the young are alert, responsive to parental signals, imitative, and able to run about and feed; they are described as "precocious" in being so fitted for aerial life within hours after emergence from parent or shell. The young porcupine, which becomes increasingly independent and weans itself in favor of a vegetable diet when only a few days old, is an extreme example of a precocious mammal.

The opposite condition, an "altricial" offspring which is helpless and dependent upon parental care for food (as are human babies, the young of mice, and squabs of pigeons) represents a compromise in embryological development. Since they are routinely born at earlier stages of life, and since they complete after birth a great number of growth processes that are finished and ready for use in a precocious organism, they presuppose instinctive organization within the parental nervous system that leads to a continuation of their constant care.

The development of a placenta whereby the embryo receives nourishment and accomplishes respiratory exchange and excretion is not confined to the mammals, although the mechanism reaches its highest development there. Aristotle described a "placental dogfish"—a shark of the Mediterranean in which there is a functional interconnection between young and mother. Rare examples are to be found in every other vertebrate group excepting cyclostomes and birds. The presence of a placental connection precludes the possibility of the animal laying eggs, so that all such organisms bring forth active young and are said to be **viviparous** (from *vivus* = alive, *parere* = give birth). But many kinds of animals lacking placentae are also viviparous—some fish, a few amphibians, numerous snakes, and lizards such as some horned toads (Photo 232), and others. These retain the yolky eggs (usually with no shells) within the body of the mother until development has reached a normal hatching age. The young issue from the parental cloacal opening in an active condition or in the amniotic sac, usu-

ally as miniatures of the parent. Sometimes the word **ovoviviparous** is used to distinguish these animals from **oviparous** (egg-laying) and the viviparous types where a placenta is involved (and the egg lacks both yolk and albuminous covering).

Among mammals, all degrees can be found between strictly oviparous and viviparous with placentae. The Australian anomalies, the spiny anteater (Echidna) and the duckbilled platypus (Ornithorhynchus—Photo 363), lay

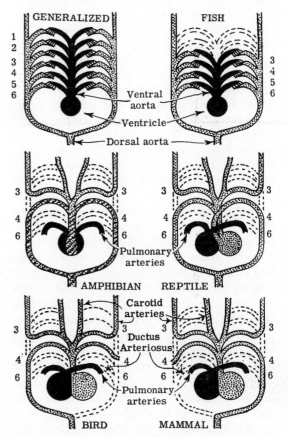

FIG. 18-19. *The initial circulation of a vertebrate embryo soon develops a ventral aorta from the original single ventricle of the heart. Six pairs of aortic arches connect the ventral aorta to the dorsal aorta. In a mature fish, the six arches have dwindled to four pairs serving the gills. In amphibians, reptiles, birds and mammals the third aortic arch on each side and a continuation of the ventral aorta remain as the carotid arteries; the sixth aortic arches become the pulmonary arteries. Still greater reduction is evident in adult bird and mammal, but the connection between pulmonary artery and dorsal aorta remains in the embryo as the ductus arteriosus (see Fig. 18-18).*

yolky eggs, incubate them, and then nourish the emerging young on milk from mammary glands. The marsupials, such as opossum and kangaroo (almost all restricted to the Australian region), provide no yolk or placenta, and give birth to extraordinarily immature "larvae" after only a few days of uterine development. The young at this stage have relatively well-developed fore legs with claws, and are able to crawl up the wetted under surface of the maternal abdomen into the pouch-like **marsupium;** here each larva able to find a nipple swallows it and remains attached for two months or more. In the case of the American opossum, as many as 22 young are born, with but 13 nipples available. Late-comers find all places taken and soon starve to death. At this stage they are just under 13 days old and about 11 mm long, with no apparent eyes and with only buds of hind limbs and tail. While supported by the two clawed fore paws, the larval body acts as a pendulum that keeps the direction of crawling always in an upward path—from vaginal opening to marsupium. It is only after much further growth, during which the remaining body systems reach full development, that the larval mouth expands sufficiently to allow removal of the nipple. The nipple itself is long, and probably extends down the gullet directly into the larval stomach. After the young reach sufficient size and maturity to free themselves from the nipple, they leave the marsupium for progressively longer periods until each is weaned and independent.

That this style of embryonic development —involving birth at a remarkably early stage of development—is successful, can be seen from the range of kinds of marsupials known. In the Australian region they include representatives from mouse-size to that of the large kangaroos of the open forests and plains (Photos 359-362, 364). They have occupied almost every ecological situation—subterranean (mole-like); terrestrial (cat-like and dog-like); arboreal; herbivorous; insectivorous; flesh-eaters; burrowing, running, hopping, climbing, volplaning (like flying squirrels). Lack of competition with the more efficient placental mammal types appears to have al-lowed full expression of the marsupial pattern in this one part of the world.

Metamorphosis

Thus it is difficult to see any clear-cut distinction between embryonic and post-embryonic development. The hatching of an egg or the birth of a fetus represents an enormous change in living conditions, but this event may come at various stages in the development of the individual without interfering with the final outcome. Growth and differentiation continue, and eventually the organism reaches a reproductive stage in its own right.

In some animals, there is a sharp division of the post-embryonic life into a feeding, growing stage, and a later, more definitely reproductive, phase. Among insects the acquisition of wings and functional sex organs follows a feeding period. Where the immature stages are like the parent in most other details, they are referred to as "nymphs" (if terrestrial) or "naiads" (if aquatic); examples are grasshoppers, cicadas, aphids, and dragonflies. Where the immature stages are highly specialized for feeding, and where there is a pronounced change (metamorphosis), a pupal stage is often required—in which feeding is suspended entirely, and in which the organism lives temporarily on food stores while previous (larval) structures are broken down and new (adult) organization is brought to completion. This is characteristic of beetles, moths, true flies, and wasps. Here the adult (*imago*) differs strikingly in structure and habits from the larva. During pupation provision is made for reproductive organs and for better means of finding mates and disseminating the species—by running, flying, and so on. Eating may take a secondary place or be eliminated entirely, as is characteristic of many adult moths and the entire insect order Ephemeroptera.

Metamorphosis occurs most conspicuously also among the amphibians, where an aquatic stage gives way to a terrestrial mode of life. In the frogs and toads, this involves replacement of gills with lungs, of a swimming tail with leaping legs, of herbivorous or omnivorous habits and a long, much coiled intestine, with carnivorous habits (and extensile tongue, improved vision and other sensory changes) and a shortened intestine, and many more fundamental alterations in physiological mechanisms and structural details. In newts and salamanders the changes are less pronounced, but like the frogs and toads, the acquisition of adult characteristics includes not only functional reproductive organs and related behavior, but also the development of a characteristic pattern in the pigmentation of the skin.

A scattering of animal kinds that belong to groups in which a metamorphosis is customary have developed a short-cut to reproduction in that the sex organs and mating behavior reach functional stages while the remainder of the body is still in an immature condition. The case of the Mexican axolotl was described in connection with its pituitary deficiency (p. 166). One of the true flies (Diptera, of the genus Miastor) similarly fails to reach the adult condition, but reproduces while still a maggot. The common tiger salamander exhibits a near approach to these situations; if it is prevented from crawling out on land as maturity approaches, it will retain its larval gills and some other characters while becoming sexually active and reproducing.

3. PLANT EMBRYOS

Members of the various phyla of thallophytes exhibit both asexual and sexual reproduction. A distinction between gametophyte and sporophyte generations may be present. But the growth of a fertilized egg into a filament or a thallus is not sufficiently patternful to describe as an embryo.

The remainder of the plant kingdom regularly pass through embryo stages, and are grouped in the subkingdom Embryophyta. In bryophytes, psilopsids, lycopsids, sphenopsids, and the class Filicineae of the pteropsids, the sperm cells swim to the eggs through a film of liquid water. Dew or rain is required in just the proper quantity—neither too much nor too little, neither too misty nor too torrential.

Among gymnosperms and angiosperms these difficulties are bypassed through additional sporophyte structures and by reduction of the gametophyte generation to a parasitic, microscopic link in the steps whereby a parent sporophyte provides for the welfare of a large number of seeds, each of them an embryo sporophyte of the succeeding generation. So important is the seed habit that an analysis of its stages permits better understanding of the familiar and economically valuable seed plants.

One specialization found among fossil tracheophytes of each subphylum, and again in the modern members of the lycopsid genus Selaginella, is found uniformly among seed plants: all of them have two kinds of spores. Those spores that can develop into ♂ gametophytes, the microspores, are produced in **pollen sacs** (= microsporangia) on special sporophylls ("microsporophylls"). Spores that develop into ♀ gametophytes are megaspores, produced in megasporangia, on megasporophylls.

In seed plants the megasporangium contributes its outer layers (**integuments**) to the embryo as the **seed coats** of the seed. For this reason the megasporangium of a seed plant is referred to as an **ovule.** Each ovule is borne on a megasporophyll. In gymnosperms the ovule lies on top of the megasporophyll, and the seed developing within the ovule is said to be "naked." In angiosperms, by contrast, the megasporophyll folds around and encloses the ovule in a **carpel** (Photo 241), leaving only a small gap (the "micropyle") through which the pollen tube can enter for fertilization (Photo 242). This is the fundamental distinction between the "naked-seeded" and the "enclosed-seeded" tracheophytes.

In both groups of plants, the sporophylls are arranged in a spiral toward the end of an abbreviated stem. Whether each sporophyll represents a modified leaf (one theory) or a modified branch (another theory) is debatable.

In many gymnosperms, the spiral of sporophylls contains either microsporophylls or megasporophylls, but not both. In the former instance, the reproductive structure is said to be **staminate;** in the latter case, it is **ovulate;** in either situation, the sporophylls may be woody and form a **cone.**

In angiosperms, the spiral of sporophylls is a **flower.** If it includes both staminate and carpellate sporophylls, it is referred to as **perfect.** An **imperfect** flower, on the other hand, lacks either the stamens or the carpels.

staminate cones

pollen sac = microsporangium

stamen = micro-sporophyll

microspore mother cells

MEIOSIS

spore tetrad

4 pollen grains

ovulate cones

cone scale = megasporophyll

young ♂ gametophyte

wing

cotyledons

stem

root

seed coat

GERMINATION

wing

embryo

seed coat

♀ gametophyte

ovule = mega-sporangium

POLLINATION

one-year ovulate cone

spore mother cell

MEIOSIS

4 spores (3 degenerate)

pollen tube

two-year ovulate cone open, shedding seeds

cone scale = mega-sporophyll

mature ♀ gametophyte

young ♀ gametophyte from one spore

FERTILIZATION

egg cell in reduced archegonium

Fig. 18-20. *The life cycle of the pine.*

The life cycle of the pine (Fig. 18-20) is often assumed to be representative of the gymnosperms. Actually the pine and other conifers are somewhat more like the angiosperms in one respect: their sperm cells are nonmotile. The cycads (Photo 185) and ginkgo (Photos 186-187) have swimming sperms.

The obvious feature of conifers is the cones in which spores are produced. Some of these cones produce microspores, which become pollen grains and are distributed by the wind; these are the staminate cones. Other cones produce megaspores; these are the ovulate cones. Although ♂ gametophytes are formed by microspores in staminate cones and ♀ gametophytes develop within the ovules of ovulate cones, it is not correct to describe the cones themselves as ♂ or ♀ since they are part of the asexual sporophyte generation.

Before being shed from the staminate cone, each microspore germinates into a young ♂ gametophyte. Two cells of this, one inside the other (Fig. 18-20), are important. The enclosed cell is the "generative cell"; around it is the "tube cell." If wind carries the young ♂ gametophyte to the immediate proximity of a developing ♀ gametophyte on a sporophyll of an ovulate cone, the tube cell commences to grow an extended **pollen tube.** The nucleus of the tube cell (the "tube nucleus") leads the way, and appears to control tube growth. As the tube reaches the ♀ gametophyte, the generative cell undergoes mitosis and cytokinesis; each of the new cells is a sperm cell, still surrounded by the cytoplasm of the tube cell. The sperm cells migrate toward the tip of the tube. Although the distance involved is only a fraction of an inch, these growth changes are so slow that from the time of pollination (arrival of the pollen on the carpel) to fertilization (fusion of the sperm cell with an egg cell) may be one or more years.

Within each ovule is a single megaspore-mother cell, which undergoes a special kind of division (to be discussed in Chapter 19) to form four megaspores. Of these, three degenerate; the last one germinates into a ♀ gametophyte. Eventually the gametophyte tissue fills the ovule, and two or more archegonia are formed, each with one egg cell (Fig. 18-20). A sperm nucleus can fuse with an egg cell to fertilize it and start growth of a new sporophyte plant.

The embryo grows and becomes differentiated into precursors of root, stem and first leaves; all of this is accomplished while the embryo is still enclosed by the ovule integuments and surrounded by a mass of ♀ gametophyte tissue. The first leaves are called **cotyledons;** a pine may have a dozen or so. Eventually the embryo reaches a resting stage, with low metabolic rate, and is a "ripe" seed, ready for "shedding" into the wind. This is helped by a gradual rotation of the carpellate cone until all of the carpels hang down. Then the cone dries out and the seeds fall from the spaces between the sporophylls. In pine this event occurs two years after pollination, one year after fertilization.

Along with the dormant embryo, the seed includes (1) a food-filled mass of ♀ gametophyte tissue serving as reserve for the seedling; (2) the seed coats contributed as the remains of the enclosing ovule wall (the integuments); and (3) a scale from the surface of the sporophyll, which serves as a wing in wind dispersal. The pine seed is ready to fall on moist ground, and reawaken from dormancy as a seedling sporophyte. Its cotyledons are the first needles, and surround the apical meristem of the trunk-to-be.

Angiosperms

The flowers of angiosperms correspond to the cones of prominent gymnosperms. At the tip of the floral stem are the carpels, each hollow and containing one or more ovules. Below the carpels is a spiral or whorl of stamens, each typically consisting of a slender **filament** supporting at its end a pair of two-lobed structures collectively described as the **anther;** each of the four lobes contains a microsporangium in which pollen grains will develop. Still farther down the abbreviated stem of the flower is a whorl of more leaf-shaped structures, the **perianth,** which covers the more apical, inner parts of the flower while it is still a closed bud.

Often the carpels are fused together or reduced in number to a single representative.

In either case they are commonly specialized into a basal enlargement (the **ovary**) containing the ovules, an intermediate slender portion (the **style**), and a more protruding glandular tip (the **stigma**) to which pollen grains adhere easily. Collectively the ovary (whether simple—of one carpel—or compound), the style, and the stigma, are termed the **pistil** of the flower.

Often the perianth is specialized into two unlike series of parts: (1) that nearer the stamens, usually showy, as the **petals** of the **corolla;** and (2) that farther from the stamens, commonly green, as the **sepals** of the **calyx.**

The most generalized flowers are those with the largest and least-fixed number of each of these flower parts. Waterlilies, buttercups, peonies, and magnolia are good examples. Other flowers show a reduction in one or more details, and trends toward regularity. Vestigial parts may become glandular, with **nectaries** secreting substances appealing to the sense of smell and taste in animals. The secretion may include energy-rich sugars that reward visitors.

In many dicots, the floral parts occur in fives (as in wild rose and morning glory) or fours (as in mustard). In monocots, the flower parts are arranged in threes or multiples of three (as in tulip, lily, and palm). Or whole sets of organs may be missing: the sedges and grasses have no perianth. Or the flower parts may be fused together. Thus a tubular corolla is characteristic of morning glory; the stamens are fused into a sheath-like group in the pea and daisy families. Or one set of flower parts may be joined to another. Thus the stamens arise from the corolla in mints and snapdragons; both perianth and stamens are fused to the ovary wall in daisies, parsley, and amaryllis. Flowers may not only be grouped in clusters, but borne in large numbers on the flattened end of a single stem, as in the daisy family.

A great many flowers are radially symmetrical. Examples of this are rose, tulip, and morning glory. Other flowers are as distinctly bilateral in their symmetry. This is true in the mint, pea, and orchid families.

Although there are almost as many forms of flowers as there are kinds of angiosperms, and although so many flowers appear to be important in attracting animals that help with pollination, the structure of flowers appears to be one of the most conservative features in plant anatomy. For this reason, similarity in flower form corresponds closely to similarity in life-history details, serological reactions, and the like. In identifying an angiosperm, the study of its floral anatomy provides the fastest and most reliable characteristics (Fig. 18-21, Photos 234-239, 253-254).

The reproductive history of the staminate and carpellate parts of flowers shows many parallels to and some important differences from the corresponding history among gymnosperms:

1. As in the formation of pollen grains in the microsporangium of a staminate pine cone, the angiosperm pollen sac (microsporangium) contains a large number of microspore-mother cells which undergo a special type of division (to be discussed in Chapter 19). Each microspore-mother cell forms four microspores in a compact group called a **tetrad** (as in Fig. 18-20). These microspores separate, and within each one a simple ♂ gametophyte develops, similar to that of the pine in containing two important cells: a generative cell inside a tube cell. At this stage the ♂ gametophyte is ready to be carried to the stigma, and the microspore wall with enclosed ♂ gametophyte is described correctly as a pollen grain. Unlike the pollen grain of pine, however, an angiosperm pollen grain contains no additional, nonfunctional cells of the ♂ gametophyte (Fig. 18-23).

2. The ovule, surrounded by the carpel in an angiosperm, is like the exposed ovule of a pine in containing a single megaspore-mother cell which, by special division, produces four megaspores. Three of these disappear. The remaining megaspore undergoes three successive mitotic divisions without cytokinesis, so that it comes to contain eight nuclei (Fig. 18-22, *3*). Walls may form around the eight after they have taken up characteristic positions within the ovule. This is the complete ♀ gametophyte. It develops no archegonia. Instead, one of the eight nuclei is the egg nucleus, in an egg cell. Two more nuclei (or by their mitotic division four or eight or even twelve or sixteen) remain in a central position as **fusion nuclei** (Fig. 18-

234. Alder, with long pendant staminate catkins and short, sessile carpellate catkins (at the end and along the side of the stem) open these reproductive parts and use wind in pollination well before the leaves unfold in the spring.

235. Maple, with distinct stamens to the right (a branch from one tree) and carpellate flowers with long red paired stigmatic surfaces to the left (branch from another tree).

236. Willow, with carpellate flowers as an aggregation of ovaries (*left branch*) and staminate flowers reduced to a mass of stamens (*right branch*). Both types of flower secrete nectar, and pollination is at least partly through insect activity.

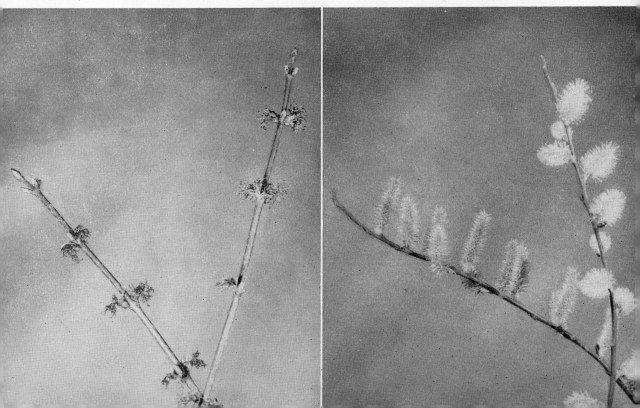

237. Apple blossoms, visited and pollinated by honeybees and other insects.

238. Skunk cabbage flowers in very early spring emit a fetid odor attractive to pollinating flies.

239. Bright hibiscus blossoms are visited by hummingbirds which brush against both the five outstretched button-like stigmas and the many stamen anthers arising from the sides of the long, fused style.

RANUNCULACEAE
The Crowfoot Family

Includes buttercup, anemone, hepatica, meadow rue, marsh marigold, larkspur. Pistils one to many, separate; fruit a one-seeded achene. Stamens many, number indefinite, attached below the pistil(s). Petals 3 to 15 or absent, separate, attached below the stamens. Sepals 3 to 15, separate, attached below the petals. Herbs or woody vines, leaves alternate, without stipules. Juice commonly bitter.

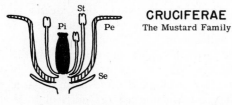

CRUCIFERAE
The Mustard Family

Includes water cress, shepherd's-purse, mustard, radish, cabbage, cauliflower, turnip. Pistil single; fruits a silique or silicle with many seeds. Stamens 6, 2 lower and shorter, attached below the pistil. Petals 4, separate, attached below the stamens. Sepals 4, separate, attached below the petals. Herbs with alternate leaves, no stipules.

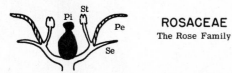

ROSACEAE
The Rose Family

Includes plum, cherry, spiraea, strawberry, bramble, rose, hawthorn, apple, pear. Pistils one to many, distinct; fruit usually fleshy. Stamens 5 to many, separate, attached with the petals to the rim of a disk lining the calyx tube. Petals 5, separate, attached with the stamens to the calyx. Sepals 5, either united at base, attached below the pistil(s), or united with the pistil, as in apple. Trees, shrubs, and herbs with regular flowers, alternate leaves with stipules free or attached to the petioles.

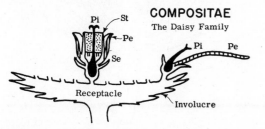

COMPOSITAE
The Daisy Family

Includes aster, goldenrod, ragweed, sunflower, everlasting, thistle, hawkweed, dandelion. Pistil one, style 2-cleft; fruit an achene. Stamens 5, anthers united as a tube surrounding the pistil, attached to the corolla; or stamens lacking. Petals 5, fused but 5-lobed as a cup around stamens and pistil in disk florets, or fused and strap-like in ray florets, attached to ovary. Sepals united, variable, fused with ovary, or absent. Herbs with multiple flowers in a close head on a common receptacle surrounded by an involucre. Leaves alternate, without stipules.

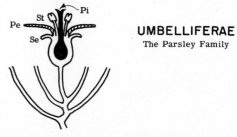

UMBELLIFERAE
The Parsley Family

Includes carrot, celery, caraway, poison hemlock. Pistils 2, fused, 2 styles; fruit 2 seed-like dry carpels. Stamens 5, separate, attached to a ring on the side of the ovary. Petals 5, separate, attached to a ring on the side of the ovary. Sepals 5, united and fused with ovary. Herbs with flowers grouped in umbels. Leaves alternate, usually compound, the petioles expanded or sheathing the stem.

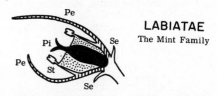

LABIATAE
The Mint Family

Includes mint, thyme, sage, catnip, horehound. Pistils 4, united but distinctly lobed; fruit 4 seed-like nutlets. Stamens 2 or 4, united and attached to the tube of the corolla. Petals 5, with 2 upper petals united, 3 lower petals united, all attached below the pistil. Sepals 5, united, attached below the petals. Herbs with square stems, opposite, aromatic leaves without stipules.

LEGUMINOSAE
The Pea Family

Includes lupine, clover, locust tree, wisteria, pea, bean. Pistil one, free; fruit a legume. Stamens 10, attached together into one or two groups surrounding the pistil, attached below it. Petals 5, usually unequal, partly fused, one superior (next to the axis of the flower cluster), attached below the pistil. Stamens 5, regular, partly fused, attached below the petals. Trees, shrubs and herbs, alternate leaves with stipules.

FIG. 18-21. *Representative flower forms among familiar families of plants.*

22, 4). The ♀ gametophyte is now ready for fertilization.

3. Through the assistance of wind or animals, the pollen grain (immature ♂ gametophyte) may arrive on the stigma of its own species of pistil. Within minutes (in dande-

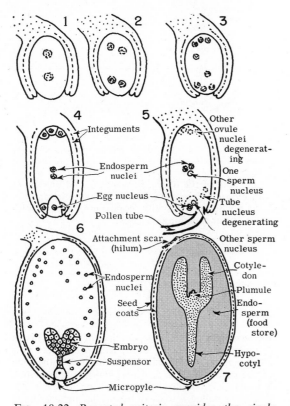

FIG. 18-22. *Repeated mitosis provides the single cell in the ovule with eight nuclei (3). Cell walls form about six of these (4), but only three of the eight—although they represent the entire gametophyte—continue to have any significance; the other five nuclei may disappear (5). The remaining nuclei are an egg nucleus and two endosperm nuclei. Upon entry of a pollen tube (5), two sperm nuclei are contributed. By double fertilization, one sperm nucleus fuses with the egg nucleus to form a zygote, whereas the other sperm nucleus fuses with the two endosperm nuclei to form the beginning of a nutritive tissue, the endosperm. A pore, the micropyle, remains where the pollen tube entered between the ovule walls. The zygote, adjacent to the micropyle, divides transversely into two cells. That farther from the micropyle grows (6) as the embryo. The cell nearer the micropyle develops into a special extraembryonic structure, the suspensor, growth of which presses the embryo into the nutritive endosperm. At first the endosperm consists of cytoplasm with a large number of endosperm nuclei; eventually (7) cell walls form, organizing the endosperm into a tissue in which the parent plant stores food which will be used by the embryo.*

lions and lettuce) to hours (in most flowers) or several months (in oaks, alders, and witch-hazel), the ♂ gametophyte extends a pollen tube down into the stigma, through the tissue of the style, out into the cavity of the carpel, and into a region of the ovule where its integuments leave a pore (the micropyle).

Unlike the gymnosperm, however, an angiosperm uses both sperm cells in the pollen tube (Fig. 18-23). One of them fuses with the egg cell, and the fertilized egg begins to grow as the new sporophyte embryo. The other sperm cell, in a unique process known as **double fertilization,** fuses with the two (or four or eight or twelve or sixteen) fusion nuclei and starts the growth of a new tissue, the **endosperm.**

4. Growth of the endosperm (Fig. 18-22, 7; Photos 242, 244-245) soon fills the ovule; thereafter ovule and endosperm enlarge together, establishing a large mass of food-rich tissue. Meanwhile growth of the embryo presses it into the endosperm. Differentiation

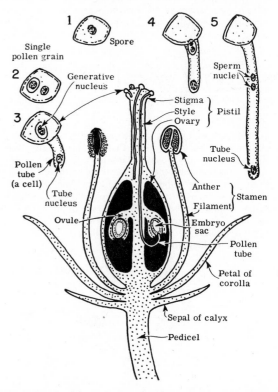

FIG. 18-23. *The steps in development of the pollen grain occur chiefly after it has reached the stigma of another flower, and are the prelude to double fertilization.*

240. Cross-section of the whole ovary shows the three cavities and six lines of ovules.

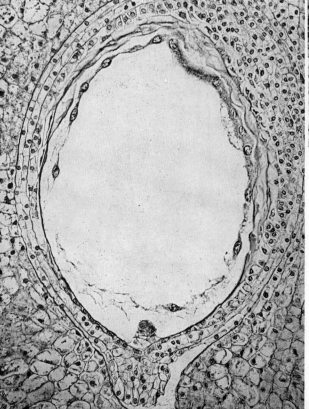

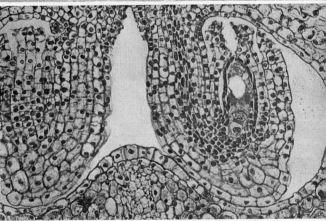

241. The ovule waits for a pollen grain to send its tube up the neck and contribute two sperm nuclei.

242. The one fusion nucleus has begun to develop an embryo above the closed neck while the other fusion nucleus is dividing to provide endosperm tissue that will nourish the embryo. At this stage no cell walls have formed in the endosperm, and these nuclei are seen in a row around the sap-filled cavity of the ovule.

THE DEVELOPMENT OF A MONOCOT EMBRYO

(Lilium)

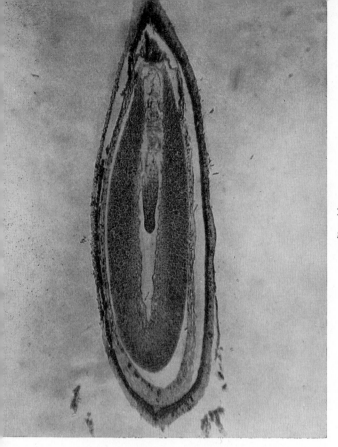

243. Longitudinal section through a gymnosperm (pine) embryo, surrounded by the food-rich ♀ gametophyte, all within the seed coat.

245. Gradually the dicot embryo may absorb the nourishment from the endosperm and obliterate this tissue. Note the two cotyledons which will be the first leaves of the embryo sporophyte.

244. The young dicot embryo is surrounded with loose endosperm tissue rich in nutrients.

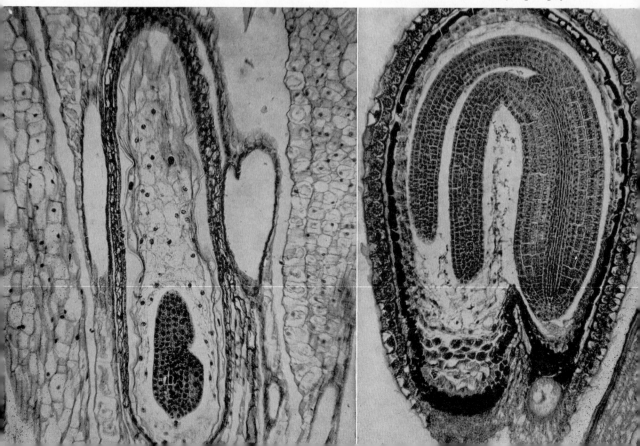

of the embryo tissues produces a precursor of a root (complete with a root cap and terminal meristem), of a stem (with a terminal bud), and one *or* two cotyledons (= "seed leaves"). In dicots there are two cotyledons, whereas monocot seeds have only one.

In most dicot seeds, by the time the embryo has reached its dormant stage and the seed is "ripe," all of the endosperm food has been transferred into the cotyledons. The latter then contain the food supply for the seedling, and the endosperm has effectively disappeared. Exceptions to this, with extensive endosperm remaining in the ripe seed, are to be found in the carob, honey locust, mesquite, and castor oil bean. In monocot seeds, the endosperm ordinarily remains to maturity. Thus in a kernel of corn (maize), the yellow part is endosperm, and the embryo plant lies dormant as a white scale on one side of it.

5. Hormones diffusing from the developing embryo and endosperm tissues affect the carpel (ovary) wall. Sometimes adhering parts of the flower or the distal end of its stalk (the **receptacle**) respond also. Each affected tissue becomes meristematic, and grows to produce a **fruit** surrounding the seeds.

Hence an angiosperm embryo is enclosed successively in (1) any remaining endosperm; (2) the seed coats, contributed by the ovule from its integuments; and (3) the fruit, as a ripened ovary wall and any adhering parts.

In a strawberry, the "seeds" are actually small fruits (each with its embryo, seed coats, and thin, hard, ovary wall) embedded in the enlarged end of the receptacle. An apple is chiefly the thickened calyx, surrounding and fused to the ovary; the thin shiny membranes left in the core of an apple are the ovary's linings, and each of the seed-filled cavities represents a carpel of the original five-part compound pistil; the calyx tips usually remain visible at the end of the apple opposite the stem; sometimes the style and stigma can be found too, sunken into the end of the ripe fruit. In monocots such as wheat and corn, the familiar kernel is itself a fruit, with the ovary wall and the seed coats fused together into a "grain coat" of special type.

The term "seed" is applied to very different structures in connection with conifers, dicot angiosperms, and corn kernels (Fig. 18-24; Photos 243, 245). Yet in each instance, a true seed represents a separate fertilization. It develops within the parent sporophyte from a parasitic gametophyte. Hence no accumulated

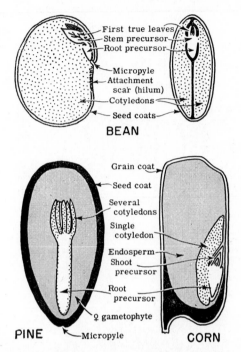

FIG. 18-24. *The food store available to the dormant embryo is in ♀ gametophyte tissue of a pine seed, in endosperm of a corn kernel, and in the paired cotyledons of a bean. In this respect corn is a typical monocot, and the bean a typical dicot angiosperm; the pine is characteristic of gymnosperm seeds.*

food stores are risked by the plant until the seeds themselves are dispersed. And each seed, by containing an embryo sporophyte already well differentiated, is able to react more promptly to suitable living conditions. It resumes growth, and becomes a new, active, plant individual (Fig. 18-25).

Dormancy

Seeds usually require a period of dormancy before they will germinate. Throughout this period they must remain alive, slowly using up the food stored with the embryo. In some, such as willows and orchids, dormancy is brief and germination must come (if at all) within a few weeks from the time of shedding. The other extreme seems to be an "extinct" relative of the sacred lotus (Nelumbo) of tropical and subtropical Asia, seeds of which remained viable in a Manchurian bog for about 1,000 years. These seeds, since their recovery in 1923, have been shown by radiocarbon dating to be far older than the 400-year estimate offered originally. Stories of the germination of seeds from the tombs of Egyptian kings, however, all prove to be fictional.

The length of dormancy is governed by more than the quantity of stored food. The embryo may still have developmental stages to complete; slow chemical changes may be in progress. Or the seed coats may be thick, cutting down on respiration, water uptake, and metabolic rate. Often bacterial action in the soil softens the seed coat. Freezing and thawing may crack it. In agricultural practice (for example, with sweet clover), dormancy may be ended by running the seed through a machine which scratches or breaks the seed coat.

Dispersal

In the life cycle of a seed plant, living cells are broadcast at two points: at dispersal of pollen, and at distribution of seeds. Pollen grains are so diminutive and contain so little nourishment that an enormous number can be sacrificed without great loss. A large proportion of seed plants produce pollen in staminate catkins or cones, and depend upon the wind to blow the grains far and wide. The winged pollen grains of pine (Photo 184) have been known to travel as much as 400 miles from one tree to another, borne entirely on air currents.

Adaptive characteristics of flowers and fruits (including seeds) related to increasing the probability of successful dispersal, are dealt with at greater length in Chapter 20.

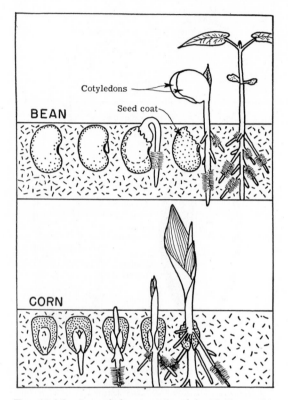

Fig. 18-25. *A cotyledon is a "seed leaf." From this landmark the seedling is named as having an epicotyl (= stem, bud and new leaves above the cotyledon) and a hypocotyl (= stem, root and growing parts in the downward direction from the cotyledon).*

HUMAN DEVELOPMENT

days (*measured from date of fertilization*)

18   1.5 x 0.8 mm in size; longitudinal axis evident (left & right, dorsal & ventral organization begun; junction of head & neck clear; almost ¾ of embryonic tissue still destined to become head)

26½   See Photo 222

weeks

4   heart beat begun; optic vesicles fully formed
5   limb buds formed (Photo 223)
6   retina of eye distinct (Photo 224)
7   oculomotor muscles of eye forming; semicircular canals of ear formed (Photo 225)
8   first reflex movements, showing nervous connection between functional sense organs & functional muscles, around mouth and along neck
12   wide variety of muscle reactions, most of them involving whole body; arms & hands rotated so that palms face each other; eyelids still fused but oculomotor muscles have nervous connections and eyeball movements begin; fovea in eye begins to develop; semicircular canals at full adult size
20   body a foot long, weighs a pound; eyes almost ready for use
22   if fetus removed surgically, makes spasmodic respiratory movements
24   some eye dimensions (e.g. distance between fovea and head of optic nerve) at full adult size, but proportion not quite final
25   respiratory movements sufficiently continuous to support life for several hours

INVIABLE IF BORN
_____

VIABLE IF BORN

28   respiratory movements adequate for life under modern care of premature; no (or rare) visual responses though eyeballs move freely and facial musculature is active; no awareness of surroundings—a condition between sleep and wakefulness
34   brief periods of awareness of environment; eyes may follow irregularly after moving objects
38   more fat deposits round out the body contours; sleep & wakefulness distinct
40   FULL TERM

months after full term birth

1   hands held primarily as fists, with fingers curled; eyes open when awake, with increase in duration of fixation on objects; monocular fixation alternates from one eye to the other
2   binocular convergence of eyes; single sounds vocalized
3   beginning of visual awareness of hands & feet, and of eye-hand and eye-foot coordinations; chuckles
4   no reaching on sight, but hands operate together, fingering one another; laughs
5   examines objects with eyes; squeals
6   reaches for and seizes objects seen, using pincer movement of thumb and fingers
7   transfers objects from one hand to the other, back and forth
12   voluntarily lets go of objects after examining them; imitates sounds, and may have a word or two
14   average age for first walking alone
24   usually 3-word sentences, including pronouns
36   more speech facility, including prepositions and plurals
152-240 enters college or university

                         —after Gesell and others

SUGGESTED READING (see pp. 507-511)

Recent and Informative: Corner, 1944; Dahlberg, 1951; Grant, 1951; Monroy, 1950; Moog, 1950; Patten, 1951; Pincus, 1951; Reynolds, H. C., 1953; Reynolds, S. R. M., 1952, 1953; Stone, 1954; Weisz, 1953.

19 · Carriers of Heredity

1. ASEXUAL REPRODUCTION. 2. SEXUAL REPRODUCTION—THE IMPORTANCE OF SEX, MEIOSIS AS A COUNTERPART TO SEX, PLOIDY, THE PROCESS OF MEIOSIS, MEIOSIS IN STRUCTURALLY SIMPLE ORGANISMS, MEIOSIS IN MULTI-CELLULAR ANIMALS, MEIOSIS IN EMBRYOPHYTE PLANTS, CHANCE COMBINA-TIONS. 3. STATISTICS. 4. SIMPLE INHERITANCE—DOMINANCE, BACK-CROSS, INDEPENDENCE, ALLELES, BLENDING. 5. DETERMINATION OF SEX. 6. SEX-LINKED INHERITANCE. 7. ORDINARY LINKAGE—CROSSING OVER, MAPPING OF CHROMOSOMES. 8. MUTATION. 9. THE NATURE OF THE GENE. 10. POLY-PLOIDY. 11. PARTHENOGENESIS. 12. PRACTICAL APPLICATIONS—HYBRID VIGOR, GENETIC IMPROVEMENT, HUMAN GENETICS, ENVIRONMENTAL INFLUENCES, ARTIFICIAL INSEMINATION OF MAMMALS, THE GENE AND INDIVIDUALITY.

ALTHOUGH all scientific understanding of inheritance dates from the present century, certain generalizations have been evident since ancient times. The statement "Like begets like" has been amended with "but not quite." It is true in the sense that a litter of pups are similar to their parents. They are not identical by any means, but they certainly are not cats.

Heredity is a tendency among individuals to resemble their ancestors and relatives. Variation is a measure of their tendencies to differ. Genetics is a branch of biology dealing with the facts and theories of both heredity and variation.

Within the past 50 years, two independent approaches to genetics have fused with happy results: (1) a study of the behavior of chromosomes, and (2) a statistical evaluation of changes in the appearance of offspring from various parental crosses. That events in the nucleus correspond exactly with the inheritability of parental characteristics was recognized in 1903 by a British biologist, W. S. Sutton. His discovery gave impetus to investigations of chromosomes in relation to heredity —the field of **cytogenetics** (cellular genetics). By 1926, one of the most productive research workers in this field (an American, T. H. Morgan) was able to summarize the factual findings into a broad theory. Subsequent

studies supported and amplified his views, and in 1933 he was awarded a Nobel prize for his contribution.

According to Morgan's theory, the chromosomes provide the hereditary bridges from one generation to the next. Moreover, along the length of every chromosome are structures in a definite and knowable sequence, each controlling the development of some one inheritable feature.

If this is a realistic interpretation of the facts, there should be a difference in the inheritability of characteristics, depending upon whether a new individual is the offspring of two different parents (through sexual reproduction) or arises from a single parent (through asexual reproduction).

1. ASEXUAL REPRODUCTION

Vegetative reproduction is known most commonly in plants. Housewives are forever cutting the longer branches of ivy and geraniums, inducing them to develop roots in water, and thus starting new plants. These are **cuttings,** and the commercial basis for propagation of sugar cane, bananas, and pineapple, for example. An "Irish" potato is an **underground stem;** the "eyes" are buds, and an eye plus part of the potato (for a food supply) will start a new potato plant. Sweet potatoes are propagated from pieces of **root.**

Many onions, tulips, and other plants with enlarged underground structures reproduce asexually by separation of the **bulbs** as new individuals. A few plants such as Bryophyllum, Kalanchoe, and African violets will grow from **leaves** partly buried in the soil. Strawberry plants send out wiry horizontal stems called **runners,** which produce new plants at the end where they touch the ground. Others, like bramble, root when stems of any kind become surrounded by high humidity—as they do when the branches curve down to the soil and become covered with fallen leaves. This is the basis of *layering* as a horticultural method of propagation.

A man-controlled extension of these methods is the nursery practice of grafting (Fig. 19-1) and budding, valuable in perpetuating varieties which would not breed true (such as most kinds of fruit trees); of propagating plants whose fruits produce no seeds, or seeds that will not germinate (such as seedless grapes, seedless bananas, and others); or of growing crops or showy ornamental tops of kinds with poor roots on the topless root system of strong-rooted relatives.

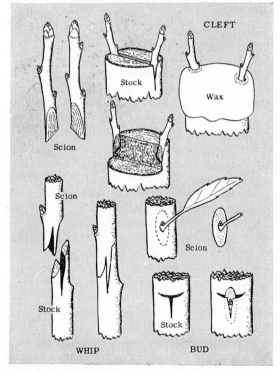

FIG. 19-1. *Artificial asexual reproduction in plants by grafting and budding.*

Asexual reproduction includes also the simple division of an ameba, a Paramecium (Photo 246), or a bacterial cell, to become two individuals in the procedure known as **fission.** It includes the production of new individuals as the result of accidental breakage of such flatworms as Planaria and tapeworm segments (though not the loading of these with fertilized eggs), or the **fragmentation** of various filamentous algae such as Spirogyra. **Budding** in the yeast cell involves mitosis and commonly produces new individuals; so does budding in Hydra and many of its relatives.[1] Other invertebrates such as sponges and moss animals (Bryozoa) reproduce by means of little masses of cells produced asexually and called *gemmules;* they are little different in origin and fate from similar structures (with the same name) arising on the surface of liverworts and other plants, or the new individuals that arise asexually around the leaf of the tropical plants Bryophyllum and Kalanchoe (Photos 247-248). **Spore-formation** among many protozoans, and among various plants (including numbers of algae and fungi) may also be asexual, and have the additional advantage of providing the new individuals with drought-resistant coverings that allow them to live through a dry spell fatal to the parent organisms.

In each asexual mechanism, the process of mitosis supplies the new individual with a nucleus, and cell divisions proceed from that point in providing final form. Since all cells have exactly the same nuclear components, there can be no significant variation from one individual to another, other than those imposed by good or bad living conditions. There is no change either for better or for worse. Hence no improvement is possible on a hereditary basis.

Sometimes it is even difficult to distinguish between parent and offspring in asexual reproduction. When Paramecium, a bacterium, or a yeast cell divides, which is parent, which

[1] Colony formation presents an aspect of asexual reproduction that is full of philosophical problems. For example, when is a colony to be considered as one organism, when as a cooperating society of individuals?

daughter? Both are individuals and there is no waste. As long as living conditions are suitable, each such cell has potential immortality. There has been no discontinuity in protoplasm between the ameba of today and that of a million years ago.

2. SEXUAL REPRODUCTION

The essential feature of sexual reproduction is the fusion of two nuclei—one from each parent. This understanding of the process has been possible only since invention of the microscope and scientific use of the instrument in study of nuclei and the gametes which contain them.

Prior to any appreciation of the importance of the gametes and their nuclei, sex and its significance had been interpreted only from observation of parent organisms and the appearance of their offspring. But the variety of steps by which plants and animals reproduce led to a maze of contradictory beliefs.

On the monuments of ancient Egypt are pictographs showing men carrying the pollen-bearing flowers of the fig tree to trees of the opposite sex, to insure a good crop of fruit. This procedure was an empiric ritual, however, with no knowledge of what happened. The concept of sex in plants was set forth first by R. J. Camerarius in 1691; he described the situation only in the flowering plants.

Sexual union of ♂ and ♀ animals was recognized for the great majority of larger kinds, but through the 17th century, men of science credited the smaller types—insects, worms, and the like—with arising from mud or filth by spontaneous generation.

The chief argument concerning conspicuous animals was whether the ♂ parent provided "form" and the ♀ only "substance" (as Aristotle had suggested), or whether both sexes contributed materially (the view of the Epicurean philosophers, espoused by many followers). These speculations were modernized in relation to new discoveries: to discovery of mammalian sperm cells—the "animalcules" described and illustrated by the pioneer microscopist, van Leeuwenhoeck, in 1679; and to a new dictum *"Ex ovo omnia"*

(everything comes from an egg) by William Harvey (familiar for his proof that blood circulates).

So arose two branches of scientific thought: the *Ovists,* who claimed everything for the egg, including the inclusion in it of a complete individual, ready to unfold (equipped already with ovaries in which were eggs, wherein were still smaller individuals with ovaries, and so on); and the *Spermatists,* who saw in each sperm cell a complete individual (in human sperm a "homunculus"— Fig. 19-2) ready to unfold and grow when

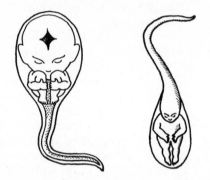

Fig. 19-2. *Imaginative microscopists claimed that the human sperm cell contained a miniature body, ready to unfold when given the proper nourishment. No agreement was found for the position of this "homunculus"—as is evident from the drawings of Hartsoeker (1694), left, and Dalempatius (1699), right.*

provided with the passive nourishment of the egg. These were the two sides to the **Theory of Preformation.**

An alternative point of view, described as the **Theory of Epigenesis,** has gradually replaced belief in preformation. This view holds that neither the egg nor the sperm is more important than the other, and that the fertilized egg develops into a new individual through progressive organization of apparently simple structure into the final complexity of form. Epigenesis assumes no structure to be unfolded, but an interacting set of chemical substances from which visible organization can arise as reactions occur. This approach emphasizes the importance of searching for the controlling mechanism and elucidating the precise steps in its operation. Today biologists have concluded that the nucleus is or contains the primary control center of each cell. But this conclusion was reached on the basis of many separate discoveries.

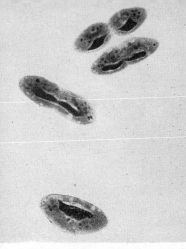

246. Asexual reproduction by fission in Paramecium (stained to show nuclei).

247. Asexual reproduction by small plant formation in notches of the mature leaves of a cultivated Kalanchoe.

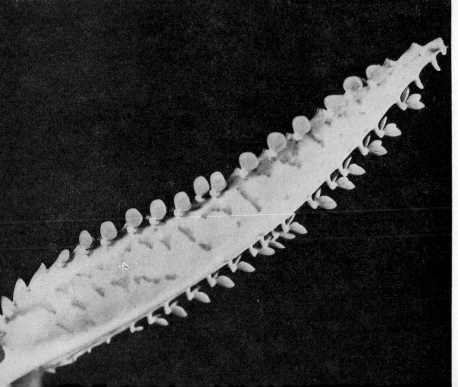

248. The same, in more detailed view. Leaflets and roots develop on each of the small plants before they drop to the ground. This represents a valuable store of nourishment contributed by the parent plant toward the survival of its asexually produced offspring.

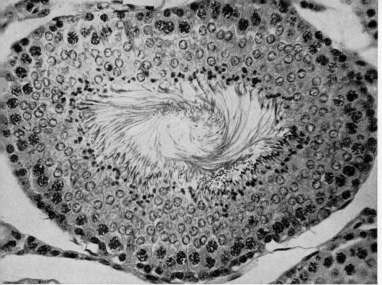

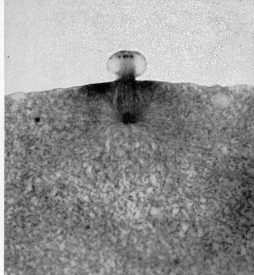

249. Stages in spermatogenesis as seen in a cross-section of a seminiferous tubule of the hamster. The tails of maturing sperm swirl out into the cavity of the tubule.

250. Polar body formation in a whitefish egg.

GAMETOGENESIS IN ANIMALS

251. A maturing mammalian egg in its follicle near the surface of the ovary.

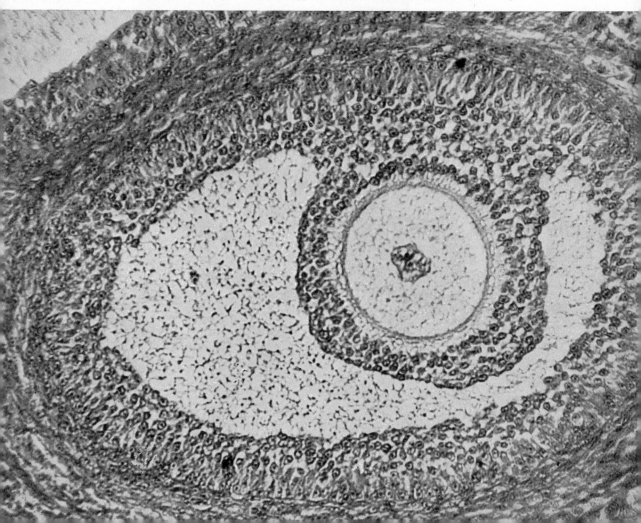

Magazines and newspapers often publish special articles entitled "Is Sex Necessary?" or something similar. Usually the implication given is that sex is a luxury, and that the ♂ could well be dispensed with. The whole point of sexual fusion is avoided, and customarily the account takes a humorous trend. The reading public must sometimes be misled, since the facts of the case are more complex and are given scant publicity.

Asexual reproduction, since it depends entirely upon mitosis, produces new individuals with exactly the same chromosomal content as the single parent. If the parent shows inheritable peculiarities, so do all of the offspring. If the peculiarity is beneficial, the outcome may be helpful to the species. If the peculiarity is detrimental, the offspring are all as handicapped as the parent.

By contrast, sexual reproduction depends upon fusion of two unlike ancestral lines. And the mechanism of gamete-formation introduces so much variation among the gametes that the probability of any two from the same parent being exactly alike is almost zero. In consequence, except for identical twins (and similar multiples which arise from a single egg fertilized by a single sperm), no two offspring of a cross are alike. The individual variation among sexually produced offspring fits some individuals better than others for any kind of environment that can be found. In the struggle for existence, this variation is most important in determining which individuals are sufficiently well adapted to living conditions to survive to a reproductive age.

The importance of sex is in terms of variability, and hence of adaptability to living conditions. The advantage over the production-line type of offspring from asexual reproduction is obvious.

Meiosis as a Counterpart to Sex

The discovery of the mechanism whereby variability is provided among gametes came as a result of an astute deduction. After he had lost his eyesight and could no longer investigate embryonic development experimentally, August Weismann began thinking about the continuity characteristic of germ-plasm (see p. 277). Several facts stood out: (1) the egg cell contains a nucleus; (2) the sperm cell contains a nucleus; (3) fertilization consists of the fusion of these two nuclei into a single nucleus; (4) thereafter, in development of the embryo, mitosis accurately duplicates every chromosome in the nucleus; hence daughter cells have the same chromosomal number and content as the previous cell.

If the nucleus in the egg cell contains N chromosomes, and the nucleus in the sperm cell contains N chromosomes, then the nucleus in the fertilized egg cell must contain 2N chromosomes. And through mitosis, every cell in the embryo and the adult must be provided with a nucleus with 2N chromosomes.

Weismann dictated a scientific paper outlining this argument and ending with a plea: Can't someone show the steps whereby cells with the 2N type of nucleus produce sex cells with the N number of chromosomes? There *must* be a special kind of division in which the chromosome number is reduced from 2N to N. Otherwise, at each sexual reproduction, the number of chromosomes would double. Since the number of chromosomes for each species is constant, reduction division must occur in any organism with sexual reproduction.

This statement and question appeared in 1885. Two years later van Beneden found and published the answer. In the formation of sex cells (whether eggs or sperms) in an animal, reduction division did occur. To the mechanism the name **meiosis** (from the Greek *meios* = less, the comparative adjective from *mikra* = small) was given. Through meiosis, new nuclei are formed with half the double (2N) number of chromosomes.

Ploidy

To analyze this process it is essential to have clear terms for each step in the sexual cycle. Each gamete contains a nucleus with a single complete set of chromosomes—one of each kind of chromosome; this is the N number. For mankind it is 24, for the fruitfly 4, and so on. Each of the 24 or of the 4 is a *different* chromosome, carrying different inherited characteristics. When fusion (fertilization) occurs, a nucleus with the N number combines with another nucleus with the N number to yield a new nucleus with the 2N number—a double set of chromosomes, two of each different kind. For mankind the 2N number is 48.[2]

The N number is characteristic of gametes, and is said to represent the **haploid** condition of the nucleus. The 2N number is characteristic of the fused product from sexual union (called the **zygote**), and is said to be **diploid.** In multicellular animals, and all plants except some thallophytes, the zygote is a fertilized egg cell. It grows by mitosis and cytokinesis through embryonic stages into a new individual.

Among multicellular animals, meiosis is a normal part of gamete formation **(gametogenesis).** It occurs in the primary reproductive organs, the **gonads** (either ovary or testis) as the final nuclear changes before the gametes become functional. Hence the only cells of a multicellular animal to be haploid are ordinarily the gametes themselves.

Among multicellular plants, meiosis is characteristic of spore formation **(sporogenesis).** The spore, and all cells of the gametophyte generation, and the gametes too, are haploid. When two gametes fuse to form a zygote, the diploid condition is established. If the zygote produces a multicellular sporophyte, every cell of that sporophyte is diploid. The last diploid cells in the cycle are the spore-mother cells which undergo meiosis to yield haploid spores.

The Process of Meiosis

In meiosis, the chromosomes of the original diploid nucleus go to equatorial positions *twice,* with two divisions in quick succession, to produce four cells, the nucleus of each being haploid.

1. The chromosomes of the diploid parent cell become shorter, denser, more stainable, as they do in the prophase of mitosis. They move to equatorial positions on a spindle.

2. The chromosomes on the equatorial plane sort themselves out in pairs and come to lie side by side, two #1 chromosomes to-

[2] See note on p. 269.

gether, two #2 chromosomes together, and so on, until there are N pairs of chromosomes, each pair being described as in **synapsis.** Since each chromosome is itself at least a double structure, consisting of two parallel chromatids within the chromosomal envelope, the synaptic process places parallel in each synaptic pair a total of 4 chromatids—a **tetrad** of

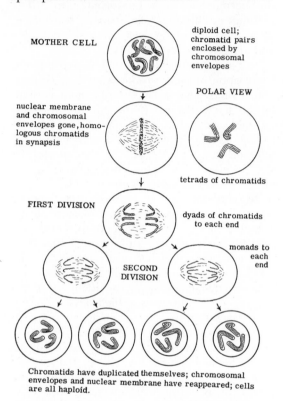

MOTHER CELL

diploid cell; chromatid pairs enclosed by chromosomal envelopes

POLAR VIEW

nuclear membrane and chromosomal envelopes gone, homologous chromatids in synapsis

tetrads of chromatids

FIRST DIVISION

dyads of chromatids to each end

SECOND DIVISION

monads to each end

Chromatids have duplicated themselves; chromosomal envelopes and nuclear membrane have reappeared; cells are all haploid.

FIG. 19-3. *The fundamental procedure in meiosis differs from ordinary cell division (mitosis) in being a two-step process, with synapsis of homologous chromosomes followed by a reduction from the diploid to the haploid condition of the nucleus. In the animal kingdom, the meiotic sequence is characteristic of gamete-formation. Among plants it occurs in spore-formation.*

chromatids. The two chromosomes of a kind which enter into synapsis are described as being **homologous** chromosomes.

3. In what appears to be an anaphase separation, *two* chroma*tids* from each tetrad migrate to each end of the cell (Fig. 19-3). This maneuver places N pairs of chromatids in polar positions. Each pair of chromatids is called a *dyad.* Cytokinesis takes place, but the chromatids do not organize themselves into chromosomes or into daughter nuclei.

4. New spindles form in the daughter cells, and the N pairs of chromatids in each cell arrange themselves on the equatorial plane.

5. In what appears to be an anaphase separation, *one* chrom*atid* from each of the N dyads migrates to each end of each elongating daughter cell. This action places N chromatids in each of the polar positions. The solitary chromatids are called *monads*.

6. In each of the four granddaughter cells, the N monads duplicate themselves by splitting lengthwise, and become N chromosomes; these organize themselves into haploid nuclei. Each of the four granddaughter cells now has the nuclear organization needed to become a spore (in multicellular plants) or a gamete (in multicellular animals).

Meiosis in Structurally Simple Organisms

Sex and the need for meiosis is not restricted to multicellular organisms. Unicellular green algae, such as Chlamydomonas (p. 213); colonial types such as Volvox; and animals such as amebae, ciliates and the like, have sexual methods of reproduction. The process may be unexpectedly complicated, as is indicated by the following examples:

1. Chlamydomonas demonstrates asexual reproduction by becoming nonmotile, and dividing the contents of a single cell into 2, 4, or 8 smaller cells which develop paired flagella, escape from the parental cell wall, and eventually enlarge to parental size. For sexual reproduction, one of the nonmotile cells may divide similarly internally, and produce as many as 32 small gametes, each with a pair of flagella. A gamete from one parent may fuse with a gamete from a different parent, to form a zygote with a thick wall. After a dormant period, the zygote cell undergoes meiotic division to yield 4 swimming cells that grow to become the familiar denizens of pond water. Since only particular pairs of gametes will fuse, it is evident that differences between them are detectable—though not through the microscope. They are said to be of different "mating types" or "strains."

2. Among protozoans are many examples of mating strains that cannot be distinguished except by behavior. Additional nuclei may complicate the picture. In the slipper animalcule, Paramecium, the ordinary active cell contains a large **macronucleus** and two (or

some other number, depending on the species) **micronuclei** of smaller size. In ordinary asexual reproduction (fission), all nuclei divide by a type of mitosis, leaving both of the daughter cells identically equipped. But when two mating strains are brought together, they cling in pairs as an initial step in **conjugation** (from the Latin *con* = together, *jugare* = to yoke). The macronucleus slowly vanishes into the general cytoplasm (as does the nucleoplasm of multicellular plants and animals). Each micronucleus divides twice (Fig. 19-4), forming 4 nuclei, of which 3 promptly disintegrate into the cytoplasm. Then, from each of the conjugating cells, one micronucleus passes through a minute opening in the cell membrane along the surface of contact. No significant amount of cytoplasm is exchanged, but the nuclei (one that originated in the cell, and one that came from the conjugating cell) fuse. Each cell is now a zygote, by a reciprocal swapping of nuclear components. The zygote nucleus in each cell undergoes a pair of divisions to produce 4 micronuclei. The two cells separate. Each reorganizes a macronu-

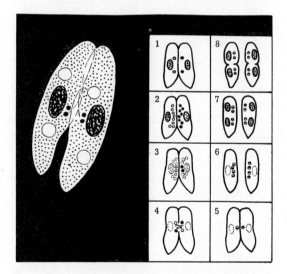

FIG. 19-4. *Conjugating Paramecium individuals cling with their oral grooves together while undergoing nuclear changes and interchanges. The inset shows the complex behavior of macronucleus and micronuclei—dividing, disintegrating, being exchanged (4), fusing (5) and dividing (6), followed by fission (8) without further duplication of micronuclear material. The meiotic division (2) precedes fusion and the exchanged micronuclei (4) must be regarded as gamete nuclei.*

cleus and undergoes fission without further duplication of the micronucleus.

For years the infrequency of conjugation in Paramecium cultures in the laboratory was a major puzzle. Then it was discovered that

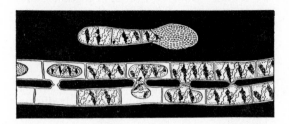

FIG. 19-5. *Conjugation in Spirogyra leads to formation of a heavy-walled zygote* (right end of lower filament), *in which meiosis occurs before germination into a new filament* (bottom).

there are as many as 8 different mating strains in a single species, and that only particular combinations will conjugate. As might be expected, the genetics of this "simple" unicellular organism proves to be highly complex.

3. The filamentous green alga Spirogyra may demonstrate sexual reproduction. Two filaments lying side by side in a pond may react to one another (Fig. 19-5). At various points, the individual cells form connecting tubes that link one filament to the other. In each cell of a linked pair, the protoplasm rounds up as though plasmolysed, and one of them becomes ameboid, moving across the bridge to fuse with the other. The passive cell can then be recognized as ♀, the moving one as ♂, and the product as a zygote. In this instance, the successive cells of one original filament may not be all of one sex, and not all cells of a filament may show conjugation. The zygotes, however, develop heavy walls that make them resistant to adverse conditions. After an extended period, these protective coverings break down and the cell within undergoes meiotic division to produce 4 nuclei. Three of these disintegrate, and the remaining one produces a single haploid filament by mitosis and cytokinesis. The diploid condition (sporophyte generation) is limited to the period between fusion of the gametes and germination of a single cell in the zygote wall.

4. In other algae, the protoplasm within cells of a filament may divide repeatedly into small bodies, each a gamete bearing 2 flagella; meiosis occurs in gametogenesis; the gametes escape through a break in the cell wall. If the gametes are so similar that neither size nor activity indicate sex, they are referred to as **isogametes.** They still are different in behavior to the extent that only certain strains will fuse in pairs. Thus, sexuality is present, although unidentifiable as to type. In other algae the strains are different in appearance— the egg cells being larger and less active, the sperm cells smaller and more energetic; they are **heterogametes.** But the fusion of a swimming gamete with another (swimming or not) is called **fertilization;** again the result is a zygote which germinates to form a new plant.

5. The black mold of bread, *Rhizopus nigricans,* is often used to demonstrate sexual strains in a terrestrial, alga-like fungus. Whenever food is abundant, Rhizopus reproduces asexually, sending up stalks bearing spores in large numbers. If one of these spore-bearing bodies is shaken over a new food supply, all of the resulting mycelia will be of the same mating type. They show this by mutual repulsion wherever their filamentous extensions approach one another.

But if two different mating types are sowed adjacent to one another, the hyphae touch instead of avoiding contact, and form cells in contact. These are haploid gametes, walled off from the rest of the mycelium. The gametes fuse, and the zygote develops heavy walls. Later it undergoes meiotic division, producing 4 spores, 2 of each mating type. Hence the visible mold plant is haploid, and of "plus" or "minus" strain. Only the zygote is diploid.

These examples suffice to demonstrate the variability and some of the complexities of the simplest kind of sexual union. The essential feature is the fusion of two nuclei. That the ♂ and ♀ cannot be distinguished until mating begins presents difficulties for the biologist studying the process, and reminds him of Roland Young's jingle:

And here's the happy, bounding flea—
You cannot tell the he from she.
The sexes look alike, you see;
But she can tell and so can he.

—from *Not for Children* (New York: Doubleday, 1930).

When meiosis occurs in gametogenesis, the animal body is diploid. Only the gametes are haploid. The process differs according to the sex of the parent. In the ♂ (Fig. 19-6, *left;* Photo 249), the cytokinetic steps during meiotic division each separate the cytoplasm into approximately equal volumes. Each of the resulting four haploid cells becomes a sperm. In the ♀, by contrast, the cytokinetic steps during meiosis favor one daughter cell and one granddaughter cell with essentially all of the cytoplasm. Of the 4 haploid cells produced, only one goes on to become an egg. The other

three disintegrate, and are called "polar bodies" from the position in which they are commonly seen (Fig. 19-6, *right;* Photo 250).

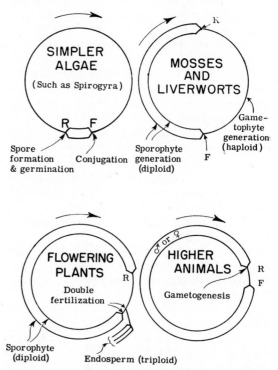

FIG. 19-7. *Reduction division (R) and fertilization (F) in plants with sexual reproduction may be spaced out by a gametophyte generation which has no counterpart among animals.*

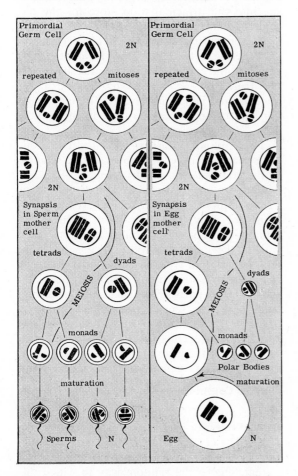

FIG. 19-6. *Gametogenesis in animals includes meiosis after the primordial germ cell in each testis* (left) *or ovary* (right) *has produced by repeated mitoses a large crop of mother cells. Each sperm mother cell (diploid), by meiosis and maturation, produces four sperms (haploid). Each egg mother cell (diploid), by meiosis and maturation, produces one egg (haploid) plus as many as three waste polar bodies (haploid).*

Meiosis in Embryophyte Plants

Meiosis is a step in sporogenesis. Its product is 4 haploid spores from each diploid spore mother cell. The spores may germinate into haploid gametophyte tissue and, still by mitosis, evolve archegonia, antheridia, and gametes—all with haploid nuclei. The zygote formed by fusion of a pair of gametes is the start of a new diploid, sporophyte generation.

The proportion of the life history occupied by gametophyte and sporophyte is markedly different in simpler plants as compared with more complex ones (Fig. 19-7).

Among seed plants, the variations in ploidy are particularly interesting:

1. The gymnosperm microspore mother cell undergoes meiotic division to produce 4 microspores (p. 278, Fig. 18-20); in each

the haploid ♂ gametophyte develops by mitosis; each sperm cell is haploid.

The megaspore mother cell in the ovule likewise undergoes meiosis to produce 4 megaspores, 3 of which abort, leaving one haploid megaspore to develop by mitosis into the ♀ gametophyte with its archegonia and egg cells.

Fertilization of an egg by a sperm starts off a new diploid sporophyte generation as an embryo surrounded by (a) haploid tissue of ♀ gametophyte, and (b) diploid seed coats from the ovule integuments—tissue of the parent sporophyte. The germinating seed casts off these surrounding parts or absorbs their nourishment into its own diploid tissue. In its own diploid cones, it eventually produces diploid megaspore mother cells or microspore mother cells (or both, in different cones), completing the cycle.

2. The angiosperm microspore mother cell undergoes meiotic division to produce 4 microspores (p. 300, Fig. 18-22); in each the

haploid ♂ gametophyte develops a total of 2 cells, by mitosis; each of the resulting sperms is haploid.

The megaspore mother cell in the ovule undergoes meiotic division to produce 4 megaspores, 3 of which abort, leaving one haploid megaspore to develop by mitosis into the 8-nucleated ♀ gametophyte.

Fertilization of the egg nucleus by a sperm starts off the new diploid sporophyte, as an embryo. Through double fertilization, the second sperm nucleus from the pollen tube unites with the 2 (or more) fusion nuclei to form a polyploid endosperm nucleus. Mitosis and eventual cytokinesis enlarge this polyploid tissue into the principal food store for the developing embryo.

In about 70 per cent of angiosperms, the endosperm is **triploid** (3N). In another 20 per cent, the endosperm nuclei arise by fusion of 4 from the ♀ gametophyte plus one sperm nucleus, and hence are 5N. The remaining 10 per cent of angiosperms range all the way to 15N.

The triploid endosperm (as the commonest situation) may be shown in its relation to the complete life history (Fig. 19-8).

Thus an angiosperm seed may consist of (1) a diploid, sporophyte embryo; (2) remains of polyploid endosperm tissue; (3) diploid seed coats contributed from the ovule wall of the preceding sporophyte generation; and (4) diploid fruit tissue, as enlarged cells of the parent sporophyte's ovary (carpel wall) and adhering parts. The husk, cob, and kernel coats of a corn seed are parental sporophyte tissue (2N); the endosperm (white or yellow, starchy or sweet) is food (3N) for the embryo (2N of the next sporophyte generation). Only the embryo can develop into a new plant.

Chance Combinations

The process of meiosis must be comprehended fully for events in inheritance to make sense. The central feature in sexual reproduction is the variety of gametes from a single parent, due to the random way in which different chromosomal contributions are segregated into gametes (Fig. 19-9).

To make this randomness evident, it is worth while to follow through the meiotic process in an organism with a small number of chromosomes. The fruitfly, *Drosophila*

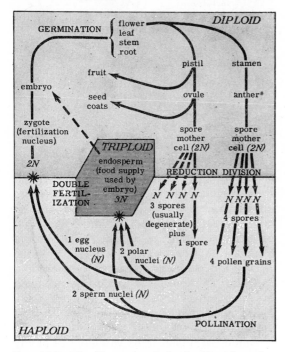

FIG. 19-8. *The life cycle of the familiar flowering plants provides each seed with an embryo of the new generation, surrounded by seed coats and fruit contributed by the parent generation, and a food supply formed by unique triple fusion.*

melanogaster, with its 2N number of 8 and N number of 4, is ideal.

In the Drosophila zygote, and in every body cell of the adult after embryonic de-

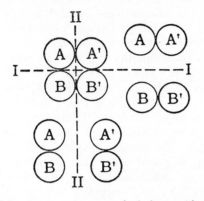

FIG. 19-9. *In synapsis, a tetrad of chromatids represents two chromatids from the ♂ parent (say A and A') and two from the ♀ (say B and B')—a homologous pair of chromosomes received originally into the zygote nucleus from the sperm and egg respectively. In the first meiotic division they may separate as the dyads (A and A' to one pole, B and B' to the other, as in I), or pair up in new combinations (A and B to one pole, as in II). In the second meiotic division, however, each granddaughter cell receives only one chromatid from the synaptic tetrad; it may be A or B or A' or B'. Hence it makes no difference whether the original separation is as in I or II. (After Marsland & Plunkett.)*

velopment, there are 8 chromosomes, 4 descended directly from contributions of the sperm, and 4 from the original egg. These eight chromosomes can be given numbers:

I, II, III, and IV from the ♂ parent;
I', II', III', and IV' from the ♀ parent.

In the primordial germ cells the 8 chromosomes are each represented by 2 chromatids. At synapsis of the meiotic division, each of the 4 tetrads on the equatorial plane consists of 2 chromatids from the ♂ parent and 2 chromatids from the ♀ parent. These four tetrads can be represented as

I	I	II	II'	III'	III'	IV'	IV
I'	I'	II	II'	III	III	IV'	IV

There is no way to predict in which plane these tetrads will separate into dyads. I will go with I' with equal statistical frequency that I will go with I. And when the gametes are formed, the only certain feature is that every gamete will have a representative of each of the 4 different chromosomes. There is an

equal chance for any particular sperm to include the representative of the I or the I' chromosome. So, too, with the II and II' chromosome, and with the others. As a result, among the many eggs or the multitudinous sperm cells in a fruitfly, there are equal proportions with each of the following 16 combinations:

I,	II,	III,	IV	I',	II',	III',	IV'
I,	II,	III,	IV'	I',	II',	III',	IV
I,	II,	III',	IV	I',	II',	III,	IV'
I,	II,	III',	IV'	I',	II',	III,	IV
I,	II',	III,	IV	I',	II,	III',	IV'
I,	II',	III,	IV'	I',	II,	III',	IV
I,	II',	III',	IV	I',	II,	III,	IV'
I,	II',	III',	IV'	I',	II,	III,	IV

Thus, when there are 4 different chromosomes (4 homologous pairs at synapsis, a haploid number of 4, a diploid number of 8), there are 16 different, equally possible combinations of whole chromosomes that combine nuclear components received from father and mother. If there had been only 3 different chromosomes involved, there would have been 8 equally likely combinations of parental chromosomes among the gametes.

Those with arithmetical ability will recognize that $16 = (2)^4$, while 8 is $(2)^3$, and that the basis for these numbers is $(2)^n$ where n is the total of different chromosomes. Those with less arithmetical background may need to be reminded that $(2)^4$ is a way of writing $2 \times 2 \times 2 \times 2$, while $(2)^3 = 2 \times 2 \times 2$. This generalization regarding the number of different gametes all appearing with equal probability holds true for man as well. In human body cells there are 48 chromosomes; the gametes contain 24 as the haploid number. Hence there are $(2)^{24} =$ about 16,750,-000 equally likely combinations of maternal chromosomes with paternal chromosomes in an individual egg or sperm cell. Stated another way, the probability of finding any given assortment of maternal and paternal chromosomes in a particular gamete is one in 16,-750,000. The possibility that a sperm will have the identical chromosome complement as the egg cell which was fertilized, or as the sperm that fused with it to start the new individual now forming gametes, is also one in

16,750,000. Another mechanism to be discussed (p. 328) makes this even more unlikely!

3. STATISTICS

Calculations of probability and statistical treatment are not new in biology. One of the earliest attempts to gain a scientific understanding of heredity used this approach. An Englishman, Sir Francis Galton (1822-1911), was one of the founders of a subscience of biology called **biometry**—the measurement of life. He began with an analysis of heights among human beings, taking 1,000 families as a sample. He measured the 2,000 parents and all the fully grown offspring. From his 1897 analysis of these data he reached no very helpful understanding of inheritance. Yet an experimental approach of which Galton was unaware had already been published. It gave the basic information on which the major part of modern genetics has been built.

This background was worked out firmly but inconspicuously by an amateur in science. The monk Gregor Johann Mendel (1822-1884), in the monastery at Brunn, Austria, achieved notable success because of a combined interest in gardening and algebra. He too was willing to deal with populations and treat his data statistically.

4. SIMPLE INHERITANCE

Mendel raised peas in the monastery garden and entertained himself by collecting their seeds, noticing what each seed produced the following season. Fortunately he saved and planted separately some seed from dwarf peas, and noticed that all of the new generation developed into dwarfs. Seeds from tall pea plants grew into either tall or dwarf plants. Mendel carefully self-pollinated his plants and prevented cross-pollination, then checked to see what the new crop of seeds would produce.

Dominance

His results were highly encouraging. All seeds from self-pollinated dwarf plants gave rise to only dwarf plants. Seeds from self-pollinated tall plants (raised from seed obtained from tall plants) gave rise either to all tall plants or to both dwarf plants and tall plants, in very nearly the ratio of one dwarf to three tall. Mendel self-pollinated again, and once more grew the seeds under his watchful eye. The results were no different: (1) all seeds from self-pollinated dwarf plants gave rise only to dwarf plants—as before; (2) all seeds from one-third of his tall plants grew only to tall plants; (3) the seeds from two-thirds of his tall plants yielded both dwarf plants and tall, again in the ratio of 1 : 3.

It is greatly to Mendel's credit that he continued these experiments several more generations. His results came out statistically the same, over and over. Then he tried crossing what he had come to call "pure line dwarf" plants with his "pure line tall" plants—and tested the cross both ways—pollen from dwarf on stigmas of tall, and pollen from tall on stigmas of dwarf. This was the first **reciprocal cross** made under scientific conditions, and the results were illuminating. All the plants from both crosses were tall.

Mendel self-pollinated these new tall plants, and in the succeeding generation found dwarf and tall in the familiar ratio, 1 : 3. Again the dwarf plants bred true when self-pollinated; so did a third of the tall plants; two-thirds of the tall plants (hence half of all plants) when self-pollinated produced dwarf and tall in the usual ratio. Hence when pure-line tall is crossed with pure-line dwarf, all offspring are tall. When these are self-pollinated, the following generation consists of ¼ pure-line tall, ¼ pure-line dwarf, and ½ "hybrid" tall.

There was need for descriptive terms with which to record these results. The German words Mendel used have not been translated literally, but instead we have equivalents in English. Thus, in the crosses outlined above, Mendel referred at once to tallness in his pea plants as being **dominant** over dwarfness, and dwarfness as being **recessive** to tallness. When a cross was made between pure-line tall and pure-line dwarf, all of the offspring showed the dominant tallness. But the recessive dwarfness was there, concealed, demonstrable by carrying the study one more generation through self-pollination.

Mendel referred to the pure-line tall parents and the pure-line dwarf parents in such an experiment as the P (for parental) generation. The offspring from the P generation were the F_1 (for "first filial") generation. When F_1 plants were self-pollinated, they formed seeds from which he grew the F_2 (second filial) generation, and so on. It was the F_2 plants that showed the 3 : 1 ratio of tallness to dwarfness. Yet the 3 : 1 ratio was deceiving. It represented a 1 : 2 : 1 ratio in terms of inheritance; the 1 : 2 : 1 ratio could be called a **genotype** ratio, whereas the 3 : 1 giving appearance only could be termed a **phenotype ratio** (from the Greek *genos* = race, and *phainein* = to show, with *typos* = model).

Clearly, a pure-line plant, whether dwarf or tall, had only one kind of pollen, one kind of ovules. But a hybrid plant, such as the F_1 when tall pure-line was crossed with dwarf, produced two kinds of pollen—one carrying the characteristic of dwarfness, the other the characteristic of tallness. When self-pollinated, there was an equal chance that a pollen grain carrying tallness would fertilize an ovule carrying tallness or one carrying dwarfness. There was an equal chance that a pollen grain carrying dwarfness would fertilize an ovule carrying tallness or one carrying dwarfness. When dwarfness and dwarfness came together (¼ of the time), the seed grew only into a dwarf plant. When tallness and tallness came together (¼ of the time), the seed grew only into a tall plant that bred true when self-pollinated. But when tallness and dwarfness came together, or dwarfness and tallness, the result (½ of the time) was a hybrid showing the dominant tallness but not breeding true.

To Mendel's algebraic mind, the representation of these events in symbols was simple and attractive. The pure-line tall plants could be represented by T × T, to show that it inherited tallness from each of its parents. The dwarf plants were all pureline, and t × t

could represent them. All ovules and all pollen grains from pure-line tall contained the characteristic T, while those from dwarf all had t. But the pollen of the F_1 from such a cross clearly were of two types in equal proportions—although no visible clue could be seen: half with T, half with t. The ovules of the F_1 were also 50 per cent with T, 50 per cent with t. In self-pollination, the complete picture could be represented by (T + t) pollen grains crossing with (T + t) ovules, and simple algebra showed that

$$(T + t) (T + t) = (T \times T) + 2 (T \times t) + (t \times t), \text{ or } T^2 + 2 Tt + t^2.$$

which could be seen as

1 pure-line + 2 hybrid + 1 pure-line
tall   tall   dwarf.

Mendel tried other characteristics of his pea plants, and found the following:

1. Round seeds was a condition dominant over wrinkled seeds.

2. Yellow cotyledons were dominant to green cotyledons.

3. Gray-brown seed coat was dominant to white seed coat.

4. Green pods were dominant to yellow pods.

5. Smooth pods were dominant to constricted ones.

6. Flowers borne in axial positions were dominant to flowers at the ends of the plants (in terminal positions).

Each of these **characters** behaved as did the tallness and dwarfness when the pure lines he developed so laboriously were crossed. Several conclusions could be drawn from the uniformity of his results:

Human Characters Showing Simple Dominance

Dominant	Recessive	Dominant	Recessive
Dimple	No dimple	Six fingers	Five fingers
Straight chin	Receding chin	Susceptibility to hernia	Normal
Pigmented iris	Albino, "pink eyed"	Resistance to tuberculosis	Susceptibility to tuberculosis
Drooping eyelids	Normal	Diabetes insipidus	Normal
Astigmatism	Normal cornea	Ability to taste phenyl-thiocarbamide	Inability to taste this compound
Nearsightedness (myopia)	Normal vision		
Cataract	Normal vision	Normal hearing	Congenital deafness

1. Each inherited characteristic could be represented by a single letter, and the plant transmitted this characteristic as a unit, never in part or in multiple. (The principle of **unit characters.**)

2. Each inheritable characteristic appeared in two forms, but a hybrid showed only one of these forms, the dominant. Capital letters could be used to represent dominant conditions of the characteristic, and lower case for the recessive. The appearance of the dominant did not indicate whether the individual was pure-line for the character, or whether it was hybrid. But the appearance of the recessive in its offspring indicated the genetic makeup of the individual. (The principle of **dominance.**)

3. When pollen grains or ovules are being formed, they receive only one unit, either the dominant or the recessive for each character, depending on the plant producing them. On a pure-line dominant plant, all of the reproductive units carry the dominant condition; on a pure-line recessive plant, all carry the recessive condition; on a hybrid plant, half of the reproductive units receive the dominant unit, half the recessive. Segregation into these reproductive units is free and unrestricted. (The principle of **segregation.**)

4. All types of pea ovules can be fertilized by any type of pea pollen. The appearance of the succeeding generation can be explained only on the basis of complete randomness in fertilization. (The principle of **random fertilization.**)

5. There is no change in the character as a result of associating with another—a dominant with a recessive. When the characters segregate from such association in a hybrid, each is exactly as it was in the previous pure line. (The principle of **purity of characters.**)

Mendel made other crosses to check his work. He cross-pollinated the F_1 hybrids and found no difference in the ratio of the progeny from that after self-pollination—indicating that the F_1 generation were all alike in their inheritance of the character. He also crossed the F_1 hybrids with the pure-line dominants—and found all dominants in the appearance of the next generation, though half were pure-line and half were themselves hybrids. He crossed F_1 hybrids with pure-line

recessive and found 50 per cent of the offspring recessives (hence pure-line), the other 50 per cent showing the dominant. Actually, however, all were hybrids.

Back-Cross

The importance of this cross between the recessive and the hybrid should not be overlooked. If an individual shows the dominant characteristic, it is impossible to tell by inspection whether it is pure-line dominant (such as TT) or hybrid (such as Tt). But if it is crossed with the pure-line recessive, a pure-line dominant produces only dominant offspring, whereas a hybrid yields 50 per cent with the recessive character. If the questionable individual is self-pollinated instead, 25 per cent with the recessive is the best expectable. With poor yields of seed, the recessive group might fail to show up altogether. For this reason, mating of an unknown with dominant appearance to the pure-line recessive is common practice; it is known as a **back-cross,** and the 1 : 1 ratio is characteristic of it for both phenotype and genotype.

Independence

During the eight years[3] of his experimental studies in the monastery garden, Mendel tried also various combinations of the seven different pure lines he had studied a single character at a time (as **"monohybrid"** crosses). Now he would follow two characters at a time, in a **dihybrid cross.** He tried one line known to be pure for round seed and yellow endosperm, mating it with another line pure for wrinkled seeds and green endosperm. All of the seeds from this cross (F_1) were round and yellow. Round was still dominant to wrinkled, yellow still dominant to green endosperm. If the parents are designated RRYY and rryy, with the R for round seeds and r for recessive wrinkling, the Y for yellow endosperm, and y for the recessive green, then the F_1 came from an

---

[3] Mendel had made earlier but nonconsecutive attempts to unravel these problems. Those ending in 1865 were the only fruitful studies. As a young monk he was kept too busy and had difficulty getting garden space for investigations that his superiors regarded as "dabbling." Later, when he became an abbot and had no time or space problems, he had become too fat to bend as needed in caring for his seeds. It is recorded that he tried smoking 50 cigars a day in the hope of losing weight—to no avail!

ovule with RY and a pollen grain with ry; they should be RrYy—all showing the dominant characteristics.

The seeds were grown and the F_1 plants self-pollinated to learn their nature. Four types were obtained in the following proportions: 315 round and yellow, 108 round and green, 101 wrinkled and yellow, 32 wrinkled and green. The phenotype ratio was roughly 9 : 3 : 3 : 1, but considered in terms of round and wrinkled alone, the 315 + 108 to 101 + 32 is very close to 3 : 1; and considered in terms of yellow and green alone, the 315 + 101 to 108 + 32 is still very close to 3 : 1. Mendel repeated his crosses and the ratios kept getting ever closer to the simple values expected on the basis of random segregation and fertilization with pure unit characters. In all dihybrid crosses Mendel tried, the 9 : 3 : 3 : 1 ratio appeared whenever two lines, each pure for two characters, were crossed and the F_1 self-pollinated. Hence he was able to add another generalization to the previous five:

6. There is no interference between two characters; each segregates independently of the other, and the random nature of pollination accounts for the results. (The principle of **independent assortment.**)

Specifically, Mendel's dihybrid crosses furnished pollen grains and ovules which combined as shown in the diagram below.

		Equal Proportions of Each of These Ovules			
		RY	Ry	rY	ry
Equal Proportions of Each of These Pollen Grains	RY	RRYY	RRYy	RrYY	RrYy
	Ry	RRYy	RRyy	RrYy	Rryy
	rY	RrYY	RrYy	rrYY	rrYy
	ry	RrYy	Rryy	rrYy	rryy

Horizontally hatched are the 9 out of every 16 showing the dominant for both characters; diagonally hatched from above to lower right are the 3 showing dominant in R and recessive yy; the opposite diagonal hatching shows those recessive in rr and carrying the dominant Y; unshaded is the double recessive rryy —one in each 16.

More than ever there is a need for terms

to distinguish RR from Rr from rr. **Homozygous dominant** is RR; **homozygous recessive** is rr; **heterozygous** is Rr. Hence also RRYY is homozygous dominant for both characters, rryy homozygous recessive for both.

Two new pure lines appear in the progeny of this cross: RRyy—homozygous dominant in R, homozygous recessive in y; and rrYY, the corresponding opposite. Of the 16 different progeny types, all found with equal likelihood, 4 are homozygous for both characters, and all 4 are different. The phenotype ratio is 9 : 3 : 3 : 1, but the genotype ratio is

1 : 1 : 2 : 2 : 4 : 2 : 2 : 1 : 1
RRYY : RRyy : RRYy : RrYY : RrYy : Rryy : rrYy : rrYY : rryy

Unfortunately, Mendel had no scientific standing outside his little community, and the one person of renown to whom he sent a report of his findings was too conservative to appreciate the importance of an amateur's work. In consequence, the only printed form in which the eight years of painstaking effort appeared was a little paper in the Proceedings of the Natural History Society of Brunn. Because no one was then interested in problems of this type, his work was overlooked completely.

From 1865, when this gem of experimental proof and analysis reached print, until 1900, no one had the benefit of Mendel's work. Then three independent research men, Hugo de Vries, in Holland, Erich Tschermak, in Austria, and Carl Correns, in Germany, worked out in preliminary form from their own studies the same ratios, the same conclusions as Mendel had reached. After recognizing the importance of their separate discoveries, each checked the literature carefully.[4] Each to his chagrin uncovered Mendel's little paper, proving that their thunder had been stolen by another. Each of the three lived up to the scientific spirit of honesty, although it was a painful duty, and published a paper in

---

[4] Proper scientific method calls for checking bibliographies *before* proceeding with experimental work. These men, like many others, learned this fact the hard way.

1900 drawing the attention of the world to Mendel's fundamental discoveries, and adding as a note: these experiments are valid; here is additional, independent proof! Thus was genetics begun.

Alleles

All of Mendel's unit characters were either dominant or recessive. As more was learned about inheritance, it became apparent that a character may exist in more than two unlike conditions. Human blood groups O, A, B, and AB are due to an inherited character of which there are two different dominant forms (with symbols A and a^B) and one recessive (a). Neither of the dominant conditions is recessive to the other, but both are dominant to a. They are hence "duplicate alleles." Eye color in fruitflies follows a whole series of "multiple alleles" operating similarly.

In human blood group inheritance, both A and a^B induce formation of antigens within the red blood cells, and inhibit formation of antibodies against these antigens within the plasma. The transfusions possible with whole blood (p. 128) depend on this. Genetically we can substitute for blood group O the symbols aa, for group A either AA or Aa, for group B either a^Ba^B or a^Ba, and for group AB the symbol Aa^B. Recently the gene A was found to be dual—actually either A^1 or A^2—although these do not differ in terms of the transfusion problem. Serological tests can demonstrate the difference, however, and this possibility extends the use of blood groupings in analysis of medicolegal suits involving disputed parenthood. Omitting the A^1 and A^2 differences, it is easy to see that only certain blood types are possible among the children of definite parents—or that granted the blood type of one parent (mother) and the child, the blood types or type among which the second parent can be claimed are fixed:

Blood Type of One Parent	Blood Type of Other Parent	Genetic Constitutions and Blood Types Possible in Children
O	O	only aa (Type O)
O	A	Aa (Type A) or aa (Type O)
O	B	a^Ba (Type B) or aa (Type O)
O	AB	Aa (Type A) or a^Ba (Type B)
A	A	AA, Aa (both Type A) or aa (Type O)
A	B	Aa^B, Aa, a^Ba, or aa (Types AB, A, B, O)
A	AB	AA, Aa (Type A), Aa^B (AB) or a^Ba (B)
B	B	a^Ba^B, a^Ba (Type B) or aa (Type O)
B	AB	Aa^B (AB), Aa (A), or a^Ba^B, a^Ba (Type B)
AB	AB	AA (A), Aa^B (AB), or a^Ba^B (Type B)

Or written in the medicolegal direction:

Mother's Type	Child's Type	Father's Type Can be	Father's Type Cannot be
O	O	O, A, B	AB
O	A	A, AB	O, B
O	B	B, AB	O, A
A	O	O, A, B	AB
A	A	O, A, AB	B
A	B	B, AB	O, A
A	AB	B, AB	O, A
B	O	O, A, B	AB
B	A	A, AB	O, B
B	B	O, A, B, AB	—
B	AB	A, AB	O, B
AB	A	O, A, B, AB	—
AB	B	O, A, B, AB	—
AB	AB	A, B, AB	O

Another antigen present in human red blood cells can be identified by developing antibodies toward it in experimental rabbits. Since no antibodies are involved in the human circulatory system, transfusion problems are not complicated by this factor. But, from the serological studies, it is clear that all human beings are carriers of antigen M, or antigen N, or both M and N; these contribute supplementary information in problems of disputed parentage since the series (which lacks dominance) is controlled by the genes MM (group M), Mm (group MN), and mm (group N).

The most recent addition to the inheritable antigens in man was discovered first in the Rhesus monkey—whence the symbol Rh. Six alleles are known in this series, with the single recessive condition rh producing no antigen in the blood cells. Unlike the M and N antigens, the Rh antigens may provoke the production of antibody in the plasma of the person who is rh rh—or, in popular terms, "Rh negative." The first transfusion of blood with Rh (any of the dominant series) causes no ill effects, but induces antibody formation. The antibodies may remain dormant for years and the incompatability show only at a later transfusion (see p. 128). Or the placental circulation may develop enough gaps that small amounts of a fetus' blood may pass into the mother's blood stream. If the fetus has received a dominant *Rh* gene from the father, and, if the mother is *rh rh,* she may develop antibodies which pass through the same gaps to the embryo, causing destruction of red cells in the embryo (*erythroblastosis*).

Blending

None of Mendel's crosses involved a character of another common type: that in which there is no dominance at all. In cattle, a red cow mated with a white bull (or conversely) gives rise to a blotched ("roan") calf that shows its hybrid character in its coat color. A pure line of red snapdragons crossed with a pure line of white yields an F_1 generation of pink snapdragons. These, if self-pollinated, produce an F_2 in which are red, pink, and white snapdragons in the ratio of 1 : 2 : 1. These are cases of **incomplete dominance** or **blending inheritance.**

Another simple form of inheritance was discovered when Mendelian principles were applied to guinea pigs, mice, rats, and rabbits. The albino, pink-eyed, white-coated individuals proved to be homozygous recessives, and each represented a *lack* of pigment. But the dominant factors that corresponded were merely for color—for pigment formation. Still other characters determine what the color will be when present, and how it will be distributed. The albino condition thus masks factors of completely separate characters.

5. DETERMINATION OF SEX

In 1901, C. E. McClung, of the University of Kansas, had noticed that in ♂ grasshoppers there was a difference in chromosome numbers from that in the ♀ ♀ of the same species. In the ♂ ♂, one of the homologous pairs in the ♀ ♀ was represented either by a single chromosome or by one chromosome plus a peculiar small one. The little chromosome received the name, the **Y-chromosome,** while its mate in synapsis, or the solitary one when no Y was found, became the **X-chromo-**

some. McClung showed that the X-chromosome corresponded in form and dimensions to one of the homologous pairs of chromosomes in the ♀. Hence the ♂ ♂ had either XY or just X, while the ♀ ♀ had XX—and these must be **sex chromosomes.** Then when the cells of the individual have chromosomes X and X, the individual is a ♀, but when the chromosomes are X and Y or just X, the individual is a ♂. This is the other way of viewing the same information, and places sex on a more mechanical basis.

These conclusions have been amply supported by further work, and we now know that in each sperm cell there is either an X-chromosome or a Y-chromosome, together with the rest of the haploid set. Eggs, on the other hand, whether in grasshoppers or fruit-flies, guinea pigs, or man,[5] contain always an X-chromosome, plus the rest of the haploid set. If an X-bearing sperm fuses with any egg, the embryo is genetically determined to become a ♀. If a Y-bearing sperm fuses with any egg, the embryo similarly becomes a ♂. Thus, sex-determination occurs at the moment of fertilization, and it depends on the chromosome content of the sperm—a matter again of random assortment during the meiotic divisions of maturation.

Since sperm cells in higher animals are not doled out singly but are furnished to the ♀ in thousands or millions at a time, and since half of them bear a Y-chromosome and half an X-chromosome, the probability that any given egg will become a ♂ is close to 50 per cent. In the human case, the likelihood of a boy baby is very slightly more than 50 per cent, although more ♂ embryos abort than do ♀ ♀. The proportion, however, is extremely close to 1 : 1 (106 ♂ ♂ to 100 ♀ ♀ among U. S. whites).

This probability has no relationship to other children born of the same parents—whether born at separate times or simultaneously (unless identical twins, which come from a single fertilized egg, are involved—Fig. 18-13). Thus, where there are two chil-

---

[5] In a few groups of insects, and in some fish and birds, the plan is different in that the ♀ is heterozygous for sex (WZ) while the ♂ is homozygous (WW).

dren from separate eggs, whether born at one or different times, there is a 50 per cent chance of the first being a boy, and a 50 per cent chance of the second being a boy. Combining these, we can see that families with two children will have equal chances of having

first a boy, then a girl (or the two at one birth if fraternal twins),
first a girl, then a boy,
a boy both times,
a girl both times.

Thus, 25 per cent of families of two will have two boys; 25 per cent will have two girls; 50 per cent will have a boy and a girl. Those with an algebraic mind will see in this the expansion of $(\male + \female)^2 = \male.\male + 2\male.\female + \female.\female$, and will be willing to gamble that in families of the three the picture will be represented by

$$(\male + \female)^3 = \male.\male.\male + 3\ \male.\male.\female + 3\ \male.\female.\female + \female.\female.\female.$$

In other words, one in eight families with three children will have (on the average) three boys; one of eight will have three girls; three of eight will have two boys and one girl; and three will have one boy and two girls.

Similarly, in families of four children, the chance of getting a boy every time (hence four boys) will be ½ of ½ of ½ of ½—hence 6.25 per cent (or one in 16). The chance of having only one girl in a group of four children is four in 16; that of having two boys and two girls is six in 16. Put another way, in a planned family of four children, the odds against three boys are 7 : 1. But if a family already has one boy, and plans on three more children, the odds against having three *more* boys is still 7 : 1. *What has happened in the past makes no difference to the random assortment on which these averages and odds must be calculated.* The entire problem of sex determination is as much based on chance as the results of an honest toss of a coin. The laws of chance govern the fusion of X-bearing sperm with X-bearing egg just as they do in the spun penny. The chance of two girls and two boys in a family of four is six in 16; so is the probability of two heads and two tails with the coins, either for a single coin flipped four times or for four coins tossed at once.

6. SEX-LINKED INHERITANCE

Although the correspondence between chromosomal behavior and inheritance of unit characters had been pointed out in 1903, and the chromosomal basis of sex determination had been demonstrated in 1901, it was not until 1910 that a clear demonstration of this relationship was available. In the meanwhile much experimental work had been in progress, but most of it—even that on inheritance in mice, rats, and guinea pigs—was concerned with checking Mendel's generalizations.

The cost of maintaining large plant-breeding stations or extensive animal colonies, and the time involved in getting through a satisfactory number of generations, provided difficulty. Then an embryologist at Columbia University turned to the new field of genetics. He was T. H. Morgan, and the suggestions of some friends gave him the lucky start on which so many rapid scientific advances depend. He began to raise large numbers of the small and common fruitfly, *Drosophila melanogaster,* which throve in his laboratory. Ordinarily, these insects nourish themselves and depend in immature stages on wild molds and yeasts that grow on exuded fruit juice from overripe fruits. To maintain them under controlled conditions, Morgan had only to borrow milk bottles from a dairy (or fail to return those that were delivered), sterilize the glassware with hot water, add half an inch of food in the bottom, cover it with a piece of filter paper or paper towel, and add a pair of flies and stopper the bottle with a wad of cotton batting. The bottles needed only shelf space in a warm room. The food was inexpensive—merely mashed overripe bananas to which a little brewer's yeast had been added. The flies mated, the female laid her eggs near the banana mash, and the maggots hatched, grew, moulted, grew, and so on; finally they pupated and emerged as adults—all in ten days to two weeks. One pair produced as many as 200 progeny in this short time, giving reasonable numbers on which to base studies of averages and ratios. The fruitfly, moreover, is greatly attracted by light, and will run or fly from the culture bottles to any other container if the light comes from a new direction. Drosophila withstood anesthesia with ether fumes, and could be examined rapidly with a hand lens, then returned to a culture bottle to revive, mate, and start a new generation.

Among the thousands upon thousands of fruitflies Morgan examined, he found little variation that looked significant. Then, one day, he found a fly whose compound eyes were white instead of the usual red. Carefully he separated the insect, placed it with a normal mate in a fresh culture bottle and watched both revive, pair, and lay the foundation for an experiment. Since white eye was probably a recessive, Morgan was not disappointed when all of the progeny emerged with red eyes. If they were hybrids and mated among one another, an F_2 generation should furnish him with some 200 flies per pair, and 50 of them should have white eyes.

But when the F_2 emerged, all the 50 white-eyed flies per bottle turned out to be ♂♂. Every ♀ was red-eyed, and so were half of the ♂ population. Were the ♀♀ all alike, or was a recessive hidden in some? Morgan made careful matings between his white-eyed ♂♂ and red-eyed ♀♀ from the F_2 population and soon had an F_3 population of two types. In approximately half of the bottles, every fly was red-eyed. In the other bottles, half of each sex bore white eyes—a 1 : 1 ratio for eye color in each sex.

This proportion resembled the back-cross percentages so strongly that Morgan concluded that his red-eyed females in these bottles must be carriers of the recessive, hence hybrid for eye color. To check this assumption he mated white-eyed ♂♂ with these ♀♀; red-eyed ♂♂ with these ♀♀; white-eyed ♂♂ with white-eyed ♀♀; and red-eyed ♂♂ with white-eyed ♀♀. The results were these:

P white-e. ♂ × white-e. ♀	white-e. ♂ × red-e. ♀
F_1 all white-eyed, ♂♂ and ♀♀	½ ♂♂ white-eyed ½ ♀♀ white-eyed
P red-e. ♂ × white-e. ♀	red-e. ♂ × red-e. ♀
F_1 all ♀♀ red-eyed all ♂♂ white-eyed	all ♀♀ red-eyed ½ ♂♂ white-eyed

Clearly the eye color followed the sex. It could be explained as a character carried on the sex chromosome, the X-chromosome, as is shown in the following diagram:

P	$X^rY \times X^rX^r$		$X^rY \times X^RX^r$			
Gametes	(X^r)(Y) (X^r)		(X^r)(Y) (X^R)(X^r)			
F_1	X^rX^r	X^rY	X^RX^r	X^rX^r	X^RY	X^rY
sex eye	♀ white	♂ white	♀ red	♀ white	♂ red	♂ white
ratio	all		1 : 1		1 : 1	

P	$X^RY \times X^rX^r$		$X^RY \times X^RX^r$			
Gametes	(X^R)(Y) (X^r)		(X^R)(Y) (X^R)(X^r)			
F_1	X^RX^r	X^rY	X^RX^R	X^RX^r	X^RY	X^rY
sex eye	♀ red	♂ white	♀ red	♀ red	♂ red	♂ white
ratio	all	all	all		1 : 1	

Two further crosses exhaust the possibilities in this inheritance:

P	red-eyed ♂ × red-eyed ♀ (wild type)	
	$X^RY \times X^RX^R$	
Gametes	(X^R)(Y) (X^R)	
F_1	X^RX^R	X^RY
sex eye	♀ red	♂ red
ratio	all	
P	white-eyed ♂ × red-eyed ♀ (wild type)	
	$X^rY \times X^RX^R$	
Gametes	(X^r)(Y) (X^R)	
F_1	X^RX^r	X^RY
sex eye	♀ red	♂ red
ratio	all	

Thus, for characters carried by the X-chromosome, there can be three kinds of ♀♀ but only two kinds of ♂♂; this is true because the Y-chromosome seems to lack the ability to carry any dominant—a fact to which interesting exceptions were found in later work. There is thus no homozygous dominant for a sex-linked character in the ♂.

X^RY
Heterozygous
♂

X^rY
Homozygous
recessive ♂

X^RX^R
Homozygous
dominant ♀

X^RX^r
Heterozygous
♀

X^rX^r
Homozygous
recessive ♀

The ability of a heterozygous ♀ to produce sex-linked recessive ♂ offspring was seen at once to explain a puzzling case of human inheritance, where the children and their marriages were so much in the public eye that no important detail was missing. This was the problem of inheritance of hemophilia, a disease characterized by excessive bleeding from minor injuries. Male offspring with hemophilia often reach middle age through continual care, but ♀ offspring almost always die before birth. From this fact, however, it should not be inferred that death in childhood of girls definitely indicates hemophilia in the royal lineage or any other.

Hence hemophilia is sex-linked, transmitted by "carrier" mothers heterozygous for the character. With normal ♂ parents, the progeny of carrier mothers can be expected to include ♂ children, 50 per cent of whom are hemophiliac, and ♀ children, half of whom are carriers; the other children should be normal. Married to a carrier, however, a hemophiliac ♂ can expect half of his sons to be plagued with the difficulty, the other half to be normal; he can also expect half his daughters to be carriers, and the other half to die in childhood. No such combination of a hemophiliac ♂ with a carrier occurs in the royal lineage cited, and only when the recessive ♂ has children with a carrier ♀ can homozygous ♀ offspring be anticipated.

Characters which cause death—and quite a few are known—are termed **lethals** (from the Latin *letum* = death). Hemophilia is a lethal when homozygous in the ♀. Not all lethals are sex-linked. In plants they may simply be the inability to form chlorophyll. In a mosaic plant, one such branch may live at the expense of the rest, but a seed lacking the ability to form chlorophyll dies as soon as its food store is exhausted.

Another sex-linked character in human beings is the inability to distinguish between red and green—one of the several types of color-blindness. This difficulty occurs in nearly 10 per cent of white race ♂ ♂, but in less than two per cent of the corresponding ♀ ♀. The incidence is not hard to understand. Since a father gives each of his sons a Y-chromosome, and each of his daughters an X-chromosome, and since color-blindness of this type is carried by the X, it is possible to state without reservation that a color-blind father never transmitted color-blindness to his sons, but he made of every daughter a definite carrier. If a color-blind ♂ has a color-blind son, the man's wife (if her vision is normal) is a carrier; half of her daughters may be color-blind. On the other hand, all sons of color-blind mothers are invariably color-blind, and the daughters may either be

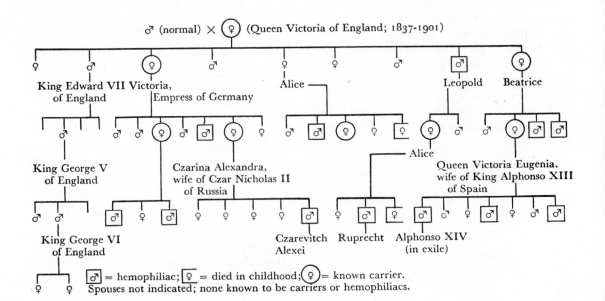

♂ (normal) × ♀ (Queen Victoria of England; 1837-1901)

King Edward VII Victoria, Empress of Germany Alice Leopold Beatrice

King George V of England Czarina Alexandra, wife of Czar Nicholas II of Russia Alice Queen Victoria Eugenia, wife of King Alphonso XIII of Spain

King George VI of England Czarevitch Alexei Ruprecht Alphonso XIV (in exile)

☐♂ = hemophiliac; ☐♀ = died in childhood; ○♀ = known carrier.
Spouses not indicated; none known to be carriers or hemophiliacs.

carriers (if the father has normal vision) or color-blind (if the father is color-blind). Thus the chances of ♂ offspring being color-blind is several times as great as that for ♀ offspring. In being a ♂, every ♂ already has a Y-chromosome with the equivalent of a recessive for every sex-linked character. A recessive on the X-chromosome is never hidden by a dominant on the Y-chromosome.

7. ORDINARY LINKAGE

As further characters were studied in the fruitfly, some were found to be sex-linked, but most were transmitted from one generation to the next in the ordinary Mendelian ratios. However, it soon became apparent that another problem was at hand. "Vestigial wing" gave good 3 : 1 ratios in the F_2 of crosses with the wild-type fly. So did "black body"; and so, too, did "white ocelli" or "hairy body." But if a vestigial-winged, black-bodied fly was mated with the wild type (normal wings, yellowish body), the F_1 generation were all wild type in appearance, and the F_2 did not show the expected ratio of 9 : 3 : 3 : 1. Instead, the F_2 flies were in the proportion of three wild type to one with vestigial wings and black body. Similarly, white ocelli and hairy body (when tested together) gave only a 3 : 1 ratio. But vestigial wing and white ocelli, or vestigial wing and hairy body, or black body and white ocelli, or black body and hairy body, all gave the 9 : 3 : 3 : 1 dihybrid ratio. More and more characters accumulated, and always they fell into the same groups:

sex-linked	group II	group III
white eye	truncate wing	hairy body
miniature wing	black body	white ocelli
cleft wing	vestigial wing	
bar eye		
yellow body		

A further character, "eyeless," turned out to belong to a fourth group. Within each group the ratios were monohybrid. Between groups they were dihybrid. Eyeless with a character from each of group II and group III gave a trihybrid ratio. Clearly the other characters were linked in their groups *and must be carried on the same chromosomes.*

Drosophila has, in addition to the X and Y chromosomes. two homologous pairs of fair length and one very short pair. The X-chromosome is a straight one. Soon it became plausible to regard the short chromosomes as involving linkage group IV, including "eyeless." And from the difference in the number of characters in groups II and group III, the conclusion was reached that the number II chromosome was the slender V-shaped one of medium length, while the number III chromosome was the longer and slightly heavier V-shaped member of the haploid set.

Crossing Over

Further study of linked characters, with larger numbers of flies tested, showed that through a poorly understood mechanism called **crossing over,** a small proportion of the germ cells of an individual heterozygous for a pair of linked characters will carry the combination in a way found in neither parent (Fig. 19-10). From such gametes a minute percentage of anomalous progeny arise—not enough to satisfy a dihybrid ratio, but too many (even one is disturbing) for complete linkage. The conclusion from these facts and others was to the effect that the inherited

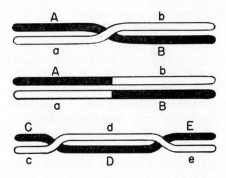

FIG. 19-10. *The mechanics of crossing over, and of double cross-over.*

characters are not only carried as units by the chromosomes, but that the site of the controlling factor in the chromosome is at a remarkably constant position along the length of the string of chromatin granules. From this conclusion arises another—that the factor controlling inheritance of a unit character is a type of organization, probably chemical, of a definite region of the chromosome. To this local, special organization the name **gene** has been applied.

Mapping of Chromosomes

Thus, the theory of the gene states that the gene can exist in at least two different conditions—a dominant condition and a recessive condition. The gene is duplicated when the chromosome splits lengthwise. In a heterozygous individual, the gene is in the dominant condition in one chromosome, in the recessive in the other. In many characters studied, one chromosome may carry the genes for two different characters both in the dominant condition, while the homologous chromosome carries these same genes at corresponding points but in the recessive condition. If no crossover occurs, the chromosomes separate in maturation divisions, the two dominants going to one set of gametes, the two recessives to the other set. But when crossover occurs, segments of chromosomes (or, more precisely, of chromatids) are interchanged, producing new combinations. This may provide a chromosome with the dominant of character *A* and the recessive of character *b,* while the other has the recessive of *a* and the dominant of *B.* Moreover, if that occurs, then the probability of a break and interchange between two characters—providing the evidence of crossing over—will be greater the farther apart the genes are located on the chromosome. By careful study of crossover percentages between linked genes, it has been possible in this way to map entire chromosomes. Such has been done to remarkable extents in Drosophila (several species), potato, corn (maize), and a number of other organisms (Fig. 19-11).

Quite early in these investigations of linkage in Drosophila, it became apparent that crossing over occurred in the ♀ fly but not in the ♂. Cytogenetic study of the steps leading to gametes in the ♂ fly indicated a possible reason. Since the synaptic step is far more rapid and close-coupled than in the ♀, there is much less opportunity for crossover. Whether this is the full explanation is still uncertain, since in most other animals crossover occurs in both sexes.

Morgan and his co-workers added new generalizations to the six Mendelian laws (pp. 310, 319). They corrected the sixth to limit its application—so that only when characters are carried by different chromosomes is assortment independent. These additional laws, sometimes called *Morgan's laws,* may be stated briefly:

6. [*redefined*] All of the inheritable characters of a species fall into linkage groups whose number corresponds to the number of homologous pairs of chromosomes. The characters are represented by genes in these chromosomes. The genes in any homologous pair of chromosomes are assorted independently of the genes in any other homologous pair of chromosomes.

7. All genes in the same pair of homologous chromosomes are linked in inheritance and maintain their original combinations from generation to generation, either 100 per cent or more than 50 per cent. The lower percentages are indication of crossing over.

8. All genes in a chromosome are arranged in a definite single linear order, and the frequency of crossing over between them is a measure of their distance apart in the series.

9. Crossing over at any point in a chromosome interferes with simultaneous crossing over at adjacent points. Double and multiple crossovers are possible. Thus, only for genes that are relatively close together is the crossover frequency an accurate measure of the recombinations—and hence of the distance between the genes.

In a consideration of linkage and linkage groups, one point should be emphasized concerning Mendel's careful work. He followed into pure lines seven different characters of his pea plants, and he found each to be independent when tested coupled with any other. We know this to mean that each character Mendel used was on a separate chromosome. By sheer chance he missed discovering linkage, since no two characters he selected happened to be controlled by genes on a single chromosome. By chance, too, Mendel stopped with seven characters. Had he identified and tested an eighth, he would have uncovered linkage—for there are only seven homologous pairs of chromosomes in the pea plant! It is amazing how much Mendel learned about inheritance. It is equally astonishing how near he came to discovering more.

The inheritance of human characteristics has been analyzed from the scattered and fragmentary family histories available, without benefit of such routine genetic tools as planned matings and back-crosses. Ordinary sex-linked characters, such as red-green color-blindness, hemophilia, optic atrophy, and so on, are clearly carried by the X-chromosome. A few others, including total color-blindness and spastic paraplegia, are carried by both X- and Y-chromosomes and hence are partially sex-linked in inheritance. Still more, like hairy ears, scaly skin, and webbed toes are restricted to males (and not related to hormones); they are carried by part of the Y-chromosome that is not homologous to any part of the X-chromosome. In addition, eight different linkage groups have been found (Fig. 19-12), free of sex, and hence carried by eight different chromosomes from the 22 nonsex chromosomes (**autosomes**) in the haploid set. Thus, cross-eyes, hair whorl, and absence of incisor teeth are in one group; myopia and finger length on another; ability to taste phenyl thiocarbamide ("P.T.C.") and ability to curl the tongue on another; and red

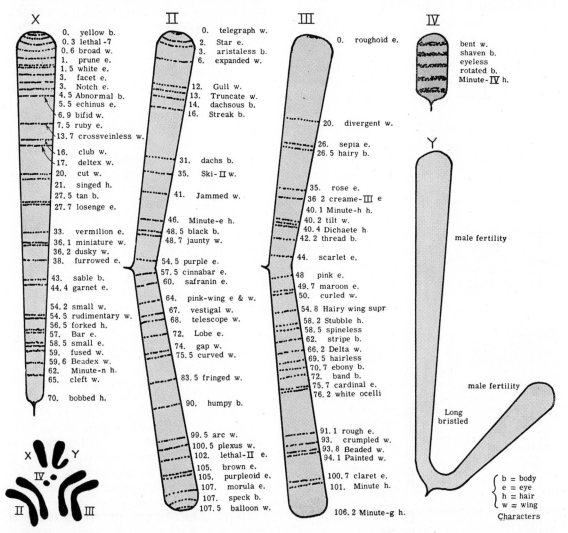

FIG. 19-11. *Chromosome map for Drosophila calculated from crossover percentages. Characters named with a capital letter are dominants. Those in chromosome IV are very close linked; those in Y have not been located precisely but long bristled is the dominant to bobbed* (see 70 in X). (*After Bridges, Morgan, Stern, and Sturtevant.*)

hair and the blood groups A, B, and O on still another. There must be 22 autosomal linkage groups altogether; gradually, information about them can be accumulated.

8. MUTATION

It is now possible to state with fair accuracy that among every 10,000 fruitflies descended from an original pair homozygous for red eyes, one will appear with white eyes. Or in a pure line of white-eyed, yellow-bodied, vestigial-winged fruitflies (clearly recessive in all three characters), one in every so many individuals will be a red-eyed, or gray-bodied, or long-winged specimen—showing the wild type characters. This change does not indicate a hidden factor. Instead it is a demonstration that the genes can change. The event is called a **mutation.**

Hugo de Vries, one of the three discoverers

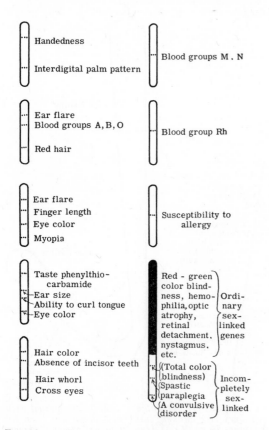

FIG. 19-12. *Human linkage groups proved from collected case histories.* (*After Snyder and others.*)

of Mendel's 1865 paper, presented the idea of mutations in a 1901 book, basing his theory upon observations in pure-line studies of the evening primrose, Oenothera. By modern standards his descriptions are vague. This is due partly to the fact that the theory of the gene was still 15 years in the future, partly to the peculiar nature of Oenothera. As a result of nearly three decades of work by other investigators, it is clear today that de Vries was confusing under his single term several different events. The word mutation has been retained for only one of these.

For any particular gene, the statistical frequency of mutation from the dominant condition to the recessive is the same as that from the recessive to the dominant. In the fruitfly, where over 500 different mutant strains have been studied, some one mutated individual can be expected in every 5,000 individuals examined. Lethal characters appear about six times as often. Probably these mutation frequencies are typical of other animals and plants.

Among wild populations in their normal surroundings, any mutation is more likely to be from dominant to recessive, and to be detrimental. This is because the "wild type" of any creature has been subjected to so continuous weeding out of misfit individuals that it is an almost pure-line composite of all the helpful adaptations. Only features that are neutral or negligibly different from the optimum can vary and be tolerated. And since a detrimental mutation that is dominant is more promptly weeded out than one that is recessive, "wild type" stock is primarily in the dominant condition for each gene.

Mutations may occur during maturation of the gametes, as **gametic mutations,** influencing every cell in the new individual. Or they may take place at some stage in embryonic development, altering only a part of the body as a **somatic mutation.** Inability to form chlorophyll is a mutation seen occasionally in plants. As a somatic mutation it affects a branch on a seemingly normal tree or bush; all leaves on the branch lack pigment, and the whole branch is parasitic for nourishment on the rest of the plant. A gametic mutation of this type would be a lethal characteristic.

Among animals both gametic and somatic mutations have been studied extensively. The somatic mutations creating greatest interest are those involving the sex chromosomes in characters that control secondary sex features. Particularly among insects, where enormous numbers of individuals have been examined carefully, part of the body may show ♂ characters, another part ♀. Such individuals are spoken of as **mosaics.** The individual bearing such a body may still be functionally either a ♂ or a ♀, although sometimes the condition is so extensive as to prevent reproductive activity. A fruitfly in which mutation has provided ♀ secondary sex characters in the head and fore legs, for example, shows interest in ♂♂. The other end of the body may carry entirely functional ♂ reproductive organs, but the wrong approach prevents the insect from mating.

An important advance in the study of mutations was made in 1927 when H. J. Muller, of the University of Texas, discovered that the rate of mutation could be speeded up greatly if fruitflies were subjected to mild doses of X-radiation. The American Association for the Advancement of Science awarded him the annual $1,000 prize for his report on this at the annual Christmas meeting; in 1946 the Nobel prize in medicine and physiology was awarded to him in recognition of his achievement and the important developments

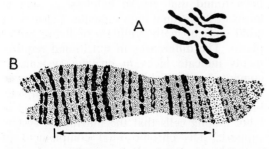

FIG. 19-13. *Distribution of bands in the small fourth chromosome of Drosphila. (After Bridges, 1936.)*

in mutation study made possible through use of this new tool. This was the second Nobel Laureate for research work in genetics.

9. THE NATURE OF THE GENE

The linear arrangement of genes in a chromosome suggests strongly a physical basis—some unit or particle in the chromosome, which might be visible. In only one place known at the moment, however, are chromo-

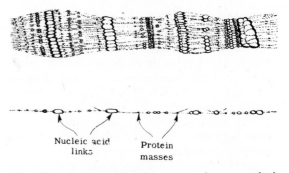

FIG. 19-14. *After a chromosome has been stretched by micromanipulation* (upper), *microchemical methods can be used to identify the nature of the visibly different parts. (After Painter.)*

somes sufficiently expanded that they can be studied closely. For some reason, the nuclei of the salivary glands in most larvae of the fly order Diptera are extraordinarily large and elongate. Their inner structure is visible under even high power magnification of ordinary microscopes. And the spacing of the denser staining parts of these chromosomes in fruitfly larval salivary glands corresponds wonderfully well with the irregular distribution of the known genes as mapped for fruitfly inheritance (Fig. 19-13).

By very delicate micromanipulation, it is possible to pull on the two ends of one of these giant chromosomes, stretching it and making visible still more structural detail. The stretched chromosome may be investigated with chemical reagents to learn its finer composition. Dark-staining bands prove to be rich in the nucleic acid DNA (see p. 52), and the less stainable bands between to be the protein bonding substance which, with DNA, composes the nucleoprotein of the chromosome.

Position is not the only reason for suspecting that DNA is the material of which genes are composed. The plant viruses and primate poliomyelitis virus, when purified enough to crystallize, have been shown to be nucleoproteins. As such they have the simplest organization showing the reproductive characteristics of living things. Yet when radioactive isotopes are used to tag first the nucleic acid portion and then the protein portion of a bacterial virus, it is found that only the nucleic acid portion takes part in infecting new cells.

DNA can exist in almost endless numbers of forms, all composed of the same four building blocks (adenine, cytosine, guanine, and thymine). The multiplicity of forms arises through differences in sequence, and through the fact that the DNA molecule is a double chain of these four units, coupled together in pairs—adenine in one chain usually matched only with thymine in the other, and guanine only by cytosine.

If DNA molecules are genes, if the genes control the synthesis of specific proteins in the cytoplasm, and if the proteins serve as the enzymes which control cytoplasmic chemistry, then further significance should be looked for in the DNA molecule. Several features of it may be very meaningful:

Firstly, either side of the chain contains all the information. If the chain were split lengthwise (as in metaphase of mitosis) and the two portions separated (as in the chromatids), each component would retain the full pattern upon which attraction of matching components from the cytoplasm could build a complete new double chain of identical DNA. Duplication of chromosomes is provided for.

Secondly, a mutation might consist of a chance improper mating, such as adenine with cytosine or guanine instead of with thymine, or of a minor rearrangement of the DNA links within one locus on the chromosome's length. If each DNA double chain determines the sequence and kind of amino acids in a particular protein, minor changes of this kind could be highly important in the cell's chemistry.

Thirdly, the pattern of four different units does appear to be enough to spell out specifications governing the arrangement of as many as 20 different amino acids in a protein molecule, if the DNA does serve as the master template for the architecture of protoplasmic proteins.

Finally, if the DNA-rich regions are the genes, then the protein fraction of the nucleoprotein entity (linking one DNA-rich area to the next) could be the site of crossing over during synaptic association of homologous chromosomes.

That genes *do* control enzyme systems (which are proteins) has been demonstrated recently in experiments upon an insignificant

pink mold—a haploid ascomycete of the genus Neurospora. This saprophytic mold thrives both in the wild state and on artificial media. The "wild type" mold requires only water, inorganic salts, sugar, ammonium compounds for nitrogen, and the vitamin substance biotin.

A mutant of Neurospora has been found which must have, in addition, the amino acid tryptophane. This is a recessive condition, and consists of the absence of the enzyme tryptophagenase in the protoplasm. The "wild type" has this enzyme and is able to synthesize tryptophane from simpler compounds among those listed. Still another mutant contains tryptophagenase but is unable to use the basic synthetic diet cited, since some of the chemical steps are lacking between ammonium compounds plus sugar and an intermediate substance (serine) of tryptophane synthesis. From these and other mutants, it has been possible to study more fully the chemical steps whereby Neurospora sustains its protoplasm on relatively simple substances. Mutants which cannot synthesize other amino acids or particular vitamins are discovered through the kind of food the mutant mold must be supplied in order for it to grow normally.

So far, no mutants of Neurospora have been found that are so helpless as man in terms of nutritional requirements. Yet man or mold ends up with synthesis of living protoplasm. The differences in nutritional requirements indicate lacks in enzyme systems as compared with mold cells. Man is simpler to the extent that his chemistry is less complete, but more complex in terms of the division of labor among cells that the nutritional system supports. His chromosomal complement of genes does not provide for synthesis of many of the building blocks for making protoplasm; but the inherited factors in his chromosomes control how that protoplasm can grow and become organized into tissues, organs, and organ systems, extending his range of possibilities far beyond that of the lowly Neurospora. Man's reach, in current scientific study, includes analysis in the captive mold of processes that are as widely distributed as life itself, and through the appearance of abnormal mutants in the saprophytic plant, of understanding more completely how his own organization is constructed. He is coming to appreciate that the unit characters of Mendel and Morgan are but the gross and cumulative changes in a whole organism in which one gene has mutated—adding or subtracting one enzymatic step.

Of course, every diploid cell of an organism contains every gene received from the

A great variety of **chromosomal aberrations** are known. Many of these abnormal situations have given important information on the normal processes. But the aberrations of greatest economic value are those which result in a zygote receiving not just the

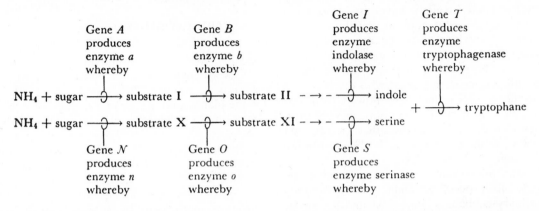

two parents. Since genes appear to control enzymes and these, in turn, govern the protoplasmic chemistry, a gene for blue eyes may well affect some growth process in a toe or kidney as that structure develops in the embryo. During the diversification of cells as seen in embryonic development, the cells themselves become different according to their position in the organism and the specializations involved. These differences and specializations must involve chemical processes, hence enzyme systems, and hence genes. Yet the gene depends for its effectiveness on materials in the cytoplasm. Thus the gene for eye color may have no effect in cells other than those of the iris of the eye—if iris cells alone possess a chemical substrate related to this gene. Although the gene would be present in all cells, non-iris cells would simply fail to call forth the particular inherited mechanism.

10. POLYPLOIDY

The chromosomal ballet evident in mitosis and meiosis is sufficiently intricate that it would be strange if the routine were followed through perfectly under all circumstances. Yet any variation in the meiotic process alters the chromosomal content of the gametes, and hence affects inheritance in major ways. In plants which are propagated asexually, a misstep in mitosis can have the same effect.

double set of chromosomes, as a diploid organism, but three sets (as a **triploid**), or four sets (as a **tetraploid**). Where the number of chromosome sets is greater than the normal two, the condition is described as **polyploidy.**

Polyploidy is rare in animals; for some reason polyploid zygotes fail to develop normally. But polyploidy is common among plants. In fact, many of our horticultural varieties, selected for size or vigor, have been found to be polyploids.

Polyploids may arise without human invention. If an abnormal gamete, diploid instead of haploid, fuses with a normal gamete, the zygote will be triploid. Or two diploid gametes can produce a tetraploid. Polyploidy may also be found among some of the adventitious growths arising from the stump of a plant which has suffered the loss of its top.

Usually a polyploid with an even number of sets of chromosomes (4N, 6N, 8N, and the like) is fertile, whereas gamete formation is interfered with in polyploids with odd numbers of chromosome sets (3N, 5N, etc.). Among plants infertility does not interfere seriously with the ability of a plantsman to obtain new specimens with the same genetic constitution—by cuttings and other asexual methods of propagation. This advantage permits the horticulturalist to expose a sterile polyploid to unusual external factors, such as chemical agents, in an attempt to alter the chromosome number still further.

The drug colchicine, when applied for periods of a day or so in dilute solutions (say 1 per cent) commonly produces doubling of the chromosome numbers in some immersed shoots. Plant breeders have used this technique as a useful tool in developing new plants. Thus in a cross between two polyploids, a 6N and a 4N, the gametes would be 3N and 2N, the F_1 a 5N—and sterile. But if the 6N parent were treated with colchicine to produce a 12N branch, and flowers from this branch were used for the cross, the 6N gametes with the 2N from the other (tetraploid) parent, would give an F_1 with 8N constitution —which would be fertile.

Even interspecies crosses can be arranged with this procedure. Thus a cross between ordinary cabbage (2N = 20) and a Chinese cabbage (2N = 18) yielded a new type of plant with 19 chromosomes. It was sterile. When treated with colchicine to make it 38 chromosomes, it was still sterile. But when this strange plant was crossed with a rutabaga (2N = 38), an entirely new type of cabbage emerged. It had 38 chromosomes, was fertile, and bred true.

Sometimes the infertility of triploids can be turned to good advantage. Grafted apple trees with triploid Baldwin tops respond to pollination, but the apples are seedless. Seedless watermelons are also triploids.

Polyploids offer so many advantages in size, hardiness, range of color, and other features that every effort is now being made to develop more of them. Fifty years ago, the garden iris plants were almost all diploids; modern ones are mostly tetraploids. Einkorn wheat is diploid (2N = 14), whereas the more desirable emmer wheats are 4N, and vulgare wheats are 6N. "Old-fashioned" roses were diploid (again 2N = 14), but horticultural varieties now include almost every multiple of N as far as 8N.

Wild plants also acquire and maintain polyploidy, or polyploidy renders fertile interspecific crosses and thereby establishes new plant types. Plant geneticists have turned detective, trying to unravel the past history of local plants, and particularly the cultivated types.

The wild ancestor of wheat, for example, is not known. Like most of our cereals (wheat, oats, barley, rye), it was domesticated before the dawn of history. As more is learned about the chromosomes of wild and domesticated plants, scientists become increasingly able to reconstruct the past and relate it to the prehistory of mankind.

11. PARTHENOGENESIS

In some organisms, unfertilized eggs can develop into complete individuals by *parthenogenesis* (from the Greek *parthenos* = virgin, *genesis* = origin). This process is known in some plants, and is a regular method of reproduction for a number of nonvertebrate animals.

Perhaps the most famous example is the development of ♂ honeybees ("drones"). Unlike the workers (sterile ♀ ♀) and queen (a fertile ♀), the drones are haploid and produce sperm cells by mitosis. The diploid queen receives from a solitary ♂ partner on her mating flight a lifetime supply of sperm cells. These she stores and maintains alive in a special sperm sac connected to her oviduct by a narrow passage under muscular control. Later, when laying eggs in the hive, the queen may relax the muscular cuff and permit sperm cells to pass through, fertilizing the eggs which are ready. Or she may prevent passage of sperms and lay unfertilized eggs. Both fertilized and unfertilized eggs hatch into maggot-like young, which are fed by the workers. Haploid maggots grow to become drones. Diploid maggots may become workers or virgin queens, depending upon the type of food supplied them and the type of cell they occupy in the comb. Queen bees, of course, produce eggs by meiosis. The remarkable adaptation in the colony is the seeming ability of the queen to control the sex of her offspring, providing an adequate population of drones at seasons when virgin queens are about to emerge.

Something similar is known among plant life (aphids). Here the ♀ insect produces in her ovary egg-like structures properly called *parthenogonidia*. These arise by mitosis, and like the mother are diploid. They develop within the mother into young ♀ ♀ which emerge only when ready to walk around and feed independently. Charles Bonnet, who discovered this phenomenon in the early 1700's, built from his observation the basis for the doctrine of preformation (p. 308).

Toward autumn, however, the same ♀ aphids—progeny of repeated generations of ♀ ♀ since spring—are able to produce two new types of ♀ ♀ whose progeny are winged and either all ♂ ♂ or all ♀ ♀. These progeny produce sperms or eggs by meiosis. The flying individuals mate, and the fertilized eggs are provided with resistant shells and a different type of protoplasm. In this stage the insect can tolerate winter, whereas the adults and young aphids all die of cold. In the spring the resistant eggs hatch into diploid ♀ ♀, which continue the parthenogenetic production of further ♀ ♀ until fall.

Since parthenogenesis provides such an interesting exception to the usual procedure, extensive experimental studies have been made, trying to find ways in which an unfertilized egg might be stimulated to develop into a complete new individual. This is actually an admission that the normal sexual method involves two unrelated steps: (1) nuclear fusion—fertilization; and (2) activation of the egg toward nuclear and cytoplasmic divisions. The first clear case of successful **artificial parthenogenesis** was presented in 1900 by Jacques Loeb. He pricked thousands of frog eggs with needles and induced development in a considerable number. Somewhat over 200 of these grew to tadpole stage, and nearly a hundred "fatherless" frogs resulted. Both sexes were represented, and all were diploid. Since that time other experimenters have succeeded with frogs and also with a variety of invertebrates, including in particular eggs of sea urchins. Shaking, abnormal temperatures, weak organic acids, and various salt solutions have proven effective, each method succeeding in "activating" the egg to the point where its nucleus will divide, then the two fuse to become diploid. Ordinary mitosis follows, producing a normal embryo and adult.

Artificial parthenogenesis in mammals has been accomplished in at least two laboratories, with rabbits as experimental subjects. Gregory Pincus, of Harvard University, succeeded in 1936 in inducing development of an unfertilized rabbit egg, using chemical and heat treatment; later he added the technique

of inserting the developing egg into the uterus of a virgin ♀ rabbit, and having the foster parent nourish the embryo until a "normal" birth took place. An extension of this technique was accomplished by Herbert Shapiro, of Hahnemann Medical College, in 1941, when he caused unfertilized rabbit ova in a virgin ♀ to develop "normally" by excessive chilling of the parent's body with ice packs on the flanks over the ovaries. These successes occasioned great excitement in scientific and lay audiences, but so far they have not led to any new developments or to any better understanding of the process.

Parthenogenesis in mankind may be said to be excessively rare. No reliable genetic records exist nor have experimental studies led man to expect such in the foreseeable future or historic past.

Parthenogenesis in animals often indicates that the ordinary bisexual method of reproduction is not well established, or that it has been suppressed. Thus the brine shrimp (Artemia) and a sow bug (Trichoniscus) have been shown to include polyploid races—almost the only instances known among animals —but these particular races produce parthenogonidia and develop parthenogenetically. Ordinary diploid races of both of these arthropods demonstrate meiotic divisions and the usual form of sexual reproduction.

In plants the corresponding production of new individuals without fertilization, but from egg protoplasm, is called **parthenocarpy**. The egg cell may develop into a haploid plant, under the stimulus of the arrival of a foreign pollen grain; both Gloxinia and Saintpaulia (African Violet) will do this. Or the egg nucleus may vanish after the pollen tube invades the egg, and the sperm nucleus take over—producing a haploid plant. Or the haploid nucleus of the egg may undergo mitosis and the daughter haploid nuclei fuse to produce a diploid nucleus, starting off a parthenocarpous diploid plant.

12. PRACTICAL APPLICATIONS

An understanding of genetics should permit an intelligent approach to breeding cultivated plants and domesticated animals, and a reasoned consideration of human inheritance.

Hybrid Vigor

Frequently hybrids show increased vigor, size, fruitfulness, speed of development, resistance to climatic extremes, diseases, and insect pests. To this phenomenon the term **hybrid vigor** (or heterosis) is applied.

Mendel's tall pea plants averaged about six feet in height, his dwarfs approximately two. The F_1 generation between these two pure lines often grew to seven feet, and heterozygous individuals in the the F_2 could often be suspected because they were taller than the homozygous dominant parents.

Although hybrids will not breed true, crops from hybrid seed can have commercial importance. Corn (maize) is a case in point (Photo 427). Although deliberate use of hybrid seed to gain from hybrid vigor was explored between 1909 and 1925, commercial application began in the early 1930's. In 1933 only 0.1 per cent of corn raised in the United States was of hybrid types, and yield averaged 22.6 bushels per acre. By 1943 more than 51 per cent of the corn crop was hybrid, yield was up to 32.1 bushels per acre, and quality had been improved at the same time.

The most usual cause of hybrid vigor is operative in crosses between parental lines with a long history of inbreeding. With his cultivated plants and domesticated animals, man selects among the offspring on the basis of a few characters important to him. To achieve stability in these, he inbreeds deliberately. He considers the crosses successful when inbreeding does not simultaneously produce homozygous recessives in genes that seriously affect desired characteristics.

In these inbred lines, however, many genes do become homozygous recessive, and of these a considerable number are actually deleterious to the growth of the organism. Thus speed of development and resistance to rust may be "bred into" a strain of wheat, at the expense of size of plant and yield of grain. A different type of wheat, grown where neither rust nor early frosts are important, may be developed for size of kernel and yield per acre. If these two inbred lines are crossed, the resulting hybrids will probably show vigor because the deleterious recessives of each parent will be concealed in heterozygous individuals by dominants carried by the other.

Genetic Improvement

The chief barriers to improving breeding stock appear to be linked genes and the relative infrequency of crossing over or mutation. To locate a few individuals with a better combination of characters, vast populations must be studied, specimen by specimen.

Often the public fails to understand why such large numbers of organisms are raised. Sometimes the horticulturalist or animal husbandryman fails to explain because he is working on educated guesses rather than from scientific knowledge. From this lack of understanding on both sides, the term "plant wizard" was applied repeatedly to Luther Burbank, although geneticists respect his procedure only in terms of statistics and sound judgment. If enough individuals are raised and examined with care by a competent observer, the selection of useful varieties is not magic but good business.

Seedless fruits, spineless cacti, and many other modifications helpful to mankind are a monument to Burbank's persistence and acumen. They do not indicate any extraordinary scientific talents.

Human Genetics

In modern human society, great emphasis has been placed (though by usage rather than by scientific planning) on maintenance of hybrid vigor through avoidance of inbreeding. So customary is the ban against matings between close relatives that a charge of immorality is brought against deviators.[6] Rumor holds that a closely inbred line dies out or degenerates.

Yet a plant breeder deliberately self-pollinates many of his plants, and an animal geneticist has no hesitation in mating brother with sister, or father with daughter, to con-

---

[6] Since every person has two parents, four grandparents, and so on, it is easy to show that (barring inbreeding completely) each human being alive today had 282 million direct ancestors 27 generations ago. But 27 human generations ago, 282 million was about the total world population of caucasioids. Hence every caucasioid is *at least* a 27th cousin of every other caucasioid alive today—a total of more than 1.4 billion people.

centrate a desired character in the next generation. It is fair to inquire whether human genetics follow different rules from those applying to plants and other animals.

Historically there is no scientific basis for the taboos against close human matings. Until the Roman Empire achieved dominance, very near kin married regularly in civilized societies. Brother-sister, father-daughter, mother-son matches were common not only among the Greek gods and goddesses but among the Greeks themselves. This close inbreeding did not lead to degeneracy, but to one of the most intellectual civilizations the world has known. The symbol of masculine desirability—Adonis—was the son of a father-daughter mating. Similarly, among the Egyptians, the royal line culminating in Cleopatra was a dynasty maintained regularly for many centuries through brother-sister marriages, with no recognizable loss in physical or mental abilities. If anything, the closest of genetic relationships provided an improvement in these characteristics.

Sight should not be lost of one key fact in this historical approach: any undesirable offspring from close unions were eliminated, just as they would be today in animal husbandry. How well this procedure can pay off is evident from the high degree of homozygosity developed in the laboratory white rat. So many repeated close matings (with discard of undesirable offspring) have been made in this mammal that the inheritance of any two animals is almost as equal as that of identical twins. Yet they reproduce somewhat more rapidly and with more viable offspring than wild rats with all the benefits of hybrid vigor. Close mating of individuals with superior inherited characteristics to concentrate the desirable dominant or recessive genes into homozygous conditions has been used successfully in other domestic plants and animals.

Close inbreeding does increase the proportion of homozygous dominants and of homozygous recessives in the population. If the homozygous individuals show characteristics that are detrimental, there is an increase in the percentage of misfit individuals. But there is a corresponding increase in the percentage of individuals in whom the deleterious character has been "bred out." And if matings are controlled, even the heterozygous individuals are increasingly recognizable, so that any particular character can be made homozygous—either dominant or recessive, whichever is advantageous—at will by proper selection. Real selection assumes, however, that unsuitable members of the population, whether homozygous or heterozygous, will not be permitted to reproduce.

This requirement for genetic improvement is easy to apply to cultivated plants and domestic animals, and has resulted in tremendous improvements in the average health and development of these organisms. But at least four difficulties arise in applying similar procedures to human populations:

Firstly, in many societies today, each individual reserves the right to choose a mate, regardless of any genetic considerations.

Secondly, each individual regards as inalienable the right to reproduce as often or as seldom as whim determines, regardless of the impact of these actions on society.

Thirdly, each individual, regardless of facts about ancestral characteristics or genetic information about self or spouse, extends the democratic maxim that all persons are born equal to claim equality in suitability either as a parent for future generations, or as a judge of those fit and unfit.

Finally, regardless of whether the individual has the physical and mental abilities to become a contributing and self-supporting member of society, the mere fact of being a member of the human species places the person in a sacred category, to be supported at the expense of normal individuals.

In the face of these four points of view, there is little possibility of widespread and sane application of genetic principles to human populations. At the best, segregation of the most unfit and prevention of reproduction among those most afflicted may be accomplished. Restriction of reproduction among close relatives of the unfit is deemed intolerable interference with human rights. Encouragement of individuals with superior physical and mental characteristics to have as many offspring as possible without impairing health is equally difficult, since this is primarily an economic problem.

In a democracy, it is most improbable that the majority—who are average in both physical and mental development—will vote to provide a higher-than-average standard of living for the minority with superior inherited characteristics. Much more likely is an affirmative vote to subsidize those unfortunates with inferior inherited characteristics, who are unable to make an income in proportion to the number of their irresponsibly-conceived offspring.

The study of human genetics and of possible ways for improving the inherited characteristics of the race is the biological field of **eugenics** (from the Greek roots signifying "well born"). Scientists engaged in such studies collect and analyze family histories and try to account for the many features found. Since planned matings are impossible among human subjects, observations and correlations are the only practical means for learning how genetics involves mankind. Students of eugenics have often misused their information by concentrating their attention on small parts of single family records. It is relatively easy to count the number of physicians, judges, and teachers on one side of a lineage, and the number of convicted criminals, mental defectives, and congenital abnormalities on another. But environment—and economic status in particular—plays such a large part in such matters that clear cases of statistical size are hard to find and prove. As a result, a counterpart of eugenics has grown up—the study of **euthenics,** which aims to study effects of environment and means for improving living conditions so that individuals with adequate inherited background will make full use of their potentialities, and of the equality of opportunity guaranteed by the Constitution.

Environmental Influences

The argument concerning the relative importance of "nature" (inherited) and "nurture" (through environment) is a basic concern of sociologists. The evidences from genetics all point to the inherited variation in ability to cope with any given constant environment. Moreover, they demonstrate the inability of environmental features to have any direct influence on the germplasm. The son of an athlete is born with no more muscular development than the child of a crip-

ple, but the training he receives from his parents may lead him to choose a different type of mate, and in that way alter the chain of inheritance. The most helpful information on this subject comes from studies of identical human twins reared together and of those reared apart. The similarities are far more striking than the differences. Thus an individual with inherited characteristics that place him in the superior category receives at conception a sort of genetic capital, the income from which may be used during his lifetime —well or badly, according to environment and choice. The principal, however—to follow the metaphor—is passed on by sharing in the act of fertilization whereby a new individual begins—with the shared capital.

Artificial Insemination of Mammals

Mammalian semen has proved to be hardy enough that it can be chilled or frozen and either shipped for long distances or maintained in a "bank." After being warmed to body temperature it can be introduced into the vagina at the best time in the reproductive cycle, and pregnancy is very likely.

Animal husbandrymen have found practical use for artificial insemination. The techniques can be applied also to mankind. Childless couples of which the ♂ is sterile, often want children. They may make arrangements through a physician for a nameless donor to supply semen for artificial insemination of the wife. At the State University of Iowa a "frozen human semen bank" has been established. Four infants have already been announced as born from mothers impregnated with semen from the frozen storehouse. Using this procedure, no barrier is in the way of a widow continuing to bear children, year after year, all fathered by her deceased husband.

Where nameless donors are used, there are important biological considerations. If the practice became popular, a donor might easily become the unknown but actual father of a hundred children in one locality. If these children, upon reaching marriageable age, marry among themselves and have children, the resulting inbreeding could be expected to lead to homozygous recessives for many undesirable characteristics appearing at a rate well above that in the normal population. As was pointed out this may far outweigh the gain from an equal number of homozygous dominant individuals with superior qualities. Ethics are involved, too.

The Gene and Individuality

The degree to which each human individual is unique can be shown from examination of the skin. Even identical twins are not completely alike (Fig. 19-15).

Human skin may be studied very personally when extracting a splinter that has entered a finger but not "drawn blood." The dead outer layers can be removed, and the underlying surface examined with a lens. The roughness evident there consists of continuous rows of small elevations **(papillae),** each very wet and shiny, bright pink with underlying capillaries full of blood.

The papillae of the skin on the palm surfaces of hand and fingers, and on the sole surfaces of foot and toes, are arranged in rows like parallel chains of miniature mountains. Over these the dead skin cells form the friction pattern characteristic of the individual. Details of the fingerprints of this pattern are used regularly in identifying people (Fig. 19-14); similar prints made from the soles of the feet of newborn babies (because their fists are clenched) are just as distinctive, and many hospitals use them for identification of children in maternity wards.

Individuality is not limited to pattern of friction ridges. It goes far deeper in the skin —into the dermis with its blood vessels. Excepting only identical twins, each individual is intolerant of skin from any other human being grafted over a wound area. Yet skin grafting is a widespread technique to help heal wounds exceeding a few square inches in area; these do not regenerate satisfactorily of their own accord, and leave ugly scars or disabling contracture if not helped.

Routine skin grafting is done by transferring small, thin sheets of uninjured skin to cover the area of loss, or to "seed" it at close intervals if the wound area is large. Except in extreme emergency, the surgeon does *not* use skin from another person. Even mother to child or brother to brother is unsuitable; such grafts heal in initially but induce antibodies in the recipient; in a few weeks the graft becomes "puffy," ulcerates, and sloughs away.

The time element for this reaction in incompatible grafts depends upon many variables. The larger the area of foreign skin used, the sooner it sloughs off. The closer the ge-

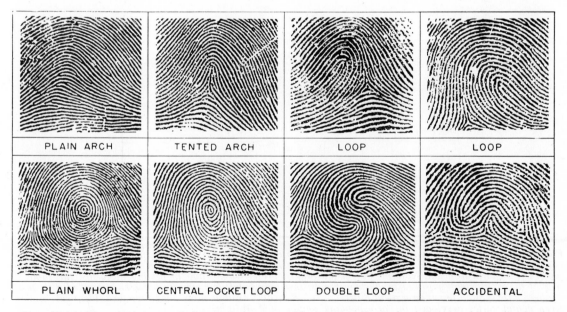

| PLAIN ARCH | TENTED ARCH | LOOP | LOOP |
| PLAIN WHORL | CENTRAL POCKET LOOP | DOUBLE LOOP | ACCIDENTAL |

FIG. 19-14. *The chief types of fingerprint pattern. (Courtesy of the Federal Bureau of Investigation.)*

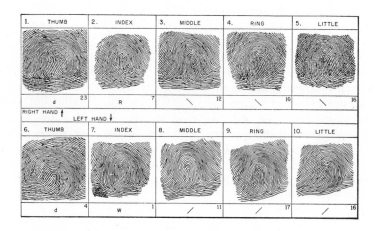

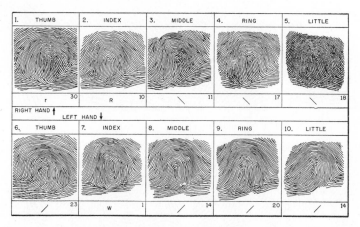

FIG. 19-15. *Identical twins with their fingerprint patterns and fingerprint classification. No two individuals —even identical twins or Siamese twins—have identical print patterns, yet each individual is constant in pattern from birth to death. Note the mirror-imaging in preferred position in folding the arms; the same is true of the comfortable position in clasping hands; one twin is left-handed, the other right-handed. I.Q. tests of these girls showed less than a point difference; on Regents' examinations they obtained identical grades. Even dental caries developed in corresponding number and position.*

netic relationship between donor and recipient, the longer will a graft stay in place. The better the general health of the recipient, the sooner separation occurs. And incompatibility becomes evident sooner when similar grafts have been tried before.

With one exception, tissues other than skin give comparable results. The exception is the cornea of the vertebrate eye—which is unique in its lack of a blood supply. A corneal graft does not induce antibody formation, and for this reason "eye banks" (of corneal tissue) are feasible. Blood banks are useful within the limitations of the antigens in the red cells and the antibodies in the recipient's plasma. The situation is different from the skin graft, however, in that the antibodies are already present, and no delay occurs before the appearance of antagonistic action.

These phenomena are not limited to mankind. They hold true for guinea pig, rabbit or cow. The only exceptions among mammals are found in the consistently inbred lines of white rats and white mice, whose genetic constitution is almost as identical as twins from a single fertilized egg.

Annual Number of Young

(numbers above two are approximate)

Elephant	1
Man	1-5
Bald eagle	2 eggs
Kiwi	2 eggs
Pigeon	2 per mating
Ostrich	3-5
Armadillo	4 identical quadruplets
Gila monster	12 eggs
Horned toad (lizard)	10-25 eggs or young
Alligator	30-40 eggs
Loggerhead turtle	80-150 eggs
House mosquito	100-300 per raft
Black widow spider	3-4 cocoons with about 300 eggs each
Chaetopterus (annelid worm)	10,000 eggs
Lobster	12,000-15,000
Toad	15,000
Bullfrog	20,000
Herring	50,000
Tobacco plant	360,000 seeds
Starfish	2,500,000 eggs
Sturgeon (eggs weigh 30% as much as parent)	3,000,000 (= caviar)
Cod	6,000,000
Mussel	25,000,000
Ling (a fish) or salmon	28,000,000
Cerebratulus (worm)	100,000,000
Oyster	100,000,000 to 500,000,000
Fungus Lycoperdon	700,000,000,000 spores

Partly from M. Burton, *The Story of Animal Life* (London: Elsevier Publishing Co., 1949), vol. 1.

SUGGESTED READING (see p. 504)

Classics and Milestones: Bonnet, van Beneden, Weismann, Mendel, Sutton, Muller, Beadle & Tatum.

Recent and Informative: Beadle, 1948; Bishop, 1955; Boyd, 1950, 1951; Chapanis, 1951; Crick, 1954; Darrow, 1950; Delbrück, 1948; Dunn, 1950; Flanders, 1950; Gamow, 1955; Goldschmidt, 1949, 1952; Gray, 1951; Hollander, 1952; Kalmus, 1952; Knight & Fraser, 1955; Mangelsdorf, 1951; Mirsky, 1953; Scheinfeld, 1950; Sonneborn, 1950; Stern, 1952, 1954; Strong, 1950; Tyler, 1954; Wiener, 1954; Zahl, 1949.

20 · The Abundance of Life

1. BIOTIC POTENTIAL—ADAPTATIONS. 2. ADAPTATIONS IN MULTICELLULAR PLANTS—IN LEAVES, IN STEMS, IN ROOTS, IN DEFENSE, IN DISSEMINATION OF SPORES, IN DISSEMINATION OF POLLEN, IN DISSEMINATION OF SEEDS. 3. ADAPTATIONS IN MULTICELLULAR ANIMALS—SEARCH AND ENGULFMENT, FILTER FEEDING, FINDING AND WINNING MATES, COMPETITION FOR MATES AND COURTSHIP, PROVISION FOR THE YOUNG, CONCEALMENT, DEFENSE AND ESCAPE, SOCIAL ADAPTATIONS, SERIAL ADAPTATIONS, GALL-INDUCING ANIMALS.

OCCASIONALLY a biologist has taken time to find out not just how many kinds of organisms there are, but also how many individuals of some particular kind. Some who were impressed with the number of earthworm castings after a rain, dug up samples of soil to count the worms in the superficial foot or two, and then computed the total per acre: a million earthworms—with a variation as high as 25 per cent above this figure and 50 per cent below it. Since there are 43,560 square feet in an acre, this represents between 11 and 45 earthworms to the square foot, for acre after acre. And this vast figure considers only those kinds of earthworms that actually come to the surface!

An entomologist (Marlatt) counted the emergence holes of a fairly large cicada (a true bug) and found 84 holes per square foot over a 20-foot circle below a fair-sized tree. Since each hole represented a separate specimen, the total from below this one tree indicated more than 33,000 cicadas. As immature stages they had fed on the roots without killing the tree.

Another entomologist (Herms) checked the number of housefly maggots in 15 pounds of stable manure; in round numbers his total was 10,000. Similarly, the puparia of brine flies emerging from Great Salt Lake, Utah, have been found to be 25 to the square inch for a beach drift area 20 feet wide all around the lake; that means that there are 370 million flies per mile of shore. And from routine soil sampling, it is evident that there are about 15 million minute insects of one particular small group in each acre of most soil-covered land areas.

In the sea (Gulf of Maine), an oceanographer (Bigelow) recorded 4,000 individuals of one kind of small crustacean in each cubic meter of water dipped up from the surface. Wherever one turns to count plants or animals, the numbers of them per unit of space is unbelievably great. The potential supply is even greater.

1. BIOTIC POTENTIAL

The late L. L. Woodruff, of Yale University, once carried a culture of the slipper animalcule, Paramecium, through 11,000 counted generations. This task required nearly 30 years, since Paramecium reproduces itself about once a day. In human beings, 11,000 generations would take about 3,000 centuries—from 298,000 B.C. to the present. But in Woodruff's glassware the single-celled Paramecia divided to become two, and each grew to full size, ready to divide again, in 20 to 22 hours.

Paramecium is only barely visible—about 0.25 mm long by 0.06 mm in each of the other dimensions. Its protoplasmic volume totals some 0.000,9 cubic mm. Yet the normal rate of reproduction doubles this volume of Paramecium protoplasm every 22 hours. *If all the offspring of one Paramecium were to survive,* there would be from each insignificant 0.000,9 cubic mm of Paramecium on January 1, a total of 1 cubic mm before January 11; a total of 1 cubic cm in just 20 generations (January 19); of a cubic meter by the 40th generation (Feb. 6); of a cubic mile by the 72nd generation (March 7); of a volume equal to that of the earth by the 112th generation (April 12); and a volume larger than that of the entire universe before Christmas time. Obviously, no such numbers were ever reached in the culture described. In the entire Woodruff study, the total volume of all 11,000 generations of Paramecia handled amounted to less than 0.1 cubic cm, because only a few of each generation were allowed to live. Whenever a cell divided, one of the daughters was removed and discarded. The remaining one, in fresh culture medium, became two in less than a day, and the process was repeated. Thus the asexual reproductive potential of Paramecium was investigated without any attempt to provide space and food for all of the offspring.

Norway rats are dependent upon their parents for the first three weeks after birth, and become sexually mature at from eight to 12 weeks of age. If given opportunity, they will reproduce three to five times a year, with litters of from four to 12. Yet even with seven young per litter and three litters a year for the three years which constitute a normal minimum for life in a well-fed rat, a single pair plus the offspring of their young total over 600,000 rats!

Every kind of animal and each species of

Year	Litter	Number of breeding pairs	Number of litters	Number of young	Total rats*
1st	#1	1	1	7	
	#2	4	4	28	
	#3	16	16	112	
Totals			21	147	149
2nd	#1	64	64	448	
	#2	256	256	1,792	
	#3	1,024	1,024	7,168	
Totals			1,344	9,408	9,536
3rd	#1	4,096	4,096	28,672	
	#2	16,384	16,384	114,688	
	#3	65,536	65,536	458,752	
Totals			86,016	602,112	610,304

* Calculations assume survival of all rats born—but only for the normal three-year life span.

plant shows this same tendency toward rise in population. The two broods each of four young bluebirds, raised each year by a pair of parents, or the 10,000 acorns dropped in the autumn by a medium-sized oak tree provide the basis for the same kind of increase in the total volume of living bluebirds or of oak protoplasm. Only the *rate* at which the population doubles its numbers (the **doubling time**) is different:

Organism	Doubling Time
Lactic acid bacterium at 40° C.	1 hour
Fruitfly Drosophila (200 offspring per pair in 11 days at 20° C.)	5.3 hours
Paramecium at 20° C.	22 hours
Norway rats (7 offspring per pair in 120 days)	53.3 days
Bluebirds (8 offspring per pair per year)	2.4 months
Man:	
Hutterites of So. Dakota	16 years
Algerian Moslems	32 years
U.S. population as a whole	40 years

The world has no room for all possible offspring of any species. Hence a contest is easy to predict: between capacity to reproduce (the **biotic potential** of a species) and the total effect of all factors tending to limit survival (the **environmental resistance**).

In a plant, the biotic potential is expressed in the number of spores or pollen grains and ovules provided in each generation as sources of the next. It is raised by any mechanism that improves the chances for survival for each sporeling or seedling, since it is the total number of these to reach reproductive maturity, compared with the total number of the preceding generation, that determines whether a species is doing well or badly.

In an animal, the number of fertilized eggs per female and the proportion of mated females in the population give a measure of the biotic potential. Every provision that betters the chances of successful fertilization or improves the likelihood of embryos living to reproduce raises that biotic potential. Every structural or functional modification in an animal or plant that delays the day of reproduction decreases the biotic potential of the species.

Devices that raise the biotic potential in one way are often at the expense of lowering reproductive capacity in another. The maple tree that shows individuality in producing lighter seeds with longer wings, enabling the wind to distribute them farther, and hence increasing the area of soil in which seedlings may find suitable living conditions, does so by decreasing the amount of food stores for the seedling—so that each has less reserve on which to grow roots and leaves to tap an independent food supply. The Pacific salmon that transfers so much of its energy store into a single enormous batch of eggs or sperm that the adult fish is spent and dies soon after the effort, shows an adaptation which effectively gambles on success of the millions of one brood of offspring—which a single disaster can destroy. Atlantic salmon reach sexual maturity in the sea and return year after year to lay a smaller number of eggs or liberate fewer sperm. Their adaptations make use of the alternate chance, since death may intervene between the first and second year, between the second and third, and so on—ending the reproduction of that parent before the "full quota" of sex cells has been expelled. There is no one best way. Many methods are almost equally successful.

Adaptations

In considering modifications of animals and plants, whereby the biotic potential of any one is raised in comparison with another, it is necessary to introduce the concept of the **generalized organism.** There is no such inhabitant of the earth as a generalized organism, just as there is no truly "typical" John Doe—"Mr. Everyman." Yet each kind of organism has certain anatomical details and physiological processes and behaviors so very like those of other, closely related species that there is some valid basis for the hypothetical being. The point of interest, however, is divergence from this generalized condition shown by individual kinds—that is, their **adaptations.** Thus there is a basic form to which all mice adhere, more or less. A special development of the hind legs and tail related to a jumping habit is characteristic of the kangaroo mouse; we say that it has longer, stronger hind legs and more elongated tail "than other mice." Therein it is adapted while other mice "are generalized." Or particularly large ears and contrasting white feet are characteristic of deer mice—and in these details lie some of their adaptations.

Primarily, adaptations affecting biotic potential might be expected to influence **fecundity**—the number of reproductive cells or of offspring which can be started on their way. Instead, adaptations may have to do with the age at which reproductive activity begins, or the number of reproductive seasons in a year, or the number of seasons over which the average parent continues to reproduce.

Secondarily, adaptations can be important if they influence the **viability** of the offspring—increasing the likelihood of survival to reproductive age, through counteracting specific factors in the environmental resistance.

In examining the life history of a plant or animal, it is usually far easier to learn what types of environmental resistance it meets (predators, parasites, adverse weather, and the like) than to evaluate its biotic potential. Adaptations related to environmental resistance are correspondingly more obvious. But they are also so varied that whole books have been devoted to analyzing their effect.

Related to both fecundity and viability are several aspects of the life cycle that can be modified by adaptations: (1) the **sex ratio** (the proportion of ♂ ♂ to ♀ ♀ in the parental population); (2) the **generation time** (the length of an average reproductive life cycle); (3) the **population density,** which both measures the success of a species and affects the likelihood that each individual will be able to find a mate.

2. ADAPTATIONS IN MULTICELLULAR PLANTS

In the sense that a plant must grow to maturity, storing energy on which to draw for reproduction, any adaptation hastening that maturity (decreasing generation time) or improving the collection and storage of energy (Fig. 20-1) in the form of food (supposedly increasing the fecundity or energy stores provided in each seed) acts to raise the biotic potential. Since plants are essentially stationary, attached organisms, the modifications in these directions are less obvious than in the case of animals, except where the adaptations are toward definite aspects of their environment—features that will be considered in the next chapter.

In Leaves

Variations among leaves show outwardly as differences in thickness, but inwardly as in-

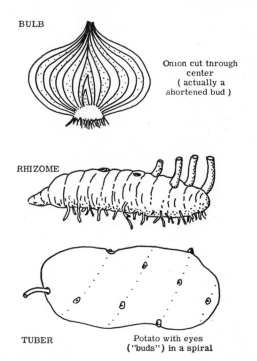

BULB

Onion cut through center (actually a shortened bud)

RHIZOME

TUBER

Potato with eyes ("buds") in a spiral

FIG. 20-1. *Food storage centers in plants produce attractive dietary morsels for animals, including man. The bulb of an onion is a terminal bud, much shortened and well stocked. The rhizome of a fern is an underground stem. A potato tuber is a specialized stem, in which the "eyes" are buds and occur in a definite spiral pattern.*

crease or decrease in the number of layers of palisade parenchyma, according to whether there is enough light to penetrate multiple layers and to bring valuable energy to chloroplastids in lower levels. Or in aquatic plants, such as the larger seaweeds or pond lilies, the possession of floats or air spaces within the tissue provides an adaptation in the form of buoyancy that keeps the tissues ready for photosynthesis at or near the surface of the water. Here the light has not yet passed through any depth of water and still contains most of its energy; the holdfasts or roots at the bottom, by comparison, are in the dark.

In Stems

Similarly, a plant that shows a perennial habit produces a woody trunk that supports a crown of leaves high above neighbors, places its chloroplastids more advantageously for collecting sun energy. A tree trunk is an adaptation—but it is also a price paid in protoplasm and secreted matter that do not contribute directly toward reproduction. The trunk is not necessary, although in a tree it undoubtedly helps in the acquisition of energy on which reproduction depends. Other plants in a forest, lacking trunks, are unable to compete successfully for direct sunlight, and in providing for their offspring they must use what energy reaches them on the forest floor. While they receive less, they do not spend any of that lesser energy on forming a trunk, and hence a higher proportion can go to reproduction. In this contrast is the fundamental fact that there are many ways of achieving the same result. Different organisms differ largely in the direction of greatest adaptation —but the modifications chiefly serve the same final end.

In Roots

In their root systems, the higher plants demonstrate three basic types, one a generalized condition, and two special adaptations. The first is the ordinary fibrous root, which is highly efficient in reaching water and dissolved nutrients in the soil. But a great many plants build an energy store in the root cortex, and make of it a tap root. Some of these load the storage center in one year, and in a second expend it in addition to new energy trapped from the sun on a remarkable display of flowers and large production of seeds. Such a plant (the carrot and hollyhock, for example) is a biennial.

Adventitious roots develop from stems and branches that are surrounded by high humidity. Some plants like strawberries extend horizontal runners (stolons) as branches which develop both leaves and roots at the tip, starting new plants in a circle around the parent, by vegetative reproduction. Or others, like so many briars, develop long slender stems which arch back to earth through their own weight. The tips, when buried by fallen leaves, are in a sufficiently humid atmosphere to start adventitious roots. In this way the plant loops over the ground, starting new individuals in a progressive series. In the tropics, where the air may be saturated with water vapor for weeks at a time, adventitious roots (Photo 237) often develop from stems far above the ground, descend to make contact with the earth, and supplement the ordinary supply of water and mineral solutes coming to the stem from the original roots—hence aiding in the achievement of mature size and reproductive activity in the plant as a whole.

In Defense

A plant might never live to become a parent were there in it no mechanisms available for attending to repair and for repulsion of attackers. Adaptations which make for prompt healing of wounds and for repulsion of attack are thus very important in protecting the vigor and life of the plant, allowing it to reach maturity or to continue in reproductive activity.

Among the more obvious means of repelling invaders is the production of gummy exudates which fill a wound, smothering attackers. The coniferous trees are particularly modified in this direction, and everyone has seen lumps of resin extruded from the break where a branch fell away or the bark was torn (Photo 238). Canada balsam, the commonest mounting medium for thin tissue sections on microscope slides, is the clear gum. Amber, used in jewelry and in making high grade varnishes, is a fossilized resin, and often contains the well-preserved bodies of insects that lit on the sticky surface and were covered over by further exudate fifty million years ago (Photos 403 to 405). The latex of rubber trees and of many other plants has a similar protective function, and it oozes quickly into a wound, drying there much like a blood clot and forming something of a scab. But other plants, which lack resin and latex, achieve much the same result by surrounding an invading insect or fungus infection with waterproof, reinforced cells—isolating the attacker in a sort of capsule or cyst—or actually by drowning the enemy in an active flow of sap.

A minority of plants show adaptations in the possession of glandular hairs on the leaves, containing substances which sting animals that brush against them (as nettles do), or stomach poisons effective on a considerable number of animals that might eat the leaves. Again, some have various kinds of thorns and spines that discourage animal approach. The honey locust has modified stipules at the base of each leaf petiole, each a sturdy spine that helps repel potential attackers. In the tropics, members of the Acacia locust group have hollow spines of greater size in which irritable stinging and biting ants make their home. When such a tree is jostled, the insects pour out of the spines and defend both homes and tree with utmost vigor.

In Dissemination of Spores

Among the spore-bearing plants, there are many adaptations for dissemination of the reproductive units. Those that are liberated into water may have flagella with which to swim. Thallophytes whose spores are scattered by wind include such familiar plants as mushrooms, puffballs, and bracket fungi. The spores are ejected horizontally on an extraordinary path—like the precise trajectory of an artillery shell—that clears the adjacent spores, to fall without hindrance through the gap between one gill and the next, and into the breeze below. Bracket fungi commonly have pores instead of gills, but the vertical tubes are also lined with spore-bearing tissue and the ballistics of spore ejection is equally exact. In puffballs, on the other hand, the whole internal mass of the fruiting body breaks down into a dust of spores. A hole opens at the top of the spherical envelope, and passing gusts of air suck out the spores in a fine mist in a manner that resembles the ejection of perfume from an atomizer. Winds of the upper air can spread such suspended spores over the entire earth, and it should come as no surprise to learn, therefore, that the thallophytes with the smallest air-borne spores are also the most cosmopolitan of plants. Their wind-blown spores have fallen literally everywhere.

In Dissemination of Pollen

For seed plants, pollen distribution occupies a place of importance comparable to that

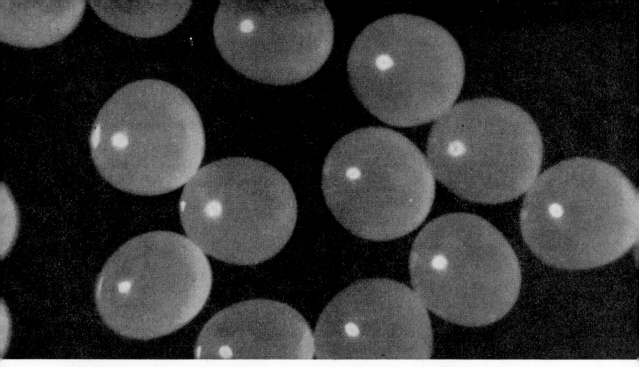

252. The shining pollen grains of corn (maize) are distributed by the wind from the staminate "tassel" to the outstretched carpellate "silk" (the stigmatic surfaces, one per kernel on the corn cob).

253. The regular flowers in the family Compositae often include sterile but showy ray florets and functional, closely packed disk florets, as in this head of sunflower. Note the central disk florets which have not yet opened, the ring of florets around these in which the stigmas are surrounded by a display of pollen, and the outer ring of florets in which the ovules have been fertilized and the accessory parts have dropped away.

254. In a poinsettia, the small yellow flowers are far less conspicuous than the bright red leaves which surround them; petals are not a part of this advertising campaign.

255. Honeybees transfer pollen from flower to flower as they search for nectar; they also collect pollen to take back to the hive as food for their queen's larvae. Here the masses of pollen are conspicuous as they are supported by special bristles on flat areas of the hind legs—the "pollen baskets" of the bees.

256. Squash pollen has a recognizable pattern. From shape of grain, size, and type of surface markings, experts can identify with certainty many kinds of pollen.

of spore dissemination among the cryptogams. There are many plants that depend entirely on wind for pollen dispersal and that cast prodigious quantities of the small cells (Photo 252) into the breezes of flowering time. Pine pollen (Photo 184) has a pair of wings on each grain that increase the surface exposed to wind and that presumably help to keep it air-borne longer—hence farther. The majority of plants depending on wind for pollination, however, live in regions where broad-leaved trees and herbs drop their leaves in winter, and the wind-borne pollen is liberated in spring before the leaves appear again. Or they are characteristic of treeless plains. In this way advantage is taken of reduced obstruction, and also in many areas of the characteristically seasonable gusty air.

Plants depending on air transport of pollen (Photos 234, 235) are said to be "anemophilous" (*anemos* = wind, *philos* = loving). Others depend chiefly on insects (Photos 236-238, 253-254) for transfer of pollen from the anthers of the stamens in one flower to the sticky stigma of the pistil in the other; such are "entomophilous" flowers (from *entomon* = insect). A few which depend on birds such as hummingbirds are "ornithophilous" flowers (*ornis, ornithos* = bird). But the mere existence of a showy flower appears to be a modification attracting some animal to the plant, and a device that improves the chance of a pollen grain being transferred to the spot where it will do the most good. Waste is inherent in such a system, but no splash or film of water (so essential in the sexual reproduction of many spore-bearing plants) is required here. Even the small volumes of liquids secreted as nectar—sugary rewards for bees, flies, or birds that visit flowers—are insignificant in contrast with the amounts of protoplasm and energy stores required for successful fertilization where swimming sperm are involved. (See also p. 301.)

Many insects, of course, feed on the pollen itself (Photo 256). The efficient flower is one that restricts it visitors as much as possible to those kinds that are fairly flower-constant; to those that enter in such a way as to leave pollen and take on a new load; and to those that do not use for food all of the pollen they take away. Honeybees and bumblebees, like so many others, stop at intervals and use spe-cial combs on their legs to remove pollen adhering to their hairy bodies. The pollen is carried in special "pollen baskets" on the hind legs (Photo 255) or under the abdomen, and is used at the nest as food for the young. Between cleanings, however, most of these insects can be enormously effective in cross-pollinating flowers. Without their activities, and those of other insects (and hummingbirds), few of our fruits would set seed or form, and the reproduction of flowering plants as a whole would fall off enormously. Thus a flower is a remarkable adaptation that greatly increases the biotic potential of the plant, through animal aid in ovule fertilization.

Some plants have gone a still farther step in the adaptation of their flower parts. In these, if insect or other pollen-distributing agent fails to bring pollen to the stigma of the pistil, the waiting egg cells are not wasted. Instead, the flower's own pollen fertilizes the egg cells. Rapid pollen growth and fertilization of the egg cells follows cross-pollination, but self-pollination occurs if no competition is offered to the slowly growing pollen tubes from the flower's own pollen grains. Self-pollination, of course, provides far less possibility of variation among the offspring, and the widespread adaptations that encourage cross-pollination seem to have as their basis the greater variation and success of plants employing these methods.

In Dissemination of Seeds

Even the seed habit is a major adaptation raising the biotic potential, since it involves both giving the embryo a partial start at parental expense before being cast out, and also an energy store to carry it further, while roots and leaves are unfolding and new sources of food obtained. Both of these are modifications tending to increase viability—so that more seedlings will become established and grow to reproductive maturity. The retention of the ♀ gametophyte embedded in the sporophyte allows the seed plant to endow the offspring with a generous energy supply; it also eliminates the dependence on liquid water for fertilization. The greater food store associated with the passive egg cell can be traced down into the thallophytes, but in the seed plants the arrangement shows its maximum development.

Among the angiosperm fruits are adaptations that increase the likelihood of improved dispersal for the seeds. The botanist recognizes such an assortment of fruits that a scheme of classification for them has been desirable (Fig. 20-2).

The following are **simple fruits:**

A. Fleshy or Succulent Fruits

These usually serve as a reward, inducing animals to aid in dissemination of the seeds; any fleshy parts not eaten by animals may rot and provide a wet fertilizer in which the seeds germinate readily.

1. Ovary wall fleshy; usually derived from a compound ovary, seen as several cavities (locules) with many seeds: *Berries* such as grape, raisin, pepper, cranberry, tomato, orange, lemon, squash, cucumber, watermelon, banana. Animals eat the whole fruit and the indigestible seeds may pass through with the feces, or only the flesh (ovary wall) may be eaten and the seeds be discarded—often at some distance from the parent plant.

2. With a skin and juicy outer part around a stony covering enclosing the seed, and only one cavity with a single seed: *Drupes* such as peach, almond, cherry, plum, olive, date. Animals seek out the fleshy part and discard the armored seed far from the parent plant, or as in squirrels, bury the stony walled seed in the ground under ideal germinating conditions—apparently as a type of hoarding instinct. No doubt some are recovered and eaten after soil bacteria have softened the hard covering around the seed.

3. With a core representing the ovary and contained seeds, but with a fleshy outer part derived from the receptacle or the calyx: *Pomes,* familiar as apples and pears, though including also the quince, walnut, pecan, hickory nut.

4. With an edible fleshy part consisting of the enlarged receptacle at the end of the peduncle, and the fruits proper consisting of small hard nutlets embedded in the surface: an *Accessory Fruit,* such as the strawberry. Like pomes and berries, these fruits provide indigestible components as well as a reward attractive to animals and capable of obtaining their unwitting cooperation in dissemination.

B. Dry Fruits

5. *Indehiscent Fruits* (which do not split or open to release enclosed seeds):

   (a) One-seeded, with a double seed coat; seed attached to the ovary wall at only one point: *Achenes,* as in buttercup, some of the rose family, and most of the huge family Compositae. Many have tufts of silk that assist in wind distribution (as on dandelion and thistles).

   (b) One-seeded, with a single fused seed coat: *Grains,* chiefly of the grass family, including oats, barley, wheat, rice, corn (maize). Like achenes they appeal to the hoarding instincts of insects, birds and mammals, and also are small enough to be carried short distances by wind and rain water.

   (c) One- or two-seeded, with a flattened wing on the ovary, aiding in wind dissemination: *Keys* or *Samaras,* as in maple, ash, elm.

   (d) One-seeded, with a hard shell of stone cells: true *Nuts,*[1] such as acorn. These appeal also to hoarding instincts of birds and mammals.

6. *Dehiscent Fruits* (splitting or opening to release the ripe seeds):

   (e) Opening by means of pores or seams, to liberate the seeds from a several chambered ovary: *Capsules,* such as poppy, iris, columbine, lily, cotton, azalea. In some cases wind and jostling of animals are depended on for knocking the seeds from the capsule; in others it is explosive, as in jewel weed and other touch-me-nots, which dry to build up sizable tensions which are released into motion when the capsule splits.

   (f) A single chamber splitting along one side (a *Follicle*) or along two sides (a *Legume*) to release the many seeds; often grouped as *Pods;* familiar as the peas, beans and peanuts (legumes) or the follicle of milkweed in which the individual seeds are provided with a tuft of silk fibers acting as a parachute that catches the wind (Endpaper Photo I). Larkspur and peony also have follicles.

---

[1] Many so-called nuts like the coconut, Brazil nut, and pine nut are merely large seeds.

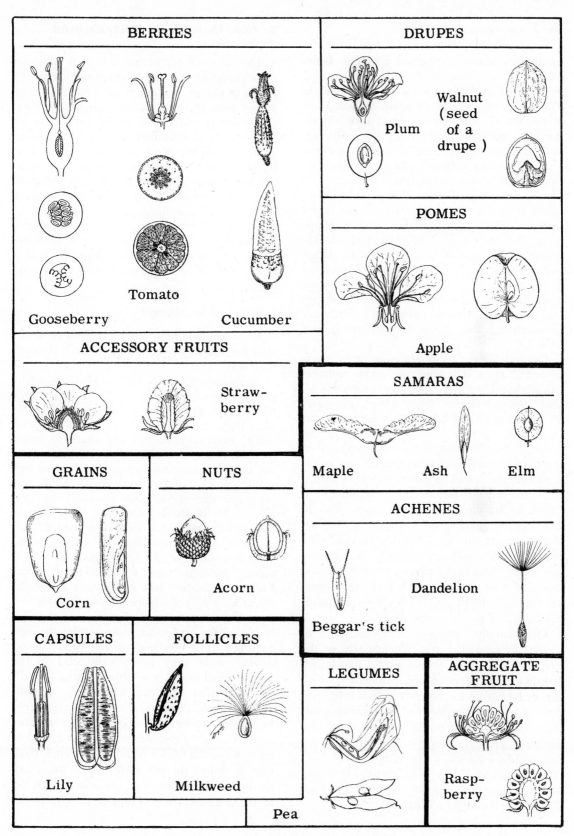

FIG. 20-2. *Representative fruits and seeds.*

In addition to these, there are **aggregate fruits** such as those of the raspberry, where several ovaries in a single flower develop into a single fruit body, and where the seeds enclosed are of the indigestible hard-covered type. There are also **multiple fruits** (the fig, mulberry, and pineapple), where the ovaries from separate flowers in a flower head combine in ripening to form a single united fruit.

The efficiency of animal dispersal of succulent fruits can be seen clearly in the speed with which a clearing in the forest is populated by raspberries, blackberries, chokecherries, and mountain ash, seeds of which had been dropped previously by birds perched in the trees. As soon as the trees were gone and light admitted to the ground, the seedlings had an opportunity to grow; under ordinary circumstances they starve for light and are not seen.

Dry indehiscent fruits are more often transported as units. The wings on maple samaras cause those fruits to spin like propellers as they descend slowly, being blown obliquely by each breeze and hence often spreading far beyond the parent tree before reaching the ground. The coconut has such buoyancy in the hard fibrous outer coat (which covers the seed ordinarily met in grocery stores) that it floats for miles from one tropic island to another, to be cast ashore by storms and to germinate at a new site (Photos 257-258). Parachutes of fine silky bristles provide wind resistance to seeds of thistles, dandelions, milkweeds, and many others, while hooks on the seed coat of beggar-tick and other burrs enable these to be carried for long distances on the fur of passing animals.

Occasionally, stranger methods are involved in seed dispersal. Particularly in the great plains region, whole plants dry into a ball-like mass of interwoven branches which comes free from the soil and which rolls over and over as a tumbleweed, scattering seeds as it goes. Or in the tropic swamps, mangrove seedlings grow to a length of a foot or more before breaking away from the parent tree. They plummet down like javelins, thrusting the root end deep into the mud of the tidal flat, where it can get a firm hold.

3. ADAPTATIONS IN MULTICELLULAR ANIMALS

The adaptations of animals that improve their chances of growing and surviving to reproduce themselves are more numerous and varied than those of plants—largely because the ordinary active life of an animal is so much more subject to variations than is the passive, fixed life of a plant. The great majority of multicellular animals go in search of food and move about in the process. Adaptations that improve their chances of finding food, of getting suitable food in larger quantities, and of spending less energy in acquiring food, are all modifications that increase the biotic potential through influences on viability, fecundity, and reduction of the reproductive cycle.

Search and Engulfment

Most animals hunt for their food or lie in wait for it, ready to capture it when it chances their way.

ARTHROPOD MOUTHPARTS. Great specialization is evident in the modified paired legs which serve arthropods as mouthparts. In insects they may take the form of jaws (Photo 262). Predatory beetles use them to catch food. Lobster, dragonfly and praying mantis use them to chew food caught with other appendages. Caterpillars and grasshoppers apply them directly to plant tissue, biting out pieces. All of these jaws work from side to side, not up and down like those of vertebrates.

An interesting modification of the side-to-side jaw plan of the arthropods is found among the spiders and a scattering of insects such as the antlion (the immature stage of the insect shown in Endpaper Photo T). Here a duct from the salivary glands joins the end of the gullet and extends as a tube through each jaw to its needle-sharp tip. In use, these animals seize prey (usually insects) in the fangs, inject into it a sizable quantity of salivary secretion, and wait while toxic ingredients paralyze the victim and enzymes begin to liquefy its internal organs. After a time, this external digestive process is complete enough for the spider or antlion to suck back into the gullet the complete body contents of the fly or ant, leaving only an empty shell, the resistant exoskeleton. Tropical tarantulas de-

257. At from 4 to 14 years of age, the tree begins producing fruit. Twelve months are required for each to ripen, but as many as 300 to 450 fruits may develop annually, weighing 4 to 5 pounds apiece. At first the husk is thin and green, the seed coat soft, its contents a jelly of endosperm. Later the jelly liquefies into the clear "milk" and most of the nourishment is laid down as the oil-rich "meat" lining the seed coat. In a completely ripe coconut, very little liquid remains.

ONE OF THE WORLD'S MOST USEFUL PLANTS—
THE COCONUT PALM

258. The husk gives mechanical protection to a coconut seed, preventing damage when it falls as much as 100 feet to the ground. It also serves as a float, permitting coconuts to be carried unharmed by salt water for long periods. They are cast ashore during storms and have colonized tropical beaches all over the world. In many places the "nuts" (seeds) taken from the husks constitute the chief cash crop (see Photos 9, 10). They may be planted by hand, or sprout where they fall, sending new leaves and strong roots through the husk at the stem end.

259. The mangrove trees which line many salt- and brackish-water shores in the tropics, repeatedly send down adventitious roots which support the plant in spite of wave action that might otherwise wash away the bottom.

260. Pines and many other conifers exude masses of resin wherever wounded. This process reduces likelihood of bacterial or fungus invasion or the attacks of insects.

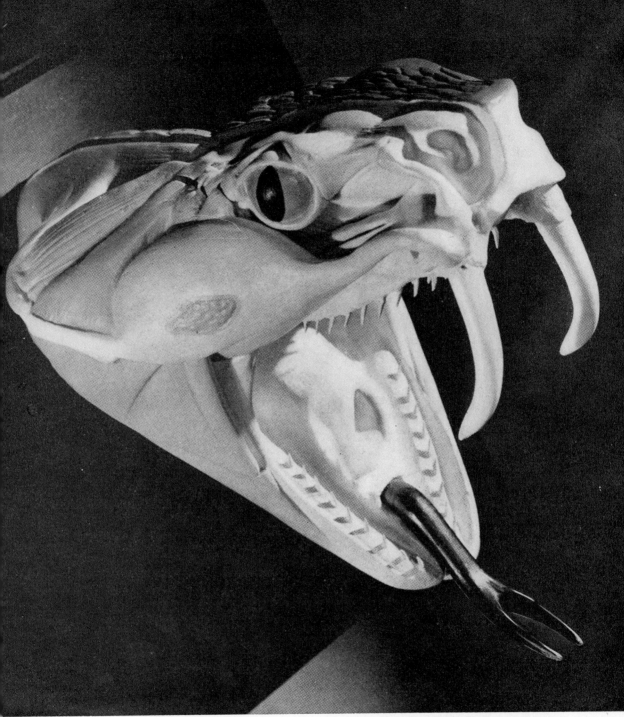

261. In this model of the head of a poisonous viper, the large poison-producing salivary gland can be seen ending in a duct which empties at the base of the erectile fang. In striking, these fangs project forward and the reptile attempts to bury them in the victim. Each fang is hollow and acts as a hypodermic needle to convey the poison from gland, through duct, through tunnel of fang, and into the tissue spaces of the prey. The forked tongue is harmless. Just behind its base is the opening to the trachea, allowing respiratory activity while prey is being swallowed.

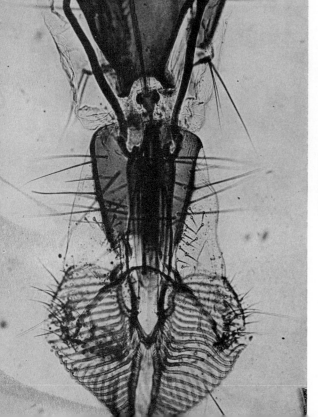

262. The powerful jaws of a stag beetle (Pseudolu-canus) are modified legs used by the ♂ principally in battling over a mate and in defence. The sturdy legs are employed in tunneling upward through the soil from the site of pupation, as much as 6 feet below the surface.

263. The "tongue" of a housefly (Musca) is a highly modified, lapping lip which spreads saliva over food materials. Dissolved materials are then sucked through a central canal. The photograph shows these parts in a slightly flattened, cleared preparation.

INSECT MOUTHPARTS ARE SUBJECT

TO ADAPTIVE VARIATIONS

vour mice, small birds, lizards (and other tarantulas) in this same way.

Other modifications of the same paired jaws and associated maxillae, upper and lower lip, form the sucking and lapping mouthparts of true bugs, butterflies and moths, true flies, bees and some wasps. Thus the long coiled tongue of a butterfly consists of the greatly elongated maxillae, which fit together as a sucking tube—a collapsible nectar straw—while the other mouthparts are degenerate. In plant louse or mosquito, the lancets with which the wound in plant or animal is opened sufficiently to get liquid to flow are again the highly modified mandibles and maxillae. The fleshy, complex lobe with which the housefly stamps over the surface of sugar, salivating and sucking up the solution again, is the specialized upper lip of the animal (Photo 263). Each follows the basic plan but exhibits differences adapting it to special food habits.

VERTEBRATE MOUTHPARTS. Vertebrates vary widely in the degree of jaw development and in the form and arrangement of the teeth with which they are armed. In each instance there is good correlation between the food used and the adaptations of the mouth region. Thus, the undercut jaw of a shark (Photo 71) with its multiple rows of sharp teeth is well suited to seizing and tearing flesh, whereas such close relatives of the sharks as skates and rays are armed with flattened modifications of the same style of tooth, and press their chinless mouths (Photo 70) over mussel beds to pick up and crush the shellfish. Bony fish, on the other hand, may have strong jaws well armed with teeth, as in the trout; or mouths with horny rims more like bird beaks, suitable for feeding on seaweeds, as in the puffer; or small pores through which microscopic particles can be sucked, as in the seahorses and pipefish.

Reptiles and birds repeat the adaptive modifications related to food types. Alligators and nonviperine snakes have many small teeth that hold prey from escaping during the rather long swallowing process. In snakes, where the engulfment of proportionately larger prey presents special difficulties, the lower jaw may be completely disengaged from the upper at will, and the two sides moved independently to shift food into the gullet. The respiratory passage, moreover, is brought

well forward in the mouth; this makes it possible for breathing to continue even though the pharynx may be blocked with prey for hours. The vipers have the additional modification of two erectile, replaceable fangs in the front of the upper jaw (Photo 261). Ducts from venom glands pass to the upper ends of these fangs and communicate with canals in the teeth themselves, effectively making them hypodermic needles that can inject poison into the lymphatic spaces under the skin of prey. Many of these dangerous snakes are called pit vipers because of a pronounced pocket that opens between eye and nostril on each side. The pit is sensitive to radiated heat, and allows rattlesnake, water moccasin, or copperhead to strike with remarkable accuracy at the body of bird or mammal—or at a hot stone, flatiron, or electric light blub—without use of the eyes.

BEAKS. Birds show some degeneration, since fossil birds had teeth as do many modern lizards. The fish-spearing, long-pointed beaks of bitterns, egrets, herons, loons, and the like are familiar modifications of this bird mouth plan (Fig. 20-3). Shovel-like beaks with strainers at the side help ducks sort worms and insect young from loose debris on the bottom of ponds. The short, strong beaks of seed-eating birds are as distinctive as the longer, sharp, chisel-like mouth structure of woodpeckers, or the slim, split-tube-like beak of nectar-sucking humming-birds. The mouth of the whippoorwill and nighthawk is an enormous, hair-fringed net with which to capture flying insects, whereas hawks, eagles, owls, and vultures have strong, hooked beaks useful in tearing the flesh of larger prey. The pelican has a combined collecting basket and funnel built into its lower jaw. All are valuable modifications of a basic design.

MAMMALIAN TEETH. Mammalian jaws are less specialized than the teeth with which they are armed, but a mammalogist can identify most of the subjects he studies if supplied with a single tooth or a jaw bone (mandible). Our own mouths are relatively unspecialized; this corresponds well with our omnivorous food habits. Rodents (mice, rats, squirrels, rabbits, and beaver, for example) have great

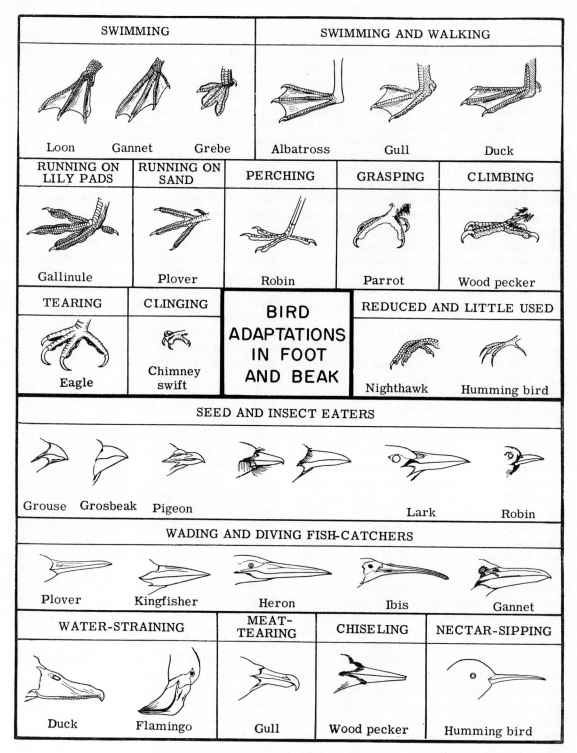

FIG. 20-3. *Bird adaptations in foot and beak.*

development of the incisors, which become chisel-like teeth with perennial roots. As these teeth wear away at the tip, the whole structure grows out from the base—continuing to serve the animal in spite of constant gnawing on all manner of woody materials.

Carnivores, on the other hand, have much less prominent incisors and relatively small molars and premolars. Instead, their canine teeth are enlarged into tearing tusks—as in the dog, cat, wolf, bear, and badger. Such an arrangement is very different from the organization in the mouth of ungulates, where the molars are particularly well developed, often with complexly folded enamel giving extra grinding surface for chewing grass and hay. Often the canines are lacking altogether. Thus, for example, in the horse there is a gap that man has found useful for installation of a bit with which to control the domesticated animal. The horse, however, has all upper and lower incisors, and browses cleanly or can bite in offense and defense. Cattle, on the contrary, lack upper incisors and sometimes canines in the upper jaw, and pluck their food by pressing the lower incisors against a firm pad of connective tissue with the grass clamped between, while the head as a whole is swung to tear the vegetation free.

GRAPPLING HOOKS AND SUCKERS. Other parts of the body are often adapted to food acquisition, hence to viability and biotic potential (Photo 264). The tentacles of coelenterates greatly expand the volume of water in which potential food can be detected. In leeches, the body is usually armed with a strong sucker at the anterior and posterior end, allowing a good hold on vertebrate prey; chitinous teeth in the mouth are used for rasping through the victim's skin, and a special anticoagulant substance produced by the salivary glands keeps the blood meal from clotting either in the wound or in the modification of the gullet described as a crop. Suckers, or suckers plus hooks, or hooks alone, allow the roundworms and tapeworms to anchor their bodies within the digestive tract of their host organisms, while in the tapeworms the expanse of surface exposed to the intestinal contents of the host is adequate to permit diffusion alone to feed the parasite, without need for any digestive tract of its own.

SHOPPING BASKETS. Animals whose food is obtained while they are particularly exposed to danger of attack (and which is relatively indigestible as well) commonly have a digestive tract adapted toward the collection of a large meal when opportunity affords, and digestive action deferred to a later time. Such are the cheek pouches of rodents (Photo 265) or the crop—a dilation of the esophagus—of the leech, the earthworm, and birds. In the last two, it is followed by a gizzard—a modified part of the stomach—armed with abrasive materials that can shred the food, leaving its fibers exposed to digestive enzymes.

Further adaptations to the type of food and its digestibility are found in the intestine. Length of the intestine and presence of blind outpocketings as ceca are related to high-cellulose diets. The intestine of a cat (carnivore) and a rabbit of equal weight (herbivore) demonstrate this striking difference in relative length and of cecal development (Fig. 20-4). The tadpole (herbivore) which becomes a frog (carnivore) shows an even more striking alteration at the time of metamorphosis, since in the same individual a long coiled

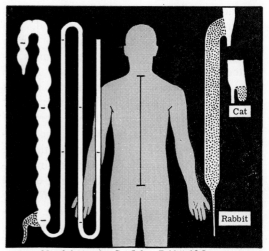

Man 8.1x trunk, Cat 5.2x, Rabbit 16.5x
(after F. Kahn)

FIG. 20-4. *The intestine of man* (left) *is about 8.1 times his trunk length* (I-shaped line). *That of a rabbit, like most herbivores, is 16.5 times the trunk length. A cat, as a carnivore, has an intestine only 5.2 times the trunk length. The cecum* (stippled) *and vermiform appendix, if any, show development in proportion to the amount of cellulose in the normal diet.*

intestine is quickly transformed into a relatively brief one, as the habits and food change on emergence from the pond to the terrestrial zone adjoining it.

FOOD-FINDING. Each animal which hunts for its food depends upon definite cues in its search. These may include the sense of smell (as with dog and buried bone); hearing (as with robin—Endpaper Photo C—and earthworm); sight (as with hawk and mouse); or even touch (as among cave animals or nocturnal feeders). Special development of any of these senses may so improve the abilities of an animal in finding food as to constitute an important adaptation increasing biotic potential. Although almost any individual kind of animal demonstrates such adaptations in sensory mechanisms related to food acquisition, some are sufficiently spectacular to earn special mention. Thus in a mole—a subsurface, burrowing mammal with degenerate eyes—the olfactory sense is very keen and the response to touch is overdeveloped.

Bats, flitting through the twilight or night, do not depend on their poor eyes for avoiding obstacles or locating insects on the wing. Instead, they utter repeated high-pitched cries (about 40,000 vibrations per second, and hence far above the range audible to human ears), and hear the echo of these sounds reflected from objects in their path (Photo 268). The nature of the echo informs the bat whether branch or bug is just ahead; and if the former, how to turn to avoid a crash. If food is flying past, the bat will change direction and pursue the insect, completing the catch by using sound waves and hearing during pursuit. Birds, on the other hand, depend primarily on acute vision (Photo 267) for finding seeds or insects, fish or mouse. Olfactory sense is almost (if not entirely) lacking, while the eyes may reach such a degree of development that, as in the owl (Photo 266), they are too large to be rotated in their sockets; instead the owl changes the direction of its gaze by rotating the whole head; and the neck is adapted through remarkable flexibility that allows rotation through more than 180 degrees on each side of "straight forward."

Filter Feeding

Among the common though less widely appreciated methods of obtaining food, the process of filter feeding has an important place. In this procedure, small animals and plants which are so diminutive that they cannot be sensed individually are strained systematically from the liquid medium. The filter feeder thus makes use of living organisms which are extremely small. This involves a comparison. For example, a whale 70 feet long uses filter feeding to pick up sardines or smaller organisms still large enough for us to see, but a clam three inches long depends on microscopic forms or those not over $\frac{1}{16}$ inch in length. The size ratios are not too different.

The whales which are filter feeders are often called the "whalebone whales" or baleen whales, since an adaptation of the roof of the big animal's mouth involves the material whalebone or baleen. Whalebone is not bone but a horny material formed in the embryonic development through the fusion of long hairs. The product resembles long narrow plates with a coarse fringed edge. These hang down from the roof of the mouth in large numbers and form a maze. As the big animal swims through the sea with mouth open, water plus the small food organisms flows between the whalebone plates. At intervals the whale closes its mouth, trapping the sardines or smaller prey. The tongue becomes inflated with blood, squeezing against the whalebone plates and forcing the living material out of the crevices into the throat to be swallowed. Thus the whalebone mechanism acts as a sort of net, preventing the small victims from escaping as the mouth is closed, and the whale seines the sea, living on those animals too small or confused to escape. Since whales are the largest of all animals, and since their numbers are kept down primarily by human depredations, it is clear that this method of filter feeding is sufficiently remunerative to allow growth and reproduction—to maintain the biotic potential of whales.

Clams and many other aquatic animals of smaller size are equipped with cilia by means of which they maintain a current of water. The current brings them food and oxygen and removes carbon dioxide and wastes. The feeding method in primitive chordates was described earlier (pp. 86, 107). In burrow-

264. The slender head, extended jaws, and narrow thorax of snail-eating beetles allow these insects to reach far into a shell after their prey.

BODY MODIFICATIONS RELATED TO FEEDING

265. The cheek pouches of the golden-mantled ground squirrel, like those of chipmunks and related rodents, allow the animal to act like an animated vacuum-cleaner whenever small particles of food are available. The unswallowed excess can be stored in underground burrows, as provisions against bad weather and poor hunting.

266. The eyes of owls admit an unusually large amount of light, the large lenses increasing sensitivity in dim light. But the eyes cannot be moved in their sockets; instead the bird swivels its whole head.

267. The eyes of hawks are far smaller but, with adequate light, remarkably keen. The retinal cells are far more slender than those of man's eyes, and acuity is correspondingly improved.

Sensory Modifications
Related to Feeding

268. Bats can see dimly, but in complete darkness they chase down insect prey victim by victim, locating and following each or dodging obstacles entirely by ear. Echoes of the bat's staccato ultrasonic calls guide the mammal with remarkable accuracy.

ing clams, the neck may extend up through three or four feet of mud, and it may constitute the only connection between the permanently buried animal and the sea above (Photos 45-47).

Various aquatic arthropods, too, act as filter feeders, but they employ none of the tactics discussed so far. Barnacles, affixed to a rock or bit of shell, open their limy plates and extend short feet armed with comb-like bristles. These create some current in the water (enough for respiration and elimination of wastes) but serve primarily to drag into the region of the barnacle's mouth microscopic organisms and the smaller visible types from the water just beyond the barnacle's shell. Water fleas and a great variety of the small free-swimming crustaceans thrive on food caught in this way—kicked, so to speak, into their mouths by bristle-armed feet which strain the still smaller food from the water.

In some places (such as Puget Sound), certain kinds of barnacles grow large enough to be collected as human food. But, for the most part, the free-swimming filter feeders never reach a directly useful size. They are, however, remarkably numerous and important. They depend ultimately for their nourishment on chlorophyll-containing microscopic algae, but themselves form the food substrate for small fish, and these for larger. Hence the sea and lake fish to which man looks for food commonly depend upon filter-feeding small crustacea, which in turn depend upon the single-celled green plants that can use energy from the sun in photosynthesis. The biotic potential of the filter-feeding crustaceans is thus an important link in the food relations of the larger forms.

Finding and Winning Mates

The female fully stocked with ripe but unfertilized eggs and the male with a ready supply of mature sperm cells, contribute little to the biotic potential of their species unless sexual union takes place. In a great many marine invertebrates this matter of fertilization is left to chance in the most casual of ways. But in a great variety of animals, there is some further degree of specialization in structure or habit that makes more probable the fertilization of the egg "capital" of the species.

Often mate-finding comes about as a result of the two sexes being attracted simultaneously to a food supply.

TOUCH. Other cues may be important. Earthworms depend on the sense of touch, and extend from their burrow mouths (plural) in various directions until two worms make contact—possibly while feeding. One reason for believing that the tactile sense is primary in this process is that mating pairs are almost invariably of equal size—small worms with small worms and large with large. Presumably, only when this correspondence is good will the longitudinal grooves on the outside of the body of one worm match with those on another to form channels through which the sperm can travel between the two.

ODORS. The extent to which olfactory cues are used among animals may be underestimated (Photos 270-271). Everyone who has had a mature ♀ cat or dog as a pet is well aware when the animal is sexually receptive—by the number of tomcats which arrive outside the house and serenade by night, or by the sudden interest in the household shown by every ♂ dog in the neighborhood.

SIGHT. Although visual cues are more familiar, the highly complex nature of the reaction between potential mates is often unappreciated. Sometimes the mechanism involves complex and special structures—as among the fish of the abyssal deeps where there is no light from the sun but where fish recognize their own kind visually through luminescent streaks and spots worn on their sides and backs. Fireflies on a summer lawn exemplify the corresponding mechanism on land. Large-eyed ♂ ♂ may fly slowly over the grass, flashing at irregular intervals. Females flash in response while perched at the tip of a grassblade or twig. If the interval between flash and response is correct within a few tenths of a second, the ♂ turns in his flight and flashes again. Further responses guide him to the waiting female.

Daytime visual cues depend to a considerable degree on the eyes that interpret them. Thus, a cabbage butterfly flitting over a field of red clover among which there are a few white daisies and a few other cabbage butterflies may feed extensively on the clover but investigate each white object—clearly unable to distinguish between the daisies and potential mates until within a distance of a very few inches. Then the difference may be recognized as much by odor as by appearance. Among birds, although vision is enormously more acute in day-active kinds, small details may determine the mating behavior. The Maryland yellowthroat, for example, is a small warbler in which the ♂ has a conspicuous black mask-like mark across the eyes; the ♀ lacks the mark. In the breeding season, ♂ Maryland yellowthroats vigorously defend a definite territory, driving off all other ♂ ♂ of the species. The degree to which they recognize their own species visually can be demonstrated by fastening a stuffed skin of a ♀ Maryland yellowthroat to a bush in the home territory of a ♂ bird. The ♂ soon discovers the addition, goes through elaborate courtship antics, and will attempt to mate with the stuffed bird. But if the experimenter uses India ink to draw on the stuffed female's head a black mask shaped like that of the ♂ in this species, the sex "difference" is recognized immediately and the ♂ which would otherwise court the effigy, dashes at it, tearing it to pieces with beak and claws.

The butterfly and warbler just described can be said to appreciate pattern. Color also has its place in cuing some organisms to prospective mates. Clearly such a method is limited to the relatively few animals in which color vision occurs. The black-crowned night heron is an example. Sexually mature ♀ ♀ differ from juveniles in that the skin of the legs turns a pinkish red. Males pay no attention to any member of the opposite sex that lacks this distinguishing color, but to those with it they accord full courtship attention. Examples of this type are less common than those involving pattern vision, but additions can be expected among any of the animals with color vision: the primates alone among mammals; most day-active birds; some day-active lizards and fish; and apparently some insects and higher crustaceans.

Even auditory cues have their place in mate-finding. Hunters make use of this fact with all manner of artificial crow calls, duck calls, and moose calls, imitating the sound produced by the ♀ ♀ in order to lure ♂ ♂ within gunshot. In the invertebrates, cicadas and members of the insect order Orthoptera (grasshoppers, katydids, and crickets particularly) offer further examples, though sound production is almost completely limited to the ♂ ♂ (Photo 270, Endpaper Photo E).

Competition for Mates and Courtship

The polygamous tendencies of the ♂ in many species have been the subject of much study and legislation. In general, there are distinct biological advantages to be gained by having a relatively few healthy, vigorous, well adapted ♂ ♂ as the parents of new generations; the vigor level of the whole population is likely to rise significantly. Having the healthy, vigorous, well adapted ♀ ♀ as the mothers of new generations, to the statistical exclusion of the less fit, is more difficult to achieve since the number of offspring possible annually for any one ♀ is far less than the number for which any one ♂ may be responsible. And among most of the animal kingdom, any nonpregnant or unmated mature ♀ is a potential mate for the first ♂ to arrive. If several ♂ ♂ reach the ♀ simultaneously, competition ensues, and the survivor or victor fulfills the sexual function. The vanquished may go elsewhere and succeed in another contest. The ♀ role is a passive one.

A great proportion of the secondary sexual characters are related to competition for mates. Some, like the peacock's tailfeather fan, can be used by the ♂ to produce an illusion of impressive size. Others like the antlers of elk and deer are weapons used in combat, one ♂ with another—butting and slashing. Similar adaptations and habits are found among invertebrates (Photos 272-273). Where the contests are largely bluff, it is common for the ♂ to employ the same series of expressive poses as a dance preliminary to mating with the ♀. The literature on animal behavior is full of the strutting and drumming of grouse, and similar actions that have a dual role: as competitive activities in which one ♂ strives to defend a territory or achieve dominance over other ♂ ♂, and as a solo dance before the ♀. It would seem that the latter activity has little biological significance, though much has been made of it as a demonstration of courtship.

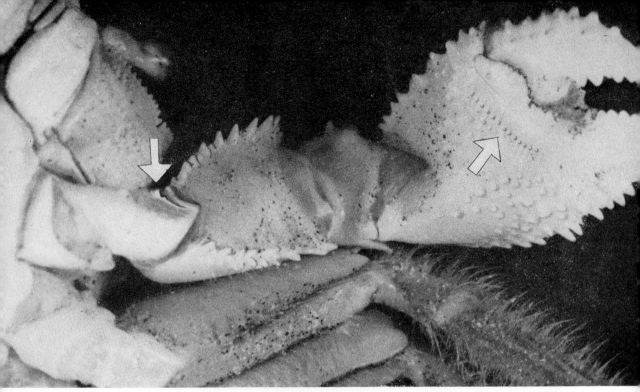

269. A scraper (left arrow) on a basal segment can be fretted across the row of pegs (right arrow) on the claw of a Ghost Crab (Ocypoda) to produce a stridulation chirp.

270. The ♂ tree cricket (Œcanthus) raises his pale green wings to rub a scraper on a series of teeth—one on one wing, the other opposite it—in producing the high-pitched trill characteristic of his kind. Other ♂♂ hear his trill and either heed its claim to a territory or approach for combat.

271. There is some uncertainty as to whether the ♀ tree cricket comes to the ♂ in response to his stridulation or as a chemical response to the secretion from an odoriferous gland exposed when his wings are raised. In any case, she nibbles on the gland upon arrival, and he combines a continuation of stridulation with secretion and mating.

272. The ♂ stag beetle (Lucanus) has enormous jaws and uses them in combat with other ♂♂. The ♀ is both smaller and equipped with small jaws.

SEXUAL DIMORPHISM IN INSECTS

273. The ♂ Hercules beetle (Dynastes) of the American tropics bears a tremendous thoracic horn which, with a head horn, forms a pair of forceps used in combat. The ♀ (not shown) lacks both horns.

More honest courtship is found among such birds as the common tern, where the ♂ catches a little fish and runs around on the beach with the food held crosswise in his mouth. If a ♀ is receptive, she approaches him and is given the fish; mating follows at once. Since the ♂ ♂ and ♀ ♀ look alike to human observers, this behavior has been described as a means whereby the ♂ bird of this species identifies a ♀ ; it is rather unlikely that this view has any basis in fact. The gift procedure, moreover, extends to many other birds where the sexes are more unlike and the ♂ , as in the black-crowned night heron, may present the ♀ with twigs such as she might use for nest building. Acceptance of the twig and mating are then the important phases of the courtship behaviors.

The competition for mates and courtship behaviors place emphasis on the success of the most vigorous and best adapted individuals in a community of animals. Hence these become the parents of a disproportionately larger percentage of the progeny in each generation. This tends to improve the species, and to increase its biotic potential in terms of health and adaptations.

Provision for the Young

Any measure that improves the chances of survival is an important contribution to the future of the species. Moreover, direct assistance from the parent to the young tends to reduce the mortality among the offspring and to allow more of them to reach reproductive maturity. Even the provisioning of the egg with a store of yolk or oil constitutes a significant gift. It relieves to some extent the urgency for the embryo to modify its form quickly from that of a fertilized egg to that of some feeding organism that can compete successfully in gaining further nourishment—regardless of what final body structure is to be achieved. Instead, the well-stocked egg can carry itself without additional feeding for long enough to allow the embryo to achieve a body form more like that of the parent, so that a metamorphosis (with its accompanying lost time or inefficient organization) is not required.

Nevertheless, the possession of a store of yolk or oil makes an egg a more valuable prize for any hungry animal. Protection of the defenseless eggs allows more of them to reach the hatching stage. Commonly eggs are secretly hidden by the parent, or the parent(s) may remain on guard until the eggs hatch, to drive away any intruders. The Surinam toad has become famous because the ♀ spreads her egg mass over her own back, where the whole hardens and the young develop through the tadpole stage before breaking out and hopping away, each from its private pit on the parent's back. In one of our common water bugs, the ♀ cements her eggs in a raft-like cluster on the back of her mate, and he skulks among the bottom vegetation with his load until they hatch. Several of the fish pick up their eggs in especially capacious mouths, and they hold them there (without feeding) until the young have reached an active swimming stage.

Simpler perhaps is the modification whereby the ♀ parent, while carrying on ordinary activities, retains within her body the fertilized eggs she might otherwise be expected to lay. If she meets with no accident, the eggs develop until hatching and the young are born in an active condition—an ovoviviparous birth. Such ovoviviparity is common among flatworms and the smaller crustaceans, and is far from rare among fish, amphibians, and reptiles. The lizard genus Phrynosoma, members of which are generally known as horned toads, contains both egg-laying species and ovoviviparous ones—indicating that no great alteration in structure is necessary for the change in degree of parental protection (Photos 232-233). A few shark species retain the eggs (Endpaper Photo K) and even develop a true placenta, while others are strictly oviparous.

Additional protection and nourishment are furnished to the embryos of the placental mammals, and a scattering of others such as the placental dogfish (a small shark of the Mediterranean Sea). Here the eggs receive less store of yolk or oil, but instead develop by cooperative growth processes an interdigitating placenta through which the embryo can respire, obtain nourishment and dispose of wastes, while developing and enlarging in a well-protected site. Mammal young have extra assistance in the form of milk secreted by the mother after they are born, and one or both parents may supplement this food supply with prey brought whole to the den (as in foxes and the like) or partly digested and regurgitated (as in the coyote and many others).

Birds are famous for the care they give their nestlings—shading them from the sun, hovering over them when the temperature falls, and bringing in food (Photo 274)— again either whole (as in wrens and other insectivorous birds) or partly digested (as in most fish- and seed-eaters). The pigeons even have glands emptying into the crop which add a nourishing "milk" during the period when the parents are regurgitating for the benefit of their squabs. The nests themselves may be remarkable for their concealment or inaccessibility (Photos 275-277).

Among invertebrates, the well-provisioned nests of bees and ants are justly famous (Photos 280-284). Both ants and termites of some kinds maintain "fungus gardens" in which an edible fungus thrives on vegetation brought in by the insects—supplying in this way a valuable supplement used in feeding the young. Various of the dung beetles, such as the sacred scarab of Egypt, form a ball from mammal feces, roll it to a suitable burial site, then inter it along with an egg or two as a food supply for the still unhatched young (Endpaper Photo L).

Concealment

Perhaps the best of all ways to survive to reproductive maturity is for an animal to live without being seen, in a region where food is plentiful. Activity and concealment are not easy to combine, however. Some animals achieve a compromise in this direction by making burrows in the earth near a supply of nourishment. The woodchuck (marmot) in a pasture hillside, or the ghost crab in a sea beach, are within running distance of food on the one hand and safety on the other (Photos 285-287). The earthworm and the clamworm in garden and mudflat, respectively, are able to extend their branching tunnels and to emerge at many points to extend themselves and forage on the surface. At a moment's notice, however, they are ready to regain the safety of their burrows.

The larger herbivores like the elk, the deer, the giraffe, and the wild horse are conspicuous by day if they feed on an open plain, and even by night can be recognized and pounced upon by keen-eyed predators—wolves, lions, and the like. Keenness of hearing and of olfactory sense are coupled in these herbivores with speed in running. And when not feeding, each seeks out the shelter of vegetation, and is adapted for blending with the background through what man calls **camouflage.** Partly this is a matter of matching the brightness or darkness of the surroundings to eliminate contrast. Partly the concealment is achieved through **disruptive coloration,** with clearly visible but meaningless markings on the body that distract the eye from the whole outline and hence from recognition. Occasionally these markings seem to resemble the vegetation among which the animal reposes (as in the tiger, zebra, badger, and bittern); sometimes it simulates to human eyes the spotty shade (as in spotted fawns of deer—Photo 289). Often the marking is a streak that runs through an eye, destroying the conspicuous circle of the sense organ, as in the wood frog and painted turtle. Or stripes may extend across quite unrelated parts of the body that are held close together in the rest position, effectively breaking the outline into unidentifiable parts, as in some of the moths and frogs. Rarely, except in insects, is the color of the animal truly adaptive in concealment—no doubt, in large part, because few except birds, some lizards, fish, and man have color vision. Insects that match the green of foliage provide fewer cues for hungry birds. Those that resemble bird droppings, or bark (Photo 290) or twigs

FIG. 20-5. *The effect of countershading is made evident when the body so marked is inverted* (center) *from its normal relation* (left) *with respect to incident light. Without countershading, the back would be bright, the underside shadowy* (right).

274. A gull with nest, egg, and nestling. Note how well the young matches the background.

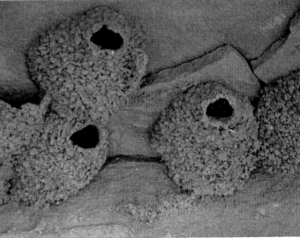

275. A pink-sided junco's nest among shrubbery on the ground in western Wyoming during July.

276. Cliff swallow nests of mud pellets, cemented to a sandstone rock wall in eastern Wyoming.

PARENTAL PROVISION FOR

YOUNG AMONG BIRDS

277. A cactus wren's nest among the dangerous spines of a cholla cactus in Arizona.

278. Newly hatched spiders clinging to the upper surface of their mother's abdomen, among river gravel in Pennsylvania.

MATERNAL CARE IN INSECTS

279. In the American tropics, a ♀ giant orb-web spider (Nephila) stands over her eggs among silk strands on a leaf.

280. Brood cells and empty comb of a yellow jacket's paper nest. Note maggot-like larvae in some open cells; these are still being fed by the parent wasps. When the larvae pupate, the parents cap the cells.

INSECTS PROVIDE FOR

THEIR YOUNG

281. Ant adults in galleries below a flat stone pick up their silk-cocooned pupae and naked larvae to carry them gently to deeper shelter.

282. The few paper cells of a pendant wasp's nest will each eventually be provisioned with food for one larval life, then capped.

283. The cicada-killer wasp with a victim. The cicada is anesthetized, not killed outright.

284. The same wasp attempting to dig in loose sand a burrow to accommodate a cicada and an egg.

GHOST CRABS (Ocypoda)

285. A remarkably terrestrial crustacean is the fast-running ghost crab, found burrowing in sandy beaches from Long Island to Rio de Janeiro.

286. The crab uses the cupped legs of one side as a sand scoop in bringing a load from below. The Y- or U-shaped burrow may go down 6 or 8 feet; its back door is at the bottom of the photo.

287. Some of the size variation within a single species found among crabs feeding at the water's edge during a July night. (See also Photo 208.)

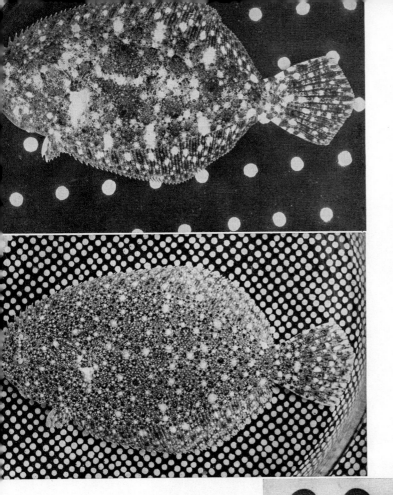

288. The flounder is able to adjust the pigment cells of its upper surface to produce
mottlings that match remarkably well the
various types of bottom—from sand (both
dark and pale) to gravel—on which it normally rests. On artificial backgrounds the
illusion is still good. Adjustment is in terms
of what the eyes see; this point has been
established experimentally beyond any doubt.

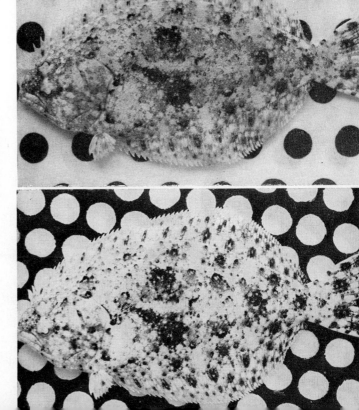

289. The dappled body of a fawn matches fairly well the spotty sunlight and shadow among the bushes where the deer leaves her young.

PATTERN

MATCHING

290. An underwing moth (Catocala) on birch bark is likely to escape detection.

291. Stick insects are near relatives of praying mantis, cricket and grasshopper. Unlike these others, however, the stick insect when alarmed stands motionless and gives a good imitation of the twigs among which it stands while feeding on foliage.

292. Tree hoppers, the adults of "spittle insects," often resemble thorns but only an accident points the spine the same way as those on a plant. The spittle is believed to protect the soft-bodied young from desiccation and from attack by birds.

RESEMBLANCE TO INEDIBLE MATERIALS

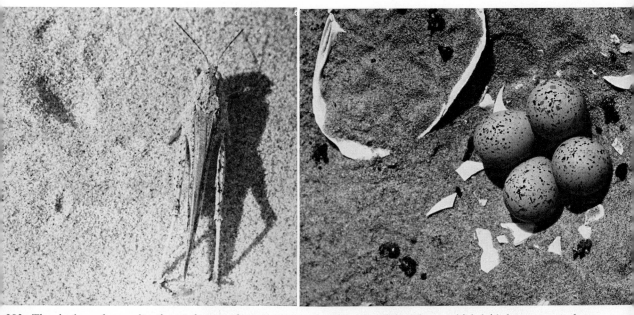

293. The shadow of many beach grasshoppers is more conspicuous than the resting insect. The depression in the sand to the left is a mark left when the insect drops to earth from a leap or flight.

294. The piping plover which laid these eggs made no nest in the sand, but from a few feet away her exposed eggs were almost invisible. How the parent finds her way back to them is unknown.

295. The harmless toad is well armed with poison glands in its warty skin. Animals which eat the toad may become what the German word "tode" means (dead).

Adaptations for Defense

296. The large pincers of small fiddler crabs are on the left hand of about half the population. They are excellent weapons for defense, and are used also in courtship dances. Female fiddlers have two small nippers, like the "bow" of the ♂ ♂, and no "fiddle" (large claw).

(Photo 291), or thorns (Photo 292), *and remain still when in danger,* are also well protected by their modified structure and pigmentation.

One aspect of animal appearance that is clearly a part of the concealment problem is the **countershading** found in so many kinds. Countershading involves having the surface of the animal normally held toward the source of light (or sun) of a distinctly darker shade than the sides of the body, whereas the surface normally away from the light is palest in its pigmentation. In this way a cylindrical body loses its identity for an observer (Fig. 20-5). Instead of there being a shine or glare of light on the back, the pigment absorbs it. Instead of the belly surface demonstrating that the body shades it, the lesser light is reflected away again as a reasonable brightness.

A very few animals match the background on which they habitually find themselves (Photos 293-294). Adjustments allowing this have been credited erroneously to the true chameleons of Africa and the false chameleon (Anolis) of the southeastern U.S. (Photo 76). These lizards, like tree frogs and several other animals, do shift from green to gray or brown through control of pigment cells in the skin, but the alterations follow temperature or emotions rather than a relationship to background and concealment. In flounders and some other flatfish, however, an ability to match the bottom is developed to an astonishing extent. Again the mechanism is one of pigment cell expansion or contraction, and the change from one pattern to another requires minutes to hours (Photo 288, Fig. 11-22). Experimental studies on these animals, using linoleum patterns for tank bottoms, were conducted by the late Francis Sumner at the Scripps Oceanographic Institution in La Jolla, California. From his research work came excellent data on both the importance of slower shifts in general coloration of other fish—from dark gray to nearly white (according to the background) —and the value of these changes in surviving attacks by fish-eating birds. Some fish do show these adaptive mechanisms, and use them to advantage in concealment and escape from attack. Most reports of similar adaptations in other groups of animals have been found to be without scientific basis.

Defense and Escape

Although a very large number of animals rely upon concealment, and another multitude upon agility in flight—by swimming, running, or flying—a sizable group show willingness to stand and defend themselves (Photos 295-304). Usually these animals have either armor in the form of scales, bony plates, or various types of exoskeletons, or definite weapons of some sort. Antlers, horns, and defensive use of teeth have been mentioned. More specialized weapons include the quills of the porcupine, which are modified hairs set among the fur (Photos 300-301). With them the animal is reasonably safe; it merely turns away from an attacker, raises its armament, and waits for an inquiring nose to come within swatting distance of the quill-studded tail or to pounce on the well-defended back. The skunk has its rectal glands, with a muscular investment and directional nozzle. The stink bug has coxal glands; the blister beetle secretes an urticating substance at knee joints and elsewhere. Many slugs can throw multiple jets of milky slime. Even Paramecium has its trichocysts and Hydra its nematocysts.

The venom of the pit vipers and the very different poisons of spiders seem often to be far more completely developed than is required in ordinary food acquisition. In defense these toxic materials can be injected into an attacker, with serious consequences. That a rattlesnake will strike chiefly when pressed or stepped upon, and will rattle a warning[2] or glide away if given half a chance, emphasizes the defensive role of these potent weapons. Toads and frogs try to escape, too, but they have strong poisons in their skins— effective against some of their enemies but not against all (Photo 295).

A more drastic method of defense that involves both loss and escape is to be found in such animals as crabs, crayfish and lobster, starfish and sea cucumbers, and various long-tailed lizards. The crustaceans mentioned are armed with strong pincers on the first pair of

[2] The rattle consists of the remains of shed skins at the end of the tail, and the snake adds a new one at each molt; terminal "buttons" also break off, so that guessing a rattler's age from its rattle is not merely a matter of counting segments.

legs (Photos 289, 306). If one of these organisms is hard pressed and can get a firm grip on its attacker with one of the pincers, the crustacean clamps the nipper and at the same time sheds the whole appendage—escaping to safety while the attacker pries itself free from the pincer's grip. The process is called **autotomy** (*auto* = self, *tomein* = to cut, hence self-multilation), and is followed within a reasonable time by regeneration of the lost appendage. Starfish held firm by an arm for some hours will free themselves by shedding the body part; if one or two arms are stroked vigorously from below in the region of the tube feet, the starfish may be induced to utilize the special mechanism that drops the appendage where it is attached to the body disk.

Far less of a loss is suffered by the many long-tailed lizards which snap off their tails when caught by the appendage. In some, the autotomized tail may itself separate into fragments, all twitching violently and likely to distract the attention of an attacker from the quick escape of the now tailless lizard. Again regeneration makes good the loss.

In a number of instances, it is enough for an animal to resemble closely one with a respectable weapon. Several harmless flies that frequent the same flowers as stinging bees and wasps are almost indistinguishable—both in appearance and behavior—from those that are properly armed. There can be little question that insect-eating animals are fooled by the imitation, since the common drone fly is repeatedly avoided by those who have been stung by the still commoner honeybees. A practiced eye is needed to distinguish between the two insects, and such critical eyes are not numerous. The biologist refers to instances of close resemblance in appearance and actions as **mimicry,** and refers to the armed species as the **model,** the unarmed as the **mimic.** Many examples have been claimed; a few stand careful investigation. The drone fly is one valid case (Photo 309).

The requirements for mimicry are rigid: (1) the mimic must be active in the same places as the model and at the same time of day and of year; (2) the mimic must be numerically less abundant than the model. If either of these requirements is not met, the predators that might prey on the mimic are not provided with sufficient unpleasant experiences through attack on the armed model to avoid both because they look alike.

Modifications promoting escape are widespread. Powerful swimming organs (Photo 311), long legs (Photo 310), and strong wings afford most obvious advantages. Burrow-making is closely related (Photos 312-314). Many of these adaptations are met as a well-knit organization in grasslands where great level stretches of a single type of vegetation provide uniformity. Most of the larger animals (chiefly ungulates) congregate in herds, feed while walking for perhaps a third of the day, and spend the rest of their time lying down inconspicuously. The smaller animals usually live in holes—ground squirrels and prairie dogs forming the food for the burrowing badgers. Birds nest on the ground. All have keen vision capable of recognizing enemies at great distances, and fleetness of foot or quickness of wing are relied upon for escape.

Each modification allowing more rapid locomotion carries with it a requirement for additional areas for muscle attachment. This is particularly evident among birds, where the flightless ostrich and some others have a relatively simple breastbone (sternum) and are classified in the subclass Ratitate (meaning raft-like, as a descriptive phrase applying to the flat breastbone). Flying birds, on the other hand, show tremendous development of the sternum into a sturdy, keel-shaped structure, whence the subclass name Carinatae (from *carina* = a keel). The muscles that force the wings downward—and hence lift the body—are spread over those sternal surfaces.

The chief modifications of running animals are in slender bodies and elongate legs. Among the hoofed mammals most of the additional length in the appendage has been achieved through extension of the digits and reduction in the total number reaching the ground. Functional hoof-tipped toes total two per limb in deer, antelope, gazelle, and others, whereas a single toe with its hoof is all that remains in the horse and its relatives. Moreover, the usual ball-and-socket articulation of the limbs has been modified in these forms

297. The cottonmouth moccasin, one of the venomous pit-vipers, is found near water in many southern states.

Poisonous Reptiles Are Few

298. The Gila monster is named for the Gila River in its native state, Arizona. The "Monster" reaches a length of about two feet, and is mottled black and peach color. It is now protected by law.

299. The only other poisonous lizard in the world is the Mexican beaded lizard, which differs in having a long slender tail rather than a short thick one, as in the Gila monster.

300. The Western yellow-haired porcupine, like its black relatives, shows few quills from the side.

DEFENSE THROUGH LOOSELY HELD QUILLS

301. The well-armed tail is used to swat quills into any inquisitive nose or careless leg.

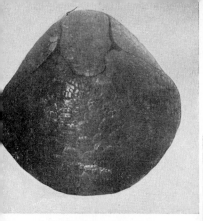

302. The armadillo, an insectivorous mammal, can curl in sides, tail and head to form an armored ball a foot in diameter.

303. A few millipedes can roll up into an armored sphere. (See also Photos 108, 109.)

304. So many wood lice can assume a spherical form when attacked that they are often known as "pill bugs."

305. While walking along, the jointed body and appendages of a wood louse show that it is actually a terrestrial crustacean.

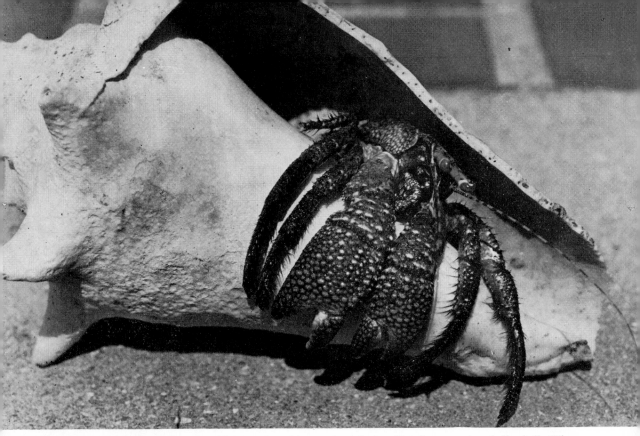

306. A hermit crab withdraws from danger into the cavity of an empty whelk shell. When undisturbed, this crab carries the shell over the distorted, unarmed abdomen.

PORTABLE SHELTERS

307. A bagworm caterpillar attaches its portable shelter of silk and plant debris, reaches out to feed, withdraws to rest, moves the shelter to a new site, and repeats the process. Eventually it pupates inside the shelter.

308. Bagworms in a locust tree all look like cocoon When ♂ bagworm moths emerge, they fly to the ♀ ♀ The latter never leave their shelters even to mate o lay eggs which will hatch into the next generation o bagworm caterpillars.

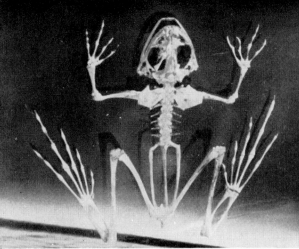

09. Fraternizing with honeybees, normally being out-
umbered by them, and both appearing and acting like
bee on a flower, are enough similarities to provide
seful safety to the drone fly (a mimic—right)
vhich lacks the sting of the honeybee (the model—
eft).

310. The frog's skeleton and body as a whole are well
adapted for leaping flight. The long hind legs form
efficient levers for throwing the body ahead. They are
supplemented by extended hip bones which parallel
the stiff tail at the end of the vertebral column.

Adaptations Aiding in Escape

311. Scallops, although clams, swim actively by expelling water from between the two valves
of the shell. Small bright eyes around the edge of the mantle may help orient this jet-
propelled swimming. The taste of starfish in the water is enough to initiate a sudden burst
of flight.

312. The burrowing legs with their flat claws show adaptations away from the general plan of turtles. Actually the flatness is due to wear; young specimens have pointed claws.

THE GOPHER TORTOISE OF FLORIDA IS A

NUISANCE TO GARDENERS

313. The burrow extends downward for many feet to a place of safety.

314. The tracks of the burrower are distinctive as they cross a cultivated field.

almost into a hinge joint in shoulder and hip —allowing movement only in one plane.

Social Adaptations

Unless animals are important to one another in a predator-prey relationship, or are competing side by side for the same food, an individual of one kind ordinarily ignores an individual of another. Except at a feeding shelf, a goldfinch means little to a chickadee. A rabbit and a deer can browse side by side without showing hostility or affection.

Exceptions to this generalization can be found in a variety of organisms. Two unlike types may regularly associate with one another—a situation to which the name "symbiosis" (= living together) is given. Within this habit, three different relationships can be distinguished: (1) Benefits accruing to each partner—the condition described as **mutualism;** (2) Benefits accruing to one partner without detriment to the other—a looser relationship, **commensalism;** and (3) Benefits accruing to one individual at the expense of the other—the feature of **parasitism.**

MUTUALISM. Only a smoothly working series of mutual adaptations has allowed the existence of the world's most numerous of large animals—the ruminant mammals, such as antelopes, bison, buffaloes, cattle, deer, gazelles, giraffes, goats, and sheep. These animals thrive on a diet of dry grass, only a minute fraction of which they can digest themselves. As was pointed out earlier (p. 218), they depend upon bacteria living in their digestive tracts, able (as the ruminant is not) to digest cellulose and some of the more complex proteins of plant food.

As is widely known, ruminants have a four-part stomach. Unchewed vegetation, swallowed while the herbivore is standing conspicuously exposed to attack by predators, accumulates in the first part—the **rumen** or paunch. Here it is mixed with a semi-liquid mass, rich with cellulose-splitting bacteria. Later, when the animal is concealed or at least lying down quietly and less obvious against the skyline, the inoculated food is transferred a lump at a time to the second section of the stomach (the "reticulum"). There it is formed into a ball, the **cud,** that can be regurgitated and chewed thoroughly, breaking the vegetable fibers and distributing

the bacteria intimately. After the food is swallowed again, fermentation continues through the third and fourth sections of the stomach and in the intestine. Indigestible residues are not discharged until the combined digestive action of bacteria and gut enzymes has worked on the food for three to ten days.

Except for green plants and the rumen bacteria, almost the only organisms that can digest cellulose form a special group of multiflagellated protozoans (p. 212) that are known only from the digestive tracts of certain insects—some termites, and a few kinds of wood-eating cockroaches.

L. L. Cleveland, of Harvard University, was able to kill the intestinal protozoans of termites without damaging the insects. He merely "defaunated" them—and they starved for nourishment while their digestive tracts became clogged with unusable wood fibers. With the protozoans restored, the termites lived normally again. Termite habits include several which insure a complete stock of the essential protozoans at all times. A termite, like any arthropod, loses its digestive lining and all contents whenever it molts. Promptly the termite acquires a new supply of protozoans through the characteristic and frequent sharing of food through regurgitation—typical of young and mature termites alike—and by eating fecal pellets which still contain living protozoans.

Our own digestive tracts harbor a considerable bacterial flora and protozoan fauna, even if parasitic worms and the like are absent. The degree to which these regular inhabitants of the digestive tract act as beneficial organisms is still under investigation. Many are no doubt properly termed commensal, but at least some are responsible for part of our ability to absorb Vitamin B complex chemicals from our food, and for our supply of Vitamin K.

The degree to which mammals may live without intestinal symbionts is under study at the University of Notre Dame. For these experimental animals to survive, they must receive a diet quite unlike the "normal" foods. Their absorption is remarkably complete. Feces are scanty and without odor, since bacterial putrefaction is absent. Complete protection from disease is matched by absence of all immunities, so that almost any microörganism can produce a fatal infection. Without disease, however, old-age symptoms appear and the experimental animals die "natural" deaths from malfunction. Their dead bodies do not decompose. Only a little self-destruction occurs, as a result of limited continuation of digestion in the gut.

Other examples of mutualism depend upon the photosynthetic abilities of unicellular algae. Several kinds of protozoans, of sponges, of coelenterates (including the "green Hydra"), and of flatworms maintain intercellular colonies of active algae. The enclosing member of the symbiotic pair furnishes protection and moves into illuminated areas whenever possible. The enclosed member (the alga) produces organic compounds which supplement or even take the place of food ingested by ordinary methods.

The giant Tridacna (Photo 98), largest of all clams, depends principally on symbiotic algae for its nourishment. Its digestive tract is somewhat degenerate, although some filter feeding does continue. But in the coral reefs of the South Pacific, the clam rests with hinge down, gape of valves up, and whenever covered with water by day, opens to spread its purple mantle edge in the sun. Algae within the superficial tissues there are not only illuminated directly, but minute flask-shaped bodies within the mantle surface diffuse the light below—increasing the depth of mantle wherein the algae can be efficient.

Mutualism is not restricted to the animal kingdom. Lichens are cooperating partnerships consisting of fungus and alga components (p. 229), the former supporting the latter in a terrestrial world, protecting the green cells from desiccation. The alga cells make food whenever water and sunlight are available simultaneously, and this food is the entire supply for both symbionts.

Pines, some other conifers, most of the heath family, and orchids generally, rely upon symbiotic fungus hyphae to take the place of root hairs in absorbing water and nutrients from the soil. These tracheophytes lack effective root hairs and cannot do without their **mycorrhizae**. The fungus, for its

part, gains sugars, amino acids, and the like from the larger plant. In terms of human interests, the successful growth of these trees and plants is dependent upon non-green soil organisms, and recognition of their role is important in providing proper conditions for commercial growth of those of value to man.

Leguminous plants, such as alfalfa, beans, clover, and peas, develop characteristic nodules upon their fibrous roots. Within the cells of these nodules are dense masses of the nitrogen-fixing bacteria Rhizobium. Similar nodules containing Rhizobium are found on alder roots and a number of other plants. In each instance the bacteria exhibit far more vigorous growth than where they are scattered in the soil. No doubt this is due to a more reliable supply of water and sugars in the root nodule. On the other hand, legumes with nodules grow more thriftily than those without, benefiting by the added supply of nitrogenous compounds made available by the bacteria. It has become good agricultural practice to mix living Rhizobium with leguminous seed, to insure good nodules and a vigorous crop.

COMMENSALISM. Usually this relationship is found where a small, unarmed animal associates with one that is vigorous or provided with weapons of some kind. Thus a fish that is relatively immune to the stinging cells of the large coelenterate known as the Portuguese man-of-war lives in the shelter of the spreading tentacles, gaining protection from them without particularly affecting the life of the floating man-of-war.

A small, round-bodied crab is met when some mussels or oysters are opened. This, the "pea crab," runs into the mollusk's incurrent siphon, and obtains shelter in the spaces of the mantle cavity. The crustacean is free to escape through the same opening, or it may remain within the clam for significant periods, feeding on the larger particles which enter in the feeding-breathing current.

Even the sharks have their associated fish —the shark sucker (Remora)—which has a highly modified dorsal fin that acts as a sucker and that allows Remora to attach itself to a shark (Photo 69). No harm is done to the shark but the shark sucker gets free transportation; when the shark catches a meal, the shark sucker frees itself long enough to pick

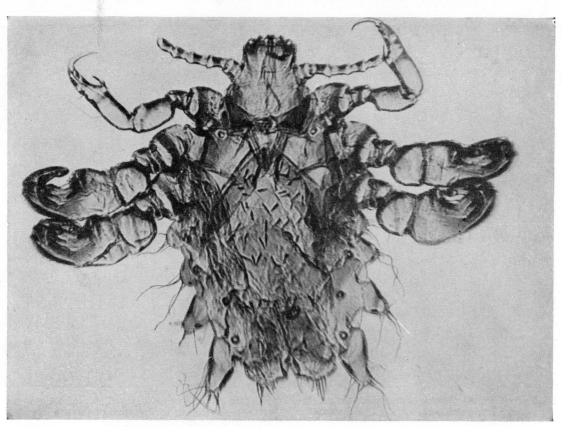

315. The crab louse, well fitted for clinging to hair in the pubic region.

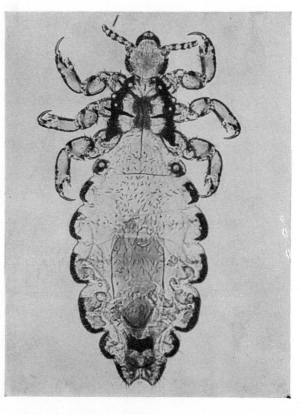

316. The head louse or "cootie," which is an important vector of diseases, also has hook-like claws with which to hold to hairs.

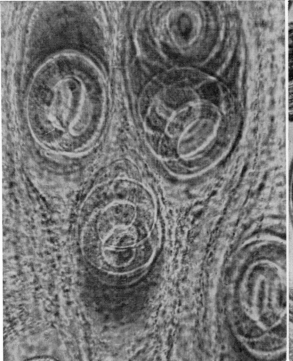

317. Trichinella, the pig and rat parasite that reaches man through uncooked pork, encysted in the muscles of a rat's diaphragm.

318. The same worms, digested out of their cysts, ready to develop in the intestine of the new host, reproduce there, and encyst once more.

Complex Life
Histories Adapt These
Worm Parasites
Affecting Man

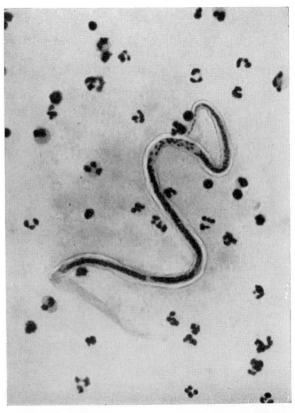

319. Filaria worms (Microfilaria) are large in comparison with human white blood cells but insect vectors have no difficulty swallowing them with a blood meal as a step in the transfer of elephantiasis.

up the scraps, and then returns to its "protector" and "provider."

PARASITISM. Adaptations permitting a small organism to live at the expense of a larger one can be considered as merely predation with the size relations reversed. The larger organism is the host, supporting the parasite.

Some parasites operate as **ectoparasites,** on the outside of the host's body. Others are **endoparasites,** entering and sustaining themselves at some internal position.

The parasite may have only a temporary dependence upon a host. This is true of the ♀ mosquito which must have a blood meal to make her eggs viable. The nonbiting ♂ requires only plant juices, as does the ♀ most of the time.

A few parasites can get along without a host, but develop more rapidly by parasitism. These are facultative parasites (from *facultas* = option, permission). Leeches are examples; they may behave as predators on snails and insects, or get nourishment faster by sucking blood from a vertebrate animal.

The opposite of a facultative parasite is one that depends entirely upon finding the right host. It is an obligate parasite (from the Latin *ob* = about, *ligare* = to bind—as in the verb *to oblige*).

Among ectoparasites, the louse, flea, tick, and leech are familiar. Most of them show remarkable adaptations for catching their hosts and for holding on while feeding (Photos 315-316). Thus fleas are able to perform great leaps through use of modified hind legs, and when hidden among fur or plumage, they make use of their flattened bodies to escape between the bases of hairs or feathers when the host is irritated into scratching. Lancet-like mouthparts enable fleas to break into the blood stream for their food. Lice, on the other hand, feed entirely on the dead skin, but they often irritate the host into breaking its own skin, leading to serious infections of other kinds. Ectoparasites in small numbers seldom cause any direct damage to the host organism, although they may transfer disease from one host to another, or be sufficiently annoying as to distract the host from important activities such as eating or reproduction.

It should be pointed out that parasites themselves are subject to parasitism; a parasite of a parasite is termed a **hyperparasite.** The series goes on and on.

Internal parasites demonstrate by far the most complex adaptations for food acquisition. Almost all of them are obligate parasites, and degeneration in structural details is accompanied usually by extreme specialization in life history. In general, internal parasites fall into two categories: those that live in and obtain their nourishment from the host's blood, and those that are found in the host's digestive tract, absorbing the host's food. Malaria, as an example of the former, was discussed on p. 214.

Parasites of the intestinal tract are extremely numerous in both total individuals and number of kinds. Since they must reach a position in the gut in order to gain their food supply, the adaptations shown are chiefly concerned with getting the host to swallow them. For the most part, these parasites not only have to eat, but have to be eaten. Simple or highly complex life cycles are involved in insuring that the parasite will be eaten—in order to eat.

Among the intestinal parasites with simple life histories, the organism causing amebic dysentery is a classical example (see p. 208). *Dysentery* comes from the Greek *dys* = bad, and *enteron* = gut, and describes the condition in a general way. Ingestion of drugs which will destroy the parasites without killing the host provide a means for recovery. Lacking such treatment, the victim may decline in general health to a point where some other, more fatal disease may invade and bring about the death of the host organism. In tropical areas where amebic dysentery is common, it is regarded as an important accessory toward the prevalent shortening of the human life span. Many of the intestinal worms act in the same vague way. They do not kill their hosts but merely lower their resistance to other diseases.

Malaria requires two hosts, amebic dysentery only one. Many intestinal parasites require at least two different organisms as hosts, although this necessitates added uncertainty in the life cycle, since one or the other host may fail to appear. Some tapeworms are good examples of the simpler sort of two-host gut parasite. The mature tapeworm is an intestinal parasite of vertebrates (Fig. 20-6). It consists of a specialized anterior end, the **scolex,** which has hooks or suckers (Photos 92, 93) or both, as anchoring structures that can attach to the duodenal wall. Behind the scolex is a linear series of flattened **pro-glottids,** each a complete individual, but produced from the scolex tip through asexual means similar to budding. The oldest pro-glottids are those farthest from the scolex; their sexual organs are mature. Those of the ♂ type liberate sperm cells into the gut contents, where they can swim to enter still older proglottids which have become ♀, and fertilize the many eggs. Proglottids with ripe eggs separate from the chain and are carried out with the feces. These are the details in the one host where sexual reproduction occurs.

The pork tapeworm is a familiar type which reaches mature lengths in the human intestine, such lengths being from six to 25 feet. If the infected human feces are eaten by man's domestic pig, development continues in the pig intestine to an immature stage which invades the intestinal blood vessels and is carried to muscle areas; there the immature tapeworms embed themselves and develop cyst walls around a resting stage—each a "bladder worm." If not blocked by a meat inspector, such pork may be poorly cooked, then eaten by man, releasing the cysts into the human digestive tract; each cyst develops into a new tapeworm. Obviously, where human feces are disposed of properly and pigs have no access to the material, the cycle is broken. Proper inspection of meat is likely to reveal infected pork. Thorough cooking of infected pork is enough to kill all of the bladder worms. Failing these, if tapeworms become established, therapy consists of oral administration of drugs that induce the worms to release their hold on the intestinal wall and of laxatives that sweep out the worms with the intestinal contents. Such remedies are called **vermifuges,** from the Latin *vermis* = worm and *fugere*

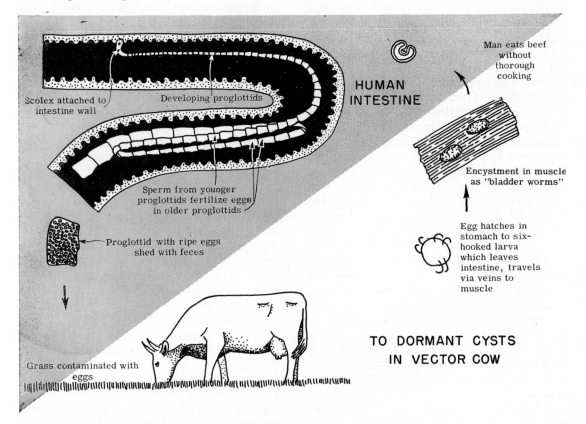

Scolex attached to intestine wall

Developing proglottids

HUMAN INTESTINE

Man eats beef without thorough cooking

Sperm from younger proglottids fertilize eggs in older proglottids

Encystment in muscle as "bladder worms"

Proglottid with ripe eggs shed with feces

Egg hatches in stomach to six-hooked larva which leaves intestine, travels via veins to muscle

TO DORMANT CYSTS IN VECTOR COW

Grass contaminated with eggs

FIG. 20-6. *The life history of the tapeworm, which man takes into his body with insufficiently cooked beef.*

= to flee. Actually, a few tapeworms do little or no significant damage to the host. The amount of food they require is small in comparison with that normally wasted by a well-fed individual. Unabsorbed foodstuffs which would otherwise appear in the feces nourish the worms instead. The largest, healthiest looking house cats frequently contain several of their own type of tapeworm or one of the others that can infect man.

The so-called fish tapeworm exhibits a life cycle involving three hosts, one of which may be man. The adult tapeworm thrives in the intestine of some mammal like a cat that eats raw fish, and it may reach a length of 33 feet. It should be remembered that these remarkable lengths represent the worm stretched out straight or wound around some measuring object. In the gut, the worm uses its muscular body wall both for absorption and also for gentle swimming movements that keep its

length well distributed in the small intestine, looped back and forth in the liquid chyme.

To continue toward another host, the proglottids of the fish tapeworm with their ripe eggs must be carried out with the feces and must get into water where there are both fish and the small crustaceans (copepods) on which they feed. The eggs in the water develop into immature stages swallowed by crustaceans and progress another step. If the crustacean is eaten by a fish, the immature tapeworms proceed farther in their development and encyst in the muscles of the fish. If the fish is eaten by a mammal while raw or inadequately cooked, the cycle is complete and a new lot of tapeworms develop in the carnivore. Fish tapeworms may have as many as 4,000 proglottids, but the

FIG. 20-7. *An American blood fluke which normally infests water birds, with pond snails as alternate hosts, occasionally enters human skin, producing "swimmer's itch" (schistosome dermatitis). The aquatic stages are shown at much greater magnification in this diagram; the larvae which invade vertebrate skin are actually microscopic, and the snails seldom over an inch in length.*

pork tapeworm is seldom longer than 1,000 such units.

To bridge the wasteful gaps in the normal life cycle, where chance is relied upon so heavily, the adult tapeworms must produce enormous numbers of eggs over as long a time as possible. Thus the statistical accident whereby the right combination of circumstances coincide for some of the offspring is made more probable, allowing the cycle to repeat itself. Hence the tapeworm must not cause significant decline in the health of its host. It must be an efficient parasite in achieving its reproduction based on food acquisition, without ruining its own future existence. Actually, most parasites are efficient in this sense. Only the relatively small number of kinds which sicken the host or which produce obvious symptoms attract attention and give parasites such a bad name. If the parasite causes disease, it is a pathogenic organism and exhibits extremely poor adaptation to its mode of life. Far more adjusted to the complexities of a parasitic existence are the efficient types which do a minimum of harm and which reach numerical abundance in a large proportion of the available host organisms without undue disturbance of the host's way of life.

Sometimes man becomes infected with parasites that do not ordinarily include a human host in their life cycle (Fig. 20-7). The other common parasite obtained from improperly cooked pork is an example. Trichinella is a roundworm, properly adapted for a two-host cycle between pig and rat. Pigs eat dead rats whenever possible, or slaughterhouse scraps and garbage containing encysted larvae, and in this way obtain the dormant stage of the trichina worm. The larvae liberated in the small intestine mature rapidly (Photo 318) and mate there. Females then burrow into the gut wall and produce larvae in enormous numbers (to 1,500 of them, each 0.1 mm long, per ♀). The larvae enter the lacteal spaces, reach the blood stream, and are carried to skeletal muscles. There each grows to about 1.0 mm in length at the expense of a single muscle cell, in which it coils up eventually and produces a cyst; this the host may impregnate

with lime, yet not disturb the encysted worm (Photo 317). Beyond this point the worms do not proceed unless eaten by another susceptible mammal—though they may await this event in a perfectly viable condition for many months. If rats can eat dead, infected pigs, the cycle is completed. Cats, dogs, and black bears—all of them scavengers with a liking for meat—can also enter into the life cycle. Man becomes involved by eating undercooked pork or bear steak, though in terms of the parasite's success, the infection of man is usually a complete loss—a blind alley because of ordinary methods of embalming and burial which either kill the cysts or which block transfer to another host.

Mild infections of Trichinella cause little damage, and one in every five people in the U.S. can be expected to have a few cysts—particularly in the muscles of the diaphragm. Heavy infections, however, produce serious symptoms (often attributed to arthritis), and even death; the disease is called **trichinosis.** In any case, muscle inflammation develops, with swelling and internal hemorrhage. Often the muscular tissue of the pericardium or the respiratory muscles is involved. At the moment the disease yields to no specific treatment but can be avoided by thorough cooking of meat—particularly pork and bear.

Many parasites are adapted to even more circuitous routes to the gut of their hosts. The hookworm, which is such a common human parasite in tropical areas, emerges as eggs in the feces, soon hatches and spends an active larval stage in and on the soil. This stage detects and attaches itself to mammalian skin (usually the bare foot), penetrates (commonly around the ankles) to enter the blood stream. The circulation returns blood plus parasites to the heart, thence to the lung capillaries, where the immature hookworms break through into the alveoli, get carried by the cilia-driven mucous currents up the bronchioles, bronchi, and trachea into the throat, where the larvae can be swallowed along with food to reach the small intestine. The chief problem in this life cycle is for the active larval stage to reach the right skin and enter before its small store of energy is exhausted. Vermifuges clear up infections, and proper sanitary precautions plus the wearing of shoes (and avoidance of contact between skin and soil) reduce the likelihood of infection. Severe infestations lower the resistance of the host, and the entry of the larvae into the alveoli opens channels for entry of disease organisms of more fatal sort.

The large roundworm of the human intestine, Ascaris by name, shows adaptations in its life cycle that can only represent a change of path with waste motion not yet eliminated. Ascaris has to be eaten, entering with food as an egg which hatches in the intestine but which cannot mature there. Instead the larva burrows into the blood stream, is carried to the lungs, follows the alveolar-tracheal route to the gullet, and back to the gut. Then it can mature! Why it is able to proceed toward sexual reproduction on the second arrival in the digestive tract but not on the first is a good puzzle. Parallelism with the route used by the hookworm suggests that Ascaris once used a different mode of attacking its host and that it still has the unneeded adaptive instincts for getting to the place where the food is. As a parasite it is not only well adapted but over-complicated. There is no other apparent explanation.

Sometimes the adaptations are not involved with the parasite being eaten by the primary vertebrate host, but by the secondary host, the vector. Such a case is characteristic of the roundworms called **filariae** (Photo 319), which so block the lymphatic circulation of man that they cause enormous enlargement, especially in the legs and scrotum. The disease they cause is called **elephantiasis.** This tropical danger is carried from one infected individual to another by mosquitos, and although only certain kinds of mosquitos can act as vector, various kinds are involved.

But mosquitos have habits with respect to feeding: some are day-feeders, some approach only at twilight or during the night. Yet whatever is the local habit of the vector kinds of mosquitos, the filariae adjust themselves in a matter of weeks to the time schedule. The filariae appear in the superficial circulation during the night if the local mosquitos are active at night, or appear during the day of the converse is true. If the local mosquitos are busy in the evening but not during the early morning hours, the filariae are soon adjusted

in their daily rhythm to be present in large numbers in superficial capillaries in the evening hours but not at other times. If the host moves from one locality to another with different mosquitos, the filariae soon adapt their activities to the timing needed for maximum use of available vectors. These adaptations are clearly related to the best interests of the parasite, but their cause is still unknown. Possibly some chemical substance in the salivas of the several different vector mosquitos provides the cue to which the rhythms become related.

Parasitology—the study of parasites—is largely an investigation of the complex adaptations shown by animals that get their energy by theft, by organisms that depend directly upon the numerical abundance of a host or hosts and that compensate for the hazards inherent in infecting new hosts by enormous reproductive activity. Of these potential individuals, only a few succeed in completing the life cycle, but it is on these exceptional individuals that the long-term welfare of the parasite depends. As in so many living things, the average individual dies young and with few progeny. It is the best adapted and statistically most fortunate organism on which continuation of each species must rely.

Serial Adaptations

Many animals show quite different adaptations at different stages in a continuous life cycle. Thus a mosquito egg hatches into a "wriggler" larva adapted in ways which permit it to hang head downward from the surface film of a pond, while breathing atmospheric air and at the same time maintaining a water current used in filter feeding (Photo 339). Later the same individual transforms into a "bullhead" pupa which floats at the surface except when not actively swimming downward; during this nonfeeding stage the organism develops structures of the flying adult—including specialized mouthparts and a functional reproductive system. The life history is a series of adaptations, changing abruptly from one set to another. Serial adaptations are thus characteristic of organisms with a metamorphosis. Metamorphosis itself is a remarkable adaptation. It achieves a division of labor between a feeding, food-storing stage and a reproducing, dispersing one (End-paper Photos N, T).

The adult stage of some insects is complicated further by adaptations that set apart a series of **castes.** Termites, ants, and bees are the prime examples. All are organisms which form colonies and provide shelter or food or both for the young. In all of them the colony includes not only ♂ ♂ and ♀ ♀ but additional types derived from genetic ♂ ♂ or ♀ ♀ through overspecialization in some directions and loss of sexual potentialities.

Ordinarily, a honeybee hive contains a single functional ♀—the queen. The drones (♂ ♂) develop parthenogenetically as haploids, from unfertilized eggs laid by the queen in response to an unknown stimulus in the hive. This stimulus coincides with overpopulation of the colony and development of new virgin ♀ ♀. Most of the colony are worker bees—sterile ♀ ♀ with a sting and instincts that lead them to keep the hive clean, build honeycomb, feed the maggot-like young (Photos 320-322), fan with their wings in maintaining circulation of air and optimum temperature, and make field flights for nectar and pollen. Food acquisition, defense, and care of the hive and its young, are thus relegated to a special, nonreproducing caste.

Among ants the arrangement is much the same, but additional castes may be present: "soldiers" with much-enlarged mandibles and spacious heads that accommodate the needed musculature, serving in defense of the colony; workers of two or more sizes, each with special instincts and capabilities. All of these extra castes are sterile ♀ ♀.

Among termites, the sterile castes include both sexes. Soldiers (Photo 34, central individual) may be supplemented by "nasutes" (from the Latin *nasus* = a nose), which bear a projecting nozzle on the back. This nozzle points forward and can be used to direct a stream of irritating acid on molesting ants or other animals.

Some of the differences in behavior between ant colonies and termites seem to arise from the fact that among ants the entire labor force consists of adults. Among termites, by contrast, the workers are the immature mem-bers of all castes. They molt periodically as they grow, and seem to lose at such times a large proportion of the conditioned reactions acquired during the previous stage.

Gall-inducing Animals

In addition to the many animals that eat plant leaves, bore in wood or root, suck plant sap, browse on pollen, quaff nectar, or ingest fruits, there is a special category that induces the plant to provide not only nourishment but a roof—a covering of highly characteristic form. They are animal parasites of plants (for the most part), and the host-parasite relationship is highly complex. In each instance, a chemical substance or substances produced by the animal acts as an irritant to the plant, causing a deviation from normal growth processes that in many ways resembles tumor formation. But usually the hypertrophy (called a **gall)** has a predictable size, shape, and detailed internal structure (Photos 323-327), so that it is possible by rather general examination of the plant to know what species of animal caused the abnormality and is (or was) inside.

Galls are not uncommon on a great variety of plants—usually as swellings of leaves or stems. Those on oak stems, with a tough, parchment-like exterior supported by radially arranged fibers around the central capsule, are often called "oak apples"; they are caused by a minute wasp which grows to mature size in the cavity at the heart of the gall (Photo 324). Another oak gall—so common on one species of European oak that the tree is called the *gall oak*—has been for many years the major source of the most important constituent of permanent inks for public documents, and is a regularly specified ingredient of formulas used by the U.S. Treasury, the Bank of England, and a number of other government agencies throughout the world. Still other galls in Asia Minor yield the dye "Turkey red." A different oak gall is a community product of small wasps which sting the leaf (Photo 323). Willows, too, are particularly susceptible to gall formers (Photo 325).

Galls are induced not only by certain insects, but also by some nematode round-worms and a variety of bacteria and fungi. The chemical induction of any structure so

320. Egg and larval stages to an age of nine days. The rapid growth shows how regularly the larvae are fed by the worker bees. Those in horizontal cells, fed one diet, become workers. Those in vertical cells, fed differently, become virgin queens.

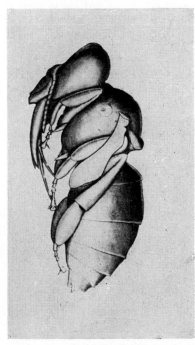

321. Pupa (drawing).

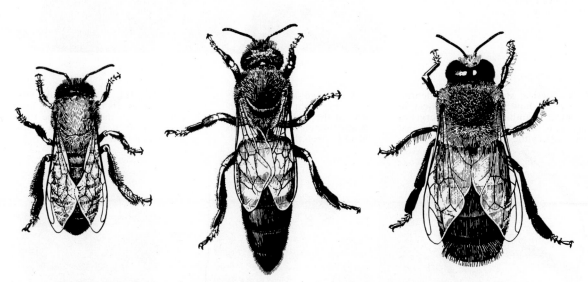

322. Workers (*left*) and queens (*center*) are ♀ ♀ developing from fertilized eggs. Drones (*right*) are ♂ ♂, from unfertilized eggs.

324. "Oak apples" produced on stems by a different wasp, with one larva per gall. These galls are more than an inch in diameter but the central chamber is small.

323. "Furry" red gall on oak leaf, cut to show chambers in which wasp larvae lived—a community dwelling.

PLANT GALLS INDUCED BY INSECTS

325. A willow crown gall sectioned to show the aborted terminal bud structure; a second with the leaves pulled away; and one of the flies that, as larvae, induced this growth as a community dwelling.

326. A normal goldenrod plant (*left*) and one with a crown gall (*right*).

327. A spherical stem gall of goldenrod sectioned to show the pupated insect in the central chamber and the emergence tunnel cut through the pith as a last preparation by the mature larva.

328. A goldenrod gallfly emerging from the trapdoor-way at the end of the emergence tunnel. It has used its head to open the door.

329. The fully expanded fly has pictured wings. Its body appears large by contrast with the emergence tunnel—an eighth-inch in diameter. The gall may be an inch across.

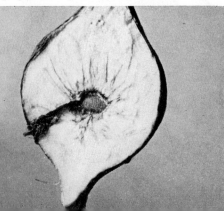

similar to a tumor or cancer is of the utmost biological and medical importance, but it is only within the last five years that anyone has succeeded in extracting from a gall insect any of the substances responsible—proving these chemicals to have such a function by applying them to the plant and eliciting the same response. The nature of the substance(s) is still

unknown. For the gall-inducing animal, the secretion of such a substance plus the adaptations in feeding habits for use of the gall tissue, involve complex changes of great significance in food finding, and hence indirectly in reproduction.

ANIMAL CALLS

When someone mentions animal calls, few think of the chest thumping of a gorilla or the drumming of a woodpecker on a tin roof. The stamp against the ground of a startled rabbit's hind feet and the simulation of a plucked string at the end of a nighthawk's plummeting dive are not noises which are typical of birds and beasts. Instead a normal call involves air passing through a confined place somewhere in the animal's throat. "Tongue and lung" have been the requirements for a voice ever since Aristotle discussed the subject twenty-three centuries ago. The sound may be the staccato bark of a dog or seal, the off-key caterwauling of a prowling puss, the whistle of a hungry groundhog or guinea pig, but it arises from taut cords vibrating in a blast of air forced from the lungs. It may take the form of a loon's eerie laughter, or the pilliwink-poddle, pollywog-poodle of a full-cropped robin on his sunset perch, but the song comes from well-controlled sinewy ridges in the bird's syrinx as air from its lungs sets up vibrations there, Or as an animal call we may remember the resonant chug-a-rumm of a big bullfrog, the trilling of toads, or the high-pitched peeping of an invisible chorus on a marsh in spring. These too are air passing back and forth from lungs to mouth, over bands that vibrate like reeds. Each vertebrate voice has this airy origin.

But among creatures that lack a backbone, sound-making takes on an entirely different form. Usually it corresponds to a fingernail run rapidly across the tips of a comb's teeth; stridulation is the correct name. Thus Ghost Crabs on the dry beach and in their tunneled hideouts, use a dozen short spines on the broad palm of their large pincer to produce a clearly audible sound. Holding the nipper close to the body, the crab rapidly raises and lowers the hand-like appendage so that the spines shuttle back and forth across a sharp ridge near the arm's base. The whole pincer vibrates vigorously in this rattling stridulation.

—LORUS J. MILNE *and* MARGERY MILNE, *A Multitude of Living Things* (New York: Dodd, Mead & Co., 1947), pp. 230-231.

SPIDER SILK

What a parachute is to an air-borne trooper, or a telephone to a lover, what tickertape is to a broker, or a blanket to a baby, so is spider silk to the spider. She has more uses for it than a cowboy for rope or an engineer for steel. Indeed, some of this exquisite gossamer is actually stronger than steel would be if drawn out to a filament of the same diameter—say, one one-thousandth of an inch.

But the engineer does not produce his steel girders out of his own body glands, nor can a falling airman create a parachute in his descent. Only a spider can do such things. To the spider, silk serves as a banqueting hall and a tablecloth, as a trapline and a foxhole, as a marriage bed and a winding sheet, as an alarm system and a fire escape, as handcuffs and a way of going places. It is the most versatile and marvelous substance produced by any living creature.

—DONALD CULROSS PEATTIE *and* NOEL PEATTIE, *A Cup of Sky*
(Boston: Houghton Mifflin Co., 1950), p. 139.

ECOLOGICAL EDUCATION

During every week from April to September there are, on the average, ten wild plants coming into first bloom. In June as many as a dozen species may burst their buds on a single day. No man can heed all of these anniversaries; no man can ignore all of them. He who steps unseeing on May dandelions may be hauled up short by August ragweed pollen; he who ignores the ruddy haze of April elms may skid his car on the fallen corollas of June catalpas. Tell me of what plant-birthday a man takes notice, and I shall tell you a good deal about his vocation, his hobbies, his hay fever, and the general level of his ecological education.

—ALDO LEOPOLD, in *Sand County Almanac* (New York:
Oxford University Press, 1949), p. 44.

SUGGESTED READING (see pp. 506-511)

Recent and Informative: Bonner, 1949; Cleveland, 1948; Dobzhansky & Murca-Pires, 1954; Farris, 1950; Hartman, 1950; Ladd & Tracey, 1949; Lyman & Chatfield, 1950; Milne & Milne, 1951, 1952; Needham, 1953; Riper, 1953; Storer, 1952; Williams, 1950.

21 · The Haunts of Life

1. BASIC HABITATS—MARINE LIFE, LITTORAL LIFE, FRESH-WATER LIFE, TER-RESTRIAL LIFE, LIFE IN ARID LANDS, PHYSIOLOGICAL DROUGHT. 2. BIO-GEOGRAPHY—AUSTRALASIAN SUPER-REALM, HOLARCTIC REALM, PALEO-TROPICAL REALM, NEOTROPICAL REALM. 3. LIFE ZONES—ARCTIC-ALPINE ZONE, BOREAL ZONE, AUSTRAL ZONE, TROPICAL ZONE. 4. SUCCESSION—AFTER VOLCANIC ACTIVITY, AFTER FIRE, AFTER MAJOR FLOODS. 5. AVOID-ANCE OF UNFAVORABLE LIVING CONDITIONS—DORMANCY, MIGRATION. 6. FOOD CHAINS. 7. ENVIRONMENTAL RESISTANCE. 8. BARRIERS AND BRIDGES. 9. EFFECTS OF LIFE ON ITS ENVIRONMENT—THE CARBON CYCLE, THE NITRO-GEN CYCLE, LIVING THINGS AS STABILIZING INFLUENCES, LIVING THINGS AS EROSIVE INFLUENCES.

MAN and his parasites seem to be distributed more universally than any other form of life. Most plants and animals are restricted rather definitely to certain geographical regions and, in these areas, to specific portions of the space available.

The study of the distribution of living things in terms that can be marked on a map is called **biogeography.** Major **realms** of the earth's surface are divided into **life zones** that show distribution in a general way, yet provide no underlying explanation.

Because animals depend ultimately on green plants for food, the distribution of animals is linked closely to the areas occupied by their food plants (Fig. 21-1). Plants, on the other hand, tend to be limited primarily by physical factors such as temperature, soil type, water availability, and sunlight.

If the distribution of plants and animals is examined in relation to environmental factors which influence it—whether physical factors or biological factors (such as food materials, predators, and parasites)—the study becomes detailed and more meaningful. It is **ecology** (from the Greek *oikos* = home), and includes consideration both of adaptations in relation to environment and of the effect of life on that environment. Ecological analysis lays stress on the precise situations (**habitats**—from the Latin for "it dwells") in which each kind of organism is normally found.

Each habitat has its own **community** of organisms—its plants and its animals. The type of vegetation with the largest volume of living protoplasm may be a unicellular alga, a grass, or a forest tree. But on these most abundant plants depend a smaller number and smaller protoplasmic volume of animals—all of them herbivores. On the herbivores prey a still smaller number of carnivores. Some one of a few large kinds of predator occupies a dominant position among the animals, as the least numerous, least preyed upon. Its position is the precarious peak of a **pyramid of numbers** (Fig. 21-2).

The abundance of the dominant predator is limited by the number of carnivores it can catch for food. The number of lesser carnivores depends on the supply of the more numerous herbivores, and upon the seriousness of attacks from the peak predator. The abundance of herbivores depends both on their ability to escape being eaten and on the supply of plant food available. The amount of plant food depends partly on conditions for growth and partly on the degree to which the herbivores destroy the vegetation. All of these relationships maintain a flexible equilibrium.

1. BASIC HABITATS

Organisms may be associated with water, as primarily aquatic types, or with land, as terrestrial plants and animals. The former may be subdivided according to whether the water is salty or fresh. Study of the life in marine situations is included in the field of

Plankton is the "grass of the sea" on which the small fish feed. They, in turn, either grow into or become food for larger fish (Fig. 21-2). The pyramid of numbers narrows gradually as size goes upward, until at the top there are a few dominant predators like

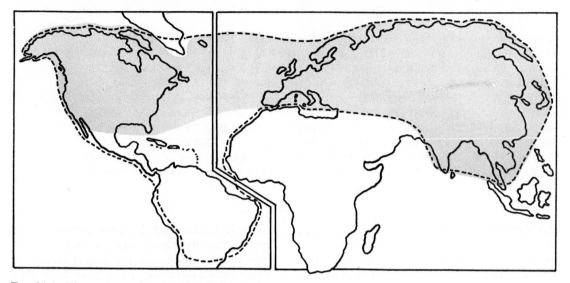

FIG. 21-1. *The correspondence in distribution between the aconite plant* (shaded) *and bumblebees* (broken line) *is too close to be coincidental. (Redrawn after Knuth, 1898.)*

oceanography. Corresponding studies in fresh water are called **limnology.**

Marine Life

In the open oceans, the smaller plants (chiefly algae) are suspended at depths to which the sun's energy can penetrate. Water movements carry these organisms passively from place to place. Together with the drifting microscopic animals, they are referred to collectively as **plankton** (from *plangktos* = wandering) and occur in unbelievable numbers. On these green plants depend a smaller number of animals, such as almost microscopic crustaceans (water fleas and the like). These small plant feeders are also remarkably numerous; they, too, have no means for directing their movements with respect to shore lines or other geographical features, and they are plankton too. Sometimes the terms *phytoplankton* and *zooplankton* are used to distinguish between the plant and animal components of this drifting type of life. That the largest animals of all—the great blue whales—subsist entirely on plankton indicates how rich is the supply.

sharks and sperm whales which prey on all smaller kinds but which have few enemies besides parasites and man. Since the fish may swim with definite directions related to their food supply or geographical features, they are spoken of as **nekton** (from *nektos* = swimming). The plankton form the food base not only for the nekton but also for a variety of animals crawling on or embedded in the bottom mud (such as clams and mussels or the various worms that are like them in using filter-feeding methods). Collectively, the bottom-dwelling life is referred to as **benthos** (from *benthos* = the depths of the sea).

Littoral Life

Plants that are aquatic—whether in ocean, lake, river, or inland sea—are classed as **hydrophytes.** Most of them, on a numerical basis, are free-drifting plankton. Others, in shallower water, are attached to the bottom if only as an adaptation that keeps them from being cast ashore by storms or washed downstream by each freshet. The physical environment of these plants is much more rigorous.

330. A combination of rocky coast with sandy bar at Bar Harbor, Maine. The bar is largely a mussel bed.

331. Closer view of the mussels and the barnacles that grow on them, and over which the mussels grow in turn.

332. A clamworm (Nereis) beside its burrow opening and castings on the mudflat at low tide.

333. A southern swamp with bald cypress hung with Spanish moss, in Georgia.

334. A temperate swamp in Pennsylvania.

335. A northern swamp with lodgepole pines in Alberta.

Currents and wave action tear at them; tides may expose them to sun and air; temporary lack of rain may allow the streams, ponds, or salt lakes in which they live to dry up, involving a lack of water over a much longer period. In winter, ice may grind them or the surfaces to which they are attached, acting as a tool with which the force of water movements is translated into enormous local pressures and shearing strains. The plants must be flexible and elastic (as are the many attached seaweeds), have firm holdfasts that can cling to wave-polished surfaces, and be resistant to desiccation and intense sunlight. That the largest aquatic plants (the giant kelps of the Pacific coast) live in this habitat, and that the rocky coasts of the world are festooned with seaweeds that thrive under such harsh conditions, indicate both the degree of adaptation possible, fitting them for the environmental conditions, and also the advantages to be gained from shallower water and the greater intensity of sunlight and availability of respiratory or photosynthetic gases there. The organisms of the shoreline are often referred to as **littoral** (from the Latin *litus* = a shore).

Sudden changes in salinity are common in littoral habitats. Most organisms that thrive there tolerate these chemical alterations in their environment. Drought on land decreases the size of rivers enough to let their estuaries become more salty. Each rainy period operates in the opposite direction. A severe storm may build a barrier beach and isolate a lagoon. A later storm may suddenly breach the land barrier.

Ordinarily these changes have only small long-term effects. One of wider importance became evident in America in the summers of 1930-31, and has received extended study ever since. The fundamental change was the near extermination of a flowering plant called "eelgrass" (*Zostera marina*) through a "wasting disease" caused by a slime mold.

Normally eelgrass is abundant in brackish water where wave action is not too violent—for example in bays and estuaries at depths to 10 or 15 feet. Eelgrass is a substrate for fish (Fig. 21-2) and a basic requirement for large populations of crabs, mollusks, geese, ducks, and other bird species. The brant, for

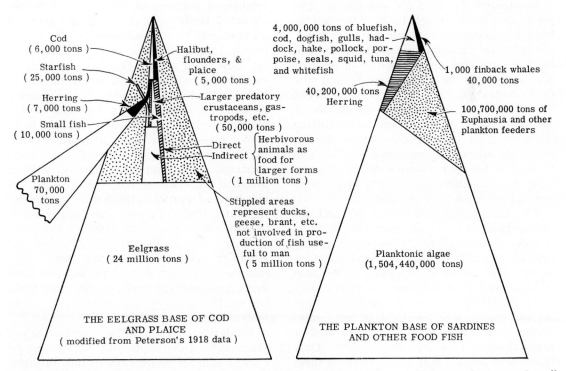

FIG. 21-2. *Pyramids of numbers always rest on a broad base of green plants, which trap the energy for all members from the sunlight falling on sea or land.*

example, depends on eelgrass for 80 per cent of its food.

When the "wasting disease" struck the Atlantic coast of America in 1930-31, it destroyed as much as 90 per cent of the eelgrass. By 1934, as a direct sequel, the continent's population of brant had fallen to about 20 per cent of its former size, and this goose-like bird no longer was available to be the favorite wild-fowl of New England diners. Coastal fishes, such crustaceans as crabs, and such mollusks as scallops, diminished rapidly.

Slowly the eelgrass is returning, and so too are the crabs, scallops, and brant. The effect on the already dwindling numbers of coastal fish may be more extended. Continuing investigations point to changes in salinity and perhaps also in water temperature as the conditions which control the virulence of the parasitic slime mold. It seems less well adapted than its host organism to the hazards of littoral life. Decreased salinity and cooler coastal waters appear to hold it in check. Changes in the opposite directions lead to epidemics.

Because of the need for sun energy, few plants live deep enough to be described as benthic. Benthic animals, on the other hand, can thrive on plankton brought down to them by water currents, or the bodies of animals and plants from the nekton that die and sink to the bottom. Even at the greatest depths of the ocean there are animals—predators of various types that depend on meals sinking down to them through the sunless depths. Many are adapted in ways that enable them to swallow for later digestion relatively enormous meals; another opportunity may not be met again for weeks or months.

The demarcation between aquatic and terrestrial habitats is abrupt where the shoreline is rocky, but elsewhere it is vague. A coastal mudflat or sand spit may be flooded by the highest tides (Photos 330-332) or by each stiff on-shore wind or storm. Through it may wind the estuaries of creeks and rivers that fill and empty with the tides or with rainstorms inland. The salt content of the mud or sand changes radically and rapidly. Only plants and animals that are adapted to these alterations can thrive in such a habitat. In tropical and subtropical areas, mangroves (Photo 259) cover the mudflats and extend on slender, multiple "knees" into the shallow water. To their knees cling oysters that are immersed at high tide, exposed at low. Between the knees run crabs of many kinds, scavenging the mudflat and feeding on dead animals or those that have been torn from their attachment places and washed ashore by waves.

Fresh-water Life

Fresh-water situations are more fully occupied by plants, probably because the tidal and salinity changes are absent. Littoral hydrophytes include some that float (such as duckweed and water hyacinth), some that are submerged (the pondweeds), some that are anchored in the bottom but extend leaves into air (such as rice, bulrush, cattail, and in the South, bald cypress), and a few with roots in the bottom but floating leaves (such as water lilies). Those extending leaves into the air are described as **emergent** types of vegetation, and the degree to which they are aquatic varies with the season—with the amount of water in the pond or stream (Photos 333-335). To the submerged surfaces of these littoral hydrophytes of fresh water cling a great variety of microscopic plants—particularly the thallophytes (algae, diatoms, and the like)—and on these feed a remarkable assortment of smaller invertebrates. This is the habitat of Volvox (Photo 140), amebas, Hydra, dragonfly nymphs, diving beetles, and many other animals available in sufficient numbers to be used in class study as "typical" representatives of their particular portions of the animal structural plan and classificatory scheme. Many of the insect members of this community have adaptations allowing them to pierce the water film to breathe atmospheric air or to walk on the film itself (Photos 336-339). And on the small invertebrates (or the adults of aquatic insect young that emerge into the air above) depend the fish and frogs that are themselves food for watersnakes and herons. Ducks may either feed directly on the invertebrates or use the plant material itself.

Fresh water is more turbid than the sea and green algae (almost its only algae) can get enough light for photosynthesis only in superficial layers. Deep waters receive only one or

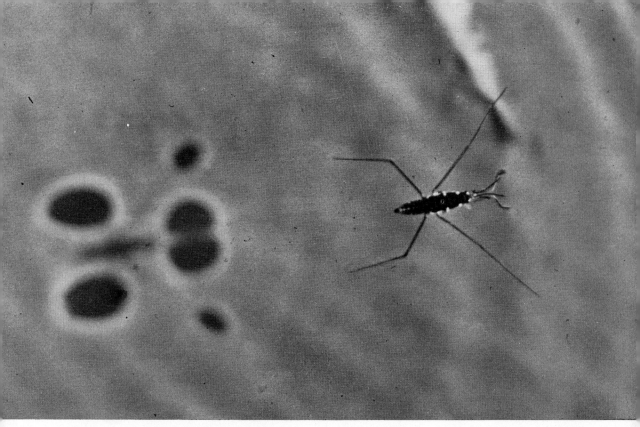

336. A water strider in sunlight casts dark shadows on the bottom, because of the distortion of this sunlight by the dimples in the water film around the insect's feet.

WALKERS ON THE WATER FILM

337. When seen from a low angle, the strider's own reflection in the water film adds point to the distorted surface below the dry-shod feet.

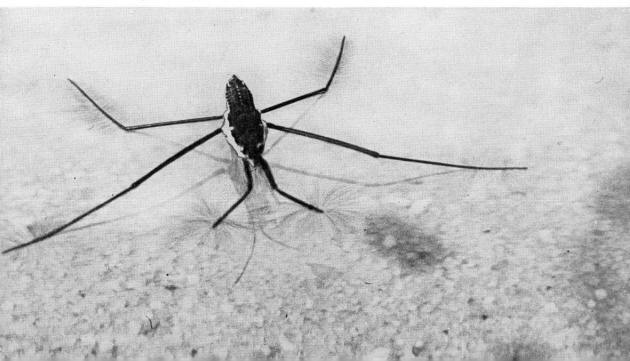

338. The giant "electric-light bug" (Belostoma) extends two long filaments from the abdominal tip to break through the surface film and inhale air.

339. A mosquito wriggler presses a special extension of its dark breathing tubes through the surface film, and rests in this position— supported by a whorl of water-repellent hairs —while taking on a new supply of air.

AQUATIC INSECTS WHICH MUST HAVE ATMOS- PHERIC AIR TO BREATHE two aerations annually (Fig. 21-3), and life at their bottoms is primarily anaerobic.

Running water has its own vegetation and life. Most of it clings to the bottom or burrows within the surface layers. Actually, the bulk of a river may be fairly free of organisms. But where the current is reduced by friction against banks or bottom, the number of living things is often surprisingly great. Even the crashing waters of the rapids just above Niagara Falls are rich in plant and animal inhabitants. The latter often emerge as adult insects in fantastic numbers, and fly to the street lights of Buffalo and adjacent cities, dying there in windrows. Some Buffalo residents even have the questionable honor of possessing a unique allergy—a sensitivity to the hairs from the wings of certain caddisflies whose young thrive by the billions in the rapids of the Niagara River.

Even the splash of water—spray from breaking waves, or the gusty mist from a

waterfall—provides an aquatic habitat which is ideal for mosses and various algae, and for the worms and insect young that feed on them. The niche may be only a fraction of an inch in thickness but may extend over enough area to support a considerable population. In the western mountain regions of North America, where streams with waterfalls and stone-filled rapids are particularly numerous, the animal population of the niche is large enough to support the water ouzel (dipper), a bird that flits or slips on foot from wet boulder to alga-covered rock to feed and find nourishment for itself and young. This bird even runs into the shallower rapids to seize insect larvae from the rocks to which they cling, and it often builds its nest in the space under a waterfall, between the tumbling water and the precipice over which it leaps. The name "dipper" is applied because of the bird's

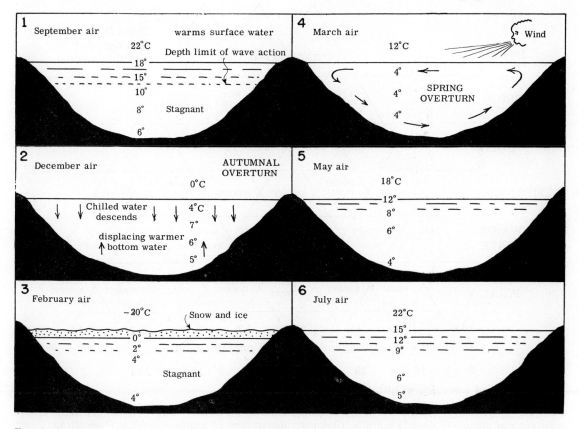

Fɪɢ. 21-3. *The anomalous peak of density shown by water at 4° Centigrade is responsible for the turnovers that aerate lakes to their very bottoms twice a year.*

curious habit of bending its knees briefly at intervals in a sort of curtsy.

Terrestrial Life

Away from standing or running water, hydrophytes do not grow well. Other types of plants, however, can thrive without buoyant support—in spite of winds, of wide variations in availability of moisture from season to season, of sudden temperature changes, and (in many parts of the world) of freezing conditions for portions of the year.

The prime factors determining what kinds of adaptations are helpful in any given site are temperature during the growing season, and availability of moisture then. These factors are linked. If the temperature is low, little water evaporates. If the temperature is high, the same amount of precipitation may

vanish from the soil by evaporation within a few hours or days (Fig. 21-4).

In temperate latitudes and altitudes, 20 inches of rain annually will support grasslands, and 40 inches a forest cover. Plants which thrive under these conditions are described as **mesophytes** since they require a "medium" amount of water (from *meso* = middle). They must have a fairly continuous supply, yet usually they will not tolerate soil that is saturated and hence almost devoid of air. Associated with these familiar kinds of vegetation are the most familiar animals.

Where the rainfall is less than 20 inches annually, only persistent cold weather can retain enough moisture for plant activity. At low temperatures, growth is retarded and moisture requirements reduced. Even so, arctic plants show many adaptations helping them conserve water against evaporative loss. All plants thriving where moisture is less

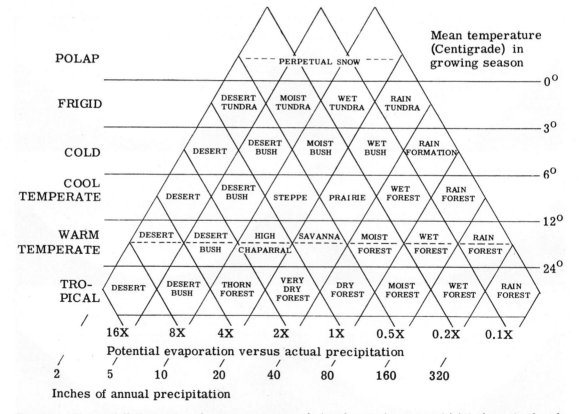

FIG. 21-4. *The rainfall* (bottom) *and mean temperature during the growing season* (right) *determine largely what kinds of plants will grow in a region. Customary descriptions of weather—polar to tropical* (left)—*are much more vague. The ratio between potential evaporation and actual precipitation is affected by temperature and, in turn, affects the amount of moisture available to plants in an area. (After Holdridge.)*

340. A prickly pear cactus (Opuntia) in western Texas. The sulfur-yellow blossoms result in scarlet, spine-studded fruits containing much sugar. Man may use them in making cactus candy, which has a delicate and distinctive flavor.

341. An Arizona plain, with cat's claw (ocotillo—*left*), cactus, and a flowering spike of century plant (Agave). Note the wide spacing between the plants, produced by competition for water by roots underground.

342. A forest of giant saguaro cactus in central Arizona. The man on the stepladder is inspecting the nest of a large woodpecker which carves out a cavity within these cacti. When saguaros fall and disintegrate, the scar tissue around a woodpecker nest is often the most resistant part.

VEGETATION OF THE ARID SOUTHWEST

343. A good stand of pine where water supplies are slightly better in central Texas. (Bastrop State Park, near Austin.)

344. Throughout the western states, from Canada into Mexico, are many species of horned toads (lizards of the genus Phrynosoma). They inhabit areas where the summer temperature rises for significant parts of the day into the range from 95 to 103 degrees Fahrenheit. At this temperature the lizards are most active, but a further rise of a few degrees may be fatal to them unless they can find shelter in cooler earth. Horned toads are known from Death Valley (below sea level) to 9,000 feet elevation, and the Texan species has been introduced successfully into the Carolinas and Florida.

345. The Texan horned toad alertly watches for an ant to come within snapping distance. (See Photo 233.)

346. An Arizona horned toad with some of its recently shed skin. (See also Photo 232.)

available show many adaptations in common, and are described as **xerophytes** (from the Greek *xeros* = dry; pronounced zeer'o-fyts).

If the rainfall is more than 40 inches annually and the temperature is higher, vegetation reaches luxuriant proportions (Photos 384, 385). The tropical rain forests represent a peak in this direction. Temperate rain forests, such as those rimming the coasts and first slopes of the state of Washington, parts of Oregon and British Columbia, are not far behind. In fact, conditions for life are so close to ideal in terms of the physical environment that the adaptations shown by plants and animals in these areas are chiefly ones related to feeding, to prevention of being fed on, and similar "social" interrelationships.

Where the humidity is regularly high, plants even grow on top of others as **epiphytes,** gaining advantage from their perches in being exposed to more light (Fig. 21-5). Their presence may do the supporting plant no appreciable harm or, as so often happens with Spanish moss and "air plants" (both bromeliads of the pineapple family), their growth may shade and weight down the vegetation over which they grow until the support is weakened or rendered an easy victim for disease. In the tropics, orchids are chiefly epiphytes. In temperate zones, mosses, ferns, and lichens occupy this site on a smaller scale.

Life in Arid Lands

Since all protoplasm requires water for activity, and photosynthesis depends upon the material as a chemical substrate, adaptations of green plants to arid situations are especially interesting. Dry seasons may be bridged in a variety of ways:

1. AVOIDANCE OF THE DRY SEASON— achieved by many small plants which become active only at the onset of the annual rains (even when this event does not occur every year). After a good rain or two, the seeds of these plants germinate, acquire a foothold in the soil, send up a disproportionately short stem, large flower, and set seeds—all before the ground dries out again. Almost overnight the desert can burst into bloom with such plants, and then in a week or two no living sign of them remains. Only their seeds await the next rainy period. Botanists refer to such

plants as "ephemeral annuals" (from the Greek *ephemeros* = for a day). The percentage of ephemeral annuals in the flora increases in proportion to the aridity.

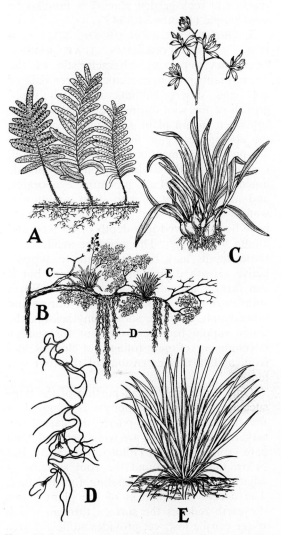

FIG. 21-5. *Representative epiphytic plants include ferns (A), orchids (C), Spanish moss (D), and "air plant" bromeliads (E). At (B), several of these epiphytes are shown in customary positions.*

2. STORAGE OF WATER—achieved by enlargement of cell vacuoles, reduction in the size of intercellular spaces, a low transpiration rate, and other modifications that are associated with **succulence.** These plants swell rapidly when moisture is available, and gradually shrivel during the dry period as they

lose and use their water store. Succulence in stems (as in cacti of America and the cactus-like spurges of Africa) and in leaves (as in the century plant and various favorite house plants and rock garden plants) is familiar to most people (Photos 340-342).

3. GREAT EXTENSION OF THE ROOT SYS-TEMS PLUS MECHANISMS THAT REDUCE TRANSPIRATION LOSS—characteristic of the larger number of nonsucculent perennials of arid and desert habitats. Through rapid growth of the root during the initial wet sea-son when such a plant germinates from seed, the absorptive region may keep up with the downward movement of water through the soil, keep ahead of the drying region that spreads downward as surface moisture evaporates, and maintain contact with deep supplies of water throughout the year. Mesquite roots have been followed to a depth of 65 feet, and alfalfa to 129 feet. The moisture available at these depths may be inadequate to support active growth during the dry season, but it can furnish enough to allow survival. When supplemented by surface moisture during and immediately after the short rainy season, the water supply becomes sufficient for sudden development of new foliage, of flowers and fruit, and further extensions of the root sys-tem.

Only a relatively small portion of the non-succulent perennial xerophyte is exposed at the surface. This may puzzle the casual ob-server since the plants are widely spaced, with bare ground between (Photos 341, 342). But below the bare ground the root systems of adjacent plants are competing for moisture. The deceptive smallness of the plant above the earth reduces the surface through which water can be lost, yet provides sufficient area to the intense daily illumination for photo-synthesis. The leaves may be reduced to spines like those of cacti; be dropped during the dry season as in cat's claw (ocotillo); or may die and then remain in place as a mulch that protects the buds at the soil surface, as in many grass-like herbs. In others, the leaves are waxy (as in creosote bush) or heavily cutinized (as in piñon pine) and remarkably stiff. They retain this stiffness even when wilted, preventing the mechanical exchange

of gases through bending of the leaf in a dry wind. The stomata may be sunken in pits and even plugged with wax temporarily dur-ing the dry season. Most such plants can tolerate a reduction in water content that would be fatal in a mesophyte. Creosote bush leaves, for example, survive desiccation to a water content equal to 50 per cent of their dry weight, whereas loss to within two to six times this value is "permanent wilting" that brings death to most mesophytes.

The animal life of the desert areas depends for its moisture as well as its food upon the xerophytic vegetation. The insects that bore into the succulents or imbibe their juices through sucking mouthparts become food for the rodents, reptiles (Photos 344-346), and birds. The rodents may gnaw on the plants or eat their fruits and seeds, but the carni-vores—though few—gain this water and nourishment at severalth hand. In flowering season, the plants squander their store of recently-acquired moisture both in growth of reproductive parts and in nectar that attracts insects and hummingbirds for a brief rush of activity. In the rainy season and immediately after, the desert is a busy place. Even snails make their appearance, emerging from hiding places in the soil to creep about and feed on the plants. Yet when the moisture is used up again, these mollusks conceal themselves, withdraw into their shells, and seal off the entrance. They go into a dormancy called **estivation** (from the Latin *aestas* = summer), with a reduction in metabolic rate and re-quirements in food and moisture that cor-respond closely with hibernation in over-wintering animals.

Physiological Drought

In addition to the arid areas of the earth, there are several other habitats in which it is difficult for plants to obtain water, and where xerophytic adaptations are of great value. They may be said to be physiologically dry.

1. REGIONS WHERE THE SOIL HAS A HIGH CONTENT OF SOLUBLE SALTS—such as the sandy shores of an ocean, or the land sur-rounding inland lakes and seas with no outlet (where evaporation takes care of all the water received from streams and rivers). Here the soil moisture is so high in salt content that it has a higher osmotic pressure than the cell sap

THE VENUS' FLYTRAP IS
A SPECTACULAR INSECTIV-
OROUS PLANT OF A SMALL
COASTAL AREA IN THE
CAROLINAS

347. Several rosettes of leaves with flower stalks. Smaller plants are more numerous and less conspicuous in the grass. The leaves are bright green. often with a reddish tinge.

348. A fly alights on the shiny, sticky-appearing surface of the outstretched leaf and accidentally brushes the six short trigger hairs.

349. Within a second the leaf closes. The initial movement is rapid enough to capture a large insect, but small ones still have a chance to escape. Then the leaf will open again in a few hours.

351. Indigestible residues are exposed to dry and blow away, leaving the trap ready for another victim. Note that the bristles along the edges of the leaf have curled out of the way. The leaf gradually opens wide—improving the chance that a breeze will clear it of debris.

350. With a large victim, the leaf intermeshes the stiff bristles along the two edges, and gradually applies the inner surfaces to the insect's body. Digestive juices are secreted, and nitrogenous products of disintegration are absorbed. Then the leaf may open again.

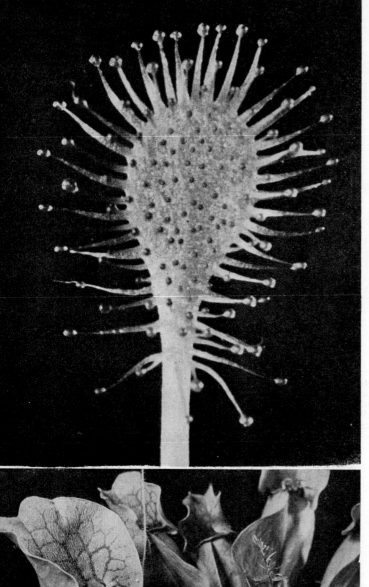

352. The glandular hairs on a leaf of round-leaved sundew glisten enough to attract insects, cling tightly to victims, wrap around them and secrete digestive enzymes, then absorb the products of breakdown. These leaves are spread in rosettes around the upright flower stalk.

353. A rosette of northern pitcher plant leaves in a cranberry bog. Melting snow and rain partly fill the pitchers and form a trap for insects. A small cluster of peat moss (Sphagnum) shows at the lower right.

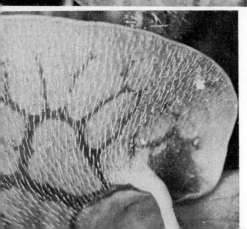

354. Close-up of a pitcher lip, showing the down-curved bristles that prevent insects from creeping upward, away from the rain water in which others have drowned and disintegrated.

355. A group of southern pitchers. The lids keep some rain from entering and in this way compensate for the heavier, more frequent downpours characteristic of these regions.

of ordinary plants and is strictly toxic through overabundance of some definite chemical substance(s). Plants that thrive under such circumstances must have means for excluding the salty environment and for obtaining their water and minerals plus nitrogen in other ways. Many of them are succulents, with

characteristically small root systems—mere anchoring structures. Those along sea coasts, moreover, are specialized in that they absorb their moisture from the humid air, and most of them die quickly of desiccation if the humidity remains low for any considerable period. Some have become so adapted to excluding water of any type from their roots that when transplanted inland and furnished adequate nontoxic soil moisture, they fail to use it and die in the drier air.

2. REGIONS WHERE THE WATER IS RICH IN TOXIC TANNINS AND OTHER ORGANIC POISONS —such as in and around peat bogs. Here the peat moss (Sphagnum) grows chiefly by pressing the older dying parts of the plant deeper into the water. The tips are green; they branch and grow, gradually spreading over the pond as a soggy, floating mat of vegetation. In a few centuries the accumulated mass may not only roof the lake but also fill it with waterlogged debris. Tannins and other chemical substances leached from the dying moss make it acid and reduce decay; they also keep down the number of other plants that can invade the quaking bog. A few evergreens, such as black spruce, deciduous conifers including tamarack, plus an assortment of leathery-leaved xerophytic shrubs like cranberry, poison oak (Rhus), Labrador tea, and bog laurel, do well. This is the habitat in which insectivorous plants (Fig. 21-6) thrive while getting their nitrogen from the decaying bodies of insects that fall into the vase-like leaves (pitcher plants) to drown in rain water there, or adhere to the glandular hairs (sundew). In each instance the plant secretes digestive enzymes and absorbs the products from breakdown of the insect bodies (Photos 347-355).

3. REGIONS WHERE THE SOIL IS CHIEFLY COARSE SAND OR GRAVEL—where the rain soaks through, getting quickly beyond all but the deepest root systems—such as along the shorelines of lakes (modern or ancient). The little organic material at the surface decomposes; the basic components are leached out and washed away, leaving a distinctly acid soil. In this the spruce, firs, and hemlocks thrive with relatively little competition in the northern belt across the country, whereas

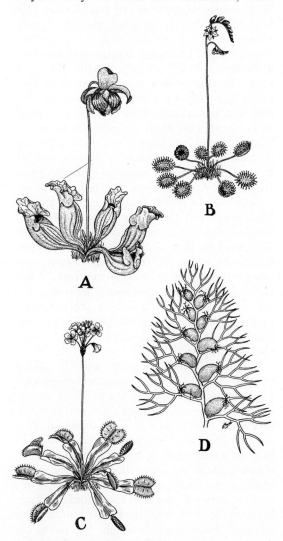

FIG. 21-6. *Pitcher plants (A) drown insects and frogs in water collected by their vase-like leaves (see also Photos 339-342). Sundews (B) capture insects on glandular tentacles (Photo 339). The Venus flytrap (C) has leaves which can snap shut on an insect or spider in less than a second (Photos 334-338). The aquatic bladderwort (D) bears small bag-like chambers the door to which opens suddenly when stimulated externally, and the chamber enlarges quickly, sucking in any small crustacean or insect larva. In each case the plant digests victims and absorbs amino acids as the chief source of nitrogenous compounds.*

farther south sugar maple, beech, yellow pine, introduced Australian "pine" (Casuarina—Photos 356, 357), and redwood take their place. In the northern phase of this habitat, fallen needles often accumulate to a depth of a foot or more, and may stifle seedlings to such an extent that the forests do not perpetuate themselves and invasion of them by other plants is very difficult. The southern ·phase, however, includes plants that return more basic organic materials to the soil, and the fertility does not deteriorate so regularly. Taken together, these soil conditions match the adaptations of our most conspicuous forests. Their value in agriculture is far less. They are the home of squirrels, bears, porcupines, and a host of other animals.

4. REGIONS OF BARE ROCK OUTCROPPINGS —such as on the almost vertical faces of recent mountains, where the drainage is perfect. In such sites a plant can get moisture from humid air or from direct rain, but not otherwise. Lichens of the several types (Photo 156), and, if shaded, mosses and ferns in little pockets of soil that accumulate from lichen decay and from dust settling, gradually pave the way for herbs and even hardy trees. With each winter, water seeps farther into cracks. It freezes and expands with force sufficient to extend the crack and to provide more space for soil, for plants with their roots, and for water that will freeze the following year. The animal population of these niches is extremely small. The frontier conditions are too precarious to support both a flora and a fauna.

2. BIOGEOGRAPHY

On a larger scale, the plants and animals of the world are limited not only by availability of water and by soil conditions, but even more by temperature and exposure. Periods when the soil is frozen and when plants above the ground are in a state of minimum metabolism for life become longer and harsher as one approaches the poles of the earth or ascends high mountains. Temperatures day and night and throughout the year become much more uniform the nearer one gets to the equatorial zone and to sea level. Adaptations which allow organisms to survive the temperature changes in a day or in a year in latitudes remote from the tropics or at altitudes high above sea level are found in many plants and animals, but the number with adequate adaptations in these directions decreases rapidly as the changes become more severe. As a result, the number of kinds of animals increases significantly as one travels from pole to equator, though the total number of individuals of each kind may show a corresponding decrease. The same is true in descending a mountain of considerable height. But on a map, the distribution of temperature is governed not only by latitude and altitude but also to a remarkable degree by the proximity to or remoteness from large bodies of water. These latter have such a profound influence that the weather in Kansas in January reaches lower temperatures than in the Aleutian Islands of Alaska, while the July maximum temperature in North Dakota exceeds that of Mississippi and Louisiana along the Gulf of Mexico. Ocean currents and prevailing winds also affect the picture. The latter, for example, bring wet warm air from over oceans onto continental slopes, causing heavy rain. When the same air, minus that much moisture, descends on the opposite side of the mountain range, it is a cool, dry wind that creates desert conditions through absence of rain and excessive desiccation.

To these climatic features must be added another factor of even greater complexity. Each organism, in expressing its biotic potential, spreads gradually over the territory available until it is limited in each direction by a barrier. The barrier may be excessive summer heat or winter chill, a mountain range or an ocean gulf, a waterless desert or the mere absence of suitable food. But during the recent history of the earth, mountains have been made and leveled; temperatures have changed from warm enough for palms in Alaska to cold enough for glaciers in Pennsylvania; the inroads of the sea have fluctuated widely, and lands now desert have been lush with vegetation, and conversely. The barriers are not permanent, and in the history of plants and animals there have been opportunities for spread that were temporary but adequate. These aspects of geologic history explain much of the present distribution of the world's flora and fauna (Fig. 21-7).

356. For decorative use and windbreak planting in the warmer parts of the United States, the "Australian pine" (Casuarina) is often employed. It is not a gymnosperm but a flowering plant.

357. The "leaves" of Casuarina are actually jointed, needle-like stems with true leaves as minute bracts at the joints. The fruits open like little cones to discharge winged seeds. The parallelism in form between this genus and the true pines is remarkable. Both are adapted to physiologically dry regions.

358. The dingo (dog) was introduced by man and is a placental exception.

MOST WILD MAMMALS OF AUSTRALIA ARE MARSUPIAL EQUIVALENTS OF PLACENTAL TYPES FOUND ELSEWHERE

359-360. Kangaroos in New South Wales.

361-362. Koalas in Healsville Sanctuary where their favorite types of gum leaves are available in quantity.

Evidence indicates clearly, for example, that Australia and the nearby islands, more than any other region, have been isolated from the rest of the land masses of the world. It is one of the marvels of biogeography—for in this area are found virtually no placental mammals (except bats, which fly in and out). Instead the marsupials (Photos 359-362, 364) have invaded niches normally filled by placentals, so that there are pouched mice, pouched moles, pouched anteaters, and pouched wolves as well as kangaroos, wallabies, koala "bears" and cuscuses, phalangers and wombats, bandicoots, and many more without equivalent. In addition are the egg-

laying mammals, found nowhere else—the duckbill (Photo 363) and the spiny anteater. Birds include an assortment of flightless types (cassowaries and emus on the mainland, kiwis on New Zealand and nearby islands) and other oddities such as birds of paradise, mound builders, and lyre birds (Photos 365-367). Actually, the islands around Australia are almost devoid of birds except for sea birds, and the mammal, reptile, and amphibian populations are negligible. Poisonous elapine snakes occur on Australia and the largest islands, and the tuatara (Sphenodon—Photo 430—the only living representative of

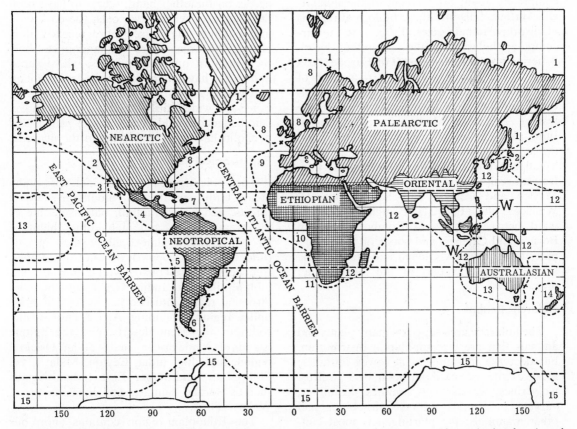

FIG. 21-7. *The biogeographical realms of the world as indicated by land organisms* (shown by hatchure) *and by shore life* (numbered areas). *Similarity between the Nearctic and Palearctic forms has led to inclusion of both in the Holarctic realm. The Ethiopian and Oriental regions similarly comprise a Paleotropical realm. South and Central America form a Neotropical realm. Wallace's Line, separating the Paleotropical and Australasian faunas and floras is indicated by W—·—W. The shore organisms group themselves into:* 1. Arctic; 2. Temperate Northwest American; 3. Transition; 4. Pacific Tropical American; 5. Peruvian-North Chilean; 6. Antiboreal South American; 7. Atlantic Tropical American; 8. Atlantic Boreal; 9. Mediterranean-Atlantic; 10. Tropical West African; 11. South and Southwest African; 12. Tropical Indo-West Pacific; 13. South Australian; 14. New Zealand; 15. Antarctic.

the order Rhynchocephalia) occupies precarious niches on the islands surrounding New Zealand. Like the egg-laying mammals, it has no counterpart elsewhere in the world. Sphenodon interests biologists not only because it is a "living fossil," but also because in it the pineal body has an eye-like form and a light-sensitive function. Australia has a lungfish—one of the few remnants of this interesting group. The plants of Australasia include most of the known kinds of eucalyptus (Photo 368), together with large numbers of special pines and cedars, mahogany, rosewood, and sandalwood.

The rest of the land masses of the earth, comprising about 80 per cent of the inhabitable surface, falls into three biological regions of disproportionate sizes. Largest is the circumpolar **holarctic realm,** including North America north of Mexico, all of Europe, Asia north of the Himalayas, and Africa north of the Sahara Desert. Smaller is the **paleotropical realm** (Old World tropics), including the rest of Africa and Madagascar, the mass of India plus Ceylon, the Malay Peninsula, and the larger islands of the East Indies as far as "Wallace's line." And finally comes the **neotropical realm** (New World tropics), including Mexico and Central and South America. Wallace's line (Fig. 21-7) angles northeastward between Bali and Lombok, between Borneo and Celebes, and south of the Philippines to set off New Guinea and many of the smaller islands as part of the Australasian area.

Holarctic Realm

The holarctic area supports many plants and animals that are circumpolar in distribution, but decrease in numbers at lower latitudes: musk ox, moose, caribou, polar bear, walrus, wolverines, weasels and ermines, lemmings, varying hares (= snowshoe rabbits), and other mammals; the ptarmigan is most conspicuous among birds. Farther south the holarctic realm contains almost all of the known chestnuts, birches, maples, lupines, heaths (including cranberries, blueberries, and the like), bears, foxes, lynxes, marmots, squirrels, deer and sheep, loons and tailed amphibia. It is divided commonly into two: (1) the **nearctic region**—consisting of Greenland and North America north of Mexico, where the forests and plains are extensive and desert regions small; and (2) the **palearctic region**—including Europe and neighboring islands, Africa north of the Sahara, and Asia (except India, Ceylon, and Malaya). Here there are considerable forests to the west, deserts along the south (Sahara, Arabian, and Mongolian), and lowland steppes to the north and east. The nearctic region is the native home of maize, pumpkin and other gourds, tobacco, skunks, pocket gophers, jumping mice, muskrat, beaver, racoon, porcupine, and rattlesnake, and formerly was inhabited widely by bison and elk. It is lacking in horses and pigs, poorly represented in ungulates. The palearctic, on the other hand, seems to have been the source of wheat, rye, oats, the cork oak, and possibly the horse; more recently it is clearly the area where rats and mice show their greatest number of kinds, where sheep and goats have their center of development, and where the common viper (*Vipera berus* L.) is the widely distributed poisonous snake. The hedgehog, wild boar, camels, panda, and pangolin have no counterpart in the nearctic.

Paleotropical Realm

The paleotropical realm includes many areas with spectacular mountains, dense forests, and heavy rainfall, but also some of the great deserts, and many other habitats. In it are found almost all of the big cats (lion, tiger, and leopard), the anthropoid apes, rhinoceros, and elephant, with cobras as common reptiles. The Indian Ocean cuts the paleotropical realm into two halves: (1) an **Ethiopian region,** including Africa and Arabia south of the great deserts, and the unique island of Madagascar; and (2) an **Oriental region,** including India, Ceylon, Malaya, the Philippines, and larger East Indian islands such as Borneo, Sumatra and Java—as far as Wallace's line.

The Ethiopian region contains enormous deserts and some of the most extensive grasslands and jungles of the world. These grasslands are the center of development of the antelope, zebra, lion, rhinoceros, hippopotamus, and the like, while in park-like plains with scattered trees are African elephants, giraffes, and further ungulates. The forested

363. The egg-laying duckbill platypus has a flat tail as well as a broad bill, and a poison claw on each hind foot.

364. The marsupial cuscus is arboreal, with a prehensile tail.

FURTHER ANIMALS OF THE AUSTRALASIAN SUPERREALM

367. The cassowary from tropical north Queensland stands about five feet high.

365. The lyrebird is Australia's finest songbird and mimic. It is confined to upland districts of southeastern Australia.

366. The ♂ lyrebird displays his magnificent tail particularly during the mating season.

368. Australia's eucalyptus forests are noted for their shadeless quality. The angle at which the leaves meet the sun is such that most of its radiant energy passes by. Some of the finest of these forests are in the mountains near Melbourne.

regions are more typically the home of the okapi, and such primates as gorillas, chimpanzees, baboons, and lemurs. Birds of the region include guinea fowls, ostriches, and secretary birds. Madagascar contains many lemurs and is the special home of the true chameleons. The Nile contains another lungfish. But bears, deer, oxen, wolves, and true foxes are almost lacking.

In the Oriental region, a greater portion is covered with jungles—partly due to the exceedingly heavy rainfall. Tigers, leopards, macaques, orangutang, gibbons, tarsiers, water buffalo, Indian elephant and rhinoceros, jungle fowl, peacock, and the sticky-toed lizards called geckos are typical animals.

Similarly, the Ethiopian region is known for its enormous baobab trees, as the source of cola nuts, and, in drier areas, as the home of the cactus-like spurges. The Oriental region is more plentifully supplied with such trees as teak, camphor, ebony, and bamboo, and it produces great quantities of the characteristic fruits—the durian and mangosteen.

Neotropical Realm

This portion of the Western Hemisphere is now so intimately connected with North America across the Mexican boundary that it is difficult to appreciate how recently (in the geological sense) the land mass became joined to that of the nearctic region. It is this that accounts for the distinctness of the biota. In the neotropical realm, the continuous north-south mountain chains such as the Andes, together with other features of topography, wind, and ocean currents, provide numerous strips of true desert at various elevations. In other areas some of the heaviest rainfall in the world is associated with extremely dense jungles. Grassy plains in northern portions of the realm are called *llanos,* in the southern part, *pampas;* much of these are on unforested tablelands.

Large mammals are almost lacking, but the area (two-thirds of it in the true tropics) supports all of the known prehensile-tailed monkeys, marmosets, true anteaters, arboreal sloths, armadillos (one has extended its range into the southern U. S.), vampire bats, jaguars, peccaries, llamas, alpacas, vicuñas, vizcachas, and most of the known opossums, hummingbirds, tapirs, and guinea pigs. Rheas, tou-

cans, curassows, guanay, condor, and motmots are birds limited to this region. Toads and frogs reach remarkable development, with one unique adaptation after another. However, oxen, sheep, horses, deer, and other large mammals are lacking entirely. The rich vegetation includes many plants that are peculiar to the region or particularly abundant there: century plant (Agave), balsa, cashew, cassava (source of tapioca), coca (source of cocaine), cacao (source of chocolate and cocoa), rubber, water hyacinth, Antarctic beech, pehuen, wax palm, various dyewoods such as logwood, cinchona (source of quinine), ebony, rosewood, mahogany, kapok, and chicle (ingredient of chewing gum). Most of the known cacti and orchids live in the neotropical realm; the others are in the nearctic. The tomato and potato apparently are contributions to our diet from the plants of the region.

In characterizing a region in a biogeographic sense, it is usual to select as "typical" the larger and more conspicuous, commoner (hence more familiar) or economically important plants and animals—yet to choose those in which the distribution coincides fairly well with the general limits set to the region. Naturally enough, a great many forms (like the cacti, orchids, and armadillo) are found overlapping the borders. Others are restricted to small areas within a realm. The recognition of a biogeographical entity is not based on the "typical" forms; these serve chiefly for discussion and diagnosis. Instead, recognition is based on distributional information about all of the plants and animals that live there. When the number that do not extend beyond the arbitrarily investigated limit is greater or more significant than the number that overlap or are restricted within, the limit is considered to have a scientific importance. Yet in each of the major realms and their subdivisions, still further distinctions can be made that are useful in studying the interrelationships of living things.

3. LIFE ZONES

An average of about two calories of radiant energy from the sun fall per square centimeter of the earth's surface, each minute—day in and day out. But the supply arrives in an extremely nonuniform way (Fig. 21-8). One side of the earth at any moment gets none, while the opposite side is in the sun. Part of the illuminated surface is between the Tropic of Cancer (22.5 degrees north of the equator) and the Tropic of Capricorn (22.5 degrees south of the equator) and is at right angles to the light energy. Part of the lighted region of the earth is between the Arctic Circle and the pole. The light there never hits a level place with less obliquity than 22.5 degrees; depending on the time of year and day, and the latitude of the level place, the angle may be anywhere between this value and zero. Yet the energy absorbed by the earth falls off rapidly as the surface is tilted away from the light. If the tilting is due to unevenness of the earth's surface, the effect is due simply to the spreading of the energy over a greater area.

Thus a slope away from the sun of as little as five degrees away from horizontal, lowers the energy receivable and hence the soil temperatures as much as does 300 miles of travel toward the pole in terms of level surfaces.

Where the tilting of the surface with reference to the sun is due to the spheroidal form of the earth and its inclination away from the light, the reduction in energy received suffers not only from the spreading of calories over more surface, but also from the absorption of energy by a greater thickness of atmosphere. When the sun is directly overhead, the air blanket cuts out nearly a quarter of the calories available, while with a low sun (as toward sundown, or in an arctic summer) only five degrees above the horizon, the oblique rays pass through about 11 times as much air—and only a feeble one per cent of the energy reaches the earth.

Thus it is not hard to understand how great is the difference in temperature on a yearly basis, in comparing points between

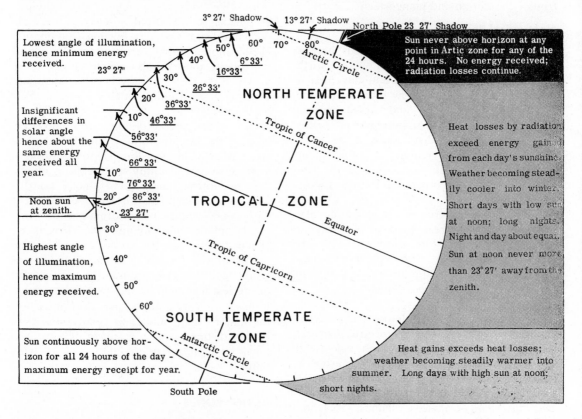

FIG. 21-8. *The angle of incidence of solar radiation has much to do with the climatic conditions and hence the distribution of plants and animals. (Shown for Dec. 21.)*

FIG. 21-9. *The life zones of North America are more distinct in the East, where high altitudes rarely compli-cate mapping, but in the West a small map is inadequate to show the distribution of each type of flora and fauna, since variations in altitude are great and influential.*

equator and poles. Each site receives and loses heat, day and night, month after month. The net effect can be expressed as an average temperature for the year, or further details can be cited. Fluctuations from year to year are not excessive. If the number of days with a mean daily temperature so many degrees above or below average are tallied, they tend to cancel out. This is the statistical basis for the practice of meteorologists in keeping a record of the number of "degree days" through a season. If the spring is cooler than average, the degree days below normal accumulate. A single hot spell may cancel them out. The expectation that they will be canceled out is the measure of how much one year is like another in terms of its long-term weather, its energy receipt from the sun, and loss to the atmosphere.

In terms of weather and of plant and animal life, certain zones and subzones can be

recognized. The life zones have been given names because their characteristics have importance in considering the interrelationships between the animals and plants that live in each, and the conditions they must be able to tolerate in order to thrive there. The life zones of North America are typical enough. C. Hart Merriam, who proposed them originally, based his divisions on temperature, connecting points having an average minimum in winter as a northern boundary, an average maximum in summer as a southern boundary. Today other factors are considered in studying the limits of life zones (Fig. 21-9).

Arctic-Alpine Zone

This is the life above tree line (the limit of tree style of plant growth) in either latitude or altitude (Fig. 21-10). Here the energy gain each year is enough to thaw the soil to only a few inches in depth; below this the ground is permanently frozen, and the term "permafrost" has been applied. In the shal-

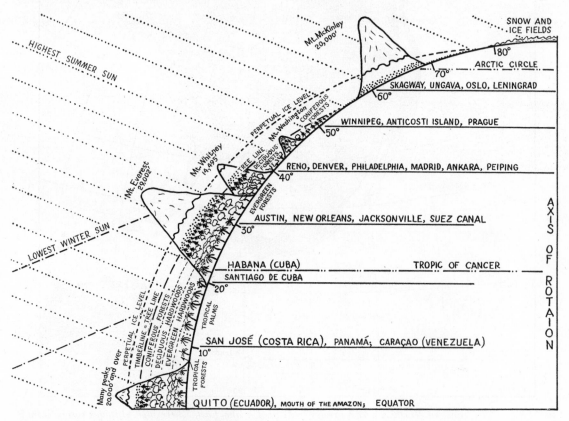

Fig. 21-10. *The effects of latitude and altitude are very comparable, for weather conditions in the arctic and on high mountain peaks are extremely similar in severity.*

369. Lichens encrust the rocks, and tundra plants such as Diapensia blossom in slow motion, subject to nightly frosts and harshly hot sun or hail by day.

370. Oeneis is a butterfly from one of the caterpillars which manage to exist in spite of such unfavorable weather.

371. Parnassius is another butterfly characteristic of high places throughout the world. Like *Edelweiss*, the alpine flower of Europe, Parnassius is much sought by collectors.

372. Looking down Pike's Peak, we see many hairpin turns of the road that mark descent to levels where climate allows tree growth. "Timber line" can be seen on various slopes in this picture.

WHERE WEATHER IS TOO HARSH, TREES CANNOT GROW

373. The transition from weather conditions in which trees can grow and those too severe for them is often so sharply marked on a mountain that a timberline is evident. Exposure to prevailing winds may be more important than elevation, so that the limit of trees follows an irregular contour.

low, thawed soil of summer there is little room for roots and the low temperature of the soil (scarcely above the freezing point) slows absorption to the point where the region is physiologically dry, although drainage is poor and water plus ice and snow stands in the open much of the summer. The plants that can grow under such conditions are xerophytes, such as mosses, lichens, grasses, sedges, dwarf rhododendrons, and Labrador tea, or ephemeral annuals, such as gentians and members of the pink family and of the poppy family. Over the area in lower altitudes range polar bear, musk ox, caribou (reindeer), arctic fox, varying or arctic hare, lemming, weasel, and Eskimo; it is the breeding ground in summer for ptarmigan, snowy owl, horned lark, snow bunting, snow goose, whistling swan, various sandpipers, and plovers. It is often described in terms of its life as the "sedge-musk ox" region, or **tundra** formation. The alpine counterpart (Photos 369-372) of the arctic region is the habitat for bighorn sheep and Rocky Mountain goats, and again for nesting ptarmigan.

In the waters off these arctic shores are surprising numbers of fur seal, walrus, whales, and many kinds of fish. They depend on the enormous numbers of algae, particularly unicellular forms, and these thrive in turn because of the large amount of upwelling of water from the bottom there, bringing nitrates and phosphates needed as nutrients by the plants. In warmer waters, as in fresh (Fig. 21-3), stratification is common and surface nutrients scarcer. Density variations with temperature and currents make the aquatic flora and fauna along arctic shores unbelievably richer than that on shore. Seals and walrus, of course, require a springtime return to the land for reproduction, but the whales, fish, and many other organisms remain in their food-rich medium all year. In general they remain all winter in broader expanses of water where icebergs do not become packed and photosynthesis continues whenever daylight reaches the arctic.

Southward from the arctic or downhill from the alpine areas beyond tree line are regions in which the weather conditions are slightly less severe. The climate is described as a "taiga," and unlike the true tundra, it allows the first indication of plants that in warmer areas would become trees. Here, in the shelter of a rock or in a shallow valley grow distorted evergreens (Photo 373), creeping birches, and creeping willows, with thick trunks twisted parallel to the earth, roots forced between boulders, and all branches conforming to the general contour of the land so that the crevice is filled by the vegetation. Any branch or twig that extends vertically reaches out into the path of winter gales, which whip away the snow and prune the plants to perfection. Nothing that protrudes can live; no bud on the windward side can develop; hence the malformed "trees" typical of these sites.

Boreal Zone

Since Boreas was the Greek god of the north wind, the significance of this regional term will be clear. It is applied to that portion of the earth that extends southward from tree line (also called "timber line") and down the mountain from the corresponding vegetative demarcation.[1] Boreal winters are long and cold, but the sun is less oblique and the summers are longer, so that the soil thaws to a much greater depth and may even lose its frost entirely by July—remaining frost-free until August or early September. Boreal areas usually receive 15 to 40 inches of annual rainfall, and maintain a fairly high humidity through much of the year. This is the region of our northern coniferous forests, with moose (Endpaper Photo B), elk, porcupine, Canada lynx, snowshoe rabbit, and breeding hermit thrush, kinglets, chickadees, various warblers, Canada jay, crossbill, and golden eagle. It may be described as the "spruce-moose" formation or be subdivided into two transverse subzones: (1) the **Hudsonian zone,** in which there are almost no deciduous trees, and the predominant vegeta-

---

[1] In terms of flowering dates and the like, A. D. Hopkins made a generalization referred to often as his *bioclimatic law* (1918): "Other conditions being equal, the variation in time of occurrence of a given periodic event in life activity in temperate North America, is at the general average rate of 4 days to each degree of latitude, 5 degrees of longitude, and 400 feet of altitude; later northward, eastward and upward in spring and early summer, and the reverse in late summer and autumn."

tion that gives form to the landscape is balsam, white spruce, black spruce and fir (Photos 374-376); and (2) the **Canadian zone,** where the conifers are diluted by sugar maple, beech, white ash, red oak, and sometimes paper birch (Photo 377), Endpaper Photo A). The Canadian zone thus represents the northern limit for upright growth of deciduous trees. The chief outliers are the prostrate, deformed, shrubby counterparts that cling to sheltered places and invade the arctic-alpine region where cover and taiga climate coincide.

Austral Zone

Derived from the Latin *auster* = south, the name of this region suggests more suitable conditions for growth among both plants and animals. Most of man's major cities are in the austral zone; civilization may be said to have its centers there. Three transverse bands of the austral region are recognized in America, each of them subdivided in terms of climate from east to west:

1. TRANSITION ZONE. Actually this is something of a catch-all, and represents an unbalanced equilibrium in terms of northward migration of Upper Austral zone organisms, counterbalanced by climatic killing off of the farthest migrants. In the eastern part of the Transition zone is the *Alleghanian* subdivision, with cold but short winters, warm summers, and between 30 and 50 inches of rainfall distributed through the year. It is the region formerly well covered by the eastern deciduous forest, with oak, hickory, chestnut, maple, beech (Photo 378), white pine (Photo 379), red pine, gray birch, poplar, and larch. It is the home of the beaver, woodchuck, red squirrel, gray squirrel, blue jay, song sparrow, and veery. It is often referred to as the "oak-deer" formation.

To the west, beyond the basin of the Mississippi, where water amounts to between 10 and 35 inches of precipitation annually, and where cold winters alternate with hot, dry summers, is the *Campestrian* subdivision, with variations from grassy prairies to poplar groves in the northern aspect, grasslands into oak groves farther south. The wild grasses are commonly the big blue stem,

grama, buffalo grass, turkey foot grass, and Indian grass, on which feed cottontail rabbits and prairie chickens. The most obvious flowers are often the sunflowers, goldenrods, asters, and coneflowers. Among the groves of trees may be racoon and red fox, although these are not restricted to this subdivision. Formerly the Campestrian was the grazing grounds for huge herds of bison (perhaps as many as 15 million head) and of elk (wapiti). It is now given over largely to agriculture, particularly cereal crops. Because of its former inhabitants, the wild grasses and American buffalo, it is often called the "grass-bison" formation. Often the number of ants is impressive.[2]

And finally, in the mountain areas toward the Pacific coast, are intergrading subdivisions called the *Okanagan* and the *Pacific,* with a western evergreen forest. In the northern extensions of these are Sitka spruce, Douglas fir, western hemlock, arbor vitae, and coastal redwood (Photo 467), growing to immense size, with epiphytic mosses, ferns, and lichens emphasizing the high humidity of warm air blown in from over the Pacific Ocean.

2. UPPER AUSTRAL ZONE. Again this represents a transverse band across the country, with considerably milder winters but summers not excessively hot for any length of time. Frost occurs with regularity and usually snow accumulates on the ground in winter. In the east is a moist *Carolinian* subdivision having a rainfall of between 30 and 50 inches annually; formerly this led to another aspect of the eastern deciduous forest, with tupelo, flowering dogwood, redbud, azalea, beech, oak, buckeye, chestnut, soft maples, wild papaw, walnut, sycamore, tulip tree, basswood, sassafras, and honey locust as prominent plants; in sandy areas, prickly pear (Opuntia) thrives. The opossum and cardinal are at home.

Farther west, beyond a southward swing of the Campestrian, is a drier *Upper Sonoran* subdivision, with 10 to 30 inches of rain each year, occurring chiefly in fall, winter, and early spring. Along the river bottoms grow

---

[2] Actually these provide aeration in the soil much as do earthworms in forested areas, and they must be regarded as ecological equivalents in this particular.

374. The Athabasca Glacier of western Alberta spreads westward to melt into the Pacific, eastward to drain into the Atlantic via Hudson Bay, and northward to send water to the Arctic through the Mackenzie River. The glacial lake at its eastward tongue floats small icebergs that break away from the retreating face. The top of the glacier is covered with debris.

SNOWFIELDS AND GLACIERS ARE REMNANTS OF THE PAST ICE AGE

375. Snowfields filling mountain valleys are common along the high western lands of Alberta. The valleys there have been scoured by greater glaciers in the fairly recent past, and the vegetation has a less settled appearance.

376. The upper austral type of vegetation in the West shows a mixture of conifers and deciduous trees. The Snake River valley in Jackson Hole, western Wyoming.

377. The upper austral in eastern states is marked by stands of white pine mixed with paper birch. On the lower slopes of the White Mountains of New Hampshire.

cottonwoods and willow, while nearby slopes bear quaking aspen and lodgepole pine, and slowly grade into more arid plains with sagebrush, greasewood and other "chaparral." Among the willows and aspen, elk browse; the sagebrush is native habitat for pronghorn antelope (Photos 463, 464), jack rabbit, badger, prairie dogs and coyote. As such it is frequently called the "sagebrush–jack-rabbit" formation. Local lakes are often alkaline, and around them and along the rivers nest white pelican, sandhill crane, prairie horned lark, western meadowlark, trumpeter swan, miscellaneous sparrows, and the avocet.

To the west again, at higher elevations or where moisture from the Pacific Ocean is more available, is a southern component of the Okanagan, with western yellow pine (Photo 14), sugar pine, Douglas fir, incense cedar, and miscellaneous other conifers and aspens of the Sierra Nevada and the central Rockies. Here is the home of the water ouzel, the golden-mantled ground squirrel (Photo 265), the western (yellow-haired) porcupine (Photos 300, 301), the mule deer, black and grizzly bears.

3. LOWER AUSTRAL ZONE. This is the final band across the nearctic realm, skirting the Gulf of Mexico and following up the east coast as far as Virginia. Snow cover is less regular; the winters never go far below freezing for more than a few days at a time; and summer temperatures may reach much higher levels. In the Gulf and eastern section is the *Louisianian* subdivision—chiefly low, swampy, or sandy soil, which receives heavy rains totaling 35 to 60 inches annually; the humidity remains high much of the time. Seen from an airplane, a surprisingly large part of the land is continually under a few inches of water. Yet on it grows a southeastern coniferous forest with long leaf pine and bald cypress, and broad-leaved evergreens such as magnolias and sourgum. Cotton, sugar cane, and pecans grow easily. Spanish moss (an epiphyte of the pineapple family) does well, particularly on swamp vegetation. Drier parts are commonly referred to as "pine barrens," with open stands of the turpentine pine. Interspersed are areas of deciduous forest with cottonwood, sycamore, beech, and papaya. Among these roam opossum, Virginia deer, racoon, wild turkey, and black snake. In wetter parts, bald cypress trees, the green lizard (Anolis—Photo 76) and alligator (Photos 75, 128) are not uncommon, and frequent snakes include the coachwhip, the diamond back, and pygmy rattlers. The mockingbird is native, and roseate spoonbills are now making a recovery because of better protection for their nesting sites. It was the home of the ivory-billed woodpecker, Carolina paroquet (Photo 457), and others that are now exceedingly rare or quite extinct.

Farther west, in Texas and beyond, a drier subdivision called the *Lower Sonoran* represents an area where rainfall is less than 10 inches annually and comes chiefly in a few weeks of fall, winter or early spring; winters may include sudden cold spells but summer temperatures reach not uncommonly into 110 to 125 degree ranges, Fahrenheit, with negligible humidity. This is the arid land of the creosote bush, of century plants (Agave— Photo 341), cat's claw (ocotillo), many cacti from small to tree size (Photo 342), of mesquite where water can be reached, of palo verde, and of yuccas including the Joshua tree (Photo 466). Here are found pocket mice, kangaroo rats and other nocturnal foragers; such lizards as the several kinds of horned toads (Photos 232-233, 344-346); the desert horned lark, cactus wren, cactus woodpecker, roadrunner, scissortail flycatcher, and magpie; the antelope jack rabbit, and armadillo. The term "creosote bush–kangaroo rat" formation is often applied, and the most conspicuous feature of the vegetation is the bare, plantless ground that separates one xerophyte from another (Photos 341, 342).

Still nearer the Pacific coast, where some moisture is taken from the air by mountains, plants are more numerous, and among them appear a few sparse evergreen forests of xerophytic pines and junipers, or broad-leaved "live oaks" whose foliage maintains the stiff character associated with arid lands.

Tropical Zone

Outliers of this type of vegetational growth reach the tip of Florida, but primarily the situation is characteristic of the lower altitudes within the true tropics of the Western Hemisphere. Here are regions in which rainfall is adequate to excessive—60 to 120 inches annually—where temperatures are medium to high all year, and where conditions for life seem optimal. It is also the region where competition for space is most severe, and where the organisms, instead of showing adaptations allowing them to survive some unfavorable feature of the physical environment, are adapted highly for getting food and for maintaining a temporary dominance in a restricted niche for long enough to complete a life cycle. The net effect is an evergreen forest that is continually shedding leaves from broad-leaved plants, especially of the legume and palm families (Photos 384, 385). Trees are hung with woody vines (lianas) or themselves send down accessory roots, as do the mangroves. On the plants cling all manner of epiphytic mosses, ferns, orchids, representatives of the pineapple family, and the like. The animals mentioned on p. 381 for the neotropical realm move quietly through the forest—so quietly that they are usually missed by the casual observer. So many kinds of animals and plants are represented, and each by so few individuals that show themselves (since their periods of activity are sharply limited in the day and in the year, and since exposure invites attack) that years can be spent in careful observation without becoming acquainted with more than a small representation. The organisms show also a vertical stratification not seen on a comparable scale elsewhere (Photos 380-385). The forest floor is relatively dark; among the fallen leaves there is the home of Peripatus— the arthropod link with the worm-like body plan (Photos 428, 429)—which creeps in search of insect prey. Tapir, anteater, and land crabs run through vague trails. Overhead are further levels of activity, with sloths and monkeys, toucans and parrot. Above the forest canopy vines spread and flower. To them come blue Morpho butterflies, such as are used in iridescent jewelry. Along waterways are ibis, flamingo, snake bird (anhinga), brown pelican, and many more. Water moccasin, swamp rattlesnake, fer-de-lance and bushmaster represent the pit vipers, but harmless snakes are not uncommon.

In tropic areas where the annual rainfall is between five and 20 inches, xerophytic plants spread bare branches much of the year, or retain leathery leaves with remarkable adaptations aiding in retention of water. Leaves often have the form of spines, or stiff petioles may remain after the blades fall, adding armament to branches frequently rendered unapproachable by stiff thorn-like twigs. This is a "thorn forest," grading into still drier regions of desert bush.

If the rainfall is less than five inches and the temperature is high, the potential evaporative rate exceeds ten times the actual rainfall. Under these conditions scarcely any plant or animal can survive, and the tropics hold some of the most lifeless deserts on earth. Sometimes, as in Peru, these lie only a short distance from the ocean. But without on-shore winds and mountains to precipitate the moisture, the soil receives almost none.

4. SUCCESSION

Within each area, regardless of its life zone, are bodies of water full of hydrophytes, shores and higher lands with mesophytes, and rocky or boggy patches actually or physiologically dry enough to be populated by xerophytes. Paralleling each of these plant communities are characteristic animals.

These conditions are far from static. Geological changes of short and long duration are supplemented by various unpredictable events, such as volcanic eruptions, floods, fires, and by the actions of plants and animals themselves.

Erosion may slowly cut through the rocky rim of a lake, draining it. The accumulation of peat moss may convert it into a bog and finally fill it. At the edges of a lake the sediments washed down by rains transform a shore where water lilies thrive into one where bulrushes grow, then into a wet, sedgy meadow, finally into a place with damp earth in which alders and willows, then larger and more permanent trees take hold. Left undisturbed, the sequence leads to a vegetation that either perpetuates itself, smothering invaders, or smothers its own seedlings as well. Such a temporary or long-term condition is spoken of as a vegetative climax, and each kind of soil in relation to rainfall, drainage, temperature (hence latitude and altitude), and exposure shows some characteristic types of plant and animal life.

378. Beech forests were once far more extensive than they are now. In the middle foreground is a clump of the waxy white flower stalks of Indian pipe—an angiosperm which depends for food upon mycorrhizal fungi capping its roots.

379. White pine stands are now more restricted than formerly. This one is at White Lake State Park, in New Hampshire.

380. Six-inch cockroaches resting for the day below a banana leaf. These insects and tailless whip scorpions (Photo 393) are conspicuous inhabitants of tree holes and caves where vampires and other bats hide in numbers.

NEOTROPICAL ANIMALS IN PANAMA

382. One of the larger hummingbirds, the Nicaraguan hermit, incubating her eggs in a nest attached to the downhanging tip of a palm frond.

381. High in the jungle trees, 6-foot iguanas feed on foliage. The white flesh of these lizards is esteemed highly by natives, who try to frighten iguanas into dropping within reach.

383. Running over the jungle floor or climbing into trees are coatis (coatimundis), omnivorous and intelligent relatives of the racoon. These versatile animals have spread northward through Latin America into Arizona. Young ones (*as shown*) become used to handling and make interesting pets.

384. A stilt palm, while still young, sends out prop roots which become equal in size to the original. The mature tree, with its top forty to sixty feet above the ground, appears to have no real trunk at earth level, and therefore no main root either.

SOLUTIONS TO THE PROBLEM OF SUPPORT FOR TALL SLENDER TREES IN THE TROPICAL JUNGLE

385. The giant Bombacopsis tree towers over the others around it, but the size of its trunk is deceivingly enlarged through the great buttresses extending to all sides as thin supporting vanes only a few inches thick.

386. The fairy shrimp (Eubranchippus) appears suddenly in temporary pools of early spring, reaches reproductive maturity (note ♀♀ with black egg masses), and vanishes for another year by bridging unfavorably warm and dry weather while in the dormant egg stage.

Answers to the

Problems Posed

by Winter

387. Swallows, like so many other birds of northern latitudes, gather for migration to warmer areas where insects are available all winter. Return in spring appears to be a matter of taking advantage of the longer days and shorter nights characteristic of summer nearer the polar regions. These conditions allow more food gathering and render easier the task of feeding broods of young.

Just described was the succession transforming a region inhabited by hydrophytes into a mesophytic climax (Fig. 21-11). Corresponding to it there is a regular succession from xerophytic to mesophytic in regions where other conditions allow. Thus the lichens that cling to bare rocks, and the mosses and ferns and few herbaceous plants that follow them when a little soil has accumulated, all add to the soil and invade each new crack as

of Krakatau in the Malay Archipelago, which was completely devastated in a single giant eruption in 1883. Here the colonizing organisms had to cross sizable stretches of water, from other islands. Yet today the island is well populated once more, even with life that could neither fly nor swim to its present location. One type after another drifted by and was

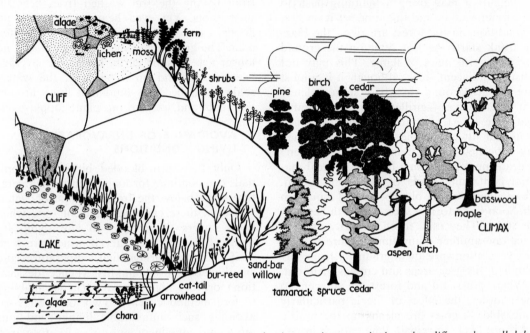

FIG. 21-11. *Plant successions follow slow changes in landscape that turn both rocky cliffs and small lakes into forested areas with a climax vegetation.*

the rock weathers and disintegrates. As the mountain becomes boulders, and as these break into smaller fragments, the vegetation changes and trees spread in. Gradually the region acquires the same climax plants as are characteristic for the latitude and altitude, when an aquatic habitat was succeeded by a mesophytic flora and fauna.

Although significant changes in such gradual successions can be noticed in a matter of a decade or two, the complete process may require centuries. Shorter-term events usually follow a biological catastrophe—a volcanic eruption, a fire, a major avalanche, or a great flood.

After Volcanic Activity

A study on a large scale involved the island

borne ashore by waves. The rate of colonization of a denuded area, however, is many times greater than the rate of spread of organisms from one region to another already occupied by a full complement of plants and animals.

After Fire

Fires are a major catastrophe that destroy climax vegetation and their associated fauna, starting the steps of succession over again from a slightly different direction. In the course of a storm, lightning may strike a tall tree and do no more obvious damage than to tear off a vertical or spiral strip of bark from base to tip. The mechanism of this is understandable: the electric current through the wettest living layer of the plant raises the temperature well above the boiling point of water, turning the sap to steam under such pressure that the tree explodes outward—blowing off the cooked part and opening an avenue for invasion of insects and fungi. Soon these weaken the living parts of the tree and cut tunnels through the dead heartwood. A second storm may touch other trees of comparable height; it may bring a lightning flash to the former victim, and this time set it on fire. If conditions in the forest are right, the blazing trunk starts the leaf litter on the ground into a general mass of flame. This may not consume adjacent trees, although it is almost sure to burn around each base so completely that the tree dies—girdled by the intolerable heat. The forest after the fire has lost much of its leaf litter, and the trees gradually shed any unburned foliage, remaining on the scene as dead specters. Passing birds drop fecal material containing seeds of birch and aspen, fireweed and sumac, blackberry and mountain ash. Soon these form a second growth between the stubs. They may reach maturity and replace one another many times before the climax vegetation spreads in gradually from surrounding fire-free areas and crowds them out.

Where grassland and forest are adjacent to one another, the effect of fire is particularly noticeable. A grass fire cleans up the prairie but is not likely to remain long enough in one place to kill the grass. At the forest edge it sets the trees to blazing and girdles many more. The sun shines down between the dead trees and grass spreads in between them. Another grass fire extends the grass still farther into the territory previously held by the forest climax. But gradually the trees spread seedlings, and these grow large enough to shade the grass and to smother it with fallen leaves, and once more the forest is established. These alterations are a succession, too, and they affect not only the plants, but also the animals that live among and on them. They are slow changes, but typical of the border zone between land which will support trees and that which has insufficient moisture for such massive vegetation.

After Major Floods

The action of floods is well enough under-

stood in terms of their erosive characteristics, breaking vegetation, drowning animals, cutting channels through soil, and removing the humus layers that hold the moisture best. After the flood, the soil remaining may be covered to a considerable depth with silt and mud, and invasion of this by smaller plants may require years. Trees not carried away by the water, in many cases, die from having considerable lengths of their trunks buried, or from having the soil washed from between their roots. Yet even heavy rains, with no floods, can cause great damage in a forested area. The ground becomes so soggy that it no longer acts as solid earth. Under the leverage exerted by wind on a tall tree, the water-soaked soil becomes mud that flows around the roots and lets the big plant topple over.

5. AVOIDANCE OF UNFAVORABLE LIVING CONDITIONS

Only the warm-blooded birds and mammals can continue for long when the temperature sinks below the freezing point of water. Not even these can find sufficient food when snow covers the ground to any significant depth. Cover is necessary if winds are high or if strong sun brings high temperatures and simultaneous low humidity (hence desiccation) or very high humidity (hence inability to lose metabolic heat). Two main ways for avoiding such unfavorable living conditions are found among organisms: (1) dormancy during the adverse period, together with some degree of protection; and (2) outright migration to another region where conditions are more tolerable.

Dormancy

The adoption of a dormant state with greatly reduced metabolism is a winter characteristic of herbaceous perennials, the deciduous trees, and an assortment of animals, the most conspicuous of which are the bats, squirrels, marmots, some bears, reptiles, amphibians, and many invertebrates. A large proportion of the simpler plants and invertebrates avoid winter by ending their life cycles in the fall of the year with a resistant stage—spores, seeds, cysts, and the like (Photo 386). In others, the changes are more complex. One feature seems to be general, however. The overwintering organism or its resistant stage transfers its water content from the free form in which materials can be dissolved, into a "bound" form that is quite different in physical and chemical features. For one thing, bound water can be chilled well below the normal freezing point without forming crystals of ice. This avoids the great difficulty experienced by living systems, since a major part of the killing effect of frost is through rupture of the cell membranes by the growth of sharp, hard, ice crystals from within the cell. Plants and animals that can withstand freezing temperatures must have their water in the bound condition if they are to survive.

Where the soil is not frozen below some definite depth, animals that cannot tolerate actual freezing have a place to go. It may be enough for a frog to bury itself in the muddy bottom of a pond—if the pond does not freeze solid during a normal winter. But too shallow a pond or too cold a winter may mean the end of life for frogs hiding from winter in the bottom mud.

With the exception of honeybees, which feed on sugar stores and engage in physical work that liberates heat and helps keep the hive temperature well above that of the surrounding air, almost every cold-blooded animal spends the winter only a fraction of a degree warmer than its immediate surroundings. The minute temperature difference is a measure of the calories produced from slowed metabolic activities. But some mammals have the adaptive ability to allow their body temperatures to sink far below the normal range. These are the types that **hibernate** (from the Latin *hiberna* = winter) in a dormant condition, curled up in some protected site. They may breathe only at irregular intervals in a five-minute period, and the heart may slow to just one or two beats a minute. At this low rate of activity, relatively little energy is being drawn from the food reserves of glycogen and fats, but life is maintained. The foodless, drinkless months between the entrance into hibernation and emergence in the spring may turn a roundly fat animal into a lean, frantically hungry one—but the winter has been avoided and the bursting buds provide new nourishment for the herbivore or for the prey on which a carnivore will feed.

Hibernating bats ordinarily hang up in caves with perpetual temperatures well above the freezing point. During the winter the flying mammals may awaken at intervals, let the blood temperature and activity level rise, fly about for a few minutes, then settle once more into dormancy. But when spring arrives outside the cave, the bats commonly leave to take up residence in protected niches closer to their food supply. That not all of them do so can be established easily by watching the nightly emergence of millions of bats from such major caves as that at Carlsbad, New Mexico, where they issue like smoke into the twilight air, to return again just before dawn.

All gradations between hibernation and general inactivity can be traced easily in the horned toads (Phrynosoma) that are familiar lizards of the Texas plains, in nearby Mexico, and in states to the west and north. These insectivorous reptiles (Photos 344-346) hibernate below frost level in the soil, emerging briefly even in winter on warm sunny days, but active on the surface for longer periods as spring advances. On soil heated to 100 to 102 degrees Fahrenheit, they react much faster and seem to show a preference for these high temperatures. Yet a further rise of a few degrees sends them scurrying for shade, or digging back into the soil to cooler depths. Exposure to 108 degrees is fatal to them if prolonged for many minutes. Since the regions in which horned toads live include Death Valley, California, and many other arid areas in which temperatures in excess of 120 degrees are not uncommon, it is easy to see that as the summer arrives, the day of the lizard is broken into two: a morning period from the initial warming of the cool soil to perhaps 10 a.m., when 105 degrees is reached, and an afternoon period from a cooling soil at perhaps 102 degrees until nearly sunset. At night and in the middle of the summer day, the conditions are not right and the lizards are dormant—the one because the temperature is too low, the other because it is too high. The need for heat to maintain the body temperature in its optimum range is shown by horned toads in early morning and late evening, when they extend the legs on one side in such a way as to tilt the flat back into a position almost at right angles to the sun's rays. While absorbing heat in this way, the lizard does not cool off as rapidly as the sands in afternoon; it heats up more quickly in the morning hours. Both allow its chemical processes to proceed at the highest safe rate, and enable the animal to be most alert for food and mates.

Similarly, at high altitudes freezing temperatures at night often alternate with very warm days. Plants and the caterpillars that feed on them are frozen stiff at night, but thaw out and continue living at a rapid rate as soon as the sun warms them in the morning. By day the plants are flexible and the animals avoid an approaching hand. By night the plants mash under foot, with none of the daytime recovery; the invertebrates are completely comatose. Yet the accumulation of growth in this intermittent pattern finally brings the plant into bloom, and allows the caterpillars to become butterflies which flit and feed, mate and lay eggs on the appropriate plants to start the precarious process all over again (Photos 357-358).

Summer dormancy, properly called *estivation,* was mentioned briefly in connection with snails in the desert areas, which escape the dry season in this way. The response is to low humidity, and can be observed during the winter season in the subtropical tip of Florida. The interesting tree snails (Liguus) of the Everglades National Park and adjacent "hammocks" of trees on slightly elevated islands in the big swamp (Photo 88) estivate in the late autumn and remain dormant until the heavy rains begin in the spring. Yet the temperature is not low, nor does it fail to rain every few days. The weather is only relatively dry, but this is enough for these snails to go into estivation. Their dormancy corresponds to significant slackening in the growth of fungi over the leaves of plants where they are found; the fungus hyphae comprise the chief food of these snails.

Allied to such estivation is the inactivity of frogs and toads which remain hidden away during much of the Florida summer. They emerge during rain storms and remain alert until the water drains away; then concealed positions and dormancy are resumed. In Egypt's Nile River the lungfish known as the bichir (Protopterus) bridges the dry summer season by burrowing in the mud, forming a

spheroidal cell in which it can curl up and remain dormant. Blocks of dried mud containing such lungfish have even been shipped to America for exhibition and study. When water was added, the fish emerged and swam about, ready for normal activities. Habits related to this adaptation for the dry period show during the rest of the year, however. The lungfish cannot depend entirely for respiration on its gills (which are fairly well sealed off during estivation), and must come to the surface at frequent intervals to replenish the air in its swim bladder, around which a capillary net is well developed, giving it a lung-like function.

Closely related to hibernation and estivation is the avoidance of unfavorable conditions through encystment, or formation of highly-resistant spores and the like. Thus bacteria of many kinds can lose moisture and become resistant to either high or low temperatures—surviving for hours at 400 degrees Fahrenheit in a hot air oven, for example. Yet these same organisms, if in an atmosphere saturated by water vapor, are unable to form spores; most of those that cause spoilage of foods can be destroyed by boiling briefly at 212 degrees; the rest are killed if subjected to water vapor at 15 pounds more than atmospheric pressure—which means a temperature of only about 275 degrees—in 15 minutes. The latter is the principle of steam sterilization such as is used for surgical instruments and bacteriological glassware.

Most of the saprophytic bacteria, protozoans, rotifers, and other microscopic animals are able to achieve desiccation-resistant forms as a puddle or pond dries up. They blow away as dust and come to life again when once more in a water supply. Freshwater sponges and the so-called moss animals (Bryozoa) of ponds and slow streams form special structures called gemmules or statoblasts, which are set free when the parent colony dies and decays in the late fall. They can not only withstand freezing and drought, but in several kinds must be exposed to temperatures of 30 degrees Fahrenheit or below in order to come out of this cyst stage later and start new individuals. Many of the fungi, such as the parasitic rusts and smuts, also have special spores that can survive the winter. Even plant lice (aphids) produce a different type of individual in the autumn—a sexual rather than another parthenogenetic type that can lay fertile eggs which can tolerate much lower temperatures. And a large number of the deciduous higher plants are unable to expand their buds into new growth until those buds have been exposed to freezing temperatures. These organisms not only have mechanisms allowing them to survive unfavorable conditions, but the mechanisms have come in some degree to depend on the arrival of the adverse climatic features they counteract.

Migration

Some bats and a great proportion of the birds in temperate and northern climates mi-

grate southward during the winter months (Photo 387). Some dragonflies and butterflies have a similar behavior. These animals avoid the cold months by shifting to a second, winter home (Fig. 21-12). In their migrations, the birds at least follow remarkably regular **flyways** along the Atlantic or Pacific coasts or down the Mississippi valley (Fig. 21-13). Thus whippoorwills raised in New England spend Christmas and the winter in the southern tip of Florida, beside wood ibis, flamingos, and other birds that remain in the Everglades or lake country there all year through. White pelican from rookeries in Nevada's Pyramid

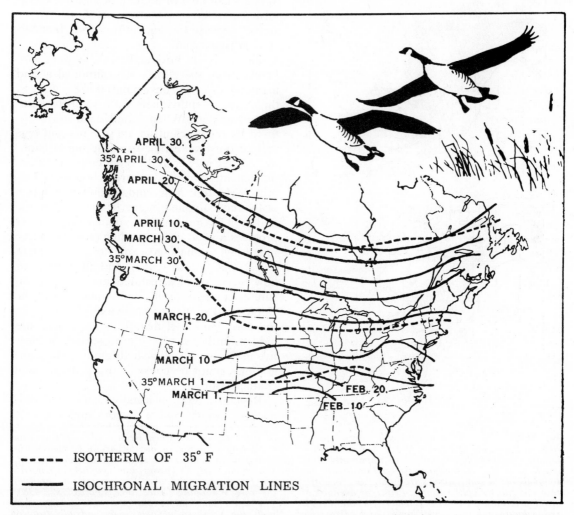

FIG. 21-12. *On any date, places with the same average temperature can be linked by a line (isotherm). Similarly, for any date, the average position of Canada goose flocks can be plotted (as an isochronal migration line). Correspondence between the two seems too close to be fortuitous.*

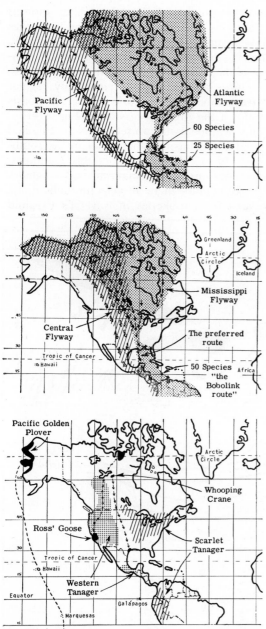

Lake and Wyoming's Yellowstone area meet along the Gulf coast of Texas, where brown pelicans live during summer as well as winter. Ruby-throated hummingbirds from the continent east of the Mississippi River (limited to this area and the only hummingbirds found there) funnel south into Florida; a few remain all winter, but the rest speed across the Gulf of Mexico to Central America. There they mingle with hummingbirds native to Mexico and southward, and with the 13 species that nest in the western United States, British Columbia, and Alaska. In spring all sort themselves out and return to their breeding grounds. No ruby-throats travel to Alaska nor rufous hummers to New England. And birds raised in one small area of an acre or two in size return year after year to the exact same acre, or spread because of competition into immediately adjacent land.

The facts of bird and bat migration are known from the efforts of ornithologists and mammalogists who have painstakingly marked thousands of individuals with numbered aluminum anklets. When found dead or recaptured by other scientists, these birds and bats may be only half a mile from the site of banding, or they may be at the other end of their annual flight. A central clearing house for records in Laurel, Maryland, allows correlation of the data supplied by the bander and by the finder. The information summarized so far provides a good understanding of *where* these migrating animals go, and to some extent *when*. But not how they find their way, or how these complex instincts arose. The pressure of competition for space and food in the tropics and subtropics is obvious. The steps in the development of the migratory instinct are hidden in the past. And most species of birds live in the tropics all year through, so that migration cannot be considered a general avian characteristic.

Regular migration usually results in avoidance of winter. Other factors are involved,

FIG. 21-13. *The annual north-south migrations of birds in temperate and arctic North America follow definite patterns. Each individual apparently "belongs" to a flyway for life, although different individuals of the same species from adjacent localities may migrate by unlike routes. Principal avenues of travel are shown by arrows, black for the Pacific and Atlantic flyways* (upper map) *and Mississippi flyway* (middle map) *and white for the central flyway* (middle map). *In the lower map the migration of Ross' Goose is shown from a restricted area in California to a region on the Arctic Circle; northbound arrows show the supposed migration route. Southbound arrows* (lower map) *connect the northern breeding ground and Texas wintering area of the rare Whooping Crane* (see Photos 437, 438). *The lower map shows also the wide difference in both the northern nesting areas and the tropical wintering areas for two species of tanager, and for the Pacific Golden Plover.*

however, in the migration of sea turtles (End-paper Photo P) to shore and fish such as salmon and eels to breeding and egg-laying regions. Mature salmon on the east coast of America approach the northern rivers, remain in the brackish water at their mouths until they become acclimatized to fresh water with its low salt content and low osmotic pressure, then swim upstream to shallow headwaters where the big fish lay eggs or spray eggs with milt before returning to the sea. On the west coast, the Pacific salmon acts in much the same way, but fails to descend the swifter rivers, and dies after a single trip. Eels, on the other hand, reach maturity in ponds, lakes, and large rivers of America or Europe (two species involved), and then descend the streams to the sea, become acclimatized, swim into a special area southeast of Bermuda, mate and lay. The adults die there. When they have grown enough, however, the young migrate back along the path their parents took—the European species to Europe, the American to America, ascend the rivers, and finish development in fresh water. Less spectacular but just as regular are the spring migrations of amphibians to fresh water, where they mate and lay, and of land crabs in the tropics to the sea, with the same outcome.

Irregular migrations of huge populations are known among animals. Some of them occur in cycles and can be predicted with some degree of success. Until control measures were instituted, the Rocky Mountain locust (a grasshopper) through regular reproduction achieved, at intervals of a few years, such truly stupendous numbers that the reactions of most individuals changed. Under the crowded conditions, they also developed longer wings. There followed mass migrations comparable to the locust plagues of Asia Minor and parts of Africa, where the flight of grasshoppers was like a cloud between earth and sun, and the devastation of their feeding cleaned every leaf from trees, shrubs, crops and lawns. Now poison bran and traps are used to control the insects and no major outbreaks are allowed.

The Norwegian lemming is often cited as an animal with spectacular but sporadic migrations. The lemming is easily mistaken for a field mouse. It lives on seeds and lichens in the far north, and is so well adapted to the difficult climatic conditions there that six to seven litters of five young each may be reared each season. The lemmings form the herbivore food base for almost all of the important fur-bearing animals in which man is interested, but in spite of these depredations the lemming populations of Norway develop to such numbers that their own food supply is inadequate. In response to the desperation of the starving, the lemmings migrate by the billion down from their barren mountains into the civilized fringe around the sea. There they overrun towns and appear in the most unlikely places, giving rise to a wealth of fallacy and fables often quoted as facts.

6. FOOD CHAINS

The difficulties due to climatic features determine to a considerable extent where each kind of living thing can survive over the years —which means not only exist but also accumulate enough spare energy in the way of food reserves to allow reproduction. The need for adequate food is quite as important as the need for tolerable physical environment.

The food requirements of plants are far simpler than those of animals. Since the non-green plants and all of the animals depend for their food on the green plants, it is possible to state quite definitely that there is a far greater total bulk of protoplasm composing green plants than composing all other organisms taken together. The number of kinds of green plants is nowhere near the number of kinds of insects alone, but the living material of the green plants is not only enough to feed all other forms of life but also to maintain the growth and reproduction of the green plants themselves. This is a fundamental fact.

It follows that if bumblebees depend for nourishment of themselves and their young upon nectar and pollen, the number of bumblebees is limited by the flowering plants that produce the nectar and pollen. Since only a small part of the flowering plant itself takes the form of nectar and pollen, the total protoplasm of the flowering plants must be vastly more than the total protoplasm of the bumblebees they support. This is the principle of the pyramid of numbers in a slightly different form.

However, if the number of bumblebees is limited by the availability of plants on which they depend, an increase in the planting of clover (for example) should result in an increase in the bumblebee populations nearby. This actually happens. But if bumblebee nests on the ground are subject to attack by field mice, then the more mice there are, the fewer bumblebees. And since clover seed depends upon insect pollination, and the clover flowers in normal years are too deep for any insects except bumblebees to pollinate them, the more mice the fewer clover flowers get pollinated and the fewer seeds are set—hence the poorer the crop in the same field in the following year. Charles Darwin first pointed out this relationship, and suggested that the more cats there were in the neighborhood of clover fields, the better would be the crop of clover seed. And if clover is grown year after year in the same field as a cattle food, there is then a relationship between cats and beef production. Later accretions to this story have indicated that since beef was the staple food of the British Navy, the more cats the stronger the Navy grew. But the absence of so many navy men from England left a large number of old maids. The old maids kept cats, which ate mice, which thereby did not destroy bumblebee nests. The bumblebees in turn pollinated the clover, which reproduced itself well and furnished food for more cattle, producing beef for a bigger and better navy, hence more absent men. Thus the biological picture seemed a self-perpetuating cycle.

Darwin's cat-and-clover story in its amplified form is admittedly overdrawn, but it illustrated clearly the nature of food chains. Similar examples can be found everywhere. Thus the unicellular green plants in a pond may be eaten by mayfly nymphs, which may be caught and devoured by dragonfly nymphs, which form part of the food of crayfish; both dragonfly nymphs and crayfish are eaten by fish, on which muskrat and kingfisher feed; mosquitos sucking blood from the muskrat may be caught by swallows, or horseflies with similar habits may be eaten by redwinged blackbirds. Or the interconnections may be in many other ways and involve the same or additional animals. But any increase or decrease of one link in the meshwork affects the numbers of the other organisms involved.

Food chains are easier to follow in restricted places such as caves (Photo 388). The only food source for cave animals may be provided by bats which go out at night to feed on flying insects, and which return for the day, and build a guano of droppings on the cave floor (Fig. 21-14). The walls of the cave (Photo 389) where the bats cling are almost sure to be sparsely populated with bat bugs—relatives of the bedbug which suck the blood of bats. Small ectoparasitic flies are other inhabitants of the same places. But the droppings of the bats are still rich in food values, and in the moist air form a suitable medium for molds. This constitutes a plant substrate on which cave crickets (Photo 392) feed—and other insects (Photos 390, 391), spiders, and scorpions (Photo 393) eat the cave crickets. A rise in mold is followed by a rise in cricket numbers, which reduces the mold until many of the insects starve to death and fertility falls off; this event gives the mold a new start. Thus a balance is struck between too many and too few crickets, but this is governed by the mold, which in turn depends upon the bats. If the bats leave the cave in favor of hollow trees during the summer, or hang up in dormancy for the winter, their droppings no longer accumulate, the mold no longer thrives, the cave crickets starve, and the many predators that eat them do likewise. The energy from the outside world is insect bodies incompletely digested by bats. On this energy many complex food chains can depend —all within a single small cave.

POPULATION EQUILIBRIUM. By interfering in complex food chains, man upsets natural balances, producing major changes in a region. Thus, in protecting domestic animals and expressing a dislike for certain kinds, man may have killed off as far as possible all hawks, owls, wolves, foxes, coyotes, mountain lions, and snakes from an area. As a result, the grass on which he sought to pasture his herds went into decline, because there was no longer any appreciable check on the mouse and grasshopper populations. No hawks, owls, foxes, and snakes meant more mice—which scoured the region thoroughly for grass seeds to feed their increasingly numerous young, and thereby stopped the grass from maintaining its normal rate of reproduction. And by killing off the wolves, mountain lions, and coyotes, there was not an adequate check on the deer and elk populations, which soon increased beyond the number for which there was food. As a result, they frantically chewed on the young growth of every tree within reach (Photo 441) on the mountainside (to which they were confined by the rancher's fences), and killed off the forest so thoroughly that the snow melted and ran off in eroding streams early in the summer, leaving the grasslands dry and parched later in the season because the water had not sunk in and become added to the water table. This picture is not overdrawn in the least. It illustrates how far-reaching may be the effects of careless or selfish interference with the complex interactions of a balanced community of animals and plants.

CYCLIC POPULATION CHANGES. Some kinds of animals show wide variability in number of individuals, with years of abundance coming at fairly regular intervals. Thus a seven-year cycle has been claimed for the snowshoe rabbit, based on the number of skins brought in to Hudson Bay Company agencies. In trying to learn the cause of this variation, investigators discovered that the maxima occur rather regularly a year prior to a maximum in the number of wood ticks, which feed extensively on the rabbits and act as vectors for rabbit diseases. The explanation became fairly clear. The rabbits reached a maximum and furnished a wonderfully expanded food supply for the ticks. They reproduced, but their attacks and the diseases they carried were so violent in the following year that rabbit reproduction sank alarmingly. The following year the fewer rabbits provided much less opportunity for ticks, and ticks declined sharply. Then normal rabbit reproduction restored the mammal population and the ticks remained a step or two behind. By the seventh year, the rabbits reached a maximum again and the

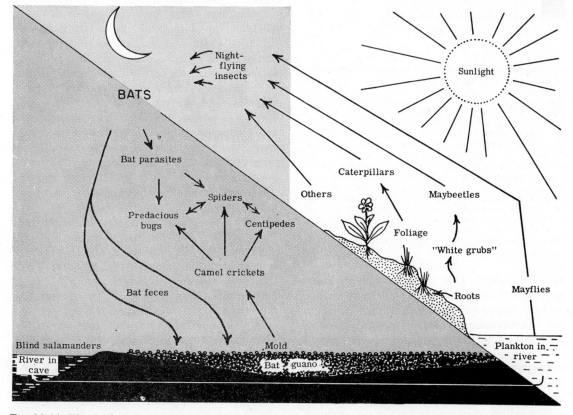

FIG. 21-14. *The food chain in a cave can be followed easily because the number of kinds of plants and animals involved is small.*

cycle started over. The term **periodicity** has been given to such major fluctuations (Fig. 21-15). Actually, they are quite widespread in the animal and plant kingdoms, but have been followed carefully chiefly in only a few forms —those wild animals in which man is finan-

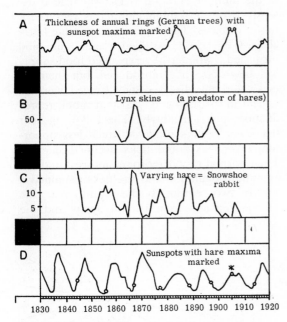

FIG. 21-15. *Periodically recurring phenomena always suggest unknown controlling factors to be sought. Curve A represents the average relative thicknesses of annual rings in German forest trees. Curve B shows the number of lynx skins purchased by the Hudson's Bay Company. Curve C indicates the thousands of snowshoe rabbit (= varying hare) skins purchased. Curve D shows the frequency of sunspots. On curve A the sunspot maxima are indicated by small circles. On Curve D the rabbit maxima are marked by small circles. (The asterisk indicates a year when unusual volcanic activity lowered the earth's temperature.) (Curves A, D, after Huntington; B, C, after Elton from H. B. Co. records.)*

cially interested. They illustrate well the interdependence of components of food chains, and the degree to which the balance swings in the two directions. The chief point of concern for the biologist is the suggested correspondence between the cycles of one animal and another, and the possible connection between these and the periodicity of sunspots or other phenomena. No conclusive evidence has been presented yet to prove the case in either direction.

7. ENVIRONMENTAL RESISTANCE

Each organism is thus hemmed in by a wide variety of restraints. Any such factor, external to an organism, that tends to reduce its biotic potential—whether by restricting the areas which it can colonize and retain, or by imposing any other limitation on its spread—is considered as part of a general **environmental resistance.**

Many of these factors are purely physical: the hardships of prolonged or especially cold winters; the lack of water or excess of it as based on precipitation or soil characteristics; the inadequacy of soil nutrients for a plant, or the toxic concentrations of salts or poisons around the roots; the shortness of the growing season; the lack of sunlight because of depth in the ocean; the excess of ultraviolet radiations at high altitudes; the continuously excessive temperatures of thermal springs, or the continuously too low temperatures of glacial waters; the mechanical difficulties of high winds or fast streams, of silt; the strains imposed by too rapid and repeated changes in temperature; and so on.

Others are biological: the absence of unoccupied earth and the competition for light and soil moisture accorded seedlings; the attacks of herbivores and disease organisms; the parasites and predators; the scarcity of food supplies; and many more. Most of these are variables. When environmental resistance decreases temporarily for a species, it expresses its biotic potential and increases rapidly in numbers. Thereupon the environmental resistance may rise and restore a balance, or overshoot and bring on a marked drop in population (Fig. 21-16).

Only when an organism can escape entirely from some major factors of its normal environment (as do introduced species that arrive without their parasites and predators) can the plant become a **weed,** the animal a **pest.** Until a new balance is struck, other species in the new area may not survive the competition —as happened to all but the opossums of the many marsupials in South America when a land bridge first allowed placental mammals to spread southward to that continent. But eventually the situation becomes relatively stabilized on a new footing. With introduced weeds and pests, man usually interferes, trying to maintain the present state rather than abide by the unpredictable consequences of the new struggle involving his crops or person.

Man is usually concerned with the welfare of some particular species—often just one at a time (as a crop)—and he becomes interested not in how that particular plant or animal fits into some special niche in the interlocking food chains, but in how to decrease environmental resistance for the particular organism so that it may grow in abundance. It is possible to list and evaluate the many aspects of environmental resistance for a single species, since once a condition of approximate equilibrium has been established (however supported or artificial it may be), the percentages from the characteristic biotic potential that are lost to each category—winter killing, parasite, predator, or whatever—are remarkably constant from year to year. This is a more local way of investigating the ecological relationships, and is inadequate because it does not take into consideration the many alternatives provided in the ordinary meshwork of food chains in any area.

8. BARRIERS AND BRIDGES

The spread of each species is limited by many factors. Some of these are its own tolerances for high and low temperatures, for inundation or desiccation, and for alternative food plants. An aquatic animal may be blocked by a land barrier, a terrestrial one by an ocean, a desert, or a mountain range. Where barriers are temporary in the geological sense, with bridges appearing at intervals, organisms are less affected and usually show distributions on both sides of the barrier.

The Gulf Stream between the tip of Florida and Cuba provides a highly effective barrier to migration of plants and terrestrial animals from this country into the West Indian island chain. Yet many plants and some animals (such as the tree snails of the genus Liguus —Photo 88) have crossed this barrier. Apparently they have been blown by hurricanes across the Gulf Stream and lodged among the vegetation along the Florida Keys. The snails

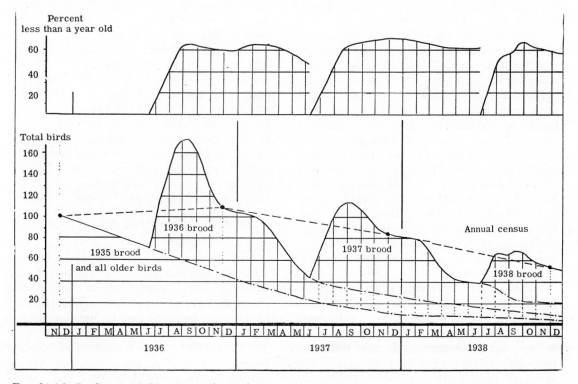

FIG. 21-16. *Decline in California quail population studied by trapping, banding, and releasing on the University of California farm at Davis. (After a report by J. T. Emlen, Jr., 1940, from 17,632 captures in three years.)*

cement themselves to trees during the dry season and could have accompanied the plant material on which they feed during a high-speed trip over the surface waters.

The entire continent of North America has changed its form remarkably in geological time, and startling changes would accompany any change in sea level (Fig. 23-11). During the glacial period less than a million years ago, the ice was formed at the expense of water from the sea—decreasing sea level as much as 300 feet in many places. The weight of ice piled on the continents also acted to press the land masses downward into the elastic core material of the earth. These movements of continents and seas were not simultaneous and they were not at the same rates; they have not ended yet. Barriers formed and disappeared in many places; inland seas became fresh water and then salt again. All of these events affected the distribution of plants and animals.

More recently, man has been the most effective means of transporting animals and plants. In some instances, he adopted organisms as domestic forms. In others, as in the case of the rat, they followed his civilization. Sometimes his food plants provided a more attractive host for local animals, and they spread back along his supply routes. The Colorado potato beetle lived inconspicuously on related plants until man arrived with potato plants. The beetles spread eastward, northward, and then westward wherever potatoes were grown—and largely deserted their previous type of vegetation. They invaded Canada (1870, Ontario; 1874, Quebec; 1878, New Brunswick; 1882, Nova Scotia; 1883, Prince Edward Island; 1884, Manitoba; 1899, Alberta; 1901, Saskatchewan; 1919, British Columbia) but are not known yet from Newfoundland or Labrador. They have crossed into Europe in spite of elaborate precautions.

Similarly, the importation of Oriental chestnut trees into New York harbor introduced a bark blight (1904) spread by wind-carried spores. Oriental trees were immune to the disease, but the American chestnut trees died out within relatively few years in spite of vigorous attempts to protect them (Photos 20, 21). Today only a few isolated American chestnut trees remain alive, and dendrologists

consider the chestnut blight to have been the most thorough in all history. Hybrids between the Oriental and American trees are often resistant, and may replace the former stands in America—perhaps supplying once more the fine wood and the tannin for which the American chestnut was the chief domestic source. Meanwhile, the blight has attacked the European chestnut, and southern Europe may be without a single tree of this kind within 30 to 40 years unless some better protective measure is discovered.

This traffic is not all one way, nor does it involve only insect pests and fungus diseases of plants. It appears that malaria was a human disease of the East Indies which had spread into regions conquered by the armies of Alexander the Great. It followed the Greek armies back to Europe and spread widely. When the Spanish Conquistadores explored Mexico and Central America, they brought malaria to America. In this disease may be the explanation for the disappearance of the civilized peoples of those areas. Certainly with so few men and without anti-malarial drugs the Spaniards could not have traveled so freely in the jungles of Central America had malaria been as prevalent then as now.

The giant land snail, Achatina, has spread remarkably in recent years, partly through voluntary assistance by the snail-eating Japanese. The lamprey (Photos 67-68), which attacks fish, is reaching the upper lakes of the Great Lakes series, clinging to boat bottoms as they pass through man-made locks and canals that bypass the rapids and falls. Similarly, automobiles and aircraft are likely to transport many organisms across barriers that would normally limit their spread.

9. EFFECTS OF LIFE ON ITS ENVIRONMENT

Not only do the physical and chemical aspects of an environment determine to a considerable degree what kinds of animals and plants can live in a region, but the presence of a particular flora and fauna may have a profound effect on the environment itself. This is evident in the formation of soil and marine deposits, in the protection against erosive forces afforded by land and coastal vegetation, and in the way many animals counteract this protection by destroying plants.

Vegetation serves importantly in trapping precipitation, affecting the availability of fresh water and hence the extent of fresh-water habitats and their biota.

Both the presence of oxygen in the atmosphere and the maintenance of an almost steady supply of this gas appear to be due entirely to the photosynthetic activity of green plants. Maintenance is seen as a cycle, with the by-product oxygen from photosynthesis being used in aerobic respiration, in combustion, and various oxidative processes. Meanwhile the solar energy bound into organic compounds by the green plants is passed along, to animals which consume them, to decay organisms, to outer space as lost heat, or is entombed for immensities of time in the form of peat, coal, oil, and natural gas. The free oxygen, however, matches in amount the total tonnage of fossil fuels and organic compounds in protoplasm plus products of its decay. It has been calculated that, at the rate animals and human activities consume oxygen (converting it into carbon dioxide), all of the

oxygen in the atmosphere would be used up in 20 centuries if photosynthesis ceased.

The Carbon Cycle

Carbon, too, can be traced in a cycle (Fig. 21-17). It is released into the atmosphere as carbon dioxide, containing no available energy, only to be captured again through photosynthesis and built into organic compounds full of stored energy. This sequence of events appears to have reached a steady state and a dynamic equilibrium with the carbonates deposited in the oceans.

It is these carbonates in warmer marine situations which enable coral animals (coelenterates), tube-building worms (annelids), and calcareous algae to build up through the centuries remarkable masses of limestone. Rock of this kind formed during recent decades is very porous, and traces of the separate organisms can be seen easily. It can be cut and trimmed with ordinary steel tools as "co-

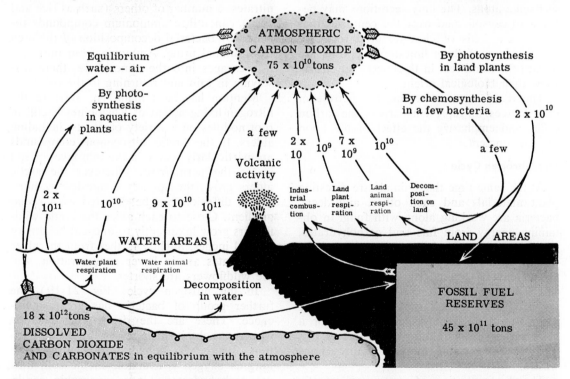

FIG. 21-17. *Since carbon is the diagnostic element in the organic compounds which give living things their active properties, it is important to trace the various routes taken by carbon into and out of protoplasm, into and out of various storage reserves. Approximate totals for atmospheric carbon dioxide, for dissolved carbon dioxide and carbonates, and for fossil fuels are given in tons. Values marked on arrows (without the word tons) are approximations for the number of tons per year following each route.*

quina rock," which dries and undergoes a slight chemical change on exposure to air. This makes of it a very hard building material used in many tropical countries and around the Gulf of Mexico.

Coral reefs fringing an oceanic island may come to enclose a shallow encircling lagoon as the island itself erodes away (Fig. 21-18). This, in turn, may evolve into the ring of low island masses on the old reef itself, around a single central lagoon, such as is characteristic

materials (such as amines and ptomaines). In the sea or the soil, however, these nitrogen-containing end-products do not remain for long. Nitrifying bacteria build them into nitrites; Nitrosomonas is particularly active in this step. Others, such as Nitrobacter, convert the nitrites into nitrates which, in turn, are the principal source of nitrogen for higher plants. Collectively these processes whereby bacteria make nitrates available, are described as **nitrification.**

Although most of the higher plants require their nitrogenous nutrients in the form of

FIG. 21-18. *Various types of coral reefs and their succession in time* (left to right).

of Pacific atolls. The limy secretions may become so consolidated over the centuries that tremendous beds of close-textured rock are found. Many of these limestone deposits are several thousand feet in thickness, yet clearly show their biological origin.

The reefs, the coal seams, the petroleum oil resources, all represent parts of the carbon cycle, and emphasize the effect of life upon the environment.

The Nitrogen Cycle

At the same time that animals are digesting plant materials and each other, and decay bacteria are working along with fungi in obtaining energy from fats and carbohydrates, still other microörganisms are breaking down the proteins of protoplasm. Each mold or microbe may be limited by its enzymes to a single step in the decomposition series. The end-product of one is the substrate for the next. But the net outcome is energy for a great variety of living things, plus free carbon dioxide, water, and inorganic nitrogenous wastes.

The decomposition of proteins is usually called **putrefaction,** and the complex, somewhat cooperative activity of the many saprophytic bacteria releases odorous and poisonous

nitrates, a number of others (such as rice and corn) can utilize ammonium compounds released by bacterial decomposition of the urea from animal urine. Ammonia from putrefaction escapes into the atmosphere, there dissolving in rain and returning to the soil.

Mention has been made (p. 360) of the nitrogen-fixing action of Rhizobium bacilli in root nodules on a variety of plants, including alders. In the Arctic, nitrogenous compounds are particularly scarce in the thin layer of soil above the permafrost. Wherever the arctic alders grow, the spread of nitrates by horizontal diffusion can be detected as a radial gradient. Close to each alder the arctic wildflowers grow luxuriantly to unusual heights of several inches. Slightly farther from the alder the nitrates are in lower concentration, and the wildflowers are shorter.

In the nitrogen cycle (Fig. 21-19) one further group of bacteria has great significance. These are the **denitrifying bacteria** which can obtain their energy by decomposition of either carbohydrates or nitrates. So long as oxygen is available in the soil, they use carbohydrates. Under anaerobic conditions they attack nitrates, obtain the oxygen from the NO_3 radicle and release gaseous nitrogen. This constitutes an important loss to the fertility of the soil. Hence suppression of denitrifying action is one good reason for keeping soil well aerated around the roots of crop plants.

The product of the many decay and putrefactive processes is a dark-colored accumulation of residues called **humus.** On the surface of the ground it may consist of recently fallen leaves. Under this are older remains of life in various stages of disintegration. In these upper levels of the soil are few mineral particles, but just below are layers with increasing admixture of inorganic matter. The rate of accumulation of humus depends partly on the soil temperature (hence the activity of the organ-

isms involved), partly on the water supply (whether arid, adequate, or excessively leaching), and partly on the frequency of fires which burn it, or winds and floods which dislodge it or cover it up. The number of organisms that find nourishment in the humus is good indication of the food values left from the slow and progressive breakdown of dead bodies. The depth to which soil can burn when exposed to a serious fire emphasizes the calories of energy there in still another way.

Proteins are the chief organic compounds in the nitrogen cycle. Many of them contain

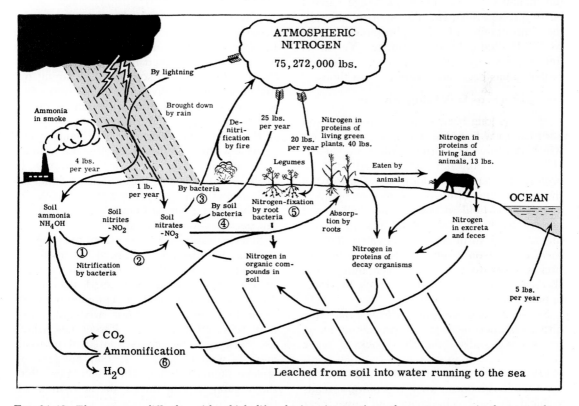

Fig. 21-19. *The extreme difficulty with which life obtains nitrogen from the vast reserves in the atmosphere is shown by the nitrogen cycle. The diagram refers to a single acre of cultivated ground—one of the 3 billion such acres man uses. The gain in nitrogenous compounds brought down by rain is approximately equalled by the loss of these substances from the soil through leaching. Another balance may be seen between nitrogen fixation by such soil bacteria as Clostridium and Azotobacter (4) and denitrification through the activity of anaerobic bacteria (3) in soil plus combustion of various kinds. A gain in soil nitrogen may be achieved through crops of legumes; in nodules on the roots of these plants are active nitrogen-fixing bacteria (5—Rhizobium). Within the soil the nitrogen is shifted from one side to another, sometimes in inorganic forms, at others in protoplasmic proteins. Green plants absorb inorganic nitrogenous compounds; bacteria shift these between ammonium compounds, nitrites and nitrates, and decompose dead tissues. Nitrifying bacteria include especially Nitrosomonas and Nitrococcus (1—producing nitrites) and Nitrobacter (2—producing nitrates). Ammonification is achieved principally by Bacillus mycoides (6). Hence the success of green plants and of the animals that feed on them depends to a major degree upon the activity of soil micro-organisms, especially bacteria.*

sulfur or phosphorus or both, and in putrefaction, these elements move into the soil in
the form of soluble sulfates and phosphates
which are important nutrients for higher
plants. When washed into fresh waters, they
are utilized by phytoplankton. In the sea they
may be combined with carbonates and calcium into mixtures of limestone and phosphate rock. If changes in sea level expose
these rocks, it is microörganisms again which
convert the insoluble calcium salts into soluble forms useful to higher plants. Since high-
energy phosphates (such as ATP) are essential in almost every energy exchange carried
on by protoplasm (whether plant or animal),
the importance of the **phosphorus cycle**
would be hard to overestimate. Yet it is
linked intimately with the nitrogen cycle, and
probably has been since very ancient times.

Living Things as Stabilizing Influences

Man has long been aware of the protection
afforded to a coastline by a barrier reef on
which the force of storms could spend itself.
He builds breakwaters as artificial reefs to
protect his harbors. Along some European
shores the value of mussels is well recognized.
These clams hold to one another and to the
bottom by means of special plastic byssus
threads, and form a "scalp" which reduces
wave erosion on sandy coasts. Legal protection is given to this scalp, even though the
shellfish represent a food of which the local
population is quite fond.

Seaweeds, eelgrass, and barnacles may furnish a smaller measure of protection along
rocky coasts, absorbing the shock of wave
action.

On land the movement of sand through
wind action is reduced when vegetation spreads
a shield above it. The great sand dunes near
Yuma, Arizona, and the gypsum dunes of the
White Sands National Monument in New
Mexico, are examples of sites where chronic
drought prevents the growth of enough plants
to anchor the shifting sands in place.

In forested localities, the protective aspect
of vegetation is more obvious. Temperature
changes occur much more slowly than in the
open. Forest cover may retard the disappearance of snow in spring for as much as five

weeks beyond the time required in exposed
areas. Reradiation of the heat acquired by
day also occurs much more slowly in plant-
covered areas.

The work of beavers (Photos 394-396)
often goes without adequate appreciation.
These industrious fur-bearers dam streams,
reducing run-off and building ponds that raise
the water table and stabilize the soil moisture.
The damage done to trees used in dam building or for food leaves is more than compensated for by the luxuriant plant growth that
they encourage and the erosion that they prevent.

Living Things as Erosive Influences

The splitting of rocks by roots, as an accessory to frost action, is well known. In
marine situations, quite a few kinds of worms
and clams are adapted in ways which permit
them to burrow into solid rock, scraping out
niches in which to live, and at the same time
weakening the rock until wave action during
storms can break it into fragments.

By eating and enfeebling the plants which
provide a shield above erodable land, animals
have an important effect on topography. In
proportion to the amount of damage done, the
soil temperatures vary more, the erosive action of heavy rains and meltwater from snowfall becomes more evident.

Starving rabbits, suffering from overpopulation or because an abnormal snowfall has
deprived them of their normal winter food,
or deer and elk similarly affected, may attack
the bark of trees and so completely girdle
them that they die. Major areas of forest
may be killed in this way. Porcupines, which
use bark as a customary source of nourishment in winter, produce regular but less extensive damage. All of these activities affect
the vegetation, and hence the soil, in much
the same way.

In arid areas sheep are the chief offenders.
They crop the plants so closely and repeatedly
that they die. Without plants the soil not only
becomes a true desert but also erodes more
rapidly, so that the humus and potentialities
for growing plants may disappear. As is discussed at greater length on p. 478, sheep-
created deserts are numerous in Spain, and
are rapidly increasing in the southwestern
United States and Latin America.

388. The inconspicuous mouth of a large cave in Pennsylvania.

CAVES AFFORD EXCELLENT OPPORTUNITIES FOR STUDYING FOOD CHAINS IN RESTRICTED QUARTERS

389. The "flowstone" formations along the walls of caves afford many niches in which bats and other animals can cling.

390-391. Predacious bugs of Texas caves feed on unwary crickets.

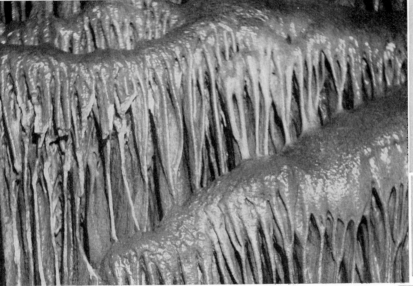

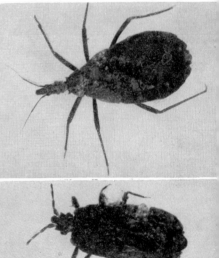

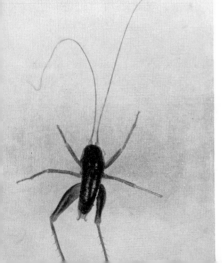

392. The cave cricket (Ceuthophilus) is wingless and relies upon long senstive antennae or bristly legs to warn it of approaching enemies.

393. Tailless whip-scorpions whose tremendously elongated first pair of legs may extend 8 inches across, catch cave crickets in Panamanian caverns.

394. A beaver house in a Wyoming beaver-made pond. In the foreground are stumps of trees felled by beaver teeth.

395. A beaver dragging one more poplar log up on the house. The apparently random combination of tangled sticks and mud makes the roof of the house almost impregnable.

396. Branches like this are often towed around until their leaves are wet and the beaver can drag the branch under to anchor it in the pond bottom where it can provide winter food after ice forms.

THE WATER SURFACE AS A LIVING SPACE

There is no scarcity of water surface on our earth, so that there should be room for all the animals that can live in this special niche. Almost three quarters of the area of the globe is ocean—nearly a hundred and forty million square miles of it. Yet relatively few creatures make any use of its surface film. Instead they are crowded on a single million square miles of lakes and rivers, ponds and streams, finding in these smaller bodies of fresh water far better living conditions than over the great depths of the sea. The oceans are interconnected and it would be easy to see how similar plants and animals could spread over these great reaches. Fresh waters, on the other hand, are often isolated. They seem peppered over the land area of the earth in little spots and streaks. Yet the similarity of living creatures on their surfaces is far greater than that of animals and plants along their banks. Showy orchids and howling monkeys do not run wild in Alaska, nor caribou and tundra plants in the jungles of Panama. But a water strider, a diving beetle and a lily pad from these two regions are indistinguishable except to a specialist. . . . It is so everywhere. Conditions of life are much more uniform over the fresh water surfaces of the globe than on the land surrounding them. For this reason, a naturalist in a foreign and unfamiliar land can feel very much at home once he rows a boat out on a pond or stream and examines the animals and plants beside his floating craft.

—LORUS J. MILNE *and* MARGERY MILNE, *A Multitude of Living Things* (New York: Dodd, Mead & Co., 1947), pp. 139-40.

THE ARCH-PREDATOR—MAN

Coyotes are the arch-predators upon sheep. Sheep are the arch-predators upon the soil of arid and semi-arid ranges. Wherever they are concentrated on ranges without sufficient moisture to maintain a turf under their deep-biting teeth and cutting hoofs, they destroy the plant life. Quail, which require cover, cannot survive too close cropping. Unless long-term public good wins over short-term private gain and ignorance, vast ranges, already greatly depleted, will at no distant date be as barren as the sheep-created deserts of Spain. Metaphorically, the sheep of the West eat up not only all animals that prey upon them—coyotes, wildcats, and eagles especially—but badgers, skunks, foxes, ringtails and others. On some sheep ranges, wholesale poisoning and trapping have destroyed nearly all of them. The surface of the earth does not offer a more sterile-appearing sight than some dry-land pastures of America with nothing but sheep trails across their grassless grounds. The free-enterprisers of these ranges, many of them public-owned, want no government interference; they ask only that the government maintain trappers, subsidies on mutton and wool, and tariffs against any competitive importations.

—J. FRANK DOBIE, in *The Voice of the Coyote* (Boston: Little Brown & Co., 1949), pp. 43-44.

NEARCTIC TREES

In giving to this continent some eight hundred tree species, of which almost a hundred are either of the highest importance as saw timber or pulpwood or tanbark or of some other value, Nature distributed them upon the continent in a grand and simple plan. There is a great band of needle-leaved trees, conifers or softwoods, stretching from ocean to ocean through Canada and Alaska, and extending in long fingers down the eastern and western mountain chains of the United States. South of this lies the finest temperate hardwood forest in the world—the broad-leaved, winter-naked trees. These are found between the Atlantic Ocean and the prairies, and they run out on the prairies along every stream course almost to the foot of the Rockies. Southward still, on the Atlantic coast, begins a forest richest of all in species, commingling southern pines, deciduous hardwoods, and evergreen hardwoods, the last typified by the live oak. Then, to complete the picture, there are two small zones that are almost all evergreen hardwood—tropical Florida with its outpost of West Indian trees, and California with its live oaks and fragrant chaparral. Add one more, the thorn forest that comes up from the Mexican highlands bringing the mesquite and cacti of tree-like growth along the southwestern border, and you have the simplified geography of the North American sylva.

—D. C. PEATTIE, in *American Heartwood* (Boston: Houghton Mifflin Co., 1949), pp. 2-3.

SUGGESTED READING (see pp. 506-511)

Classics and Milestones: Wallace, Merriam.

Recent and Informative: Bates, 1952; Bailey, 1953; Beecher, 1954; Carson, 1951; Cowles, 1932; Deevey, 1951; Griffin, 1948, 1950; Hasler & Larsen, 1955; Heilbrunn, 1954; Ingle, 1954; McDonald, 1952; Milne & Milne, 1949; Nicholas, 1955; Riley, 1952; Schmidt-Nielsen, 1949, 1953; Teale, 1951; Vevers, 1952; Walford, 1951; Waterman, 1955; Went, 1949, 1955; Yearbook of Agriculture, U.S.D.A., 1941.

22 · The History of Life

1. THE RECORD IN THE ROCKS—THE ARCHEOZOIC ERA, THE PROTEROZOIC ERA, THE PALEOZOIC ERA, THE MESOZOIC ERA, THE CENOZOIC ERA. 2. TIME. 3. FOSSILS—FOSSIL HISTORIES.

CHANGE is a challenging feature of the past. Even in the few centuries since man began to sketch on cave walls, the kinds of animals around him have altered. No longer do the familiar mammals of Europe include the bison and the mammoth, although these were drawn artistically (Photos 397, 398) by early inhabitants of the region near Ariege, in southern France. The mammoth, in fact, has been extinct for longer than written history extends. The bison of Europe in a wild state has been out of the picture for almost as long.

Within recorded time, the passenger pigeon, the heath hen, the great auk, and others have disappeared from the American scene. Despite human intervention, the Mississippi has added hundreds of square miles of delta, the Colorado River has twice switched its course (producing a new inland salt lake—the Salton Sink in California), and islands just off the Florida coast have appeared and vanished in the Dry Tortugas group.

In our western states, great glaciers (Photo 374) have receded hundreds of feet to several miles from the points at which they ended when discovered a few decades ago. At Pozzuoli, Italy, the ornate columns of the Temple of Serapis now shown to visitors are pitted with the chambers of rock-boring clams. These animals attacked the limestone pillars while this area near Naples was below sea level— covered by the Mediterranean—for a period between the time of Roman civilization and the present.

These examples are typical of the alterations in the earth's form and population that have occurred within quite recent times. For information on still earlier periods of history, it is necessary to rely upon the findings of geologists (who study rocks) and of paleontologists (who investigate fossil remains of plants and animals).

The paleontologist is interested not only in what kind of organism a fossil represents, but where—geographically and chronologically in the sequence of rocks—the fossil was found. His records constitute direct evidence showing the amount and direction of change in the flora and fauna of prehistoric times.

1. THE RECORD IN THE ROCKS

Rocks are of two main types: **igneous** ones, formed by the solidification of hot, fluid magma, and **sedimentary** ones, built up as successive layers at ordinary temperatures. Since the sediments composing sedimentary rocks are derived partly from erosion of preexisting sedimentary rocks and partly from igneous rocks that have disintegrated, it is not difficult to extrapolate the rock-building process into a remote past when there were no sedimentary rocks, but only igneous ones. But to do this requires an immensity of time, and also that ice, water, and wind be eliminated from the scene, since these are the forces that transport the sedimentary particles. If the earth were considerably warmer than it is today—say, above 100 degrees Centigrade (212 degrees Fahrenheit)—the ice and water problem would vanish, since there could be neither—only steam in the atmosphere. Without water, there could be no life as we know it today, and this concept of an originally lifeless earth, composed exclusively of igneous warm rocks, undergoing violent long-term changes through earthquakes and volcanic activity, is held widely among modern geologists.

If this explanation is correct, the earth has cooled slowly to its present temperature. Rather early in the process, the rocks and atmosphere reached temperatures where the steam could condense, rain down, and some water flow over the surface. Soon fragments of the igneous rock were being swept by water currents to lakes and seas, there to settle and consolidate. As the depth of these sediments increased, and as more water accumulated over them, pressure consolidated the particles into rocks: sandstone from sand, conglomerate from gravel, shale from the fine flake-shaped particles of mud. Some of these earliest rocks still exist. They have been elevated above sea level by mountain building, and have suffered physical and chemical changes through long periods of immense pressure and local heating by volcanic activity. Yet they are still recognizable—and they rest firmly on igneous rock that underlay them at that early date. That it is the *same* igneous rock is clear because these earliest sedimentary deposits follow the irregularities of contour of the underlying rock; they are "conformable" with it.

Often before one sedimentary deposit was followed by a later one, the first was exposed to erosive action, its surface pitted and carved by water and wind. The tilt of the exposed strata commonly is such that erosive action cut across the grain, so to speak. Then, when new sediments were laid down on top of the older, they showed a distinct difference in the layering. They were not conformable, and the **unconformity** is taken as clear evidence of a long interval of time between the deposition of the first and second sedimentary rocks. Moreover, the changes due to pressure and local heating are not so severe in the upper layer as in the lower; the second strata are less "metamorphosed" from their original sedimentary form. This too is an indication of difference in age.

In interpreting the record in the rocks geologists follow the same general rule as other scientists: a theory to account for observed data should include the fewest possible assumptions. Accordingly, they postulate that

1. events in the past have occurred at about the same rate as they do now;

2. in general, the thicker a layer of rock is, the longer must have been the time required for its formation;

3. sedimentary deposits have been accumulated in consecutive order; unless there is evidence of disturbance; the oldest layer in a series must be the bottom layer;

4. unless there is evidence indicating that fossilized organisms burrowed into a layer of rock after its formation, the fossils found in a particular stratum must represent life of the period during which the rock was being deposited.

The Archeozoic Era

If the physical conditions in the earliest seas involved temperatures such as have been suggested, the environment would not be hospitable to life as we know it today. But as cooling proceeded, the situation became more suitable. Thus, if we grant the geologists the historical development of the earth as just outlined, no fossil remains should be anticipated in the earliest sedimentary rocks. Careful study of the rocks themselves establishes the fact that there are, indeed, no fossils there of any kind. Nor is there any indication of the existence of life. This information does not prove the hypothesis, but it does not disprove it either. A fossilized human skeleton or the clear imprint of an oak leaf would render the hypothesis untenable. But the facts of the case are clear—no fossils. For convenience these oldest sedimentary strata are referred to as **Early Archeozoic** in age, with Archeozoic an immensity of time called an **era.**

There is also a **Late Archeozoic** section to this era, consisting of strata that lie unconformably on the early Archeozoic rocks. And in these later sediments are a few accumulations of graphite. From their form and position, it is believed that the graphite represents not carbon brought to the surface through volcanic action, but carbon consolidated from the dead bodies of single-celled organisms. This would be an indication of life. It is a suggestion, not a true fossil record, but this indication in the light of more recent sedimentary inclusions is sufficient to give to the era the name Archeozoic—meaning "ancient life." Archeozoic strata are exposed in North America in the Laurentian hills around Hud-

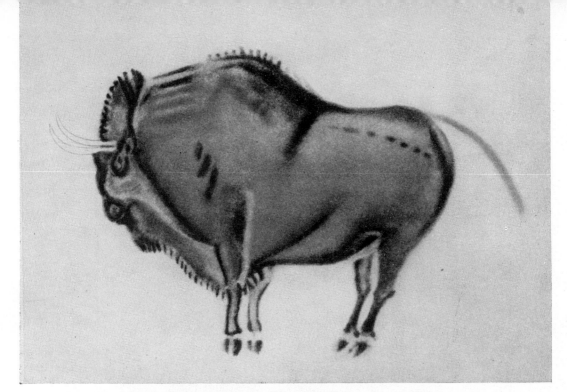

397. A European bison, possibly now extinct; as late as 1940 a few herds were maintained in private parks. As a wild animal in Europe it has been unknown for centuries. The American representative of this animal was almost exterminated a few decades ago.

Cave Paintings in the Vicinity of Altamira, Spain, Are the Work of Prehistoric Men, Possibly 20,000 Years Ago. They Represent Far More Accurate Draftsmanship and Keener Observation of Common Animals Than Is Known from Any Period until Recent Times.

398. A European wild boar, drawn to show how the legs moved in running. This illustrates early man's attempt to animate drawings in a style made successful only with the invention of moving pictures.

399. When the Colorado River eroded northern Arizona to form the Grand Canyon, it exposed an incomparable section of earth history in the successive levels of stratified rock. At this point on the north rim, the canyon is 14 miles wide and a mile deep. The south rim is 1,000 feet lower than the north, and drainage and weather on the two rims are so different that the fauna and flora on them are quite unlike.

son Bay and in the innermost gorge of the Grand Canyon (Photo 399) in Arizona.

The Proterozoic Era

A far greater unconformity and lessening of metamorphosis indicates an enormous gap in time between the laying down of the late Archeozoic sediments and those of the next more recent. During this period the Archeozoic rocks were elevated into air, eroded away, and almost obliterated. They were then lowered below sea level again by further changes in the wrinkled surface of the earth. On their remains a new series of strata were laid down. And in these, in addition to more graphite with an apparent organic origin, and iron ore deposits that may represent bacterial action, there are great layers of limestone and a few real fossils. The limestone is so consolidated that no evidence is left to indicate what kind of organisms may have produced it, but its extent, position, and form do not suggest any other possible source. The fossils are very strange ones—of alga-like plants similar to none known in later geological formations and like none alive today. It is logical to conclude from these facts that in the seas where these sediments accumulated there were no plants or animals with sufficiently rigid bodies to make good fossils. There were no woody plants, or vertebrae, or teeth; not even a clam shell is indicated. In view of the more recent sequence of fossils, these findings and conclusions are entirely harmonious. The period of time represented by these strata is described as the **Proterozoic Era,** meaning "very early life."

The Paleozoic Era

The strata overlying the Proterozoic beds are again very unconformable—indicating another great gap in the record, when rocks we can now examine were not accumulating sediments but were, instead, exposed to air and being eroded away. But there are plenty of rock formations above the Proterozoic, and all of them are rich in fossils. In that tremendous interval of time between the laying down of the Proterozoic and the beginning of the next sediments, plant and animal life had not only become widespread and abundant, but the kinds of organisms had changed. Now they had skeletal parts that could be perpetu-

ated in fossil form. Not that this is a requirement—since in these strata there are beautiful imprints of jellyfish that died and came to rest in soft fluffy mud. Limy sponges, lamp shells (brachiopods), echinoderms (called cystoids) somewhat in the pattern of sea urchins, and great numbers of a group of arthropods now long extinct (the trilobites—Photo 400—named from the three-part body), plus various kinds of worms, crept and swam between algae. Some of the limy algae are abundant in the fossil record; imprints of others are well known.

Since these fossils were discovered first in a sedimentary deposit in Wales (called *Cambria* by the Romans), they were referred to as **Cambrian period** animals and plants. Many other areas of Cambrian rocks are now known. Everywhere they emphasize the apparent suddenness in the appearance of good fossils—merely demonstrating what an enormity of time passed by in the gap in the record between the Proterozoic formations and these later sediments. The list of genera and species of Cambrian fossils grows annually, but none of them (except the remarkable little brachiopod, Lingula) represents even a family that is alive today. There are no snails, no crabs, no insects, no spiders, no vertebrates of any description. Not a single evidence of a backbone or a tooth appears in those Cambrian fossil collections. Nor is there any sign of plant or animal life that might have been on land. Every one is a sea organism, and the flora is exclusively thallophyte. There is no lack of specimens, and many of them are well preserved. Hence the only acceptable inference is that the world in those days was populated rather densely in the ocean with algae and the simpler invertebrates, but that there was neither land flora nor fauna, no vertebrates whatever.

A lesser unconformity distinguishes the Cambrian rocks from those next more recent—the **Ordovician** series, named in honor of an early tribe of European natives. In these sedimentary deposits are embedded the earliest known corals, the first coiled snail shells, clams, the first nautiloids (with chambered shells like the modern Pearly Nautilus—but with straight cones, not coiled—Photo 402), sea urchins and sea lilies, new trilobites (Photo 401), and sea scorpions (eurypterids). A few fossils indicate the first of the vertebrates—armored, flattened creatures called *ostracoderms* (literally "shell skinned"); they were limbless, jawless members (Photo 403) of the cyclostome group to which our modern lampreys belong. Apparently they developed in fresh water, and then some migrated to the seas. There is evidence, too, of a few peculiar land plants, with distinctly separate root and shoot, stomata, and sparse ducts of xylem. All of them were psilopsids (pp. 15, 253). This immediately suggests that a few algae and bryophytes (no doubt some bacteria and fungi, too) had emerged and begun to live an aerial, terrestrial existence, to change minerals into the first soil. The sea scorpions (Photo 404), moreover, appear to have been able to climb out on land for brief periods, as the first land animals. It is believed that they were scavengers, much as are the horseshoe crabs (Xiphosura) of modern days.

Again a discontinuity ushered in a new period, the **Silurian,** with sediments lying unconformably over the Ordovician wherever both are represented in the same locality. The distribution of these rocks indicates that the interval between these two periods was one of great mountain building, and that Silurian seas were much more restricted than those of the Ordovician. The plant records are little changed, but fossil animals include new reef-forming corals, starfish, giant sea lilies, new trilobites (Photo 405), and sea scorpions in great numbers and a variety of sizes—some of them as much as 12 feet long, others clearly adapted for life on land. A new branch of the mollusk group—the ammonoids—and more and bigger ostracoderm fish competed with the sea scorpions in the sea, while new groups of fish invaded fresh water. There, apparently, the first fish with jaws appeared. The existence of freshwater fish indicates that there must have been food for them in these sites, which means that smaller creatures had followed plants into fresh-water habitats.

Another unconformity is followed by more recent rocks representing the **Devonian** period. This has been referred to often as the "Age of Fishes," for the seas must have been full of them. Some fossilized forms are as long as 30 feet, with great biting jaws. Others had lobe-like fins or whole rows of fins along the sides. Both cartilaginous fish, such as sharks and rays, and bony fish, like most that are familiar in modern waters, were well represented, and a few forms of seemingly intermediate position between fish and amphibians, with developing lungs, are found in fresh-water deposits. The invertebrates included new examples of types found in earlier strata, but with the addition of a few horseshoe crabs—the beginning of a line which has continued relatively unchanged to a few species alive in modern seas (Photo 110). Although much of the exposed land surface in the Devonian period was arid, there were also the first true forests, composed of giant ferns, clubmosses, and horsetails. In addition to scorpions, there were centipedes, some spiders, and a few rather simple insects. But as far as can be learned, no flowering plants existed and the complex interrelationship between pollinating insects and nectar-producing flowers had not yet begun. The plant life, however, included many forms with good conducting tissues, and these allowed upright growth to considerable heights. It is likely that among these forests stood a few seed ferns, earliest of the seed plants.

Following the Devonian came a period when much of the continent was low and marshy. The fossils show that bigger ferns, clubmosses, and horsetails than ever before now grew in dense thickets, to heights of 100 feet or more (Photos 406-408) through the marshes, with here and there a few seed ferns and other primitive gymnosperms. But for some unknown reason there were fluctuations in the land level that successively inundated and killed these forests, then raised them enough for new growth to spread on top. Layer after layer of dead plant material was added in this way, and the accumulation did not decay into a soil but became consolidated into coal. The coal deposits in this period are so extensive, in fact, that they have given the name to the time—the **Carboniferous period.** Separation of coal seams often exposes beautiful prints of fern fronds (Photo 408), and the shales of the period include fossil dragonflies with more than a two-foot wingspread, cock-

400. A large trilobite of the Cambrian period. Many of these reached a length of eight inches or more.

401. A more ornate trilobite of Ordovician age. Note the plates on the back and the long tail spines.

402. Ordovician rocks include many straight-shelled chambered mollusk shells (Orthoceras).

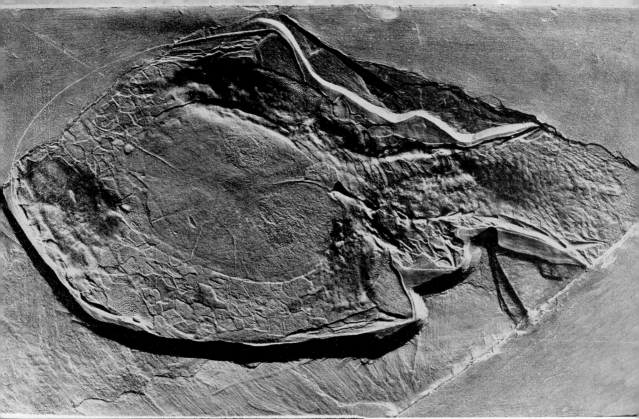

403. An armored jawless fish (ostracoderm) from the older strata of the Devonian age. (*Photo from American Museum of Natural History.*)

404. A sea scorpion in Silurian rock (*right*) and a plaster model reconstructed from study of many specimens (*left*).

PALEOZOIC ANIMALS

405. Devonion trilobites were still different from earlier types and their structure allowed them to curl up like a modern wood louse or armadillo—a feature that appears to have been an advance over Cambrian and Ordovician styles.

406. Modern techniques allow preparation of microscopic sections of fossils so that internal anatomical details can be studied. This cross section of a Carboniferous period root shows the remarkable preservation of cellular structure from which much can be learned about the plants of the time.

PALEOZOIC PLANTS

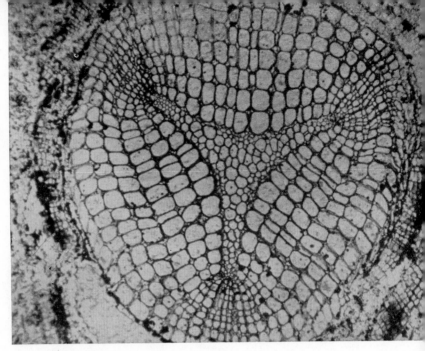

407. A fossilized stump of a "scale tree" in a Nova Scotia coal mine of Carboniferous age. Scale trees, long extinct, reached a height of over 100 feet, and had flat, stiff, scale-like leaves over trunk and branches.

408. Fern fronds in Carboniferous shales of Nova Scotia. Alternate flooding of swampy land, covering it with mud and sand, and elevation enough for ferns to grow again, preserved many good fossils.

409. A bony fish in fine-grained limestone of Permian age.

410. Fossilized logs and fragments exposed in the Petrified Forest National Monument near Holbrook, Arizona. These trees, of Triassic age, apparently were washed downstream and covered by sand. More recently, the sand was carried off by wind, leaving the fossils exposed.

roaches, and other insects, although all of them belong to orders in which no pupal stage is found. Horseshoe crabs crept over the mud-flats, and sea scorpions were still prevalent. On land the true scorpions and spiders became much more numerous, no doubt feeding on the newly abundant insect life. In the seas and fresh waters, fish continued to increase in numbers of types, but in the swamps the amphibians reached a dominant position, and then declined again toward the close of the Carboniferous as reptiles became common and successful competitors.

With a sixth period, the **Permian,** another great era of time came to an end. The Cambrian, Ordovician, Silurian, Devonian, Carboniferous, and Permian are grouped as the **Paleozoic era** (from *paleo* = old), comparable in significance with the Archeozoic and Proterozoic, and similarly set off from the rest of geological history by great unconformities in the stratified rock and by tremendous changes in the embedded fossils (Photo 409).

The Permian, which completes the era, was a time of great upheavals of the earth—the period when the Appalachian Mountain chain was raised above the rest of North America, together with thousands of feet of paleozoic rocks. Regions that were swamps became deserts, and conversely—placing great stress on the ability of living things to change and adapt themselves to new conditions. The giant ferns, horsetails, and clubmosses continued in the marshes, but the first cone-bearing trees spread toward drier areas. These were no longer the cycads and seed ferns of earlier periods but members of the Coniferales, the group to which most of our modern gymnosperms belong. Horseshoe crabs dwindled in number of kinds; trilobites and ostracoderms disappeared entirely. Simultaneously the fossil record is full of reptiles—mostly of lizard form, but of assorted sizes—from small insectivorous types to larger herbivorous and predacious kinds. Some of them are mammal-like but not mammals. None was a true dinosaur, though the scene was rapidly approaching the reptile-filled condition of the next few periods of geologic history. Nor were true turtles, snakes, or alligators represented in the Permian fauna; none of the many reptile types survived into modern times.

The Mesozoic Era

Following the Paleozoic era, the time schedule is represented by three great formations of rocks with many fossils—the periods of the **Mesozoic era** (*meso* = middle). Lowest and earliest of these sediments is the **Triassic** layer of deposits, with more diverse reptiles than ever and with the appearance of small versions of those giants of the group—the dinosaurs. Some of the reptiles had reinvaded the sea, with adaptations that made them fish- or whale-like. Others possessed the new ability to run on two hind legs, and apparently used the fore limbs as hands for holding food. Still others were so constructed that they could stand on all four legs, with belly clear of the ground, rather than drag themselves along using the limbs as levers. The flora, meanwhile, is represented among the Triassic fossils by a waning number of ferns, horsetails, and clubmosses, and by an increasing number of more modern seed plants, all of them still gymnosperms (Photo 410).

The dominant forms of life in the **Jurassic** and **Cretaceous**—the two periods of Mesozoic time that followed the Triassic—were reptiles. In the Jurassic (named for the Jura mountains in France and Switzerland, where the first formations of this period were found) was Brontosaurus, a vegetarian reptile of which everyone has heard; with its long neck and tail it reached a total length of 80 feet or more (Figs. 22-1, 23-13). Pictures of the reconstructed Stegosaurus (another huge plant-eater, with armored flaps along its back) and of the super flesh-eater Allosaurus (nearly half as long as Brontosaurus and standing 14 feet high in a bipedal gait) are familiar to every school child. There is good evidence that these enormous animals waded around in swamps, where the buoyant force of the water helped support their bulk and weight. But spectacular as these animals are, even in fossil form, they give a false notion of sizes. They are exceptions rather than the rule, since most of the reptiles were smaller. They swam, ran, crept, and even flew, for in the Jurassic are fossilized the first winged reptiles—the pterosaurs—which must have been the "sparrows" of the day.

At the same time, skeletal remains of feathers represent the first birds—though these had long tails, reptile-like bony structure, and teeth; Archaeopteryx and Archaeornis have been much publicized; they were the largest and most clearly preserved (Photo 411). Whether these first birds were warm-blooded or not is unknown, but mammals also make their appearance in the Jurassic sediments and there is little doubt that they were already controlling their body temperatures. The mammals are all small, probably insectivorous in habit, and are represented in the record chiefly by delicate jawbones and teeth. None is closely similar to any alive at the present time. During the Jurassic, the ammonoid group of mollusks seemingly went wild in complex shell production. The fish, however, have a more modern form, and the vegetation on land continued the shift in emphasis toward the gymnosperms, with more conifers and fewer ferns, horsetails, and clubmosses; the seed ferns became extinct.

In the Cretaceous period with which the Mesozoic era closed, the geological conditions were those of tremendous upheaval. In the Americas, the Rocky Mountains and the Andes were formed and much of the continental area became raised well above the sea, restricting the oceans more than had occurred for a long time. The climate changed slowly, the temperature dropping far enough for glaciers to form toward the end of the period. The reptiles reached the peak of their dominance (Photos 412-414), with such famous forms as Triceratops (a herbivore), Tyrannosaurus (a giant predator), and the pterodactyls (a flying type). On a smaller scale, the first salamanders and frogs replace the previous types of amphibians; shark-like fish and new bony fish are found instead of the "more primitive" forms of earlier strata. Warm-bloodedness was probably well established, for there are remains of many birds—all of them toothed—and an assortment of marsupial mammals. Through the Cretaceous strata, it is apparent, moreover, that the earliest marsupials were in North America, but that many kinds of them migrated for an unknown reason through the Alaskan area into Asia and downward to Australasia on the one hand, and into South America on the other. It is in the later Cretaceous, in fact, that the Australasian area with its stock of marsupials began its long period of isolation from the rest of the land masses of the world. South America also became separated, but the divorcement was of much shorter standing and the fauna and flora are correspondingly less unique.

During the Cretaceous, the angiosperms (flowering plants) appeared gradually, and such seemingly modern trees as magnolia, oak, and sycamore took a place beside the many now-extinct forms of vegetation. In the magnolia, however, there are petals. This suggests that the relationship between pollinating insects and insect-attracting flowers (complete with corolla and nectaries) began at this time. There is even an improvement in the fossil record of insects, for we have some amber of Cretaceous age—hardened gum that oozed from pine trees, catching unwary insects that

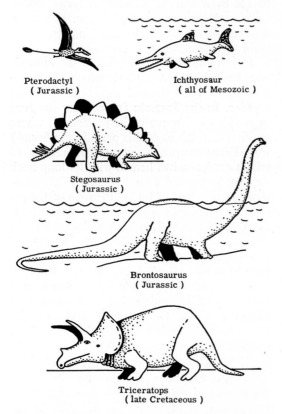

Pterodactyl
(Jurassic)

Ichthyosaur
(all of Mesozoic)

Stegosaurus
(Jurassic)

Brontosaurus
(Jurassic)

Triceratops
(late Cretaceous)

FIG. 22-1. *Most spectacular of Mesozoic animals were the giant reptiles which invaded every niche and competed successfully there for millions of years.*

411. A toothed bird, Archaeopteryx, shows one of the steps between reptilian ancestors and modern birds. The tail, with unusual feather pattern and length, is to the right.

412. A duck-billed dinosaur in process of excavation from Upper Cretaceous rocks in Alberta. Exposed bone surfaces have been varnished to protect them from weather while further rock is chipped away.

413. Reconstruction of an extinct dinosaur of medium size in a park in Calgary, Alberta.

414. Footprints of dinosaurs exposed along modern river banks tell something of the gait of these extinct animals.

415. An ammonoid from the Cretaceous (*upper right*) with a shell of the modern chambered nautilus (sectioned on its mid-line to display the internal partitions). The nautilus is the only surviving near relative which continues to secrete such a complex shell.

CHAMBERED SHELLS OF CEPHALOPOD MOLLUSKS

416. An amber fragment in a small dish.

417. The same specimen but covered by a liquid (xylol) having approximately the same optical qualities (refractive index) as the amber. This procedure makes surface scratches much less conspicuous, so that any inclusions in the amber are evident.

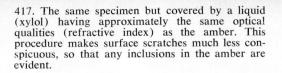

AMBER OF EOCENE AGE

OFTEN CONTAINS FOSSILIZED

REMAINS OF INSECTS

418. Closer view of wasps, spiders, and other inclusions in the fossilized gum.

alighted on the shiny surface, covering and preserving them. The insects are as perfect as though embedded in modern plastics, allowing entomologists to count every bristle and to identify each specimen nicely. Along with the insects are small remains of plants—leaves, flowers, and the like—that the wind blew against the sticky gum, that the resin covered, and that can now be studied in the hardened amber.

There can be no doubt that the climatic changes which accompanied the close of the Cretaceous were highly unfavorable for bryophytes and the larger spore plants, and for the amphibians and lizards. The aridity of major land areas reduced the ability of these plants to reproduce themselves, since they depended on rain for that process. And the cool air slowed the movements and reactions of the cold-blooded terrestrial vertebrates, making them easy prey for the small opportunistic placental mammals that appeared in numbers at this time. Even the reduction in swamp land removed much of the vegetation on which the herbivorous lizards depended for support of their large size. Their disappearance removed the meat on which the huge predacious dinosaurs based their activities.

The Cenozoic Era

A major unconformity separates the strata of the Cretaceous from all more recent formations, indicating the length of time between the laying down of the latest of known Mesozoic sediments and the earliest of the new era, the **Cenozoic.** This blank in the record conceals the final fate of the dinosaurs and ammonoids (Photo 415), for in the Cenozoic there are none, and the reptile group is almost in modern form at the very outset. Progress made by the angiosperms is also a spectacular change, for in addition to the more familiar types of flowering plants, the grasses and palms (monocots) are numerous and widespread for the first time. The grasses, in fact, formed the first prairies and opened up the higher land to new types of herbivorous mammals. The plants, indeed, seem clearly to be shifting emphasis from the tree type (with perennial growth and large size—as in the late Paleozoic and through the Mesozoic) into shorter-term annuals and biennials. They became increasingly herbaceous and matched more adequately the comparatively severe climates of the Cenozoic.

If the present time is counted as a period in the geologic scale, it must belong to the Cenozoic and compose the sixth of its divisions. The other five, in sequence, are the Eocene, Oligocene, Miocene, Pliocene, and Pleistocene. They represent an era with exceptionally active movements of the earth's surface. The Rocky Mountains, which arose in the Cretaceous, became eroded and were then elevated farther. The Sierra Nevada, including Mount Whitney (highest in the U.S.), were formed. The Colorado River cut Grand Canyon. The Alps and the Himalayas (including Mount Everest, highest of all) developed from below sea level to more than their present height. Later the Pacific Coast Range arose. Then from the Arctic and every mountain peak, glaciers crowded down over America and great areas elsewhere in the Northern Hemisphere.

The earliest of the Cenozoic rock formations, the **Eocene,** is full of fine fossils, including great quantities of amber—much of it containing insects and plant fragments (Photos 416-418). In fact, from the Baltic amber (collected along the shores of the Baltic Sea, particularly near Koenigsberg and the Sammland Peninsula) we know more about the insect fauna of the Eocene than about this group of animals in any other prehistoric period. Most of the insects were of simpler groups—those without a pupal stage, or the less specialized members of metamorphosing orders. But among them are also ants very much like those of today, and bees and wasps. Fossil bones indicate, moreover, that the Eocene mammals were much more modern in appearance, though none of them was the same as kinds alive today. Marsupials were numerous and diverse, but apparently a great bulk of the mammals no longer depended on insects as a steady diet; they employed herbivorous or carnivorous habits and were well adapted in these two basic directions. However, the predatory mammals were sufficiently active that there was emphasis on ability to escape, and the herbivores were either armored in a way comparable to the modern rhinoceros, or fleet of foot, more like deer. Small horse-like forms (Fig. 22-2) appear for the first time, and also elephant-like (Photo 419), bear-like, and rat-like mammals. Forms similar to the sea cow (manatee) lived in the swamps, and whale-like animals were living an amphibious life at the sea shore, apparently escaping to the open water whenever pursued on land. Bats are found as Eocene fossils, fully formed, using the same method of flight as the flying reptiles of the Mesozoic. And fragmentary remains suggest the existence of the first lemur-like primates.

The **Oligocene** period represents for mammals what the Jurassic did for the reptiles—a time of sudden diversification. The remains of cud-chewing ruminants outnumber all other mammal remains, but they are not clear-cut deer, or camels, or cattle. The famous sabre-

toothed cats (Fig. 22-3) are members of the fauna—apparently well adapted for penetrating the thick armored hide of the larger, slower herbivores. Other mammals, however, are sufficiently unlike modern types that a

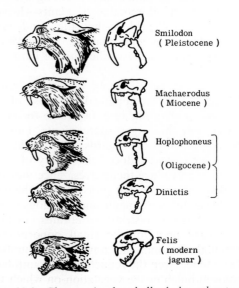

FIG. 22-3. *Changes in the skull of the sabre-tooth cats paralleled a specialization in progressively larger prey. When these latter became scarce during the Pleistocene, the sabre-tooth cats died out entirely.* (*Redrawn after Wells, Huxley & Wells.*)

present-day biologist would have difficulty assigning them places without detailed comparative study. Some were pig-like, some beaver-like, and some elephant-like; yet the distinguishing features of pigs, beavers, and elephants (Photo 419) are specializations these animals lacked. Porcupines, however, would be identified easily; apparently they arose in Africa, spread to South America, thence eventually to North America. South American fossils include marsupials of Oligocene age that were large carnivores the size of bears. And in the seas were sea cows much more like modern manatees, and an assortment of true whales. Of primates, several types are known, each represented by jaw-bones and teeth.

In the **Miocene** the climate was cooler again. The fossils represent perhaps 50 per cent of the modern groups of animals, in recognizably recent form. The sabre-toothed cats were bigger than before, and the elephants larger and more elephant-like (Photo 419). Dogs and bears that a modern anato-

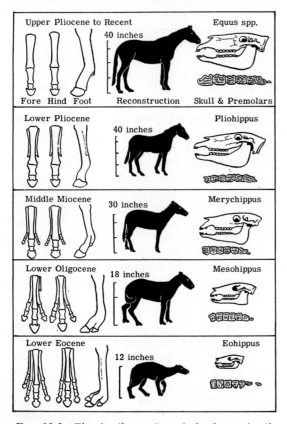

FIG. 22-2. *The fossil remains of the horse family are complete enough to be arranged in a series showing gradual increase in size and in modifications for running.*

mist would describe as "very generalized" apparently preyed on the herds of herbivores —the ungulates, rabbits, and rats. In North America the fossils include rhinoceros, camel, and tapir. In Europe, in addition to deer, there were antelopes and giraffe-like mammals. Seal and walrus appeared, and whales reached a peak of development not equaled in any other period. The mastodon, with its four tusks, represented the elephant group in northern North America at the end of the Miocene, although what it found to eat in sufficient bulk is something of a mystery. Vegetation was of much more modern type, but the cool weather placed further emphasis on annuals and monocotyledons like grasses. This was the scene in which lived the first primates of which satisfactory fossil remains have been discovered. One was gibbon-like, another clearly ape-like (Dryopithecus). In South America and Australia, meanwhile, the marsupials reached new heights of development, with cat-like, dog-like, and other highly-adapted forms.

The **Pliocene** period brought still cooler weather, more dominant growth of grasslands, and further ungulate country. Hoofed mammals, cattle, goats, and sheep were abundant in the palearctic area but none is known from North America. Horses and camels browsed on American plains, however, and the mastodon spread into South America as well. In spite of these oddities, perhaps 80 per cent of the animal population would be recognizable —though different in species and often in genus from any modern types. Dogs, wolves, foxes, bears, hyenas, and others were abundant, as were also the smaller rats and mice, lemmings, and the like on which they fed.

During the Pliocene two land bridges provided new avenues for animal migration: (1) between North and South America, allowing the mastodon and a great variety of placental mammals to go southward, a few marsupials and armadillos to come northward; at this stage, South America had even marsupial sabre-toothed cats, but the competition with placental mammals was too unequal and soon the marsupials largely disappeared; and (2) between North America and Siberia, allowing late in the period a major movement of ungulates from the palearctic realm into the nearctic; by this time, however, the weather

was sufficiently cool that only the hardier, cold-tolerant types came over, and none of them ever reached South America. Similarly, the cold weather seems to have driven the ungulates from Europe into Africa, so that it is possible to compare more accurately the grassy plains of Pliocene Europe with the velds of modern Africa; both are characterized by their ungulates.

In the **Pleistocene** the chill in the weather reached such proportions that glaciers began to advance over the holarctic realm from the North Pole, and from every mountain range farther south out into the plains. The term "Ice Age" is applied commonly and with reason. Actually, there were two glacial sessions of long standing, with a sizable interglacial period between, and in each of the glacial times the ice advanced twice, with a major retreat separating the two. Rain fell so widely that the Sahara Desert and our western arid lands turned into territory suitable for plant growth, but near the ice itself the cold winds restricted vegetation to tundra and taiga. Enormous numbers of the earlier types of life failed to adjust fast enough— either by changing geographical distribution or becoming adapted to the cool conditions and altered food available; instead they declined into extinction. Horses weathered the change both in Eurasia and North America. For a long while, camels continued on this continent; finally they went under. So too did the mastodon and the sabre-toothed cats, the giant elk (Megaceros), the ground sloth (Megatherium), and giant armadillo (Glyptodon). Yet in this adverse environment are found the first relics of human and subhuman primates, indicating the beginning of man. One of these primates, probably Cro-Magnon man, is responsible for the cave drawings of mammoths and giant elk, of sabre-toothed cats, and herds of European bison (Photo 397), since none of these survived the Pleistocene into the recent period—the modern "Age of Man."

These are the fossil records. They clearly indicate a sequence from the simpler to the more complex in both plant and animal life; from the sea to fresh water to land; from cold-bloodedness to the advent of fur, feathers, and controlled body temperature in mammals and birds; and from dependence upon water for reproduction in plant and animal to means for obviating this dependency. The gaps are plain but the lack of confusion in the sequence makes the gaps less important. It is a single story, not a series of separate and complete pictures. Throughout, the interdependence of animals and plants upon one another and upon climatic features is most evident and understandable. The present is but a continuation of a very ancient past. It has reached modern form by many slow steps, as has the very shape of the North American continent.

2. TIME

The *relative* dates of the different strata of sedimentary rocks are known with almost complete certainty. The *actual* dating is also interesting. Several methods for estimating past time are available, yet the evidence from each fits well into a single schedule:

1. The present rate at which sediments accumulate can be measured. It averages about one foot in 1,000 years. From the thickness of strata in each geological era or period, a minimum number of years for its formation can be calculated.

The rate of decay or erosion of sandstone, and of dissolution or transfer of limestone in surface water, can be studied under a variety of weather conditions. A representative value can be chosen. Wherever erosion has removed measurable amounts of strata, the minimum time required can then be calculated from the representative erosion rate.

Durations for deposit and for erosion can be added together. Except for a major factor of uncertainty in the big gaps between one era and the next, good estimates can be made of the length of each period and minor unconformity.

Taken together, these calculations suggest that the first sedimentary rocks (of Archeozoic age) were formed at least 2 billion years ago.

2. The ocean is growing saltier as new dissolved materials arrive in river water, along a route that must have been in use ever since the oceans formed. Using the most precise techniques of quantitative chemistry, the rate of increase in salt concentration can be measured. If this rate has been uniform during the past, an extrapolation can be made to learn how long ago the oceans were fresh—as recently condensed steam. The calculation indicates 2 billion years ago as the most probable date.

3. Samples of igneous rocks of obvious antiquity, such as those underlying Archeozoic sediments, include many containing both lead and uranium. Four isotopic forms of lead are present: Pb^{204}, Pb^{206}, Pb^{207}, and Pb^{208}. Uranium is in two isotopic forms: U^{235} and U^{238}.

It is known that U^{235} affects the proportions of the lead isotopes, by increasing the concentration of radioactive Pb^{207}. Correspondingly, U^{238} causes an increase in the amount of radioactive Pb^{206}. The amount of increase in radioactive lead isotopes is a known function of the time that the lead and uranium have been in close proximity. The proportions of all of these isotopes can be measured for any given sample.

For comparison with these ancient rocks, a lead-bearing sample is needed that contains an insignificant amount of uranium and the same proportion of the four isotopes of lead as was characteristic of the earth's crust when it was formed. Recent meteorites from outer space have been taken as this reference point. By comparing the proportions of lead isotopes in these and in uranium-bearing specimens of the earth's crust, a time can be calculated as the period during which the uranium present could have accounted for the entire change in proportions of lead isotopes.

Admittedly this method employs a number of risky assumptions. But the calculation comes out as 4.5 billion years to represent the age of the earth's crust. The value is somewhat greater than the 3.3 billion years obtained from other methods of estimation. No one knows, however, which is the better value. Percentagewise the difference is not great.

4. Astronomers have found that the various galaxies of the universe are speeding away from one another and from a central point at a constant rate that can be measured. If the present distances apart and the rate of expansion are used to compute a time in the past when all of the material in the universe might have occupied the central position—

perhaps ready for some vast explosion—a value of 6 billion years ago is obtained as a date for the origin of the universe.

All of these extrapolations are estimates and subject to error. But the error is not likely to be greater than a factor of two. Hence, when a geologist or geophysicist states that a certain rock sample must have been formed about a million years ago, his calculations indicate that this is the minimum. He would be satisfied with anything between one and two million years. The one-million figure is more conservative than the other, but the uncertainty is still there.

These qualifications should be kept in mind when considering the following table—an indication of the proportions of the past involved in each stage of geological history. In parentheses following the name of the period is the total time in millions of years to the end of the period since the end of the preceding one:

The method depends upon several facts: (1) in the upper atmosphere, nitrogen atoms are modified by cosmic-ray action to form carbon-14 (C^{14}), an unstable radioactive isotope of ordinary carbon-12; (2) almost at once, carbon-14 is oxidized to form radioactive carbon dioxide ($C^{14}O_2$); (3) radioactive carbon dioxide becomes thoroughly mixed with ordinary carbon dioxide in the atmosphere; (4) from the moment of its formation, carbon-14 decays at a fixed rate, such that 50 per cent of the change (its "half life") is complete in 5,568 years; (5) over immensities of time, the rates of formation and of decay of carbon-14 have reached an equilibrium, with approximately one atom of carbon-14 in every trillion atoms of carbon; (6) there is a relatively fixed total quantity of carbon participating in the carbon cycle—about 2.75 trillion tons in the atmosphere, plus perhaps 66 trillion tons in equilibrium

Chronology of the Geologic Past

Recent	today from at least 30,000 years B.C.
Cenozoic—Pleistocene (1)	30,000 B.C. to at least 1,000,000 B.C.
—Pliocene (7)	1,000,000 to 8,000,000 B.C.
—Miocene (12)	8,000,000 to 20,000,000 B.C.
—Oligocene (15)	20,000,000 to 35,000,000 B.C.
—Eocene (20)	35,000,000 to 55,000,000 B.C.
——————— Interval	perhaps 20,000,000 years
Mesozoic—Cretaceous (45)	75,000,000 to 115,000,000 B.C.
—Jurassic (35)	115,000,000 to 150,000,000 B.C.
—Triassic (45)	150,000,000 to 195,000,000 B.C.
——————— Interval	perhaps 55,000,000 years
Paleozoic—Permian (25)	250,000,000 to 275,000,000 B.C.
—Carboniferous (60)	275,000,000 to 335,000,000 B.C.
—Devonian (100)	335,000,000 to 435,000,000 B.C.
—Silurian (40)	435,000,000 to 475,000,000 B.C.
—Ordovician (75)	475,000,000 to 550,000,000 B.C.
—Cambrian (90)	550,000,000 to 640,000,000 B.C.
——————— Interval	perhaps 100,000,000 years
Proterozoic (650)	740,000,000 to 1,390,000,000 B.C.
——————— Interval	perhaps 200,000,000 years
Archeozoic (600)	1,590,000,000 to 2,190,000,000 B.C.
Oldest igneous rocks	4,500,000,000 B.C.
Origin of universe	6,000,000,000 B.C.

In 1952 a fresh method was found for estimating the age of carbon-containing objects less than 30,000 years old. Because this time span includes most of the period during which mankind has existed, information on the age of sedimentary deposits, fossils, and artifacts is particularly helpful.

with it although dissolved in fresh water and the oceans of the earth, or as ions or carbonic acid, or as bicarbonates, or bound in limestone and similar carbonates (Fig. 21-17); compared to these amounts the total in living organisms is trivial.

These facts suggest that the proportion of

C^{14}-containing carbon dioxide is essentially constant both in water and in the air around us. At the University of Chicago, W. F. Libby pointed out that plants carrying on photosynthesis obtain $C^{14}O_2$ at this fixed, low rate, and incorporate it into organic compounds. If the plant is eaten, the C^{14} is transferred into organic compounds in an animal.

So long as plant or animal is alive, it maintains among its carbon atoms the same proportion of C^{14} to C^{12} as is characteristic of atmospheric carbon dioxide. But once an organism dies, no new C^{14} is added. The amount already present decreases steadily at the known fixed rate—50 per cent in 5,568 years. By comparing the proportions of C^{14} and C^{12} in fossils, the length of time during which the C^{14} has been decaying can be computed. This is the "carbon-14 method of dating." It is limited only by the accuracy with which a sample can be measured for C^{14}. At present this limit is about 30,000 years (six half-lifes of C^{14}).

3. FOSSILS

Great credit must be given to the paleontologist, who, with infinite patience and care, pieced together this fossil record. He has shown the ingenuity usually ascribed to detectives in fitting scattered clues and in drawing conclusions from them. The nature of fossils must be appreciated in order to see to what lengths the scientist must go, and how specialized his information must be. The following are the chief sorts of fossils.

1. Reasonably intact specimens or parts of them.
   (a) Bones and teeth of vertebrates or complete mummified bodies, found in arid areas or in such sheltered sites as caves; water causes their decay and dissolution; occasionally they are preserved in polar ice, or in tar pits and asphalt lakes such as those at La Brea, California, or in sandstones (Photo 408).
   (b) Insects, spiders, flower parts, leaves, and the like, embedded in amber (Photos 416-418).
   (c) Clam shells, snail shells, other mollusk shells, lamp shells (brachiopods), worm tubes, coral formations, calcareous sponges and calcareous algae, embedded in limestone.
   (d) Silicious skeletons of radiolarians (protozoans) and diatoms, accumulated in ooze at the bottom of the ocean, often to great thicknesses, more or less consolidated. Calcareous skeletons of foraminiferans (protozoans) also accumulated as an oceanic ooze, later becoming consolidated as fossils.
   (e) Pollen grains and larger plant parts kept from decay by the toxic acid nature of the bogs in which they accumulated.

2. Petrified specimens or parts of them.
   (f) Part-for-part replacement of bone or chitinous exoskeleton or shell or plant tissue with silica, while these remains are covered in sandy sediments which later become sandstone. Later the sandstone may be eroded and blown away by wind, exposing the fossils, as has occurred in the Petrified Forest National Monument of Arizona (Photo 410) and elsewhere, or water may uncover the specimens. The fineness of grain of the fossils is much in favor of their resistance to erosion while the surrounding matrix falls away.
   (g) Part-for-part replacement with calcium carbonate.

3. Casts of specimens, particularly in fine-grained sandstone and in shales of muddy origin, where the specimen itself has not remained. Even jellyfish have been fossilized in this way. Sometimes a clam shell is embedded in sandstone, later dissolved out and the space filled by silica, forming a cast. The mold may be of the outside of the shell or of the inside, or in many instances records merely a burrow in the beach or other ground.

4. Tracks of specimens, made in mud, preserved by gentle covering of the firm footprint with soft sediments which later hardened.

5. Accumulated products secreted by living organisms, such as coral reefs, which later became consolidated into limestone.

6. Accumulated products from the incomplete decay of organisms, such as petroleum oil, coal, some graphite, some "bog iron ore."

7. Fossilized fecal pellets or regurgitated pellets, called "coprolites."

8. Gizzard stones of dinosaurs, called "gastroliths."

A moment's consideration will convince anyone of the difficulties experienced by the paleontologist in correlating all these types of evidence. Thus a fragmentary specimen in the form of a skeleton may correspond to a characteristic fecal pellet and a definite track. Associating them correctly after so many thousands or millions of years depends on close attention to fortuitous clues, and an encyclopedic familiarity not only with the living habits of all kinds of animals and plants alive today but with the nature of all forms in the past geologic eras.

Fossil Histories

The fullest of the fossil records, in tracing the origins of modern species, are to be expected where bones are large and conditions for their preservation good. The horse, elephant (Photo 419, Fig. 23-10), rhinoceros, and camel are modern descendants of many ancestors which are now well known from fossil remains. In the horse, for example, there is an excellent series (Fig. 22-2) starting with the dog-sized forest dweller, Eohippus of the Eocene (about 11 inches high at the shoulder, with three hind toes and four front ones on the ground, though only the third toe carried the weight in each case); the larger Miohippus of the Oligocene (24 inches to the shoulder, with lateral toes no longer touching the ground); the still larger Merychippus of the Miocene (40 inches); Pliohippus of the Pliocene (45 inches, with the lateral toes progressively shorter); and the true horse, Equus, of the Pleistocene and recent (60 inches, with lateral toes reduced to mere rudimentary splint bones at the base of the elongated third toe). The skull form and folding of the enamel in the grinding molar teeth follow the same sequence: Eohippus had a full set of 44 small teeth with no cement between the slight folds of the enamel; Miohippus and later genera mentioned show addition of cement and the gradual development of the present complex form of horse molars, in keeping with the change of habit from browsing to grazing. In Miocene rocks and later formations are other genera, clearly descendants of Eohippus but types that gave rise to no modern horses. The causes of their extinction are not known, but from the details of their skulls, teeth, and leg structure, it is clear that they are not part of the main line that led to Equus. Similarly, more than 10 species of Pleistocene Equus in North America failed to survive.

SUGGESTED READING (see pp. 507-510)

Recent and Informative: Deevey, 1952; Janssen, 1948; Rush, 1952.

23 · The Problem of Life Itself

1. THE INFERENCES FROM EMBRYOLOGY—INDIRECTIONS, UNUSED ORGANS, PARALLELISM. 2. THE INFERENCES FROM COMPARATIVE ANATOMY—HOMOLOGIES, VESTIGIAL ORGANS. 3. THE INFERENCES FROM COMPARATIVE PHYSIOLOGY—INTERCHANGEABILITY, SEROLOGY, COMPARABLE PIGMENTS, SUSCEPTIBILITY TO DISEASE, BLOOD SALT CONTEXT. 4. INFERENCES FROM BIOGEOGRAPHY—WALLACE' LINE, ISLAND LIFE. 5. INFERENCES FROM GENETICS—SELECTION UNDER DOMESTICATION, NATURAL FACTORS, INTERSPECIFIC CROSSES, POLYPLOIDS. 6. FACTS AND THEORIES. 7. GENERAL DEDUCTIONS—SPECIAL CREATION, EVOLUTION THROUGH INHERITANCE OF CHARACTERS ACQUIRED OR LOST BY USE OR DISUSE, EVOLUTION THROUGH PROGRESSIVE ELIMINATION OF THE LESS FIT BY NATURAL SELECTION, EVOLUTION THROUGH NATURAL SELECTION OF MUTATIONS, EVOLUTION THROUGH NATURAL SELECTION OF CHARACTERS INHERITED THROUGH THE CYTOPLASM. 8. THE MODERN SYNTHESIS. 9. THE ORIGIN OF LIFE AND OF THE PHYLA. 10. TREES OF DESCENT—DIVERGENCE. 11. BIOLOGICAL "INVENTIONS"—LOCALIZATION OF CHEMICAL REACTIONS, MULTICELLULARITY, SEXUAL REPRODUCTION. 12. REREADING THE FOSSIL RECORDS—EFFECTS OF CLIMATE, NONADAPTIVE (CONSERVATIVE) CHARACTERS, OVERSPECIALIZATION, TERMINAL ADAPTATIONS, EMBRYONIC SIMILARITIES. 13. THE POSITION OF MANKIND—CULTURES, FOSSIL HISTORY, HOMO AFRICANUS, HOMO ERECTUS, HOMO SAPIENS, MODERN MAN, HUMAN POPULATIONS.

BECAUSE life has existed on the earth for at least two billion years and during this time has changed radically, science is obliged to account for life's beginnings and explain the many changes.

Since the beginning of the Paleozoic, the fossil record suggests strongly that the plants and animals were subjected to living conditions scarcely differing from those to be found today. The temperature must have been such as to allow water to be liquid, and not to exceed 40° C. since above this point most proteins and enzyme systems are destroyed. The atmosphere must have contained nitrogen and oxygen and carbon dioxide, although not necessarily in modern proportions.

These conditions for life are rather special. None of the other planets in our solar system appears to possess a climate and atmosphere meeting these requirements. But there is no scientific reason to assume that our planet is the unique home of protoplasm, or that different types of life may not now exist on other planets in our solar system.

Astronomers believe that at least 10,000 planets around other stars in the universe may correspond closely to earth in climate and atmospheric conditions. Some day it may be possible for man to explore far enough to learn whether life exists elsewhere.

Similarly, since the fossil record from eras prior to the Paleozoic is of a different type, it is entirely possible that the earth at that time provided environmental conditions quite unlike those of the present. In seeking a reasonable account linking the factual information of the fossil record to the fuller knowledge of living kinds of life, it is important that each piece of evidence be given its proper place.

A fertilized egg is a very special package. It contains not only the inherited chromosomal and cytoplasmic features that determine whether it will develop into a worm, snail, fish, turtle, or man, but also the raw materials with which to carry on the building operation up to the point where the embryo can tap a fresh supply. From the time the egg leaves the ovary until the new individual is organized well enough to obtain additional nourishment, the embryo is on its own. In almost every instance, each hour of its embryohood is fraught with dangers against which the developing individual is entirely helpless. Hence the briefer the embryonic period, the more embryos can be expected to survive. Balanced against this is the fact that the embryo can achieve full size and reproductive capacities sooner (and hence with less likelihood of accidental death on the way) if the path of development is a straight one, without too much in the way of what might be called side trips—specializations apart from those of parental type merely for the sake of getting food earlier.

Put in terms of the manufacture of automobiles, it would be poor economy to spend twice as long on each unit by starting out putting wheels on a bare chassis so that it could be run around the shop to accumulate other parts gradually, if in half the time the "embryo" car could proceed passively in a straight line while power plant, brakes, lights, and body were set in place, acquiring wheels only when complete and ready to roll on its own to the sales room. Detours in an embryonic history are expensive. There must be an excellent reason for any that are present. The inferences to be drawn from comparative embryology are concerned, for the most part, with these expensive digressions from the main business at hand—the completion of a food-getting individual.

Indirections

If a complex mechanism is to be made in a machine shop, there must first be a master plan. From this, detailed drawings are prepared for each of the parts. The stock is distributed from the supply department to match each part, and the separate pieces are machined to size. Then they go to an assembly room and are fitted together into a workable mechanism matching the original master plan in every way. The details are completed first, and the whole emerges only when they are assembled.

An embryo does not do things in that way. It may well be that 12 hours after the egg is fertilized half of its cells will be ectoderm and half endoderm, but the first division of the egg does not set apart these two types of organization. Instead, the embryo consistently builds a whole. First cleavage occurs time after time until there is a three-dimensional mass of cells that could be called a colony. But the colony reorganizes itself to leave a large blastocoel at the center, and, after some further cell divisions, one half of the ball draws up inside the other half so that the embryo becomes a two-layered cup. The process of gastrulation identifies the cells of the ectoderm from those of the endoderm and at the same time produces an open archenteron which will become the cavity of the gut. At this stage, however, there is no separate mouth and anus, even though this may be typical of the organism into which the embryo will grow; there is a single opening to the outside world and it may close slowly as a blastopore. The infolding of the endoderm in the process of gastrulation almost obliterates the blastocoel. But now cells begin separating from the external layer of the embryo, pushing into the blastocoel and taking up definite positions there as the third layer of the developing body—the mesoderm.

Similarly, no single cell produces a nervous system. Instead, the nervous system of a vertebrate comes from an infolding and separation of a dorsal tube of ectodermal cells from end to end on the surface, and this later becomes organized into a brain and cord, into the details of the final anatomy. The embryo works from the general to the particular—blocking in the general outline and then completing details in a thousand places simultaneously.

Since the plan of the whole organism is inherent in the "simple" fertilized egg cell, and since the outcome is so definite and clear, it has seemed strange to biologists that all embryos should go through these same steps.

The similarity between a 64-cell mass of freshly cleaved cells and a crude colony is good; the correspondence between the blastula and such a coordinated colonial organism as a Volvox is astonishing; the body plan of the gastrula suggests that of a coelenterate with its two body layers; the fact that mesoderm arises in the same way in worm, fish, and man is remarkable—almost alarming. That all the vertebrates should get their nervous systems in the exact same way, whereas paired nerve strands are derived in the various invertebrate groups in as many different ways, makes one look for an explanation. With so different a final structure in prospect, why should a lamprey embryo and a human embryo go so much along the same route? More than that, why should the features that are vertebrate be added after those that are both invertebrate and vertebrate? Why should the details of mammalian structure come last in forming a mammal, and then by following just a few steps farther than was enough to complete a fish?

To be specific about a single vertebrate organ—the eye—why does every vertebrate —whether fish, amphibian, reptile, bird, or mammal—form the eye as an outgrowth from the brain plus induced parts from the head ectoderm plus mesodermal material, when this construction results in the characteristically inverted retina, requiring the light to pass through not only the chief media of the eye but also the blood vessels, nerve fibers, and ganglionic tissues of the retina before reaching the sensory cells? This mechanism introduces additional scattering and absorption of light—reducing sensitivity, acuity, and contrast discrimination. That such an eye design is not necessary is shown in the cephalopod mollusks, where octopus, squid, and cuttlefish also have a camera type of eye (very much like that of the vertebrate but differently derived) with a retina wherein the sensitive cells face the lens, not away from it. It would seem that the vertebrates agree with a strange uniformity in going about eye formation the hard way. Certainly no optical engineer would design an eye in the vertebrate plan, when the cephalopod style was available.

Unused Organs

If an embryo is on its way to become a reptile, bird, or mammal, why should its organization require the expenditure of time, energy, and material in developing structures that never will be used, though they would if the embryo were to become a fish or amphibian? Yet, in the regular course of its development and through the usual processes of differential growth, every embryo reptile, bird, or mammal arrives at a stage when four or five grooves on each side of the pharynx match up with corresponding furrows on the outside of the body, and these isolate aortic arches (Fig. 18-18) by what can only be referred to as gill slits. Occasionally, even in a human being, one of these slits may remain open as an abnormality at birth—a "cervical fistula" that must be closed by corrective surgery. In a fish or tadpole, the gill slits become functional as part of the breathing mechanism in the regular aquatic life. They close in an amphibian when it metamorphoses to the adult. The embryos of reptiles, birds, and mammals form the complete set of gill slits and vascular supply, and then go through the metamorphosis—obliterating them and most of the aortic arches—as one step in their normal development.

Similarly, in the vertebrates there are three different types of kidney organization, each distinct from the others in structure and position (Fig. 8-35). One is functional in cyclostomes. The second is the kidney of adult fish and amphibians. The third is characteristic of reptiles, birds, and mammals. But again, the embryo does not proceed with formation of the final kidney type if it is to become a mammal. Its cells organize themselves into the first type of kidney. This is now reorganized into a second type of kidney and still the embryo is not born. Finally, another major change occurs and the final kidney forms, and the remnants of the former types are slowly absorbed. Why all these steps?

Or if an embryo is to become a guinea pig or a human being, with no appreciable tail,[1] why should the embryo form a complete tail, equipped with functional muscles and nerves,

[1] The guinea pig's tail is so short that the uninitiated are often told solemnly, "If you pick up a guinea pig by its tail, its eyes will fall out!"

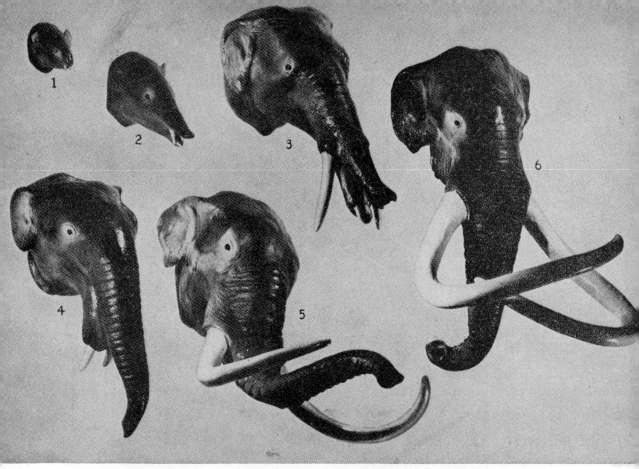

419. Models illustrating the fossil history of the elephant, based on restorations by Professor R. S. Lull of Yale University. The Eocene form (No. 1, with a 22-inch head); lower Oligocene type (No. 2, with 36-inch head); Miocene forms (Nos. 3 and 4, with 80-inch heads); a Pliocene elephant (No. 6) and the Pleistocene Mastodon (No. 5), both with 104-inch heads. All show gradual extension of the nasal region and tusks. See also Fig. 23-10 (p. 433) for the geographical distribution of these and related forms.

ATAVISM IN MAN

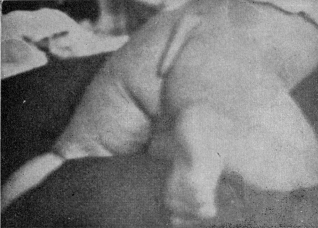

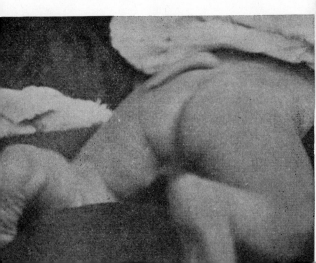

420-421. Unretouched photographs of a tailed child which was normal in every other way. Such tails are less unusual than is widely believed. The midwife or attending physician usually snips it off and does not tell the parents. The scar soon disappears.

422. The twisted head of a flounder is the product of a process which begins after the symmetrical young fish begins to swim. The eye from the under side migrates as a whole to the upper side when the young flounder commences to lie flat on the bottom.

exactly as though the tail were to be used—and then outgrow the tail so that it can scarcely be seen? Again there are occasional abnormal human embryos which complete their development and the tail keeps pace. Among some groups of people, babies born with tails are not uncommon (Photos 420-421). Rarely is the tail photographed; seldom does the event receive publicity; the medical attendant snips off the tail, and soon not even a scar marks the spot; even the parents may never be told.

At seven weeks of age, the human embryo is clearly a mammal, but just *which* mammal cannot be told yet. The tail is well developed, the hands and feet are generalized "paws," (Photos 222-225) and the body may be covered with a dense coat of hair called *lanugo*. Within a week the human characteristics appear, and the fur ordinarily is lost. Why was it formed? Sometimes a baby is born with its embryonic hair coat, though otherwise the infant is entirely normal; the covering is soon shed but the parents usually recall the shock felt when first they saw their child. The list of such structures formed and then lost again without finding use is a long one. Similar examples can be quoted from among the invertebrates. All through the animal kingdom the embryos follow a pattern of development that seems full of indirections. There must be a good reason. The indirections, moreover, all follow a definite pattern (Fig. 23-1). The pattern must be significant.

Parallelism

The sequence of steps in embryonic development corresponds with remarkable fidelity to the sequence of fossils in the geologic record. The invertebrates were alone among

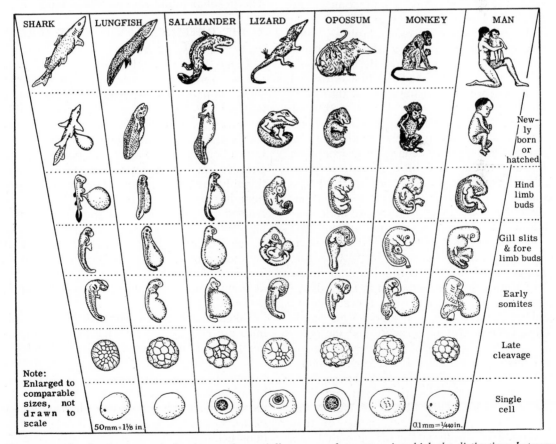

FIG. 23-1. *The development of chordate embryos follows a regular pattern in which the distinctions between classes appear first, then those between orders, and finally those between species. (Redrawn after an exhibit by the American Museum of Natural History.)*

animals until the late Ordovician. They included single-celled organisms, colonies, blastula-like spheres such as Volvox is today, gastrula-like coelenterates with two body layers, and many forms that had a mesoderm —but no fish. The early part of embryonic differentiation transforms a single fertilized egg cell through stages suggesting these invertebrates. Then the fossil record includes fish with no jaws, but with the dorsal tubular nervous system, ventral heart, and aortic arches passing between the gill slits. The embryo of a vertebrate next installs these features. The Silurian-period fossils show indications that jaws were in use by fresh-water fishes. The embryonic jaws form by the ventral fusion of the first pair of gill arches, and the jawbones originate as the supporting cartilage accompanying the aortic arches there. Before the Carboniferous period, some of the vertebrates had lungs instead of gills, achieved by the usual amphibian metamorphosis. Such a metamorphosis follows in the embryos of reptiles, birds, and mammals. By the Jurassic period, with the advent of the first birds and mammals, we can assume that the four-chambered heart was in use. In a bird or mammal embryo, the disappearance of gill slits is followed by a transformation of the busily pumping heart, changing it from two chambers to three to four. Simultaneously the kidneys are altered to reach the third-type condition. Precursors of feathers or fur develop. And still there is no clear indication in a mammalian embryo of the final outcome —beaver, pig, goat, or man. The diversification of the mammals is found in the Cenozoic section of the fossil record—latest of all in time. Embryonic specialization in these directions also waits until the other organization and reorganization is well along. This parallelism between the fossil record and the regular growth processes in a developing egg is too detailed to be ignored. The obvious inference from embryology is that the seeming inefficiencies and indirections correspond to part-way stages in the history of life on the earth. The embryo retreads much of that historic path—even taking detours that are no longer needed.

The conspicuous metamorphosis which separates the aquatic, swimming, herbivorous tadpole from the terrestrial, leaping, insectivorous frog or toad, traces the phylogenetic path but exhibits clear adaptations useful in the two types of food-getting. In the flatfishes, a somewhat similar metamorphosis transforms a completely bilateral symmetry in the young fish to a degenerate condition in which the animal lies on one side. This alteration is also a post-embryonic adaptation to feeding habits, and allows the flatfish to lie on the bottom in wait for prey to come along. The outlines of the body become the dorsal and ventral fins (Photo 288), and the lower eye migrates to the upper surface at the same time that the mouth develops a distinct twist (Photo 422). Yet the origins of all of these structures are as normal as in any other fish. A straight path toward the adult form is not found. Instead, the embryo progresses as though to produce a fish of ordinary shape. The peculiar modifications follow later.

2. THE INFERENCES FROM COMPARATIVE ANATOMY

Long before anything appreciable was known about paleontology or embryology, scientists had been busy comparing the plants and animals, seeking both characteristic differences that allowed recognition of each and the similarities between some that were worth remembering. Of these two purposes in comparative studies, identification was unquestionably the primary goal. The two questions man has asked through the ages as he examined any plant or animal are: "What is it?" and "What is it good for?" In making use of his environment, it has been imperative that he know one kind of organism from another. The basis for such recognition is comparative anatomy, and the inquiry becomes: "What is it like?"

Likenesses between plants or between animals are not necessarily hard to see. In temperate zones, most people distinguish quickly between evergreen and deciduous trees, and in the more southern climates between the broad-leaved evergreens like magnolia and the needle-leaved pines. A northern observer of trees may point out that the larch (= tamarack) is a needle-leaved, cone-bearing tree that drops its leaves in winter—hence is a deciduous type. Similarly, among animals there is seldom any hesitation in recognizing a fish apart from a bird or a mammal. This merely states that fish are more like one another than like birds or mammals. Actually, the similarity extends far beyond general body form and such features as gills and scales, to internal details and full embryological development and to the physiology of water balance and the chemistry of the blood. As with the larch, there are a few partial exceptions to any broad generalization, but the feature that is exceptional is not so impressive as the countless details of complete agreement.

Homologies

There are far more differences between a porpoise and a shark than between a porpoise and a cow. For all its aquatic habit and carnivorous diet, the fish-eating porpoise is a warm-blooded mammal—with only a few bristles to represent hair, it is true, but with placental nourishment for its embryos and milk from mammary glands available to the newborn. In its anatomy there are many specializations adapting the porpoise to swimming and its type of food (Fig. 23-2), but the preponderance of the structural plan is that of a mammal—and one not too different from an ungulate.

The flipper of the porpoise is not supported only by cartilaginous or bony rays, as are the fins of the shark or of a bony fish. Instead there is a pattern of bones consisting of a humerus (like the upper foreleg bone of the cow), a fused radius and ulna (corresponding to the lower foreleg bones that are

fused also in the ungulate), a series of carpals and metacarpals (as in the cow's high-placed "wrist" joint) and a series of five phalanges representing five fingers (Fig. 23-3). The cow has lost the use of some of its

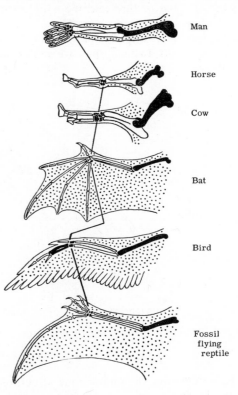

FIG. 23-3. *Adaptive radiation in the fore limb of vertebrates.*

toes in the adaptations that provide long legs used in flight from enemies on grassy prairies. The porpoise has not lost the digits but retains them within the muscular flipper.

This correspondence of bony structure in the flipper of the porpoise or whale can be found again by comparisons involving salamander or frog, lizard or turtle, bird (wing), bat (wing), cat, or man. All of these, moreover, whether eventually used in swimming, walking, flying, or writing, have the same mode or origin in the embryo, with the same blood vessel connections, the same plexus of spinal nerves, and even the same distribution of muscles—including sites of origin and insertion. To emphasize this similarity in origin and basic plan and to overlook differences in

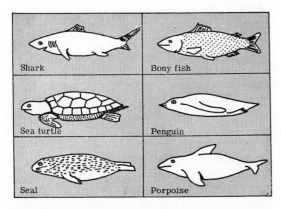

FIG. 23-2. *Adaptations for swimming include a spindle-shaped body and some means of propulsion. Various groups of animals have achieved such modifications, as convergences.*

final form and use, these anterior paired appendages of vertebrates are said to be **homologous.**

In contrast, there is a complete lack of similarity in anything except final use between the wing of a bat or bird and the wing of an insect such as a bat-sized moth. These are not homologues; their origins and structure are unlike (Fig. 23-4). Instead, they are **analogous** appendages.

a honeybee to the egglaying structures in a cricket.

That homology is not merely a matter of size may be empasized in connection with the anterior paired appendages of vertebrates. The flipper of the whale has the same bony support as the wing of a hummingbird or the front leg of a small mouse. Many tropical insects are much larger than the hummingbird or mouse, but their legs and wings have an entirely different plan and arise in a manner in no way resembling the vertebrate se-

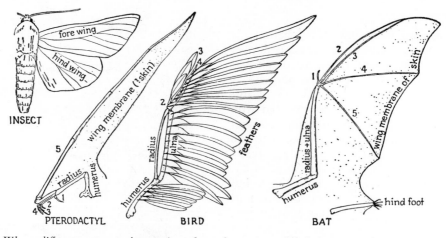

FIG. 23-4. *Where different groups of organisms have become modified for a single type of activity, only those with comparable embryonic development show homologous structures; all other similarities are analogous.* (*From T. I. Storer,* General Zoology, *McGraw-Hill Book Co.*)

The recognition of homologous structures and the separation of analogues is one of the tasks of comparative anatomists. In terms of an appendage, the problem is usually an easy one. Other features involving finer details are not so simple. There was a long wait, for example, before embryologists and anatomists concluded that a change in the hinging of the lower jaw in the embryonic transition between fish-like and later stages of amphibians released both a gill slit to become the Eustachian tube and also the single ear bone (*columella*) found in the middle ear of a bullfrog. Or that a further change in the hinging released two more pieces to yield the three familiar ear bones of man and other mammals. The homology of the ear bones to parts of the jaw mechanism was established only after long and careful research. The same is true of the homology of the many types of mouthparts among insects, or of the sting of

quence. The legs of an insect, however, are homologous with each other, with the legs of a crayfish or lobster, with the antennae and mouthparts (including the lateral jaws) of all of the arthropods, with the swimmerets under a lobster's abdomen (used in creating a breathing current, in mating by the ♂, and in carrying the eggs by the ♀), and with the side pieces of the powerful tail fin with which these crustaceans can drive themselves backward through the water. This is obviously **serial homology,** involving a series of fundamentally similar segments. In vertebrates, a corresponding series is limited to the anterior and posterior pair of appendages, both of which arise in the embryo as almost identical limb buds with a definite position, innervation, and blood supply but with no immediate indication of eventual use.

Homologies suggest strongly that organisms possessing them have a similar history. Varying degrees of similarity can be seen, and these have been used extensively in classification to indicate relationship. Homologous structures are less usual than analogous ones when members of two different phyla are compared. Homologous structures are numerous between members of the same phylum, still more abundant between members of a single class, and almost complete as a part-for-part correspondence among orders or lower categories. This is another way of saying that organisms which are basically similar in embryology and structure may be well adapted for a variety of ways of life, and that in classification those with homologous structural details are grouped together. In this way the classification (representing careful studies in comparative anatomy) comes to record basic similarities through the taxonomic grouping of plants and animals into the various categories.

Vestigial Organs

In anatomical investigations, quite a number of strange facts have come to light. For example, neither the whale nor the snake has any visible hind limbs. Yet in the whale's body, in the right place, are the remains of hind leg skeletal elements and musculature. In pythons there is a pelvic girdle of much-reduced form, and to it are attached bones ending in little claws that project through between the scales beside the cloacal aperture and that are used in copulation as claspers. In the hoactzin (a South American bird), the young are born with workable fingers with claws on the featherless wings. These are used in clambering in the tree near the nest. Finally the feathers grow and the use of the claws is lost, but the skeletal elements that support them and the muscles used in moving these fingers are strictly homologous with the corresponding part of a human hand.

In our own bodies a number of such rudimentary structures are known (Fig. 23-5). One is the vermiform appendix—a slight extension from the cecum, of no particular value to us in our omnivorous digestion, but representing a structure which is greatly elongated and important in the breakdown of cellulose through bacterial decay in such herbivores as the rabbit. Another rudiment

is the small fold of tissue at the nasal side of the eye, which represents the nictitating membrane of reptiles and amphibians—a third eyelid that a frog can close over its eye from the medial toward the lateral corner, and that in birds reaches particularly full development as transparent goggles protecting the eyes in landing and sometimes also in flight. Some mammals have a nictitating membrane, but the rudiment of this structure appears in the accessory tissues of our eyes (also those of other primates and the whale group) at what might be called the amphibian stage of their development, and remains as a visible clue into our old age.

Still another human rudiment can be seen in many human ears, as a little lump with cartilaginous support, that points downward and forward from the upper rim of the pinna. In the embryonic development this point begins as an upward projection, which later folds over, leaving a smooth contour to the

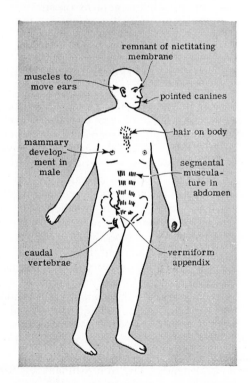

FIG. 23-5. *The human body is well supplied with vestigial organs, the homologues of which can be found in functional operation elsewhere among the vertebrates.*

rim of the ear. In other primates the same lump arises, but comes to final form as the tip of the upward pointed ear. Charles Darwin was the first to draw attention to the lump and point out its homology; it has been known as "Darwin's Point" ever since. The other feature of human ears that seems quite useless and a rudiment of a mechanism of value only in other kinds of animals, is the musculature for moving the pinna. Some people learn to use some of these muscles in very minor ear movements, but the complete musculature is there, just as in the dog or horse, suitable for rotating the pinna—if it were free to rotate and if the muscles were more fully developed and under better nervous control.

From comparative studies of homology and analogy, and of rudimentary organs, it is clear that more than chance is required to explain the consistent similarities in animals with unlike habits, and to indicate a reason for the presence in an adult organism of structural features in even a rudimentary condition, where these have no use whatever.

3. THE INFERENCES FROM COMPARATIVE PHYSIOLOGY

In the field of horticulture, man has taken extensive advantage of the close similarity in functional details between one plant and its near relatives. Thus, if one kind of apple tree has worthless fruit but grows a fine root in a given kind of soil or climate, the horticulturist may raise many such trees to sturdy sapling size, only to chop off their tops a little above the ground. The root with its short trunk becomes the "stock" into which he grafts "scions"—shoots cut from trees with fine apples but unsatisfactory root systems. The surgery requires some care, but thereafter the root of one kind supplies water and minerals to the stem, leaves, flowers, and fruit of another. The fruit always has the form of the scion type—with no indication whatever of the nature of the root system on which it depends. The nourishment elaborated by photosynthesis in the leaves of the scion is entirely suitable for the cells of the root system, and diffuses through the scar tissue between the two parts without undue

difficulty. Thus the stock and scion are "compatible." Similar grafting is standard procedure with ornamental cacti, and a great variety of fruiting bushes and trees. It is not uncommon in Florida or California to see on a single root several branches, one bearing oranges, one lemons, one grapefruit, and so on.

It is possible in many instances to graft together two vertebrate animals into a pair of artificial "Siamese" twins. This is **parabiosis,** life side-by-side. If one twin has been deprived of its thyroid and the other of its pituitary, the hormones will travel across the vascular bridge between the two in sufficient quantities for both individuals to develop normally.

Vascular unions have been successful in dogs (Fig. 23-6), which served science by showing that when one animal received a meal and the food passed from its stomach to its duodenum, the hormone secretion was released into the common blood stream. The pancreases of the two animals then gushed digestive juice into the intestines, both of the one containing the food and of the other with none.

Grafts of this type allow a study of compatibility. Usually different races of the same species are compatible, different species incompatible. But in one salamander, tadpoles from different parts of the country not only

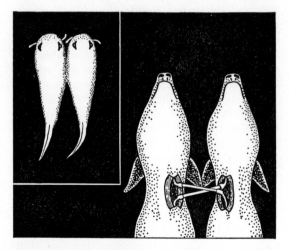

Fig. 23-6. *Interchangeable cellular contents and blood chemicals can be demonstrated and investigated through use of artificial Siamese twins—enforcing a type of life known as parabiosis. Salamander tadpoles* (left); *dogs with blood vessels interconnected* (right).

failed to knit together, but the one "physiological race" produced toxins fatal to the other.

Interchangeability

Use is made of the chemical homologies between plants and between animals in all manner of hormone applications. It is an important part of biological and medical practice, and the basis of the highly valuable methods whereby human subjects are not required for initial study of a drug or hormone, but whereby information gained from experimental work on other mammals can be applied to the human problems. Thus, diabetes symptoms similar to those in man are obtained in experimental dogs when their pancreases are removed. The hormone insulin was identified in such studies, and the information used promptly in therapy for the pathological condition of human diabetes mellitus, thereby saving many lives. Hormone injections, vitamin supplements, and the great variety of antitoxins, antivenins, inoculins, and vaccination materials all depend on the interchangeability of chemical materials between other mammals and man, and upon the fact that these substances elaborated by one animal under experimental conditions can be used by another in time of need. Nowhere can a more compelling case be made for the essential chemical similarity of the mammals than in these practices. Actually the entire vertebrate group, not just the mammals, show this compatibility with respect to hormones and vitamins; many of the Vitamin A and D supplements are made from fish liver extracts, and the chief reason for obtaining hormones and inoculins from mammals is the availability of the glands in slaughterhouses and the volume of inoculin that can be withdrawn from one large, treated animal.

The plant hormones are effective when transferred from one plant to another but usually act as foreign poisons when injected into animal systems. Sight should not be lost, however, of the fact that the source of auxins from which analysis led to recognition of indole-3-acetic acid was human urine. Invertebrates have hormones, too, and within members of the same class or phylum a considerable amount of interchangeability has been demonstrated. Those involved with pig-

ment control or with molting in crabs seem alike among the crabs, but not efficient in eliciting similar responses in insects or mollusks.

Serology

The protoplasm of one organism differs in its complex constitution from the protoplasm of every other species, but the degree of difference varies widely. This aspect has been investigated in the study of serology—the research usually being confined to the constituents of blood plasma or of plant sap. For these problems, a stock of healthy experimental animals is maintained—rabbits or roosters or some others from which blood samples may be drawn from time to time. The experimental animal is sensitized to the aqueous extract of the crushed cells of one species of plant, or to the blood plasma of some one animal, until it has built up a full set of antibodies for this one particular set of foreign proteins. When this has been accomplished, a drop of serum from the experimental animal is so potent that when mixed with a drop of extract or blood from the organism to which it has been sensitized, it causes clumping of cells and precipitation of proteins in less than a minute. The production of similar clumping and precipitation (but in a longer time) is the result of using the animal's serum with the extract or blood of an organism similar to but not identical with the sensitizing type.

Thus a rabbit sensitized to human blood gives the precipitin-clumping reaction promptly when its serum is added to human whole blood, drop for drop. But with gorilla blood the reaction is somewhat slower; with lemur blood it is slower still; with nonprimate blood nothing happens at all. Or with a rooster sensitized to extract of sumac, the reaction with sumac material is prompt; with poison oak (another member of the same genus), slow; with plants not of the genus Rhus either very slowly or not at all. The speed of the reaction can then be used as a measure of the similarity in the precipitated proteins in one organism (the sensitizing type) and another. With few exceptions, the similarity in proteins indicated by these tests corresponds closely to similarity in structure, in embryology, and in fossil history. The test is very helpful, for this reason, in trying to learn the affinities of plants or animals which have so many differences from others in struc-

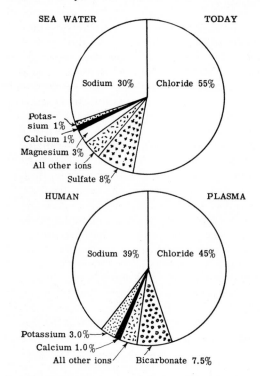

FIG. 23-7. *A comparison between the salt content of modern sea water* (above) *and human blood plasma* (below).

ture that their position in the classificatory scheme is not clear.

Comparable Pigments

In general, the basic chemistry of life is outlined on a broad scale. Thus the two commonest respiratory pigments in animals are hemocyanin—in the arthropods and some mollusks, and hemoglobin—in the vertebrates (and a scattering of annelids and insects). The one contains copper, the other iron, but both have a similar structure responsible for the oxygen-carrying capacity of the big molecule. Similarly, the chlorophylls among the plant kingdom are alike—whether neatly packaged in chloroplastids or diffused in the cytoplasm (as in the blue-green algae). With all the different habitats occupied by plants,

a whole range of different photosynthetic pigments might be expected if there is no good reason for uniformity. And a good reason should be an obvious one.

The light-sensitive pigments of vertebrate eyes, which are located in the terminal segments of the rod and cone cells in the inverted retina, show a remarkable uniformity also.

Susceptibility to Disease

Biochemical similarities are frequently evident in the way viruses and pathogenic organisms attack different host species. Mycologists (who study fungi) have tried to use susceptibility to specific fungus parasites as helpful cues in settling disputes on flowering plants when systematic botanists have difficulty determining the family to which a genus belongs. That the rhesus monkey and chimpanzee are susceptible to so many of the diseases affecting mankind, whereas nonprimates are ordinarily immune, implies a fundamental chemical correspondence.

Blood Salt Content

The inorganic substances carried in blood plasma are remarkably similar to those found in sea water (Fig. 23-7). Biologists have often wondered whether the functions of a modern blood stream were handled in early animals by sea water taken from the environment into their bodies. In this case, blood should be considered as a sort of artificial sea water, animal-made, carried internally as a private sea bathing the tissues.

If this hypothesis comes close to the truth, it should explain both the qualitative and quantitative aspects. Animals fall into two main groups in terms of blood salt concentration: (1) various crustaceans, such as crabs and lobsters, and the elasmobranch fishes, such as sharks and rays; and (2) most other multicellular animals with blood. The former have blood concentrations closely matching that of modern sea water. The latter are much more dilute by comparison.

The amount of salts can be estimated collectively in terms of the freezing point of the blood. Thus the blood of bony fish (both fresh-water and marine), of frog, turtle, desert snake, bird, man, and whale, all have freezing points between —0.55 and —0.74° C. The sharks and their kin, and marine crustaceans, have a blood salt concentration preventing their blood from freezing above −1.90°. For comparison, modern sea water freezes at about −1.85° and lake water at −0.03°— not at 0.00° as does distilled water.

In attempting to correlate this type of information, A. B. Macallum offered in 1903 a definite hypothesis: (1) that at a time when the sea's salt·concentration was such as to give it a freezing point around −0.60°, the ancestors of modern bony fish, land vertebrates, and whales migrated from marine situations into fresh water; (2) that they were able to desert the ocean only because they had a new mechanism that isolated their blood streams from the environment and maintained the salt concentration in the blood that bathed all tissues; (3) that through the intervening ages, no major change has occurred in the salt balance maintained by these animals; and (4) that the elasmobranch fishes, like many marine crustaceans, have always been marine and merely kept up with the increasing salt concentration of the ocean; presumably they never isolated their blood from the environment, and faced no osmotic problems such as are met by animals in fresh waters.

This explanation is not in conflict with the fossil record or any other factual information. The constancy of the salt concentration of the cellular environment thus appears to have been maintained by the living system through millions of years (Fig. 23-8).

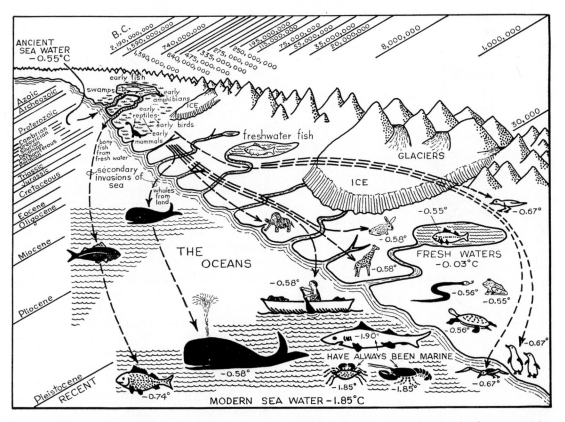

FIG. 23-8. *The change in salt concentration in the oceans and the relationship with blood salt concentrations in modern animals. By mid-Paleozoic the concentration in the sea was enough to lower the freezing point by 0.55° C. Early vertebrates with blood concentrations matching that of sea water apparently migrated at this time into fresh water and retained the blood salt concentration without change. Land vertebrates and the bony fish and whales which returned to colonize the seas have kept these early concentrations—even when they are now associated with modern sea water freezing at 1.85° below zero C. Sharks and crustaceans, however, have not left the ocean, and their blood concentrations have changed gradually to match modern sea concentrations.*

4. INFERENCES FROM BIOGEOGRAPHY

Certain facts stand out when maps are drawn to show the distribution of plant and animal species, genera, families, orders, or classes on a world basis. Some types, such as hummingbirds and cacti, are clearly restricted—in these cases to the Western Hemisphere. Others, such as ungulate mammals, are found native on every continent except Australia.

Since each kind of organism tends to produce more offspring than can find food if the geographical range is limited, every species is likely to spread over an increasing area until further progress is blocked by a barrier. Barriers may be physiological (such as intolerance for heat or cold or desiccation), or physical (such as oceans, high and long mountain ranges, and great deserts). It is chiefly when a species passes a barrier that the full rate of its potential expansion is demonstrated (Fig. 23-9).

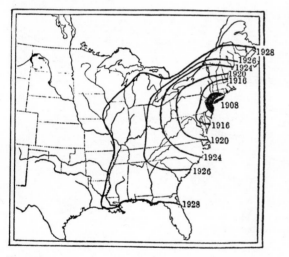

FIG. 23-9. *The spread of the introduced European starling has been followed with interest and concern.* (After Z. P. Metcalf.)

Yet barriers are seldom permanent. Old mountain ranges erode away; new ones form. Continents become linked together by chains of islands or isthmuses, and then are isolated again. Each of these events leaves a lasting effect that a biogeographer can detect.

This type of evidence is enough to allow predictions beyond those suggested by fossils available at the time. This recommends certain areas as likely ones in which to search for new fossil relics. New tangible discoveries of this sort may either support the hypothesis or make it untenable. The hypothesis, if supported, becomes an acceptable migration route (Fig. 23-10).

As a further example of this type of deduction, the marsupials can be considered. The presence of so many of these peculiar mammals in Australia, of the single species of North American opossum, and of the several species of Central and South American opossums, suggests that once there was a land connection between these areas. Did the American opossums come from Australia, or did the Australian marsupials come from America, or did all of them spread out from some intermediate point—say, Asia?

Other features of the Australian fauna, such as the presence of egg-laying mammals, and the lack of native placental types, indicate that it is an area that was isolated during the period when placental mammals were becoming diverse and widespread. Australia's connection to other land areas must have occurred prior to this diversification. Early traffic could have been in either direction, or both.

The fossil record must be consulted to learn the answer to these problems in modern distribution. The answer then becomes clear. The first marsupials (Eocene) were in North America, and they spread to both South America and Australia during the late Eocene, and were isolated and reached great development in both outlying areas during the Oligocene and Miocene. Placental mammal competition in North America, meanwhile, ended all of its marsupials except the opossum, and when a land bridge to South America appeared in the Pliocene, the placentals spread southward and the South American marsupials similarly disappeared—leaving only fossils and a few small opossums. Australia remained separated until the recent period, and consequently retained a relict fauna, rich in these older mammalian types.

Wallace' Line

The distinctness of the Australasian fauna from the Oriental phase of the Paleotropical led A. R. Wallace to explore the East Indian islands rather carefully during the middle of

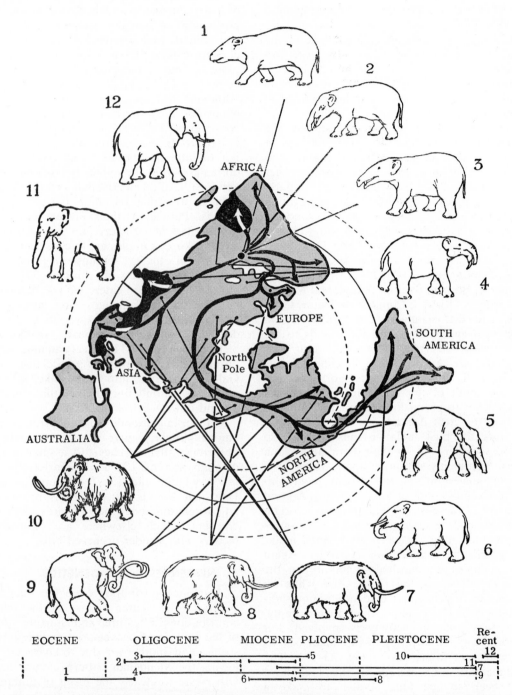

Fig. 23-10. *The probable migration of ancestral elephants is shown by arrows in solid black; this would account for the known distribution of fossil forms (1 to 10) and modern types (11, 12). The distribution of each in the fossil record is shown by the horizontal lines at the bottom. The earliest (1) was amphibious. A downward bending of the lower jaw, evident first in (4), permitted elongation of the trunk. The name "mastodon" has been popularized for (6) to (8), whereas (10) is the "woolly mammoth." (Modified from Z. P. Metcalf, 1932.)*

the 19th century. This thoughtful and competent biologist noted a gradual transition—fewer and fewer animals characteristic of the Asiatic mainland as the island chain was followed toward New Guinea and Australia. Similarly, though to a lesser extent, the marsupials of Australia seemed to have spread to New Guinea and westward.

The biggest change came between the island of Lombok and the adjacent island of Bali. The Australasian cockatoo extended to Lombok but not Bali. The Asiatic tiger stopped on Bali. The flora was similarly divided. Wallace followed this segregation northward, and grouped the larger islands of Borneo and Celebes with Bali and Lombok respectively. The outcome was "Wallace' line," dividing into two the maze of islands in this region (Figs. 21-7, 23-11). Bali, Java, Sumatra, Borneo, the Philippines, and Malaya are seen as Oriental; Lombok to Timor, Celebes, and the islands of the Banda Sea to Papua (New Guinea) and the islands to the east, with Australia, Tasmania, and New Zealand, are Australasian. The line extends through the Macassar Straits, northeastward to the south of the Philippines, and across the Pacific to group the Hawaiian Islands as part of the great Australasian complex.

Since the East Indian islands are now so close together, yet in their flora and fauna seem continents or more apart, there is a strong suggestion that the present geographical proximity is not of long standing. A great number of these islands are of volcanic origin and could have arisen by stages, as a series of stepping stones between the oriental mainland and the continent of Australia. Again the geologist is consulted to inquire on the history shown by the rocks. And while he agrees in principle, his evidence is not sufficiently complete to allow a satisfactory reply. Not only volcanic activity is involved, but also raising and lowering of the major islands with respect to sea level (Fig. 23-11). The sedimentary rock records in this area have not been studied fully enough to make a full answer available.

Island Life

Off the west coast of South America, on the equator opposite the shores of Ecuador, is another group of oceanic islands—the rocky Galápagos (Fig. 21-13). More than ordinary interest is attached to these outlying possessions of Ecuador because of the plants and animals that survive the hot, dry, windy climate. Charles Darwin was the first to explore the life of these little land masses, and he was struck by the differences among them. Although they are rather close together and about 600 miles west of the South American coast, even the birds on some islands show differences from those on others. All are similar to different species found on the Ecuadorian coast but the relatively few kinds present must have taken advantage of the range of habitats available on these barren volcanic islands. Paralleling their present habits are peculiarities of structure. In this respect the most striking examples are finches now known as "Darwin's finches" because they were so influential in affecting his thinking. Ordinarily any finch is a seed-eater, with a short stout bill. But on the Galápagos some have parrot-like beaks, others "straight woodboring beaks, decurved flower-probing beaks, slender warbler-like beaks" used in insect catching, and so on. The species which, as a specialist on the Galápagos, drills into wood like a woodpecker, is the only finch known that can climb up and down vertical surfaces.

On oceanic islands this diversity of form among closely similar species is a frequent occurrence that matches (1) a small number of kinds present, (2) a wide variety of habitats available, and (3) few enemies. In the Hawaiian Islands the pattern is repeated in an entirely different group of birds, the honey creepers, which elsewhere are only nectar feeders with slender decurved bills.

5. INFERENCES FROM GENETICS

A major contribution from the science of genetics is a clearer picture of the relative contributions of "nature" and "nurture." Many of the differences between one individual of a species and another are due to characters following the Mendelian pattern of inheritance. Others are as clearly the result of differences in opportunity—temperature, food, or some other environmental factor. We know, moreover, that the inherited characteristics may involve processes which show as structural changes (such as eye color, height, and so on)

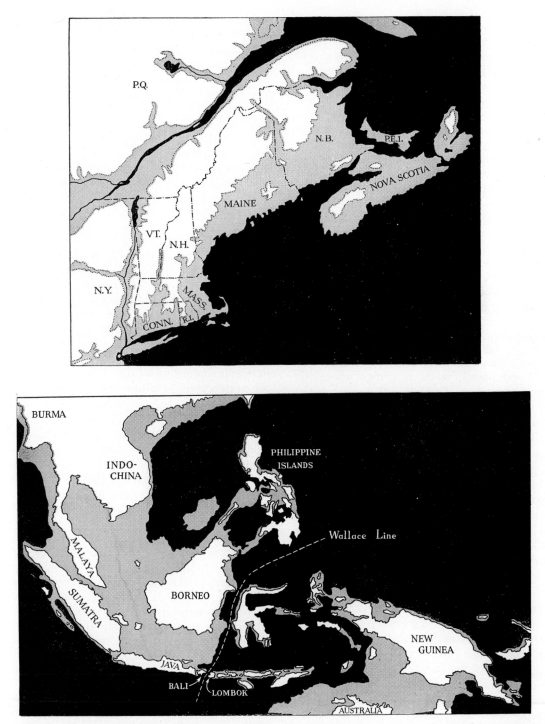

FIG. 23-11. *Changes in the relative levels of land and sea have taken place innumerable times during the history of the earth. A 200-foot depression of New England and adjacent areas would produce widespread flooding (stippled). Emergence of the East Indies to an elevation of 200 feet above present shorelines would link many islands (stippled) but leave intact the barrier of Wallace' Line.*

or as functional tolerances (such as diet requirements or the ability to withstand high or low temperatures). Furthermore, we are certain that while the general run of any population (perhaps 99.8 per cent) will continue in a state of nature with the character in the dominant (or recessive) condition, the few (0.2 per cent or less) will occur with statistical certainty and represent predictable mutations, from dominant to recessive or the converse. Under ordinary circumstances this trifling minority does not become evident. If the mutation involves some character that decreases the biotic potential (as most mutations do), those individuals or their progeny are weeded out automatically. Genetics thus has allowed man to see the regularity with which mutation occurs, and something of its scientific background—the ordinary variability of populations due to sexual reproduction.

Selection Under Domestication

From man's success with domesticated animals and plants, much is known about the cumulative effect of selection from among the natural variability of living things. In the dog —possibly the first to become part of man's household, as scavenger, hunting helper, burglar alarm, and the like—the number of true-breeding strains is enormous. The domestic fowl is not far behind. The horse, cow, sheep, goat, rabbit, pigeon, and others have been diversified in the name of "improvement," by the selection and breeding of interesting variants. Generally the change has been in body conformation and hair development, but the more recent accomplishments with food animals have been in terms of meat content and milk production—both quantitative and qualitative alterations being involved. Among plants, the horticultural varieties are a further evidence of the effects of rigid selection and propagation of the statistically infrequent mutations, segregating and recombining to achieve more attractive flowers or better fruits—including seedless types—or spineless bushes and cacti. Grains tolerant of northern climates (Photos 423-426) and corn wih greater yield per acre (Photo 427) are other genetic accomplishments of recent years.

Natural Factors

These requirements of man's devising, applied conscientiously over only relatively few centuries at the most, have taken wild species and changed them in spectacular ways —in several instances preserving species that have otherwise disappeared. But under natural conditions, there are a multitude of other factors acting to eliminate certain variations and to render others distinctly advantageous, and hence molding each species in some one or more directions. These forces have been at work not only in the late Pleistocene and the recent period, but for as long as each kind of animal or plant has existed. In a species with a sizable range, it is prevented from further spread by different barriers in the various directions. Each barrier acts as a molding influence that slowly alters the relative proportions of variations in the population, allowing some to survive to reproduce in that area in greater numbers than others. It would indeed be surprising, judged in the light of man's short-term experience with selection, if these natural selective agencies did not soon result in visible and physiological differences among the populations so influenced.

Interspecific Crosses

Further evidence for the similarity in chemistry and function can be found in the genetic study of crosses between species. A horse (*Equus caballus*) and the donkey (= ass, *Equus asinus*) may be mated. A jack (♂ donkey) mated with a mare (♀ horse) produces a mule; a jennet (♀ donkey) mated with a stallion (♂ horse) produces a hinny. Except rarely, both mule and hinny are sterile, although the endurance and sure-footedness of the mule is far superior to that of the horse, and its strength is much greater than that of the donkey. Interspecies crosses are always either less viable (often aborting as embryos) or completely sterile—or at least with definitely reduced fertility. Yet the fact that two kinds of protoplasm can be sufficiently compatible for sexual union into a zygote indicates greater similarity than is found between species of different genera. Thus, the genetic evidence indicates that there are all degrees in differences between organisms. Members of the same species are ordinarily interfertile. Members of the same genus may

423-426. Improvement in cultivated plants arises from experimental study and selection of useful mutant strains. Thus Marquis wheat, for years the best available for crops in the short summers of northwestern grain lands, has been replaced by other types.

423. The field is of Saunders wheat, which ripens first and is most resistant to spring frosts (but is third choice in terms of yield and of resistance to rust).

426. Over 58 per cent of spring wheat now grown in Canada is of the Thatcher type, which has the highest yield and greatest resistance to stem rust, but is slowest ripening and second in resistance to spring frosts. Each type thus represents a compromise. No one is ideal on all counts.

425. Redman wheat is second in time of ripening, in yield, and in resistance to rust, but is least resistant to spring frosts as compared with Saunders and Thatcher wheat.

424. A head of Saunders wheat. This variety accounts for nearly 7 per cent of wheat now grown in Canada.

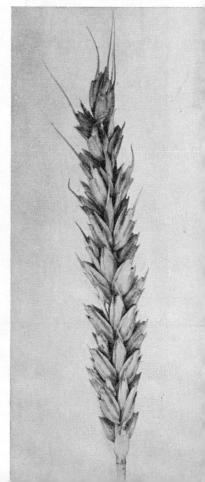

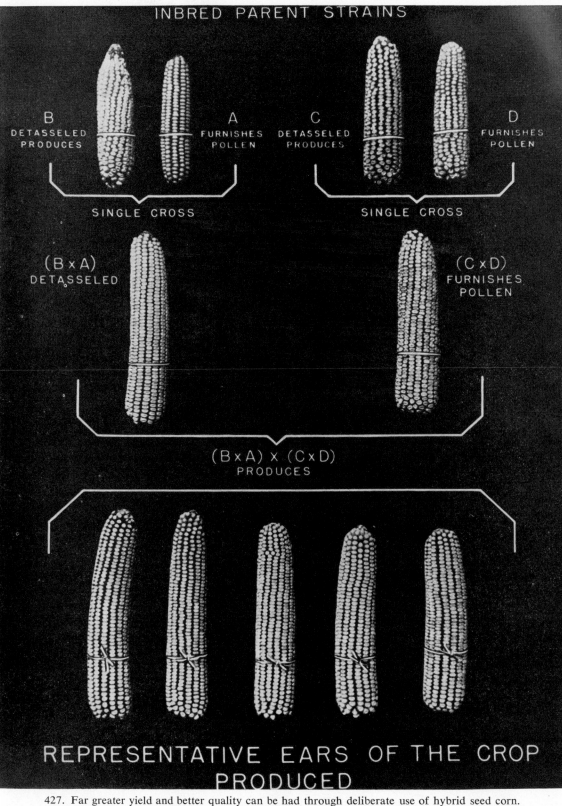

B
DETASSELED
PRODUCES

A
FURNISHES
POLLEN

C
DETASSELED
PRODUCES

D
FURNISHES
POLLEN

SINGLE CROSS

SINGLE CROSS

(B x A)
DETASSELED

(C x D)
FURNISHES
POLLEN

(B x A) x (C x D)
PRODUCES

REPRESENTATIVE EARS OF THE CROP
PRODUCED

427. Far greater yield and better quality can be had through deliberate use of hybrid seed corn. In this family tree the steps in preparing hybrid seed [(B × A) × (C × D)] are shown, from the four inbred parental strains to the crop.

sometimes give rise to offspring, but the reproductive capacities of the offspring are deficient. Sterile interspecies crosses that have gained some publicity include the liger (from lion and tiger, both of genus Felis), and the tangelo (from lemon and tangerine, both of genus Citrus). Members of different genera are rarely compatible enough for grafting together as stock and scion, or as artificial parabiotic twins for hormone studies. Hence the basic chemistry of the protoplasm is demonstrated in the experiments of genetics.

Polyploids

Among plants, where polyploidy is common and usually results in larger, more vigorous individuals, the chromosome number and kindred information have yielded many clues concerning the probable interrelationships between species and the significance of modern geographical distributions. Most classic of such studies is that of N. I. Vavilov on wheat (1928) whose origins in the Caucasus mountains he traced to a wild diploid species which had many native outliers of tetraploid and hexaploid nature (2N = 14, 28, 42). Other workers have followed up a variety of cultivated and wild plants, trying to find relationships and to interpret distribution.

One general conclusion is that, of the species of flowering plants, more than half are polyploids today. It would seem, however, that the proportion of polyploids is related to the extremes of temperature and other adverse physical conditions to which the plants are exposed, suggesting that the cytological irregularities which initiate polyploid formation have this pathological background. Many of the polyploids are perennials, while their diploid antecedents were strictly annuals. The polyploids are also more variable, which may explain the fact that in so many instances the geographic range of a polyploid extends in every direction beyond that of its diploid antecedent and relatives. This indicates ability to push on toward new barriers. It also brings the logical inference that separation of what the taxonomist would recognize as species may occur through polyploidy and various chromosomal abnormalities. In the field of cytogenetics, the evidence of such changes is collected and analyzed and the interpretations sought in terms of the sources of modern vegetation.

The study of inheritance has established the facts of variability and the effects of selection on this variation. The long-term effects of natural selection by environmental factors can only be an inference to be used in the interpretation of the history of life before human-interference. As such it can be a supplemental source of information where there are gaps in the fossil records.

6. FACTS AND THEORIES

As was pointed out in Chapter 2, scientists accept a dual obligation: to uncover, describe accurately and in detail every pertinent or possibly pertinent fact; and to group all available facts into a general theory which will account for them.

The anatomical differences upon which modern and fossil organisms can be distinguished are facts. So are the findings on geographical distribution, geological horizon, ecological relationships, and inheritance. The developmental steps in the embryological history of a plant or animal, and every detail of its life cycle, are facts. Similarities in chemical constitution, in function, in structure, and in mode of development, are all facts.

Facts may be subdivided through later study, but they cannot be changed. They may be interpreted in many ways, each a different hypothesis. A small number of facts may fit a variety of hypotheses. But when additional facts are considered, there is a narrowing of the number of possible explanatory accounts. The more a theory is found to accommodate all new facts, the more confidence can be placed in the theory. *It* does not become a fact, however. It merely is seen to lie close to the truth.

7. GENERAL DEDUCTIONS

Only recently has the evidence outlined on the preceding pages been drawn together. General recognition of the true nature of fossils is scarcely a century old. Paleontology was born with the work of Georges Cuvier in the early 1800's. Previously and until much later, many people believed fossils to be plants or animals that had been struck by lightning and turned to stone. Others thought them to be the casts that the Creator had used in mass-producing the living things on the earth. Still others, less respectful, suggested that fossils were errors—animals and plants made by the Creator but discarded because they did not function properly.

Another Frenchman, Jean Baptiste de Lamarck (1744-1829) presented in 1801 the hypothesis that **evolution** had taken place, that modern organisms were descended with changes from earlier types of life.

Lamarck's idea was not new, but previous writers had never offered factual evidence in support of the concept. As far back as Roman times, Saint Augustine had held that species of plants and animals inhabiting the earth had changed, and that creation (although a special event) included the process by which new species arose from fewer previous ones. This view did not conflict noticeably with a literal interpretation of the Judaeo-Christian Bible or with other writings approved by the early Christian church.

Lamarck's evidence that evolution had occurred was sketchy, though well presented. It was information of a technical sort, which only trained scientists could properly evaluate. Yet virtually all biologists were affronted by it. For half a century they had been laboring to catalogue the species of modern plants and animals, using the system introduced by Linnaeus. If species were not fixed, the value of classification would be small—or so they thought. If evolution were in progress, the entire task might have to be redone every few centuries!

From the perspective of present knowledge, the attempts to defend the *status quo*—to insist on fixity of species and **Special Creation** of each—seem comical. At the time the scientists were in dead earnest. Biologists split into camps—the evolutionists and the anti-evolutionists. Gradually their debates spread into public places, until nonscientists took sides as well.

Resistance to the idea of evolution was largely emotional, and relied upon arguments and written words rather than on scientific facts. In the heat of verbal duelling, the essential duality of the problem was largely overlooked:

1. Unless a supernatural, special creation did occur, spontaneous generation must have been possible in the remote past, to produce the first protoplasm from nonliving precursors. Life on earth must have had a beginning unless the past was infinitely long.

2. After protoplasm came into existence, either all modern organisms were present in addition to all extinct types from the very beginning, or the kinds alive today have evolved in their genetic descent from fewer, earlier, different types.

That the first of these problems was neglected until very recently is understandable since belief in spontaneous generation continued widespread until the second half of the 19th century. Larger animals and plants were known to come only from pre-existing parents. But bacteria and many types of small multicellular organisms had not been shown to obey the same general law.

Special Creation

Since the scientific discussions pro and con, regarding evolution, arose in Europe during the past 150 years, the protagonists were men with a Judaeo-Christian background. Rather than take time to demonstrate factually that species were fixed and had been so since first created, the biologists and public siezed upon written words of unknown authorship and unproven scientific significance as "evidence." They quoted the Judaeo-Christian Bible, particularly Chapters 1, 2, 6, and 7 of "The First Book of Moses, called Genesis." These told how the earth and its inhabitants arose—actually in two different accounts: both man and woman simultaneously (Chapter 1, Verses 26 and 27); and woman from a rib removed from Adam's side (Chapter 2, Verses 21 and 22). Chapters 6 and 7 told of a flood that killed off all living things except those in Noah's ark. To Special Creationists, this episode furnished a satisfactory explanation for sedimentary rocks and fossils alike.

Unfortunately, Genesis did not explain the survival of both marine and fresh-water organisms in the face of catastrophe; nor the solution to the space requirements of two of each kind of terrestrial animal (plus Noah and his family), plus assorted food—enough for the 40 days of deluge and for a new growing season afterward—for all these hungry mouths; nor the fate of the plant kingdom on which all animals depend.

Moreover, the sedimentary record shows that the many strata were laid down at widely different times. Cuvier overcame this objection by suggesting that there must have been many floods, and repeated special creations to repopulate the earth after each. Noah simply rode out the most recent general flood. This was the doctrine of *catastrophism*.

As the progressive nature of the changes in the fossil record came to light, this position became equally untenable. No version of the biblical story provides an explanation for the lack of vascular plants or vertebrate remains in the Cambrian sediments, although even jellyfish were preserved well. Or for the regular sequence of changes from extinct toward modern forms in each phylum after its appearance. None gives clues to the geographic peculiarities of distribution, the vestigial organs, the roundabout procedures in embryonic development, the chemical uniformities and differences. These are too tangible and too numerous to be passed off as due to chance alone.

To be satisfied without an all-inclusive explanation is not the way of science. Yet no matter how inadequate Special Creation may seem today, it cannot be disproved. It is immune to proof and disproof since it is not based upon observable facts.

The scientific approach is to seek for an explanation based upon all proven facts, and hence acceptable equally to scientists in any land, regardless of religion or educational heritage. Progress is dependent upon the honest attitude expressed by Charles Darwin: "I have steadily endeavored to keep my mind free so as to give up any hypothesis however much beloved (and I can not resist from forming one on every subject) as soon as facts are shown to be opposed to it."

Nor is it scientific to yield little by little—to say (in effect) that biogenesis or evolution must be admitted in instances where the evidence is overwhelmingly complete, but apply spontaneous generation or special creation to all other, less proven cases. Calling upon the supernatural as an explanation for the natural is retention of a position shown repeatedly to be based upon ignorance, and also a denial that further facts can be helpful.

Evolution Through Inheritance of Characters Acquired or Lost by Use or Disuse

When Lamarck presented his hypothesis in 1801, he recognized that he needed to show clearly why he believed a larger number of present-day species to have evolved from a smaller number of pre-existing species. He saw too that these changes must be the result of some general principle affecting the reproductive process. He gave both points careful consideration, and later revised and amplified his views in *La Philosophie Zoologique* (1809) and *L'Histoire Naturelle des Animaux san Vertèbres* (1815).

In these works, Lamarck postulated that all species, including man, had descended from other, different species. He was the first to reach this conclusion from careful study of specimens, and seems to have been led to the entire idea by the difficulty of distinguishing species and varieties, by the almost perfect gradation of forms in certain organic groups, and by the analogy of domestic plants and animals.

More precisely, Lamarck reached the conclusion that evolution must have taken place or still be in progress while he was identifying such animals as snails. The specimens lay before him, and to one side was the manuscript for the 1815 monograph. Lamarck's quandary arose not because his collections were too small, so that he did not have representatives of the species that were described in the technical literature. Instead, the collection was too large, and in many instances specimens before him seemed to bridge the gaps between species. It was the dilemma familiar to every systematic zoologist: what constitutes a reliable characteristic for distinguishing between two species? Something that lacks variation is ideal, but such features are often hard to find, so that the decision is not a clear alternative. Instead, one kind appear to intergrade with another. The discontinuities that Linnaeus had supposed to occur, and that are a necessary basis for binomial nomenclature, are often lacking if structure alone is studied.

Lamarck's difficulty is easy for a modern biologist to appreciate, since now the major museums have such extensive collections in most groups of animals and plants that the problem has multiplied itself again and again. That the quandary should have arisen within 50 years of Linnaeus' *Systema Naturae* indicates merely the progress made by collectors, and the growing interest in the comparison of longer series of specimens, to find better means for identifying each kind. But that the explanation of the problem should have come in terms of changes in the structure, by an orderly process of evolution, reflects credit on Lamarck. Like many another astute guess, it was better than he knew, for at that time the study of paleontology had barely begun, the cell doctrine was far in the future, the embryonic germ layers had not been recognized, and even the concept of homology as contrasted with analogy remained undefined. Thus the conclusion was reached entirely on the basis of comparative anatomy—in terms of applications of structural study to problems of classification.

That evolution had taken place, and that the specimens before him were the products of complete and incomplete separations between pre-existing species, became a fixed idea in Lamarck's mind. He extended this point of view in his writings, to the effect that all modern species were the outcome of descent with change from former, fewer species; that not all former species had survived; that species with a common ancestry and the link not too far back were those grouped as genera; and that species with a common ancestry but with the point of junction more remotely in the past were those now recognized as families (or, if still farther into the past, as orders, or classes, or phyla). It was Lamarck's view that spontaneous generation explained the presence of the simple unicellular animals of the present time, and that these, allowed to survive and reproduce, could change into the higher forms. Thus for him the process was dynamic—a continuing operation, and the product a gradual "improvement" by increasing complexity and specialization.

Point two of Lamarck's hypothesis—that a basic principle must explain the change in inherited characteristics—led him to choose an idea that seemed plausible enough at the time. According to this view, structures would develop or diminish in future generations according to how much they were used by the parents. Giraffes "must" have acquired their long necks through generations of stretching them—reaching higher into trees for the foliage on which they fed. Slugs "must" have lost their shells through living under fallen logs where no shell was needed.

Lamarck's attention was primarily on adaptations that helped an animal get food or escape from enemies—long legs for flight, keen vision for detecting danger. The "for" was foremost in his mind. The organism in which a need arose transferred to its offspring a slight improvement in the solution to the need. The accumulation of improvements in the many directions (as many as the needs of each species) resulted in changes which distinguished species, genera, and the like on structural grounds.

The premise that evolution must have occurred was a conclusion of broad connotation and one that most of Lamarck's contemporaries either overlooked or completely scorned. The corollary that the simplest forms of present-day life must be arising continually by spontaneous generation did not concern anyone greatly, since the doctrine of biogenesis was not applied to single cells until the work of Pasteur (1862); the inadequacies of this appendix to the main premise did not destroy the premise anyway.

But the explanation for the mode of operation of evolution, through use and disuse, was open to experimental study. Followers of Lamarck measured and cut off the tails from 500 generations of mice, to see whether lack of a tail from an early age would influence the inheritance of a tail or bring about a shortening of the organ. It had no effect at all. The experimenters might have considered the feet of the feminine members of Chinese nobility of the day, bound in childhood so that they would remain small (and deformed)—a tradition carried out for untold generations. Yet any unbound foot grew just as big as that of a peasant girl. Or the infant sons of blacksmiths would have been a helpful case, since these show no difference in muscular development at birth (or later unless with special exercise) just because their fathers' arm muscles were so enormous. Test after test was applied; the explanation of use and disuse was discarded as an impossible answer. The activities engaged in by an organism do not alter the inherited characteristics in its germplasm. The genetic factors are hidden deeply; they carry along from generation to generation potentialities that have proven satisfactory over a very long period of time, and variations in these potentialities that follow the Mendelian pattern of inheritance. But Mendel's work, showing the regularity of inheritance of variations, remained buried for almost a century after Lamarck first presented his explanation of evolution.

The curious reaction to failure of the explanation of evolution by use and disuse was not that a better explanation was needed, but that the fact of evolution should be discarded. This was the equivalent of saying that since an explanation of gravitation proved untenable, apples no longer fell from trees. As long as the explanation of disuse and use had no factual basis, biologists in general dismissed the notion of evolution and chose to ignore the difficulties Lamarck had encountered in dividing his snails into genera and species.

Evolution Through Progressive Elimination of the Less Fit by Natural Selection

Although genetics remained an aspect of biology on which there was no sound information available, Charles Darwin had the advantage of the growing evidence from paleontology, and far more information from comparative anatomy and embryology. Darwin himself had traveled widely as the naturalist aboard H.M.S. *Beagle* on a world cruise extending from 1826 to 1835. It was a combination, in fact, of his observations made during the expedition—particularly in South America and the Galápagos Islands—together with an idea gained from reading T. R. Malthus' *Essay on Population*[2] that started Darwin toward his study of "natural selection." His principal contribution was in presenting such an avalanche of evidence indicating (1) that evolution (in the Lamarckian sense) had actually occurred, and demonstrating (2) the unspectacular nature of the selective forces which could bring about the changes noted.

Darwin explained these changes on the basis of normal variability of living things

[2] First published anonymously in 1798.

and the selective elimination of the least well adapted by normal, natural competition for food and mates. Implied in this is the belief that the variability stems from inherited characteristics, and that the reproductive cells of the various phases of a single species differ— hence breed true, perpetuating the differences. The first detailed account appeared in 1859 in Charles Darwin's book, *The Origin of Species by Means of Natural Selection.* Darwin considered it an abstract only, since he did not present the full evidence and the topic was treated rather broadly. He followed it with *Variation of Animals and Plants under Domestication* (1868), *The Descent of Man, and Selection in Relation to Sex* (1871), *Effects of Cross- and Self-Fertilization in the Vegetable Kingdom* (1876), and *Different Forms of Flowers on Plants of the Same Species* (1877).

The evidence was drawn with care from the whole gamut of biological information, thoughtfully arrayed, and published with full acknowledgment to previous workers. So tremendous was the impact on the scientific world of these facts, cited one after another, that it is not unusual for people to credit Darwin with initiating the theory of evolution. That it was Lamarck's is made amply plain on the first page (and subsequently) in *The Origin of Species*. Some two dozen others between 1801 and 1859 are mentioned as having the same point of view, but Darwin alone added materially to the form of the theory in which Lamarck left it.

Almost a century has passed since the publication of Darwin's "Abstract," and an enormous body of evidence has been added to it. It is a remarkable fact that the suggestions and conclusions of a man who was so broadly versed in outdoor observation should have sent so many biologists scurrying indoors to their collections of specimens and to their microscopes and microtomes to seek out the answers to predictions and to prove Darwin wrong or right about the existence of the evolutionary process. Many of these investigators were spurred on by a multitude of non-scientists, all bent on disproving Darwin's claims concerning the fact of evolution. In this they were often highly emotional. But the evidence they uncovered merely added to the probability of evolution having taken place. In spite of their initial dislike for the proposition, the biologists became convinced, and soon came to see what a unifying gift the entire theory provided. Isolated facts now fitted into a great pattern for the first time. Predictions could be made, and they were. In research work to check on these predictions, not only did the predicted information come to light, but with it more evidence—always in the same direction.

Except for the Copernican explanation that the earth was a rotating sphere that traveled an orbit around the sun, no scientific pronouncement in history has received so great opposition as the doctrine of organic evolution. Like the Copernican view, however, it survived its critics, and with increased wealth of factual support has become a basic concept in biology comparable in acceptance with Newton's "law" of gravitation. Through the work of Darwin and later scientists, Lamarck's suggestion has been amplified and extended. All factual evidence points in this one direction.

Darwin's other contribution was his explanation of how evolution came about. For this he had to make certain assumptions: (1) that variation in form and function within a species was due to inherited characters—in other words, that variation was on a genetic basis; (2) that the biotic potential of every kind of animal and plant was so great that only a small fraction of the offspring could possibly survive in the struggle for food and mates and against enemies; and (3) that those members of the population which lost out, starving or failing to find mates, or succumbing to enemies, were those least well adapted—the weakest, least resistant members of the variable group of individuals.

Of these, point *one* was an astute guess, since there was no adequate evidence available on genetics. Mendel had not yet performed his crucial experiments, and even these were not published in a widely-read form until after Darwin's death. Point *two* was merely the extension of Malthus' comments on overpopulation, broadened to include all living things—the old story of the

abundance of life. Point *three* was a logical inference, and the essence of "natural selection." It is the wild counterpart of the arbitrary selection of variants by man in his improvement of domestic animals and cultivated plants.

It will be noted that Darwin, like Lamarck, had his eye primarily on those features of structure and function that were of adaptive value to an organism in the struggle for survival. Nonadaptive features were given no consideration. Presumably they were either of importance and subject to selection at some stage in the past, or were linked in some way to features of adaptive significance. The term "survival of the fittest" is often applied to Natural Selection; probably "elimination of the least fit" is a better description, since a great number of mediocre individuals do reproduce themselves. Variation in the adaptation of some organ, function, or habit extends over a range. At the low end are individuals poorly adapted, and eliminated in the struggle for perpetuation; at the high end are overadapted individuals, and the excessive adaptation may even act to their detriment —it does them no better than the minimum adaptation that will succeed in the struggle —unless more of their progeny may be equipped beyond this minimum level. As one professor of biology used to remark: "An animal has just about enough adaptations and sense to get by; much more does it little good." But much less eliminates both it and its progeny, and contributes to the gradual change in the species.

One further point should be mentioned in discussing Darwin's contribution to biological understanding. His *Origin of Species* would not have appeared in 1859 had not friends hurried him into publication. As early as 1844, Darwin had a sizable part of his "abstract" in a rough draft that he showed to some members of the Linnaean Society of London. He was still working on it at his own rate (limited considerably by poor health), when Alfred Russell Wallace sent him a manuscript for transmission to the Linnaean Society for publication—a brief work in comparison, but detailing the evolutionary process and its basis in natural selection, as a conclusion reached entirely independently. Wallace' work came directly from the East Indies, where its author was studying the distribution of animals in particular, and trying to account for what he found. Darwin endorsed the treatise and had it published as Wallace had asked, complimenting its author on his care and contribution to science. Only his friends knew how much evidence Darwin had already accumulated on the subject, and how thoroughly thought through were his conclusions. They urged him to present what was already organized, and he brought out the "abstract" which is now history.

Again and again this coincidence of ideas has occurred in all phases of civilization. The biologists of the world cannot be said to have been ready for the doctrine of evolution or for the explanation in natural selection. But the increase in information had reached a level where such an understanding of the whole was sure to occur to some one or two alert scientists—to those not too immersed in details for appreciation of the whole picture. Darwin got his first inkling while on the *Beagle* voyage; 15 years later he was still working on it. Wallace, more impatient, readied his account for publication with fewer supporting facts, and sent it to London in 1859. To him as well as to Darwin belongs the credit for our understanding of natural selection. The stage was set. The announcement was bound to come within a period of a very few years—whether by Wallace, by Darwin, or by some other person. The independent rediscovery of the laws of genetics and of Mendel's paper by de Vries, Correns, and Tschermak in 1900 is an exact parallel.

Evolution Through Natural Selection of Mutations

Known usually as the "Mutation Theory," this is an addition to the Darwinian view, proposed in 1901 by Hugo de Vries, based on his studies in the inheritance of the evening primrose, Œnothera. Like so many other scientists at that time, de Vries was concerned lest normal variation among living things be inadequate to explain evolution through natural selection. He called attention to the sudden changes he found in his flowers, laying in this way some of the important background for Morgan's theory of the gene. Since the correspondence between inheritable variations and mutations is now understood far better

than it was in 1901, de Vries' suggestion is merely incorporated into the Darwinian version of natural selection. It provides the nuclear basis for the variation Darwin counted on, and which he predicted would have an inherited background. For de Vries, too, it was an astute guess, since the nuclear role in the process was not appreciated until considerably later. Several of de Vries' mutations turned out to be cases of polyploidy and other chromosomal abnormalities.

Evolution Through Natural Selection of Characters Inherited Through the Cytoplasm

Based entirely on the work of I. V. Michurin and T. D. Lysenko, and of assistants under their direction, this view received strong promotion in official publications of the U.S.S.R. until 1955, and stronger condemnations elsewhere. Extravagant claims were made (such as changing oats into rye in a few generations) but descriptions of the experiments were too inadequate for free scientists to see why repetitions elsewhere with good controls failed to substantiate any of the assertions of the Russian group. At the time these reports were published, the easily repeated experiments of Mendel and Morgan were denied categorically.

Scientists in the free world do not deny that characters may be inherited through the cytoplasm as "plasmogenes." Several instances of this are known, and some (such as tassel-less maize) are used by plant breeders. All of them may be explained equally well on the basis of virus diseases carried from generation to generation through egg cytoplasm. And the situation is met far too seldom to have the broad significance claimed for it in the Russian publications.

8. THE MODERN SYNTHESIS

That evolution has taken place; that all modern forms of life are the direct descendants through countless generations from single-celled organisms (or simpler) that existed in Archeozoic seas; and that natural selection occurs and could account for a considerable part (if not all) of the evolutionary changes producing the variety of life today from the few beginnings in the past, is the considered judgment of virtually all biologists today.

The process is visualized as still actively in full operation, with a future as well as a past. From less than 3,000 years of written history, plus his studies of fossils and of the internal structure and workings of living things today, man is now ready to describe in fair detail what happened to living things not only during the 50,000 years of his own existence as man, but also during the previous two billion years of the geologic sequence. He regards it as a most orderly process, governed partly by the potentialities of variable protoplasm, and partly by the environmental factors—both physical and biological. The variations he has seen develop into distinct varieties or races while under cultivation or domestication, he is willing to concede could produce in a somewhat longer time the differences between distinct species, or between genera in still longer,[3] and so on up to the highest categories. Thus classification takes on a new significance. It is not only a convenient tool for referring to individual kinds of living things; it now expresses also the most probable ancestral relationships between them. The degree of proximity or remoteness on the classificatory scheme is believed to indicate the position in time when two lines of evolution diverged from one another.

9. THE ORIGIN OF LIFE AND OF THE PHYLA

A spontaneous origin for life, transforming an initial Azoic period into the Archeozoic, must always remain hypothetical. But as the physical and chemical specifications of protoplasm become better known, speculations on the subject have more meaning.

We can scarcely think of life without liquid water, nucleoproteins, and energy. Or without some phosphorus-containing compound, perhaps far simpler than ATP, as an energy-transfer mechanism. The nucleic acids appear to provide the basis for self-duplication and mutation, and be an essential part even of a virus molecule. Apparently their organization

[3] On the basis of the excellent fossil records of the horse, G. G. Simpson has estimated that each generic separation required 5.6 million years.

can spell out the sequence and kind of amino acids in each protein. And with proteins as enzymes, amino acids can be converted into carbohydrates, and these into fats, giving the full range of naturally occurring organic compounds.

Nucleic acids are not much more complicated than amino acids. If the spontaneous origin of amino acids could be demonstrated, nucleic acids and then proteins would seem a logical sequence. The first step has been observed in the laboratory. In 1953, S. L. Miller discovered that an electrical discharge in an artificial atmosphere consisting of water vapor, carbon monoxide, methane, ammonia, and hydrogen, produced several different amino acids in milligram amounts.

This mixture of gases was chosen because geologists have postulated it as the probable ingredients of the earth's early atmosphere. They suggest that the "air" did not become oxidative until after the great Laurentian mountain-building period in the late pre-Cambrian.

Without free oxygen, amino acids formed through the action of lightning and perhaps ultraviolet components of sunlight could accumulate. Evaporation of water from shallow lagoons and ponds left by storms could concentrate an originally dilute solution, and do so in just the situations where solar ultraviolet could be most effective.

Carbon monoxide could serve as a substrate for a modified photochemical process (utilizing the high energy content of ultraviolet radiations), or in chemosynthetic oxidations comparable to those found today in a few bacteria (see p. 75).

Without oxygen, the more soluble compounds of phosphorus (the phosphites and hypophosphites) could exist, whereas with oxygen present, all phosphorus-containing compounds are relatively insoluble. In the presence of carbon monoxide, ammonia, hydrogen, and ultraviolet radiations, soluble phosphorus compounds could be built into high-energy substances capable of serving in transfer of metabolic energy. Hence a primitive organism could manage without the specializations found in modern protoplasm, needed for concentration of relatively insoluble phosphorus compounds into high-energy phosphates such as ATP.

A few nucleic acid molecules in a dilute pool of amino acids, adjacent to an energy-transfer mechanism of primitive type, might easily react, blueprinting and synthesizing a few proteins. With nucleic acids and proteins together, nucleoproteins could form. Even the origin of the nucleic acid DNA would lay the basis for mutations, producing fresh sequences of the four units of the DNA molecule, and blueprinting new and sometimes helpful enzymes.

Somewhere in this sequence, it is necessary to postulate the formation of plasma membranes, putting boundaries to the earliest living things. Yet, if these speculations approximate the truth, life would have arisen in a host of different chemical forms. None of them need have been anything like even the viruses of today. They would still fit one recent definition of life: an autocatalysing complex of proteins capable of self-nourishment, duplication, and evolution.

The earliest protoplasm may have consisted of particles of Rickettsial dimensions. Its chemosynthetic and photosynthetic activity could have been supplemented or even supplanted by fermentation. It could still take full advantage of the enormous surface-to-volume ratio inherent in small size.

Fermentation, however, would release carbon dioxide into the sea water. Slowly an equilibrium between dissolved, dissociated, and atmospheric carbon dioxide and precipitated carbonates (see p. 401) could have been achieved. Still no photosynthesis of modern type or aerobic respiration would have been possible.

With carbon dioxide and light available, photosynthesis as we know it would depend upon the invention of compounds comparable to bacteriochlorophyll or chlorophylls. Once developed, tremendous possibilities would be open. But simultaneously, free oxygen would enter the picture for the first time.

It seems likely that these and other early changes brought major crises to primitive organisms:

1. With oxygen in sea water, the soluble phosphites and hypophosphites would be oxidized into meagerly soluble substances. A mechanism for concentrating and utilizing these minute supplies would be a requirement for survival.

2. With oxygen free in sea water, amino acids dissolved there would be oxidized into simpler compounds. Abiogenesis would end.

3. With oxygen available, carbon monoxide as a nutrient would be replaced by carbon dioxide. Organisms dependent upon the monoxide would become extinct. Only those developing chemical processes permitting use of the dioxide could continue. Some modern plants can use either substrate.

4. With oxygen available, the door to aerobic respiration and more efficient use of food would be opened wide. This would lead, in turn, to establishment of the great cycles of carbon and nitrogen, all powered by solar energy (Figs. 21-17, 21-18, 24-1). It would also support the more vigorous activities of animals, and emphasize the value of predatory habits. Survival might soon depend upon increased reproductive rate, or armor, or speed in escape. The development of armor introduces a greater chance for fossilization.

5. With oxygen in the atmosphere, an ozone blanket at high altitudes would develop gradually, shielding the seas from most of the ultraviolet in sunlight. Organisms dependent upon a primitive type of photosynthesis based on ultraviolet would vanish. The survivors would be those with chlorophyll or chlorophyll-like compounds. Since most, if not all, of these contain as a structural core the porphyrin complex found also in the respiratory enzymes, it is likely that the entire metabolic process required rebuilding to match the presence of oxygen.

This hypothesis conflicts with no known fact and provides a place for much recent information. It implies that the greatest evolution of all was chemical and occurred during the Archeozoic. Presumably the development of structures permitting division of labor came somewhat later: the nucleus, perhaps plastids. Refinements such as autotrophic and heterotrophic ways of life, active predation and parasitism, saprophytism and the scavenging habit, sex and multicellularity, would be later additions. Even hemoglobin appears to have been a relatively recent invention, again using the porphyrin design of organic molecule.

All of the phyla of invertebrates and of

thallophytes seem to have separated as distinct ways of life before any of them achieved fossilizable firmness and size. This suggests that secretions of lime, silica, or cellulose, larger size, and body stiffening even as feeble as in a jellyfish, came later. Physiological diversity and the body architectural characteristics of the many phyla certainly preceded these developments.

Evolution since the Archeozoic is more obvious because of the fossil record. But it is far less spectacular than the origin of life and of the phyla. Moreover, in this view, viruses would be a very ancient way of existence—perhaps the first parasites. Chemosynthetic bacteria would come a close second. Purple bacteria and blue-green algae would represent the only modern relics of early photosynthetic organization. An anaerobic bacterium could be more primitive than an aerobic one. A facultative aerobe, such as brewers' yeast, would suggest the way in which advantage was taken of oxygen when first it became available.

When interpreted in this way, the green plants with chloroplastids and the animals that eat them seem far more modern developments. Yet it is these two categories that furnish almost all of the fossil record.

10. TREES OF DESCENT

Whether all modern plants and animals represent the descendants of a single style of original life may always remain unknown. If more than one fundamental type of ancestor is postulated, then several distinctly different series of living organisms would be expected. They should be unlike chemically and structurally. No sharp division of this kind is evident.

The biologist finds it useful to summarize his conclusions about the past history of life in the form of "family trees" (Fig. 23-12). In this way he emphasizes the continuing nature of the evolutionary process, with new branching every year. Moreover, each branch is relatively independent of events elsewhere in the terminal portions of the tree.

Amebas have many characteristics in common with man or pine. They also have many special features found only among protozoans.

Presumably those features shared by amebas, men, and pines were developed by common ancestors. Those peculiar to protozoans can be regarded as features added since the division of the lines of descent.

There is no thought that amebas will evolve into mammals or gymnosperms. Each is engaged in testing out adaptations in a special way of life. Mammals are becoming progressively more mammalian.

Adaptations are often described as though they were so many inventions developed by the various phyla. In this it is neither necessary nor desirable to attribute foresight or intelligent choice to the organisms involved. Man can recognize that environmental resistance poses certain problems for living things. But the normal variations and mutations seem to provide enough basis for natural selection to make progressive changes. The Second Law of Thermodynamics can be invoked to account for the one-way character of these alterations, and for the repeated dichotomy of the lines of descent.

The tabular summary on p. 448 shows the cumulative aspects for part of the animal kingdom. This presentation emphasizes how the more specialized organisms have added one helpful adaptation after another, and gained thereby in independence and physical dimensions.

Divergence

Since annelid worms do not develop warm blood and hair, mammary glands, and the like, the biologist concludes that these adaptations are not provided for in their nuclei. Instead, each splitting of the ancestral line appears to commit the descendants on definite limitations. In becoming more worm-like the annelids have seemingly yielded the possibility of becoming more mammal-like.

In the late 1800's, divergence of descending lines was believed to follow an "urge" for improvement. This view was in line with the vitalistic thinking prevalent then. The improvement is real enough; it can be demonstrated in the laboratory in 7,000 generations of a bacterial population. But at present the "urge" is denied. In its place is a longer-term application of natural selection, constantly weeding out the least fit, the misadapted. Adaptations, for their part, are seen as genetic changes and combinations of changes with a fortunate outcome.

The underlying mechanism appears to be ordinary Mendelian segregation of inherited characteristics, supplemented by mutations and chromosomal irregularities. Most changes are minor or detrimental. Occasionally a combination may arise which has definite advantage, and it will be made a permanent part of the inheritance of the species.

Advantageous variations depend for their success upon both time and place. For centuries or millions of years they may be unimportant parts of the normal variation. Then a change in habitats available or in the way of life allows the variation to enhance reproductive opportunity. The neglected feature promptly becomes a valuable adaptation to the new situation.

Organisms seem to become diverse simply through selection of adaptations matching them to the diversity of environments on the earth. Whenever adaptations in two different directions are selected simultaneously in two parts of the total population of a species, the stage is set for division of that species into two. The one step needed is "reproductive isolation," whereby the one portion of the population is prevented from breeding with the other.

Reproductive isolation may be provided by a geographical barrier, a difference in time of the mating season, or of activity (into nocturnal and diurnal populations, for example). Each incipient species is then free to vary independently, to become progressively more adapted to its new way of life. Eventually,

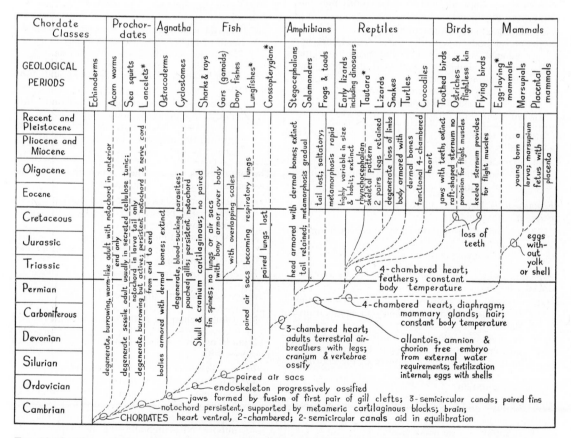

FIG. 23-12. *The probable relationships of the chordates, with indications of fossil and modern representatives shown in solid lines, inferred connections in broken lines, and "living fossils" with an asterisk (*). (Partly after Gregory.)*

physiological differences can be expected to show externally as structural dissimilarities on which a taxonomist may base identification.

11. BIOLOGICAL "INVENTIONS"

Once life was established, the inherent variability of protoplasm permitted exploration of an enormous range of adaptive possibilities. Presumably most of the combinations

Among *protozoans:*

1. the protoplasm is in cellular units;
2. mitosis duplicates the genes carried by chromosomes, and these are organized into one or more nuclei;
3. contractile fibrils may be present, as simple versions of the contractile elements in muscle cells;
4. a neural mechanism of conducting strands shows in part of a single cell many features characteristic of neurons;
5. locomotory extensions of the cell are equivalent to structures carried by epithelial cells in more complex animals;
6. sexual fusion and meiotic division are represented.

Coelenterates show all of these adaptations plus additions or refinements:

7. multicellular construction;
8. plural body layers, the outer (ectoderm) associated with sensation and protection, the inner (endoderm) related to digestion and absorption;
9. a special digestive cavity, connected to the outside world via a mouth;
10. differentiation of a nerve-cell network.

Flatworms show these 10 adaptations and have additionally:

11. mesoderm, including muscle cells;
12. a central nervous system, showing cephalization of neurons.

Roundworms have lost none of these 12 characteristics, and have added:

13. a production-line digestive tube, opening at an anus;
14. blood, conveying materials within the body.

Annelids embody all 14 adaptations and have introduced a few more:

15. separation of a closed circulatory system from the coelom, adding efficiency in blood transport;
16. hemoglobin, aiding in transport of oxygen;
17. coelom-clearing ducts (nephridia) comparable to the most primitive features of the chordate kidney;
18. segmentation.

The *chordates* add a few adaptations to the 18 listed above:

19. a hollow, dorsal nerve cord;
20. a firm supporting notochord immediately below the nerve cord;
21. gill arches and their circulation;
22. a glandular liver extending beyond the wall of the gut.

Cyclostomes include all of these features, and add:

23. a cartilaginous skeleton, further protecting the nervous system and giving support to the body;
24. a pair of camera-style eyes;
25. a pair of semicircular canals on each side as specializations toward equilibration;
26. blood cells and an effective clotting mechanism;
27. a ventral muscular heart with two chambers.

The *sharks* and their relatives possess all 27 of these adaptations, plus new ones:

28. paired appendages;
29. jaws;
30. placoid scales and teeth, homologous with the teeth of higher vertebrates;
31. a third semicircular canal on each side.

Bony fishes include all of these features and more besides:

32. replacement of cartilage with bone, firm enough to support the body in air;
33. a respiratory lung, sometimes bilobed, opening into the pharynx—best developed in lung fishes.

The *amphibians* carried these adaptations with no loss into air, on dry land, and added:

34. jointed appendages, with toes and other features of the pentadactyl form, useful in locomotion away from water;
35. a separate pulmonary circulation and a third chamber in the heart, permitting more efficient use of lungs;
36. an auditory ear, with eardrum and earbone.

Reptiles went farther, still without losses:

37. claws on their toes;
38. a fourth chamber in the heart (in some).

Mammals retained all 38 adaptations and extended the series with:

39. reasonably constant blood temperature;
40. hair, helping in temperature control;
41. mammary glands, emphasizing parental care for the young after birth;
42. a placental connection between mother and unborn offspring, allowing the latter to develop to greater complexity before birth and exposure to environmental dangers.

with survival value are shown either in the fossil record or by surviving species. Certain of these biological adaptations are particularly striking.

Localization of Chemical Reactions

One early dichotomy of the ancestral line related to the degree of localization of activities within the cell. One group restricted its adaptations to those possible in small size, taking advantage of surface-to-volume characteristics at this level. Some continued with photosynthesis, either with chlorophyll (the blue-green algae) or bacteriochlorophyll (the purple bacteria), or by chemotrophic reactions (the iron and sulfur bacteria). Still others became saprophytes and parasites (the remaining bacteria).

The other branch of living things appears to have started as nucleated, sexless cells, perhaps similar to many Euglenophytes. This line probably divided into those which were ancestral to animals, and developed no plastids, and those which were ancestral to more obvious plants. In both of these subdivisions, unicellularity, multicellularity, and sexual reproduction appear to have offered advantages, since several combinations are evident. Probably plastids arose in the plant line alone, since no undisputed animal forms them.

Multicellularity

Division of labor among cooperating cells is only as efficient as the coordinating mechanism. For sessile multicellular plants, chemical coordination has been sufficient to support the most enormously productive energy-storage system known. The more active life of animals, however, became supported by both endocrine and nervous mechanisms. Multicellularity in animals extends beyond the tissue level seen in plants, to organization of organs and organ systems.

The advantages of multicellularity are numerous:

1. Different cells may be specialized toward greater efficiency in energy capture, absorption, storage, structural enlargement, coordination, and reproduction.

2. With increased size, inner cells are more protected from attack or desiccation, and may

be used to store energy needed in surviving periods of adverse living conditions.

3. Storage of energy (whether starch and oil in parenchyma cells, or glycogen in a liver and fats in adipose tissue) permits division of the life history into periods of growth, food-gathering, and reproduction.

4. Duplication of parts, whether as leaves on a plant or metameric segments in an animal, may provide structures all of which contribute to the organism's general welfare, yet structures some of which can be expended if attacked or mutilated by accident. As an extra gain, metamerism seems to place emphasis upon paired appendages, and these have proven highly advantageous.

5. Vascular tissues permit efficient transport of food, hormones, respiratory gases, wastes, and the like.

6. The basis is laid for parental care for new members of the population, whether through enclosure, stocking with food, attachment of parts improving chances for successful dissemination, or in contributions of food (and sometimes knowledge) after the new individual is relatively independent.

Sexual Reproduction

Two fundamental types of reproduction are evident. One places emphasis upon rapidity, on shortness of life cycle, and exploitation of any local supply of food. It is characteristic of organisms distributed in the encysted state by wind and water. It is the way of bacteria, of the great variety of unicellular algae and simple fungi, of the protozoans and small multicellular animals which can dry up and blow around as dust.

In this style of life, mutations and chromosomal irregularities apparently provide enough variation to allow slow evolution. Among many of these organisms, sexual reproduction is possible but often suppressed through long periods, or replaced by parthenogenesis.

The alternative system is met among plants and animals with longer lives and life histories. Populations of these species show remarkable stability in that, without human interference, the number of pine trees or woodchucks may vary little on a square mile of ground over several centuries. Few offspring or seed-lings reach reproductive maturity. Only at long intervals, when a forest fire, a disease epidemic, or some similar catastrophe opens a way for the then current crop of young, is there a test of variation in recolonizing the land area suddenly made available.

Sexual reproduction, through the endless recombinations of parental characteristics, provides a maximum of variation and keeps it available for use on short notice. With longer lives and life cycles, there is less advantage in having every adult member of the popula-tion a parthogenetic mother or a fruit-producing plant. Pollen-bearing seed plants and male animals are needed in each genera-tion, as devices increasing the variability available for testing whenever, at long inter-vals, a real opportunity for this arises.

12. REREADING THE FOSSIL RECORD

With the principle of evolutionary change in mind, far more meaning can be read into the fossil record. It is worth while to return and reconsider the account given in Chapter 21. The chief question is as to which from among the many fossils is most likely to be close to ancestral lines of later types, if not the actual ancestors.

In many instances, present-day species are seen as "living fossils," the remnants of once-abundant groups which have become all but extinct. The psilopsids, horsetails, clubmosses, cycads, and Ginkgo, are certainly representa-tives of this type among vascular plants. The brachiopods (lamp shells), the chambered nautilus (Photo 415), the onychophorans (Photos 428, 429), the lancelets, lungfishes, and egg-laying mammals, qualify in the An-imal Kingdom.

In every phylum the basic plan varies more and more (Photo 431), yet retains its indi-viduality. Thus early Cambrian fossils include onychophorans and trilobites (both arthro-pods) and annelid worms. All of these exhibit serial homology of appendages and a meta-merically segmented body. A remote but com-mon ancestry is called upon to explain the similarities.

However, the trilobites of the Cambrian are far too specialized to be ancestral to the rest of the arthropods. Hence, in the Protero-zoic, the arthropod stem must have given off an onychophoran line, a mandibulate line (leading to trilobites and crustaceans, to the precursors of millipedes, of centipedes, and of insects), and a chelicerate line (ancestral to horseshoe crabs, eurypterids, and arach-noids).

Fresh water and the land appear to have been invaded in relatively quick succession, in Silurian or early Devonian times. Organisms which could make the shift to streams must have been those which already were equipped to (1) concentrate needed mineral sub-stances from the far more dilute solution; (2) overcome the increased uptake of water forced into the protoplasm by osmosis; (3) tolerate greater variation in water flow, hence aeration, and temperatures; and (4) bridge dry seasons.

Life surrounded by air added dangers in the way of (1) desiccation; (2) still more rapid and extreme changes in temperature; (3) the battering effect of wind; (4) toxic effects of ultraviolet radiations which are filtered out by water but not by air; and (5) lack of buoy-ant support.

Accordingly it is no surprise that the first aquatic plants to leave the sea seem to have been phytoplankton, and the earliest to in-vade the land were low-growing, with sup-porting tissues and coverings resistant to aerial conditions. The animals followed this pattern too.

Effects of Climate

At the present time, with both tropical and arctic climates available for study in relation to flora and fauna, certain generalizations may be made concerning the evolutionary process. Where the climate is seasonably variable, either in temperature or in water availability, the limiting factors are those of survival through the cold or dry periods when life is at its lowest metabolic rate. Hence emphasis is not on perfection of adaptations to condi-tions of activity, but on variations that effect survival in a comatose condition. The chief adaptations that can be important under such circumstances are increase in fecundity, ac-celeration of development (including means for obtaining food faster or in greater quanti-ties), and such physiological mechanisms as

428. Peripatus, a "missing link" between annelid worms and arthropods, is a widely distributed tropical curiosity found among rotting logs and decaying vegetation.

429. The mouth and paired tentacles of Peripatus are unlike those of any other animal. The body structure combines features found elsewhere only among annelids and arthropods.

430. The tuatara (Sphenodon) is now protected on islands off the New Zealand coast, where it lives in burrows—the sole surviving species of the Rhychocephalia, a once-prominent order of reptiles.

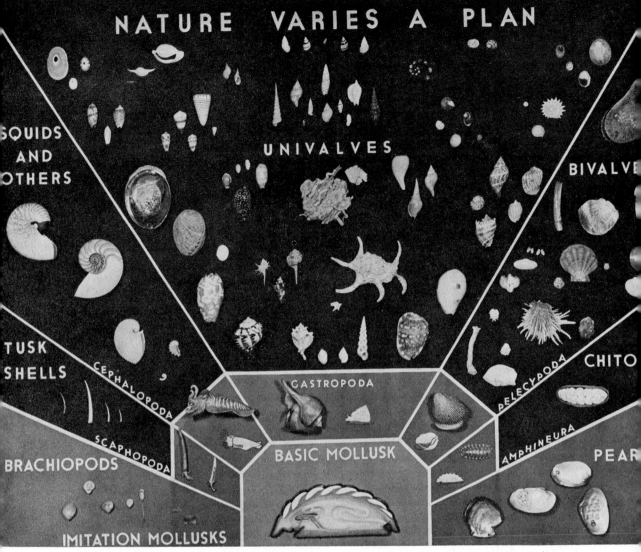

NATURE VARIES A PLAN

SQUIDS
AND
OTHERS

UNIVALVES

BIVALVE

TUSK
SHELLS

CEPHALOPODA

GASTROPODA

PELECYPODA

CHITO

SCAPHOPODA

AMPHINEURA

PEAR

BRACHIOPODS

BASIC MOLLUSK

IMITATION MOLLUSKS

431. The differences in molluskan architecture are extreme enough to have interested man since prehistoric times.

432. In the South Pacific some backward people of the present still use strings of money cowrie shells in bartering.

tolerance for low temperatures or desiccation. Adaptations toward cold or drought are likely to be simple ones like burrowing, and many of them lead into evolutionary blind alleys. Under seasonal variability of climate, the number of species of plants and animals is relatively small, though each may be represented by enormous numbers of individuals during the short period of annual activity. Usually the animals show little social adaptation, and are remarkably unafraid of man. All these features point to physical conditions which vary only between more and less harsh, and the former kill off great proportions of the populations apparently on a random basis that can contribute little to evolutionary advance.

Where the climate is less variable, on the other hand, the physical factors seldom influence the numbers or adaptations to any great degree. Food acquisition is largely a problem of being active without being preyed upon, since the biological environment is very exacting. As a result, tropical animals avoid one another, and this shyness often gives the impression that no animals are present. Vast numbers of kinds of plants and animals are represented by relatively few individuals apiece, but the niches into which their lives are restricted are so narrow as to require complex adaptations, and the individuals themselves are subject to a surprising variability. Complex social relationships plus the variability lead to much more effective natural selection. There are, so to speak, more frequent evolutionary challenges—hence more adaptations and more long-term responses to the environment that result in species formation. Thus, in a tropical region, emphasis is less on fecundity, or on speed of development, or on means for getting food quickly and in bulk; it is more on detailed adaptations that fit the organism very perfectly into some particular niche. The high variability, however, allows quick shifts from one niche to another when pressure of competitors allows the spread. Evolution in the tropics is far faster and more spectacular than in regions with more variable climate. Mimicry and protective resemblance reach heights far beyond anything in temperate regions; commensalism between organisms and social communities among the animals reach a peak of development.

From an appreciation of the contrast between evolutionary opportunities in variable and almost constant climates comes better understanding of the role of glaciation in species formation. With advance of the ice sheets, as in the Permian, Cretaceous, and Pleistocene periods, group after group of organisms is eliminated, since each lacks the adaptive variability needed for a radical shift in its location or its mode of life. Retreat of the glaciers, on the contrary, provides an enormous opportunity for the variable species in the tropics and subtropics. Those that can follow onto the newly exposed areas have a temporary freedom from competition —temporary in the geologic sense. It should not be surprising, then, to find the variable species following a glacial retreat. It is a fact that each retreat of glaciers has been followed by a disproportionate shift of variable tropical forms into the exposed areas where evolution has then proceeded with great rapidity (still in the geologic sense of time) and where great areas have been colonized.

As the ice retreated, the vegetation and animals followed. This was very largely due to pressure of other organisms in which tolerances did not allow so close an approach to the cold weather around the glacier. The forward march of the organisms carried them to the north on the level, or up any mountain slope. Always the tundra type of life was in the vanguard, followed by taiga, then by the spruce forests which preceded the deciduous trees and grasslands. Northward and upward they went, until at present the tundra extends across the arctic lands beyond the spruce forests of the Hudsonian zone, and tips the peaks of mountains high enough to have a timber line. Farther south a mountain must be more than 12,000 feet in elevation to reach climates of arctic severity and maintain a tundra top. In Maine a mere 5,000 feet is sufficient. In Quebec, north of the St. Lawrence River, a few hundred feet is adequate. Farther yet, tundra reaches sea level. Many other factors complicate this subject, so that phenology (the relationships between climatic factors and growth of organisms) requires full study for appreciation of the effects of winds, water currents, bodies of water, large land masses, and major mountain barriers in the distribution of plant and animal life. The history in terms of the latest glaciation, however, is very clear, and demonstrates the importance of knowing not only the present positions of living things, but also their relationship to the fossil record.

Nonadaptive (Conservative) Characters

One aspect of the explanation of evolution on the basis of natural selection is the lack of importance of the great bulk of the characters of an organism. As long as they do not directly affect the biotic potential of the species, they are free to continue and to express their genetic variability in a completely random manner. Some new environmental factor may arise which will affect some such "neutral" character and raise it to a position of significance in survival; when this occurs the variability is restricted gradually as one end of

the series of variants is progressively eliminated. This character will then be less subject to variation or it may vary in new directions. No alterations take place toward the old that was detrimental—if the elimination is sufficiently regular over a long period of time.

As a result, every organism contains in its adult and embryonic constitution an enormous number of features that are no longer of adaptive significance in its modern way of life. They are characteristics that were important in some ancestral form, but now they remain as rudimentary organs of no value whatever. They are spoken of as "conservative" features.

Overspecialization

Among the spectacular forms of life that vanished with the Pleistocene glacial period were the sabre-toothed cats, the mammoth, the Irish elk (Megaceros), and many others. Similarly, the Cretaceous put an end to the remarkable coiled nautiloid mollusks and the Ammonites, and to the dinosaurs and all but a few other reptiles. The Permian eliminated the trilobites and eurypterids. Most of these, toward the end of their days, showed one feature in common: overspecialization. In each instance the organism had lost variability to such an extent that it was unable to adapt for the changes in climatic conditions and food available. It had gone up an evolutionary blind alley.

Thus, in terms of prediction, the most likely candidates for a long future and a diversity of descending lines are those living things that now are relatively small and unspecialized (Fig. 23-13). Among mammals the rat holds an enviable position. It is omnivorous and of medium size, with a high reproductive rate and a reasonable development of all mammalian characteristics, including an adequate brain. The rat may well survive mankind, but in the meanwhile it makes use of man's food and transportation and acts as a vector for a number of his diseases (typhus, trichinosis, and several more). Man's chief claim to a future, on the other hand, is in his hands and brain, with which he has learned already to control his environment but not yet his reproduction or devastation of natural resources. Man has achieved no balance with natural conditions except where civilization is at a

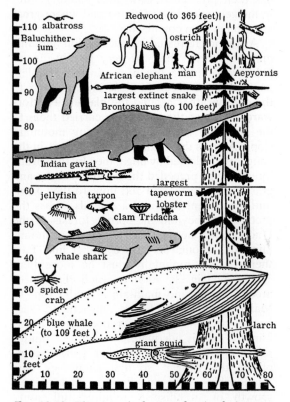

FIG. 23-13. *The size of plants and animals is sometimes a clue to overspecialization and a possible factor in extinction through loss of adaptability to new conditions. (After Wells, Huxley & Wells.)*

low ebb. Until this is reached, the prediction of a future is on shaky foundations.

Terminal Adaptations

Something inherent in the evolutionary process clearly prevents an organism from climbing any distance down its own family tree. Occasionally a genetic combination of characters turns up in any species that seems to be a "throwback," exhibiting features found among ancestral types. In man, birth in a full coat of lanugo or with a cervical fistula representing an unclosed gill slit, are good examples. Each is referred to as an *atavism* (derived from the Latin *avus* = grandfather) or a *reversion* to former types. These are rather negligible exceptions to the rule just mentioned, since they represent such rare individuals and involve only one feature at a time.

Far more characteristic is the fact that when the ancestors of modern whales began their Eocene journey from the south coast of the Mediterranean Sea as shore dwellers taking up aquatic sites in the Sea itself, they did not develop gills or a typical fish tail or scales. The adaptations that gradually permitted them more and more freedom in the water were not achieved by changing the direction of development when their mammal-style embryos reached the gill-slit, fishlike stage. Instead, they carried through specializations into the mammalian form, in an anatomical conformation clearly on the ancestral line of the modern ungulates, and then used new adaptations allowing invasion of marine situations. Their tail is a transverse sculling oar that no doubt is helpful in diving; their paired pelvic appendates degenerated, although the bony framework and muscles for a five-toed limb still remain in modern whales; their pectoral fins developed with a five-fingered skeleton showing that the ancestral types once were possessed of digits. The blow-hole is a strictly cetacean device, carrying the nasal apertures to a common opening directly above the pharynx,[4] and not interfering with the filter feeding of the big animals, or with the active lives of those like porpoises and toothed whales that have predaceous habits. All of these animals, however, possess in their re-

---

[4] In toothed whales; in whalebone whales there are two openings side by side.

spiratory functioning a whole array of special adaptations that allow them to dive deeply, where hydrostatic pressures are enormous; they remain submerged for 15 minutes or more, holding their breath, without being incapacitated by carbon dioxide accumulation or oxygen deficit. These are all modifications of a mammal, allowing it to compete successfully with the gill-breathing fishes, while invading a habitat for which fishes have been becoming progressively better fitted since the Ordovician or before. Thus evolution adds at the end only, and any changes involving the embryo are by slow elimination of roundabout stages—not by secondarily making use of embryonic features when there is a return to an earlier habitat.

The various specializations of mammal structures that allow whales to operate successfully in the marine situation demonstrate how adaptation for a way of life may be reached by a new or different route. The procedure is referred to as **convergent evolution,** as contrasted with the divergent changes that tend to make organisms more unlike, more specialized for different modes of existence. Thus the whale can be said to have converged toward the adaptation pattern of fishes, while at the same time diverging from the remainder of the original ungulate group. Similarly, the bats show a convergence with the flying reptiles, the birds, and the winged insects. Many of the confusions between homology and analogy have convergent evolution—independent development of adaptations helpful in a single way of life—as a background.

Embryonic Similarities

Vertebrate embryos go through many comparable stages, regardless of whether they end as fish or fowl, mouse or man. Each proceeds toward its own final form. But the similarities (Fig. 23-1) led to the idea that each vertebrate "climbed its own family tree" during embryonic development. This concept is now outmoded, since exceptions to it are numerous and more important than are the best examples supporting the idea. The resemblances result from processes that are common. Each of these processes is an expression of relative growth and the inherited genes.

13. THE POSITION OF MANKIND

The fossil record of the genus Homo (Fig. 23-14) and of the family Hominidae extends backward only into the Pliocene; and that of the order Primates possibly into the beginning of the Eocene. The other evidences of man's existence on earth take the form of objects he has used for tools or clothing or utensils. They are the **artifacts** of the ethnologist—objects on which man has left an imprint of his handiwork, however crude. Each year, as parties from museums and universities excavate the remains of early human habitations, more of this documentary evidence comes to light, and interpretations of man's past come to be on a progressively firmer footing.

Cultures

To date, the early history seems to fall rather naturally into several periods. First of these is the **Eolithic culture** during the Pliocene, from about seven to one million years B.C. During this time, human types emerged from prehuman ancestors, and although we have no known skeletal remains of man, the presence of a tool-wielding organism is indicated by the earliest, crudely-chipped stone implements.

A **Paleolithic culture,** often referred to as the "Old Stone Age," followed—through the Pleistocene into the recent—up to about 12,-000 B.C. It is marked by slow advances in implements into a diversity of finely-worked types, some being stones fastened to the side of a shaft. Bone tools were developed, and the earliest art is found on cave walls and roofs where man sought shelter (Photos 397-398). Some of these drawings are far more accurate representations than any until the Renaissance in Europe.

From 12,000 to 6,000 B.C., a **Mesolithic culture** or "Middle Stone Age" is recognized, in which man gathered together on a community basis and in which a degree of specialization appeared. Some men excelled in hunting, others felled trees and built boats; a different group made millstones (which implies that the cultivation of some cereals had begun), and further men made pottery that was crude but useful. The domestication of the dog occurred at this time, perhaps in more than one region on an independent basis.

The **Neolithic culture** began about 6,000 B.C. when the domestication of further animals and a variety of food plants laid the basis for agriculture and animal husbandry. These arts made possible more permanent living quarters and larger settlements; these, in turn, gave rise to further division of labor, to better pottery and housing, to community life, and to the development of social, political, and religious organizations. The transition ending neolithic times has been more variable. Nearly all primitive people of the present day were in the neolithic stage when first discovered: the American Indian, Australian aborigine, and others. Yet, at its highest point, the neolithic organization produced the civilizations of the Maya, Aztec, and Inca empires of Central and South America, with high development of architecture, stone-working, and ornamental design.

Use of metals (copper, then alloys of copper with tin to make bronze) has been used as a criterion of the "Copper-Bronze Age," when city- and town-sized communities developed in Egypt, Mesopotamia, the Indus Valley, Crete, and China (4,000 to 1,200 B.C.). The metals allowed more rapid working of stone, and seem to have led to radical improvements and diversifications in arts and industries. The first written records are from this period, and architecture reached the proportions where the great pyramids were designed and built in Egypt (2,900 to 2,630 B.C.).

In the Mediterranean area, between 1,200 and 500 B.C., the "Early Iron Age" developed, with the rise of Classical Greece (often referred to as the "Homeric Age" in honor of Homer, whose life included the year 900 B.C.). The use of iron led to the development of tools with keener edges, and to the expansion and migration of militaristic tribes now equipped with iron weapons. Roman civilization began, and in the Far East both Confucius and Buddha were born (551 and 500 B.C., respectively).

Fossil History

The remainder of the record falls into two categories: (1) the most recent 2,500 years, when written history gives a far fuller picture of man's activities over much of the world; and (2) the remote past—Pliocene and before —where inferences can be drawn only from the fragmentary remains of primates. Since the appearance of Charles Darwin's book *The Descent of Man,* and the inclusion of man in the evolutionary scheme, interest in these early evidences of human presence or of ancestral types has not only been keen but has been subjected to the most detailed scrutiny. For a while it was believed that no subhuman "missing links" would be found, but since 1891 a whole series of such forms have rewarded ethnologists and paleontologists, so

that there is now no significant break in the story of man that might set him on the pedestal he so obviously craves.

Before considering these primate remains, it is important to review some of the features of modern members belonging to this order of mammals. Many of them are familiar to most people from visits to zoological parks, where the monkey house is a major attraction. Three main groups of primates are recognizable: (1) the lemuroids, in which the second toe has a claw instead of a nail—including the potto of Asia and Africa, the lemurs of

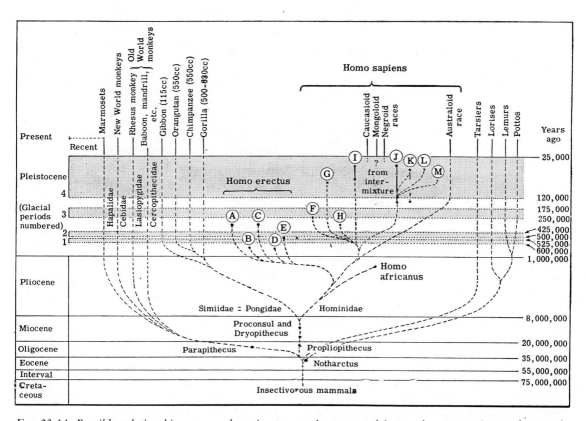

FIG. 23-14. *Possible relationships among the primates can be presented in tree form on a time scale extending back through the Cenozoic. Recent studies suggest that all fossil relics of man can be referred to some one of 3 species, although special genera were proposed for most of them. Five separate fossil discoveries may be grouped as* Homo erectus: *A, "Java man"; B, a Chinese giant; C, "Peking man"; D, a Javanese giant; and E, "Heidelberg man." None of these seem to have left modern descendants. Extinct also is* Homo africanus, *the "southern ape." The remaining species,* Homo sapiens, *consisted of at least 3 stocks: one producing the present Australian aborigines, the australoid race; a second, the "Cro-Magnon" stock, may be ancestral to the 3 other modern races of man; the third, the "Neanderthal" stock, is either extinct or was partly absorbed by intermixture. Of the Cro-Magnon stock, fossil finds include F, the Swanscombe remains; G, the Fontéchévade remains; H, the Kanjera discoveries; and I, the true Cro-Magnon collection. The Neanderthal stock is represented by J, a well-known European phase; K, "Rhodesian man"; L, "Solo man"; and M, "Florisbad man." Cranial capacities are shown for anthropoid apes; corresponding values for the fossil men and other information concerning them are given on pp. 457-459.*

Madagascar, Indo-China, and adjacent parts of Africa and Asia, and the lorises of Asia; in most of these the snout is prominent, the tail long and bushy, the habits solitary; they are tree dwellers with omnivorous habits and inferior intelligence; (2) the tarsier—the single species of the genus Tarsius—in the Philippines and Australasian islands; these are small, squirrel-sized animals, with claws on the second and third digits and nails on the others; they have a long naked tail and remarkable extensions of the hind feet enable them to leap like a frog after insects and lizard prey; all digits end in rounded pads; they are nocturnal, with large ears and relatively enormous eyes; and (3) the anthropoids, all of them with nails and no claws, with diurnal habits and more nearly human form; the monkeys and apes.

The fossil record of the primates is sufficiently good to be able to reconstruct much of their history (Fig. 23-14). Apparently they arose from some group of Cretaceous insectivorous mammals that developed arboreal habits. A mechanical aid to clambering in trees can be seen in the peculiar skeletal modifications that produced a link via the clavicle between shoulder girdle and sternum—our so-called "collar bone." In most mammals the clavicle floats freely as a rudiment of little value. The primate feet and hands, moreover, are characteristically flexible, each with five digits, usually armed with nails rather than claws; the innermost toe and the thumb are normally opposable to the other four digits, allowing the appendage to be used in grasping branches.

Notharctus in the Eocene seems to show some of the characters that distinguish lemuroids from tarsiers or anthropoids. Hence the conclusion is reached that two divisions of the main stem occurred—first the branching that led to the lemuroids, then that to the tarsiers, both in Eocene times. The remaining anthropoid stock divided in the early Oligocene, separating a monkey line represented by Parapithecus from an ape line indicated by Propliopithecus in the later Oligocene. The diversification of monkeys following Parapithecus seems to have followed geographical boundaries, with an "Old World Monkeys"

division and a "New World Monkeys" group. The latter are highly adapted for arboreal life in Central and South America, and in some instances have developed prehensile use of the tail; none has cheek pouches, and there is a flat space on the head between the nostrils; the marmosets compose the one family (Hapalidae), whereas such monkeys as the howler, capuchin, and spider monkey are members of the other (Cebidae). Similarly, the Old World Monkeys have characters in common; the tail is never prehensile, the nostrils are close together, directed downward; some have cheek pouches; most have hairless, calloused areas on the buttocks, which may be brightly colored as a sexual character ("ischial callosities"). One family (Cercopithecidae) has become secondarily terrestrial, and includes the baboons and mandrills of southern Arabia and Africa. The other (Lasiopygidae) includes the macaques or rhesus monkeys of Asia Minor and India into Malaya, and the Barbary apes of Asia and Gibraltar.

Following Propliopithecus on the ancestral line leading to the apes is the Miocene fossil Dryopithecus. It is believed that shortly after this time, but still in the Miocene period, the stem forked into two, one side leading to the great apes (family Pongidae = Simiidae) and the other toward man (Hominidae). In the former the arms are longer than the legs and the canine teeth are enlarged. In hominids the legs are longer than the arms and the canine teeth scarcely exceed their neighbors in length.

Further branching of the ape group, probably in Pliocene times, segregated the gibbons of Malaya from the stem that forked to separate the gorillas of West Africa from the line leading to the orangutan of Sumatra and Borneo, and the chimpanzee of West Africa.

The family Hominidae appears to contain only a single genus—Homo—with three distinct species. Only one of these, *Homo africanus,* may be as old as late Pliocene. The others have been distinguished from fossil remains in the Pleistocene—all within the past one million years. One, *H. erectus,* seems to have left no modern descendants. The remaining species, *H. sapiens,* resembles *H. erectus* in the spread of distribution, and may have been the competing factor which ended the existence of *H. erectus.*

This species was described originally in 1925 from one incomplete skull of a child, found in a cave near Taungs, Bechuanaland, South Africa. To it the name *Australopithecus africanus* was applied; newspapers called it the "southern ape." Later two adult skulls, with bones of arm and leg and with fragments of toes, were uncovered. Then almost complete skeletons came to light. As a result, the species is now rather well known.

The brain volume ranged between 440 and 733 cc, with an average at about 600. This is somewhat greater than that of the largest gorilla, but is far larger if related to body size (Fig. 23-15). The teeth are quite human in type, although set in a jaw protruding to a degree intermediate between that of modern man and that of present-day apes. The bony knobs by means of which the skull articulates with the first cervical vertebra are farther forward than in any living ape, implying a relatively erect posture. The leg bones are of a form corroborating this view. The hip girdle has the broad, flat, human character markedly different from the long, narrow form in apes. The arms show none of the overdevelopment associated with an arboreal habit.

Homo erectus

To this species, five separate discoveries have been referred. Originally each of these fossil men was given a separate generic, as well as specific, name. No justifications for this practice seems evident.

"Java man" (*Pithecanthropus erectus*) was described in 1890 from a skull and a femur. Until 1937 no additional material was found. Then skulls and leg bones of three other specimens were recovered in the same geological formation, near Trinil, Java. The sediments appear to be of middle Pleistocene age. The 1937 fossils were accompanied by crude stone implements of Eolithic type.

"Peking man" (*Sinanthropus pekinensis*) is known from a single tooth found in 1903, a partial skull excavated in 1929, and a series of over 40 more since that time.

"Heidelberg man" (*Palaeoanthropus heidelbergensis*) was identified from a single complete jaw with teeth, found near Mauer, Germany, in 1907. The chin is not prominent, but the teeth are strong and the jaw itself is far heavier than that of any other fossil man or of living man.

The Chinese *Gigantopithecus blacki* and Javanese *Meganthropus paleojavanicus* were described from jaw fragments of extraordinary size.

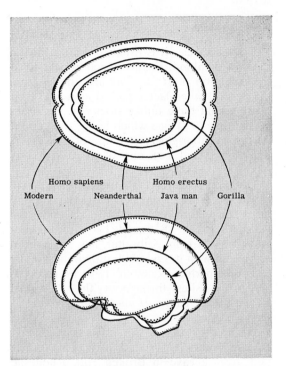

FIG. 23-15. *Brain dimensions show a gradual increase in the human stock toward modern times, either as seen in outline from above* (top) *or side* (below).

From these remains it is possible to derive a fair picture of *Homo erectus*. He varied from moderate to large in size, and stood erect or nearly so. His forehead retreated and his jaw projected, although less so than in modern apes. He lacked a chin, and his teeth were massive.

The size of the brain was particularly variable. The Javanese skulls range from a brain-case volume of 775 to 900 cc, with 860 a good average. The Chinese skulls present a scale from 850 to 1,300 cc, with 1,075 cc the average value. These are well ahead of the gorilla's 500 cc, though behind the average value of 1,350 cc for modern man. The intelligence of *H. erectus* probably fell between. Peking man, at least, lived in caves, used fire, and had weapons made of stone, bone, and deer antler.

Thus *Homo erectus* appears to have spread widely in early Pleistocene times, but to have died out, perhaps in the second interglacial period.

Homo sapiens

To this species it is usual to refer all living races of mankind. Fossils which appear to fit the definition of *H. sapiens* are known from the second interglacial period onward. It is possible that three unlike stocks were present at that time: (a) one which led to the present Australian aborigines; (b) one of "Neanderthal" type; and (c) one of "Cro-Magnon" type.

Of these, "Neanderthal man" is best known. It was recognized from skeletal remains found near Düsseldorf, in Germany's Neanderthal valley, between 1856 and 1861. An earlier find (1848) from Gibraltar has since been associated with it. Over 100 individuals, many as almost perfect skeletons, have been recovered from sites throughout the Palearctic Realm. The name *Homo neanderthalensis* seems unnecessary.

Neanderthal-like fossils have been uncovered in South Africa and Java. The former find, from a cave in Broken Hill, Rhodesia, was named *Homo rhodesiensis*. It consisted of a nearly complete skull, part of another upper jaw, pieces of limb bones and of a pelvic girdle. The Javanese fossil collection was uncovered between 1931 and 1933 along the Solo River, near Ngandong. It includes 11 partial skulls and a tibia, to which the name *Homo soloensis* was given. An earlier representative, "Florisbad man" from near the tip of South Africa, agrees with "Rhodesian man" and "Solo man" in differing little from the Neanderthal type, and in fitting within the time scale of true Neanderthal fossils.

The Neanderthal type can be reconstructed easily. The posture was stooped, and a height of 5 feet or less was usual. The hands and feet were disproportionately large, the legs bowed. The gait must have been a shuffle rather than a walk. The skull was large, thick-boned, with prominent eyebrow ridges and receding forehead. The neck was thick, since the spinous processes of the cervical vertebrae are exceptionally large.

Neanderthal man's cranial capacity ranged from 1,234 to 1,660 cc, with 1,450 cc an average figure. This is larger than that of modern man, but two facts militate against crediting Neanderthal with as much intelligence. The impressions of the cortex on the inner surface of the brain case indicate convolutions of less complexity than those of modern man. The cerebellum was larger, the cerebrum smaller, and the whole skull had a relatively flat roof.

Cro-Magnon man, by contrast, had an elongate skull with ample room for cerebral cortex. Erect posture is indicated by the articulation of skull and first cervical vertebra, by the straightness of the leg bones, and by the form of the pelvic girdle. Correspondence to modern races of mankind is much more striking. The fossil records of this type include numerous remains. Most are from caves in western Europe (especially France and Spain). Apparently related, although much earlier in geological time, are specimens from Kanjera in East Africa (probably of second interglacial period), from Swanscombe in England, and from Fontechevade in France.

Culture among the Cro-Magnons attained the highest of the Paleolithic. The paintings with which these men adorned the walls and ceilings of their cave homes are remarkable for their accuracy and artistic standards (Photos 384-385). Many of these drawings seem to have been made by blowing pigments through a straw at a wetted stone surface. Some are line drawings. A few include indications of how the animals moved their legs, and suggest modern animated cartoons. Others have shading to indicate three-dimensional form. The same caves have yielded sculptures, and also stone spears and stone axes.

Several other, minor, collections of human skeletons add a little to the picture and indicate where gaps remain. In England, skulls found at Galley Hill and others (named *Palaeoanthropus palestinus*) from Mount Carmel in Palestine, seem intermediate between Cro-Magnon and Neanderthal man, and may represent a hybrid produced by interbreeding. Somewhere a broad-headed race should be found, since such a race must have interbred with the long-headed Cro-Magnons during Neolithic times to produce the variety of skull forms among modern races.

Modern Man

Anthropologists are still uncertain whether the **australoid** type of man is derived from a separate line of descent, and hence should be considered a separate species—*Homo australiensis*. It may even be ancestral in type to the other three groups of modern man.

The australoid build is on the small side of average; the hair is wavy and develops into full beards and considerable body covering in the ♂. The skull is narrow and forehead sloping, so that the average brain volume is 1,200 cc, with only 1,100 cc fairly common. The brow ridges are more prominent than in any other living type of man.

Australoid culture is scarcely as high as that of the Neanderthal group. But unlike these fossil forms, the australoid has hands the size of other modern men and he makes his few tools to match. A suspected relative of the australoid is the low-caste Veddah that represents the aborigines of Ceylon.

Incidence of Human Blood Types*
(BY PER CENT)

Racial group	AB	A	B	O	M	N	Rh-neg.
Australoid	0.6	48.1	2.4	48.9	3.0	67.4	0.0
Caucasioid							
basques	2.2	39.7	1.3	56.8	?	?	28.8
nordic	3.4	43.3	9.4	43.8	29.0	21.5	13.7
mediterranean	2.5	32.0	10.0	55.5	22.4	25.2	13.1
alpino-armenoid	4.8	54.7	9.7	31.7	32.0	21.0	5.9
semito-arabic	6.5	34.8	19.0	39.5	29.0	16.5	?
ainu	?	?	?	?	17.8	31.9	?
Negroid	4.4	24.3	24.8	48.5	28.5	27.5	6.0
Mongoloid							
north asiatic	8.2	32.9	28.3	30.8	38.6	15.8	0.5
south asiatic	5.3	23.1	28.6	43.3	38.2	14.9	0.0
polynesian	0.5	59.0	2.0	38.5	?	?	0.0
North American Indian	0.0	9.0	1.0	90.0	58.3	5.0	0.0
South American Indian	0.0	0.0	0.0	100.0	80.0	0.7	0.0

* Largely from N. Lahovary in *Science* for March 13, 1953.

The three other racial groups all have a much larger brain, more complex civilization, and far more vertical forehead with scarcely any brow ridges. Of the three, the **caucasioid** is the most archaic and exhibits the greatest variability. They have the doubtful honor of being hairiest; skin color ranges from pink to

dark brown, hair color from palest blond through dark brown, eye color from blue through dark brown, and hair form from straight to wavy (but never woolly). The skull sutures are complex—the frontal one being most serrated; the forehead is high and prominent, the chin well developed but the face not prognathous; the root of the nose is high, the nasal spine (to which the nasal cartilage is attached) is large and sharp; the lips are usually thin and the upper rim of the upper lip tends to form a complex bow. The caucasioids include the Ainu tribes on islands off northeastern Asia (the hairiest of all mankind), the Dravidians and Afghans of India, the Ethiopians of Abyssinia, the Berbers of northwest Africa, the Arabs, the Armenoids and Mediterranean peoples, the Alpine groups in Europe and eastward, and the blond Nordics of northern Europe—particularly of Scandinavia.

The **negroid** races have less hair—that on the body being much less prominent than in caucasioids and that on the head being woolly or kinky or even so scanty as to be arranged in "peppercorns." The hair is always black, as are the irises of the eyes. The skin is dark brown to black. The face is more prognathous than in other human groups, but the everted lips are less ape-like than those of any Primate; the bow of the upper lip's margin is simple and the chin is less prominent than that in other races. Broadly flaring nostrils and short noses may be related to the tropical environment in which so many negroid groups live—where heating the air inhaled is of no significance. Partly, however, this nasal character is due to the low root of the nose, the very wide angle at which the bones that make up the bridge of the nose meet one another, and to the smallness and roundness of the nasal spine. The skull sutures are mostly simple, that at the back of the head the most complex. The forearm and lower leg bones are usually much longer in proportion to the rest of the body, and the calves have somewhat underdeveloped muscles; the buttocks may be abnormally large; commonly the heel projects more than in other races. In addition to the African negroids—the Negro, the Bantu, the Bushman, and the Congo pigmies—other groups in this category include the Negrito of the Philippines to New Guinea, and the Melanesians (including Papuans) of the Australasian islands.

Mongoloid races, by contrast, have coarse, straight, black head hair, scanty body hair, and skin yellow to yellowish brown. The skull sutures are relatively complex; the cheekbones are the widest of any modern man. In addition, there are commonly fatty deposits around the eyes and cheeks that alter the appearance of the face; an epicanthic fold over the inner corner of the eyelid may give the eyes an oblique appearance. The upper incisor teeth are peculiar in that a ridge of enamel on each side produces a depressed inner surface —a feature often described as "shovel-shaped." There is a tendency toward short, solid build. These features apply to the Mongols and Tatars of Asia, the Indonesians and Polynesians of the Pacific islands, the Eskimos, and the American Indians (properly called Amerinds) of both hemispheres in the New World.

Interbreeding tends more and more to destroy the distinctions between modern races of man, so that "pure" specimens of any group are increasingly difficult to find. This is due largely to the increased ability of man to travel over the world, and to his present emphasis on economic position rather than physical or mental characteristics in mate selection. Even the distributions of the racial groups mentioned are the results of complex migrations and intermixtures. These facts make it difficult for man to see where his evolution has brought him or is taking him at present.

Human Populations

Until the end of the Paleolithic period (say, 12,000 B.C.), all of mankind apparently depended upon foods which grew naturally— wild animals, or herbs, or both. On this basis, about two square miles of fertile hunting territory are required to support each human individual. Since the entire earth has only about 20 million square miles of land of this quality, the maximum possible population at the end of the Old Stone Age must have been about 10 million people.

A sharp rise in population was possible with the development of agriculture and the domestication of animals for food and burden. Urbanization and division of labor helped in the same direction. Yet the world population doubled itself less than six times in over 13,-000 years, since in 1650 A.D. the total stood at about 545 millions.

This growth is slow compared to that which can be shown since the Industrial Revolution. Fortunately, good statistics are available to follow this most recent increase:

Year	1650	1750	1800	1850	1900	1950
Population (millions)	545	728	906	1171	1608	2400
Europe (per cent)	18.3	19.2	20.6	22.7	25.0	23.3
Anglo-America	0.2	0.2	0.6	2.2	5.0	6.9
Latin America	2.2	1.5	2.1	2.8	3.9	6.6
Australasia	0.4	0.3	0.2	0.2	0.4	0.5
Africa	18.3	13.0	9.9	8.1	7.5	8.3
Asia	60.5	65.8	66.5	63.9	58.4	54.2

Two general conclusions can be reached from study of this table. One is that the rate of increase in population is greatest in Europe plus America—changing from a fifth of the world's population in 1650 to more than a third of it in 1950. The second is that the population is increasing more rapidly at present than in any recorded period.

Europe plus America contain primarily caucasioid peoples. To complete the total of this racial group it is necessary to add in the Arabs and others mentioned on p. 459. When this is done, it is seen that of the world's present population, about 57 per cent are caucasioid. By contrast 34 per cent are mongoloid, and only about 9 per cent negroid. In terms of the total picture, the Europeans and their descendants seem to be reproducing themselves more rapidly than any other group.

The rate of increase at present must be considered as an explosion. In the century following 1650, the world's population added a third to itself. In the succeeding century it added two thirds to itself. And in the century ending with 1950, it more than doubled. How long this can continue is an important biological problem facing mankind.

In the past 12,000 years, we have grown from being a relatively insignificant member of the world's animal population to become its most dominant organism. We have surpassed all other mammals in geographical distribution, in control of environment, and probably also in sheer numbers.

The figures quoted in the table above for 1950 are based upon reports submitted to the United Nations, and an estimate of world populations prepared by the Statistical Office and the Population Division of that agency. Of the several separate estimates made from various lots of data, the world population was seen to lie between 2,350 and 2,471 million. Hence 2,400 million is a good round number.

If these millions were distributed evenly over the 57 million square miles of land, there would be 42 inhabitants per square mile. But the six million square miles of Antarctica are uninhabited, and so are 14 million more square miles consisting of ice sheets, tundras and deserts on other continents. Nor are the remaining 37 million square miles equally useful to man. As a result the density of population varies widely:

	Human inhabitants per square mile
Manhattan Island, New York City	63,000
Java	1,000
Belgium	740
Japan } Puerto Rico }	600
Western and Central Europe	310
Northeastern U.S.A.	180
United States as a whole	50.7

About two-thirds of mankind live in the Far East, India, western and central Europe, and the northeastern United States. These areas account for less than 8 per cent of the total land surface of the earth—about 4¼ million square miles. How many more people the earth can support receives analysis in the following chapter.

God has ordered His creation by weight and measure.

J. VON LIEBIG (1803-1873)

THE WORLD OF LIFE

Why animals and plants are as they are, we shall never know; of how they have come to be what they are, our knowledge will always be extremely fragmentary, because we are dealing with only the recent phases of an immense and complicated history, most of the records of which are lost beyond all chance of recovery, but that organisms are as they are, that apart from the members of our own species, they are our only companions in an infinite and unsympathetic waste of electrons, planets, nebulae and suns, is a perennial joy and consolation.

—WILLIAM MORTON WHEELER in Science 57:71 (January 19, 1923).

SUGGESTED READING (see pp. 505-511)

Classics and Milestones: Malthus, de Lamarck, Darwin & Wallace, Darwin.

Recent and Informative: Bibby, 1953; Boyden, 1951; Blum, 1951, 1955; Bradley, 1952; Bogert, 1953; Broom, 1949; Brues, 1951; Colbert, 1949; Deevey, 1954; Dobzhansky, 1950; Dodson, 1952; Eiseley, 1948, 1953, 1954; Gamow, 1951; Hooton, 1945; Huxley, 1942; Jarvik, 1955; Krogman, 1943, 1948, 1951; Lack, 1953; Mangelsdorf, 1953; Moody, 1953; Movius, 1953; Oakley & Weiner, 1955; Oparin, 1938; Ryan, 1953; Simpson, 1949, 1950; Stebbins, 1951; Waddington, 1953; Wald, 1954.

24 · Looking Toward the Future

IN THE PAST few thousand years, the human species has found ways to transfer from one generation to another far more than the hereditary characters carried by the genes. Through speech, writings, and handiwork, man has been able to benefit from group experience, to evolve in a mental and technical sense far faster than in physical changes affecting his body or its protoplasmic chemistry.

Prime among the gains in this cumulative heritage have been the substitutions of agriculture and animal husbandry for food gathering, and of medicine for dependence upon natural immunities to diseases and other parasites. Technological advances permit activity during adverse weather, and storage of food in quantity. Added together, these changes overcome environmental resistance in large measure.

Every organism exploits its surroundings to the limit of its abilities. Only by doing so can nonhuman kinds maintain a balance between biotic potential and environmental resistance, and continue in evolutionary diversification. Any adaptation or passage of a barrier that suddenly lessens the effect of environmental resistance permits an explosive increase in numbers of the species. Mankind has reached that stage (p. 460).

Judging from the fossil record of species released suddenly from environmental pressures, and from our current understanding of ecological relationships, man's future course seems to depend largely upon whether he can spread beyond the limits of the earth. If he can migrate in numbers to fresh areas with untapped food supplies, the normal incidence of mutations would be subjected in these new areas to an unusual variety of fresh limiting factors. In each isolated new region, specializations could develop, perhaps resulting in rapid diversification of the present single species into a large number of separate ones. But unless mankind can escape into outer space and conquer new worlds, this possible future appears unlikely. Isolation on earth is becoming more difficult each year, and past diversification may be lost through racial intermixtures.

If man's release from control by environmental resistance results merely in a population increase within the same geographical limits, there is little hope that the rate of food production can long keep up with the number of mouths to be fed. Man is becoming a "weed species," comparable to deer wherever natural predators have been eliminated.

When the demand for food exceeds the amount that green plants produce beyond their own needs, vegetation disappears, leaving eroding soil and deserts. At first the animal species causing this change may suffer only from malnutrition and increasing fatalities from diseases which are unimportant when nutrition is good. Then a virulent form of some common disease or outright starvation eliminates so much of the population and so weakens the rest that the species dies out locally. If mankind reaches this stage, "locally" may well read "world-wide."

In comparing mankind with other organisms and seeking to predict the future, several important differences must be kept in mind. Some of these differences are detrimental; others are helpful.

1. Through medical care and skilful surgery, many human beings who would have been eliminated in previous centuries by disease or malformations now live to be parents. Susceptibilities to disease or malformations may be inheritable features. The number of defective individuals in the population is rising because these factors no longer eliminate "unfit" individuals as parents. Medical statistics show that this increase is already quite measurable.

2. No other species of animal or plant taxes the more vigorous and productive members of its kind for the support of the less vigorous. Humanitarianism is a factor which uniquely influences human evolution. It is likely to be a potent one.

3. No other species has released agents increasing the natural environmental level of radioactivity. Radiations affect the mutation rate of mankind and all other autocatalytic systems—including viruses. What effects this will have upon human beings and the organisms with which they share the earth cannot be foretold at the present. Harmful effects are far more likely than beneficial ones.

4. Man is able to examine his own actions objectively. His extreme awareness of "self" may lead him to appreciate his ecological place in nature. He could introduce self-regulatory procedures to take the place of the environmental resistance he has eliminated so thoroughly. To be effective, any deliberate action of this kind would have to be handled consistently, with full awareness of alternative consequences, and be introduced before the downward spiral of disease and starvation gets well started.

In looking toward man's future, his real needs must be evaluated carefully. Because he is a living organism, these basic requirements are those of protoplasm: a continual supply of energy, and particular atoms for maintenance and growth.

Energy is comparatively easy to analyse. Although man has made great progress in harnessing power for industrial use, and raises food with a single-mindedness that is nearly unique in the animal kingdom, his energy still comes almost entirely from the sun (Fig. 24-1). So far, he has not been particularly successful in utilizing solar power directly.

Only the most meager attempts have been made to use volcanic heat or the force of the tides. And whether atomic fission (or fusion) will furnish energy for more than war and heavy industry remains to be seen. No one knows how to dispose of the dangerous radioactive "wastes" produced. Places to hide these wastes where they will not interfere with potential resources, until the radioactivity has decayed into harmlessness, may be so hard to find that use of atomic power will always be limited.

From Fig. 24-1 it is easy to see which parts of solar energy become available to man in food, and which can be used in work. So long as solar energy remains the principal power source, man's activities are circumscribed by the degree to which he can increase the rate of energy trapping, the efficiency with which he uses his share, and the amount of the total available that he can divert from one channel to another.

One limitation in efficiency lies in man's own dietary choices. Since he is anatomically an omnivore and can be either strictly vegetarian or almost as strictly a carnivore, there is wide variation in the relative importance of *direct* utilization of plant food and *indirect* consumption of vegetation as the meat of herbivores.

Man is between 7 and 10 times as efficient in his use of plants when he eats them directly, although the results in terms of human vigor are not comparable (as will be pointed out on p. 495). Yet, no matter which form of food is more desirable or available, man must be vitally concerned with the welfare of green plants. His future depends on their success alone.

Green plants, in turn, have their own requirements: carbon dioxide from the atmosphere, sunlight, water, and certain soil nutrients. Carbon dioxide and sunlight are seldom as variable in supply as water and soil nutrients. For the most part, human activities tend to decrease both the water and the soil solutes available to plants, and to increase the carbon dioxide.

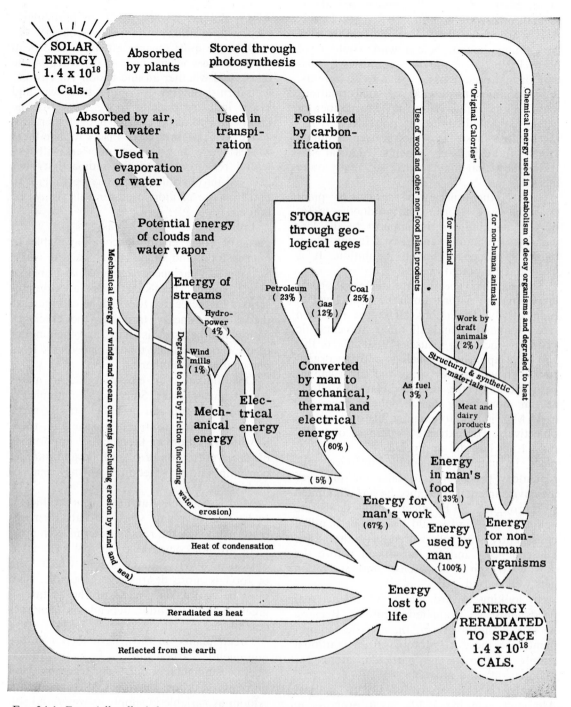

FIG. 24-1. *Essentially all of the energy man uses comes directly or indirectly from the sun. He takes a third of his share in food, the rest in mechanical, thermal and electrical energy used in his work. How much he can increase this share by tapping energy supplies now lost to life, or by competing for energy now used by other living things is a question for the future. (After Calvin, 1952.)*

Soil and water, like plants and animals, are renewable resources. Man's exploitation of them reduces both the rate of renewal and the actual existence of living resources. In part this has been due to ignorance of cause and effect. To a greater extent it has been from callousness toward the future—even the foreseeable future—in a desperate drive for immediate gain.

No practical application of biological science approaches in importance the insurance of a food supply for future man. The critical point has already arrived. Change will come during the lifetime of children already born. Whether the change will be one insuring man's survival depends upon his own decisions. The problem is to introduce the needed modifications in human ways before our modern world-wide civilization falls from the same cause as brought down the more local civilizations of the past: heedless exploitation of the land on which green plants grow.

To study human resources and calculate the number of people a given environment can support, is to engage in a study of **demography.** To find ways in which renewable resources can be utilized on a crop basis so as to continue their availability into an indefinite future is to explore the field of **conservation.**

Man's opposable thumb, binocular vision, upright posture, and related development of the cerebral cortex seem to have led to speech, writing, and technology. They have enabled the human race to exploit its environment to the point of endangering the future supply of soil, water, and living things.

In addition, man has become dissatisfied with living "like an animal," on the fringe of starvation. He wants the "better things of life"—paid vacations, education, automobiles, libraries, churches. But if he chooses to raise the general, world-wide standard of living, can he also have all the children his biotic potential will allow?

I. ENVIRONMENTAL RESISTANCE

Scarcity of food, contaminated water, poisons taken carelessly, and degenerative changes in his own body, remain the central factors killing people and limiting the population the world can support.

1. DISEASES

Progress in medicine and public health within the past century has been so spectacular that it is difficult to realize how recent is our knowledge of diseases.

Some Advances in Medical Techniques Since 1850

1851—introduction of ophthalmoscope for eye examination
1852—first hypodermic syringe
1860—discovery of antiseptic action, with phenol (carbolic acid)
1867—trial use of phenol spray in surgery
1870—first major test of vaccination against smallpox, although Jennings discovered the method in 1796
1870—introduction of catgut sutures and adhesive tape
1875—discovery of hemolysis after transfusion of alien blood (see 1902, 1920's, 1940)
1876—Koch demonstrated that disease anthrax was due to a bacillus, establishing the "germ theory of disease" (see also 1882)
1879—first local anesthesia, with cocaine
1880—Pasteur demonstrated artificial immunity, toward fowl cholera
1881—Laveran discovered the parasite of malaria; Nobel prize 1907 (see also 1897)
1882—Koch discovered the bacillus of tuberculosis; Nobel prize 1905 (see also 1894)

1883—Klebs discovered the diphtheria bacillus
1884—Koch discovered the cholera organism
1884—Metchnikoff discovered phagocytosis; Nobel prize 1908
1886—first steam sterilization of instruments
1892—filter-passing characteristic of a disease-causing agent recognized, identifying tobacco-mosaic virus as a new type of disease agent; in 1936 Stanley showed this particular agent to be a pure protein, as the first identification of the true nature of a virus, and received a Nobel prize 1946
1894—Trudeau began his sanitarium for tuberculosis patients, at Saranac Lake, N.Y.; in 1954 it was closed for lack of patients
1896—first sphygmomanometer for clinical measurement of blood pressure
1897—Ross discovered the vector of malaria to be the Anopheles mosquito; Nobel prize 1907
1899—first spinal anesthesia (anesthetic action of nitrous oxide—"gas" used in dental offices today had been discovered in 1800; first public use of ether in surgery, 1846; of chloroform, 1847)
1899—discovery of aspirin
1898-1902—discovery of the relationship between fleas and rats and human epidemics of typhus fever (= bubonic plague)
1902—Landsteiner discovered human blood groups; Nobel prize 1930 (see also 1940)
1905—Schaudinn discovered the spirochete of syphilis
1907—Wasserman introduced a sero-diagnostic test for syphilis
1908—Ehrlich found arsphenamine ("Salvarsan" or "606") for treatment of syphilis; Nobel prize 1908
1920's—first routine use of blood transfusions
1922—Banting discovered insulin; Nobel prize 1923
1927—Minot and Murphy discovered use of liver to combat pernicious anemia; Nobel prize 1934; active principle now known to be vitamin B_{12} in the liver
1928—first iron lung
1934—discovery of sulfanilimide as the first "sulfa" drug— by Domagh; Nobel prize 1939; other sulfa drugs followed: sulfathiazole 1938, sulfadiazine, 1946, etc.

1936—Kendal discovered cortisone; Nobel prize 1950; cortisone synthesized 1944; pituitary control of cortisone secretion, through ACTH, found 1949
1940—Landsteiner and Wiener discovered the Rh factor responsible for erythroblastosis and other difficulties
1945—first clinical use of penicillin by Florey and Chain; drug had been discovered by Fleming in 1929; Nobel prize shared by all three men, 1945
1945—Waksman discovered antibiotic value of streptomycin; Nobel prize 1952
1948—Dugger discovered antibiotic action of aureomycin
1953—Robbins and Enders discovered a culture technique for poliomyelitis viruses; Nobel prize jointly, 1954

Much of the credit for fundamental work proving the role of micro-organisms in disease belongs to Louis Pasteur and Robert Koch, who demonstrated it for a wide range of afflictions (Fig. 24-2). They also developed techniques for handling microbes for study (Fig. 24-3), and alerted the public to the need for better sanitation. At first, Joseph Lister was one of the few medical men to pay attention to the new ideas. He attempted to

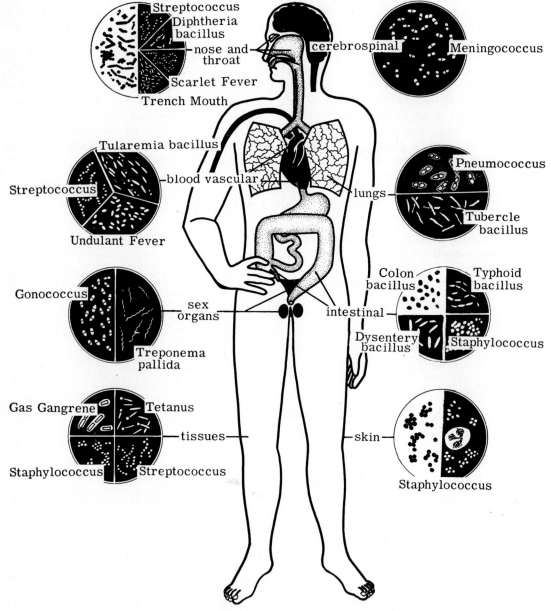

FIG. 24-2. *The major bacteria of the human body.*

reduce infection from the invisible agents during surgery. His success, cited in terms of numbers of patients surviving, was so much better than in hospitals where antiseptic routines were not followed, that others were impressed and insisted on similar measures.

As the public and medical men became conscious of the avenues of infection, procedures were broadened to reduce transmission. At the same time, laws were passed and enforced, regulating the purity of drugs and foods. Administering these laws required efficient organizations.

Organizations

Health supervision in civilized areas is organized in an ascending scale, beginning with parental responsibilities at the family level. Physicians and nurses are required by law to report all communicable diseases to an officer in each community—the **public health officer.** Each town has its Board of Health, each city its Health Department. At higher levels, the State Department of Health coordinates local efforts in cities and towns, and

supervises the various divisions of the State Board of Health.[1]

In 1953 a Department of Health, Education and Welfare was created by Act of Congress, with its Secretary a member of the President's Cabinet. This Department includes the U.S. Public Health Service (directed by the Surgeon General) with officers in uniform. Part of this organization is housed in great research centers of the National Institutes of Health at Bethesda, Maryland, and the Communicable Diseases Center at Atlanta, Georgia. Also included is a Commissioner of Food and Drugs, superintending a vigilant group who keep constant check on the safety of these commodities for public use. A Narcotics Bureau of the U.S. Treasury Department cooperates with them.

[1] With divisions dealing with communicable disease control, crippled children's services, dental hygiene, food sanitation, industrial hygiene, nursing; and a diagnostic laboratory to which physicians and public health officers can send specimens for identification.

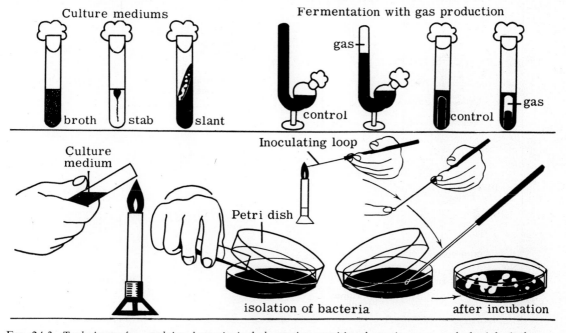

FIG. 24-3. *Techniques for studying bacteria include testing nutritional requirements and physiological processes. The micro-organisms may be grown in a broth, or as a stab culture in nutrient agar, or on the surface of an agar slant. Some will produce gas. Handling the cultures requires care* (lower illustrations): *flaming the mouth of the culture tube to prevent contamination while pouring an inoculated broth into a sterilized Petri dish; using an inoculating loop* (wire in a handle) *sterilized by flaming, to pick up a bacteria sample to be incubated on nutrient agar in another sterilized Petri dish. The form and color of colonies after incubation are useful characteristics in identification.*

Shortly after the end of World War II, 26 nations collaborated in forming a World Health Organization (WHO); additional nations have joined since. This organization strives toward international action which is likely to reduce tuberculosis, malaria, cholera, typhus, syphilis, and leprosy. It has supervised large numbers of immunizations for tuberculosis, using this temporary measure to relieve local situations. It also encourages study of nutrition, and is attempting to get cooperation in the field of drug addiction.

Results

In countries where medical skill and a public understanding about health and disease are widespread, sweeping changes are evident (Fig. 24-4). Communicable diseases no longer create a high death rate. Infant mortality has been decreased. Life expectancy tables have required upward revision time

after time. Yet this is due to more people living out a full life rather than extension of the maximum age. The net result is a changed distribution of age groups in the population (Fig. 24-15).

People live long enough to succumb to degenerative diseases. Some of the apparent rise of heart diseases, of cancer, and of cerebral vascular failure ("apoplexy"—thrombosis and hemorrhage) may be due to changes in diet or mode of life—particularly increased fat intake and nervous tension. Nearly 9 deaths in 10, however, are due to 13 diagnosed causes shown on p. 469.

Progress is apparent in many directions affecting human welfare, but not in all. The communicable diseases, now seen to be due to parasites transmitted from person to person, can be blocked in large measure by better public health measures and modern medical care. The environmental diseases are more varied: better understanding of dietary needs allows elimination of avitaminosis problems;

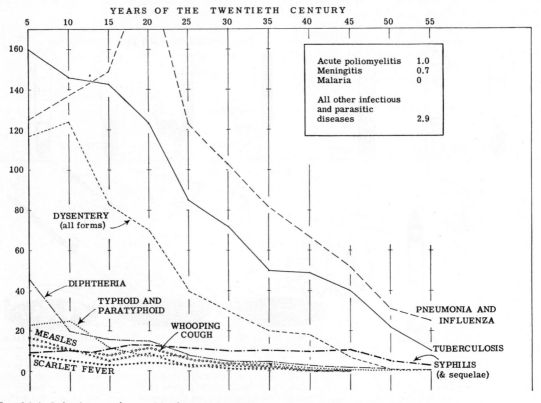

FIG. 24-4. *Infectious and parasitic diseases in 1955 were responsible for less than 5 per cent of deaths in the United States. Changes in the impact of these diseases during the twentieth century* (5-year intervals shown at the top) *are best compared in terms of death rates* (left) *per 100,000 of population.*

<table>
</table>

Rank	Degenerative diseases	Infectious diseases	Kill 1 in	Per cent of total
1	Heart		3	37.4
2	Cancer		6	16.0
3	"Apoplexy"		9	11.2
4	Accidents		16	6.2
5		In infancy	23	4.3
6		Influenza & pneumonias	27	3.7
7	Arteriosclerosis		48	2.1
8	Diabetes mellitus		61	1.6
9	Congenital malformations		71	1.4
10	Senility		73	1.4
11	Kidney		83	1.2
12		Tuberculosis	87	1.1
13	Cirrhosis of liver		88	1.1
—	All other causes of death			11.3

many sources of chemical poisonings are now recognized and guarded against. Constitutional diseases, such as glandular disorders, for slaking his personal thirst, cooking, bathing, operating laundries, fire control, watering lawns and gardens, and other domestic and municipal purposes. Often the presence of a water supply for domestic use determines where man locates his communities. This water is chiefly runoff water, plus a little cutoff water taken from wells.

The second greatest use of runoff water is in transportation of wastes, particularly sewage and the discharge from industrial plants. Subsidiary to these, and seldom interfering seriously with other water uses, are demands for water to drive hydroelectric power stations (manufacturing about 30 per cent of all electric power used) or transport boats, or serve in refrigeration systems. Use of runoff water for irrigation, by contrast, decreases the direct supply for man, sewage disposal, and industry.

Pollution

Even silt from eroding fields makes a stream so turbid that all except the least valuable fishes are suffocated. Inert industrial wastes, such as particles from ore-crushing and washing equipment, are particularly destructive. Proper agricultural methods on the one hand, and use of settling tanks on the other, can prevent discharge of these harmful substances into streams.

Sewage from human communities is often dumped into lakes and rivers without pretreatment of any kind. Although this practice contributes nourishment to filter-feeding organisms such as clams, it pollutes the water with bacteria. Hence purification plants are required to make the water fit for drinking. Pollution also adds many organic wastes which become oxidized by removing dissolved oxygen needed for normal respiration of aquatic wildlife such as fish.

Water *is* needed for collection and transport of sewage, but all sewers should lead to a treatment plant. Sewage from homes is over 99.9 per cent water, and this water can be salvaged, reclaimed and purified before being returned to the stream or lake.

At a sewage treatment plant, inorganic solids such as gravel, sand, glass and metal particles can be screened out quickly. Chemical treatment may be needed to hasten settling

of an organic "sludge" from a clear "effluent." Bacteria in the latter can be filtered out, the filtrate disinfected and aerated until it is purer than many town water supplies. Meanwhile the sludge can be reorganized by activity of nonpathogenic bacteria until it is a valuable fertilizer free of disease organisms and safe to use even with plant crops which are not cooked.

Water-borne wastes from business enterprises are of many kinds, and require as many different treatments to avoid pollution of lakes and rivers. Wherever possible, industrial users of water should be encouraged to locate their factories beside the ocean and use salt water. The limited supply of fresh must be conserved since it is so vital to man and a wide variety of living things. If they cannot use salt water, industrialists could be forced to reclaim all fresh used and to dispose of wastes in ways that do no harm to fresh-water supplies.

Forests and Cutoff Water

Since reliability of a water supply is so urgent, any factor which tends to stabilize runoff water becomes important. Forests have this function. They provide the principal trap for moisture sinking into the soil (Fig. 24-6) to become cutoff water, and to emerge as the springs which feed streams month in and month out.

Grasslands serve as water traps too, but their importance is secondary. Grass is fundamentally a form of vegetation that thrives where annual precipitation is too scanty for tree growth. Since man is concerned with in-

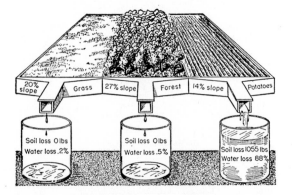

FIG. 24-6. *The effectiveness of plant cover in trapping rain is evident from the runoff and soil loss on equal areas planted to grass, forest, and row crops* (*with rows ascending the slope*).

creasing the volume of pure water available to him and to his crops, it is to forests that he must look for help.

The chief difficulty with forests as water traps is that they appear to be idle—contributing nothing to man's welfare. Why not cut the trees as a source of immediate profit, or expose the land they occupy for agricultural crops?

A lumbering operation or a fire can eliminate the trees quickly. Reforestation may take a century. Yet loss of continuous cover vegetation on high country is soon followed by erosion of the exposed soil. Then comes a rapid decline in the moisture seeping to adjoining valleys between one rainy period and the next. Moreover, during a storm, runoff is excessive and carries soil with it as pollution for the streams.

The water-conserving function of intact plant cover is hard to evaluate. Conservation measures are correspondingly hard to defend on their own merits. Fortunately, however, a forest has other values of long-term importance, and combined arguments often prevail. Thus, beyond insuring a continuous supply of fresh water in rivers and protecting valleys against spring floods, a forest yields a timber supply that can be harvested on a crop basis (p. 489), a haven for wildlife, and a recreational attraction. At least 75 per cent of the forest land in the United States today has a major or moderate importance in watershed protection. The remaining 25 per cent is in swamplands or other areas of mild topography, such as along coasts.

3. FOOD

Deliberate cultivation of plant crops and raising of domestic animals for food is so widespread today that it is hard to realize how uniformly primitive man depended upon fruits he could pick, roots he could dig, and animals he could catch.

As recently as 1776, it took 19 agricultural workers to provide food enough beyond their own needs to support one nonagricultural worker. In 1950 the same 19 workers in agriculture supported more than 80 nonagricultural workers, with even larger quantities of food. Unfortunately, some of this record is through exploitative methods which destroy the soil.

Plant Crops ("Original Calories")

Although less than 5 million square miles of the earth's surface are cultivated for plant crops, essentially all areas that can be described as either "good" or even "fair" for agriculture are already in production. The rest is difficult to use because of its short growing season, its chronic drought, or its inadequacy of mineral nutrients.

Plants require more than sunshine to grow thriftily on a crop basis. They need water, soil minerals dissolved in the soil moisture (but not too much), oxygen in the soil, reasonable freedom from metallic poisons in air and soil, and some protection from diseases, insects, and competition from weeds.

WATER. Agricultural practice limits cultivation of crops to areas where water is available in the soil naturally, or where it can be brought in by irrigation. In either case, enough must be on hand to support healthy, transpiring plants—the only kind capable of rapid growth.

The availability of moisture in the soil depends upon the flow of subsurface water, the capillary rise of enough to supply the needs of vegetation, and the evaporative rate into air passing over the soil surface. The importance of an unbroken plant cover to capture cutoff water has been considered (p. 470). This is the moisture which becomes added to the "water table," and forms the most important source for plant crops.

Runoff water is often used for irrigation in areas where rainfall is low or evaporative rate high. Unfortunately, river water (from surface streams or artesian wells reaching subterranean rivers) is not freshly distilled, as are dew and rain. Instead, it contains dissolved minerals. As the plants and evaporation remove the irrigation water, these solutes are left in the soil. Finally the accumulation reaches toxic levels, and agriculture ends in that area. It has become, with man's help, a "salt desert." On a long-term basis, irrigation can never substitute for rain. Irrigation is an emergency measure.

SOIL. According to the 1948 *Yearbook of Agriculture* (p. 425) "The soil comes first. It is the basis, the foundation of farming. Without it nothing; with poor soil, poor farming, poor living; with good soil, good farming and living." Yet the needs of soil are not widely enough understood.

One common fallacy is the belief that water and dissolved minerals are all that a green plant requires from the land. Yet soil consists of both living and nonliving components. Each must be present to give the stability upon which good crops depend.

Living components of soil are extremely numerous: 800,000 algal cells, a million fungus plants, 20 million bacteria, and a million protozoans may inhabit a single gram of soil. An acre of ground, to the depth ordinarily turned in plowing, contains about a billion grams of soil. In this billion grams the weight of living organisms may account for from 0.5 to 2.5 per cent—5 to 25 tons per acre. Most of these plants and animals are of microscopic dimensions. A majority of them are decay organisms, adding importantly to the continuity of supply in nitrogenous compounds, phosphorus and sulfur in the soil.

Of the inorganic components, clay is the most important. Clay particles are so small (less than 2μ in diameter) that they expose enormous surfaces on which ions may be adsorbed. Since clay particles arise from the weathering of silicate rocks, they are chemically inert. But their permanent negative electrical charge enables them to attract and hold positively charged ions such as calcium, magnesium, potassium, iron, zinc, copper, manganese, boron, and cobalt. By adsorbing these ions, clay particles prevent cutoff water from leaching them downward beyond the reach of plant roots. Instead, the ions remain adsorbed until living root cells exchange for them (see p. 56), making use of the "fertility" the clay particles provide.

Complex organic compounds of humus also retain ions and add to fertility. Moreover, like sand, they tend to keep the soil open. Oxygen can then diffuse downward from the atmosphere or be carried in with rain.

OXYGEN IN THE SOIL. Oxygen permits respiration in growing roots, reaching these by diffusion. It supplies the respiratory needs of the soil organisms that carry on decomposition, as part of the great cycles of carbon, nitrogen, and the like (Figs. 21-17, 21-19).

And by maintaining aerobic conditions in the soil, oxygen keeps inactive the anaerobic denitrifying bacteria which, otherwise, will destroy nitrates useful to roots.

Oxygen enters the soil naturally through the burrows of ants, earthworms, moles, and smaller organisms. It is driven to deeper levels by cutoff water. Man aids this penetration of both rain and oxygen by harrowing and plowing. The latter process loosens the soil to a depth of six inches or more, and has the additional advantage that the soil is inverted, burying weeds and "discouraging" them.

If the clay content is high and the humus content low, cultivation makes no lasting improvement. To render close-textured soils more porous, they may be mixed with sand, or (preferably) with humus materials. Recently developed synthetic substances, such as Krilium, are even more effective. Only their high price prevents use of these in large-scale agricultural undertakings.

On any ground, plowing followed by drought and wind can be disastrous. The soil dries to powder and blows away (Photos 436-438). Infertile subsoil exposed in one place is matched in others by smothered vegetation, homes, and hopes. "Dust bowl" storms of this type have been common in northern Texas and Oklahoma. Areas of this character should never be plowed. Even their use for crop-raising is highly questionable.

Plowing fields that slope can be equally short-sighted, unless the furrows follow the contours (Photo 435). Contour plowing delays runoff until the water can sink in. Otherwise it rushes down the furrows (Photos 433-434), carrying away topsoil and polluting the streams with it.

Improper cultivation or the wrong crop can destroy the soil. At present, one fifth of the total agricultural area of the United States has been destroyed through faulty methods (Figs. 24-7, 24-8). Another fifth is endangered. Of the grazing lands in the West, three-fourths are so overworked that yields have dropped to 50 per cent or less, as compared to reasonable expectations.

Where water is scarce, colonization of eroded land by plants is slow. They have difficulty storing enough foods to last them from one rain to the next. If grazing animals are allowed to raid these scanty stores, the plants die and the land becomes a desert. A meat animal may be fed only *excess* food stores. If drought is chronic or the soil is poor, there is no excess. No grazing whatever is permissible under these circumstances.

Soil nutrients. Examination of a sample of soil may show that it needs additions in

FIG. 24-7. *In 1776 the average depth of the top soil throughout the United States was about 9 inches. So great has been the erosive loss of topsoil from the areas used for growing food that the average depth of topsoil for the country is now less than 6 inches.*

the form of fertilizer to compensate for definite mineral inadequacies, or humus, or both. That *anything* must be bought to add to soil comes as a painful shock to many farmers. Instead of taking the long view, they have depended upon minerals and humus already in the soil when the trees were cleared by the pioneers. Unless the soil is cared for, this resource does not last. The major tragedy is in farmlands that have been abandoned when the soil gave out, while the irresponsible inhabitants moved on to other areas to repeat the exploitation.

As an alternative, the standard of living may drop to match the depleted soil—as has happened at some points in the Southeast. There repeated crops of corn, cotton and tobacco have reduced the original thin, sandy

soil to a state where only low-grade pines can grow and yield a little turpentine and lumber.

The chief lack of understanding of soil nutrients is as to which organisms are to be fed. The short-term "cure" is to feed the crop plants, according to their specific needs as far as these are known. They continue, however, to draw additional nutrients from the soil, and thereby deplete it still more. The long-term treatment is to feed the soil organisms until the living soil can hold all ions available.

Perhaps the simplest method for enriching soil is through use of leguminous plants such as clover and alfalfa. If nodule-bearing legumes are grown as one of the crops in a rotational sequence, the nutrient value of the land is increased in terms of nitrogen. Still more can be accomplished if the legume is not harvested, but instead is plowed under as a "green manure." If left to decay, it provides both nitrogen and humus toward improvement of future crops of other plants.

Metallic poisons. From industrial centers come a variety of toxic substances, usually in smoke or wash water. They may kill all vegetation near by, and leave residues effective for centuries. At Ducktown, Tennessee, the radius of the blighted area is about seven miles. Like others of its kind, this is evidence of a callous attitude toward the land and people. It shows willingness to save a few dollars at public expense rather than install filters to clear the smoke or wash water of poisons.

Protection from attack. Man has chosen his cultivated plants because their leaves are large, their fruits generous, their whole habit of growth thrifty. They are ideal hosts for parasites and food for insects. Man sows them in close rows, making spread of infection or infestation particularly easy.

Occasionally it is possible to find a strain of the crop plant which is resistant to disease. Advantage may even be seen in sacrificing a few desirable features in the quality of the product in order to avoid the expense and bother of using chemical treatments.

Often a virus, bacterium, or fungus disease of crop plants has an alternate host, or is distributed by an insect vector. If man can eliminate the alternate host or the vector, the source of infection may vanish.

If these approaches are impractical, a chemical substance harmless to the crop plant, yet effective against the pest, may be found. Frequently, however, the fungicide or insecticide ("pesticide") is poisonous to man. Then the grower has the expense both of applying the substance and of removing it afterward, before selling his product.

For plant lice and other sucking insects, the poison must be a substance that is absorbed through the integument (as is DDT) or into its respiratory tract. For caterpillars and other chewing insects, a stomach poison may be effective, since the organism will swallow insecticides spread on leaves or fruit.

Over the years, pesticides tend to become progressively less effective. The organisms they are intended to control become immune to the poison. New chemical substances must then be tried, and no end to this difficulty can be seen. Possibly no chemical control measure should be used routinely, since it merely tends to make the pest species evolve into types resistant to any chemical agent that will not kill the crop plant.

The preferred method is **biological control** —making use of the living enemies of each pest. These agents may be bacterial or virus diseases, parasitic protozoans, or worms; more commonly they are insects. Thus tachina flies (order Diptera), ichneumon flies, braconids, and chalcids (all of order Hymenoptera) parasitize insects. Each is remarkably specific as to host attacked. Yet some natural enemies of this type can be found for practically any insect pest man has encountered.

The great advantages of biological control lie in its self-perpetuating nature, in the way any rise in pest numbers is followed by a controlled rise in parasite numbers, in the effectiveness with which the parasites seek out their host organisms, and in the rapidity with which any change in the habits of the host species is followed by a matching adjustment

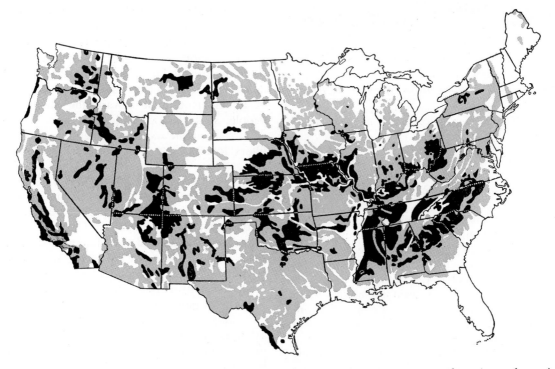

FIG. 24-8. *The extent of erosion in the United States varies from one area to another. Areas shown in black have lost from 76 to 100 per cent of their soil; shaded areas have lost from 25 to 75 per cent; white areas have lost less than 25 per cent. Unfortunately, many of the areas shown in white or shading are of little use in raising food because of insufficient water, excessively steep or rocky topography, or inadequacy of soil minerals.*

in the parasite. The two evolve together. In addition, the parasites seldom attack other species, and hence upset no other ecological balances.

Application of chemical substances, by contrast, endangers foe and friend alike. Insecticides may kill honeybees, producing a loss for the beekeeper and simultaneously limiting the number of bee visits to flowers, hence reducing pollination and the amount of fruit formed. Moreover, a great range of insects die as a result of each application of insecticide. Parasites and predators are killed, leaving few of them to help control the explosive character of any new outbreak of the pest species.

Insects from which man has found neither personal benefit nor harm die of general application of insecticides. Even if insect-eating birds are not poisoned by eating the stricken insects, their food supply has been cut. Their numbers decrease. Again man has hurt his own allies in pest control. With biological control, by contrast, it is easy to give encouragement to insectivorous birds, predacious insects such as praying mantis, lady beetles, and the caterpillar-hunting ground beetles and wasps.

Pests are largely introduced organisms. Relative freedom from enemies, prolific reproduction, and resistance to adverse climatic conditions permit them the rapid increase in numbers. Most pests of cultivated plants have been accidental immigrants on imported plants and fruits, or "stowaways" in shipments of quite unrelated goods. A few have been escapees of insect kinds imported for a serious purpose—for example, with the idea of raising silk in America.

Inspectors at points of entry, and programs striving for control of both plant and insect pests, are measures provided by the Department of Agriculture's Bureau of Entomology and Plant Quarantine. Fumigation of incoming seeds and nursery stock eliminates most of the insect pests. Plant diseases are given an opportunity to develop in quarantine, where they can be detected. Inspection at borders intercepts many others.

Often the red tape involved in handling plant materials leads thoughtless or irresponsible people to avoid legal entry of these commodities. Their action adds to national diffi-

culties, contributing a few new pests annually. Millions of tax dollars are spent trying to eradicate infestations as they arise at unpredictable points within the country.

Scouts from the Bureau of Entomology and Plant Quarantine seek to learn the parasites and diseases of foreign pests which get started in the United States. These natural enemies are brought back alive, studied for many generations to test efficiency, hardiness, and possible alternate hosts available in America. Then the parasite may be freed in a field study at a site of major infestation.

Our native birds are highly efficient in consuming native insects, which may or may not have a present economic importance. Nuthatches, woodpeckers, and chickadees hunt out overwintering eggs and pupae. Flycatchers, swallows, swifts, nighthawks, and whippoorwills capture adult insects on the wing. Warblers, vireos, and wrens devour quantities of caterpillars and other insects on foliage. Even seed-eating birds such as sparrows, finches, and juncoes turn to insect-catching when feeding their nestlings. Growth is faster on meat than on a seed diet.

COMPETITION FROM WEEDS. Any vigorous, well-adapted plant that can compete on better-than-average terms with man's crop plants becomes a weed. Usually it is a rapid-growing, profuse-flowering, abundant-seeding, easily-dispersed organism with a high enough biotic potential to be able to compete successfully along field borders under wild conditions. When man cultivates a field, plants a crop, and adds fertilizer, the weed promptly moves in.

Most weeds are immigrants from other countries. They have followed man as impurities in seed, as seeds in soil, or in other ways. Often they are relatively free from insect attack and from serious diseases.

A weed is harmful merely in occupying space that could serve a crop plant. From the soil it removes both moisture and nutrients that otherwise could go to the crop. It may also serve as a secondary host for disease organisms or insect pests.

The time-honored methods of weed elimination are hand pulling, cultivation with a hoe, or upsetting the soil around the crop plant by machine. Each of these is time-consuming, and leaves enough of each kind of weed to serve as a breeding stock.

Since most weeds are broad-leaved dicots, they may be eradicated from among monocot crops (such as corn, rice, wheat, and other cereals) by application of a selective herbicide (e.g., 2,4-D). This technique enables man to raise some crops in almost pure stands, and by remarkably remote control.

Rice lands in Louisiana, for example, can be prepared in the fall of the year. When spring rains have raised the water level (making the fields almost impassable to a machine on the surface), the rice can be sown by airplane. Later, dustings and sprayings with insecticides, fungicides and herbicides are applied from low-flown planes. They keep the rice crop almost free from attack and competition. Even fertilizer can be added in this way. Only when the rice is ripe and the fields dry out, is it necessary for a ground crew to move in, to harvest the crop and prepare the ground for next year's sowing.

Herbicides are not so effective with crops of dicot plants. A relatively recent technique has been introduced to handle this situation. It depends upon the normal competition one kind of plant can give another, and is called **replacement control.** Like biological control for insect pests, it is usually far less expensive as a long-term solution.

So far, replacement control has been used effectively against a number of introduced plant pests. One of these is a summer annual, the Russian thistle, which serves in the West as a secondary host to the beet leafhopper—an important, sap-sucking insect pest.

To eliminate Russian thistle, mustard is planted. It grows earlier and later in the year (becoming a winter annual in many areas) and crowds out the Russian thistle. The mustard, however, is also a secondary host of the beet leafhopper—vector of the virus disease called "curly top." But if downy chess, a winter annual grass, is introduced on land in which the mustard has eliminated the thistle population, the grass soon replaces the mustard.

Downy chess is not a host to the beet leafhopper, and yields far better forage for stock than either of the others. It affords better protection from erosion for the soil. The change from bare land with Russian thistle to a firm covering of downy chess may take as little as five years.

Under proper conditions, the chess itself is a temporary cover that is replaced naturally by native perennials—both grasses and shrubs—that provide a more stable cover, more reliable forage, and still are not hosts for the beet leafhopper.

In eliminating weeds already here and preventing establishment of new ones, man should do everything possible to encourage his natural allies in weed control. Of these the seed-eating birds, such as sparrows and finches, are pure gain. Mice and ants help to a remarkable degree. Often they collect the weed seeds by the thousand and hide them far below the surface, in storage spaces from which no germinating sprout can emerge.

THE FUTURE OF LAND-PLANT CROPS. If man does everything he can to help his crop plants, by improving the soil, reducing competition by weeds, control of plant diseases and insect pests, and introduction of improved varieties as fast as research in horticulture allows, he can expect more food per acre. These improvements will be gradual. A six-fold increase has been cited as the maximum to be expected. In the end, man will remain limited by his food supply, by the number of Calories he may take from the land plants without endangering the plants themselves or the soil on which they depend.

New crops may be helpful. A Division of Plant Exploration and Introduction (in the Bureau of Plant Industry, Soils and Engineering, of the U.S. Department of Agriculture) is alert for plants from other parts of the world. But since new eating habits must follow new plants, even slower progress seems likely.

Animal Crops ("Secondary Calories")

Prior to the domestication and improvement of various breeds of cattle, pigs, sheep, ducks, fowl, and turkeys, man depended for meat upon those animals he could catch. With luck he might kill something large—bison, deer, caribou, bear, tapir, antelope, or elephant—but otherwise he ate insects, mice, rabbits, squirrels, groundhogs, and any bird he could lay hands on.

With domesticated animals available, he distinguished between "tame" meat and "wild." The latter became something of a luxury, and a demonstration that in spite of raising crop animals, men who were MEN could still live "off the country" by bringing home wild meat. If the prize supplied horns, antlers or tusks which could be saved as trophies of the successful hunt, so much the better. As an extension of this, men became interested in killing and retaining as mementos the heads of as large as possible a variety of mammals, whether their meat was acceptable as food or not. The "game" hunter came into existence.

Domesticated animals can be raised on land which is unsuited to vegetable crops or grains. About 9½ million square miles of the United States are used for pasture because they are too steep, too stony, too deficient for agriculture. Seldom does the husbandryman understand how dependent his animals are upon nutrients in the plants they find for food. Almost every mineral element required by livestock must come from the plants. Low calcium or phosphorus, cobalt or magnesium, iron or copper, and the like in the soil means deficiencies of these for the animals pastured there. And only a plant whose roots have a good source of nitrogenous compounds can elaborate the amino acids the animal must have to build meat proteins.

Animals are selected for breeding toward ever greater production of meat, milk, or eggs. An animal which stands still most of its life puts on weight faster than one which runs around. For this reason, wariness has been bred out. In its place, man provides protection from predators.

DOMESTICATED FOOD BIRDS. Most of the fowl in which man is interested for food are scavengers and seed-eaters. They may be raised in the open in fenced yards or in special houses. The former method may afford food without cash outlay, whereas otherwise the grower must feed grain and mash and pay for these.

Keeping a flock safe from parasites—worms, mites, insects, and diseases—is part of the business. Fumigants and insecticides must be chosen with special care. They must be effective yet leave no residue to flavor the meat.

The poultryman tends to class as "varmints" all snakes, rats, and mice (which attack food supplies, eggs, and young birds); skunk, weasel, fox, and coyote (which eat occasional adult birds as well as chicks and sometimes eggs); crows, hawks, owls and eagles (attacking adults and chicks); and the carnivorous snapping turtle (which takes ducklings whenever possible). Although the birds caught may have been sick ones, each victim seems to the poultryman to be a martyr —at top market value.

The biologist prefers to examine the evidence. He studies the stomach contents of reasonably large samples of each of these predatory animals. He is then willing to group rats with the snapping turtle as completely undesirable. He suggests that mice be excluded from the feed bins—left alive to eat weed seeds and supply natural food for fox and coyote, hawk and owl. Snakes, fox, coyote, and skunk can also be excluded from poultry runs, and left to live. They have an importance to man in controlling insects and rabbits as well as mice. Most hawks and owls should be encouraged. For every dollar's worth of domestic bird they eat, the country benefits by from $10 to $100 worth of food grown because the predator has destroyed insects, rabbits and mice which, otherwise, would have taken this toll. Even the crow does more good than harm.

Eagles need enthusiastic protection. An eagle is at the top of the pyramid of numbers, and has trouble finding an adequate diet. Yet eagles form an essential ceiling over such herbivorous mammals as rabbits, groundhogs, and mice.

An occasional hawk, owl, crow, or coyote becomes a habitual raider on man's domestic animals. But this is no justification for eliminating all of their kind. The offender can be destroyed as an individual. Thus a study of 8,339 coyote stomachs showed the diet to consist of rabbits (33%), carrion (25%), rodents of various kinds (22%) and miscellaneous other items (20%). In the last category came vegetable matter, insects, and the occasional chicken or lamb.

DOMESTICATED FOOD MAMMALS. According to statistics published by the U.S. Department of Agriculture, livestock on farms and ranches in 1953 totalled some 94 million cattle, 48 million hogs, 27 million sheep. The meat harvest for that year came to over 12 million tons, of which half was beef, 40 per cent was pork, the remainder veal, lamb, and mutton.

These animals furnished the human population with a per-person total of 150 pounds of meat, 350 pounds of fluid milk and cream, and over 40 pounds of ice cream, cheese, butter, and other dairy products. Additional amounts were purchased and put into dead storage to maintain prices at high levels. No other nation produced, consumed, and stored away so much.

Most of the cattle and sheep were raised on the range. A few, like the pigs, were fed in restricted quarters. Range cattle may be brought, when full grown, to pens for final feeding on grains. This fattens them and makes the meat more tender, flavorful, and salable.

Range for livestock tends to be land on which plant crops cannot be grown profitably. In mountainous or rocky terrain, there is little opportunity to use the plow, seeding machine, cultivator or harvesting equipment without by-passing many weedy areas and risking expensive tools among jagged boulders. Cultivation also sets the stage for rapid erosion. Cows and sheep can climb the hills and forage between the boulders, making use of the weeds along the way.

In our western states and Canadian provinces, range land may be marginal in the sense that rainfall there is too slight to support agriculture on an economic basis. In a biological sense, this is merely a restatement of the seeming inefficiency of an animal in using its food supply. The steer, like the cod, requires 10 times its weight in fodder. If the food is weeds that need not be planted or purchased and handled as seeds, the profit on the meat may be considerable. If grass must be allowed to grow (perhaps as part of a crop rotation) and then mowed and stored as hay, the cost in time and seed cuts into the gain from stock-raising. But if land that could be growing a cash crop must be used to raise cattle feed, with the animals unable to browse

at any time more cheaply, the price of meat would become prohibitive. Hence the emphasis on "waste" land for stock country.

It is not true that we now raise cattle where buffalo roamed in former days. Wherever the soil and climate in buffalo country will stand the strain, we raise cash crops of plants—as well as in the great areas where once there was forest, between the Atlantic Ocean and the western edge of the Mississippi basin. Cattle-raising is pushed, instead, to the limits of buffalo range—fringing on deserts, and into the deforested mountain areas where the soil eroded away quickly and left no basis for economic agriculture.

Tragically, however, this procedure is still one of exploiting the land. Every pound of meat shipped to the great stockyards represents soil nutrients that are not being replaced. Steadily the ranges grow poorer. Whether the answer is to increase the cost of meat by the price of fertilizer and proper soil conservation procedures, or to turn depleted ranges back into wilderness areas, is a decision still to be reached. The present price of meat, though ridiculously high, does not include sound use of the land as an investment toward a future for man.

Cattle-raising on marginal land presses sheep-raising still farther into the mountains or toward the desert. Sheep can and do crop the vegetation much closer to its roots than even a half-starved range cow or steer. They leave so little of the plant to carry on photosynthesis that sheep lands cannot be browsed continually. The sheep must be driven *through* an area. Then it needs time for plant recovery.

Even the sharp hooves of sheep make life difficult for vegetation. They cut into sod and break the humus layer. It is thin enough in the best of these marginal lands. As a result, desiccation is quick and erosion follows all too often (Photo 439).

One would think that the well-understood sheep-made deserts of Spain and elsewhere would serve as a clear object lesson to sheep-raisers in this country. But those who exploit the land know little of precedents elsewhere. They seem to care even less about the future. Opportunism of this kind blocks its own continuation. Our sheep-made deserts are developing, as extensions of natural desert

433. Topsoil and rain water hurrying down an 8 per cent slope in a Maryland corn field.

434. Once this was a corn field with a 12 per cent slope in Missouri.

435. Contour plowing provides a series of horizontal valleys that trap the rain and help it sink into the earth as a needed contribution to the water table and the roots of coming crops.

 EROSION OF FARM LAND BY WATER, AND ITS PREVENTION

436. A South Dakota farm stripped to the subsoil by wind after plowing and a stretch of dry weather.

437. The short-term answer: a temporary cover crop of cane and sudan grass as a start toward developing a new layer of topsoil knit together by roots.

438. The long-term answer: rows of windbreak trees. These are still too far apart, and the soil below them is being carried away by wind. A planting of legumes there will provide a cover to bind the soil among the tree trunks.

EROSION OF FARM LAND BY WIND, AND ITS PREVENTION

439. Complete loss of topsoil in characteristic "sheet erosion" due to sheep on a dry hillside.

EFFECTS OF OVERGRAZING

440. The shallow roots of beech and other trees exposed through the activity of livestock in an Indiana pasture.

441. An overpopulation of deer, which developed after predators had been killed off, starves to the point of eating all seedlings and trimming trees to a conspicuous "browse line." Such forests cannot perpetuate themselves and die out, leaving bare hills that erode rapidly.

442. Excessive logging on the privately owned land to the left has allowed melting snow and rain water to begin destruction of the topsoil. Federal forest land to the right has been cropped of marketable trees without danger of erosion and loss of useful land.

areas. They may be expected to engulf thousands of square miles of depleted land that previously grew enough grass to feed cattle. The process continues, eroding into lands where plant crops have exhausted the soil. Only public sentiment or financial dilemmas can put an end to this abuse of our most important natural resource.

Stockmen have prolonged public belief in a fallacy inherited from Europe: that man's enemies include all bobcats (wildcats), pumas (also called panthers or mountain lions), lynxes, wolves, and coyotes. According to a common view, each of these animals should be shot on sight or trapped to extermination.

Admittedly stockmen do suffer losses from these animals. The losses fall into two categories. One is sick or maimed domestic animals which cannot keep up with the herd. The other (and far rarer) victim is a healthy animal killed by the few individual predators that have acquired a liking for fresh tame meat. That a small proportion of the human species consists of murderers and arsonists is scarcely argument for extermination of all mankind. And the ordinary bobcat, puma, wolf, or coyote has an important role in ecological balance. There is no justification for eliminating them, for encouraging their decimation, or for paying bounties to hunters who bring them in.

The native predators form a natural check on the normal, healthy reproduction of native herbivores, and serve especially in weeding out the less vigorous individuals. Without the predators, the numbers of herbivores fluctuate widely. Diseases spread as epidemics, since sick animals continue to roam. In peak years, forage for the herbivores is inadequate, and they starve because of their own successful and unopposed reproduction.

Without predators, deer and elk become weed species. When cyclic abundance reaches a crest, they eat all seedling trees and chew on bark until seed-producing trees are girdled and die. Whole forests on watersheds have been destroyed in this way (Photo 441). Steep country, without its forest cover, no longer holds the snow and spring rains. Adjacent bottom lands are scoured by floods or choked with silt, and then lie parched because the season's precipitation has run off,

leaving little water in the soil. The remaining grass either goes into dormancy or dies. Now the rich bottomland offers food neither for the surviving wild herbivores nor for the livestock in which man is interested.

By contrast, if predators are curbed to the extent of hunting out known killers of stock, the rest can control the wild herbivores (including deer, rabbits, rodents, and insects), letting man profit more.

WILD ANIMALS AS FOOD. When white men first came to America, the supply of wild animals suitable for food seemed endless. Market hunters (who sold their kill of game and fish) used efficient, low-cost methods. Soon they made tremendous inroads on animal populations.

Bison herds on the plains, for example, numbered between 50 and 100 million animals. They were slaughtered by the thousands, used as food by the railroad builders, and as a source of hides. "Buffalo Bill" Cody's fame rested on records such as 69 bison killed in one day, 4,862 in a single year. To some extent this extermination program was organized as a means of subduing the Indians—starving them out by destroying their food supply. By 1889 the work was so completed that, when the U.S. government sought to buy the remainder as living curiosities, less than 600 bison could be found.

Passenger pigeons vanished completely, the sole survivor dying in a zoo in 1914. In less than three centuries, man had caught and sold by the carload essentially all of these once-abundant birds.

At present, game mammals and birds are seen to be primarily a byproduct of good land —of farms that include small wooded areas and "waste" corners. Federal and local agencies have done much to increase the annual crop of upland game birds and waterfowl (see p. 492).

The total modern harvest of wildlife amounts to about 120,000 tons of meat annually—including deer, elk, antelope, bear. waterfowl (principally ducks and geese), and upland game (primarily pheasants, grouse, and quail).

There is no way to learn how much of this wild meat is used. One estimate holds that the total weight eaten from wild birds and mammals about matches the total food weight from all fish caught by sports fishermen. If this is approximately correct, then the cost per pound of the meat eaten can be calculated. Since American hunters and fishermen spend annually between $2 and $4 billion on their hobby—a sum 10 times the cost of all spectator sports—the wild meat eaten (fish and game) would cost between $8 and $16 per pound.

Only rarely do these figures include any payment to the man who owns the land on which the wildlife grew. They pay for no fertilization or soil-conservation measures to replace value removed from the land. An animal that dies on its home ground, like a tree that falls, contributes to the soil important humus materials maintaining that soil. But a game animal taken away (and then often dumped in the refuse) makes no such contribution. It represents continued exploitation of the land.

Since 120,000 tons of meat annually is only about one per cent of that raised as a crop (12 million tons of mammal and 1.4 million of bird flesh, weighed dressed for sale), and since the cost per pound is completely out of line with commercial meat prices, wild animals contribute negligibly to human food supplies. Hunting and fishing are classed more honestly as avocations (as on p. 41).

INTRODUCED GAME ANIMALS. Repeated attempts have been made to introduce new game animals, always with the excuse that they will furnish meat or hides or fur, and hence pay for themselves. One example will suffice in refutation of these claims:

Late in 1859, two dozen wild European rabbits were imported by an estate owner in southeastern Australia. He liberated them as breeding stock. Within six years he had killed 20,000 of their descendants, and estimated that another 10,000 remained alive. By 1869 they had invaded northeastern Australia, overrunning thousands of square miles of the best land on the continent.

People enjoyed hunting them. Business boomed with an annual export of as many as 70 million rabbit skins and nearly 16 million frozen carcasses as meat. Australians built 7,000 miles of supposedly rabbit-proof fence to hold the rabbits back. They spent millions of dollars of tax money trapping, poisoning, trying to stop the explosion—all with little effect. Rabbits ate the vegetation on which the native herbivorous marsupials depended, and the numbers of these shrank rapidly.

After 1870 the experience was repeated in New Zealand. New Zealanders now kill more than 16 million rabbits annually. Exported skins and frozen carcasses bring in more than $5 million a year. But the rabbits do damage estimated at twice that amount.

Five rabbits eat as much as one sheep. Both Australia and New Zealand produce fewer sheep in proportion to the success of the rabbits. Worse still, excessive grazing of rabbits and sheep combined is causing rapid depletion of the soil.

In 1950 biological control was begun, by releasing rabbits inoculated with a virus disease (myxomatosis) obtained from South American rabbits. Each infected rabbit sickens, infects others, and dies. Sheep ranchers did their best to spread the disease. People who made a living by killing rabbits for fur or meat or bounty tried to block the control.

Europeans visiting Australia were delighted with the effectiveness of the disease and carried it home. Quietly they introduced it in France (1952) and England (1953). Farmers were overjoyed. Sportsmen were aghast, and Frenchmen who depended on rabbit-catching to extend their meat diet raised a great cry.

Whether Australasian native wildlife will recover with rabbit pressure decreased, is a question for the future. In some areas, immune rabbits began to increase again by 1953. What adjustments will occur in the European fauna is equally problematical. But these problems are no longer foreign to the U.S.A. A federal law banning importation of European rabbits was circumvented in 1954 by sportsmen in Pennsylvania, who wanted the animals for targets. How fast they will spread is unknown. They will compete here with native rabbits. If the disease is introduced, it will affect native rabbits too.

Epidemics of this type are referred to as **epizootics** (pronounced eppy-zō-ŏtics) and correspond to human plagues. Few known have the deadly power of myxomatosis.

THE FUTURE OF ANIMAL CROPS ON LAND. In the United States and Argentina, where cattle are raised primarily for meat, there is good cause to question whether too many are not now being pastured. If perpetual use of the land is to be planned, rather than short-term exploitation, then some areas should be withdrawn immediately from range use, and steps should be taken to improve the soil on the remainder. For sheep the situation is even more critical (see p. 478).

A different use of cattle in Europe points to another approach toward animal proteins. There cattle are primarily part of the dairy industry. An acre of land with grass, alfalfa, and corn as fodder can produce about 3,000 pounds of milk, containing 120 pounds of protein. By contrast, under good management an acre of farmland with the same fodder plants can yield about 50 pounds of beef as meat.

Elsewhere in the world, cattle serve more as draft animals. The largest concentration of cattle in the world—perhaps 200 million animals—is in India. They consume about three times as many Calories as are eaten by the human population. Only about a third are draft animals. The rest are useless but protected by religious conviction and popular sentiment, even though the people starve and call upon other nations to help soften the strain of periodic famine!

The pressure of increasing human population is all in the direction of restricting pasture areas. Man may be forced by his own reproduction to change dietary habits toward vegetarianism, and use of "original" Calories. A smaller supply of meat per person seems more likely than a larger one. A smaller amount available per person is certain as human reproduction continues at its present rate.

Food from the Water

Almost three-quarters of the earth's surface is covered by oceans—140 million square miles of water area. Another million square miles is lake and stream, pond and waterfall. Throughout this wet realm are fish of 15,000 kinds. Some of them are useful to man. Counting both fish and shellfish, he extracts about 20 million tons annually of edible materials—about 280 pounds for every square mile.

All but about 2 per cent of this catch is from waters of the Northern Hemisphere, largely because the demand for fish is from countries in this region. Both demand and abundance of fish vary widely. In Japan, seafoods account for most of the animal protein in the diet. In the United States, only about 7 per cent (11 pounds per person per year) is obtained from this source.

Almost all fish are dependent for their growth upon planktonic organisms—algae and the small animals that feed on the microscopic plants. Since the pyramid of numbers depends upon photosynthesis, fish are concentrated near the surface of oceans and fresh waters. But the algae grow best only where dissolved nutrients such as nitrogen and phosphorus are available. This depends upon circulation patterns in the ocean and upon the proximity of continents from which rivers bring the dissolved mineral matter.

In 1950, the catch of fish in the United States and surrounding waters totalled about 468,000 tons, in the following proportions:

Fresh or frozen (chiefly blue pike, cod, flounder, haddock, hake, halibut, ocean perch, pollock, rockfish, salmon, sauger and whiting)		21.9%
Canned—consisting of		77.6%
salmon		23.8%
U.S. catch	6.0	
Alaska	17.8	
sardines		17.3%
Maine	3.6	
California	13.7	
tuna & kin		16.8%
mackerel		5.0%
fish used as food for domestic animals		12.0%
all other		2.7%
Cured		0.5%

In addition, 38,000 tons of shellfish were sold as food, and imports of fish and shellfish exceeded exports by 96,500 tons.

How much the catch of fish from oceans and fresh waters can be increased to feed a larger human population is unknown. Areas of ocean within reach may simply not support the tonnage of fish man would like to use. Too little has been learned of the life histories of fish. Many are migratory. Often their life cycles include points of extreme vulnerability to man's activities (other than fishing).

Certainly American waters are no longer the haven they provided when man first came from Europe to these shores. Then fish abounded to such an extent that it was worth while to send ships all the way from Spain and Britain to New England just for fish that could be dried, salted, or otherwise preserved as food for Europe. Codfish ran in large numbers close to shore and in the greater bays.

The annual catch of cod in North Atlantic waters has shrunk in the past 70 years to less than a third. Atlantic halibut have decreased to less than 10 per cent. The New England lobster catch is down 50 per cent. The same situation is characteristic of the Pacific coast. Until recently, California sardines (pilchards) accounted for a quarter of all fish brought in at American ports, but recently they have almost disappeared. The Alaskan salmon catch is only about a third of its former dimensions.

Some of these changes can be accounted for. Others apparently are the result of a gradual decrease in the fertility of the water, due largely to human activities on land.

OVERFISHING. The clearest cases involving commercial fisheries are those of the Pacific halibut and the Alaskan salmon. Depletion of halibut was detected as early as 1916—a year after the catch in the four chief fishing areas had totalled 34,500 tons. In 1924 an International Fishery Commission was formed by the U.S.A. and Canada to study the resource and draft a treaty. This agreement was strengthened in 1930, again in 1937, and broadened in 1953. Quotas for catch were established in four areas; a fifth was set aside as a nursery or sanctuary. Meanwhile the catch sank to a low of 21,500 tons (1931). Then it rose under strict conservation to better than double the best previous annual take. Possibly the Atlantic halibut fisheries could be brought back by similar study and control. They have sunk from over 7,000 tons annually to 217 tons in 1951.

Greed led Alaskan salmon fishermen to work the rivers so intensively that most of the fish were caught on their way upstream to the spawning beds. The annual catch dropped to about a third of earlier levels, yet a great cry arose when the U.S. Fish and Wildlife Service insisted on a two-day vacation from fishing at the height of the season each year, to let adult salmon go up to reproduce. About 70 per cent of Alaska's tax revenue comes from the salmon industry, and "intelligent management of the resources, based on scientific knowledge, would increase the overall production in Alaska by at least 50 million pounds, worth some 10 million dollars annually."

In offshore fisheries world-wide, moving nets swept through the water and over the bottom have gradually replaced stationary nets and hooks. Dragging and trawling do yield more fish, but fish are captured indiscriminately. Often the small are crushed between the large. Smaller sizes are taken, often removing immature fish before they have had a chance to reproduce. Valuable fish may be sorted out for food; the rest may be brought home as a cheap source of fertilizer. In this and other ways the fisheries industry has helped to cut its own throat.

BARRIERS. Of the annual tonnage of fish marketed in the United States and Canada, a quarter is salmon from the Pacific coast. Nearly half of this comes from the Columbia and Fraser Rivers. As Alaskan salmon crops decrease, this proportion from the Columbia and Fraser rises.

Formerly salmon entering the Columbia River along the border between Oregon and Washington state traveled all the way to Canada to spawn. Power dams now block their way. As a result, the Columbia accounts for only about 10 per cent of the combined U.S.-Canadian harvest. A number of the lower dams on the Columbia are by-passed by fish-ladders (Photos 443-444) but the success of these is limited.

Fraser River salmon are netted from international waters in Puget Sound, before they enter the river itself. In 1913 the crop reached an all-time high of 30 million fish. But just prior to the spawning run of that year, a landslide at Hell's Gate (a narrow part of the Fraser 130 miles from the sea) blocked off the river completely for long enough to prevent all of the 1913 migrants from reaching

443. The fishway facilities at Bonneville Dam on the Columbia River cost about $7½ million, and require constant upkeep as well as staff to count the fish using them and the visitors admiring them.

444. The information sign shows that an average of less than two fish per human visitor use the fishways in the upstream direction.

SECTION OF FISHLADDER

ALL FISH MIGRATING UP THE COLUMBIA RIVER BEYOND THIS POINT MUST PASS THROUGH THESE FISHWAYS, AND ARE COUNTED AND CLASSIFIED AS TO SPECIES.

THERE ARE THREE LADDERS AND SIX FISH LOCKS PROVIDED FOR UPSTREAM MIGRANTS. DOWNSTREAM MIGRANTS (FINGERLINGS) MAY USE THE ADULT FISH LADDERS OR SEVEN OTHER ADDITIONAL BYPASSES.

THE HELPING HAND FOR FISH

445. By replacing metal numbered tags on spawning trout, the migration of individuals can be followed.

446. Mid-season activity in the U. S. government fur seal reservation on St. George's Island, Alaska.

447. The sea otter, once believed extinct, has come back to a surprising degree because of strict protection. Three adults and a pup on rocks of Amchitka Island, Alaska.

spawning territory. Subsequent runs were greatly hindered, and the Fraser River salmon dwindled rapidly.

In 1937 international agreements were finally concluded and efforts were made to restore the Fraser River salmon fishery (Photo 445). Concrete fish-ways were constructed around difficult parts of the river, and spawning grounds were improved. Since completion of these engineering tasks in 1945, salmon have returned in ever greater numbers. In 1953 the catch was four million fish; in 1954 nearly 10 million. After a few more of the four-year spawning cycles, the annual catch may well top 25 million. According to treaty, it will be divided equally between fishermen of the United States and Canada.

POLLUTION. Exposure of the soil for agriculture has increased the erosive effect of runoff water and loaded the streams with silt. In spring, floods sweep out the plant life on which young fish might feed, or bury it under mud and sand so that its growth cannot be normal. The silt itself makes aquatic respiration difficult. Lakes, rivers, and dam backwaters become shallower as they fill with debris from the land. The shallower water warms up more in summer. Since the bulk of the year's precipitation goes to the sea in spring floods, rivers flow more slowly otherwise. Deltas become exposed to the sun. Lakes grow stagnant. Estuary areas increase rapidly in salinity, contrasting greatly with the low salt content of flood time. Industrial wastes and human sewage add to the difficulty. For the large number of fish species that migrate toward shore or into fresh water to spawn, these changes have often been disastrous.

Close to shore, the effect of pollution is dual. Enormous potential supplies of excellent food, chiefly shellfish, become unfit for human consumption as soon as the bacterial count of *Escherichia coli*[2] reaches 150 per 100 milliliters of water. Fish which try to spawn in polluted waters are often unsuccessful in finding safe places for their eggs.

The latter difficulty affects many kinds. Ocean-going fish such as shad, smelt, and others on which fish of larger kinds feed, have the habit of laying in brackish or fresh water. They commonly fail to leave progeny because

[2] A universal intestinal bacterium in man, used as an indicator of pollution.

their eggs cannot survive. Smelt, for example, go to the head of tidewater and deposit their eggs on rocks or gravel. If these surfaces are slippery with a coating of sewage, the eggs slip from the position in which the parent places them, tumble to the bottom, and are smothered in the sewage silt.

The problem is one of major public concern and joint responsibility. At present the populations of coastal towns and of cities that dump their sewage into the host of rivers that flow to the sea see no reason to tax themselves for sewage treatment plants. If fish become too expensive, some other article of diet must take its place; fishermen can find other occupations. The fishermen cannot be expected to provide sewage disposal plants for even coastal communities, so that "their" fish can reproduce in brackish water of river mouths.

The governments of states and nations, which tax both groups of people, have not yet felt the political pressure to make these extra taxes and new laws necessary. The problem is acute and may soon be beyond solution. All the sewage-disposal plants and industrial waste-control techniques in the world cannot bring back salmon or shad once they are extinct.

ARTIFICIAL PROPAGATION. Since each ♀ fish produces enormous numbers of eggs, and every ♂ has enough sperm to fertilize even larger quantities, raising fish in hatcheries seemed to be the way to counteract the decline in fish harvests evident during the 1800's. About 100 Federal fish hatcheries and some 500 State fish hatcheries were established. Yet even introduction of fingerling salmon into streams unblocked by dams (to which mature fish would presumably return) has not had encouraging results. Gradually this program is being reduced, as being commercially ineffective.

Commercial fisheries in fresh water account for only about 3 per cent of the total tonnage of fish caught in American waters. Hatcheries have been able to help most with noncommercial enterprises, such as the stocking of newly constructed farm ponds and the restoration of useful fish to shallow lakes after an especially cold winter has destroyed the previous inhabitants.

PREDATORS. In the ocean, at least, man takes fish from situations where they are in a state of ecological balance. The predators recognized are chiefly sharks and lampreys that raid stationary nets. Starfish and oyster drills (snails) may damage shellfish beds.

Sharks are no longer regarded as a major problem. Instead, a commercial use has been found for them: large sharks yield livers from which vitamin-rich oil can be extracted; small sharks have a market in zoology laboratories.

Improved methods for destroying starfish are now in use. Formerly the angry shellfishermen broke each starfish in two and threw the pieces overboard. Each piece promptly regenerated into a whole starfish. Now mop-like gear is trailed over the shellfish beds. The starfish become entangled, are caught and destroyed thoroughly.

A new menace to fisheries has developed recently in the Great Lakes chain. Commercial fish there are sufficiently large to be attractive to lampreys (Photos 67-68). But until man built canals to let his ships by-pass the rapids and falls, the lampreys were unable to reach these large bodies of fresh water. Now they cling to ship bottoms as the vessels steam through the canals and locks.

Lampreys appeared first in Lake Ontario —nearest to the ocean—and did great damage to whitefish and others there. Now these jawless predators have passed Niagara Falls into Lake Erie, and even into the rest of the chain. Strenuous efforts to find a means of destroying the lampreys are in progress. Again civilization has brought the fisheries industry into desperate straits, all through activities of people in other lines of work.

THE FUTURE OF FOOD FROM WATER. Probable improvements in the yield of fish from the ocean and fresh water seem about balanced by probable decreases. New gains might be anticipated if refrigerated fishing vessels were to operate in oceans of the Southern Hemisphere. But the expense of bringing the catch across the Equator may be prohibitive until population pressures are very high.

Both fish and shellfish can be cultivated in closed systems—small lakes and ponds, or along protected coasts. Additions of fertilizer minerals improve algal growth and feed larger populations. Removal of the large fish without disturbing the small ones may permit the latter to grow to full size. Inadequate fishing *of the large fish* often results in malnutrition and stunting for all. Thus a lake may recover faster from overfishing than from underfishing.

Oysters, clams and mussels can be encouraged to the point where half a ton of meat can be harvested per acre per year on good inshore bottom. The area available for shell fisheries and the demand for seafood of this type are the chief limits at present.

A very different approach to food from water has been advocated in recent years. Fresh-water algae, such as the unicellular Chlorella, could be produced commercially (see p. 217, Fig. 13-12). They are capable of rapid photosynthesis and reproduction, yielding protoplasm rich in proteins, carbohydrates and fats.

Chlorella is still not beefsteak. But from dried Chlorella it might be possible to prepare a substitute for hay, and feed this to cattle, sheep, and perhaps other animals. The chief problem is to find sites for factories, where there would be simultaneously and year-long plenty of sunlight, fresh water, and warm weather but not hot (which would require expensive air conditioning to protect growth).

4. POSSIBLE FUTURE RESOURCES

Raw materials depend upon two natural sources: living and nonliving. Both are the concern of the chemist and engineer, although for many years living resources attracted the attention only of biologists and such applied biologists as agriculturalists and foresters.

No one with any sense of perspective would ask a chemist or engineer whether every possible use had been found for each chemical element available on earth. The discovery of new uses is a repeated occurrence. Nor is it reasonable to conclude that the uses to which man can put plants and animals are limited to those discussed in Chapter 4 of this book, or any extension of that list based upon present knowledge.

The number of kinds of nonliving resources is essentially fixed. It is determined by the number and arrangement of the components of each type of atom. Except for chemical elements of high molecular weight (which are too unstable to survive in the earth's crust),

449. Flight formation over the Tule Lake Sump, where nests are common now that a wildlife refuge has been established.

448. Marshlands along the principal flyways have been set aside as public lands and administered in the interests of larger crops of waterfowl. The photo shows one such area on the border between California and Oregon, with Mt. Shasta in the background.

WATERFOWL

CONSERVATION

450. A nesting goose in Crab Orchard National Wildlife Refuge (Illinois) on the Mississippi flyway.

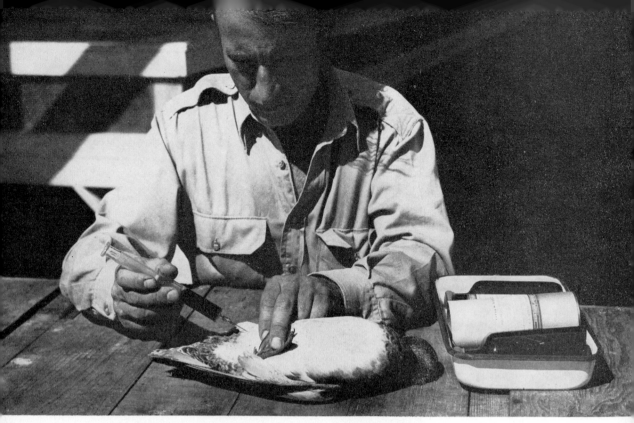

451. Giving antitoxin to a victim of "western duck sickness."

452. Applying a numbered metal anklet toward learning more about migration habits.

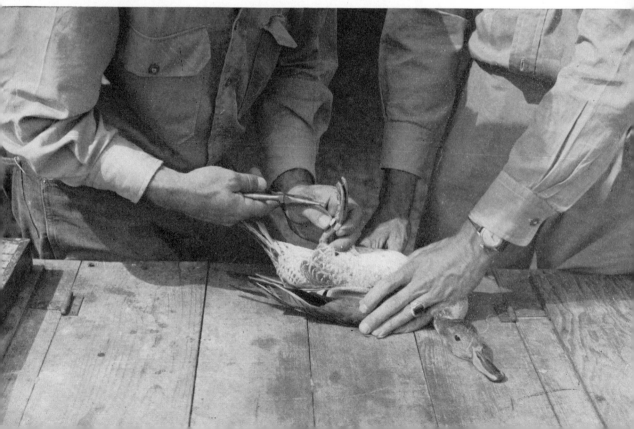

the chemist and physicist have studied every possible kind of fundamental chemical substance. Moreover, a number of the unstable elements have already been manufactured for special investigations. An atom is sufficiently simpler than a living organism that the chemist and physicist working together can synthesize each of the 90-odd kinds from components of others. If some one element were to disappear or to be consumed completely, science has a way to make more of that element.

To let any species of plant or animal vanish is to lose permanently all opportunity to find in it a valuable raw material. No matter how useful a passenger pigeon might become, there is no way to make a live one. The plants and animals alive on earth today are the ancestors of all plants and animals there will ever be. Extinct species are gone, and all their potential progeny and varieties with them.

Often it is the inconspicuous, the scarcely known species, which can contribute the most. Until the discovery of penicillin, few even among biologists gave much thought to the fungus organisms living in soil. Now they are being sought out and studied wholesale, with new products succeeding one another, each a valuable aid to human health. Or the parasitic insect which, in its native habitat, kept another insect under control, may be entirely unknown until entomologists scouting for natural enemies of a new pest work out the life history in all its ecological connections. Wild relatives of the tomato plant, growing unnoticed in South American fields and forming fruits of grape size, are being used in horticultural development of new commercial tomatoes with a higher content of vitamin C.

To retain for future use the largest possible variety of living resources, it is not enough to grow representative patches of each in a botanic garden, or to maintain them in a zoo. Reproductive rate and variability both fall off in confinement. It is essential to protect samples of every kind of habitat and have these areas of reasonable size. Each is a living museum of plant and animal resources. Each has a far greater importance for man's own future than any collection of paintings and sculpture, antique cars and furniture. Man's nonliving products are all replaceable. His companions among the living animals and plants, like his children, are impossible to retrieve once they are gone.

Many species are already extinct as a result of man's activities: the European bison, the Labrador duck, the Carolina paroquet, the passenger pigeon, to name a few. A host of others are tottering (see p. 494). The American bison narrowly escaped. In it we have the last of bison kind on earth.

Some of these losses were due to direct attack on a species. Others arose and continue to arise through encroachment on breeding grounds as man takes land for crops and cities.

In Anglo-America, it is difficult to realize how firmly a new philosophy gripped the pioneers. Or how outmoded this viewpoint has become. When the early colonists arrived they were overwhelmed by the seemingly endless abundance of trees, land, fish, birds, and mammals. Their astonishment was based upon previous experience in the Old World, where forests belong to the State or to some wealthy private owner. In Europe the edible birds are so few that starlings and house sparrows appear on tables as delicacies. Deer, rabbits, and pheasants are raised for their owners only.

The colonists broke quickly from these traditions. The trees were free. The animals belonged to anyone who could shoot them. That there might be a limit to the land or its wildlife occurred to scarcely anyone.

Now wilderness has almost ceased to exist. Man looks to interstellar space for new worlds to explore. In a few thousand years he has regimented the earth into categories: ocean, desert, pasture, fields for crops, forests. There are crop plants and useless ones, domestic animals and game, the economic and the insignificant. And the oceans yield less fish, the pastures produce poorer livestock, the fields and forests shrink, the deserts advance upon the land.

Many see the signs. Few do anything about the situation. Man can use his living resources as a crop with indefinitely sustained yield. Or he can deplete them until the untapped resources are gone and the crops yield enough only for chronic famine.

5. POISONS, NARCOTICS, AND STIMULANTS

Every year a few families in the United States become violently ill and some members die as a result of eating poisonous mushrooms —or even harmless ones which have been in contact with poisonous types for the short time required for the powerful alkaloids to spread through a basketful. Annually deaths are reported of families for whom the cook has prepared a fine dish of rhubarb *leaves,* not knowing that only the *stalks* are safe to eat, the foliage loaded with deadly oxalates.

Deaths from poisonous foods differ only in degree from fatalities following an overdose of sleeping tablets, or internal use of a medicine valuable only externally. Statistics show that one person in ten *can* drink methyl (= wood) alcohol without obvious injury; blindness or death threaten the other nine. Yet many an alcoholic has chosen to test his own reaction, and been buried as an outcome.

For many toxic substances, the physiological reaction is two-fold when they are taken in small doses. They stimulate the body, inducing the liver to convert glycogen into glucose and affecting the organism in many other ways that resemble the effects of slight secretion (or injection) of adrenalin. People who are mentally or physically tired, with spare time to dispose of, often resort to stimulants. But the second action of these substances is unavoidable and more prolonged: a compensatory stupor with much-reduced sensitivity and activities, commonly with a headache.

The use of any known toxics is to be discouraged as contrary to health of the organism. But it would be considered a problem only for the human individual were it not for some side effects and the fact that sales of the poisons provide such profits as to constitute big business. Different nations take diverse views on how much these businesses should be controlled.

NARCOTICS. In the United States and the British Empire, certain poisons are grouped as **narcotics.** Their manufacture, sale, possession, and use are regulated and limited to medical applications.

Almost all of these substances are alkaloids. They may be relatively pure and crystalline or crude mixtures of varying content. Morphine, cocaine, and others are examples of the first. Opium and marihuana represent the second.

Oriental nations have not been particularly interested in curtailing these businesses, although the deterioration of health, moral irresponsibility, and financial straits of those addicted to drugs is obvious and deplorable. Thus, on an international basis, tolerance is in proportional to the number of users—as is so characteristic of vices.

Enough nations have viewed narcotics with alarm to have established supervision of their legal distribution through the office of the World Health Organization of the United Nations. Lack of cooperation by some of the member nations makes it necessary for each nation wishing strict control to have its own narcotics agents—both in ports and throughout the nation—to intercept peddlers and to raid storage centers.

ALCOHOL. The use of alcohol is equally widespread and affects a different part of the the world's population. Where narcotics are used freely, alcoholic beverages are less in demand. Again, however, so much money can be made by manufacturing, selling and distributing alcoholic beverages that very strong pressures are placed on governments to permit free operation. In turn, the governments gain a considerable fraction of their total tax support from legalized sale of alcoholic beverages. Hence they are reluctant to enforce control or make moves in the interest of public health, since such measures would reduce tax returns.

From the standpoint of biology and economics, two aspects of alcohol use are important: (1) the number of individuals whose health is measurably impaired, whose family life is harmed, and hence whose reproductive responsibilities are neglected; and (2) the number of individuals suffering physical or financial loss as a result of the activities of people under the influence of alcohol.

If the problem were only one of deterioration of those using alcohol, the topic might be regarded as a peculiarly human mode of eliminating the mentally unstable—dragging their offspring with them into progressively lower levels of the social structure. But the loss of life and destruction of property due to

454. Less than 35 of these whooping cranes remain.

453. Two of the last few known whooping cranes, wintering on the Aransas Refuge in Texas.

TWO SPECIES WHOSE CONTINUED EXISTENCE IS STILL IN THE BALANCE

455. A family of trumpeter swans, the largest waterfowl in the world, near the highway in the Federal Elk Refuge near Jackson, Wyoming.

456. The passenger pigeon died out completely about 1914. To some extent, this was due to the numbers killed and to reduction of lands where the previously abundant birds could feed in peace. But an introduced disease of pigeons is believed responsible for their end. (*Photo from National Audubon Society.*)

457. The Carolina paroquet was last seen alive in 1920.

458. The dodo of Mauritius was exterminated in 1693, partly by direct action of man, partly by the free-ranging hogs he introduced. The hogs ate eggs and young birds. The flightless parents had no way to build nests beyond reach.

the unrestrained activities of those whose nervous control has been damaged by alcohol constitute a public problem of major dimensions. They become a physical danger adding to the usual environmental resistance.

Whether it is a man killed in a fight, a sober pedestrian run over by a drunken driver, a drunken pedestrian killed by a sober driver who thereafter becomes neurotic, a two-car collision brought about by alcoholic indulgence by one driver, or merely a telephone pole knocked down by a car out of control for the same reason, the public loses far beyond what can be tolerated. This tolerance is asked on the basis of three "rights" in a widespread wrong: (1) the right of the individual to drink whatever he chooses; (2) the right of the alcoholic beverage manufacturers to make and market their product, doing everything possible to give its use a universal, fashionable appeal; and (3) the right of the government to get all the taxes possible from the sale of these toxics and to suppress all who make them tax-free.

TOBACCO. On a far less significant scale, the same arguments apply to the nicotine in tobacco—another drug to which millions become addicted with the approval of a government gaining in taxes with every unit sold, and of an industry manufacturing and marketing these units. There is never any argument as to which product containing nicotine is *not* harmful. Advertising and thinking are all in terms of which is *least* harmful. Least harmful of all is *none*.

Tobacco is used in several ways: by chewing, by inhalation of the powdered form (snuff), by combustion in pipes, or as cigars and cigarettes. Smoking consumes most of the annual output of tobacco products. Smokers also account for the start of about a quarter of all forest fires, through careless disposal of the still-burning match-end, and unquenched butts of cigars and cigarettes (Fig. 24-9). About 23,000 square miles of woodland are burned out by forest fires annually; this places the bill to nicotine stimulation at about 6,000 square miles, plus a good share of the $50 million spent each year on fighting forest fires. A few small towns are wiped out, some human lives lost, as a result of this carelessness. Additional deaths and property damage arise annually through nonforest fires, such as those started by the smoker who falls asleep with a cigarette in his fingers, or the man who touches off a gas or gasoline explosion by entering the region of fumes while smoking.

Snuff-taking is usually followed by a sneeze, spreading droplet infections of disease organisms for others to inhale. Chewed tobacco implies spitting of the loaded saliva at frequent intervals. If cuspidors are not used, a still wider spread of disease organisms is provided for.

Smoking does not enter the picture from the standpoint of spreading disease. But both statistical analysis and laboratory experiments have demonstrated a relationship between cigarette-smoking and lung cancer. Since 24,000 people die of lung cancer each year in the United States alone, the health problem is significant. According to figures released in 1955 by the American Cancer Society, deaths from lung cancer per 100,000 of population fell in the following categories:

1. Never smoked	less than 5
2. National incidence, smokers plus non-smokers	14.6
3. One-time regular smokers who quit	102
4. Smoking less than a pack a day	128
5. Smoking one to two packs daily	227
6. Smoking more than two packs daily	460
For comparison:	
National death rate from heart disease, the #1 killer today	343
National death rate from cancer of all types, the #2 killer	147

6. DANGEROUS ANIMALS

Man's success in reducing to insignificance the hazard of attack by wolves, pumas, lynxes, and bears was referred to earlier (p. 479). At present his attention is turned to far smaller enemies: the mites and insects that serve as vectors of disease, and the animals which reduce the potential supply of food, timber, and other materials.

A few poisonous snakes (see p. 33) and other venom-bearing organisms continue to give occasional trouble. Some have been brought so close to extermination that conservationists fear for their complete disappearance. In Arizona the Gila monsters have been given legal protection—the sole legally pro-

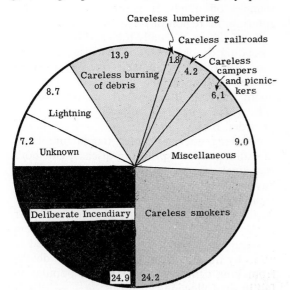

FIG. 24-9. *A careful study of the causes of forest fires by the U. S. Forest Service discloses that natural causes account for less than 20 per cent. The major causes are criminal incendiarism, careless smokers, and carelessness of other users of wooded country.*

tected poisonous reptile—to save some of them alive in the desert as curiosities!

There can be no doubt that these changes in the proportions of predator and preyed-

upon affect the entire ecological picture in which man lives. The environmental pressures have been altered for all of the component plants and animals. Since these pressures are the forces selecting and eliminating the least fit from among the variant members of each species, they modify the directions of evolution.

Some of these effects are rapid enough for man to see in a single lifetime. As a result of widespread use of the insecticide DDT since 1940, a new type of housefly has emerged. It is still *Musca domestica* L., but it is resistant to DDT and can detoxify the poison as fast as it penetrates the integument.

Of all the animals dangerous to mankind, one met in civilized communities exceeds in effect all the rest. Man is his own worst enemy. In World War I, the United States lost 116,563 human lives through enemy action. In World War II, the total was just under 408,000. Motor vehicle accidents alone account for this many deaths each decade: in 1953 (an average year) they totalled 38,310, or 24.2 per 100,000 of population. In that year suicide accounted for another 16,090 and homicide 7,880. Together, under conditions of peace, man killed man more than a third as often as cancer killed man. Yet the accident rate has remained amazingly level (Fig. 24-5). Only unremitting and universal care can decrease it.

II. BIOTIC POTENTIAL

The physical limitation in human reproduction is the number of children a mother can bear and a family rear to independence. If the reproductive age-span of woman is from 15 to 45, there are 30 years available for pregnancies. Between 30 and 40 children might be born—not counting multiple births—to one mother. Half this number is a more usual limit. And unless her diet is ideal and the family's finances strong, the likelihood that her health will last and all children live is almost negligible. In countries where pregnancy follows birth regularly with brief delay, the women are "old" at thirty.

In Occidental areas, poor diet normally is accompanied by lowered reproductive rate. A correspondence can be noted in the United

States between deficient soils, poor crops, sickly animals, and substandard people. The files of the Selective Service examinations have made this point abundantly clear. Low calcium in the soil was related to tooth troubles. Low phosphorous matched mental inadequacy. Where man, domestic animals, and wildlife eat the local plants, this dependence upon soil is ordinarily reflected in birth rates, maladies, and age at death. In some Oriental areas, by contrast, birth rate seems to be unaffected even by starvation.

To the biologist it is evident that any nonreproductive outlet for human energy represents a partitioning of man's biotic potential. Instead of turning every effort toward children, toward food to feed them and the

461. A desert mountain sheep (ram) in the Kofa Game Range near Yuma, Arizona.

459. From a small number of bison, far larger herds have been growing in the National Bison Range of Montana and other sanctuary areas.

460. Part of the bison herd in Jackson Hole, Wyoming, where the flavor of the Old West is more nearly preserved than elsewhere in the nation.

462. Elk using the Federal Elk Refuge at Jackson, Wyoming, where space and suitable feed are available as a replacement for lands taken over for ranching.

463. A pronghorn antelope buck in the Desert Game Refuge near Las Vegas, Nevada.

464. A young pronghorn antelope in Jackson Hole's sagebrush meadows, near Moran, Wyoming.

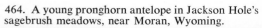

parents, we often use our creative force on houses, cars and boats. Each is a sublimation of the sex drive. To a large extent, civilization is built on this substitution. Herein lies much of man's uniqueness.

For no other animal is there any indication of biotic potential to spare. There is a limit to how far man can afford to spread his. To the scientist examining man's chances for continuation, as compared with probability for early extinction (in the geological time sense), any factor detrimental to the human organism is of prime importance. Each way in which man habitually unbalances ecological situations, or reduces his own physical health, or expends his energy unwisely, becomes significant.

Thus technology can be looked upon as an indirect outlet for biotic potential. In a number of aspects, this indirect outlet is involved with organisms important to biological science.

1. INDIRECT OUTLETS

Human activities related to more food for more people commonly interlink with technological problems. Thus the forest on a watershed furnishes trees for industry; the dams that control irrigation water may furnish hydroelectric power and permit navigation; measures assisting in flood control or survival of wildlife may serve in public recreation. The degree to which these activities overlap can be seen in the multiplicity of government agencies related to these matters.[3]

TREES. By far the largest crop man harvests is wood. Over half of the total cut is used as fuel. About a third goes into construction work. The rest is divided nearly equally between paper-making and all other uses.

---

[3] The Department of Agriculture, with its Forest Service, Soil Conservation Service, and such active bureaus as Animal Industry, Entomology and Plant Quarantine, Plant Industry, Soils and Agricultural Engineering.

The Department of Interior, with its Fish and Wildlife Service, National Park Service, Geological Survey, Office of Land Management, plus the bureaus of Reclamation, and Indian Affairs.

The Department of the Army, which builds and maintains major dams through its Corps of Engineers, supervises the fish ladders at Bonneville Dam on the Columbia River.

The Tennessee Valley Authority, in six states along the Tennessee River.

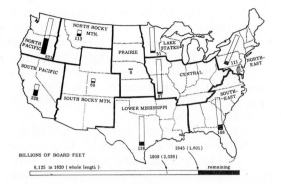

FIG. 24-10. *The U. S. Forest Service keeps records of the rate at which our timber resources are used in various areas of the country. The rectangular insets have lengths proportional to the total in billions of board feet. Black indicates the amount still remaining in 1945, white the additional amount believed present in 1620.*

Originally, forests covered about 23 million square miles of the earth's surface. Man's activities have already consumed or destroyed more than a third of this. Wood is still being used far more rapidly than it grows. About 10 million square miles produce trees at a rate which would be suitable as a crop. Few of them are being managed in this provident way. Nearly 5 million square miles of forests are close enough to transportation facilities for the wood to be harvested with the best of modern techniques. Even this is not being done.

When the Pilgrim Fathers landed at Provincetown in 1620, nearly half of the United States was forested—1.3 million square miles. The trees seemed endless. A forester would have calculated some 8,125 billion board feet of virgin timber.

By 1909 this original supply, plus second growth of much inferior quality, had been cut back to about 35 per cent of the original amount. Of this remainder, 44 per cent was used in the years between 1909 and 1945 (Fig. 24-10). In spite of reforestation efforts, we are using saw timber 1½ times as fast as it is being replaced by new growth.

Today, trees for whose planting no man can take credit—since they are part of remaining patches of virgin forest—still account for more than half of the standing wood resources in the United States.

More than two-thirds of the remaining

timber is in the West. About a quarter of it is now under close supervision from the U.S. Forest Service, in national forest areas. In these areas, timber is cropped scientifically and conservatively, trying to build reserves from which the yield can be high. Publicly-owned forests of this type produce a tenth of the nation's timber crop.

In the western states, more than half of the existing forest area is publicly owned and operated. In the East and South, by contrast, public ownership is less usual. Farmers and other small owners hold title to about 57 per cent of the total commercial forest lands. Lumbering industries own only about 18 per cent. Yet these tax-paying forests produce about 90 per cent of the annual timber crop. Unfortunately most of the cutting is done with no thought for the erosion begun, the watersheds denuded, the wildlife cover and recreational areas destroyed.

The average size of the private (nonindustrial) holdings is small—only a tenth of a square mile. This fact, plus the spirit of free enterprise, make conservation work difficult. The Forest Service describes two-thirds of the cutting under private management as "poor or destructive." A number of states have adopted regulatory measures, but most of their standards are so low as to be ineffectual (Photo 426). Both State and Federal governments have an obligation to step in and prevent malpractice wherever removal of trees is done in a fashion which will bring loss of topsoil, silting of streams, spring floods, summer droughts, crop failures, and reduction in water supplies for valley towns.

Statistics on forest land can be very misleading (Fig. 24-11). Of American areas described as "commercial forest land," three-fourths lie east of the Great Plains—mostly in the Southeast. Yet the timber on this land is mostly scanty and of low grade. Correspondingly, of the 250,000 square miles of "national forest" land, only about half bear trees of any consequence. Many of these areas were logged out years ago, or are situated where the soil is so poor or rain so inadequate that new growth has barely begun. Another 65,000 square miles listed as saw timber are on other Federal lands (such as national

parks) and on areas controlled by state and local governments.

In the United States, supervision of public lands is by the Forest Service. In Canada the equivalent control is handled by the Forestry Branch, Department of Resources and Development. In Mexico, although attempts have been made to set aside national forests and national parks under the Dirección General Forestal y Caza, lumbering and overgrazing continue in the designated preserves. Pressure for acreage to feed a population already on a low-calorie diet, and a long history of corrupt politics, make law enforcement difficult. Even watersheds are not respected in a land limited chiefly by drought. How long before population pressures in the United States bring us to a similar dilemma is a practical problem for the present.

Without immediate improvement in timber management, the United States will reach the effective end of its supply by 1970. Under the best conditions, a century must elapse before seedings and planted trees are ready to harvest. Wherever erosion has depleted the soil, still longer time is needed.

"Nature's lumbermen" are insects, tree diseases, and fire. Chemical control of the first two is not practicable, yet the demand for wood makes man wish to do so. Lumbering accounts for 89.1 per cent of the annual removal of marketable wood from forest lands. Insects and disease destroy about twice as much as fire. Insects, in fact, are the biggest factor in forest drain. Usually they are most destructive in overage and overcrowded stands. Vigorous, young, well-spaced, fast-growing trees are normally most resistant to attack. Foresters, entomologists, and lumbermen can cooperate in selective operations whereby the insect-, disease-, and fire-resistance of a stand are improved at the same time that a crop is being harvested.

Important reforestation programs have been adopted by many West Coast lumber companies. Seeds (often coated with a chemical repelling hungry rodents) may be sown by airplane, or the forest may be thinned or cut in blocks to leave seed trees within proper distance for natural wind dissemination. According to the West Coast Lumbermen's Association, "tree farming" by proper methods can pay $25 an acre every year—once the

465. Washingtonia palms are native to a small canyon near Palm Springs, California. They are now protected as part of an Indian reservation.

466. Joshua trees are great branching members of the lily family, restricted to certain desert areas in California and Nevada. To preserve some of the best stands, the Joshua Tree National Monument lands have been set aside in California.

467. Thanks to the designation of preserves for public parks, future generations may walk among the giant boles of a stand of California's coastal redwood.

proper balance has been achieved. This is more than the yield per acre of the same land as pasture.

One temptation is to let domestic animals graze on forest land, thereby getting a cash crop in meat while the trees grow. Within limits this is possible. But since seedling trees are eaten, the forest fails to perpetuate itself.

SEALS. Often conservation of renewable natural resources becomes an international undertaking. This has become true of seals, whales, and other mammals of marine waters, and probably will become increasingly urgent for fish as well.

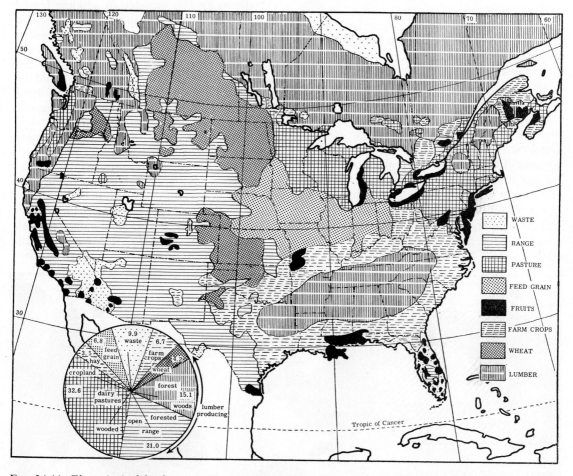

FIG. 24-11. *The principal land uses in the United States are shown by variations in shading, and their totals as proportions of the circular diagram at the lower left. Extensions of these uses are indicated across the Canadian border. In the United States, the 9.9 per cent cited as wasteland includes areas of inherent infertility (desert, dune, swamp, tundra, and rock outcrop) as well as those man uses for roads, railroads, parks, and human habitation. The remaining area includes many with multiple uses, so that statistics can be cited in many ways. "Original Calories" are grown on less than 11 per cent of the area—indicated as farm crops (with 1.4 per cent fallow) and wheat; farm crops include edible commodities such as vegetables, potatoes, rice, and inedible fibers (cotton, flax) and tobacco. Fruits and nut crops complete the list for original Calories. "Secondary Calories" in the form of meat animals are raised on a far larger area— nearly 64 per cent of the total. Partly this is through use of marginal lands, such as 11 per cent which are arid almost to being desert, or too rugged for agriculture. Partly it is through grazing on forested land (9.7 per cent) and pasturing in woodlands (7.1 per cent). Partly it is through use of crop lands for growing feed grains (corn, oats, barley, sorghums—6.8 per cent) and hay (3.5 per cent). Some crop lands (about 3.6 per cent annually) are used for dairy pasture. Hence only about 21.0 per cent of the total area of the country is used primarily in lumber production. Often a value of 37.8 per cent timbered land is cited, by including also the forests and woodlands in which domestic animals feed. (Statistics from 1950 Census of Agriculture, vol. 5, part 4; 1952.)*

When the Pribilof Islands off Alaska were discovered in 1786, the seal population numbered about four million. They were cropped by "fishermen" of many nationalities. Soon depletion was evident. By 1867, when the United States bought Alaska and adjacent islands from Russia, the number of seals had shrunk to three million. Continued exploitation by citizens of Canada, the United States, and Japan, led to further reduction—to 130,000 animals by 1910.

The U.S. Fish Commission (one precursor of the present Fish and Wildlife Service) sought and arranged an international treaty, effective in 1911, forbidding pelagic sealing. The United States (which owns the breeding grounds of the seal herds) took over all sealing operations. A share of the profits from sale of furs was paid annually to Canada and Japan. Careful management has brought the seal herd back to 3,600,000 animals (1947 census), with an annual yield of between 60,000 and 70,000 skins (Photo 446).

WHALES. Whaling is an even older industry, extending back at least 1,000 years. But one whaling ground after another has been depleted, leading whalers to move on to more distant oceans. Shortly after 1900 the industry began operating in the last great unexploited area, the Antarctic Ocean.

Since fisheries biologists in many of the two-dozen nations engaged in whaling feared a repetition of the exhaustion of whales—a condition that would then be world-wide—the League of Nations was induced to form a committee and to seek international conventions at which whaling regulations could be formulated. Several such conventions have been held, with definite and far-sighted results (Fig. 24-12). The participating nations, which include most of the important whaling countries, share responsibility for enforcement.

NATIVE BIRDS. As recently as fifty years ago, it was common practice in the United States to keep songbirds of many kinds in cages as pets, and to shoot a wide variety of egrets, herons, terns, and gulls (as well as the roseate spoonbill) for feathers with which to adorn ladies' hats. A large number

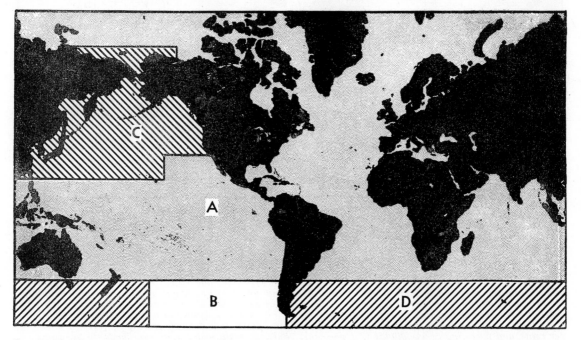

FIG. 24-12. *The present enormous demand for whale oil and other products of the whaling industry has led to international agreements. About 75 per cent of the world's whaling is now conducted pelagically from factory ships in the Antarctic. Such ships for taking baleen whales are not allowed in area A, but they may operate in C without restriction. In area D, these factory ships may take baleen but not humpback whales, and must cease operations at the end of the season without permission to shift to other waters. Area B is a proposed sanctuary for baleen and humpback whales. (U. S. Fish & Wildlife Service.)*

of songbirds were killed annually as tasty additions to human food supplies.

Private individuals who felt concern over the rapid extermination of bird life banded together in 1905 as the National Association of Audubon Societies for the Protection of Wild Birds and Animals, Inc. Step by step this group enlisted support from legislators until laws were passed protecting the birds and forbidding the importation of plumes, to end the demand and discourage poaching. The movement has grown into the National Audubon Society, cooperating with bird clubs, wildlife groups, and government agencies interested in conservation of animal life.

The Audubon groups provided a public counterpart to a federal agency established in 1896—the Biological Survey Commission— whose task it was to study depletion of migratory birds and of larger mammals, and to recommend legislation to reduce further losses. The activities of the commission overlapped so much with the work of the U.S. Fish Commission (begun in 1872) that the two were merged in 1940 as the Fish and Wildlife Service.

Attempts to remedy the depletion of game birds have been reasonably successful, particularly as to waterfowl. Mostly this has been through setting and enforcing realistic bag limits. These reflect the fact that, although the season may seem absurdly short at any one place, the birds are under almost continuous hunting pressure as they migrate. Regulation by flyways (see p. 394) permits this cropping of waterfowl to be fairer to all.

Since 1903 a total of more than 28,000 square miles of the United States have been set aside at National Wildlife Refuges. But a majority are operated in support of a program of "Ducks Unlimited"—to supply the legal limit for every sportsman who buys a license ("duck stamp"). These refuges lie along the Atlantic, Mississippi, and Pacific flyways, and provide marshy areas in which young can be raised or where migrating birds can find a respite from firearms while on their twice-annual flight. Some refuge areas allow limited hunting (Photos 448-450).

In terms of general sanctuary for wildlife and preservation of natural habitats, many of these refuges count for little. They are manipulated too much to be natural areas, and

control measures are biased consistently in the direction of bigger annual harvests of waterfowl. Other species gain or lose according to how well their needs match the manipulation. Habitat maintenance is far more valuable in the 16,200 square miles of National Parks, in which no animal or plant may be destroyed, and where little is done to alter the normal succession of vegetation toward climax conditions.

Since ducks, geese, and most other migratory birds do not stay within national boundaries, international agreements have been sought. Canada and Alaska contain most of the breeding areas of North American waterfowl. The United States, Mexico, Central America, and parts of South America contain the wintering grounds. A Migratory Bird Treaty (1916) between the United States and Canada called for cooperation in protection. A similar agreement (1937) with Mexico includes also the game mammals.

Bird banding (Photo 452) has provided a means for analysis of migratory movements and details of the life history of each species. More than 5 million birds have been marked in this way. About 375,000 returns have come in from five continents and many islands of the Pacific. It is clear that birds usually belong to a single flyway for life. This fact is counted on in controlling hunting on the flyway basis.

In spite of supervision, a number of birds have approached extinction and may continue for some time at such low levels that continued existence is uncertain for them. The whooping crane (Photos 453-454) is down to 31 known birds, 27 of them in a Texas refuge each winter. The California condor is represented by less than 60 individuals. The ivory-billed woodpecker is almost gone.

In 1938 the trumpeter swan population had fallen to 1,931 birds. By 1949 only 500 were known in the United States. Every effort is being made to see that this largest of the world's waterfowl (Photo 455) does not disappear as did the great auk (1844), the Labrador duck (1878), the passenger pigeon (1914—Photo 456), the Carolina paroquet (1920—Photo 457), the Eskimo curlew (1932), and the heath hen (1933). Publicity aimed at enlisting public support for conservation measures has made these extinct birds of

America as well known as the giant, ostrich-like Aepyornis of Madagascar, the dodo (Photo 458) of Mauritius, and the moas of New Zealand.

NATIVE MAMMALS. The near-extinction of the American bison was described earlier (p. 479). In sanctuary areas, the surviving herds have been built up to better than 5,000 individuals (Photos 459, 460). Most of these are in the National Bison Range in Montana, the Wichita Refuge of Oklahoma, and Yellowstone National Park.

Because of its food value, salable hide and magnificent antlered head, the American elk (wapiti) was hunted almost to extinction. The pronghorn antelope was regarded as doomed in the early 1920's. The black bear and the grizzly disappeared from most of their former areas. Big-horn sheep (Photo 461) and mountain goats likewise dwindled away. Fisher, kit fox, marten, timber wolf, and wolverine shrank into rarity.

Now the elk are on the increase again in the Jackson Hole country of Wyoming, where winter food is provided for thousands (Photo 462) which move down from surrounding mountains in the fall to avoid deep snow. Hart Mountain National Antelope Refuge in Oregon and similar areas in Nevada were created especially for pronghorn antelope (Photos 463, 464; Endpaper Photo R). The Desert Game Refuge in southern Nevada has saved the desert bighorn sheep (Photo 461). Others have continued and may increase in the protected lands of National Parks and National Monuments.

Outside refuge areas, hunting is regulated in the interests of conservation. This does not mean locking up the wildlife for the future. Instead it is a program calculated with great care to allow an annual "harvest" of birds and mammals without endangering the supply. It is a procedure whereby man takes the place of the predators he eliminated as the regulator of abundance in game birds and game mammals.

The chief danger is depletion. With nearly 30 million hunting and fishing licenses sold annually, there is strong pressure toward relaxing regulations. Fortunately, measures which help wildlife help soil conservation, watershed protection, and flood control—hence agriculture. They avoid stream pollution and assist fisheries. So long as biological surveys are maintained on a scientific basis and their recommendations carried out honestly by those serving the public, long-term improvement can be expected.

NATIVE PLANTS. Between rapid reduction of natural forest areas by lumbermen, cultivation of immense farm areas, and pasturing of livestock on any other land where plants will grow at all, the native vegetation has difficulty surviving. Anything spectacular or unusual has a slightly better chance (Photos 465-467). But anything inconspicuous remains the concern chiefly of such public-spirited organizations as the International Union for the Protection of Nature (with headquarters in Brussels, Belgium), The American Nature Study Society (Washington, D.C.), and the Wild Flower Preservation Society, Inc. (also of Washington). The general problem is studied by the Wilderness Society, and the Nature Conservancy.

Local groups have been highly effective in preserving some of these living resources for the future. Californians banded together and pressed for legislation to protect groves of redwood (Sequoia sempervirens—Photo 467) and of the "big trees" (Sequoia gigantea). These are now reasonably safe in state parks, National Monument areas, and additions to National Parks.

Those who bemoaned the inroads made upon the Florida Everglades swampland had a large part of it set aside as a National Park. One of the last virgin stands of giant cypress (the "Corkscrew Swamp") was bought recently in cooperation with the National Audubon Society, to preserve this relic of a south-Florida forest.

Presidential decree has been utilized in the same direction, to set aside as National Monuments particularly fine groves of Joshua Trees (California), of saguaro cactus (Arizona—Photo 466), and even fossil vegetation: Fossil Cycads in South Dakota, and Petrified Forests in Arizona. State action has preserved the last native stand of Torrey pines, just north of San Diego. (See also pp. 41-42.)

Constant guard must be maintained over these areas to keep selfish local interests from making inroads on the lumber, mineral or wildlife resources on these public lands, or from covering them with backwaters from dams for power and irrigation purposes.

2. DIRECT OUTLET

Although the total possible number of off-spring per pair of human parents is rarely approached except in countries where standards of living are at starvation levels, the population of mankind is increasing rapidly (Fig. 24-13, and see p. 460). In civilized areas, modern medicine shrinks infant mortality, reduces communicable diseases to negligible proportions, and extends the average life span well beyond the end of reproductive function. A major strain is placed upon food available when it must be shared with people upon whom environmental resistance rests so lightly.

Quantity of Future Mankind

One of the earliest men to see any logic in the widespread scarcity of food was T. R. Malthus (1766-1834) who, in 1798, published an *Essay on Population*. The conclusions he reached so frightened Malthus that he presented them anonymously, and claimed credit only when support was found for his views. Essentially they included only two points:

1. Increase in food productivity is slow; a little is added each year.

2. Increase in human populations is rapid. Hence a struggle for food and inequalities in its distribution are inevitable.

In many parts of the world, the sole factor preventing increase in population at faster-than-observed rates is starvation. Neither a high standard of living nor education, however, reduce the birth rate to the point where the population size remains level. The recent rise in the United States proves this point. It is important, therefore, to compare food availability with population size.

The average food energy requirement for basal metabolism (pp. 65, 79) is usually about 1,700 Calories per day per person. At 16 hours of light physical activity (such as office work, slow walking, average housework), the energy required rises to between 2,200 (♀ ♀) and 3,000 (♂ ♂), with 2,800 an acceptable average. Heavier people, or

those engaged in vigorous exertion, require more.

For this "average adult" at 2,800 Calories daily, an adequate diet will include about 70 grams of proteins (half of them of animal origin) and a reasonable balance between carbohydrates and fats. The proteins will contribute about 400 Calories. The other two need to supply about 2,400. In addition, the daily intake should include 1.0 gram of ab-

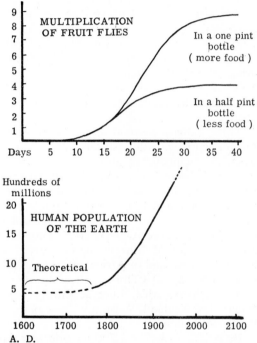

FIG. 24-13. *The multiplication of animals with a limited food supply usually follows an S-shaped curve. Although man's food supply cannot be greatly increased, no leveling off of population can be detected. (After Marsland; modified.)*

sorbable calcium, 12 milligrams of iron in soluble form, and the following vitamins:

carotene (vitamin A)	4,700 I. U.[4]
thiamin (vitamin B_1)	1.6 mg
riboflavin (vitamin B_2)	2.3 mg
niacin	16 mg
ascorbic acid (vitamin C)	70 mg

This biological measure of an adequate diet was compared with the average intake for

[4] International Units.

a total of 70 countries in a survey conducted by the Food and Agricultural Organization of the United Nations. Java (with its 1,000 inhabitants per square mile—see p. 461) and the United States (with its 50.7) represented the two extremes of actual diet.

In Java the average daily intake per person was about 2,000 Calories, of which only 43 grams were proteins. All but four grams of this was of plant origin. This daily intake over a year required about 800 pounds of food altogether for each adult in the country.

By contrast, in the United States each adult consumed on the average 1,300 pounds of food, not counting the water in milk. The daily Calorie count came to over 3,200 Calories, of which proteins totalled 88 grams. Most of the 88 were of animal origin and hence more available to the human metabolic process.

Three ranges of food intake were seen: (1) a low range, with less than 2,250 Calories daily, characteristic of about 50 per cent of the world's population—particularly those of Asia, Egypt, all of Central America, and parts of South America; (2) a medium range, with 2,250 to 2,750 Calories daily, characteristic of about 20 per cent—especially people in most of southern Europe, certain areas of South America, and of Africa; and (3) a high range, over 2,750 Calories, characteristic of all of Anglo-America, much of Europe, Australia, New Zealand, Argentina, and parts of the Soviet Union.

Daily intakes below 2,250 Calories per day per person are scarcely more than enough to maintain life. No energy can be spared for combatting disease, performing useful work, or participating in activities of social progress. Even at 2,500 Calories daily there is a change in thought processes. Everything seems worth sacrificing toward maintenance of the *status quo*. Inventiveness and enterprise seem dangerous. The herd spirit takes its place.

As diet deteriorates, more and more stress is placed upon agriculture. Seven to ten times as many people can live as vegetarians on a given area as can depend on it for a carnivorous diet of "secondary Calories." Consequently, wherever people are exceedingly numerous and dietary standards shrink, the principal foods come to be vegetable ones. If hunger is just around the corner, it is unreasonable to ask anyone to relinquish seven to ten Calories of plant food in order to have one Calorie of meat—even if it *is* better for them. It is also unreasonable to expect any sale of food to buy fertilizer in order to have a better crop next year. Soil deteriorates, making starvation very real.

Since animal products represent inefficient use of land, their price is always high. And since they are expensive foods, the diet of the poor or thoughtless becomes loaded with cheap cabbage and potatoes, rice and beans, bread or tortillas, breadfruit and cassava (manioc), cornmeal products of many kinds, macaroni and spaghetti. These give a sense of fullness and yield Calories that can produce fat and a happy state of mind. But they do not afford a balanced diet and support no high level of human activity.

A survey of food resources world-wide indicates that the combined production of land and water furnishes on the average some 5,760 billion Calories per day. If no increase is made in this yield, it provides a world average per person per day of

2,800 Calories for 2,010 millions, or
2,400 Calories for 2,400 millions, or
2,000 Calories for 2,880 millions, or
1,700 Calories for 3,490 millions, or
1,440 Calories for 4,000 millions, etc.

The 2,400 million mark was passed in 1950. If the rate of increase recorded between 1900 and 1950 continues to the year 2000, the total population of the world will be 4,000 millions.

To feed 4,000 million people the minimum adequate diet of 2,800 Calories daily will require more than just doubling the present food supply. To get animal protein into the diet, the proportion of "secondary Calories" must be increased. Hence the total Calories of food raised must be treble or quadruple the present amount. Whether this *can* be done is a good question. Whether man will see that it *is* done—and at the same time get into better balance with his environment by ending exploitation—is the main problem in looking toward the future.

WAYS OUT. Numerous plans have been offered in an attempt to escape the consequences of continued rise in human populations. Each has economic drawbacks or goes contrary to present policy in many countries.

1. Man can put an end to opportunism and depletion. He can stop desperate overfishing, agriculture that destroys the soil, deforestation, pollution of fresh waters and tidal areas, and contamination of the atmosphere. International agreement and policing can be instituted wherever needed. Only in this way can the balance of nature be restored.

2. Man can support enthusiastically all programs of breeding and selection which seem likely to increase the yield of eggs per hen, milk volume or butterfat per cow, beef per steer, grain weight per acre (without harming the soil), or the vitamin content of fruit. He can encourage agencies developing rust-resistant wheat or watermelons that reach maturity in a short growing season. These gains can be had on existing land areas, through more efficient types of domesticated animals and cultivated plants. They would supplement long-range programs for land and sea areas.

3. Man can eliminate wastage of food, both by buying only what will actually be eaten and by scrupulously avoiding spoilage of stored products. He can encourage storage of apples and wheat and butter to keep these foods available over greater parts of the year *consistent with low price* (and hence wide sale). He can discourage storage of these and other commodities—or their destruction—*to keep the price high.* There is strong reason to doubt that any group of people, even when they have bought the land and pay their share of taxes, have the right to create artificial scarcities of food for their own economic gain.

It is time to re-examine humanitarianism. Should gifts or unrepayable "loans" of food (or purchasing power to buy food) be made to groups—local or national—where the additional food merely permits an increase in population? To do so is to squander the wealth (= biotic potential) of the producers without achieving any desirable long-range result.

Each of these suggestions deliberately avoids the one direct approach to the problems of human overpopulation. Measures can be taken to insure that no further rise in numbers occurs. To date, however, very few groups of human beings have developed customs which maintain a population in equilibrium with the land they live on.

The unspoiled aborigines in Australia have one system. They match into family units young girls with old men, and young men with old women. This sharply reduces the likelihood of pregnancies and keeps the population from increasing beyond its food supply. In Ireland, the Irish have come to postpone marriage until, at the death of a man's parents, their meager plot of agricultural land is passed on to him. Since the average bride and groom are in their thirties or forties, only a few years of childbearing remain to them. The population in Ireland remains essentially stable. (See p. 30.)

Toward the other extreme is the situation in India, where marriage normally encompasses all of the potentially childbearing years. Discouragement of child marriage is one of the measures now being tried there to reduce the high birth rate.

In this country a swing in the opposite direction became apparent during World War II, as a change in general custom. Postponement of marriage until a young couple had become self-supporting was regarded as an intolerable delay. The years of education extended so far, and parental wealth permitted an adjustment. More and more parents accepted the economic cost of an early marriage for their children, extending the long period of parental care for which mankind is noted, until it included even the support of grandchildren. A spectacular rise in birth rate has accompanied this change in custom.

Deliberate prevention of pregnancies within a marriage in the interests of the welfare of the children, or the health of the wife, or the economics of the family, implies a high degree of responsibility. At present the only alternative seems to be an overwhelming increase in the numbers of mankind.

Quality of Future Mankind

It is not enough to know that man will have food and drinking water in his future. It is important also to inquire what kind of human beings will receive the heritage. We need to know what groups of *Homo sapiens* are reproducing themselves, and at what rates.

This can be done without much difficulty on an ethnic basis (see pp. 460-461). But when it is attempted within the confines of a democratic nation, emotions often replace reasoned judgment.

Yet it is this factor of differential reproductive rate which is central in determining how man will evolve in his future, and hence how that future will be spent. All the emphasis on advance in science, literature, and the arts means nothing over a dozen centuries if the people representing mankind at that time lack the ability to use the heritage.

The rate of change is far faster than is generally supposed. The simple fact that children from large families tend to become parents of large families (and conversely) produces remarkable changes in as little as 150 years—five generations (Fig. 24-14):

The question which must be answered is whether group A is "good stock" or "poor." This is far more difficult to decide than to relate demonstrated fertility to, say, education, income, or occupation. These categories are not simple ones either, for each depends upon factors that are partly economic, partly a measure of inherent ability.

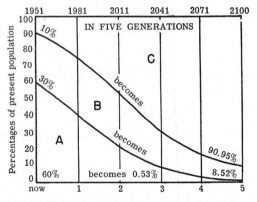

FIG. 24-14. *Children from large families tend to become parents of large families, and conversely. The result of differences in birth rate, on national or international bases, can be traced into remarkable changes in the population's inheritance within five generations. The proportions of one-child families (A), of two-child families (B), of three- and four-child families (C) in present populations are altered as each new generation reaches maturity. If the group A represents poor stock, few children are a fine thing. If group C is poor stock, race degeneracy can be foretold. If A is good stock, the race dies out. If C is good stock, race betterment results. (After Laughlin.)*

Thus in 1935, a study of "native-white, urban families" showed that the birth rate that year could be analyzed as follows:

87 births per 1,000 wives with college education
91 births per 1,000 wives with high school education
105 births per 1,000 wives who went beyond 6th grade but not to high school
118 births per 1,000 wives who went no farther than 5th grade

Or by family income (remembering that a dollar in 1935 bought as much as $1.94 in 1955):

76 births per 1,000 families with income above $2,000
81 births per 1,000 families with income between $1,500 and $2,000
90 births per 1,000 families with income between $1,000 and $1,500
117 births per 1,000 families with income below $1,000 but self-supporting
147 births per 1,000 families on total relief

Or by occupation of fathers:

86 births per 1,000 business men
94 births per 1,000 professional men
100 births per 1,000 skilled workers
115 births per 1,000 unskilled workers
147 births per 1,000 unemployed (on total relief)

These and similar studies suggest that reproductive rate is inversely proportional to intelligence and responsibility. If so, the unintelligent and irresponsible will rapidly take the dominant position. Civilization will adjust itself accordingly. At the moment, nations with the highest standard of living are beset by this dangerous situation. Progress is being betrayed by differential reproductive rate.

The interplay of economics and biology is inescapable. If children are not only self-supporting at an early age but also aid in the financial problems of the family, there is an advantage in having many children. But if public opinion is strongly against child labor, so that children must be supported into their teens (or even after they have children of their own), then the economic advantage is all on the side of fewer offspring.

There is close correlation between popularity of small family size and legal action to prevent exploitation of children by parents, enforcing schooling to 12 or 16 years of age. A responsible citizenry thinks carefully before adding to the family another child, when the addition represents a financial drain on parental resources of from $5,000 to $20,000, depending on the amount and type of education provided. The higher the educational group and the more responsible the citizen, the smaller by comparison is the usual family.

Thus, in countries enjoying the highest standard of living, two new factors of environmental resistance have taken the place of food scarcity and disease. These two—cost of normal parental care, and discriminatory taxation—exert an important pressure modifying reproductive rate and hence human evolution. Conditions of life have changed greatly since pioneer days (Fig. 24-15). Too often at present they discourage self-advancement or thrifty habits through failure to reward those with creative ability and responsible attitudes.

In the evolutionary sequence shown by the fossil record, by the geographical distribution of plants and animals, and by their ecological relationships, it is clear that organisms which cease to progress die out. Maintenance of the *status quo* is a strong urge. But it does not lead forward. It is the characteristic of radially symmetrical animals, of sessile ones like barnacles, and of parasites. Wherever action of a democratic group is such as to eliminate risk, to avoid anything new, to emphasize security rather than progress, degeneration is assured.

A small group of social workers and biologists have sought methods which could be counted on to improve the inherited characteristics of the human species. Only modest suggestions seem worth making. Yet the need for action is clear.

In all kinds of living organisms except man, environmental pressures weed out the least well adapted, denying them as much opportunity to reproduce. By contrast, civilized man requires a significant part of the labor of the fit members of the community to be used in supporting the misfits. This is true in medical practice, in procedures for handling habitual criminals, in the public and private institutions for the mentally and physically inadequate, and in the "social reforms" aimed at aiding through public expenditure those groups whose failure in general competition leaves them living in slum areas and on substandard diets. Man's sympathy for the less fortunate may well be the critical factor that

will change his inheritance and the course of his civilization.

Two proposals have been made to help improve the quality of mankind. Neither can

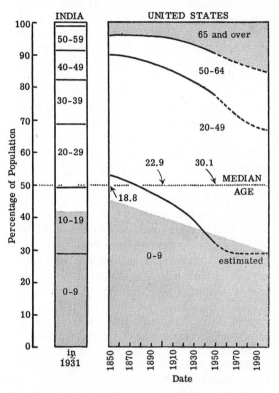

FIG. 24-15. *Improved sanitation and medical care permit a far larger proportion of babies born in the United States to live beyond age 65. As a result the proportion of the entire population now over 20 years of age* (lowest curve) *has risen from 47 per cent in 1850 to over 70 per cent. The median age* (dotted line) *has changed from 18.8 years in 1850 to 30.1 in a century. Shading indicates the financially dependent* (non-productive) *fraction of the population as a fairly constant proportion. These distributions of age groups can be compared with India* (data for 1931) *in the column at the left, to contrast an industrialized with a non-industrialized nation. With an increasing number of older people, conservative action in a democratic nation becomes more probable than enterprise and progress.*

provide an adequate answer in the face of the overall birth rate. Neither has found wide support, partly because each is controversial (affecting the "Dignity of Man"), and partly because state policies as advocated might have adverse side effects. One proposal is contrary to some religious beliefs, and for this reason branded as "unethical."

1. The prevention of reproduction among certain classes of the population has been suggested: those with known inherited deformities, such as "lobster claw" (split hand or foot, a dominant character) and microcephaly (small-headed idiots; a recessive character); those with habitual criminal activities; and a considerable variety of the mentally and physically handicapped who cannot function as responsible parents.

The surgical techniques are simple, and do not alter the personality, living habits, build, or other characteristics of the individual in any way. A number of states have present laws allowing such surgery after a carefully selected board of review has passed on each case. Few beyond the walls of public institutions have been so treated.

Thus, when a biologist reads in the newspaper that five members of a family—children of one pair of parents—have been allowed to see again by corneal transplants to replace corneas clouded by inherited corneal dystrophy, the reaction is twofold: How wonderful for the children! How foolish for the human race! Surgical relief could be available at state expense, offered gladly, but only to benefit the afflicted individuals. The relief could be purchased from society with the only sure guarantee that no new sufferers from the same trouble will come from the particular family—sterilization of parents and children as well.

This principle applies to other afflictions that prevent the victims from carrying their share in community responsibilities. The price to society in general for the continued reproduction of these people is far too great. With a world population already beyond its food supply,[5] reproduction must become a privilege and no longer a right.

2. Financial aid in the form of subsidies for children has been advocated. It would be awarded at public expense to those married couples in whom tests can show a much better-than-average combination of desirable physical and mental characteristics. With public assumption of the costs of additional chil-

---

[5] The food supply available in the United States on a sustained-yield basis is enough to feed 100,000,000 persons—not the 162,187,000 as of June 1, 1954.

dren, these superior types supposedly would be led to a greater reproductive activity than the rest of the population.

If such a move had the desired effect in birth rate, it would certainly swing the average physical and mental ability in the right direction. But a public policy of this kind meets little popular support in the face of a fundamental unscientific attitude: Each individual believes he or she is "as good as anybody else," and hence that opportunity is all that prevents any citizen from becoming a Beethoven or an Einstein, a Pasteur or a Morgan.

SUPREMACY. In trying to see a way out for mankind, it is natural to compare his supremacy among living things with corresponding situations at other levels of organization. Man's increase in numbers is now in a closed system, limited by the soil of the planet Earth. Yeast cells in a closed system exhaust their oxygen, change to anaerobic fermentation, and continue their reproduction and its energy-obtaining metabolism until the food is exhausted or the by-products of fermentation accumulate in killing concentrations. The yeast cells cannot foresee this alcoholic death. Otherwise they might remain aerobes, with a low rate of reproduction matching the inward diffusion of oxygen.

Yeast cells in a sugar solution are not comparable to mankind in that their environment includes no living companions of other cell types. Perhaps within a single multicellular organism, the interaction of cells competing for the organism's food can be likened more closely to man's position among plants and other animals. In the multicellular animal, if one type of cell begins to multiply with no regard to need, racing along in reproduction, it soon takes food from neighbors. We call it cancer. Within closed cavities, the new growth may cause pressure. In a short time the cancer cells invade the space previously occupied by other types of cells. This direct extension corresponds in many ways to man's destruction of forests, extermination of animals, and inroads upon the soil.

In suggesting this analogy, Alan Gregg compared metastasis of the malignant growth with colonization of the Western Hemisphere and Australasia by the white race. In the slums of our great cities he saw a parallel to the necrosis at the center of a tumor—death and dissolution of individual cells cut off by surrounding growth from the circulation of all-important food.

The quality of a cancer cell is unlike that of a normal one. It is hard to avoid employing words like "irresponsible" to the inordinate need for more food, the irrepressible reproduction, the intolerance of healthy tissues that have food and normal growth.

Cancers are not cured by feeding them. The whole organization suffers from inclusion of a malignant growth. The analogy to "our plundered planet" hardly needs elaboration. The yeast cell, the cancer tissue, and mankind all achieve supremacy. Only mankind has a mind with which to see the consequences.

III. THE DRIVING FORCE

Ignorance is no longer a valid excuse for civilized man to exploit his living resources and their habitats. He can see what is happening. The human population curve is rising in a geometric progression. The curve of food availability is rising in an arithmetic progression, much of the rise being at the price of depleting the soil—turning cropland into pasture, then into desert.

Man cannot eat his soil and have it too. He cannot enjoy the benefits of modern medicine and a heritage of domestic plants and animals—all shrinking environmental resistance for mankind—and also maintain his birth rate and his callousness toward plants and animals for which no economic use has yet been found.

He has been too successful in his struggle for existence. At this point, nature's paradox is plain: No organism can afford to win the battle, to overcome its environmental resistance completely. "To the victor belong the spoils" is true only for as long as there are spoils to be consumed. When these are gone, the victor starves to death.

Some scientists believe that the carnivorous dinosaurs of the Mesozoic became too dominant, that they wiped out their own food supply and became extinct for no other reason. Certainly deer threaten to do that when man removes the chief predators and fails to harvest a large enough annual crop.

One trouble is that ideas are so much harder to change than "things." Famines do not alter a Chinaman's insistence upon becoming an ancestor—producing daughters and sons so as to have sons. Starvation does not lead to butchering the sacred cattle of India, even though they consume more Calories of food than the people do. "Dust-bowl" conditions in Oklahoma and the Texas panhandle do not bring a complete change in the uses to which the remaining arid soils are put. The sheep-made deserts of Spain and the alternate parching and flooding of Mexican valleys whose watersheds have been denuded of vegetation have taught nothing to the western rancher or the man who owns a hilltop clad in trees.

If a person talks conservation, it is usually in terms of restricting exploitation to allow for those ecological factors that have been identified so far. How much will it cost today to have ducks in five years? How can a tree farm be made to pay its way until the crop will be ready for harvesting a century hence? Why hold back this year when even a person's children may not live to reap a benefit? Why worry about great-great-grandchildren a man will never even see before he dies? What has posterity done for us?

On this basis, no conservation effort can ever be large enough to count. When put on a cash basis and in terms of 10 or 50 or 100 years, the price of adequate measures is far too high. Economic motives will never supply an adequate driving force when each change in action means at once a lowered economic return.

Ideas do change, though slowly. Primitive peoples, like the American Indians three centuries ago, regarded themselves as one with nature. Their simple tools permitted them to kill no major part of the wild animals. Human diseases kept their numbers low enough that a modest yield of cultivated plants and a tolerable use of the soil sufficed. Moreover, they sensed an indebtedness to the land. In ceremonial proceedings they asked the pardon of the animals they killed. And killed only enough to eat.

Modern man shrugs off these early ways as superstition. He may say Grace before meat, and once a week thank his Creator for Sunday dinner cooking in the automatic oven. But he may also oil his gun, pay his license fee, and rush off on a holiday that would astonish any honest savage.

Theologians of the Middle Ages believed firmly that the universe had been created for man's benefit alone. Some of the 17th Century philosophic scientists suggested that man might at least discover some use for every living thing. One of England's first great biologists, John Ray, objected to both views. He substituted the statement that man's chief gain from plants and animals was to be found in appreciating through them the wonder and beauty of God's handiwork. A century ago, Henry Thoreau wrote with intent to shock his contemporaries a secular version of the same idea: "This curious world which we inhabit is more wonderful than it is convenient; more beautiful than it is useful; it is more to be admired than to be used."

Our present need is not for more ducks or trout or shorter working hours, but for a reason to be less successful. We lack something mental or spiritual that would lead us to relent in our persecution of nonhuman life, to give loving care to the soil that supports all protoplasm. Instead of assuming as his birthright the freedom to exploit the world and its organisms, mankind needs most to become humble, to accept happily a kinship to the animals, and to sense the responsibility and custodianship that accompany the unique possession of a great brain and manipulative hands.

The modern biologist, when he takes time to think, realizes that his own enthusiasm stems from a sense of limitless wonder. Each structural feature of a living organism exhibits orderliness bordering on perfection. The ultimate limits of this regularity are beyond the scope of his most powerful instruments. Every new discovery emphasises this fact.

Physiological processes are not those a man might conjure up. Each shows constancy in the face of wide variations in environmental conditions, and yet adaptability under a host of special circumstances. No nonliving human product shows this sequence of organization, level above level, from the electron whirring about an atom's core to the unfolding flower or a bird dancing before its mate.

A community of plants and animals in unstable ecological balance shows a continuity, a stability, a detailed organization that conceals beauty of immense appeal to the research man. In his study he can see the regularity of lifeless Creation supporting the flexibility of life. Yet how can it be defined, and listed like the chemical elements or the orbit of the earth? Living protoplasm is so much more wonderful that respect for it can be boundless. In exploring and clarifying real knowledge of life's myriad aspects, man finds joy and inspiration with an emotional pull close to and sometimes substituting for formal religion.

If any force can be compelling enough to make conservation a way of thought for man, it must exceed the enlightened selfishness of the "practical" conservationist, and have a firmer foundation than mere sentimentality. It must be something that will make a man happy to leave unexploited much of the useful as well as all of the "useless." If man is to continue, he must quickly find this ethic on which to base his actions. It must be convincingly demonstrated to those who would sell a sunset if they could wrap it up. For if we do not have the mind to respect beauty even more than usefulness, the universe will soon cease to harbor man.

THE WILDERNESS AND ROADS

To build a road is so much simpler than to think of what the country really needs. A roadless marsh is seemingly as worthless to the alphabetical conservationist as an undrained one was to the empire builders. Solitude, the one natural resource still undowered of alphabets, is so far recognized as valuable by ornithologists and cranes. . . . The ultimate value in these marshes is wildness, and the crane is wildness incarnate. But all conservation of wildness is self-defeating, for to cherish we must see and fondle, and when enough have seen and fondled, there is no wilderness left to cherish.

A MONUMENT TO THE PASSENGER PIGEON

On May 11, 1947, in Wyalusing State Park, the Wisconsin Society for Ornithology dedicated a monument to the extinct passenger pigeon. A thoughtful conservationist wrote down his interpretations of this event.

We have erected a monument to commemorate the funeral of a species. It symbolizes our sorrow. We grieve because no living man will see again the onrushing phalanx of victorious birds, sweeping a path for spring across the March skies, chasing the defeated winter from all the woods and prairies of Wisconsin.

Men still live who, in their youth, remember pigeons. Trees still live who, in their youth, were shaken by a living wind. But a decade hence only the oldest oaks will remember, and at long last only the hills will know. . . .

For one species to mourn the death of another is a new thing under the sun. The Cro-Magnon who slew the last mammoth thought only of steaks. The sportsman who shot the last pigeon thought only of his prowess. The sailor who clubbed the last auk thought of nothing at all. But we, who have lost our pigeons, mourn the loss. Had the funeral been ours, the pigeons would hardly have mourned us. In this fact, rather than in Mr. DuPont's nylons or Mr. Vannevar Bush's bombs, lies objective evidence of our superiority over the beasts.

—ALDO LEOPOLD, in *A Sand County Almanac* (New York: Oxford University Press, 1949), pp. 101, 108-110.

SUGGESTED READING (see pp. 505-511)

Classics and Milestones: Malthus, Pasteur, Koch, Fleming.

Recent and Informative: Allen, 1954; Applegate, 1951; Applegate & Moffett, 1955; Ayres & Scarlott, 1952; Boyd-Orr, 1950; Brown, 1954; Byerly, 1954; Cain, 1949; Carlson, 1942; Chapman, 1947; Deevey, 1950; Dice, 1952; Dresser, 1948; Eiseley, 1950; Eliassen, 1952; Fawcett, 1947; Fenner, 1954; Gilmore, 1955; Gray, 1949; Kellogg, 1950; Kimble, 1950; Krogman, 1949; Krutch, 1953; Leopold, 1949; Leopold, 1955; May, 1953; Metcalf, 1952; Muller, 1947, 1950, 1955; Osborn, 1948, 1953; Remington, 1936; Riley, 1949; Salisbury, 1954; Schubert, 1955; Sears, 1947; Smith & Allen, 1954; Snyder, 1955; Spoerl, 1951; Swanson, 1953; Thompson, 1950; Trowell, 1954; Vogt, 1948; Waksman, 1940; Warren, 1954; Weaver, 1954; Yearbook of Agriculture, U.S.D.A., 1955; Zinsser, 1934.

Suggested Reading

1. CLASSICS AND MILESTONES. 2. RECENT AND INFORMATIVE.

THE STUDENT who wishes to achieve perspective on the biological sciences will want to read the excellent histories published:

Nordenskiold, E. 1946 *The History of Biology*. New York: Tudor.

Singer, C. J. 1950 *The History of Biology*. New York: Abelard-Schuman.

These books chronicle the major scientific advances and lay the basis for better appreciation of new discoveries as these are reported. In order that more readers could have access to the true flavor of significant work, as described in the words of the men whose achievements made history, compilers have presented extracts and translations:

Gabriel, M. L. & S. Fogel. 1955 *Great Experiments in Biology*. Englewood Cliffs, N. J.: Prentice-Hall.

Hall, T. S. 1951 *Sourcebook of Animal Biology*. New York: McGraw-Hill.

The living and non-technical approach also has its place, and carefully chosen selections compose anthologies of wide appeal:

Beebe, W. 1948 *The Book of Naturalists*. New York: Knopf.

Krutch, J. W. 1950 *Great American Nature Writing*. New York: Sloane.

Peattie, D. C. 1936 *Green Laurels: The Lives and Achievements of the Great Naturalists*. New York: Simon & Schuster.

Brief references cited at the ends of chapters draw attention to related reading that is readily available, either as popular books or magazine articles—especially in *American Scientist* (Amer. Sci.), *Scientific American* (Sci. Amer.) and *Scientific Monthly* (Sci. Mo.). To emphasize the names which have made history, the "Classics and Milestones" have been separated from a more general category of "Recent and Informative."

CLASSICS AND MILESTONES

Aristotle (384-322 B.C.) *Biological Treatises* in Great Books of the Western World (ed. R. M. Hutchins), vol. 9; 1952, Encyclopædia Britannica, Inc.

Banting, F. G. & C. H. Best. 1922 The internal secretion of the pancreas. *See* Gabriel & Fogel, pp. 64-69.

Bayliss, W. M. & E. H. Starling. 1902 The mechanism of pancreatic secretion. *See* Gabriel & Fogel, pp. 60-64.

Beadle, G. W. & E. L. Tatum. 1941 Genetic control of biochemical reactions in *Neurospora*. *See* Gabriel & Fogel, pp. 273-279.

van Beneden, E. 1883 Researches on the maturation of the egg and fertilization. *See* Gabriel & Fogel, pp. 245-248.

Bonnet, C. 1745 Parthenogenesis proven. *See* Hall, pp. 174-176.

Darwin, C. 1839 *Journal of Researches . . . during the Voyage of H.M.S.* Beagle *round the World*. London. Many editions, under the title "Naturalist's Voyage in H.M.S. *Beagle*."

———— 1859 *Of The Origin of Species by means of Natural Selection* in Great Books of the Western World (ed. R. M. Hutchins), vol. 49; 1952, Encyclopædia Britannica, Inc.

———— & F. Darwin 1880 Sensitiveness of plants to light. *See* Gabriel & Fogel, pp. 142-146.

———— & A. R. Wallace. 1859 Joint publication of arguments in favor of natural selection. *See* Gabriel & Fogel, pp. 282-295, or Hall, pp. 607-622.

Eijkman, C. 1897 An attempt to combat beri-beri. *See* Gabriel & Fogel, pp. 74-77.

Fleming, A. 1929 On the antibacterial action of cultures of a *Penicillium*. *See* Gabriel & Fogel, pp. 127-131.

Flemming, W. 1879 Contributions to the knowledge of the cell and its life phenomena. *See* Gabriel & Fogel, pp. 240-243.

von Frisch, K. 1950 *Bees: Their Vision, Chemical Senses, and Language*. Ithaca, N.Y.: Cornell.

Harvey, W. 1616 On the Motion of the Heart and Blood. *See* Hall, pp. 113-126.

Hooke, R. 1665 Description of cells. *See* Gabriel & Fogel, pp. 3-6.

Koch, R. 1878 Investigations upon the etiology of the traumatic infective diseases. *See* Gabriel & Fogel, pp. 119-123.

de Lamarck, J. P. P. A. 1809 Evolution through environmentally produced modifications. *See* Hall, pp. 578-597.

van Leeuwenhoek, A. 1674, 1676, 1677, 1679 Protozoa and bacteria discovered; first published account of sperm. *See* Hall, pp. 155-157, 434-437, and Gabriel & Fogel, pp. 106-109.

Linnaeus, C. 1788 Taxonomy applied to man. *See* Hall, pp. 31-38.

Malthus, T. 1798 & 1803 Population and nutrition. *See* Hall, pp. 571-578.

Mendel, G. 1865 *Experiments in Plant Hybridization*. Reprinted 1941, Cambridge, Mass.: Harvard.

Mendel, G. 1867 Letter to Carl Nägeli. *See* Gabriel & Fogel, pp. 228-233.

Merriam, C. H. 1895 The geographic distribution of animals and plants in North America. *Yearbook of the U.S.D.A.* for 1894, pp. 203-232.

Muller, H. J. 1927 Artificial transmutation of the gene. Science 66: 84-87. *See* Gabriel & Fogel, pp. 260-266.

Pasteur, L. 1862 Memoir on the organized corpuscles which exist in the atmosphere. *See* Gabriel & Fogel, pp. 110-118.

Pavlov, I. P. 1928 Conditioned reflexes. *See* Hall, pp. 326-334.

Priestley, J. 1774 Of the restoration of air infected with animal respiration, or putrefaction, by vegetation. *See* Hall, pp. 189-196.

Redi, F. 1688 Early experimental studies. *See* Gabriel & Fogel, pp. 187-189, or Hall, pp. 362-368.

Schwann, T. 1839 The general cell theory. *See* Hall, pp. 443-447.

Stanley, W. M. 1935 Isolation of a crystalline protein possessing the properties of tobacco-mosaic virus. Science 81: 644-645.

Sutton, W. S. 1902 The chromosomes in heredity. Biol. Bull. 4: 231-251; or *see* Gabriel & Fogel, pp. 248-254, or Hall, pp. 667-674.

Theophrastus (370-286 B.C.) *Enquiry into Plants* in Readings in Biological Sciences (ed. I. W. Knobloch), pp. 9-12; 1948, New York: Appleton-Century-Crofts.

Thompson, D'A. W. 1944 (2nd edit.) *On Growth and Form*. New York: Macmillan.

Wallace, A. R. 1876 Delineation of zoogeographical areas. *See* Hall, pp. 697-706.

Weismann, A. 1889 The continuity of the germ plasm as the foundation of a theory of heredity. *See* Gabriel & Fogel, pp. 199-204.

Went, F. W. 1926 On growth-accelerating substances in the coleoptile of *Avena sativa*. *See* Gabriel & Fogel, pp. 148-152.

RECENT AND INFORMATIVE

Allen, D. L. 1954 *Our Wildlife Legacy*. New York: Funk & Wagnalls.

Allen, F. 1951 The visual apparatus as an optical instrument. *Sci. Mo.* 72: 71-74.

Applegate, V. C. 1951 The sea lamprey in the Great Lakes. *Sci. Mo.* 72: 275-281.

———— & J. W. Moffett 1955 The sea lamprey. *Sci. Amer.* 192 (4): 36-41.

Arnon, D. I. 1955 The chloroplast as a complete photosynthetic unit. *Science* 122: 9-16.

Ashby, E. 1949 Leaf shape. *Sci. Amer.* 181 (4): 22-24.

Astbury, W. T. 1951 Flagella. *Sci. Amer.* 184 (1): 20-24.

Audus, L. J. 1955 Growth substances and plant development. *Endeavour* 14: 205-211.

Ayres, E. & C. A. Scarlott. 1952 *Energy Sources—The Wealth of the World*. New York: McGraw-Hill.

Bahm, A. J. 1944 Teleological arguments. *Sci. Mo.* 58: 377-382.

Bailey, H. S., Jr. 1953 The voyage of the *Challenger*. *Sci. Amer.* 188 (5): 88-94.

Baitsell, G. A. 1955 The cell as a structural unit. *Amer. Sci.* 43 (1): 133-147.

Bates, M. 1952 *Where Winter Never Comes*. New York: Scribner's.

Beadle, G. W. 1948 The genes of men and molds. *Sci. Amer.* 179 (3): 30-39.

Beecher, W. J. 1954 The Coriolis force and bird navigation. *Sci. Mo.* 79: 27-31.

Beidler, L. M. 1952 Our taste receptors. *Sci. Mo.* 75: 343-349.

Biale, J. B. 1954 The ripening of fruit. *Sci. Amer.* 190 (5): 40-44.

Bibby, T. G. 1953 History in a peat bog. *Sci. Amer.* 189 (4): 84-88.

Bishop, D. W. 1955 Sperm maturescence. *Sci. Mo.* 80: 86-92.

Blum, H. 1955 Perspectives in evolution. *Amer. Sci.* 43: 595-610.

———— 1951 *Time's Arrow and Evolution*. Princeton, N. J.: Princeton.

Bodian, D. 1950 The paralytic plague. *Sci. Amer.* 183 (2): 22-26.

Bogert, C. M. 1953 The tuatara: why is it a lone survivor? *Sci. Mo.* 76: 163-170.

Bonner, J. T. 1949 Chemical warfare among the plants. *Sci. Amer.* 180 (3): 48-51.

———— The social amoebae. *Sci. Amer.* 180 (6): 44-47.

———— 1949 Volvox: a colony of cells. *Sci. Amer.* 182 (5): 52-55.

Bosshard, H. H. 1955 Structure of a classic raw material. *Sci. Mo.* 81: 224-233.

Bovarnick, M. R. 1955 Rickettsiae. *Sci. Amer.* 192 (1): 74-79.

Boyd, W. C. 1950 *Genetics and the Races of Man*. Boston: Little, Brown.

———— 1951 Rh and the races of man. *Sci. Amer.* 185 (5): 22-25.

Boyden, A. A. 1951 The blood relationships of animals. *Sci. Amer.* 185 (1): 59-63.

Boyd-Orr, J. 1950 The food problem. *Sci. Amer.* 183 (2): 11-15.

Bradley, J. H. 1952 (2nd edit.) *Patterns of Survival*. New York: Grune & Stratton.

Braun, A. C. 1952 Plant cancer. *Sci. Amer.* 186 (6): 66-72.

Broom, R. 1949 The ape-men. *Sci. Amer.* 181 (5): 20-24.

Brown, F. A. Jr. 1954 Biological clocks and the fiddler crab. *Sci. Amer.* 190 (4): 34-37.

Brown, H. 1954 *The Challenge of Man's Future*. New York: Viking.

Brues, C. T. 1951 Insects in amber. *Sci. Amer.* 185 (5): 56-61.

Burkholder, P. R. 1952 Cooperation and conflict among primitive organisms. *Amer. Sci.* 40 (4): 601-631.

Burnet, F. M. 1951 Viruses. *Sci. Amer.* 184 (5): 43-51.

—— 1953 The influenza virus. *Sci. Amer.* 188 (4): 27-31.

Burnet, M. 1954 How antibodies are made. *Sci. Amer.* 191 (5): 74-78.

Byerly, T. C. 1954 Role of genetics in adapting animals to meet changing requirements for human food. *Sci. Mo.* 79: 323-331.

Cain, S. A. 1949 Plants and vegetables as exhaustible resources. *Sci. Mo.* 68: 321-328.

Calkins, G. N. 1932 *The Smallest Living Things.* New York: University Soc.

Carlson, A. J. 1942 Food and fitness. *Sci. Mo.* 55: 403-407.

—— & V. Johnson 1953 (4th edit.) *The Machinery of the Body.* Chicago: Univ. of Chicago.

Carson, R. L. 1951 *The Sea Around Us.* New York: Oxford.

Chapanis, A. 1951 Color blindness. *Sci. Amer.* 184 (3): 48-53.

Chapman, E. M. 1947 The wealth of the ocean. *Sci. Mo.* 64: 192-197.

Chapman, V. J. 1950 *Seaweeds and Their Uses.* London: Methuen.

Clayton, R. K. & M. Delbrück 1951 Purple Bacteria. *Sci. Amer.* 185 (5): 68-72.

Cleveland, L. R. 1948 An ideal partnership. *Sci. Mo.* 67: 173-177.

Colbert, E. H. 1949 The ancestry of mammals. *Sci. Amer.* 180 (3): 40-43.

Collins, J. L. 1948 Pineapples in ancient America. *Sci. Mo.* 67: 372-377.

Conklin, G. 1949 Cancer and environment. *Sci. Amer.* 180 (1): 11-15.

Constantinides, P. C. & N. Carey 1949 The alarm reaction. *Sci. Amer.* 180 (3): 20-23.

Cooley, J. S. 1951 Origin of the sweet potato. *Sci. Mo.* 72: 325-331.

Corner, G. W. 1944 *Ourselves Unborn.* New Haven: Yale.

Cowles, H. C. 1932 The ever-changing landscape. *Sci. Mo.* 34: 457-459.

Crick, F. H. C. 1954 The structure of the hereditary material. *Sci. Amer.* 191 (4): 54-61.

Crowder, W. 1926 Marvels of Mycetozoa. *Nat. Geographic Mag.* 49 (4): 421-443.

Dahlberg, G. 1951 An explanation of twins. *Sci. Amer.* 184 (1): 48-51.

Danielli, J. F. 1952 On transplanting nuclei. *Sci. Amer.* 186 (4): 58-64.

Darrow, G. M. 1950 Polyploidy in fruit improvement. *Sci. Mo.* 70: 211-219.

Deevey, E. S. Jr. 1951 Life in the depths of a pond. *Sci. Amer.* 185 (4): 68-72.

—— 1952 Radiocarbon dating. *Sci. Amer.* 186 (2): 24-28.

——1954 The end of the moas. *Sci. Amer.* 190 (2): 84-90.

—— 1950 The probability of death. *Sci. Amer.* 182 (4): 58-60.

Delbrück, M. & M. 1948 Bacterial viruses and sex. *Sci. Amer.* 179 (5): 46-51.

Dice, L. R. 1952 Heredity and population betterment. *Sci. Mo.* 73: 273-279.

Dobzhansky, T. 1950 Evolution in the tropics. *Amer. Sci.* 38: 209-221.

—— 1950 The genetic basis of evolution. *Sci. Amer.* 182 (1): 32-41.

—— & J. Murca-Pires 1954 Strangler trees. *Sci. Amer.* 190 (1): 78-80.

Dodson, E. O. 1952 *A Textbook of Evolution.* Philadelphia: Saunders.

Dresser, P. 1948 The future of the Amazon. *Sci. Amer.* 178 (5): 11-15.

Drinker, C. K. 1949 The physiology of whales. *Sci. Amer.* 181 (1): 52-55.

Dubos, R. J. 1955 Second thoughts on the germ theory. *Sci. Amer.* 192 (5): 31-35.

—— 1949 Tuberculosis. *Sci. Amer.* 181 (4): 30-41.

Dunn, L. C. 1950 Genetic monsters. *Sci. Amer.* 182 (6): 16-19.

Eiseley, L. C. 1948 Antiquity of modern man. *Sci. Amer.* 179 (1): 16-19.

—— 1953 Fossil man. *Sci. Amer.* 189 (6): 65-72.

—— 1953 Is man alone in space? *Sci. Amer.* 189 (1): 80-86.

—— 1950 Is man here to stay? *Sci. Amer.* 183 (5): 52-55.

—— 1954 Man, the fire-maker. *Sci. Amer.* 191 (3): 52-57.

Eliassen, R. 1952 Stream pollution. *Sci. Amer.* 186 (3): 17-21.

Emerson, R. 1952 Molds and man. *Sci. Amer.* 186 (1): 28-32.

Evans, R. M. 1949 Seeing light and color. *Sci. Amer.* 181 (2): 52-55.

Fairchild, D. G. 1930 *Exploring for Plants.* New York: Macmillan.

—— 1938 *The World Was My Garden.* New York: Scribner's.

Farris, E. J. 1950 Male fertility. *Sci. Amer.* 182 (5): 16-19.

Fawcett, C. B. 1947 The numbers and distribution of mankind. *Sci. Mo.* 65: 181-198.

Fenner, F. 1954 The rabbit plague. *Sci. Amer.* 190 (2): 30-35.

Flanders, S. E. 1950 Control of sex in the honeybee. *Sci. Mo.* 71: 237-240.

Fox, H. M. 1950 Blood pigments. *Sci. Amer.* 182 (3): 20-22.

Fruton, J. S. 1950 Proteins. *Sci. Amer.* 182 (6): 32-41.

Funkenstern, D. H. 1955 The physiology of fear and anger. *Sci. Amer.* 192 (5): 74-80.

Gamow, G. 1955 Information transfer in the living cell. *Sci. Amer.* 193 (4): 70-78.

—— 1951 The origin and evolution of the universe. *Amer. Sci.* 39: 392-406.

Gerard, R. W. 1948 The dynamics of inhibition. *Sci. Amer.* 179 (3): 44-49.

—— 1940 *Unresting Cells.* New York: Harper.

Gilmore, R. M. 1955 The return of the gray whale. *Sci. Amer.* 192 (1): 62-67.

Goldschmidt, R. B. 1949 Phenocopies. *Sci Amer.* 181 (4): 46-49.

———— 1952 *Understanding Heredity.* New York: Wiley.

Gottlieb, B. 1948 A new theory of tooth decay. *Sci. Amer.* 179 (4): 20-23.

Grant, V. 1951 The fertilization of flowers. *Sci. Amer.* 184 (6): 52-56.

Gray, G. W. 1953 Human growth. *Sci. Amer.* 189 (4): 65-76.

———— 1951 Sickle-cell anemia. *Sci. Amer.* 185 (2): 56-59.

———— 1948 The great ravelled knot. *Sci. Amer.* 179 (4): 26-39.

———— 1949 The antibiotics. *Sci. Amer.* 181 (2): 26-35.

———— 1955 Unknown viruses. *Sci. Amer.* 192 (3): 60-70.

Green, D. E. 1949 Enzymes in teams. *Sci. Amer.* 181 (3): 48-51.

———— 1954 The metabolism of fats. *Sci. Amer.* 190 (1): 32-36.

Greene, H. S. N. 1948 On the development of cancer. *Sci. Amer.* 179 (6): 40-43.

Greulach, V. A. 1955 Plant movements. *Sci. Amer.* 192 (2): 100-106.

———— 1952 The rise of water in plants. *Sci. Amer.* 187 (4): 78-82.

Griffin, D. R. 1950 The navigation of bats. *Sci. Amer.* 183 (2): 52-55.

———— 1948 The navigation of birds. *Sci. Amer.* 179 (6): 18-24.

Gumpert, M. 1948 Vesalius: discoverer of the human body. *Sci. Amer.* 179 (5): 24-31.

Haagen-Smit, A. J. 1952 Smell and taste. *Sci. Amer.* 186 (3): 28-32.

Hartman, C. G. 1950 Playing 'possum. *Sci. Amer.* 182 (1): 52-55.

Harvey, E. N. 1952 Luminescent organisms. *Amer. Sci.* 40: 468-481.

———— 1948 The luminescence of living things. *Sci. Amer.* 179 (5): 46-49.

Hasler, A. D. & J. A. Larsen 1955 The homing salmon. *Sci. Amer.* 193 (2): 72-76.

Hayashi, T. & G. A. W. Boehm 1952 Artificial muscle. *Sci. Amer.* 187 (6): 18-21.

Heilbrunn, L. V. 1951 Calcium and life. *Sci. Amer.* 184 (6): 60-63.

———— 1954 Heat death. *Sci. Amer.* 190 (4): 70-75.

Hollander, W. F. 1952 Lethal heredity. *Sci. Amer.* 187 (1): 58-61.

Hooton, E. A. 1945 *Up From the Ape.* New York: Macmillan.

Howard, R. A. 1953 Captain Bligh and the breadfruit. *Sci. Amer.* 188 (3): 88-94.

Huxley, J. S. 1942 *Evolution: The Modern Synthesis.* New York: Harper.

Ingle, R. M. 1954 The life of an estuary. *Sci. Amer.* 190 (5): 64-68.

Jacobs, W. P. 1955 What makes leaves fall. *Sci. Amer.* 193 (5): 82-89.

Janssen, R. E. 1948 The beginnings of coal. *Sci. Amer.* 179 (1): 46-51.

Jarvik, E. 1955 The oldest tetrapods and their forerunners. *Sci. Mo.* 80: 141-154.

Johnson, F. H. 1954 Heat and life. *Sci. Amer.* 191 (3): 65-68.

Jones, G. N. 1951 On the number of species of plants. *Sci. Mo.* 72:289-294.

Kabat, E. A. 1949 Allergic mechanisms in nervous disease. *Sci. Amer.* 181 (1): 16-19.

Kalmus, H. 1952 Inherited sense defects. *Sci. Amer.* 186 (5): 64-70.

Kamen, M. D. 1953 Discoveries in nitrogen fixation. *Sci. Amer.* 188 (3): 38-42.

Katchalsky, A. & S. Lifson 1954 Muscle as a machine. *Sci. Amer.* 190 (3): 72-76.

Katz, B. 1952 The nerve impulse. *Sci. Amer.* 187 (5): 55-64.

Kellogg, C. E. 1950 Soil. *Sci. Amer.* 183 (1): 30-39.

Kelner, A. 1951 Revival by light. *Sci. Amer.* 184 (5): 22-25.

Kemeny, J. G. 1955 Man viewed as a machine. *Sci. Amer.* 192 (4): 58-67.

Kilgour, F. G. 1952 William Harvey. *Sci. Amer.* 186 (6): 56-62.

Kimble, G. H. T. 1950 The changing climate. *Sci. Amer.* 182 (4): 48-53.

Knight, C. A. & D. Fraser 1955 The mutation of viruses. *Sci. Amer.* 193 (1): 74-79.

Kopac, M. J. 1950 Microsurgery. *Sci. Amer.* 183 (4): 48-51.

Kraus, E. J. 1954 The significance of growth regulators in agricultural practice. *Amer. Sci.* 42 (3): 439-460.

Krogman, W. M. 1948 The man-apes of South Africa. *Sci. Amer.* 178 (5): 16-19.

———— 1949 The record of human illness. *Sci. Amer.* 180 (1): 52-55.

———— 1951 The scars of evolution. *Sci. Amer.* 185 (6): 54-57.

———— 1943 What we do not know about race. *Sci. Mo.* 57: 97-104.

Krutch, J. W. 1954 Conservation is not enough. *Amer. Scholar* 23 (3): 295-305.

Lack, D. 1953 Darwin's finches. *Sci. Amer.* 188 (4): 66-72.

Ladd, H. S. & J. I. Tracey, Jr. 1949 The problem of coral reefs. *Sci. Mo.* 69: 297-305.

Lansing, A. I. 1953 Experiments in aging. *Sci. Amer.* 188 (4): 38-42.

Leopold, Aldo 1949 *A Sand County Almanac.* New York: Oxford.

Leopold, A. S. 1955 Too many deer. *Sci. Amer.* 193 (5): 101-108.

Li, C. H. 1950 The pituitary. *Sci. Amer.* 183 (4): 18-22.

Linderstrom-Lang, K. U. 1953 How is a protein made? *Sci. Amer.* 189 (3): 100-106.

Long, E. R. 1955 The germ of tuberculosis. *Sci. Amer.* 192 (6): 102-110.

Lüscher, M. 1953 The termite and the cell. *Sci. Amer.* 188 (5): 74-78.

Luria, S. E. 1955 The T2 mystery. *Sci. Amer.* 192 (4): 92-98.

Lwoff, A. 1954 The life cycle of a virus. *Sci. Amer.* 190 (3): 34-37.

Lyman, C. P. & P. O. Chatfield 1950 Hibernation. *Sci. Amer.* 183 (6): 18-21.

McDonald, J. E. 1952 The Coriolis effect. *Sci. Amer.* 186 (5): 72-78.

McLean, F. C. 1955 Bone. *Sci. Amer.* 192 (2): 84-91.

Mangelsdorf, P. C. 1951 Hybrid corn. *Sci. Amer.* 185 (2): 39-47.

—— 1950 The mystery of corn. *Sci. Amer.* 183 (1): 20-23.

—— 1953 Wheat. *Sci. Amer.* 189 (1): 50-59.

Maramorosch, K. 1953 A versatile virus. *Sci. Amer.* 188 (6): 78-86.

Matzke, E. 1942 The finest show on earth. *Sci. Mo.* 55: 349-354.

May, J. M. 1953 The geography of disease. *Sci. Amer.* 188 (2): 22-27.

Mazia, D. 1953 Cell division. *Sci. Amer.* 189 (2): 53-63.

—— 1956 The life history of the cell. *Amer. Sci.* 44: 1-32.

Melnick, J. L. 1953 Viruses within cells. *Sci. Amer.* 189 (6): 39-41.

Metcalf, R. L. 1952 Insects v. insecticides. *Sci. Amer.* 187 (4): 21-25.

Milne, L. J. & M. J. 1947 *A Multitude of Living Things.* New York: Dodd, Mead.

—— 1950 Animal courtship. *Sci. Amer.* 183 (1): 52-55.

—— 1952 How animals change color. *Sci. Amer.* 186 (3): 64-67.

—— 1948 Insect vision. *Sci. Amer.* 179 (1): 42-45.

—— 1948 Right hand, left hand. *Sci. Amer.* 179 (4): 46-49.

—— 1949 Temperature and life. *Sci. Amer.* 180 (2): 46-49.

—— 1951 The eelgrass catastrophe. *Sci. Amer.* 184 (1): 52-55.

—— 1954 *The Mating Instinct.* Boston: Little, Brown.

—— 1956 *The World of Night.* New York: Harper.

Milner, H. W. 1953 Algae as food. *Sci. Amer.* 189 (4): 31-35.

—— 1955 Some problems in large-scale culture of algae. *Sci. Mo.* 80: 15-20.

Mirsky, A. E. 1953 The chemistry of heredity. *Sci. Amer.* 188 (2): 47-57.

Monroy, A. 1950 Fertilization of the egg. *Sci. Amer.* 183 (6): 46-49.

Montagu, A. 1950 Social instincts. *Sci. Amer.* 182 (4): 54-59.

Moody, P. A. 1953 *Introduction to Evolution.* New York: Harper.

Moog, F. 1948 Gulliver was a bad biologist. *Sci. Amer.* 179 (5): 52-55.

—— 1948 The biology of old age. *Sci. Amer.* 179 (6): 40-43.

—— 1950 Up from the embryo. *Sci. Amer.* 182 (2): 52-55.

Morrison, P. & E. 1949 Natural history of a virus. *Sci. Amer.* 181 (5): 50-53.

Movius, H. L., Jr. 1953 Archeology and the earliest art. *Sci. Amer.* 189 (2): 30-35.

Muller, H. J. 1947 *Genetics, Medicine and Man.* Ithaca, N.Y.: Cornell.

—— 1955 Radiation and human mutation. *Sci. Amer.* 193 (5): 58-68.

—— 1950 Radiation damage to the genetic material. *Amer. Sci.* 38 (1): 33-59, 126; (3): 399-425.

Naylor, A. W. 1952 The control of flowering. *Sci. Amer.* 186 (5): 49-56.

Needham, P. R. 1953 The mortality of trout. *Sci. Amer.* 188 (5): 81-86.

Nicholas, G. 1955 Life in caves. *Sci. Amer.* 192 (5): 98-106.

Oakley, K. P. & J. S. Weiner 1955 Piltdown man. *Amer. Sci.* 43: 573-583.

Oparin, A. I. 1938 *The Origin of Life.* New York: Macmillan.

Osborn, F. 1948 *Our Plundered Planet.* Boston: Little, Brown.

—— 1953 *The Limits of the Earth.* Boston: Little, Brown.

Page, I. H. 1948 High blood pressure. *Sci. Amer.* 179 (2): 44-47.

Pappenheimer, A. M. Jr. 1952 The diphtheria toxin. *Sci. Amer.* 187 (4): 32-36.

Parker, G. H. 1953 Criteria of life. *Amer. Sci.* 41: 614-618.

Patten, B. M. 1951 The first heart beats and the beginning of the embryonic circulation. *Amer. Sci.* 39: 225-243.

Pauling, L., R. B. Corey & R. Hayward 1954 The structure of protein molecules. *Sci. Amer.* 191 (1): 51-59.

Pearson, O. P. 1953 The metabolism of hummingbirds. *Sci. Amer.* 188 (1): 69-72.

—— 1954 Shrews. *Sci. Amer.* 191 (2): 66-70.

Pfeiffer, J. E. 1948 Enzymes. *Sci. Amer.* 179 (6): 28-39.

Pincus, G. 1951 Fertilization in mammals. *Sci. Amer.* 184 (3): 44-47.

Platt, R. 1947 *Our Flowering World.* New York: Dodd, Mead.

Pollard, E. C. 1954 The physics of viruses. *Sci. Amer.* 191 (6): 62-70.

Potter, R. K. 1950 Frog calls. *Sci. Amer.* 182 (5): 46-47.

Pramer, D. 1955 Antibiotics against plant diseases. *Sci. Amer.* 192 (6): 82-90.

Quisenberry, K. S. 1954 The world's principal food plants. *Sci. Mo.* 79: 241-247.

Rabinowitch, E. I. 1948 Photosynthesis. *Sci. Amer.* 179 (2): 34-35.

—— 1953 Progress in photosynthesis. *Sci. Amer.* 189 (5): 80-84.

Rahn, O. 1945 *Microbes of Merit.* New York: Ronald.

Raper, K. B. 1952 The progress of antibiotics. *Sci. Amer.* 186 (4): 49-57.

Remington, R. E. 1936 The social origins of dietary habits. *Sci. Mo.* 43: 193-204.

Reynolds, H. C. 1953 The opossum. *Sci. Amer.* 188 (6): 88-94.

Reynolds, S. R. M. 1953 Circulatory adaptations to birth. *Sci. Mo.* 77: 205-213.

—— 1952 The umbilical cord. *Sci. Amer.* 187 (1): 70-74.

Ribbands, R. 1955 The honeybee. *Sci. Amer.* 193 (2): 52-60.

Riley, G. A. 1949 Food from the sea. *Sci. Amer.* 181 (4): 16-19.

Riley, H. P. 1952 Ecological barriers. *American Naturalist* 86 (1): 23-32.

Riper, W. van 1953 How a rattlesnake strikes. *Sci. Amer.* 189 (4): 100-102.

Rodbard, S. 1953 Warm bloodedness. *Sci. Mo.* 77: 137-142.

Rose, S. M. 1949 Transformed cells. *Sci. Amer.* 181 (6): 22-24.

Rush, J. H. 1952 Tree rings and sun spots. *Sci. Amer.* 186 (1): 54-58.

Russell, P. F. 1952 The eradication of malaria. *Sci. Amer.* 186 (6): 22-25.

Ryan, F. J. 1953 Evolution observed. *Sci. Amer.* 189 (4): 78-82.

Salaman, R. N. 1952 The social influence of the potato. *Sci. Amer.* 187 (6): 50-56.

Salisbury, P. F. 1954 Artificial internal organs. *Sci. Amer.* 191 (2): 24-27.

Salk, J. 1955 Vaccines for poliomyelitis. *Sci. Amer.* 192 (4): 42-44.

Saunders, F. A. 1948 Physics and music. *Sci. Amer.* 179 (1): 32-41.

Scharrer, B. 1951 The woodroach. *Sci. Amer.* 185 (6): 58-62.

Schery, R. W. 1952 *Plants For Man.* Englewood Cliffs, N.J.: Prentice-Hall.

Scheinfeld, A. 1950 *The New You and Heredity.* Philadelphia: Lippincott.

Schick, B. 1948 Allergy: a definition. *Sci. Amer.* 179 (1): 26-29.

Schmidt-Nielsen, K. & B. 1953 The desert rat. *Sci. Amer.* 189 (1): 73-78.

—— 1949 The water economy of desert mammals. *Sci. Mo.* 69: 180-185.

Schneirla, T. C. & G. Piel 1948 The army ant. *Sci. Amer.* 179 (6): 16-23.

Schocken, V. 1949 Plant hormones. *Sci. Amer.* 180 (5): 40-43.

Schrader, F. 1952 *Mitosis.* New York: Columbia.

Schubert, J. 1955 Radioactive poisons. *Sci. Amer.* 193 (2): 34-39.

Sears, P. B. 1947 *Deserts on the March.* Norman, Okla.: Univ. of Oklahoma.

Shapiro, S. 1951 The control of blood clots. *Sci. Amer.* 184 (3): 18-21.

Simpson, G. G. 1950 History of the fauna of Latin America. *Amer. Sci.* 38: 361-389.

—— 1949 *The Meaning of Evolution.* New Haven: Yale.

Smith, C. S. 1954 The shape of things. *Sci. Amer.* 190 (1): 58-64.

Smith, H. W. 1953 The kidney. *Sci. Amer.* 188 (1): 40-48.

Smith, R. F. & W. W. Allen 1954 Insect control and the balance of nature. *Sci. Amer.* 190 (6): 38-42.

Snyder, L. H. 1955 Human heredity and its modern applications. *Amer. Sci.* 43: 391-419.

Sognnaes, R. F. 1953 The skin of your teeth. *Sci. Amer.* 188 (6): 38-42

Sonneborn, T. M. 1950 Partner of the genes. *Sci. Amer.* 183 (5): 30-39.

Spoerl, E. 1951 The lethal effects of radiation. *Sci. Amer.* 185 (6): 22-25.

Stebbins, G. L. Jr. 1951 Cataclysmic evolution. *Sci. Amer.* 184 (4): 54-59.

Steinbach, H. B. 1951 The squid. *Sci. Amer.* 184 (4): 64-69.

Stent, G. S. 1953 The multiplication of bacterial viruses. *Sci. Amer.* 188 (5): 36-39.

Stern, C. 1952 Man's genetic future. *Sci. Amer.* 186 (2): 68-74.

—— 1954 Two or three bristles. *Amer. Sci.* 42 (2): 213-247.

Stone, A. 1954 The control of fertility. *Sci. Amer.* 190 (4): 31-33.

Storer, J. H. 1952 Bird aerodynamics. *Sci. Amer.* 186 (4): 24-29.

Strong, L. C. 1950 Genetics and cancer. *Sci. Amer.* 183 (1): 44-47.

Stumpf, P. K. 1953 ATP. *Sci. Amer.* 188 (4): 85-92.

Surgenor, D. M. 1954 Blood. *Sci. Amer.* 190 (2): 54-62.

Swanson, C. L. W. 1953 Soil conditioners. *Sci. Amer.* 189 (2): 36-38.

Szent-Gyorgyi, A. 1949 Muscle research. *Sci. Amer.* 180 (6): 22-25.

Teale, E. W. 1951 *North With the Spring.* New York: Dodd, Mead.

Thimann, K. V. 1950 Autumn colors. *Sci. Amer.* 183 (4): 40-43.

—— 1954 The physiology of growth in plant tissues. *Amer. Sci.* 42: 589-606.

Thompson, E. O. P. 1955 The insulin molecule. *Sci. Amer.* 192 (5): 36-41.

Thompson, W. S. 1950 Population. *Sci. Amer.* 182 (2): 11-15.

Tinbergen, N. 1954 The courtship of animals. *Sci. Amer.* 191 (5): 42-46.

—— 1952 The curious behavior of the stickleback. *Sci. Amer.* 187 (6): 22-26.

—— 1951 *The Study of Instinct.* New York: Oxford.

Trowell, H. C. 1954 Kwashiorkor. *Sci. Amer.* 191 (6): 46-50.

Tyler, A. 1954 Fertilization and antibodies. *Sci. Amer.* 190 (6): 70-75.

Vallee, B. L. 1951 The function of trace elements in biology. *Sci. Mo.* 72: 368-378.

Vevers, H. G. 1952 Animals of the bottom. *Sci. Amer.* 187 (1): 68-69.

Vogt, W. 1948 *Road to Survival.* New York: Wiley.

Waddington, C. H. 1953 Experiments in acquired characteristics. *Sci. Amer.* 189 (6): 92-99.

—— How do cells differentiate? *Sci. Amer.* 189 (3): 108-116.

Waksman, S. A. 1940 Microbes in a changing world. *Sci. Mo.* 51: 422-427.

Wald, G. 1950 Eye and camera. *Sci. Amer.* 183 (2): 32-40.

—— 1954 The molecular basis of visual excitation. *Amer. Sci.* 42: 73-95.

—— 1954 The origin of life. *Sci. Amer.* 191 (2): 45-53.

Walford, L. A. 1951 The deep-sea layer of life. *Sci. Amer.* 185 (2): 24-28.

Walter, W. G. 1954 The electrical activity of the brain. *Sci. Amer.* 190 (6): 54-63.

Warden, C. J. 1951 Animal intelligence. *Sci. Amer.* 184 (6): 64-68.

Warren, H. V. 1954 Geology and health. *Sci. Mo.* 78 (6): 339-345.

Waterman, T. H. 1955 Polarized light and navigation. *Sci. Amer.* 193 (1): 88-94.

Weatherwax, P. 1950 The history of corn. *Sci. Mo.* 71: 50-60.

Weaver, W. 1954 People, energy, and food. *Sci. Mo.* 78: 359-364.

Weiss, F. J. 1952 The useful algae. *Sci. Amer.* 187 (6): 15-17.

Weisz, P. B. 1953 The embryologist and the protozoon. *Sci. Amer.* 188 (3): 76-82.

Went, F. W. 1955 Air pollution. *Sci. Amer.* 192 (5): 62-72.

—— 1955 The ecology of desert plants. *Sci. Amer.* 192 (4): 68-75.

—— 1949 The plants of Krakatoa. *Sci. Amer.* 181 (3): 52-54.

White, P. R. 1950 Plant tissue cultures. *Sci. Amer.* 182 (3): 48-51.

Wiener, A. S. 1954 Parentage and blood groups. *Sci. Amer.* 191 (1): 78-83.

Williams, C. B. 1953 Insect breathing. *Sci. Amer.* 188 (2): 28-32.

—— 1950 The metamorphosis of insects. *Sci. Amer.* 182 (4): 24-28.

Witt, P. 1954 Spider webs and drugs. *Sci. Amer.* 191 (6): 80-86.

Wood, W. B. Jr. 1951 White blood cells v. Bacteria. *Sci. Amer.* 184 (2): 48-52.

Wyckoff, R. W. G. 1951 Visualizing macromolecules and viruses. *Amer. Sci.* 39: 561-576.

Yearbook of Agriculture, U.S.D.A., 1941 *Climate and Man.*

—— 1948 *Grass.*

—— 1952 *Insects.*

—— 1953 *Plant Diseases.*

—— 1949 *Trees.*

—— 1955 *Water.*

Yerkes, R. M. 1925 *Almost Human.* London: Cape.

Zahl, P. A. 1949 The evolution of sex. *Sci. Amer.* 180 (4): 52-55.

Zinsser, H. 1934 *Rats, Lice and History.* Boston: Little, Brown.

Index

Index

C

D

E

T

S

R

Q

A

P

CAPTIONS ARE ON PAGE XIII